SCOTT FORESMAN-ADDISON WESLEY

*"We did not weave the web of life,
we are merely a strand in it.
Whatever we do to the web, we do
to ourselves."* –CHIEF SEATTLE

Biology

The Web of Life

ERIC STRAUSS • MARYLIN LISOWSKI

Scott Foresman
Addison Wesley

Editorial Offices: Menlo Park, California • Glenview, Illinois
Sales Offices: Reading, Massachusetts • Atlanta, Georgia • Glenview, Illinois
Carrollton, Texas • Menlo Park, California

1-800-552-2259

http://www.sf.aw.com
http://www.biosurf.com

SCOTT FORESMAN-ADDISON WESLEY

Biology
The Web of Life

Program Components

STUDENT EDITION

TEACHER'S EDITION

TEACHER'S RESOURCE PACKAGE
Laboratory Manual
(Teacher's Edition)
Unit Review Modules
Consumer Applications
Issues and Decision Making
Biotechnology Manual
Overhead Transparency Preview
Project Biology
Teacher's Curriculum Guide

OVERHEAD TRANSPARENCY PACKAGE

LABORATORY MANUAL
Student Edition

TECHNOLOGY
Biology Alive! Video Series
Rewind: *The Web of Life*
Reteach Videos
Animated Biological Concepts
Videodiscs and Worksheets
TestWorks CD-ROM
Interactive Biological Simulations
CD-ROM and Worksheets
Teacher's Resource Planner
CD-ROM
Biología: la telaraña de la vida
CD-ROM (Spanish Student
Edition)
bioSURF Internet Site
The Biology Place Internet Site
Published by Peregrine Publishers, Inc.

Cover photograph: Tim Davis/Davis-Lynn Images

About the cover: Wolves and aspen trees are just two of the millions of species that comprise the web of life. The effects of the wolf's removal from and reintroduction to ecosystems demonstrate the delicate and complex connections among living things.

GeoSystems Global Corporation and Addison Wesley Longman are the publishers of the maps included in this textbook. The information contained in these maps is derived from a variety of sources. While every effort has been made to verify the information contained in such sources, the publishers assume no responsibility for incon- sistencies or inaccuracies in the data nor liability for any damages of any type arising from errors or omissions.

ISBN 0-201-86954-3

2 3 4 5 6 7 8 9 10 - VH - 01 00 99 98 97

Brief Contents

Contents

Unit 1 The Basis of Life 30–125

Unit 2 Genetics 126–225

Unit 3 Change and Diversity 226-321

Unit 4 Monerans, Protists, and Fungi 322–393

Unit 5 Plants 394–495

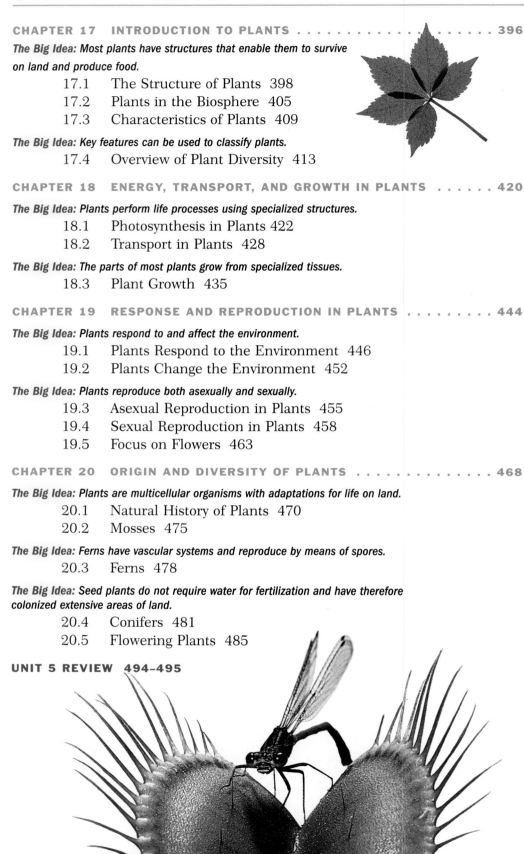

Unit 6 Invertebrate Animals 496–587

Unit 7 Vertebrate Animals 588–687

Unit 8 Human Biology 688–849

References and Resources

Big Ideas

There is much to learn in every chapter of this textbook. The Big Ideas! will help you organize and understand the essential knowledge and skills that comprise biology. Build a framework of biology by learning and connecting these Big Ideas.

Unit 1 The Basis of Life

- Living things share many characteristics, including organization and adaptation. 1.1–1.2
- Scientists use careful observation and controlled experiments to study the natural world. 1.3
- Living things are made of chemicals with characteristic structures and functions. 2.1–2.2
- Life processes depend on breaking and forming chemical bonds in chemical reactions. 2.3–2.4
- Life processes depend on the properties of water and the characteristics of solutions. 2.5
- Cell structures of living organisms perform life functions. 3.1–3.3
- Cells of major groups of organisms can be distinguished by their structural differences. 3.4
- Cells exchange materials with their environment by chemical and physical processes. 3.5
- All organisms get energy by breaking down the chemical compounds in food and making ATP and other molecules. 4.1–4.3
- Energy from sunlight passes through a series of living organisms. 4.4
- Cell division is the basis of reproduction and development 5.1–5.2
- Chromosome number is reduced in meiosis. 5.3–5.4

Unit 2 Genetics

- Traits are inherited in a consistent pattern. 6.1–6.2

- There are patterns of inheritance that make some traits predictable. 6.3–6.5
- The structure of DNA, the molecule of heredity, enables the molecule to copy itself. 7.1–7.2
- Genes, sections of DNA that code for a specific trait, are linked together on chromosomes. 7.3–7.5
- Genes are sequences of DNA bases that can be translated into proteins or parts of proteins when they are activated. 8.1–8.2
- Changes in DNA can cause changes in phenotype. 8.3–8.4
- Genotypes can be changed through selective breeding and genetic engineering. 9.1–9.2
- Technology enables us to find out about genotype and use this knowledge to affect phenotype. 9.3–9.4

Unit 3 Change and Diversity

- Populations change over time through natural selection. 10.1–10.2
- Scientific analysis of fossils and modern organisms supports the theory of evolution. 10.3
- New species can originate through natural selection and other changes in a population's gene pool. 10.4–10.5
- Evidence indicates that organic molecules and cells may have formed spontaneously on ancient Earth. 11.1
- Our planet and the organisms that inhabit it have changed greatly over time. 11.2–11.3
- Primates are mammals with binocular vision and dexterous hands and arms. 12.1
- There have been many different hominid species over time, each species with its own unique characteristics. 12.2–12.3

- Scientists classify organisms into a hierarchy of groups based on evolutionary relationships. 13.1–13.2
- Classification has numerous applications, including identifying species. 13.3

Unit 4 Monerans, Protists, and Fungi

- Viruses are particles that depend on living things to replicate. 14.1–14.3
- Monerans are microscopic organisms that lack a membrane-bound nucleus and membrane-bound organelles. 14.4–14.6
- Protists are a diverse group of eukaryotes that include unicellular and multicellular organisms. 15.1
- Protists can be classified into three groups—protozoans, algae, and molds. 15.2–15.4
- Protists have a major ecological impact as food sources, decomposers, and infectious agents. 15.5
- Fungi are stationary organisms that live as heterotrophs. 16.1–16.2
- Fungi act as decomposers and symbiotic partners of humans and many other organisms. 16.3

Unit 5 Plants

- Most plants have structures that enable them to survive on land and produce food. 17.1–17.3
- Key features can be used to classify plants. 17.4
- Plants perform life processes using specialized structures. 18.1–18.2
- The parts of most plants grow from specialized tissues. 18.3

- *Plants respond to and affect the environment.* 19.1–19.2
- *Plants reproduce both asexually and sexually.* 19.3–19.5
- *Plants are multicellular organisms with adaptations for life on land.* 20.1–20.2
- *Ferns have vascular systems and reproduce by means of spores.* 20.3
- *Seed plants do not require water for fertilization and have therefore colonized extensive areas of land.* 20.4–20.5

Unit 6 Invertebrate Animals

- *Animals have evolved a number of adaptations enabling them to perform essential functions of life.* 21.1
- *Sponges are sessile animals without specialized tissues and organs.* 21.2–21.3
- *Cnidarians are radially symmetrical animals with specialized tissues and stinging tentacles.* 21.4–21.5
- *Sponges and cnidarians provide food and protection for a large number of organisms.* 21.6
- *Flatworms and roundworms have bilateral symmetry and specialized tissues.* 22.1
- *Mollusks share a common body plan that includes a muscular foot, a visceral mass, and a mantle.* 22.2
- *Annelids are wormlike animals with a segmented body.* 22.3
- *Arthropods are segmented invertebrates with jointed appendages and an exoskeleton.* 23.1
- *In general, arthropods are classified by the number of body segments they have and the structure of their appendages.* 23.2–23.4
- *Arthropods, as members of the largest phylum, have many important roles in the biosphere.* 23.5
- *Echinoderms are marine animals with spiny skin, an endoskeleton, and a water vascular system.* 24.1
- *Invertebrate chordates represent possible evolutionary links between invertebrates and vertebrates.* 24.2

Unit 7 Vertebrate Animals

- *Vertebrates are animals with backbones.* 25.1
- *Fishes are a diverse group of vertebrates that are adapted for life in the water.* 25.2–25.4
- *Although amphibians share some fish traits, they are adapted to life on land.* 25.5–25.7
- *Reptiles represent the first vertebrates with adaptations that enable them to live their entire lives out of water.* 26.1–26.3
- *With the development of feathers, birds were the first vertebrates able to maintain a constant body temperature.* 26.4–26.6
- *Although different species have unique adaptations, all mammals are endothermic vertebrates with hair and mammary glands.* 27.1–27.2
- *Mammals live almost everywhere on Earth and play important roles in ecosystems.* 27.3
- *Animal behaviors are adaptations that maximize survival and reproductive fitness.* 28.1–28.3
- *Animal behavior involves interactions between individuals, between groups, and with the environment.* 28.4

Unit 8 Human Biology

- *The human body consists of twelve systems.* 29.1
- *The body's skeleton provides support and protection.* 29.2–29.3
- *Muscles contract to move the body.* 29.4–29.5
- *The skin covers and protects the body's internal organs.* 29.6
- *The digestive system breaks down food into usable compounds.* 30.1–30.3
- *The excretory system eliminates nitrogen-containing wastes and helps maintain homeostasis.* 30.4–30.5
- *The vital exchange of oxygen and carbon dioxide occurs in the respiratory systems of animals.* 31.1–31.3
- *Circulatory systems transport materials necessary for life.* 31.4–31.6

- *The immune system protects the body from harmful organisms and substances.* 32.1
- *The immune system consists of specialized cells, organs, and organ systems that respond to the presence of a pathogen.* 32.2–32.3
- *A healthy immune system requires a healthy lifestyle.* 32.4
- *The endocrine system controls long-lasting internal changes.* 33.1–33.3
- *Reproductive systems make possible the continuation of life.* 33.4–33.6
- *Nervous systems control our detection of and response to the environment.* 34.1
- *The human nervous system consists of the brain, spinal cord, nerves, and sensory organs.* 34.2–34.4
- *The health of the nervous system can be affected by injury, disease, and substance abuse.* 34.5

Unit 9 Organisms and the Environment

- *Life depends on the relationships between living and nonliving parts of the environment.* 35.1–35.2
- *Regions of the biosphere have distinguishing characteristics.* 35.3–35.4
- *The size of a population is affected by living and nonliving factors.* 36.1–36.2
- *How populations interact determines the structure and characteristics of a community.* 36.3
- *Biotic and abiotic changes in a community alter the community structure.* 36.4
- *In an ecosystem, the flow of energy moves in one direction.* 37.1–37.2
- *Nutrients are recycled in ecosystems.* 37.3
- *Human use of essential natural resources can affect the web of life.* 38.1
- *Land, water, and air are invaluable natural resources.* 38.2–38.4
- *Humans can affect the future of the biosphere in a positive way.* 38.5

Labs and Activities

🔵 Discover It!

🔵 Think About It!

Features

Discover

The Web of Life

You are about to explore the amazing and wondrous web of life.
Your textbook will serve as a valuable tool for your journey through
the world of living things. Use the next few pages to become familiar
with the organization and features of this textbook. Then begin your
travels and enjoy biology!

Hit or Myth?

The amazing stories of **Hit or Myth**—
sometimes fact and sometimes
fiction—reflect the relevance of
biology to today's world.

bioSURF

Connect the *Web of Life* to
the World Wide Web using
the **bioSURF** internet site.

Chapter Opener

We introduce you to the chapter with
a story that puts the content in con-
text. Use the **LAB ZONE Discover It!**
activity to begin your exploration of the
chapter material. Practice expressing
your knowledge, ideas, and experiences
as you **WRITE ABOUT IT!**

Identify and Connect

The Big Idea

There is much to learn in every chapter of this textbook. **THE BIG IDEA!** will help you identify and connect major biology concepts.

What you'll learn

The **objectives** describe what you should be able to do after you have read the section. New **key terms** are listed at the beginning and shown in bold type so that you can recognize them easily. Each key term is accompanied by a definition.

Everyday Biology and In the Community

Recognize that biology is everywhere by doing an activity in **In the Community** and by reading the often surprising and always interesting information in **Everyday Biology**.

Science, Technology, and Society

Information about the role of biology in your life and the lives of others is identified and categorized as **Environmental Awareness**, **Issues in Biology**, and **Frontiers in Biology**.

Visual Learning

Develop an understanding of the processes, cycles, and diversity of life by analyzing the **visual learning** figures found throughout the textbook. You can even see the illustrations "come to life" by viewing the **Animated Biological Concepts** and **Interactive Biological Simulations CD-ROM.**

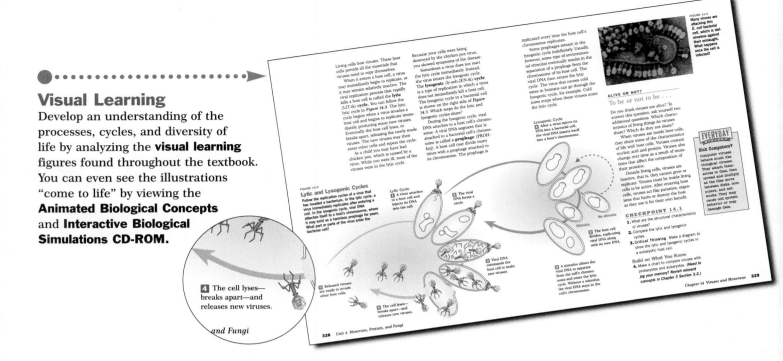

Interact and Explore

Lab Zone Activities

LAB ZONE Investigate It! activities give you an opportunity to experiment in much the same way a biologist does: You will use a variety of skills to hypothesize, experiment, observe, analyze, conclude, and apply your conclusions to other situations.

LAB ZONE Discover It! activities provide opportunities to explore ideas and discover characteristics of life—before you read about them.

LAB ZONE Do It! activities provide quick and effective hands-on applications of science concepts and skills.

LAB ZONE Think About It! activities provide practice in analyzing and applying concepts.

Review and Extend

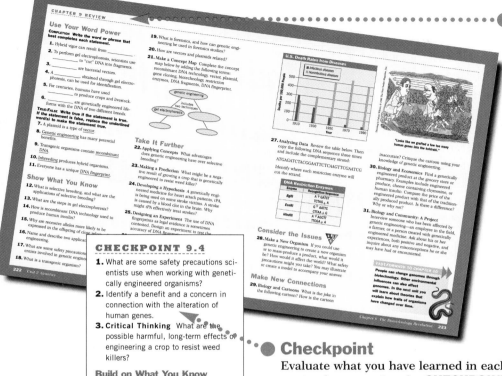

Use Your Word Power

COMPLETION Write the word or phrase that best completes each statement.

1. Hybrid vigor can result from _____.
2. To perform gel electrophoresis, scientists use _____ to "cut" DNA into fragments.
3. _____ are bacterial vectors.
4. A _____ obtained through gel electrophoresis, can be used for identification.
5. For centuries, humans have used _____ to produce crops and livestock.
6. _____ are genetically engineered life-forms with the DNA of two different breeds.

TRUE-FALSE Write true if the statement is true. If the statement is false, replace the underlined word(s) to make the statement true.

7. A plasmid is a type of vector.
8. Genetic engineering has many potential benefits.
9. Transgenic organisms contain recombinant DNA.
10. Inbreeding produces hybrid organisms.
11. Everyone has a unique DNA fingerprint.

Show What You Know

12. What is selective breeding, and what are the applications of selective breeding?
13. What are the steps in gel electrophoresis?
14. How is recombinant DNA technology used to produce human insulin?
15. Why are recessive alleles more likely to be expressed in the offspring of close relatives?
16. Name and describe two applications of _____ engineering.
17. What are some safety precautions scientists involved in genetic engineering _____
18. What is a transgenic organism?

19. What is forensics, and how can genetic engineering be used in forensics studies?
20. How are vectors and plasmids related?
21. Make a Concept Map Complete the concept map below by adding the following terms: recombinant DNA technology, plasmid, gene cloning, biotechnology, restriction enzymes, DNA fragments, DNA fingerprint.

Take It Further

22. **Applying Concepts** What advantages does genetic engineering have over selective breeding?
23. **Making a Prediction** What might be a negative result of growing a crop that is genetically engineered to resist weed killer?
24. **Developing a Hypothesis** A genetically engineered medicine for heart attack patients, tPA, is being used on some stroke victims. A stroke is caused by a blood clot in the brain. Why might tPA effectively treat strokes?
25. **Designing an Experiment** The use of DNA fingerprints as legal evidence is sometimes contested. Design an experiment to test the accuracy of DNA fingerprints. _____

27. **Analyzing Data** Review the table below. Then copy the following DNA sequence three times and include the complementary strand.

ATGAGATCTACGGAATTCTCAAGTTCGAATCG

Identify where each restriction enzyme will cut the strand.

DNA Restriction Enzymes

Enzyme	Recognition Sequence
BglII	A ▼ GATCT TCTAG ▲ A
EcoRI	G ▼ AATTC CTTAA ▲ G
HindIII	CTTAA ▲ G A ▼ AGCTT TTCGA ▲ A

Consider the Issues

28. **Make a New Organism** If you could use genetic engineering to create a new organism or to mass-produce a product, what would it be? How would it affect the world? What safety precautions might you take? You may illustrate or create a model to accompany your answer.

Make New Connections

29. **Biology and Cartoons** What is the joke in the following cartoon? How is the cartoon

"Looks like we grafted a few too many human genes into the kohlrabi."

inaccurate? Critique the cartoon using your knowledge of genetic engineering.

30. **Biology and Economics** Find a genetically engineered product at the grocery store or pharmacy. Examples include engineered produce, cheese containing chymosine, or human insulin. Compare the price of the engineered product with that of the traditionally produced product. Is there a difference? Why or why not?

31. **Biology and Community: A Project** Interview someone who has been affected by genetic engineering—an employee in the field, a farmer, or a person treated with genetically engineered medicine. Ask about his or her experiences, both positive and negative, and inquire about any misconceptions he or she may have had or encountered.

LOOKING FORWARD TO CHAPTER 10
People can change genomes through biotechnology. Other environmental influences can also affect genomes. In the next unit you will learn about theories that explain how traits of organisms have changed over time.

Chapter Review

Test your knowledge of the **words** and **ideas** presented in the chapter by answering questions. Challenge your understanding by answering the **critical thinking** questions in **Take It Further.** Use the questions in **Consider the Issues** and **Make New Connections** to extend the Chapter content.

CHECKPOINT 9.4

1. What are some safety precautions scientists use when working with genetically engineered organisms?
2. Identify a benefit and a concern in connection with the alteration of human genes.
3. **Critical Thinking** What are the possible harmful, long-term effects of engineering a crop to resist weed killers?

Build on What You Know

4. How could the scientific method help resolve safety and ethical issues related to biotechnology? *(Need...*

Checkpoint

Evaluate what you have learned in each section by answering the **CHECKPOINT** questions. A **critical thinking** question gives you an opportunity to demonstrate your understanding. And the **Build on What You Know** question connects concepts in different chapters.

Unit 2 Review

THE BIG IDEA Answering the following questions will help you to link ideas and grasp the core concepts.

Connect the Chapters

1. Compare recombination as it occurs in crossing over with the recombinant DNA technology used to produce insulin.
2. Explain why gene therapy for cystic fibrosis does not prevent the malfunctioning gene from being passed on to offspring.
3. Compare Mendel's breeding experiments with pea plants to biotechnology.
4. Contrast the use of test crosses and DNA markers to identify carriers of recessive genes.
5. How are chromosomes, genes, codons, anticodons, and proteins related?
6. Explain how Griffith's 1928 experiment with bacterial strains was an early example of genetic engineering.

Connect the Units

7. Cells do not need as much energy to produce RNA polymerase as they need to produce other proteins. Why?
8. Identify one event in the process of gene expression in a eukaryotic cell for which active transport is essential.
9. Explain the function of DNA polymerase during the interphase portion of the cell cycle.

Connect to Themes

10. **Unity and Diversity** How does eukaryotic gene expression show unity and diversity?
11. **Patterns and Changes** How do linked genes affect the Law of Independent Assortment?
12. **Systems and Interactions** How does the concentration of lactose control lactose digestion in E.coli?

project plans

1. In the past, marriages in European royal families were arranged to strengthen political alliances. The bride and groom were often related to some degree. Such inbreeding was widespread among the descendants of England's Queen Victoria. Unfortunately, strong political alliances did not lead to equally robust genes. One problem was the incidence of the genetic disorder hemophilia. Make a poster displaying a pedigree of Queen Victoria's lineage. Identify the descendants who carried the hemophilia gene, and those who expressed the gene.

2. As a class, research and experiment with varieties of a flower or vegetable. For example, find out how many varieties of tomatoes can be grown in your area. Then design an experiment to find the variety best suited for local soil and weather conditions.

CRITIC'S CORNER

The Double Helix, by Nobel Prize winner James D. Watson, tells the story of scientists and their determination to discover the structure of DNA. The book describes a scientific team working together to decipher a mystery (with a little help from x-rayed molecules). Each scientist had his or her own job to do, each had a unique way of helping out. The unity of these scientists, and their often humorous relationships with each other, make this book a page-turner for students of all interests and backgrounds.

A BOOK REVIEW BY STACIE SIMMONS OF KANSAS CITY, MISSOURI

The Double Helix
James D. Watson

SPOTLIGHT ON CAREERS

DR. KEITH BLACK
Neurosurgeon, UCLA Medical Center;
professor of neurosurgery at UCLA
Education: Neurological surgery residency;
general surgery internship; M.D., B.S.

"I specialize in brain tumors. Most of these tumors are very complex, and about half of them are malignant. One part of my work is surgery, because malignant tumors cannot be cured without it. I also do research—I try to find ways of curing or improving the treatment of brain tumors. One of the newer treatments is gene therapy. We aim to develop a brain-tumor vaccine. We've learned that tumors release proteins that turn off the ability of immune cells to fight disease. We genetically modify tumor cells so that they no longer release these proteins, then we can take the modified cells and inject them back into the patient. That way, the person's immune system can recognize the tumor's cells and fight them."

bioSURF Learn more about Dr. Black's cancer research at UCLA Johnson Cancer Center by visiting http://genetics.biosurf.com for more information.

"Science is a lot of fun. It's like solving a mystery, and you have to choose the way to find the answers." —ANAMARIA CRAICI

ANAMARIA CRAICI
College Intern at the National Cancer Institute,
National Institutes of Health
Education: College junior majoring in biochemistry and molecular biology; high school diploma

"I have always known that science was where I wanted to go. You work with an unknown, a question. I study the systems plants have to defend themselves against all kinds of pathogens. A pathogen is an organism that can cause a disease— a bacterium, or a virus, for example. My professor, Dr. Craig Tepper, is looking for genes that 'turn on' when a plant is attacked. My job is to do

nonradioactive DNA sequencing. By studying how plants defend themselves, we hope to learn how to induce plants to grow in places where they normally wouldn't, or grow plants that are dying."

bioSURF Find out about internships at the National Cancer Institute at the National Institutes of Health by visiting the site http://genetics.biosurf.com.

Unit Review

Integrate all the concepts you have learned throughout each unit by answering the questions and doing the activities in the **Unit Review**. Read a student's review of a book, film, or CD-ROM in **The Critic's Corner**. And through **Spotlight on Careers**, meet people whose lives exemplify biology in action.

The Authors...

Eric Strauss

In the years he has been teaching at Boston College, Eric Strauss has quadrupled enrollment in an introductory biology course for non-science majors. In addition, Eric helped start the Boston College Environmental Studies program and serves as the program director. His dynamic approach to teaching biology extends beyond the college classroom. High school students, college undergraduates, and graduate students conduct original research on animal behavior and ecology at a Cape Cod field research station run by Eric and his former high school teacher.

Marylin Lisowski

Before becoming professor of science education at Eastern Illinois University, Marylin taught Biology, Environmental Science, and Middle Level Science. She also directed a marine research station. Marylin shares her research experience with high-school teachers and students as she leads international expeditions and field programs. Dedicated to improving science education, Marylin has been the recipient of dozens of awards, including Ohio Science Teacher of the Year, Florida Honor Science Teacher, and Illinois Environmental Educator of the Year.

and others who have helped us

Content Reviewers

David M. Armstrong, Ph.D.
University of Colorado, Boulder, CO

John Ebinger, Ph.D.
Eastern Illinois University Charleston, IL

Paul R. Ecklund, Ph.D.
Cornell University Ithaca, NY

Dana M. García, Ph.D.
Southwest Texas State University San Marcos, TX

Alison Hill, Ph.D.
University of North Carolina Chapel Hill, NC

Rebecca A. Pyles, Ph.D.
East Tennessee State University Johnson City, TN

Gerald Skoog, Ed.D.
Texas Tech University Lubbock, TX

Teacher Reviewers

George Bacon
Crystal River High School Crystal River, FL

Mary Bonetati
Klein ISD Spring, TX

Bob Hembree
Newman-Smith High School Carrollton, TX

Michael Lopatka
Edgewater High School Orlando, FL

John Madden
Mountain View High School Tucson, AZ

Kim Mosely
The Colony High School The Colony, TX

Anne Tweed
Eaglecrest High School Aurora, CO

Jill Wallace
Lewisville High School Lewisville, TX

Dear Student Biologist:

Welcome to biology. We are delighted that you will be joining us in this exploration of life. Your teacher, your classmates, and this text-book are all part of a team that will guide you through the web of life. As biologists, we are excited by and inspired about the living world. As authors, we hope that you will come to share our excitement and inspiration.

Biology, like all of the sciences, is a process of discovery. It is a process with an impressive history and an incredible future. We want you to understand and appreciate the contributions of the past—as well as recognize and respond to the numerous possibilities that lie ahead. The biologists of today started their journey in a classroom similar to yours. Our program weaves current research and discoveries with insights made hundreds of years ago. Throughout your study, you will have the opportunity to make your own discoveries.

Many of these discoveries will apply to your everyday life. This may not surprise you: Biology is closely connected with all aspects of our day-to-day activities. Biology is also closely connected with the decisions you will be making about your future and the future of the planet Earth. It is our hope that your experience with this textbook and the "stuff" of biology will make you aware of and sensitive to the living world around you.

This is an exciting time to be learning biology. So, welcome aboard. Enjoy your discoveries. And, have fun!

Eric G. Strauss

Marylin Lisowski

CHAPTER 1
The Study of Life

You can find out more about the study of life by exploring the following Internet address:
http://basis_of_life.biosurf.com

In this chapter . . .

FEATURES

Everyday Biology
• Measurement Made Easy
• Get Organized!
• Fossil Walls
• Pasteur's Process

In the Community
Science in the News

 Environmental Awareness
Humans and the Web of LIfe

Issues in Biology
Science and Society

LAB ZONES

Discover It!
• Observing Ants

Do It!
• Comparing Living and Nonliving Things
• Observing Biodiversity

Think About It!
• Identifying Experimental Controls and Variables

Investigate It!
• Designing a Scientific Experiment

A CLOSER LOOK

All scientific knowledge begins with a search for answers to questions about our world. For example, imagine that you are on a central Texas plain where you notice a group of red insects. You kneel down to take a closer look. What do you see? There are two large ants and some smaller ones, as well as fine bits of gravel and things that appear to be eggs. Your observations leave you with many questions to be answered: What are the ants doing? Are they building something? Are they eating? Why are two ants so much larger than the others?

In science, the process of finding answers often leads to more questions. And each major scientific advance, such as the invention of the microscope, provides a new way of looking at our world that may lead to as many mysteries as it solves. Science is human curiosity at work, and biology is human curiosity about life. What do you, the biologist, see in the living world around you that you would like to know more about?

LAB ZONE Discover It!

Observing Ants

You need a small amount of sugar and salt, and some sand or very small pebbles

1. Locate an ant colony. (Be careful—some ants bite!) Some places to hunt are along cracks in pavement and in sandy areas in lawns or along streets. By observing carefully you should be able to find the main entrance to the nest. Observe the ants' activity.

2. Sprinkle some sugar near the nest and some salt in another area near the nest. Did the sugar and salt affect the ants' activity? If so, how?

3. Now drop several pebbles or some sand into the nest opening. What happens? After recording your observations, remove the salt, sugar, and pebbles.

Ants live in highly organized social groups. They respond as a group to threats to their safety and to new sources of food. They mark trails chemically, and the trails can easily be disrupted by objects or events.

A microscopic view of an ant

WRITE ABOUT IT!

Imagine that you, as a human and a member of society, are responding to threats from creatures the size of huge buildings. Write a story that describes how you would feel and react.

3

1.1 Similarities Among Living Things

What you'll learn

IDEAS
• To compare different theories of the origins of life
• To summarize the properties of life

WORDS
biosphere, organisms, spontaneous generation, biogenesis, cell, tissues, organs

A recipe for life?
Practiced in medieval times, alchemy was a blend of philosophy, early science, and magic. By following the right steps, alchemists thought they could transform common materials into precious metals or even create a formula for immortality. Of course, they never managed to make lead into gold or find the secret of life. However, alchemists did develop many of the first scientific instruments and techniques.

FIGURE 1.1
Before spontaneous generation was disproven, people actually wrote recipes for living things. The Roman poet Virgil wrote this recipe for bees.

Recipe for Bees

1. Kill a bull during the first thaw of winter.
2. Build a shed.
3. Place the dead bull on branches and herbs inside the shed.
4. Wait for summer. The decaying body of the bull will produce bees.

WHAT IS LIFE?

A very special status

We live in a part of Earth called the biosphere. The **biosphere** is the thin layer of air, land, and water that is home to all living things on Earth. Within the biosphere, the planet teems with life—from the microscopic bacteria that live on your skin to the huge humpback whales that cruise the Atlantic Ocean. The biosphere makes up much less than one percent of Earth's mass, yet when it comes to a discussion of life, this is where the action is!

All living things are called **organisms.** Organisms obey the same laws of physics and chemistry as do nonliving things. So what makes life special? How can we clearly recognize some things as being alive and other things as not? For most people, this distinction usually seems obvious. But this was not always so.

During much of human history, most cultures believed in a view of life called vitalism. According to this view, living things exist because they have been filled with special forces called ethers, which bring nonliving things to life. The Greek philosopher and scholar Aristotle, who lived 2300 years ago, held this view of life. Vitalism dominated Western culture for nearly 2000 years. During the Dark Ages in Europe, it gave rise to the idea of spontaneous generation.

Spontaneous generation is the process by which life begins when ethers enter nonliving things. You can see one example of a spontaneous generation "recipe" in *Figure 1.1.* In addition to this belief about the origin of bees, mice were thought to come from discarded rags, geese from the mud banks of rivers, and salamanders from wood and fire. Although these ideas may seem foolish now, they were accepted as facts many years ago.

In 1668 the Italian physician Francesco Redi performed two experiments to test spontaneous generation. His experiments involved maggots, wormlike larvae that develop into flies. According to the theory of spontaneous

FIGURE 1.2

Spontaneous Generation or Biogenesis?

Scientists in the early 1600s thought life came from nonliving things and ethers. Redi conducted experiments to test this theory. What did his experiments demonstrate?

1 Maggots were thought to come from rotting meat. When jars were left open, maggots did appear on rotting meat. Redi tried to prove whether this change was due to spontaneous generation or to biogenesis.

2 According to the theory of spontaneous generation, maggots did not appear in sealed jars because ethers could not enter the jars. According to the theory of biogenesis, maggots did not appear because flies could not enter the jars.

3 When jars were covered with cloth, maggots did not appear. Although the theoretical ethers could enter the jars in this setup, flies could not. The absence of maggots supported biogenesis.

generation, maggots emerged when rotting meat was filled with ethers. Redi suspected that the maggots came from flies. As you can see in *Figure 1.2,* Redi demonstrated that flies did account for the appearance of maggots on rotting meat. You will learn more about the scientific method Redi used in his experiments later in this chapter.

The debate over whether spontaneous generation occurred lasted for hundreds of years. The theory that eventually replaced spontaneous generation in the late 1800s is called biogenesis. **Biogenesis** is the principle that life comes only from life. "Bio-" literally means "life" and *genesis* means "beginning." According to this theory, each type of living organism produces more of its own kind, or species.

Another theory, sparked by the work of Redi and others, is called mechanism. According to this principle, both living and nonliving organisms obey the same laws of physics and chemistry. Living things, however, have a special status because of their complexity. But as you will see later, sometimes it is not so easy to distinguish between organisms and nonliving things. Stay tuned!

Ideas about what distinguishes a living organism from a nonliving thing have changed dramatically over the past 500 years. During this time, the rise of science as a tool for answering questions and solving problems has increased our understanding of how the world works.

New tools, such as the telescope and the microscope, allowed scientists to see things that had never been seen before. New theories about the structure of the natural world emerged during this time as well. The English physician William Harvey, for example, demonstrated that the human heart was a mechanical pump

Measurement Made Easy

The metric system of weights and measures made scientific communication much easier. The metric system is the international standard. Although we still use some English measurements, metric units are also common in the United States. Where have you seen metric units?

FIGURE 1.3
Organization

The snowflake has a very complex and structured organization. The plant root also has a regular pattern of organization. What differences make the root a living thing?

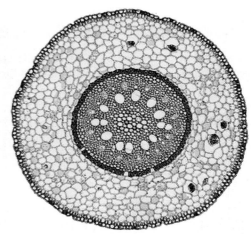

for blood and not the organ of emotion. Most important, the scientific revolution encouraged the study of the natural world and the development of new ideas.

PROPERTIES OF LIFE

To be or not to be

At this point, you may be wondering if there really is a difference between living and nonliving things. Would you be surprised to learn that at some physical level, the answer is actually no? Both living and nonliving objects are composed of the same materials. They are all made from the elements present on Earth, and they all obey the same laws of nature.

It is clear that organisms have characteristics that make them different from the nonliving world—characteristics that you can usually recognize. The characteristics of living things are organization, energy, growth and development, reproduction, and response and adaptation.

Many of these characteristics are not unique to living systems. Some can be found in nonliving objects as well. Clouds move across the sky; highly organized ice crystals appear to grow across a cold windowpane; fire consumes energy and can reproduce by starting other fires. But clouds do not adapt, ice crystals cannot reproduce, fire is is not made of cells, and it is not organized. So although some nonliving things have some of the characteristics of life, none show all of these characteristics.

Organization Living things are highly organized. Specialized structures perform specific functions at every level of organization, from a single bacterial cell to the multicellular human body. In most multicellular organisms, structures are organized according to repeating patterns.

The basic unit of organization in living things is the **cell.** All organisms are made of cells. Some organisms, such as protists and bacteria, are unicellular; they are made of only one cell. Others—multicellular organisms—are made of many cells. Multicellular organisms, such as plants and animals, can be composed of trillions of cells. Each cell of every organism displays the characteristics of life.

Energy Physicists—scientists who study the properties, changes, and interactions of matter and energy—have discovered that energy exists in many forms. Forms of energy include sound, light, and chemical energy. Each of these forms is important to living things. We use light energy, like that produced by the match shown

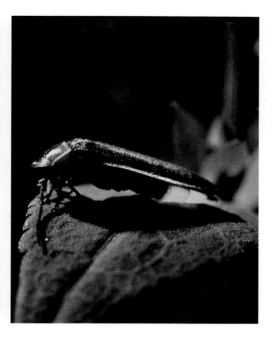

FIGURE 1.4
Energy
The match and the firefly both use energy. How do they differ? What characteristics make the firefly a living organism?

in *Figure 1.4,* to see. Living things also use energy for life processes. The firefly shown in *Figure 1.4* uses chemical energy to grow, fly, and produce its greenish glow.

Where does the energy needed for life processes come from? All organisms are able to take in energy from the environment and use it for their life processes. For example, light energy enables plants to make food from carbon dioxide and water. Some organisms take in chemical energy as food and use it for many daily activities.

Growth and development

Compare your body with the body of an infant. How have you changed? Humans, like all living things, grow and develop. Growth is an increase in size. Development is a change in shape or form. Look at the cloud and the butterfly shown in *Figure 1.5.* What makes one example living and the other nonliving?

The magnitude, or amount, of growth varies among living things. Some organisms grow very little. A single ameba, for example, does not change much in size. There is great change in the size of some organisms, however. An elephant grows from a

single fertilized egg cell into an enormous adult animal.

The nature of development also varies from species to species. Do you think that your body has changed much as you've grown? Compare the changes you have gone through with the development of a caterpillar or a tadpole, and you will soon realize that other organisms undergo developmen-

FIGURE 1.5
Growth and Development

Have you ever compared cloud shapes to living things? Although changes in the size and shape of clouds are similar to growth and development, clouds are not organisms. How do these cloud changes differ from the changes a caterpillar undergoes when it becomes a butterfly?

FIGURE 1.6
Reproduction

Although a camera can copy images, it cannot reproduce living things. The bacterium can reproduce—making a new bacterium.

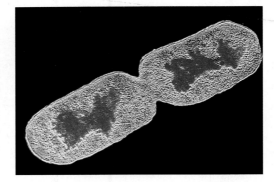

FIGURE 1.7
Response

A plant responds by growing toward a light source. How does this response compare with the response of the wheel to the water?

tal changes even more dramatic than those you have experienced.

Reproduction As you have learned, biogenesis explains that living things come from other living things. The process through which new living things are formed is called reproduction. Reproduction involves making new cells. A new cell can be part of an existing organism, part of a new organism, or an entirely new, independent unicellular organism.

Like growth and development, reproduction is part of the life cycle of many organisms. Without reproduc-

tion, there would be no living things to replace those that die. Although it is not necessary for each organism in a population to reproduce, reproduction is necessary for the survival of a species. Reproduction can result in an exact duplicate of the parent, or in duplication with variation.

Response and adaptation Have you ever blinked when your eye was irritated? Or sneezed in response to dust? Responding to stimuli is another characteristic shared by all living things.

Growth, migration, color changes, and movement are just a few of the many ways in which living things respond to environmental stimuli. Some seeds, for example, sprout in response to the presence of water. Some bird species respond to the change of seasons by migrating from place to place. What type of response is shown in *Figure 1.7*? How does the response of the plant differ from the response of the water wheel?

Adaptation is a way for an entire population of organisms to respond to long-term changes in their surroundings. Adaptations are passed on from generation to generation. You will learn more about adaptations and the theory of evolution later in this chapter and in Unit 3.

Each species has unique adaptations that enable it to survive in its particular environment. As a result, life can exist under some very extraordinary conditions. For example, one type of bacterium can survive the sub-freezing temperatures of the Arctic ice fields because it is able to produce a biological "antifreeze." Tube worms and giant clams live in the sulfur-rich vents of the ocean bottom where water temperatures reach the boiling point!

Wherever life is found, organisms must meet the challenges of survival. To varying degrees, all living things need water, temperatures within a certain range, and a source of energy. Most organisms also need oxygen. The more extreme the conditions, the more specialized organisms must be in order to survive.

THE ORGANIZATION OF LIFE

The architecture of the living world

As you now know, one of the characteristics of living systems is organization. The organization in the biosphere can be broken down to many different levels. You can see some of these levels illustrated in *Figure 1.8* on page 10. Biologists study life at each level of organization.

Some of these levels of organization are universal—present in all living things. For example, all organisms have cells and are part of a population, community, and ecosystem. Other levels of organization are present in some organisms but not in others. Humans and other animals have specialized tissues, organs, and systems. Bacteria, however, do not have these levels of organization.

The smallest level of organization

Do It!

Comparing Living and Nonliving Things

Can you tell which of two materials is made of living things and which is not? You can find out if you . . .

Try This

1 Examine the two substances that your teacher has given you. Use any instruments—magnifying glass, ruler, balance—you have available, and record your observations of appearance, weight, texture, and odor.
2 In a small bowl, mix each of the substances with the same amount of warm sugar water. Observe what takes place. Were there any changes in the characteristics you recorded in step 1?
3 Think of one more test you can perform that might provide a clue to whether the materials have a property of life.
4 Share the results of your tests with other class members.

Analyze Your Results

1 Did you or your classmates observe any signs of life? If so, which property of life might be demonstrated in the observation?
2 Do you think neither, one, or both of the substances are alive? Explain your answer.

of all things, living or not, is the atom. Atoms often bond to one another to form molecules. Molecules can consist of as few as two atoms, but most biological molecules are made of hundreds, or even thousands, of atoms. Biochemists and molecular biologists study the molecules essential to living organisms.

Cells are the fundamental units of life that exhibit all of the characteristics of living things. Even the largest organisms begin life as a single cell. Thousands of unicellular organisms, which you cannot see with the unaided eye, inhabit Earth.

Inside the cell are specialized "compartments" in which life's functions take place. The cell can be thought of as a complex factory that manufactures the products of life. Biologists who study cells are called

FIGURE 1.8

Levels of Organization

Each living thing can be made of atoms, molecules, cells, tissues, organs, and organ systems. The biosphere is made of individuals, populations, communities, and ecosystems.

1 Atom, molecule
Atoms are the smallest units of organization. They bind together to make molecules.

2 Cell
The cell is the basic unit of living things. Muscle cells are one of the types of cells that make up your heart.

8 Ecosystem
The ecosystem includes all of the communities in an area and all the nonliving things, such as snow, water, soil, and air.

3 Tissue
Muscle tissue, like all tissue, is made of a group of cells that work together to perform a specific function.

4 Organ
The heart is an organ. Several types of tissue, including muscle tissue, cardiac tissue, and connective tissue, make up this organ.

7 Population and community
A population is a group of similar organisms, such as turtles, living in the same place. The turtles and all the other populations in an area, including the reeds at the water's edge, make up a community.

6 Individual
Large multicellular organisms, such as this turtle, are made of several organ systems.

5 Organ system
The circulatory system is one of several organ systems that enable a turtle to survive.

cellular biologists or cytologists ("cyt-" means "cell").

In many multicellular organisms, cells are organized into tissues. **Tissues** are made of cells working together to perform a specific function. In the turtle shown in *Figure 1.8,* muscle, bone, and blood are examples of different types of tissues.

In many multicellular living things, tissues are further organized to form organs. **Organs** are made of several different types of tissues that function together for a specific purpose. Roots and leaves are organs found in members of the plant kingdom. The heart is a common organ in animals. What human organs can you identify?

In many organisms, organs are further organized into organ systems, made of several organs working together to perform a function. The circulatory, digestive, and reproductive systems are some of the organ systems in the human body. Together, the organ systems make up an individual organism. Doctors, zoologists, botanists, and other specialists study organ systems in different types of organisms.

The field of biology does not end with an understanding of individual organisms, however. After all, individual organisms interact with other living things. Population biologists study all the members of a particular type of organism living in an area. A population is a group of organisms of the same species that live together in a particular location. The turtles in a pond, the sugar maples in a forest, and the pigeons in a city are examples of populations. How would you describe your population?

Scientists who study the interactions of populations within an area focus on communities. Communities include all of the organism populations in a particular location. A lawn is an example of a community. The lawn community includes populations of grasses, insects, worms, bacteria, and other organisms. What populations share your community?

If you add all of the nonliving parts of a location to the community, you have an ecosystem. Ecosystems include all the living and nonliving elements in a location. Environmental biologists and conservation biologists study communities and ecosystems. Their studies confirm the long-held belief that there are no truly isolated areas on Earth. Events taking place in one part of the globe can have an effect on living organisms hundreds or even thousands of miles away! All forms of life are interconnected.

You are a new biologist. With this textbook, you will begin your study of biology by considering life at the smallest level of organization. You will discover how the basic characteristics of life are rearranged in an almost infinite number of ways to produce the diversity of life on Earth. When you have completed your study, you will increase your understanding and appreciation of the biosphere, which some scientists view as the largest living system of all.

Get Organized

There are different levels of organization in many fields. Our government has federal, state, and local levels, You may by familiar with your school's organizational levels—for example, school committee, principal, teaching staff, and student body. What other kinds of organization can you identify? Consider areas such as work, school, sports, or extracurricular activities.

CHECKPOINT 1.1

1. Compare the principles of spontaneous generation and biogenesis.

2. List and describe the characteristics of living things.

3. Choose an organism and identify the levels of organization that characterize it and its environment.

4. Critical Thinking A copier machine displays many of the characteristics of a living thing, including the use of energy and the ability to reproduce. Explain why it is not alive.

Build on What You Know

5. Which levels of organization have you studied in previous science courses?

1.2 Adaptation and Interdependence

What you'll learn

IDEAS

• To explain how organisms respond and adapt to their environment
• To compare the various interdependent relationships of organisms
• To summarize the role of humans in the ecosystem

WORDS

predator, prey

Heading for the north country
Edith's checkerspot butterflies, found along North America's Pacific coast, are homebodies. An entire population can live in a small area for many generations. Yet these butterflies have begun steadily moving north—perhaps in response to the gradual warming of the Earth's atmosphere. In the increasingly warm south, checkerspots are dying out.

ADAPTATION

The struggle to survive

Earth has a very long history—over four billion years! During that time, conditions on Earth have changed a great deal, and they will surely continue to change. The ability to respond and adapt to changes in the environment is one of the most important characteristics of living things. This ability includes adjustments for short-term changes, such as the temperature difference between day and night, and long-term changes, such as the warming or cooling of Earth over thousands of years. Living organisms must have characteristics that enable them to cope with these changes or they will die out.

Responses to most short-term changes can often occur quickly and easily with a change in behavior. For example, the Bengal tiger shown in *Figure 1.9* may wake up cold at dawn and move into the direct rays of the rising sun to warm up. At midday, however, the tiger may escape the heat of the sun by seeking the shade of a tree.

But what about the long-term changes that tigers face? The Bengal tiger's natural environment has changed dramatically during the past century. Cities and towns have formed in what used to be the animals' hunting ground. How will the tigers adapt to changes in the supply of food, water, and living space? These adaptations require changes in the very nature of the entire species. In fact, the characteristics and behaviors of modern tigers are the result of adaptations that allowed the tigers to cope with changes in the past.

Until about two hundred years ago, the idea of a changing world was unacceptable. Throughout recorded human history, life seemed very stable. Tigers have looked and acted relatively the same for as long as anyone has been observing them and writing about them.

FIGURE 1.9
Daily life for this Bengal tiger requires reacting to various changes in its environment, such as temperature fluctuations.

By the 1700s, however, geologists had uncovered evidence that Earth's history was full of change. Older layers of Earth's crust reveal organisms that flourished millions of years ago, and these organisms are different from those living today. For example, fossils reveal the existence of the saber-toothed tiger, a cat species quite different from the Bengal tiger. Compare the saber-toothed tiger skull shown in *Figure 1.11* with the Bengal tiger shown on page 12. How are these species similar? Different?

Species that no longer exist are said to be extinct. The saber-toothed tiger is an example of an extinct species. You may be familiar with other extinct groups, or species, such as dinosaurs, woolly mammoths, and dodo birds. The extinction of a species is a concern for several reasons. Species are interdependent—they rely on one another. The loss of a species always affects other organisms.

Fossil evidence shows that many species have become extinct over Earth's history. The discovery of fossil evidence of an extinct species was clearly at odds with the traditional view that Earth and its inhabitants had remained unchanged since they came into being. By the middle of the nineteenth century, the evidence for a changing Earth was strong.

What was missing, however, was an explanation of how Earth's changes might lead to changes in organisms. Charles Darwin, the English naturalist, proposed a theory to answer this important question. While earlier scientists had used the term evolution, it was Darwin who first explained how evolution may be involved in changes in organisms over time.

Darwin viewed life as a competitive struggle for Earth's limited resources. Most often, more living things are born than can survive. Only those organisms that can successfully compete for Earth's resources can survive and reproduce. The traits that enable an organism to survive are passed to its offspring. The theory of evolution states that these traits can eventually become adaptations for the entire species.

EVERYDAY BIOLOGY

Fossil Walls

In New York City you can take a tour of fossils on display in an unusual place—on the surfaces of public buildings! Ancient stone used in construction often contains fossilized remains. Check stone buildings in your area for fossils.

FIGURE 1.11
This skull belongs to a large predator known as the saber-toothed tiger. Now extinct, this animal roamed North America during the late Pleistocene period.

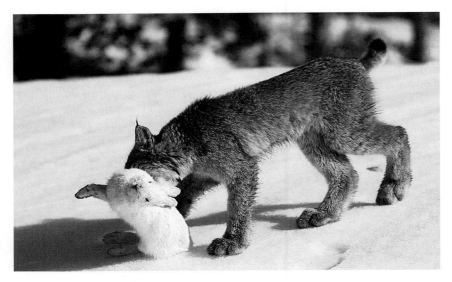

FIGURE 1.12
The lynx population is dependent on the hare population for survival.

INTERDEPENDENCE

The web of life has many connections

Organisms have complex interactions with their environments. Each species requires a very precise combination of temperature, moisture, soil composition, and other environmental conditions in order to survive. Organisms are tightly connected to the nonliving world in which they live. Complex relationship webs also connect organisms to other

organisms. As you read this textbook, you will learn about many of these relationships. Each chapter about a specific group of organisms includes a section that explains the roles that group plays in the biosphere.

Many of the roles that organisms play involve food—how they obtain food and how other organisms might use them for food. Many organisms depend upon a specific plant or animal for food. This relationship is called a predator-prey relationship. A **predator** is an organism that kills and eats another organism. The organism that is eaten is the **prey.** Consider the predator-prey relationship shown in *Figure 1.12*. Which animal in the photo is the predator? Which animal is the prey?

In a predator-prey relationship, the need of one organism to respond and adapt to evolutionary changes drives the process of adaptation in both species. For example, if the predator population begins to use a new, more efficient way to hunt and catch prey, the prey population must develop new ways to avoid getting caught. If

FIGURE 1.13
The crab *Lybia tessellata* carries a pair of anemones on its claws. In this mutualistic relationship, the crab gets protection from the anemones' stinging tentacles, while the anemones benefit from the crab's mobility.

the prey species began to escape its predators, how would the predator population be affected?

The predator-prey relationship is one of the many types of interrelationships you will read about as you study living things. In other types of relationships, one organism depends on another living thing for shelter, for protection from predators, and for access to resources such as light or water. Relationships in which different species depend upon each other are known as symbiosis. Symbiosis is one of the characteristics of the interdependence among organisms. There are three types of symbiosis—mutualism, commensalism, and parasitism.

In mutualism, both partners in a symbiotic relationship benefit from their association. *Figure 1.13* shows one example of mutualism. The crabs benefit from the relationship with anemones because they are protected by the anemones' stinging tentacles. The anemones also benefit from their relationship with crabs. When crabs feed, some food particles are scattered into the surrounding water. The anemones take in this food with their tentacles.

Commensalism, a second kind of symbiosis, is a relationship in which one partner benefits and the other partner is unaffected. The bromeliad and tree shown in *Figure 1.14* are partners in a relationship that demonstrates commensalism. Bromeliads growing high on tree branches benefit by gaining greater exposure to sunlight. The tree, on the other hand, is neither helped nor harmed by the presence of the bromeliad. How does this relationship differ from mutualism?

In parasitism, the relationship between an organism and its partner is one-sided. One member of a partnership (the parasite) benefits from the relationship, and the other (the host) is harmed. How do the

parasites shown in *Figure 1.15* affect their hosts?

Understanding the interdependence among organisms helps us to understand the fragile nature of the biosphere. The relationships may have evolved over millions of years and may be quite specialized.

Even a small change to one type of organism, such as a change in its population size, can have a major impact on all the other organisms in an environment. If long-term relationships change before all the organisms involved can adapt, some organisms will become extinct. It is often difficult, if not impossible, to predict how a change in one species or one aspect of the environment could affect the other organisms in the area. The connections among living things are like a spider's web. Each thread in the web of life is a species. If one thread is disturbed, the entire web can be threatened.

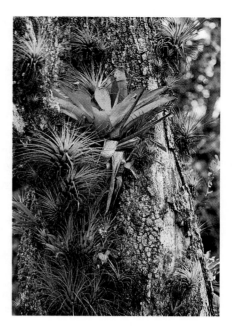

FIGURE 1.14
This bromeliad lives on the trunk of a tree and benefits from the tree's height.

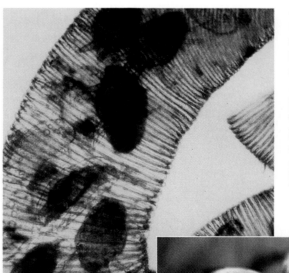

FIGURE 1.15
Many parasites can seriously injure or kill their hosts. The tracheal mite (left) lives and breeds in the tracheal tubes of honeybees, obstructing the flow of oxygen and killing the bee. The velvet mite (below) is a plant parasite that harms or kills its host.

Humans and the Web of Life

You are part of the web of life—the "structure" that represents the interconnectedness of living things. As part of that web, you affect and are affected by the living things around you. Without an understanding of biology, you will not be able to make wise decisions about many issues that affect you, your family, and your community.

Take a look around you. How many objects can you identify that are living, made from living things, or made from the products of living things? Did you include all the wood products? How about plastics, clothing, and paper? All these things and many more are made from or by organisms. Biology affects many aspects of everyday life, including food, clothing, shelter, and health.

Biotechnology is the use of organisms to produce things that people need. For example, using bacteria to turn milk into cheese or yogurt is a biotechnology technique people have practiced for centuries. Modern techniques, such as genetic engineering, have greatly increased the applications of biotechnology. Biotechnology is essential for farming, livestock management, food processing and preservation, medicine, and many other human needs.

Food You cannot live more than three months without food, which gives you energy to carry out all your activities. All foods are made directly from living things or indirectly from the products of living things.

The science of biology has helped improve the quantity and quality of food available to people all over the world. As you may know, plants we use as food can grow in the wild. Many animal food sources, such as fish, are also wild. At one time in human history, people depended on wild, unmanaged resources for all food. Today most of the food supply for people comes from managed areas, such as the sheep farm shown in *Figure 1.16*. Farmers use biology to plan their farms and cultivate crops. Ranchers use biology to feed, breed, and care for their animals.

Medicine Living things provide many solutions to medical problems. The discovery and production of

FIGURE 1.16

Natural and Managed Ecosystems

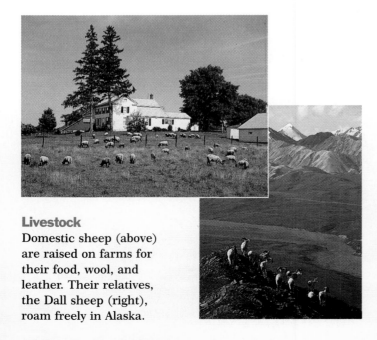

Livestock
Domestic sheep (above) are raised on farms for their food, wool, and leather. Their relatives, the Dall sheep (right), roam freely in Alaska.

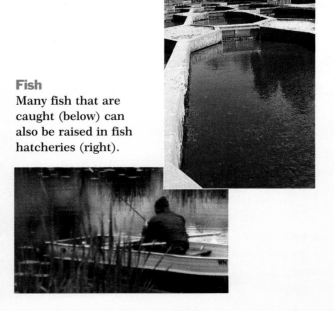

Fish
Many fish that are caught (below) can also be raised in fish hatcheries (right).

medicines has changed many diseases from fatal illnesses into minor inconveniences. The role of biology in health goes beyond the treatment of illnesses. Healthful community practices of water treatment, garbage disposal, and food handling can prevent many kinds of human suffering.

Clothing Most clothing is made from biological products. Wool, silk, and leather come from animal products. Cotton and linen are common plant materials used for clothing. Biotechnology has expanded the types of living things we can use as sources for clothing. Rayon, for example, is made using wood chips.

Additional resources Many fuels are made from the remains or the products of organisms. For example, wood comes from plants and coal comes from the fossilized remains of plants. Petroleum products, such as oil and gasoline, are made from the decayed remains of tiny marine organisms that lived millions of years ago. Together, petroleum and coal are referred to as fossil fuels.

We rely on living things for many other materials and products as well. As you can see in *Figure 1.16* below,

some trees are farmed and some flowers are cultivated. We use trees and other plants to build structures and make paper. We also rely on trees in managed and natural ecosystems to recycle oxygen and carbon dioxide and provide shade and shelter from the wind. What other living resources can you think of?

Living things are priceless

Perhaps the most important reason to gain an understanding of biology is to help protect the diverse life of the biosphere. Biology reveals the interactions between organisms and their environments.

It is not always easy to predict the value of a species. Although some plants and animals may seem at a given time to have little impact on human survival, nothing could be further from the truth. For example, in the early 1990s the Pacific yew tree was found to contain a chemical that may be useful in treating certain types of human cancer. The yew tree tends to grow among valuable timber

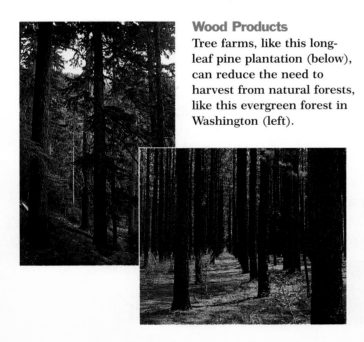

Wood Products
Tree farms, like this long-leaf pine plantation (below), can reduce the need to harvest from natural forests, like this evergreen forest in Washington (left).

Flowers
Wildflowers can be seen blooming in many habitats, such as the field of paintbrushes in California (below). Flowers can also be planted in cultivated gardens (right).

Do It!

Observing Biodiversity

The biodiversity of an ecosystem refers to the numbers of organisms that have adapted to live there. You can explore the biodiversity of your community when you . . .

Try This

1 Go to a park, woodland, or other unpaved outdoor location. With nails or pegs, measuring stick, and string, mark out an area one meter square.
2 Take a census of living organisms in the marked-off area (a hand lens will help). Count, as accurately as you can, the number of individual organisms you find. Sketch and describe the different types of plants and animals you observe. Record your observations.
3 When you are done, remove your materials and leave the location as you found it. Record the time, place, and weather conditions of your study.

Analyze Your Results

1 How many different types of organisms did you find? Which types were the most abundant? Was it easy or hard to count individual organisms? Why?
2 How different do you think your results would be if your study had taken place at a different time of year, a different time of day, or in a different location or climate?

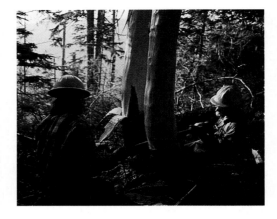

FIGURE 1.17
The bark of the Pacific yew tree contains a chemical called taxol, effective in treating certain types of cancer.

environment? It is impossible to predict whether or how living things will adapt to future changes. But it is possible to understand, appreciate, and protect the intricate, delicate web of life.

CHECKPOINT 1.2

1. Choose an organism and describe a typical response. How is the species adapted to its environment?
2. Describe ways in which organisms depend on other organisms.
3. How do humans rely on other organisms?
4. Critical Thinking Give an example of a type of organism that humans depend upon for survival. How would life change if this organism became extinct?

Build on What You Know

5. List three examples of nonliving products developed from living things. Describe which properties of life they have, and which they do not have. *(Need to jog your memory? Revisit relevant concepts in Section 1.1.)*

trees and is considered by the lumber industry to be a weed. Before the discovery of its medicinal value, the yew tree was almost driven to extinction.

Without the knowledge that biology brings, it will be impossible for the growing human population to exist alongside the other species on Earth, and guarantee the continued survival of all of Earth's diverse species. Many people wonder about Earth's future. Will most organisms survive the rapid changes currently taking place in the

What are the characteristics that living things share?

1.3 Doing the Science of Biology

Who is a scientist?
What does your mental image of a scientist look like? Someone in a white lab coat? A scientist is generally defined as a person having expert knowledge in science. But you can begin learning to do science right now, like the students in the photograph, who are collecting samples to test the water in their community.

What you'll learn

IDEAS
• To summarize the scientific method
• To explain the role of science in society

WORDS
scientific method, hypothesis, variable, control setup, theory

SCIENTIFIC METHOD

The "how to" of science

We all observe the world around us, in order to survive! We observe our surroundings so we can reach destinations without running into obstacles. We observe the weather so we can wear appropriate clothing. And so on. What makes the observations of a scientist different from those of the casual observer? The answer lies in understanding the process of doing science in general, and of doing biology in particular.

The work of science, and of any other discipline, involves the careful observation of events. Scientists make meaningful connections between their observations and past observations made by themselves and others. Mastering science is like mastering any other discipline, such as law, art, and philosophy. In science and in

FIGURE 1.18
Making Observations

Smell
The unpleasant odor of the giant carrion flower may give clues about interactions with its environment.

Sound
Observations made by sound, such as the trumpeting of an elephant, can be sensed by the ears or enhanced with technology. The scientist above is recording bird songs.

Sight
Observations made by sight can give clues about physical variance within a species. The male and female argus pheasants have a very different appearance.

FIGURE 1.19
The development of the microscope allowed scientists to make observations on a cellular level. A light microscope was used to photograph fat cells (near right), and a scanning electron microscope was used to photograph fat in human skin cells (far right).

other disciplines, researchers build upon the historical record and follow logical paths to reach new conclusions about their field of expertise.

Science has some unique features that make it different from other fields of study, however. One of those features is a sequence of logical steps to generate new ideas, answer questions, and draw conclusions. Although the exact sequence of these steps can vary depending on the nature of a question, the characteristic steps in a scientific inquiry are commonly called the scientific method.

The **scientific method** is a process that involves making predictions, designing an experiment that tests those predictions, making careful observations of that experiment, and interpreting those observations. Often, the results of one experiment form the basis for predicting the results of the next experiment.

As you read earlier in this chapter, spontaneous generation was at one time an accepted scientific idea. Now the principle of biogenesis is used to explain life. But how did scientists first support biogenesis? They used the scientific method.

Observations The process of science begins with making careful observations. Sometimes, making observations requires little more than

carefully looking at an object. But there is much more to life than can be observed with the unaided human eye.

Many of the tools used by scientists enable them to observe things that cannot otherwise be seen. The progress of modern science is therefore tied directly to the invention of tools that help scientists observe. For example, the invention of the microscope hundreds of years ago enabled scientists to learn about the cellular nature of life. Medical equipment allows doctors to observe changes within a patient's body. A Geiger counter, which converts radiation into audible clicks, enables scientists to observe invisible radioactivity.

Observations are often confused with conclusions. Conclusions are assumptions that are based on observations. What would you think, for example, if you observed a pot of boiling water? Would you conclude that the water temperature was 100°C? Many people would probably draw this conclusion. However, you cannot know the temperature of the water, without measuring it. Factors such as air pressure and dissolved substances can result in water boiling at different temperatures. The water could, in fact, be 105°C or 95°C. How might you accurately determine the water temperature?

In science, it is very important to distinguish between observations and conclusions. As you conduct experiments, make sure you record your observations carefully. Consider your observations thoughtfully before drawing conclusions.

Hypotheses Observations inspire curiosity, which can then lead to a hypothesis. A **hypothesis** is a possible explanation for an event or set of observations. Hypotheses are sometimes confused with the observations themselves. Suppose, for example, that you observed a scene like the one shown in *Figure 1.20*. You might think that hyenas kill zebras. This explanation of an animal's behavior is a hypothesis. It proposes an explanation for your observations. Spontaneous generation, the explanation that living things come from nonliving things, was a hypothesis that was used to explain the birth of new organisms.

Often scientists formulate several hypotheses before designing an experiment. The zebra below, for example, may have been killed by other animals, such as lions. The hyenas may be scavengers. Before you begin any experiment, consider many different possible hypotheses.

Although hypotheses are not facts, they are not simply wild guesses either. Scientific hypotheses are based on investigating scientists' observations, including the results of experiments. A hypothesis serves as a prediction about the outcome of an experiment.

Experiments To test a hypothesis, a scientist must design an experiment that focuses directly on the problem being investigated. The hypothesis must be clearly stated at the beginning of the experiment. The results of the experiment will either support or disprove the hypothesis.

All experiments have variables. A **variable** is a factor that can change in an experiment. Temperature, length of time, size, and chemical composition are possible variables with which you may be familiar. Scientific experiments are designed so that only one variable is tested in each experiment. The variable being tested is called the experimental variable.

A scientific experiment is not considered valid if there is more than one experimental variable. To add certainty to the cause-and-effect

FIGURE 1.20
How would you explain the scene shown here? What other information would you need to support any hypothesis you make?

FIGURE 1.21
Pasteur's Scientific Experiment
How does Pasteur's experiment demonstrate the scientific method?

Control setup

One year passes

Experimental setup

One day passes

1 The broth is heated. The curved neck of the flask prevented dust from entering the broth.

2 After one year, Pasteur observed the broth again and there were still no bacteria!

1 The straight neck allowed dust from the air to settle in the broth. All other variables were kept constant.

2 After one day, the broth was cloudy. When Pasteur observed a sample under the microscope, he found bacteria.

relationship between the experimental variable and the observed results, all other variables must be controlled. In a **control setup,** all factors remain the same during the experiment, except for the change in the experimental variable.

In 1862 the French chemist Louis Pasteur performed an experiment that helped to support biogenesis. Although Redi and others had disproved spontaneous generation in various ways, the scientific steps used by Pasteur finally convinced most of the remaining skeptics. The experiment still serves as an elegant model of scientific experimentation.

Louis Pasteur was one of many scientists who challenged the idea of spontaneous generation. Prior to Pasteur's discovery that microorganisms cause disease, doctors did not understand why surgical patients died of infection so often. His discovery of this relationship, called the germ theory, changed modern medicine forever.

Supporters of spontaneous generation observed that microorganisms could grow in broth where there had previously been no life. They claimed that life arose from an "active principle" that was present in the broth.

After repeated observations of microorganisms, Pasteur hypothesized that the bacteria that grew in broth were carried by dust particles falling from the air, and that the bacteria did not arise spontaneously from broth. To test his hypothesis, Pasteur designed a controlled experiment.

He set up two different flasks—one with a curved neck and the other with a straight neck. The variable Pasteur chose to isolate in this experiment was the exposure to dust from the air. He exposed each flask to dust in the air. However, dust that entered the flask with the curved neck remained in the neck and did not reach the broth.

In order to isolate this variable, Pasteur had to control the other variables, such as temperature, light, and the amount of broth. To ensure that both flasks were free of contaminants, Pasteur boiled the broth in both flasks. With the experimental variable isolated, Pasteur conducted

Pasteur's Process

You may have seen the word "pasteurized" on milk cartons. It means that the milk was heated to a high temperature to kill disease-causing microorganisms. This process is named for Louis Pasteur.

his experiment. *Figure 1.21* shows Pasteur's results.

When Pasteur observed the results of his experiment, he found bacteria in the flask with a straight neck, but no bacteria in the flask with the curved neck. This observation supported the hypothesis that exposure to dust resulted in the appearance of bacteria.

Theory A hypothesis that is supported by many experiments done over a period of time is called a **theory.** Like hypotheses, theories can be confused with facts. Theories are not facts. Theories are probable explanations for events that are supported by a wide range of evidence.

There are many theories that explain the characteristics of living things. Biogenesis is a theory. It is supported by experiments performed by Redi, Pasteur, and other scientists. Other scientific theories you will learn about in this textbook include the cell theory, the theory of evolution, and the germ theory.

It might surprise you to learn that one of the main characteristics of science is uncertainty. Theories are constantly challenged and refined as new discoveries are made. Throughout this course, you will read about and participate in experiments that test theories. You will also learn more about current debates among scientists and about refinements or changes to theories. We encourage you to thoughtfully question theories, propose hypotheses, and analyze the information presented in this textbook. Questioning, hypothesizing, and analyzing are important scientific skills.

ISSUES IN BIOLOGY

Science and society

For a subject to be studied scientifically, one must be able to observe and test it. Questions about ethics and values cannot be tested scientifically. Scientists

Identifying Experimental Controls and Variables

While conducting his experiment on spontaneous generation, Redi was careful to have only one experimental variable and to control all other factors that might change during the course of the experiment. Learn how to evaluate variable and control conditions by analyzing Redi's experiment.

Analyzing the Experiment

1 Study the setups in Redi's experiment shown in Figure 1.2 on page 5. What is the variable in Redi's experiment? How are the conditions of the experiment altered using this variable?
2 What factors were the same in both the experimental setup and the control setup? That is, what were the controlled variables in the experiment?
3 How could the experiment be altered to test a new variable?

cannot construct experiments to answer such questions.

All people, including scientists, must carefully consider the way they use the products of science. The products of science can be of great benefit to humans and to the environment. However, science can also deliver products that have the potential to cause harm. Often, the question of what to do with scientific discoveries must be considered along with the ethics and values of society. The question of how a particular scientific breakthrough can be used is usually determined by scientists. How it is actually used depends, at least in part, on the values of society.

Science and scientists If experimental results, or data, support a hypothesis, scientists can use the results to make further hypotheses. Two very important features of science relate to experimental results.

First, experimental results must be made public along with the methods

FIGURE 1.22
A scientist points to some fur caught in the bark of a damaged tree—presumably from an Alaskan brown bear. How might such observations about the environment influence public policy?

by which the experiments were conducted. This process is called peer review. Scientists provide all important experimental data to others working in their field so that others can analyze the results. After a panel of peers agrees that the experiments were sound, the work can be published and made available to other scientists and to the general public.

Science that is examined in this rigorous way is often published in scientific journals. Currently there are more than ten thousand peer-reviewed journals in the field of biology alone! The experiments that you will conduct as student-scientists will follow a similar path, as the data are reviewed by your teacher and fellow students.

The second important aspect of science is that the results of experiments must be repeatable. Once the experimental results are published, other labs will try the same experiments in order to get the same results. If the same results can be achieved by other scientists, the original work can be considered a legitimate contribution to the field of science.

Sometimes scientists must be patient. Experiments may take a long time to conduct, and experimental results may not reach a target audience for a long time. The most important factor is the honesty of the science and the validity of the results. But caution is necessary because the information will become part of the scientific foundation upon which new knowledge will be built. When he commented on the historical nature of experimental science, Sir Isaac Newton (1642–1727), the great English mathematician and inventor of calculus, stated eloquently, "We see farther because we can stand on the shoulders of giants."

Science and change Another feature of science is its changeable nature. Scientists do not consider their ideas to be absolute facts. One cannot accept scientific theory on faith. Scientists must always be ready to change or reject an idea if new evidence disproves it.

New techniques and tools often provide such evidence. Innovative technology may open up new branches of science. For example, the field of genetic engineering grew

FIGURE 1.23
You do not have to be a scientist to make an impact on the living world. The volunteers working to save these beached pilot whales come from many different professions.

from the development of techniques to alter the traits of bacteria.

Sometimes the needs of society change the direction that scientific progress takes. For example, many significant scientific breakthroughs resulted from our exploration of space. On the other hand, scientific developments can change the direction that society takes. Can you think of examples of scientific developments that have affected your life?

Science and public policy Data collected by scientists are often used to make public policy. Many of the laws and regulations in our society are the direct result of scientific evidence collected in response to a problem. Laws about environmental issues, food and drug safety, and wildlife management are most often based on biological data collected by experimentation.

Most science is funded by grants from public agencies such as the National Science Foundation. These agencies are supported by tax dollars from citizens like your family members.

Therefore, all citizens have a voice and a contributing role in the progress of science.

Science cannot answer all of the questions of society or address all of the conditions of planet Earth, however. Remember that the scientific method requires a question that can be approached experimentally. The unknowns, or variables, must be clearly identifiable, and the results repeatable. Some of the important questions that stir the human soul may never be answered by science.

CHECKPOINT 1.3

1. Describe the scientific method.
2. How can scientific experiments affect society?
3. **Critical Thinking** Design and describe an experiment to test whether temperature alone can affect the growth rate of a plant.

Build on What You Know

4. How are politicians and other non-scientists involved in protecting fragile environments?

What is the scientific method? ?

Designing a Scientific Experiment

WHAT YOU WILL DO Design and carry out a scientific experiment

SKILLS YOU WILL USE Estimating, predicting, observing, recording data

WHAT YOU WILL NEED Living plants or seeds, other materials and measuring instruments

Propose a Hypothesis

You know that plants need water and light for healthy growth. What other factors or substances might affect a plant's growth? Soil conditions? Fertilizer or nutrients? Music or human conversation? Choose a variable, then propose a hypothesis about how the presence and absence of that factor affects the growth or survival of a plant.

Conduct Your Experiment

1 Outline the steps of your experiment. Identify the variable and the controls in your experiment. (Remember, there should be only one experimental variable—the presence or absence of the factor you are testing.)

2 Select a time period for your experiment.

3 Specify the data that you will observe in the experimental and control setups. Choose data that can be accurately measured and compared.

4 Conduct your experiment and record your observations.

Analyze Your Data

1 Compare the measured data from the experimental and control plants.

2 Organize your data into a table.

3 Make a graph to display your results.

Draw Conclusions

Did the presence of your experimental variable make a difference in the growth of the experimental and control plants? Was the effect more or less than you had proposed?

Design a Related Experiment

Design an experiment that would give information on another factor that might affect plant growth.

Designing a Scientific Experiment

Variable: soil type
Control: water
light
temperature

Chapter 1 Review

 THE BIG IDEA!
> **1.1–1.2** Living things share many characteristics, including organization and adaptation.
> **1.3** Scientists use careful observation and controlled experiments to study the natural world.

Sum It Up

Use the following summary to review the main concepts in this chapter.

1.1 Similarities Among Living Things

- Redi's experiments in 1668 disproved spontaneous generation, showing that organisms arise only from other organisms.
- Although some nonliving things share some of the characteristics of living things, none displays the entire set of characteristics.
- The characteristics of living things are organization into cells; processes that are fueled by energy; growth and development; reproduction; response and adaptation.
- There are many levels of organization in the biosphere: Atoms make up molecules, which are the components of cells. Cells can be organized into tissues, and tissues into organs with specific functions. The organ systems make up an organism. Organisms form populations, and populations form communities within an ecosystem.

1.2 Adaptation and Interdependence

- Fossils of extinct species show that life has changed over time. Darwin explained how competition for resources could account for the evolution of species.
- Organisms are connected to one another and to the environment through complex webs of relationships. Relationships between organisms can be one-sided or beneficial to both partners.

- Symbiotic relationships include mutualism, where both partners benefit; commensalism, where one partner benefits without harming the other; and parasitism, where one partner benefits and the other is harmed.
- Humans are dependent on other organisms for food, medicine, clothing, fuel, and shelter.

1.3 Doing the Science of Biology

- Scientists make careful observations, develop hypotheses based on observations, and design experiments to test hypotheses.
- Scientists distinguish between observations and any conclusions that may be based on observations.
- To test hypotheses, scientists design experiments in which they control all variables except the one being tested.
- Scientific theories are challenged and refined as scientists submit their data for peer review. Scientific results must be repeatable.
- Results of scientific experiments are made public. Often public policy is based on scientific data. Scientific research is often funded by public agencies.

Use Terms and Concepts

**Use each of the following words or terms in a complete sentence.
If you need to review a meaning, turn to the page indicated.**

biosphere (p. 4)

organisms (p. 4)

spontaneous generation (p. 4)

biogenesis (p. 5)

cell (p. 6)

tissues (p. 11)

organs (p. 11)

predator (p. 14)

prey (p. 14)

scientific method (p. 20)

hypothesis (p. 21)

variable (p. 21)

control setup (p. 22)

theory (p. 23)

Use Your Word Power

COMPLETION **Write the word or phrase that best completes each statement.**

1. The smallest unit of life that displays all the characteristics of life is the _____ .

2. The process that involves designing experiments to test hypotheses is called the _____ .

3. A(n) _____ contains several different types of tissues that function together.

4. The _____ is that part of Earth in which life exists.

5. The size of the _____ population can affect the size of a predator population.

6. Any factor that can change during an experiment is called a(n) _____ .

7. Bacteria, butterflies, grasses, and bears are all examples of living things, or _____ .

TRUE-FALSE **Write true if the statement is true. If the statement is false, replace the underlined word(s) to make the statement true.**

8. The process by which organisms arise from other organisms is called <u>spontaneous generation</u>.

9. A possible explanation for a set of observations is a <u>theory</u>.

10. All the cells in a <u>tissue</u> work together to perform a specific function.

11. In a control setup, <u>all</u> variables must be controlled.

12. In the relationship between lynxes and hares, the lynx is the <u>predator</u>.

13. Biogenesis is a <u>theory</u> about the origin of new organisms.

Show What You Know

14. How did the discovery of fossils change scientific thinking about species?

15. How do an ecosystem and a community differ?

16. What was Darwin's explanation for the evolution of species?

17. What is biotechnology? Give a traditional and a modern example of biotechnology.

18. What is symbiosis? Name and describe the three types of symbiosis.

19. Describe four ways in which your daily activities are affected by biology.

20. What is the advantage of using a control setup?

21. What is the relationship between a hypothesis and a theory?

22. **Make a Concept Map** Complete the concept map below by adding the following terms: adaptation, atom, cell, community, ecosystem, energy, development, growth, individual, molecule, organ, organization, organ system, population, reproduction, response, tissue.

For help in making concept maps, see Appendix E.

Take It Further

23. **Applying Concepts** Pharmaceutical companies often test new medicines by giving pills with the medicine to one group and pills without the medicine to a second group. Neither the doctors nor the patients know which pills they are using. Identify the variables and controls in this procedure. What is the advantage of this procedure? Would the experiment work as well if the second group took no pills? Explain.

24. **Developing a Hypothesis** In 1847 doctors in Vienna ridiculed Ignaz Semmelweis when he urged them to wash their hands with germ-killing solution before examining patients. In 1865 Joseph Lister was successful in this regard. What might have made the difference?

25. Designing an Experiment Plan an experiment to find out the effects of preservatives on bread. What variable will you be testing? What variables will you need to control? Make a hypothesis about your experimental results.

26. Interpreting a Graph The graph shows eight countries ranked by land area and population. What inferences can you make about their population densities? What information would enable you to calculate their population densities exactly?

Countries Ranked by Land Area and by Population

27. Analyzing Data In 1974 the federal government reduced speed limits on highways to 55 miles per hour (89 kilometers per hour) to conserve gasoline. Some people predicted that the lower speed limit would also save lives. Use the table to decide whether that prediction was accurate. What other variables might have affected fatality rates between 1960 and 1990?

Motor Vehicle Traffic Fatalities

Year	Registered Vehicles	Traffic Deaths	Fatality Rate*
1960	74,444,000	36,399	5.06
1965	91,673,000	47,089	5.30
1970	111,243,000	54,180	4.92
1975	137,915,000	44,525	3.36
1980	161,491,000	51,059	3.35
1985	177,098,000	43,825	2.47
1990	193,057,000	44,599	2.08

*Deaths per 100 million vehicle miles

Consider the Issues

28. Publish or Perish Sometimes the first person to make a scientific discovery does not get the credit for the discovery. Credit is usually given to the first person to publish the new findings. How does science benefit from this practice? What problems might arise if researchers rush to get their work into print?

Make New Connections

29. Biology and Art Recalling what you have learned about the properties of life and its levels of organization, draw or photograph some organisms living in your area. Make an exhibit of your work, adding captions to explain how each image represents a property or level.

30. Biology and History Research and report on what the world was like in the late 1600s and early 1700s, when Redi and Pasteur were conducting their experiments. What was medicine in Europe like? What was the United States like at that time in history?

31. Biology and Technology Many experiments require measurements of time and temperature. Trace the development of accurate devices for measuring these variables.

FAST-FORWARD TO CHAPTER 2

All life processes depend on interactions between molecules. In Chapter 2, you will learn about chemical reactions and the kinds of molecules that are essential for life.

Which of these statements about the world around us and inside us are fact, and which are fiction?

Hit *or* Myth?

The hydra, an organism the size of a pencil point, has fewer **chromosomes** than an alligator.

(Fiction. Both organisms have 32 chromosomes, structures that contain genetic material. The size of an organism has no bearing on chromosome number. For example, one type of fern has 1010 chromosomes.)

If birds stored energy as **carbohydrates** instead of **fat,** they would weigh so much that they couldn't fly.

(Fact. Fat stores energy in a highly concentrated form that is also very light—it contains more than twice as much energy per gram as carbohydrates do.)

Celery has **zero** calories.

(Fiction. Celery has 18 Calories per 100-gram serving. However, this is such a small number that you may burn more calories chewing the crunchy vegetable than it actually contains.)

DAY 1
1

DAY 2
**10,000,000,
000,000,000,
000,000,000,
000,000,000,
000,000,000**

Bacteria reproduce so rapidly that the number of bacteria produced in just two days **surpasses** the number of humans that have ever lived.

(Fact. In the right environment some types of bacteria reproduce—by dividing—every 20 minutes.)

Muscles get **sore** during exercise because they overheat.

(Fiction. Lactic acid makes muscles sore. This waste product is created when your muscles generate energy during strenuous exercise, such as running a long distance.)

There are more **cells in your body** than there are stars in the Milky Way.

(Fact. There are about 50 trillion cells in an adult human, which is about 500 times more than the number of stars in our galaxy.)

Spider silk is **stronger** than steel.

(Fact. A strand of a spider web, which is made of protein, is stronger than a piece of steel of the same thickness.)

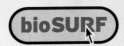

You can find out more about the chemical processes of living things by exploring the following Internet address:

http://basis_of_life.biosurf.com

A Bee's Eye View of the World

A beehive shelters many thousands of bees. Bees can be divided into groups. There are worker bees, drones, a queen bee, and developing bee larvae, seen here about to emerge and join the life of the colony. Each individual bee is a complex organism of many parts. The architecture of the hive is also made of smaller units. Honeycomb, which is made from beeswax, is formed into thousands of hexagonal building blocks, and sheets of honeycomb form the "walls" inside the hive.

You can compare the structural units of a beehive—hexagons—with the units of matter—atoms. Just as the individual hexagons together form the honeycomb, atoms link to one another to form larger units.

In this chapter you will learn more about the units of matter in living and nonliving things. Although all matter consists of atoms, different chemicals make up living and nonliving things. The chemical substances that are vital for all living things are carbohydrates, lipids, proteins, and nucleic acids. The honeybee colony is a good example of how these essential chemical substances are integrated into living systems.

LAB ZONE Discover It!

Observing a Chemical Reaction

You need a small plastic or glass container of dark iced tea and a lemon cut into quarters

1. Squeeze the juice from one lemon quarter into the iced tea. Record the result in your lab notebook.
2. Repeat step 1 until all the lemon quarters are used up.

What happened to the appearance of the tea? The tart taste of lemon comes from a chemical called citric acid, and the change in the tea results from a reaction between citric acid and the chemicals that give tea its brown color.

WRITE ABOUT IT!

In your science journal, list examples of possible chemical reactions that occur around you at home, school, or work every day. If you need ideas, think about how the lemon juice affected the tea in the activity above. What substances that are used in the kitchen or in the laundry have a similar effect?

2.1 Chemicals in Organisms

What you'll learn

IDEAS
- To identify the four groups of substances that make up most living things
- To compare the functions of each of those four groups

WORDS
carbohydrates, lipids, proteins, nucleic acids

You are what you eat
Does that mean this bat is really a flower? Of course not. But the bat and the flower are both made of the same basic substances. Although there is an almost endless variety of living things on Earth, most living things are made of four kinds of chemicals—carbohydrates, lipids, proteins, and nucleic acids.

CARBOHYDRATES

How sweet it is

The night before a big event many athletes "carbo-load"—they eat foods rich in carbohydrates. Why? Many carbohydrates provide a usable energy source. Your body breaks down carbohydrates and uses the energy in their chemical bonds to fuel the activities of life. **Carbohydrates** are a group of chemicals that include sugars, starches, and cellulose. Carbohydrates store energy and provide shape to organisms.

Sugars, such as those that make up the honey in *Figure 2.1,* are relatively small, simple carbohydrates. Simple sugars are the easiest chemicals for your body to break down. Have you ever had a sudden burst of energy after eating something sweet? Sweet foods usually contain sugars. Sugars commonly come in two forms: monosaccharides ("single sugars") and disaccharides ("double sugars").

Many monosaccharides and disaccharides can be linked together into more complex carbohydrates called polysaccharides ("many sugars"). Organisms form various complex carbohydrates for energy storage. Most plants store energy in a polysaccharide called starch. When you eat a potato, you are taking in the potato plant's stored starch. Animals store energy in a polysaccharide called glycogen, formed in muscles and the liver.

When athletes carbo-load before an event, they eat foods high in starches, which their bodies break down to simple sugars. Their liver and muscles convert the simple sugars into stored glycogen. The glycogen can be broken down into simple sugars when energy is needed.

FIGURE 2.1

Chemicals in a Beehive

Making honey
Honeybees gather nectar from plants and change it into honey. Both nectar and honey are made of carbohydrates.

Beeswax, a mixture of lipids
Honeybees produce beeswax, which they use to build the honeycomb.

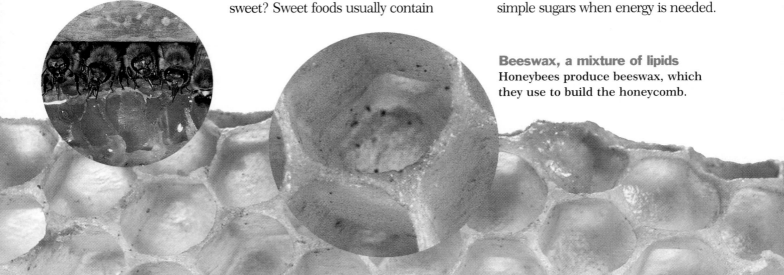

Plants and animals use different carbohydrates to store energy. Most plants store energy in the form of starch. When you eat a potato, you are taking in some of the plant's stored starch. Animals store energy in a carbohydrate called glycogen. Glycogen is formed in muscles and in the liver.

Simple sugars can also be joined together to make structural carbohydrates, such as cellulose. You may not be familiar with the word *cellulose*, but cellulose is all around you—in desks, pencils, paper, and any other plant material you see. In fact, cellulose is one of the most abundant biological molecules on Earth.

LIPIDS

Greasy molecules store energy for organisms

Carbohydrates are used for some energy storage. When energy is to be stored for an even longer period of time, carbohydrates are converted into a different chemical—fat, a kind of lipid. **Lipids** are a group of chemicals that include fats, oils, waxes, phospholipids, and steroids. Beeswax, shown in *Figure 2.1*, is a mixture of lipids.

Pollen contains proteins
The pollen covering this bee comes from a flower.

Fats, oils, and waxes are the most common lipids. Fats and oils provide long-term energy storage. Fats also act as insulation by helping to keep animals such as whales and penguins warm. Waxes provide a different kind of protection. They repel water. Fruits and leaves produce waxes to keep water in and thus prevent the plants from drying out. Ducks and other water fowl produce waxes that make feathers more waterproof.

Phospholipids are important structural chemicals in cells. These molecules form the membrane, or protective covering, that surrounds cells. Phospholipids help control the substances that enter and leave cells.

The last group of lipids, steroids, serve structural and control functions in your body. Some steroids, such as cholesterol, are components of the membranes that surround your cells. Although cholesterol is essential to life functions, too much of it can be harmful to your body. You will learn about the control functions of the steroid hormones in Chapter 33.

PROTEINS

An amazing variety

More than one half of the dry weight of your body is made up of a third kind of chemical—protein. **Proteins** are large, complex molecules composed of many smaller molecules called amino acids. The pollen shown in *Figure 2.1* is the most important source of protein for bees. The pollen eaten by bees may contain as much as 28 percent protein.

FIGURE 2.2
Molecules of Life

Below are representations of three molecules of life. The color key identifies the elements present in the molecular structures. Which elements are part of all three molecules?

Carbohydrate

Lipid

Protein

Molecular Model Color Key	
■	Carbon
■	Hydrogen
■	Nitrogen
■	Oxygen
■	Phosphorus

FIGURE 2.3

Proteins have many functions. Which functions are most familiar to you? Which ones are surprising?

Functions of Proteins

Function	Example
Movement	Actin and myosin are proteins necessary for contraction of muscle fibers.
Structure	Collagen, the most abundant protein in the human body, forms bones, tendons, ligaments, and cartilage.
Regulation	Proteins called enzymes help control chemical reactions in cells.
Transport	The protein hemoglobin in red blood cells carries oxygen through the bloodstream.
Nutrition	The protein casein in milk stores amino acids for use by some newborn animals.
Defense	Antibodies are proteins that help animals fight off invasion by viruses and bacteria.

FIGURE 2.4

Nucleic Acids

Nucleic acids, such as the spiral-shaped DNA molecule (left), contain the genetic information of organisms. A queen bee (right) lays eggs that contain copies of her DNA.

Proteins are important for many reasons. *Figure* 2.3 lists some of the various functions that proteins perform in living things.

Although their functions may differ, all proteins are similar in composition. Organisms use only 20 amino acids to make proteins. Different combinations of amino acids produce different proteins.

One group of proteins—enzymes—helps control chemical reactions. Enzymes can speed up some reactions by more than a billionfold. For example, enzymes are involved in digesting food, releasing energy during cellular respiration, and building up proteins.

NUCLEIC ACIDS

Molecules of heredity

Killer bees are more aggressive when threatened than other types of bees. What makes these bees behave differently? Some of their characteristics (and some of yours) are inherited. Inherited characteristics are controlled by molecules called nucleic acids. **Nucleic acids** are large, complex molecules that contain hereditary, or genetic, information.

There are two kinds of nucleic acids—deoxyribonucleic acid (DNA) and ribonucleic acid (RNA). DNA and RNA differ in their structures and functions. Similar to a blueprint for a builder, DNA carries instructions that control the activities of a cell. Similar to a builder, RNA uses those instructions to make proteins.

CHECKPOINT 2.1

1. What four groups of substances make up most living things?
2. Compare the functions of each of the four groups of substances.
3. **Critical Thinking** Wood is made mostly of cellulose. Using what you know about wood, describe the properties of cellulose.

Build on What You Know

4. Relate these four groups of chemicals to the properties of living things. (*Need to jog your memory? Revisit relevant concepts in Chapter 1, Section 1.1.*)

2.2 Basics of Chemistry

Worth your salt

Sodium is a metal that reacts explosively with air or water. Chlorine is a poisonous gas. When these two chemicals join together, they form . . . ordinary table salt. Today salt is inexpensive and plentiful, but in ancient times salt was so valuable that it was sometimes used as currency. Soldiers of the Roman Empire were paid in salt. Where do you think we got the word *salary*?

What you'll learn

IDEAS
• To distinguish elements from compounds
• To describe how atoms form different chemical bonds

WORDS
element, compound, organic compounds, ion, isotopes, chemical bonds

ELEMENTS AND COMPOUNDS

Countless combinations

Just as all the words in a dictionary are made from combinations of the 26 letters of the English alphabet, all the matter on Earth is made from about 100 elements. An **element** is a substance that cannot be broken down by chemical processes into simpler substances. Common elements include aluminum, gold, iron, and oxygen. The molten iron in the photo (right) in *Figure* 2.5 is an example of an element. The table lists the elements that make up most of the human body.

Sometimes elements exist in nature in a pure form. Usually elements exist in combinations called compounds. A **compound** is a substance made of two or more elements chemically combined in definite proportions. In *Figure* 2.5 the red blood cells in the small photo contain the compound hemoglobin. Hemoglobin contains the element iron.

All of the substances you read about in section 2.1—carbohydrates, lipids, proteins, and nucleic acids— are compounds, and all of these substances contain the element carbon. Almost all compounds that contain carbon are called **organic compounds.** Organic compounds are generally associated with living things.

Other compounds, for example, water and table salt, are inorganic compounds. Most inorganic compounds do not contain carbon.

Each element has its own distinct characteristics, or properties. But, as you read in the introductory story, when elements combine, their properties

Some Common Elements			
Element	Symbol	Approximate % by Weight	
		Human Body	*Earth's Crust*
Oxygen	O	65	46.6
Carbon	C	18	0.03
Hydrogen	H	10	0.14
Nitrogen	N	3	Trace
Calcium	Ca	2	3.6
Phosphorus	P	1	0.07
Potassium	K	0.4	2.6
Silicon	Si	Trace	27.7
Aluminum	Al	Trace	8.1
Iron	Fe	Trace	5.0

FIGURE 2.5
Molten iron is an element. Iron also is part of the compound hemoglobin in red blood cells. Using the table (left), compare the percentages of elements found in the human body and in Earth's crust. Which elements show the greatest differences?

FIGURE 2.6
This artificially colored scanning electron micrograph shows the geometric arrangement of uranium atoms in a crystal.

change. How do the properties of table salt differ from the properties of sodium and chlorine?

Scientists use symbols to represent the elements. These symbols can be one or two letters. For example, the symbol for hydrogen is H; the symbol for oxygen is O. All of the elements and their symbols appear in the periodic table on pages 944–945.

ATOMS

Atomic particles take charge

An atom is the smallest particle of an element that has the properties of that element. Atoms are the building blocks of matter. All atoms are made of smaller particles—protons, neutrons, and electrons—arranged in a specific way.

Protons are positively charged (+) particles located in the center, or nucleus, of an atom. Neutrons, which have no electrical charge and are described as neutral, are also in the nucleus. Protons and neutrons account for about 99 percent of an atom's mass.

The atoms of each element have a distinctive number of protons. For example, all hydrogen atoms have 1 proton. All oxygen atoms have 8 protons. All gold atoms have 79 protons.

Electrons are negatively charged (–) particles that are much smaller than either protons or neutrons. Electrons are located outside the nucleus in regions called energy levels. Electrons are in constant motion, forming a "cloud" around the nucleus. Because it is difficult to represent the movement of an electron, electrons are sometimes drawn as dots in circular energy levels. See *Figure 2.7*. Because the number of positively charged protons is always equal to the number of negatively charged electrons, an atom is electrically balanced, or neutral.

Ions An atom is most stable, or unlikely to react, when its outermost energy level is completely filled. Each energy level has a set maximum number of electrons. Atoms can lose or gain one or more electrons and thereby achieve an outer energy level with the maximum number of electrons.

An atom that has lost or gained electrons is called an **ion.** Atoms that lose electrons become positive ions. Atoms that gain electrons become negative ions.

In *Figure 2.8* you see an illustration of how a sodium atom becomes a sodium ion. How many electrons do the sodium atom and sodium ion have in their outermost energy levels?

Isotopes All atoms of the same element have the same number of protons. And, as neutral atoms, they have the same number of electrons. However, individual atoms of the same element can have different numbers of neutrons. Atoms of the same element that have different numbers of neutrons are called **isotopes** of the element.

FIGURE 2.7
The Parts of an Atom

Protons
Protons are located in the center, or nucleus, of an atom. Protons have a positive charge.

Neutrons
Neutrons have no charge. They are located in the nucleus of an atom.

Electrons
Most of the volume of an atom is occupied by its moving electrons. Electrons have a negative charge.

Sodium atom   Sodium ion

FIGURE 2.8
A sodium atom is neutral. It has the same number of protons and electrons. However, this atom can lose its outermost electron and become a positively charged ion.

About 50 naturally occurring isotopes are radioactive. A radioactive isotope has an unstable nucleus that breaks apart spontaneously, giving off energy in the form of radiation. Although radiation can harm living organisms, some radioactive isotopes are useful tools for biologists. Radiation from isotopes can be measured to determine the age of fossils, rocks, and artifacts. Radioactive isotopes can also act as tags or tracers. *Figure* 2.9 shows images of a brain formed by a positive emission tomography, or PET, scan. In a PET scan, radioactive isotopes show where chemical processes are occurring in body tissues. Radioactive isotopes are also used to preserve food and treat cancer.

CHEMICAL BONDS

Let's get together

As you have read, sodium chloride—salt—is a compound. But what holds the elements sodium and chlorine together in a compound? The answer is chemical bonds. **Chemical bonds** are the attractions that hold two or more atoms together to form a compound. Whenever a chemical bond is formed or broken, energy is either absorbed or released.

LAB ZONE **Think About It!**

Examining Isotopes

In nature most elements occur as a mixture of two or more isotopes. The atomic mass given for each element in the periodic table is an average value based on the percentage of each of the isotopes found in a naturally occurring sample. Generally, the average atomic mass of an element will be closest to the actual mass of its most common, or most abundant, isotope.

Analyzing the Periodic Table

Consult the periodic table located on pages 944–945. Answer the following questions for each pair of isotopes:

- C-12 and C-14
- S-32 and S-33
- Si-28 and Si-29
- N-14 and N-15

1 What is the average atomic mass of each element?
2 How many neutrons are in each isotope?
3 For each pair of isotopes listed above, which isotope would you expect to be most abundant?

Ionic bonds Positive and negative ions attract each other because of opposite electrical charges. An **ionic bond** is the chemical bond formed from the attractive force between ions with opposite charges. The resulting compound has no electrical charge. In an ionic bond, electrons are lost by one element and gained by another

FIGURE 2.9
PET scans measure the amount of physiological activity in the brain, with red indicating the most active areas. These images show how, at any moment, the amount of activity varies in different parts of the brain.

Tough Spots

Protein-rich stains left by milk, egg, or blood are difficult to remove from fabric. Other types of stains tend to dissolve in water—but not protein stains! Some detergents contain enzymes that break the bonds in proteins so detergent and water can do their work.

element. You can see an illustration of the bonding process in *Figure 2.10*. Sodium has one electron in its outer energy level. As you have learned, an atom is most stable when its outermost energy level is filled. The sodium atom's lone outer electron represents an unstable arrangement. The chlorine atom's outermost energy level would be filled with the addition of one more electron.

When sodium reacts with chlorine, the sodium atom loses its outermost electron and becomes a positive ion. The chlorine atom gains that electron and becomes a negative ion. How many electrons are now in the outer energy level of each ion?

The attractive force between the positively charged sodium ion and the negatively charged chlorine ion is very strong. The two ions come together to form an ionic bond. The compound that forms is sodium chloride, or table salt.

Covalent bonds Some compounds have bonds in which electrons are not gained or lost, but are shared

by atoms. This type of bond is called a covalent bond. (Think of the "co-" in *cooperative* as a reminder that sharing takes place.) Water, carbohydrates, lipids, proteins, and nucleic acids all have covalent bonds.

In covalent bonds, atoms may share electrons in several different ways. If atoms share two electrons between them, a single bond is formed. If atoms share four electrons, a double bond is formed. If atoms share six electrons, a triple bond is formed. *Figure 2.11* illustrates the structure of each type of covalent bond.

The units that are formed by covalent bonds are called molecules. Most molecules are made of atoms from different elements. Some molecules, however, consist of atoms from the same element that are covalently bonded. Oxygen gas, O_2, and nitrogen gas, N_2, are two common examples. Each molecule exists as a pair of atoms bound by a covalent bond.

Polar molecules In some covalent bonds, atoms do not share electrons equally. As a result, some

FIGURE 2.10

Ionic Bonds

In this chemical reaction, an ionic bond has formed between a positive and a negative ion. The compound formed—sodium chloride—is shown at right in crystallized form, artificially colored.

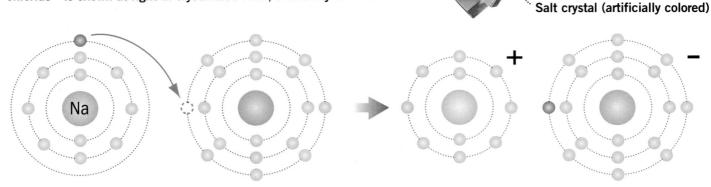

Salt crystal (artificially colored)

Sodium atom
This atom loses the lone electron from its outer energy level.

Chlorine atom
This atom gains an electron from the sodium atom, filling its outer energy level.

Sodium ion
The sodium atom is now an ion, and it carries a net positive charge.

Chlorine ion
The chlorine atom is now a negative ion. The sodium and chlorine ions form an ionic bond.

FIGURE 2.11
Covalent Bonds

Single bond
In the water molecule, each of the two hydrogen atoms is sharing two electrons with the oxygen atom.

Double bond
In the carbon dioxide molecule, each oxygen atom is sharing four electrons with the central carbon atom.

Triple bond
In the atmospheric nitrogen molecule, two nitrogen atoms are sharing six electrons with each other.

atoms in the molecule have a slightly negative charge and other atoms have a slightly positive charge. Molecules with a slightly negative end and a slightly positive end are called polar molecules.

Water is a polar molecule. *Figure 2.12* shows a diagram of a water molecule. In a water molecule, shared electrons are attracted more to the single oxygen atom than to the two hydrogen atoms. As a result, the oxygen end of the water molecule has a slightly negative electrical charge, and the hydrogen end has a slightly positive charge. How do you think the polar water molecule affects the charged parts of ionic compounds?

Other chemical forces As you have read, ionic and covalent bonds hold atoms together. In addition, there are other forces of attraction between molecules. These forces are much weaker than either ionic or covalent bonds, but they have a significant effect on organic compounds.

One kind of relatively weak attraction between molecules is called the hydrogen bond. Hydrogen bonds hold together molecules that contain hydrogen, such as water molecules, and they also exist in some proteins and nucleic acids. Hydrogen bonds are important in determining both the properties of water and the chemistry of living things.

CHECKPOINT 2.2

1. Compare compounds and elements.
2. Explain how atoms form the following types of chemical bonds: ionic, covalent, and polar.
3. **Critical Thinking** How are polar molecules similar to ionic compounds? How are they different?

Build on What You Know

4. Compare the levels of organization in matter with the levels of organization in the biosphere. *(Need to jog your memory? Revisit relevant concepts in Chapter 1, Section 1.1.)*

FIGURE 2.12
Unequal sharing of electrons causes the water molecule to be polar.

What kinds of chemicals are living things made of?

2.3 Chemicals at Work

What you'll learn

IDEAS
- To explain what happens during a chemical reaction
- To show how an enzyme functions

WORDS
chemical reaction, enzyme

Animal antifreeze
Not all organisms have a place to go when it gets cold. Some insects, such as the cabbage white butterfly shown here, produce chemicals that protect them against harsh winters by lowering the freezing point of the insects' body fluids. One of these substances, glycerol, is similar to the antifreeze used in cars.

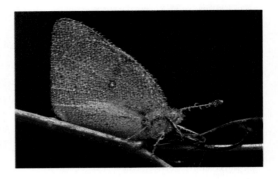

CHEMICAL REACTIONS

Changing atomic partners

Your body obtains energy by breaking chemical bonds in compounds such as carbohydrates. Carbohydrates, like all compounds, result from chemical bond formation. Both of these processes require chemical reactions. In a **chemical reaction,** one or more substances is changed into a new substance by the breaking or forming of chemical bonds.

When a cracker dissolves in your mouth, the breakdown of starch that occurs is an example of a chemical reaction. As you may remember, starch is a polysaccharide—a complex molecule made of a long chain of sugars. As you chew the cracker and it mixes with enzymes in your saliva, a chemical reaction occurs and the bonds between the sugar molecules in the starch are broken. You begin to notice a sweet taste. The appearance of one or more new substances, in this case sugar, is a sign that a chemical reaction has taken place.

You will often see chemical reactions represented by an equation like the one in *Figure 2.13*. Chemical equations are a shorthand way of showing what happens during a reaction. The letters are symbols for elements, and they can also be combined in chemical formulas to represent compounds. A chemical formula indicates the elements and numbers of atoms in the smallest unit representing a substance.

Typically, equations are "balanced," meaning that the kind of elements and total number of atoms of each element on the left side of the arrow equal the kind and total number on the right

FIGURE 2.13

A Chemical Equation

This chemical equation represents the formation of water molecules (H_2O). H is the chemical symbol for hydrogen; O is the symbol for oxygen.

The original substances, called reactants, are located on the left side of the arrow.

$$2H_2 + O_2 \longrightarrow 2H_2O$$

This represents the number of hydrogen molecules involved in the reaction.

This subscript represents the number of atoms in each molecule of oxygen.

Substances appearing on the right side of the arrow are the products of the reaction.

FIGURE 2.14

Color change, heat, and light are typical evidence that chemical reactions are occurring. What evidence of reactions is shown in these photos?

side of the arrow. How many molecules of water are formed in the reaction in *Figure 2.13*?

All chemical reactions involve energy. Energy can be either absorbed or released in a chemical reaction. When water is formed from hydrogen and oxygen gases, energy is released. When water is broken down, energy is absorbed. The energy that is given off when a substance is formed is equal to the energy needed to break it down.

REACTION SPEED

Faster than ever

Chemical reactions, such as the ones shown in *Figure 2.14,* take place around us every day. Some chemical reactions are involved in life processes, such as the growth of an eaglet or the chemical breakdown of fruit. Other chemical reactions occur in nonliving matter, such as a rusting car or exploding fireworks. All of these reactions take place at different rates of speed, however. Can the rate of a chemical reaction be altered?

It is possible to speed up a chemical reaction by increasing the temperature. The speed of the reaction increases because the higher temperature makes the atoms or molecules move faster and collide with each other more often.

Another way to change the speed of a chemical reaction is with a catalyst. A catalyst is a substance that speeds up or slows down a reaction

LAB ZONE Do It!

What Does a Chemical Reaction Look Like?

Chemical reactions cause substances to change into new substances. You can observe a chemical reaction if you . . .

Try This

1 Mix 5 grams (g) of baking soda and 120 milliliters (mL) of water in a glass jar. Write your observations about the mixture.
2 Mix 5 mL of vinegar and 120 mL of water in another jar. Again, note the results.
3 Mix 5 mL of vinegar and 5 g of baking soda in another jar. What happens?
4 Combine the baking-soda-and-water mixture with the vinegar-and-water mixture.

Analyze Your Results

1 Which combinations resulted in chemical reactions?
2 What happened to the ingredients in the mixtures that reacted and in those that did not?
3 What do the results of this lab indicate about the reactivity of water with baking soda and with vinegar?

1 Enzyme and substrate are available.

Substrate (sucrose)

Chemical bond

Enzyme (sucrase)

Active site

2 Substrate binds to enzyme's active site.

Chemical bond

3 Chemical bond breaks. Substrate is converted to products.

Glucose

Fructose

4 Products are released. Enzyme is not changed.

FIGURE 2.15
The enzyme sucrase breaks down molecules of sucrose by breaking the bonds holding the glucose and fructose molecules together. How do the shapes of the substrate and the active site compare?

without being changed or used up in the reaction. Because the catalyst does not change, it is highly effective in small amounts. All living organisms contain catalysts. These catalysts are called enzymes. As you may recall from Section 2.1, an **enzyme** is a protein catalyst that speeds up the chemical reactions within an organism. Enzymes work quickly, typically taking part in about a thousand reactions per second.

Consider one enzyme that is involved when you digest sucrose (table sugar). A molecule of sucrose is made up of two simple sugars. The enzyme sucrase binds to sucrose and breaks the bond between the two simple sugars, glucose and fructose.

Figure 2.15 illustrates how an enzyme works. The reactant, or substance to be changed (in this case, sucrose), is called the substrate. The region on the enzyme where the substrate attaches is called the enzyme's active site. At that site, the substrate is changed slightly by the enzyme so that a specific chemical bond is weakened. This weakened chemical bond allows sucrose to break apart quickly.

Specific enzymes catalyze specific chemical reactions, much as a key works with a specific lock. Some enzymes cause compounds to break apart. Others cause compounds to be formed. Enzymes provide a way to speed up life's essential functions without raising the temperature of an organism's body.

CHECKPOINT 2.3

1. Summarize what happens during a chemical reaction.

2. Make a labeled drawing that shows how an enzyme works.

3. Critical Thinking Suppose that when you mix two colorless liquids, they turn bright blue. You then observe a blue solid slowly settle on the bottom of the beaker. Has a chemical reaction taken place? Explain why or why not.

Build on What You Know

4. Do enzymes follow chemical or physical laws that are different from the laws governing nonliving substances? *(Need to jog your memory? Revisit relevant concepts in Chapter 1, Section 1.1.)*

Analyzing a Chemical Reaction

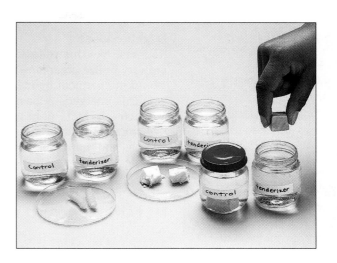

WHAT YOU WILL DO Observe the effects of meat tenderizer on starch, fat, and protein

SKILLS YOU WILL USE Observing, predicting, controlling variables, collecting and recording data

WHAT YOU WILL NEED 6 empty baby food jars with lids, tape, permanent marker, metric balance, meat tenderizer, 2 pieces of rotini pasta, 2 pieces of beef suet, 2 pieces of ham

Propose a Hypothesis

Meat tenderizer contains an enzyme that breaks down proteins. Propose a hypothesis about the effects of meat tenderizer on starch, fat, and protein. Record your hypothesis in your lab notebook.
Caution: Be careful when working with glassware to avoid breakage.

Conduct Your Experiment

DAY 1

1 Use the tape and the marker to put your name on each jar. Then label the six jars *Control Starch*, *Control Fat*, *Control Protein*, *Tenderizer Starch*, *Tenderizer Fat*, and *Tenderizer Protein*.
2 Fill each jar with water. Use the metric balance to measure 9 g of meat tenderizer. Add it to one of the *Tenderizer* jars and stir until completely dissolved. Repeat for the other two *Tenderizer* jars.

3 You have two samples each of starch (pasta), fat (suet), and protein (ham). Place the samples in their assigned *Control* and *Tenderizer* jars, as shown in the photograph. Put the lids on the jars.

DAY 2

4 Examine both pieces of pasta. How do they look? How do they feel? Squeeze the pasta between your fingers. Record the look and feel of both pieces.
5 Repeat step 4 for the suet and the ham.

Analyze Your Data

1 Were there any differences in look or feel of the two pieces of pasta on Day 2? If so, explain.
2 Were there any differences in look or feel of the two pieces of suet on Day 2? If so, explain.
3 Were there any differences in look or feel of the two pieces of ham on Day 2? If so, explain.

Draw Conclusions

1 Why do you need the control jars?
2 Was the hypothesis supported by your observations? Why or why not?

Design a Related Experiment

Design an experiment to compare the effects of substances used in marinades (for example, vinegar or lemon juice) on proteins.

Analyzing a Chemical Reaction

		Look	Feel
Pasta	Tenderizer		
	Control		
Suet	Tenderizer		
	Control		
Ham	Tenderizer		
	Control		

2.4 Chemistry in Life Processes

What you'll learn

IDEAS

• To describe different life processes

• To explain that life processes are based on chemical reactions

WORDS

metabolism, homeostasis

Mighty mouse
Rodents, like this yellow-necked mouse, are very active organisms. Their energy is stored in chemical bonds in the food they eat. This energy is released by chemical reactions. In fact, all of an organism's life processes, including reproduction, growth, and maintenance, depend on chemical reactions.

FIGURE 2.16
The slow metabolic rate of this python, combined with its ability to consume large prey, means that it eats much less often than birds or mammals. Many large snakes eat only eight to ten times a year.

METABOLISM AND ENERGY

Fuel for life

During your lifetime your body never stops functioning. Even when you are in a deep sleep, comfortable and motionless, your body is busy. It is producing chemicals that help you sleep, and it is regulating your heartbeat, blood flow, and body temperature. Twenty-four hours a day, your body works to keep you alive by carrying out a series of chemical changes. The combination of all the chemical changes that take place in an organism is called **metabolism.**

The chemical changes of each organism's metabolism are coordinated to allow the organism to obtain and use energy to perform its body functions. Organisms require energy for just about everything they do, including moving, growing, taking in food, and reproducing.

Organisms use compounds that contain energy in chemical bonds as sources of energy. As you learned earlier, when sugars and starches are broken down in your body, energy is released. Plants and some other organisms can use sunlight to make energy-rich compounds. You will learn more about the synthesis and breakdown of energy-rich compounds in Chapter 4.

In addition to supplying energy, food compounds also contain elements that your body needs as building blocks. Your body uses the elements in food compounds to make all of the materials your cells need to stay alive. These materials include proteins, lipids, and carbohydrates.

The products of the chemical reactions in your body include heat and

FIGURE 2.17
This anole is growing a new tail after losing the original one. The process of growing back a lost body part is called regeneration.

wastes. Humans and other organisms need heat to stay alive, but too much heat is harmful and must be removed. Carbon dioxide, food wastes, and salts are examples of body wastes. Such wastes are poisonous, so your body must eliminate them.

GROWTH AND REPAIR
A look at a lifetime

During their life span, some organisms undergo many, sometimes dramatic, changes. Think of how you have changed since you were an infant, and how you expect to change in the years to come. In some organisms very complex changes can occur, such as the metamorphosis of a tadpole into a frog. The changes that occur as organisms grow and develop are the result of many complex chemical reactions.

To grow and develop, the cells of organisms must make many new carbohydrates, proteins, and lipids. The nucleic acids in cells control the production of these materials. You will learn more about the chemical control of nucleic acids in Chapter 8.

In addition to growing, organisms must repair damage from injuries. For example, when an anole such as the one in *Figure 2.17* loses its tail, it can grow a new one. In the repair process, chemical reactions are needed to produce new cells to replace the injured cells. When you break a bone, the broken bone heals by producing new bone cells in a process that involves many chemical reactions.

HOMEOSTASIS AND CONTROL
Staying in balance

In section 2.3 you read that chemical changes are constantly occurring in living things. For an organism to stay alive, those changes must be controlled. The internal conditions of the organism must remain constant, or stable. The tendency of an organism to maintain stable internal conditions is called **homeostasis.** You might think of homeostasis as an internal balance system.

Just as it takes many tiny motions to steady a gymnast on a balance beam, it takes millions of chemical reactions to keep the internal conditions of living things stable. Consider the sagebrush in *Figure 2.18*. This plant may be immobile, but chemicals inside the sagebrush are in constant motion. Chemical reactions and physical processes help the plant maintain the proper water balance and temperature. They also help the plant absorb nutrients to keep the cells healthy and to make new cells.

Throughout this textbook you will learn about many kinds of controls that are involved in maintaining homeostasis. For example, many chemical reactions in cells are controlled by feedback loops. A feedback loop is a series of reactions in which the products of the last reaction cause the first reaction to start or stop. In multicellular organisms, some feedback loops are controlled by hormones, such as the protein insulin, that are sent from one organ to another.

FIGURE 2.18
Plants keep their internal conditions in balance through chemical and physical processes. This desert sagebrush draws water from the soil through a physical process. Water balance greatly affects the main chemical processes of the plant.

FIGURE 2.19
This male silk moth is attracted to a potential mate by the female's pheromones. The male moth's large antennae can detect as few as 100 molecules of the female's pheromone combination in 1 mL of air.

COMMUNICATION AND RESPONSE

"Talking" without words

In the world of living things, communication takes place both within an organism and between organisms. In many animals, internal communication occurs in the nervous system. Chemicals called neurotransmitters carry impulses across the small spaces between nerve cells. You will learn more about this process in Chapter 34.

Communication between organisms can take place through sight, sound, touch, smell, and taste. For insects and many other animals, communication occurs through chemical signals called pheromones, which the animals smell or taste. Pheromones are produced by chemical reactions. In a beehive, for example, the queen produces a substance called queen mandibular pheromone, which worker bees lick from the queen's body. This pheromone stops worker bees from rearing new queens. What are some other examples of organisms using odors and tastes for communication?

REPRODUCTION

Making new life

One of life's most amazing processes is reproduction. During reproduction, parents create offspring by providing the necessary chemical information to begin and continue life. That information, as you learned in section 2.1, is carried in nucleic acids such as DNA.

The chemical characteristics of DNA enable it to carry the information needed for producing new cells. In a series of chemical reactions, enzymes duplicate DNA. Other enzymes translate the information in DNA into materials needed for new cells. Reproduction requires the doubling of almost all of the materials in a living cell. Doubling the materials in a cell involves countless chemical reactions. Ultimately, DNA's characteristics enable organisms to reproduce. You will learn more about the structure and function of DNA in Chapter 8.

CHECKPOINT 2.4

1. Name the major life processes discussed in this section.
2. Explain how each of those life processes is dependent on chemical reactions.
3. **Critical Thinking** An ant can move along a path that other ants can later follow. Propose a hypothesis to explain this phenomenon.

Build on What You Know

4. How are the processes discussed in this section related to the characteristics of life? *(Need to jog your memory? Revisit relevant concepts in Chapter 1, Section 1.1.)*

Why are chemical reactions important for life?

2.5 Water and Solutions

The blue planet
As this view from space shows, Earth seems to be more water than land. The overwhelming expanses of blue that cover three quarters of the planet's surface are testament to the crucial roles that water plays in life on Earth. What things in your life are not affected by water?

What you'll learn

IDEAS
• To identify the properties of water that support life
• To distinguish between acids and bases

WORDS
solution, acid, base, pH scale

SOLUTIONS

Molecules all wet

Water, though common, is an extraordinary substance. Its chemistry allows it to form solutions easily. A **solution** is a uniform mixture of two or more substances. Water solutions are important because all of life's chemical processes occur in solutions.

In a solution, two or more substances are mixed together so completely and evenly that they cannot be distinguished. Think of what happens when you pour sugar into a glass of water. Although visible at first, the sugar soon disappears. The sugar molecules become evenly distributed throughout the water to form a sugar solution. There is no chemical change in the sugar or water molecules.

Solutions have two components. The dissolved substance in a solution is called the solute. The dissolving substance is called the solvent. In the sugar and water solution, sugar is the solute and water is the solvent.

Most ionic compounds dissolve readily in water because of the polar nature of the water molecule. For example, as a crystal of common table salt, or sodium chloride (NaCl),

dissolves, the positive regions of the water molecules attract the negative ions of the NaCl crystal. The negative regions of the water molecules attract the positive ions of the NaCl crystal. These attractions separate the ions, and the salt dissolves into sodium ions (Na^+) and chloride ions (Cl^-).

Covalent compounds that are polar can dissolve in water. As you may recall, polar molecules have regions of slightly positive and slightly negative charge. Because water is also polar, water dissolves many polar molecules. The ability of water to form solutions so readily has earned it the title of "the universal solvent."

Most living things depend on water to survive. Most organisms can live without food for a longer time than

FIGURE 2.20
Solid crystals of copper sulfate are added to a solvent (water). What is happening in each picture?

FIGURE 2.21
The Cohesion of Water Molecules

Water in plants
The cohesion of water molecules allows plants such as this tree to move water through a tissue called xylem from the ground up to its leaves.

Xylem

Water strider
The surface tension of water supports the weight of this water strider, allowing it to "skate" across the surface.

they can live without a fresh supply of water. The seeds of plants and the spores of certain plants, fungi, and bacteria can exist without water only if they are dormant. In order to become metabolically active, their water content must increase. In fact, the very presence of water prompts most seeds and spores to germinate.

TWO FEATURES OF WATER
How bugs water-ski

In addition to being the universal solvent, water has other important characteristics, many of which are related to hydrogen bonding. Hydrogen bonds, as you have learned, are weak chemical attractions between hydrogen and other atoms. Two characteristics related to hydrogen bonding in water are cohesion and expansion.

Cohesion means "sticking together." Hydrogen bonding causes water molecules to cling to each other. Cohesion produces surface tension, which causes a filmlike boundary to form on the surface of water. The water strider in *Figure 2.21* is supported by the surface tension of the water in the pond.

The cohesion characteristic of water also is important for the movement of water through the trunks of tall trees. Water molecules stick together and are literally pulled up narrow tubes called xylem in the trunk. You will learn more about this process in Chapter 18.

You have probably seen ice floating on top of water. This common phenomenon demonstrates another important characteristic of water—it expands as it freezes. (Most substances shrink as they freeze.) Because water expands as it freezes, ice has a lower density than liquid water. This lower density causes ice to float on water. Because ice floats on water, ponds freeze from the top down, enabling pond-dwelling organisms to survive in the cold liquid water beneath the ice.

ACIDS, BASES, AND SALTS

Keep that balance

When an ionic compound is placed in water, forming a solution, the compound breaks apart and releases ions. A compound that releases hydrogen ions (H^+) in water is called an **acid.** Hydrogen chloride (HCl), for example, produces hydrogen ions (H^+) and chloride ions (Cl^-) when dissolved in water. In solution with water, HCl is called hydrochloric acid. Hydrochloric acid is present in the digestive juices in your stomach. Other acidic substances include orange juice and vinegar.

A **base** is a compound that produces hydroxide ions (OH^-) when dissolved in water. Sodium hydroxide (NaOH) is a base. When dissolved in water, it produces sodium ions (Na^+) and hydroxide ions (OH^-). Examples of bases include soaps and egg whites. You can find examples of other acids and bases in *Figure* 2.22. Strong acids and bases that do not occur naturally in food can be extremely dangerous and should be handled with care.

Compounds that yield ions other than hydrogen or hydroxide ions when in solution are called salts. Sodium chloride and potassium chloride are examples of salts.

The degree or range of acidity is defined by the pH scale. The "p" can be thought of as standing for "power," and the "H" stands for the hydrogen ion. The **pH scale** is the standard measurement of the concentration of hydrogen ions (H^+) present in a solution. The pH scale ranges from 0 to 14.

Examine the pH scale in *Figure* 2.22. Notice that a pH value of 7 indicates a neutral solution, one that is

pH of Common Substances			
Property	**Substance**	**pH**	**Color**
Strong base	Lye	14	■
	Bleach	13	■
Weak base	Baking soda	9	■
	Egg white	8	■
	Blood	7.4	■
Neutral	Pure water	7	■
	Many soils	6	■
	Coffee	5	■
Weak acid	Tomatoes	4	■
	Vinegar	3	■
	Digestive juice	2	■
Strong acid	Battery acid	0.5	■

FIGURE 2.22
You can use the pH scale to measure the acidity of a substance. Standard pH paper indicates the pH of a substance by changing to the characteristic color shown in the table. What is the most acidic food substance on this chart? The most basic?

neither an acid nor a base. In a neutral solution the concentration of hydrogen ions equals that of hydroxide ions. A substance with a pH of less than 7 is an acid. The lower the pH number, the more acidic the substance is. Conversely, the higher the pH reading, the more basic that substance is.

LAB ZONE Do It!

What Is the pH of Common Foods?

Standard pH paper responds to a wide range of pH values. You can use pH paper to find the pH of common foods if you . . .

Try This

1 Assemble samples of a variety of foods. (Oranges, apples, potatoes, bananas, and milk are some good choices.)
2 On a paper towel, line up enough squares of pH paper to test each of your samples.
3 For each sample, apply the cut surface of the food or a drop of the liquid to a clean pH square. Avoid touching the pH paper because substances on your hands could affect your results.
4 Compare the color of each pH square to the chart on the pH paper dispenser. Record the pH of each sample.

Analyze Your Results

1 Make a class chart displaying the pH of some common foods.
2 Which substance is the most acidic? Which is most basic?
3 What characteristics do acidic foods share? Basic foods?

FIGURE 2.23
Acid rain can have very damaging effects on plant life. How did acid rain in the soil affect the Frasier firs?

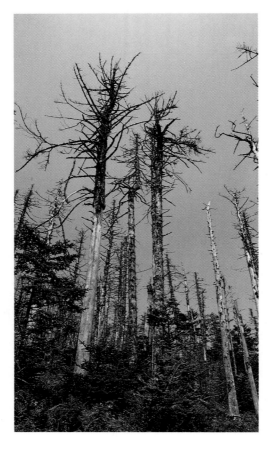

Almost all chemical reactions of living things take place at pH levels between 6 and 8. The pH of your blood is constant at about 7.4, which is slightly basic. If it were to become more acidic than 7, or more basic than 7.8, you would not survive more than a few minutes. However, in your stomach the presence of digestive gastric acids results in pH levels as low as 2. Because of the stomach's protective mucous coat, the acidic pH does not harm the stomach lining.

The chemical reactions that take place in your body are very sensitive to the presence of hydrogen ions. Even a small change in pH can cause some enzymes to stop functioning effectively. For this reason, your body has a control system to regulate the pH level of your blood and ensure homeostasis.

ENVIRONMENTAL AWARENESS

When it rains acid

Fossil fuels are used as energy sources all over the world. Burning fuels such as coal, oil, gas, and gasoline releases sulfur and nitrogen compounds into the air. These compounds react with water in the atmosphere and fall to Earth in raindrops containing sulfuric acid and nitric acid.

Rain water with a pH of less than 5.6 is called acid rain. Acid rain is a persistent threat to the environment. Acid rain (including acid snow, fog, and dew) washes away vital minerals from soil. The acids also release some metals, such as aluminum, from soil particles. High levels of some metals in soil can kill many plants.

Lakes are also vulnerable to acid rain, which kills aquatic organisms and throws off the balance of the ecosystem. The problems of acid rain can be resolved, in part, by reducing the amount of pollutants in the air.

CHECKPOINT 2.5

1. List and explain the properties of water that support life.

2. Compare acids and bases, and give an example of each.

3. Critical Thinking The cohesive properties of water allow it to absorb heat without indicating a large increase in temperature. How does this property help your body to maintain a constant temperature?

Build on What You Know

4. Use the scientific method to design an experiment testing the effects of pH on a plant species. *(Need to jog your memory? Revisit relevant concepts in Chapter 1, Section 1.3.)*

Why is water important to life processes?

Chapter 2 Review

 2.1–2.2 Living things are made of chemicals with characteristic structures and functions.
2.3–2.4 Life processes depend on breaking and forming chemical bonds in chemical reactions.
2.5 Life processes depend on the properties of water and the characteristics of solutions.

Sum It Up

Use the following summary to review the main concepts in this chapter.

2.1 Chemicals in Organisms

- Organisms use the energy stored in carbohydrates as fuel for life activities.
- Some lipids provide long-term energy storage and heat insulation. Other lipids serve structural and control functions.
- Twenty small molecules called amino acids make up the many complex proteins with their diverse functions.
- Large molecules called nucleic acids store genetic information.

2.2 Basics of Chemistry

- An atom is the smallest particle of an element. Uncombined atoms are neutral because they contain equal numbers of protons (+) and electrons (–).
- Atoms of different elements combine to form compounds, which are held together by chemical bonds. Ionic bonds form when atoms gain or lose electrons. Covalent bonds form when atoms share electrons.

2.3 Chemicals at Work

- Chemical equations represent chemical reactions. During a chemical reaction, bonds are broken and new bonds are formed. Energy is absorbed or released.
- Enzymes are protein catalysts that speed up or slow down the chemical reactions in living organisms.

2.4 Chemistry in Life Processes

- The metabolism of an organism comprises all the chemical reactions that occur, including those involved in obtaining energy, producing new cells, maintaining homeostasis, communicating, and reproducing.

2.5 Water and Solutions

- Life's chemical reactions all occur in water solutions. Because water is a polar molecule, it can dissolve many kinds of compounds.
- For an organism to function properly, the degree of acidity, or pH, of internal fluids such as blood must be maintained within a narrow range.

Use Terms and Concepts

**Use each of the following words or terms in a complete sentence.
If you need to review a meaning, turn to the page indicated.**

carbohydrates (p. 34)
lipids (p. 35)
proteins (p. 35)
nucleic acids (p. 36)
element (p. 37)
compound (p. 37)
organic compounds (p. 37)

ion (p. 38)
isotopes (p. 38)
chemical bonds (p. 39)
chemical reaction (p. 42)
enzyme (p. 44)
metabolism (p. 46)
homeostasis (p. 47)

solution (p. 49)
acid (p. 51)
base (p. 51)
pH scale (p. 51)

Use Your Word Power

COMPLETION Write the word or phrase that best completes each statement.

1. The combination of all the chemical reactions that take place in an organism is _____ .

2. Large molecules that carry genetic information are called _____ .

3. The maintenance of a stable set of internal conditions is called _____ .

4. The _____ measures the concentration of hydrogen ions in a solution.

5. Carbon compounds that are associated with living things are called _____ .

TRUE-FALSE Write true if the statement is true. If the statement is false, replace the underlined word(s) to make the statement true.

6. A protein catalyst that speeds up chemical reactions in organisms is called an <u>enzyme</u>.

7. A <u>base</u> is a substance that releases hydrogen ions in solution.

8. <u>Lipids</u> are composed of smaller molecules called amino acids.

9. An atom that has lost or gained electrons is called an <u>ion</u>.

10. The forces that hold two or more atoms together are called <u>chemical bonds</u>.

Show What You Know

11. Why is the compound water considered essential for life on Earth?

12. Compare acids and bases. Include a discussion of the pH scale in your answer.

13. What are isotopes? How are some isotopes used in biological research?

14. Compare the properties of protons, neutrons, and electrons.

15. What is a solution? Describe what happens when table salt and water form a solution.

16. What occurs during a chemical reaction? Give an example of a chemical reaction.

17. Which type of organic compound contradicts water's reputation as a "universal solvent"? Give a specific example to support your answer.

18. How are elements and compounds similar? How do they differ?

19. **Make a Concept Map** Complete the concept map below by adding the following terms: carbon, carbohydrates, lipids, nucleic acids, proteins, and enzymes. For help with making a concept map, see page 952.

Take It Further

20. **Designing an Experiment** Design an experiment to compare the speed with which ionic, non-polar covalent, and polar covalent compounds dissolve in water. Ionic compounds include table salt and baking soda. Non-polar covalent compounds include vegetable oil and sugar. Polar covalent compounds include acetone and hydrogen chloride. Predict the results of your experiment.

21. **Applying Concepts** Explain why you should not put a sealed container that is completely filled with a water solution in a freezer.

22. Designing an Experiment Suggest one or two simple experiments to determine whether a solid white substance is a lipid or a carbohydrate. What evidence would you need to support each hypothesis?

23. Interpreting a Graph The bar graph below shows the total amount of product formed from a chemical reaction that was performed at three different temperatures for the same time period. The same enzyme was involved each time in the chemical reaction. Describe the results at each temperature. Explain why you think these results were obtained.

Effects of Temperatures on a Reaction

24. Analyzing Data The three boxes below are part of the periodic table. From the information in the boxes, answer the following questions: What is the name of each element? What is the chemical symbol for each element? What is the atomic number of each element? What is the average atomic mass of each element? How many protons and electrons are there in an atom of each element? How many neutrons are in the most common form of each element?

6 **C** Carbon 12.011	7 **N** Nitrogen 14.007	8 **O** Oxygen 15.999

Consider the Issues

25. Conflicts About Foods Many organizations publish recommendations about the quantities of carbohydrates, fats, and proteins that people should eat. Sometimes the nutritional guidelines disagree. Describe the information that you would need to decide if the nutritional recommendation of a particular group was based on fact or opinion.

Make New Connections

26. Biology and Art Make three-dimensional models of organic compounds such as single sugars and amino acids. Refer to illustrations in this textbook or in other reference books.

27. Biology and Chemistry Research an element from the table in *Figure* 2.5. When was the element discovered, and how did it get its name? What is the key function of the element in the human body? What foods are sources of the element? What happens to the body if the element is missing? Prepare a poster or short written report to summarize your findings.

28. Biology and Community After discussing your plans and safety procedures with your teacher, collect precipitation (rain and snow) and water samples from local sources, such as puddles, ponds, lakes, or streams. Test the pH of your samples and present your findings to the class.

FAST-FORWARD TO CHAPTER 3

Atoms are the building blocks of cells. Cells are the building blocks of organisms. The next chapter describes the structure of a cell and how the cell functions as the unit of all living things.

CHAPTER 3
Cell Structure and Function

bioSURF

You can find out more about cell structure and function by exploring the following Internet address:
http://basis_of_life.biosurf.com

THE UNSEEN WORKFORCE

Numerous things we associate with modern life—cars, computers, even shoes—are made as the result of many processes coming together under one roof, a factory. Factories organize the manufacturing process by breaking it down into separate, smaller tasks, which enable the product to be made in the most efficient way. In a sense, this approach was in use long before the first factory ever opened its doors, because a factory mimics the organization of living cells.

Factories and cells are organized around the same principles: Keep processes flowing evenly. Do not allow raw materials or products to pile up. Supervise every level of operation. Be ready to respond to changing conditions and needs. Repair and replace equipment regularly.

As you look at this cell, try to envision the workings of a factory. Imagine that you are taking a tour—exploring the complex system of loading docks, conveyor belts, and elevators. As you visit the factory floor, imagine that you see the supervisors analyzing production and hear them giving instructions. Imagine that you hear the clatter and feel the heat of the machines working. Try to picture some of the workers repairing machinery, while other workers are moving raw materials into the factory and sending finished products out.

Multicellular organisms have millions, even billions, of these microscopic factories—all operating at once. Throughout its lifetime, a plant or animal depends on the smooth and effective operation of nature's unseen assembly lines.

Using a Hand Lens

You need a hand lens, black and white and/or color newspaper pictures, comics, or magazines

1. Look at a picture from the newspaper without magnification. Then examine the same picture with the hand lens. What do you see now that you could not see before?
2. Go on a hunt. Try to find an object in the classroom that reveals something unexpected when you look at it under the hand lens. You may want to try looking at fabrics, school supplies, or plants.

Most hand lenses magnify objects only about 1.25 to 1.5 times. Biologists have more powerful tools—microscopes—for examining cells and their structures, which are invisible to the unaided eye. Light microscopes, such as the ones you will use later in this chapter, have the ability to magnify objects up to 1000 times.

WRITE ABOUT IT!

In your science journal, write an imaginative description of one or more things you examined under the hand lens. You might want to start by thinking of an analogy—a comparison between the object you saw and something it resembled.

3.1 A Look at Cells

What you'll learn

IDEAS
• To explain the key ideas that make up the cell theory
• To summarize the role of the microscope in the development of the cell theory

WORD
cell theory

Seeing cells

Marcello Malpighi (1628–1694), a physician in Bologna, Italy, was one of the first to use microscopes in medicine. His discovery of capillaries, the smallest blood vessels, provided the missing link in the understanding of blood circulation. Malpighi was also the first to see and describe red blood cells, shown here moving through a capillary. Because he questioned long-held beliefs about living organisms, Malpighi struggled throughout his career against his colleagues' disbelief and resentment.

FIGURE 3.1

These cells are magnified 700 times their actual size. What differences do you observe?

WHAT IS A CELL?

Where life happens

You read in Chapter 1 that a cell is the smallest unit of life that can carry out all the functions of a living thing. The size, shape, and structures of cells are very diverse, as you can see from the six kinds of cells in *Figure 3.1.*

Living things may be either unicellular (consisting of one cell) or multicellular (many-celled). Bacteria are one type of unicellular organism. Most of the organisms you are familiar with—including yourself—are multicellular.

As you see in *Figure 3.1,* cells can also vary greatly in size. Notice that the smallest cell is a bacterium. About 8000 of the smallest bacteria could fit inside one of your red blood cells. The longest cells are the very thin nerve cells of large animals. These cells can be more than a meter long. The cell with the greatest volume is an unfertilized ostrich egg. It has about a liter's worth of contents, including stored food.

Notice also that the shape of cells can vary greatly. A cell's shape is related to its function. A long nerve cell, for example, can carry messages from your spine to your toes. Long, slender muscle cells that are grouped together form long, slender muscle tissues. The contraction and relaxation of muscle tissue is responsible for movement in animals.

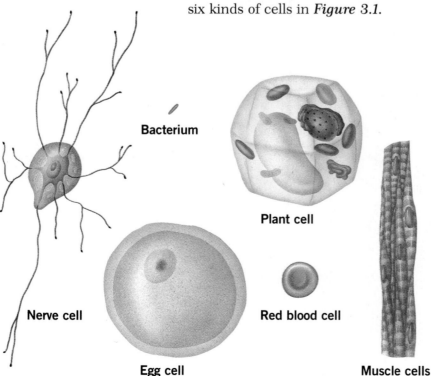

Bacterium

Plant cell

Nerve cell

Red blood cell

Egg cell

Muscle cells

FIGURE 3.2
Robert Hooke's drawings of cork seen through a microscope show rows of empty spaces. What did he call these spaces?

DISCOVERY OF CELLS

A small new world

You are living at a time when a great deal is known about microscopic life. However, in the beginning of the 1600s people knew only about organisms they could see with the unaided eye. They certainly had no knowledge of the existence of cells.

The invention of the microscope was one of the most important breakthroughs in biology. The microscope was invented by a trio of Dutch eyeglass makers in the late 1500s. It consisted of a tube with lenses ground from rock crystal, and it magnified objects up to nine times their actual size. Many other inventors produced variations of this simple model in the early 1600s.

In 1665 the British scientist Robert Hooke published a set of drawings illustrating what he had observed with a microscope. One of these drawings is shown in *Figure 3.2*. Hooke called the empty chambers he saw "cells" because they reminded him of the small rooms, or cells, in a monastery. Scientists later learned that the cells Hooke observed had once contained living matter.

In the early 1670s Anton van Leeuwenhoek (LAY-vun-hohk), a Dutch fabric-store owner, began to grind lenses as a hobby. Leeuwenhoek used his handheld microscopes to examine materials such as pond water and blood. To his amazement, he discovered a world of microscopic organisms and living cells.

CELL THEORY

Biologists build a theory

The invention of the microscope led to many advances in the study of science. By the 1830s many biologists were using the microscope as their chief investigative tool. Some of the key discoveries biologists made during the 1800s are included in *Figure 3.3*. Three of these advances were especially important in building one of the key theories in biology.

Matthias Schleiden was a botanist, a scientist who studies plants. He found that the plant parts he examined were made of cells. In 1838 Schleiden made the generalization that all plants are made of cells.

About the same time, Theodor Schwann was studying animals. His microscopic investigations of animal parts led him to generalize that all animals are made of cells. He further proposed that all organisms are made of cells.

FIGURE 3.3
Discoveries with the Light Microscope

1665 Robert Hooke (English) publishes *Micrographia*, which contains drawings of cork and other objects he has observed.

1674 Anton van Leeuwenhoek (Dutch) begins to make single-lens microscopes that magnify objects about 200 times.

1838 Matthias Schleiden (German) concludes that all plants are made of cells.

1839 Theodor Schwann (German) concludes that all living things are made of cells.

1855 Rudolf Virchow (German) infers that all new cells come from existing cells.

1862 Louis Pasteur (French) publishes his theory that microscopic organisms cause contagious diseases.

1879 Hermann Fol (Swiss) is the first person to see an egg cell being fertilized by a sperm.

1882 Walther Flemming (German) publishes his discovery of chromatin, a threadlike material in cell nuclei, and the steps of cell division, or mitosis.

FIGURE 3.4
A micrograph of cells from an *Elodea* plant is shown at left. Matthias Schleiden determined that all plants are made of cells, but he did not understand how new cells are formed.

FIGURE 3.5
These three photographs of paramecia were taken using different light microscopy techniques. Which technique provides the most contrast and detail?

Bright-field micrograph

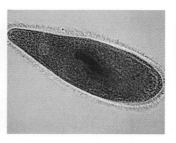
Dark-field micrograph

Phase contrast micrograph

FIGURE 3.6
Milestones in Microscopy

1931 Ernst Ruska builds the first electron microscope.

1950s Biologists begin to use electron microscopes to study living things.

1965 Electron microscope shows fossilized cells that are 3.5 billion years old.

Transmission electron micrograph of sperm

Scanning electron micrograph of sperm

During the 1830s most people, including many scientists, thought that new living things could appear spontaneously from nonliving matter. You may recall from Chapter 1 that this idea was called spontaneous generation. In 1858, a German doctor named Rudolf Virchow disputed the idea of spontaneous generation. Virchow reasoned that new plant cells arise only from existing plant cells, and new animal cells arise only from existing animal cells.

The ideas of Schleiden, Schwann, and Virchow make up what is now called the cell theory. The **cell theory** consists of three principles:

- Cells are the basic units of all life.
- All organisms are made of one or more cells.
- All cells arise from existing cells.

The cell theory emphasizes that all organisms are composed of cells, the fundamental units of life. Historically the cell theory has provided direction for the work of many biologists and physicians as they study life processes, genetics, and diseases.

FRONTIERS IN BIOLOGY
Seeing smaller

The progress of biology often depends on the advances of technology. In fact, the study of life has paralleled the invention of tools that extend scientists' ability to observe and analyze information. One of the most important tools used by biologists is the microscope.

Until the 1950s all available microscopes were light microscopes—instruments that use either sunlight or artificial light to view objects. One of the main advantages of the light microscope is that it can magnify many microscopic organisms while they are alive. However, if the object being studied is too large, it has to be sliced thin to allow light to pass through it.

Light microscopes can magnify objects such as tiny organisms up to about 1000 times their actual size. If you try to obtain a larger magnification, the image begins to look blurry. Over the years, scientists have found ways to observe objects better by increasing the contrast between different parts of a specimen.

One way to increase the contrast is by using dyes to stain or color a specimen. Dyes improve contrast by selectively staining certain parts of the specimen. The stained areas then become more visible. One drawback to the staining method, however, is that the dyes usually kill the specimen. Another way to increase the contrast is by manipulating the light. Notice how contrast affects the three images in *Figure 3.5*. How do the three views compare?

Since the 1950s biologists have been using microscopes that use electrons instead of light. Electron microscopes can magnify objects up to a million times their actual size. Before

FIGURE 3.7
This image was created using SIAM, a microscope that can resolve features as small as 1 nanometer (nm), which is about five times the size of an individual atom.

a specimen can be viewed, all parts of it must be fixed, or locked in position, and placed in a vacuum. Consequently, electron microscopes cannot be used to view organisms that are alive.

Electron microscopes work in two ways to produce images. Some microscopes pass, or transmit, electrons through a thin slice of an object. These microscopes are called transmission electron microscopes (TEM).

Scanning electron microscopes (SEM) examine, or scan, the outside of an object. Compare the images produced by two kinds of electron microscopes in *Figure 3.6*. How does the TEM differ from the SEM?

A new microscopic technique has recently been developed. It uses some principles of the light microscope but has the potential to allow the imaging of single atoms. Called a scanning interferometric apertureless microscope (SIAM), it produces about 500 times better resolution than is possible with existing light microscopes.

For biologists the SIAM could be an important tool for studying DNA because it can be used to view and identify individual molecules.

LAB ZONE Do It!

How Do You Use the Microscope?

You will use a compound light microscope in many activities throughout this textbook. You can learn how when you . . .

Try This

1 Cut a 2-centimeter (cm) piece of one of your hairs. Without the microscope, examine the hair and record your observations about its color, thickness, shape, and texture.
2 Follow instructions in the Appendix under "Using a Microscope" (p. 947) and reexamine the piece of hair using low and high power. Add to your observations about the hair's characteristics.
3 Compare the cut end of the hair with the natural end. How are they different? Why?

4 Exchange samples with a classmate and compare his or her hair with your own. Record your observations.

Analyze Your Results

Compare the level of detail you saw without the microscope, with the microscope on low power, and with the microscope on high power. Give examples of the way the hair appeared in each case.

Currently, mapping genetic profiles of organisms takes years. In the future, with SIAM's help, DNA sequencing might be accomplished much faster.

CHECKPOINT 3.1

1. Explain the key ideas of the cell theory.
2. Summarize the role of the microscope in the development of the cell theory.
3. Critical Thinking Why do you think that most biologists were unimpressed when the microscope was first invented?

Build on What You Know

4. Compare the relationship between structure and function in chemicals and in cells. *(Need to jog your memory? Revisit relevant concepts in Chapter 2, Section 2.1.)*

3.2 Basic Cell Structures

What you'll learn

IDEAS

• To describe the structure and function of the cell membrane, the cytoplasm, and the nucleus

• To contrast the cell structure of prokaryotes and eukaryotes

WORDS

cell membrane, phospholipid, cytoplasm, cytoskeleton, nucleus, chromosomes, nucleolus, prokaryotes, eukaryotes

When stains are good

In 1880 German biologist Walther Flemming was the first to describe a complex material located in the nuclei of cells. The new material was called "chromatin" because the tightly bundled fibers readily absorbed colored stains. "Chroma-" comes from the Greek word for color. You can see darkly stained nuclei in these cheek cells. Many structures in cells become visible when stained.

THE CELL MEMBRANE

Controlling the flow

As you now know, all living things consist of one or more cells. Although cell structure may vary from one organism to another, certain features are common to the cells of animals, plants, and many other living things. *Figure 3.8* shows a cross section of a cell and highlights three common features: the cell membrane, cytoplasm, and nucleus.

The cells of all organisms are surrounded by a cell membrane. The **cell membrane** is a thin layer of lipid and protein that separates the cell's contents from its environment. Cell membranes are 5 to 10 nm thick. A stack of 10,000 membranes is about equal to the thickness of this page.

Nucleus

Cytoplasm

Cell membrane

FIGURE 3.8

The cutaway diagram of a cell is shown above. Notice the cell's three principal features: cell membrane, cytoplasm, and nucleus. Can you locate these features in the micrograph on the right?

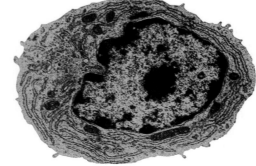

The cell membrane functions like a fence with gates, controlling what enters and leaves the cell.

Membranes are made mostly of phospholipid (fos-foh-LIP-id) molecules. You can see a phospholipid molecule in *Figure 3.9*. A **phospholipid** is a type of lipid made from glycerol, two fatty acids, and a phosphate group.

The two ends of the phospholipid molecule have different properties in water. The phosphate head of a phospholipid is hydrophilic (hy-droh-FIL-ik), meaning "water-loving." The phosphate head dissolves easily in water. The lipid tails of the molecule are hydrophobic (hy-droh-FOH-bik), meaning "water-fearing." The lipid tails do not dissolve in water.

When dropped in water, phospholipids will form two layers, called a lipid bilayer. The phosphate heads on both sides of the bilayer face the water. The lipid tails of each layer face each other. You can see the structure of a lipid bilayer in *Figure 3.9*.

The structure of cell membranes is based on a lipid bilayer. The phosphate heads face the watery fluids inside the cell and outside the cell. Lipid tails are sandwiched inside the bilayer. The phospholipids in the cell membrane are constantly being formed and broken down by chemical reactions in living cells.

Protein molecules are embedded in the lipid bilayer. About 30 percent of the proteins are attached to one side of the membrane. The rest extend all the way through the bilayer. There are many kinds of proteins in membranes. For example, red blood cell membranes contain more than 50 different proteins. Some of these proteins help move materials in and out of the cell. Others serve as identification badges that enable cells to recognize each other.

Cell membranes are fluid and have the consistency of vegetable oil. The lipids and proteins are always in motion, like the surface of a soap bubble. The phospholipids drift across the membrane, changing places with one another. Cholesterol molecules interact with the phospholipids, helping to keep the membrane intact, yet fluid.

Proteins in and on the membrane form patterns, or mosaics, on the membrane, such as the one shown in *Figure 3.10*. These proteins move sideways across the membrane like slow-moving ships at sea. Because the membrane is fluid with a mosaic of proteins, scientists call the modern view of membrane structure the fluid mosaic model.

Water
Hydrophilic phosphate head
Hydrophobic lipid tail
Hydrophilic phosphate head
Water

Lipid bilayer

Phospholipid molecule

THE CYTOPLASM

Inside the great membrane

The material between the cell membrane and the nucleus is called the cytoplasm. The **cytoplasm** is a semifluid substance made primarily of water and organic compounds. Various structures called organelles, or "little organs," are suspended in the cytoplasm. Organelles are structures that work like miniature organs within the cell to perform specific functions. You will learn more about these important structures and their specific functions in section 3.3.

FIGURE 3.9
The phospholipid molecule consists of a phosphate head and two lipid tails. The cutaway view of a lipid bilayer shows the orientation of the lipid molecules. Why are the lipid tails located facing each other?

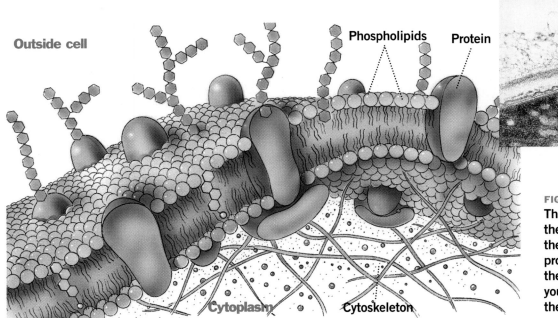

Outside cell

Phospholipids   Protein

Cytoplasm   Cytoskeleton

FIGURE 3.10
The illustration (left) shows the fluid mosaic model of the cell membrane. The proteins can drift across the cell membrane. Can you locate any proteins in the micrograph above?

Nucleus   Nuclear   Chromosomes
           envelope   Nucleolus

FIGURE 3.11

The image above (left) shows a cutaway view of a nucleus. Why are the pores on the nucleus important? The micrograph (right) shows the nucleus of a human cell.

No Room for a Nucleus

Upon reaching maturity, a human red blood cell actually spits out its nucleus. It uses the space for hemoglobin, the protein that enables red blood cells to carry oxygen from the lungs to the rest of the body.

One of a cell's most intricate components is its cytoskeleton. The **cytoskeleton** is a network of protein fibers and tubes extending throughout the cytoplasm. The network gives the cell support and helps it to maintain or change its shape. The cell membrane and some organelles are anchored to the cytoskeleton. Materials are transported throughout the cell on the cytoskeleton. Also, the cytoskeleton enables the cell itself to move. For example, amebas move by a coordinated flow of cytoplasm caused by the elongation and contraction of their cytoskeleton.

THE NUCLEUS

Chromosome keeper

Within the cytoplasm lies the most prominent of a cell's organelles, the nucleus. Often called the control center of a cell, the **nucleus** contains most of the cell's genetic material. As you can see in *Figure 3.11,* the nucleus is surrounded by a double membrane called a nuclear envelope. Like the outer membrane of a cell, each membrane of the nuclear envelope is a lipid bilayer. Together the two membranes separate the nucleus from the cytoplasm. In a microscopic view, the nuclear envelope looks pitted. The surface is pierced by tiny pores

through which proteins and other compounds can pass.

Most of a cell's genetic information is kept in distinct structures called **chromosomes.** The nucleic acid in chromosomes carries the genetic information. All organisms have a definite number of chromosomes. Human body cells have 46 chromosomes. Chromosomes contain the genetic "blueprints" that control all cellular activity, such as growth and cell division. You will learn more about chromosomes in Chapter 7.

Another identifying structure of the nucleus is the nucleolus. Organelles called ribosomes are formed in the **nucleolus** (plural: *nucleoli*). Ribosomes help make proteins. Cells that are primarily involved in protein synthesis have rather large nucleoli and many ribosomes.

TWO KINDS OF CELLS

Nucleus or not?

Living things are classified into two large groups, based on the presence or absence of a nucleus in their cells. Organisms whose cells have no definite nucleus are called **prokaryotes.** Organisms whose cells have a nucleus surrounded by a nuclear membrane are called **eukaryotes.** Bacteria and

Prokaryotic cell
Prokaryotic cells contain no nucleus or membrane-bound organelles. This micrograph shows a bacterium.

Eukaryotic cell
The eukaryotic cell contains a nucleus and membrane-bound organelles. This eukaryotic cell is a human pancreatic cell.

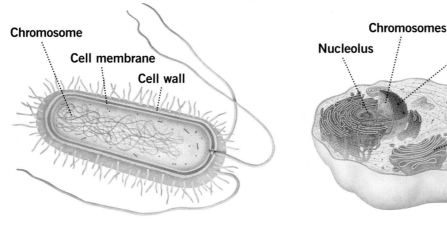

Chromosome
Cell membrane
Cell wall

Chromosomes
Nucleolus
Nucleus
Organelles
Cell membrane

|—— 0.1 to 1.0 micrometer ——|

|—— 1.0 to 10.0 micrometers ——|

FIGURE 3.12
Compare the structure of the prokaryotic cell and the eukaryotic cell. Notice the size indicated on the scale below each cell.

their relatives are prokaryotes; all other organisms, including plants and animals, are eukaryotes.

The cells of prokaryotes are called prokaryotic cells. The cells of eukaryotes are called eukaryotic cells. Prokaryotic cells and eukaryotic cells are easily distinguished by their structural differences, as you can see in *Figure 3.12*. What similarities and differences do you see?

Prokaryotic cells are typically much smaller than eukaryotic cells. Most prokaryotic cells are tiny—about one-tenth the width and one-thousandth the volume of eukaryotic cells. The tiny size of prokaryotic cells is the reason scientists could not view their internal structures before the invention of the electron microscope.

Prokaryotic cells have a less complex internal structure than eukaryotic cells. Prokaryotic cells do not have a nuclear membrane and most lack organelles surrounded by membranes. Although prokaryotic cells contain

fewer internal structures, they can perform all of the activities of life, including reproduction and response to the environment. Because of their small size and comparatively simple structure, prokaryotic cells are considered the forerunners of eukaryotic cells.

CHECKPOINT 3.2

1. Describe the three main parts of a eukaryotic cell. What are the functions of each part?
2. How does a prokaryotic cell differ from a eukaryotic cell?
3. Critical Thinking What characteristic of eukaryotic cells gives them a greater capacity for specialization than prokaryotic cells have? Explain.

Build on What You Know

4. You have learned about the chemicals that make up living things. Match each chemical with the cell structure(s) for which it is a main component. *(Need to jog your memory? Revisit relevant concepts in Chapter 2, Section 2.1.)*

3.3 Cell Organelles

What you'll learn

IDEAS
• To describe the function of key organelles
• To compare and contrast the characteristics of cilia and flagella

WORDS
ribosomes, endoplasmic reticulum, Golgi apparatus, mitochondria, lysosomes, cilia, flagella

Many parts and functions
Cells have many different parts, each of which performs a specific task. The tiny hairs, called cilia, on human tracheal cells (right) are one type of specialized cell structure. The waving cilia move a coating of mucus through the airways to help remove dust, bacteria, and other foreign matter from the body. Cilia perform different functions in other types of cells.

ORGANELLES IN CYTOPLASM

Little machines

Despite their small size, cells are by no means simple structures! Cells function like miniature factories, constructing new molecules from raw materials. At any moment, cells may be taking in nutrients; making new molecules; sorting, secreting, and storing chemicals; and breaking down foreign materials. Organelles are the cell structures that perform these specific functions. In many ways organelles are like machines in a factory, each with a specific role.

Organelles called **ribosomes** (RY-buh-sohmz) make the proteins needed by cells. Groups of ribosomes function like an assembly line, helping to make proteins from amino acids. Ribosomes are found suspended in the cytoplasm or bound to membranes.

Both prokaryotes and eukaryotes have ribosomes. Other organelles, all membrane-bound, are found only in eukaryotes. *Figure 3.13* illustrates some of the different organelles found in a eukaryotic cell.

The **endoplasm reticulum** (en-do-PLAZ-mik ri-TIK-uh-lum) or ER, is an extensive network of membranes that produces materials for the cell. There are two types of ER: rough and smooth. Rough ER has ribosomes on its surface and functions in the syn-

thesis of proteins that will be secreted by the cell. Rough ER also manufactures new cell membranes. Smooth ER makes lipids, processes carbohydrates, and modifies chemicals that are toxic to the cell.

Molecules that are produced in the ER are transported by the Golgi apparatus (GOHL-jee). The **Golgi apparatus** is a series of flat, membrane-bound sacs where molecules are sorted, often modified, packaged, and distributed to their destination. For example, the Golgi apparatus distributes some molecules to the cell membrane for secretion. The Golgi apparatus is the cell's conveyor belt, transporting materials.

Most of the energy necessary to power the cell's activities is generated in organelles called mitochondria (my-tuh-KAHN-dree-uh). **Mitochondria** (singular: mitochondrion) change the energy stored in food compounds into a form useful for the cell—the energy-storing molecule adenosine triphosphate (ATP). You will read more about ATP in Chapter 4. Mitochondria are similar to a factory generator that changes mechanical energy into electrical energy.

Inside many cells, large molecules are digested inside of saclike organelles called lysosomes (LY-suh-sohmz). **Lysosomes** contain digestive enzymes that help break down large molecules

FIGURE 3.13

Organelles—
Machines in the Cell Factory

Assembling proteins

Ribosomes are protein assemblers. Whether free-floating in the cytoplasm or attached to rough endoplasmic reticulum, they help assemble long chains of amino acids that are called proteins.

Generating energy

Mitochondria are energy-producing organelles. The folded inner membrane of a mitochondrion surrounds a space called the mitochondrial matrix, where ATP is produced. Most cells have hundreds or thousands of mitochondria.

Ribosomes

Mitochondrion

Endoplasmic reticulum

Processing materials

The endoplasmic reticulum is a complex network of tubules and sacs. It connects the nuclear membrane to the cell membrane. Rough ER, shown here, helps make protein secretions, such as hormones, and assists in membrane production. Smooth ER makes lipids and rids the cell of toxic waste. What makes rough ER rough?

Lysosome

Nucleus

Golgi apparatus

Packaging and transporting

The Golgi apparatus sorts, packages, and transports substances in the cell. These substances may include products of the endoplasmic reticulum.

Preparing raw materials

Lysosomes are small sacs containing digestive enzymes. Large molecules are absorbed into the cell in membranous sacs. Lysosomes fuse with the sacs and release digestive enzymes into them. The enzymes break down the molecules for the cell's use.

FIGURE 3.14
Compare the micrograph of cilia (left) with the micrograph of a flagellum (right). How do the two different structures enable organisms to move?

of carbohydrates, proteins, and lipids. Lysosomes also digest old organelles that are no longer useful to the cell. Because the digestive enzymes are isolated in lysosomes, the rest of the cell is protected. Lysosomes are like a factory furnace that melts down scrap metals into materials that can be used again. How might a cell use lysosomes for defense?

STRUCTURES FOR MOVEMENT

Getting around

You may recall reading about the cytoskeleton and its role in cellular mobility. Many cells have unique extensions of their cytoskeleton for movement. These specialized cellular appendages are called cilia and flagella. They are composed of bundles of cytoskeletal proteins wrapped in the outer cell membrane. Although both cilia and flagella are used for movement, they are different in structure and function. You can see cilia and flagella in *Figure 3.14*.

Cilia (singular: *cilium*) are short, hairlike projections that usually occur in large numbers on the surface of certain cells. Some unicellular eukaryotes, known as ciliates, eat and move using their cilia. Ciliates are found mostly in fresh water. The movement of cilia closely resembles that of oars,

with alternating strokes generating the force needed for locomotion. Cilia are also found in multicellular organisms. In fact, cilia on the cells lining the human trachea, or windpipe, aid in the removal of debris from this area.

Flagella (singular: *flagellum*) are long, tail-like projections. Unlike ciliates, flagellates usually have one flagellum. Prokaryotic flagella differ structurally from their eukaryotic counterparts. The movement of prokaryotic flagella also differs from that of eukaryotic flagella. Prokaryotic flagella spin like propellers, whereas eukaryotic flagella move with a whip-like motion.

CHECKPOINT 3.3

1. Describe the function of five key organelles.
2. How do cilia and flagella differ in structure and function?
3. **Critical Thinking** Would you expect skin cells to contain more or fewer mitochondria than muscle cells? Explain your reasoning.

Build on What You Know

4. What substances are affected by the digestive enzymes of the lysosomes? What is the general term for all materials that are acted upon by enzymes? *(Need to jog your memory? Revisit relevant concepts in Chapter 2, Section 2.3.)*

 What are some cell strucures, and what do they do?

3.4 Cell Diversity

How many cells in a termite?
There are probably more cells than you think. The termite is a relatively complex organism with many specialized cells, but it could not feast on wood without the help of the unicellular protists that live in its digestive tract. Each stowaway protist, (in turn), is home to bacteria, whose ability to digest cellulose enables both termite and protist to survive.

What you'll learn

IDEAS
• To contrast the components of plant and animal cells
• To describe some similarities and differences in the cells of unicellular and multicellular organisms

WORDS
cell wall, chloroplasts, vacuole

PLANT AND ANIMAL CELLS

The little things that keep us apart

You have just finished reading about the organelles and other cell parts that are common to many cells. But not all cells are identical. Among the eukaryotes, there are great differences between the cells of plants and animals. You can see some important structural differences between plant and animal cells in *Figure 3.15*.

One of the most significant differences is that plant cells have a cell wall. The **cell wall** is a tough, rigid outer covering that protects a plant cell and helps it maintain its shape. The cells of fungi, algae, and bacteria also have cell walls. Animal cells lack cell walls, but they have other structures, such as cytoskeletons, for support.

Another difference is that plant cells contain organelles called chloroplasts. **Chloroplasts** are structures that enable the plant to make sugars through photosynthesis. Animal cells do not have chloroplasts and cannot make their own food. Animals get

FIGURE 3.15
Plant and animal cells share many of the same features, but some specialized structures distinguish them. Which structures are present only in plant cells?

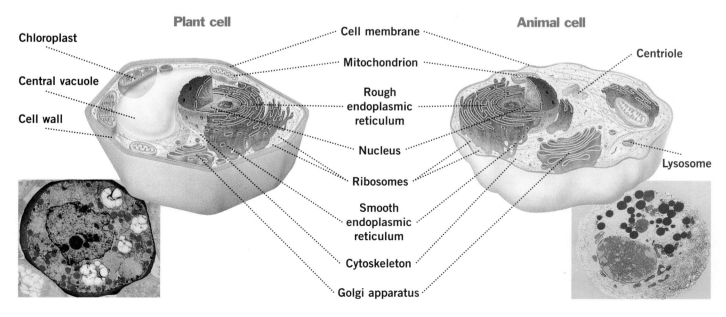

Plant cell — Animal cell

Chloroplast

Central vacuole

Cell wall

Cell membrane

Mitochondrion

Rough endoplasmic reticulum

Nucleus

Ribosomes

Smooth endoplasmic reticulum

Cytoskeleton

Golgi apparatus

Centriole

Lysosome

FIGURE 3.16
This table shows structural similarities and differences between different kinds of cells. What structures do all of these cells have in common?

their nourishment by eating other organisms or their products.

All plant cells also contain a large central **vacuole,** a membrane-bound compartment that serves many functions. Vacuoles may absorb water, or they may store proteins, ions, and the waste products of metabolism. Animal cells lack a large central vacuole but may contain smaller vacuoles.

COMPARING CELL DIVERSITY

Together or apart

There is great diversity among cells. As you have learned, there are differences between plant and animal cells, and between prokaryotic and eukaryotic cells. The diversity of cells can be explored in a number of ways.

As you have already done with plant and animal cells, the structures in cells can be compared. In contrast to eukaryotic cells, prokaryotic cells do

not have a nucleus or membrane-bound organelles. In addition, some prokaryotic cells have cell walls, similar to plant cells.

Cells can also differ with respect to their associations with other cells. For example, some cells exist alone as unicellular organisms. Unicellular organisms perform almost all life functions as individuals. Some unicellular organisms do interact when they combine briefly for reproduction.

Conversely, some cells live together as multicellular organisms. Multicellular organisms depend on the interaction of many cells, which generally cannot survive as separate cells outside the organism.

The cells of multicellular organisms typically are specialized to perform different functions. For example, specialized cells in animals are adapted for reproduction, digestion, or movement. A unicellular organism must perform all of these functions. *Figure 3.16* summarizes the diversity of the cells that you have studied.

CHECKPOINT 3.4

1. Describe two differences between plant and animal cells.
2. Name the main differences and some of the similarities between unicellular and multicellular organisms.
3. **Critical Thinking** How do the cell walls, chloroplasts, and vacuoles of plant cells illustrate the idea that cell structure mirrors cell function?

Build on What You Know

4. How is the organization of the cells of the human body similar to the organization of a eukaryotic cell? **(Need to jog your memory? Revisit relevant concepts in Chapter 1, Section 1.2.)**

A Comparison of Cells			
Structure	**Prokaryotic Cells**	**Eukaryotic Cells**	
		Animal	*Plant*
Cell membrane	Yes	Yes	Yes
Cell wall	Yes	No	Yes
Nucleus	No	Yes	Yes
Chromosomes	Yes (one circular strand of DNA)	Yes (many)	Yes (many)
Ribosomes	Yes (small)	Yes (large)	Yes (large)
Endoplasmic reticulum	No	Yes	Yes
Golgi apparatus	No	Yes	Yes
Lysosomes	No	Yes	No
Vacuoles	No	Yes (small or none)	Yes
Mitochondria	No	Yes	Yes
Chloroplasts	No	No	Yes
Cytoskeleton	No	Yes	Yes

 What is the relationship between cells and organisms?

LAB ZONE Investigate It!

Comparing Plant and Animal Cells

Elodea cell

Human cheek cell

WHAT YOU WILL DO Compare and contrast the structures of plant and animal cells

SKILLS YOU WILL USE Hypothesizing, observing, recording data

WHAT YOU WILL NEED Compound light microscope, leaf from *Elodea* plant, forceps, medicine dropper, water, slide, coverslip, prepared slide of human cheek cells

Propose a Hypothesis

Based on what you have read in the chapter, list the similarities and differences you expect to see in the cells of a plant and an animal. Propose a hypothesis about how the differences in structure of plant and animal cells are related to differences in function.

Conduct Your Experiment

1 Make a three-column chart in your notebook. Label the columns *Leaf Cells, Cheek Cells,* and *Both Types of Cells.*
2 Make a wet-mount slide of an *Elodea* leaf taken from the tip of the plant, where there is new growth. Use forceps and handle the leaf carefully.
3 Observe the specimen with the microscope on low power. This will show the outermost cell layer.
4 Draw several of the cells you see and label the cell structures that are visible. Record the cell structures on your chart.

5 Observe the specimen on high power. What other cell structures are now visible? Add them to your drawing and chart.
6 Using a prepared slide of human cheek cells, repeat steps 3–5.

Analyze Your Data

1 In the third column of your chart, list the structures you saw that are common to plant and animal cells.
2 Which organelles are unique to plant cells? To animal cells?
3 What makes a leaf green?
4 The cells in the lining of your cheek are organized in sheets. Did the cheek cells in your slide look different? If so, what might have affected their appearance?

5 As you viewed the cell structures in the plant leaf with the microscope, how could you make the structures more visible?

Draw Conclusions

Was your prediction supported by your observations? Were there any organelles that you expected to see, but did not? How do you explain this?

Design a Related Experiment

Imagine you are given a slide of unidentified cells. Explain the procedure you would use to determine if they are plant or animal cells.

Leaf Cells | *Cheek Cells* | *Both Types of Cells*

3.5 Cells and Their Environment

Waiting for water
How can a plant that appears brown and shriveled come back to life? The cells of several types of resurrection plants like this one are able to endure extreme dehydration. When rain falls, water diffuses from an area of abundance to an area of scarcity—from the outside to the inside of the leaves—and the plant becomes green again. This process is an example of one way that cells exchange materials with their environment.

FIGURE 3.17
Diffusion

Initially, the concentration of a substance outside the cell is higher than inside.

Later, the substance has diffused into the cell so that the concentration is the same on both sides of the membrane.

INSIDE AND OUTSIDE

Be prepared to stop

All cells live at least partly in touch with a water solution. In order to live, all cells must take in nutrients and eliminate wastes. Somehow nutrients and waste materials must cross the cell membrane between the solution outside the cell and the solution inside the cell.

A **semipermeable** membrane lets certain molecules pass through and prevents other molecules from crossing. Cell membranes are semipermeable membranes. Small molecules, such as water, can enter and leave the cell freely. Large molecules, such as proteins and carbohydrates, cannot. And even though they are small, particles with strong electrical charges, such as ions, cannot pass easily through the membrane. The electrical charge prevents the ion from moving through the lipid bilayer.

Several processes are involved in moving materials across the cell membrane. These processes can be classified either as passive transport or active transport. **Passive transport** is the movement of a substance across a cell membrane without the input of the cell's energy. **Active transport** uses cellular energy to move substances across a cell membrane.

DIFFUSION

Going with the flow

The most common form of passive transport is simple diffusion. **Diffusion** is the random movement of molecules from an area of higher concentration (more molecules) to an area of lower concentration (fewer molecules). Simple diffusion enables oxygen and carbon dioxide to cross cell membranes. *Figure 3.17* illustrates the process of diffusion.

The rate of diffusion depends on the temperature and the size of the molecules involved. Molecules diffuse faster at high temperatures than at low temperatures, and small molecules diffuse faster than large ones.

Diffusion always occurs down a concentration gradient. A concentration

FIGURE 3.18
During facilitated diffusion, carrier proteins shuttle molecules across the lipid bilayer of the cell membrane.

Carrier protein

gradient is the difference between the concentration of a particular molecule in one area and its concentration in an adjacent area. When the molecules have been dispersed evenly, there is no concentration gradient. A state of equilibrium has been reached, and diffusion stops.

Some molecules diffuse across cell membranes with the help of carrier proteins in the membrane, as shown in *Figure 3.18*. This form of passive transport is called facilitated diffusion. In facilitated diffusion, molecules always move down a concentration gradient, from higher concentration to lower concentration. Facilitated diffusion increases the rate that some molecules cross the cell membrane, such as large molecules or ions. For example, facilitated diffusion enables the transport of glucose from the blood into body cells.

OSMOSIS
Water's way

Water moves freely across cell membranes by diffusion. The diffusion of water across a semipermeable membrane is called **osmosis.** Osmosis like all diffusion, is a form of passive transport.

Osmosis occurs when the concentrations of solutes in the solutions on the two sides of a semipermeable membrane are different. Like other diffusing molecules, water moves down its concentration gradient. In other words, water moves from solutions with higher water (lower solute) concentration to solutions with lower water (higher solute) concentrations. *Figure 3.19* shows what happens during osmosis.

Cytoplasm is a solution of water and many dissolved solutes. The different concentrations of solutes in the cytoplasm and in the surrounding solution cause water to move in or out of a cell by osmosis.

The natural tendency of water to move from low solute concentrations to high solute concentrations has an effect on cells, as you can see in

FIGURE 3.19
Water moves by osmosis across a semipermeable membrane. How has the concentration of the solute changed in the beaker on the right?

Do It!

Observing Osmosis and Semipermeability

You can observe the results of osmosis through a cell membrane when you . . .

Try This

1 Record the appearance of a raw egg in its shell. Measure and record its circumference.
2 Gently place the egg in a jar and cover it with white vinegar. Put the lid on the jar. Record your observations.
3 After 72 hours record the egg's appearance after being in the vinegar. Then remove the egg from the jar and measure its circumference.

Analyze Your Results

1 Compare your recorded observations. How did the egg change?
2 What happened to the egg's circumference after 72 hours?
3 What kept the contents of the egg from seeping into the vinegar?
4 Propose an explanation for the changes you observed.

Figure 3.20. For example, in a hypertonic solution, the fluid outside the cell has a higher concentration of solutes than the cytoplasm inside the cell. Water diffuses out of the cell.

You can see the effect of hypertonic conditions by placing a small piece of lettuce in a bowl of salt water. As you will see after a few minutes, the lettuce wilts because its cells have lost their water to the salty, hypertonic environment. In an isotonic solution, the concentration of solutes outside the cell equals the concentration of solutes inside the cell, so osmosis does not occur.

In a hypotonic solution, the concentration of solutes is lower outside the cell than inside, and water moves into the cell. The flow of water into the cell causes it to swell. Distilled water is very hypotonic because it contains no solutes. Animal cells placed in distilled water will swell and often burst because of osmosis. Plant cells do not burst in distilled water. Can you explain why? A piece of lettuce in distilled water becomes firm and crisp because of the diffusion of water into its cells. Good cooks know that they must keep lettuce damp and chilled if they want to serve crisp salad.

ACTIVE TRANSPORT

Movin' on up

Passive transport allows molecules to cross a cell membrane without using the cell's energy. Molecules always move down a concentration gradient during passive transport. However, a cell must use energy to move molecules across the membrane against a concentration gradient, from areas of lower concentration to areas of higher concentration. This process is called active transport.

FIGURE 3.20

Effect of Solution Concentrations

The cells in this figure depict reactions to the osmotic effects of different solution concentrations. In what direction has the water moved in each of these examples?

Normal cell

Hypertonic
The concentration of solutes outside is higher than it is inside the cell.

Isotonic
The concentration of solutes outside the cell is equal to that inside the cell.

Hypotonic
The concentration of solutes outside is lower than it is inside the cell.

Very Hypotonic
This cell has burst due to the large amount of water entering it.

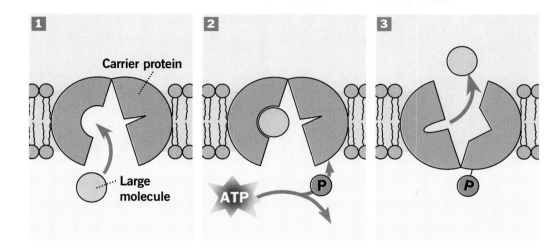

FIGURE 3.21

Active transport of molecules and ions against a concentration gradient requires membrane-bound carrier proteins and the energy of ATP. What happens in each of these three steps?

Like facilitated diffusion, active transport often involves carrier proteins. These carrier proteins use energy to pump ions and molecules across the membrane. The energy for active transport usually comes from ATP, as illustrated in *Figure 3.21*.

Active transport is especially important in maintaining proper ion concentrations inside cells. Animal cells, for example, pump sodium ions out of the cell and potassium ions into the cell. This sodium-potassium pump uses about one third of a cell's available energy. As a result of active transport, the concentration of potassium ions remains high inside the cell, while the accumulation of sodium ions remains high outside the cell. These gradients are important for the contraction of muscles, the transmission of nerve impulses, and the absorption of nutrients.

Active transport is vital to all organisms. In plants, active transport enables the roots to absorb nutrients from the soil. Plant nutrients are more concentrated inside the roots than in the surrounding soil. Without active transport, these nutrients would diffuse out of the roots. Overall, active transport is one of several ways that an organism maintains homeostasis.

BULK MOVEMENT

Package and handling

When a cell needs to transport large molecules such as polysaccharides or proteins across its membrane, it uses several processes, all of which are classified as bulk movement. During bulk movement large molecules move across the cell membrane by being packaged in membrane-bound sacs. Cells typically rely on two types of bulk movement, exocytosis and endocytosis.

LAB ZONE Think About It!

Analyzing Ion Concentrations

The graph at the right shows the relative concentrations of different ions inside (red) and outside (yellow) an animal cell. Use this information and what you have read in the chapter to answer the following questions.

Analyzing the Graph

1 Which ions are transported into the cell by active transport?

2 Which ions are transported out of the cell by active transport?

3 Explain how you determined your answers.

FIGURE 3.22
Exocytosis (left) and endocytosis (right) are both
forms of bulk transport.
What are the steps of exocytosis? Endocytosis?

Exocytosis

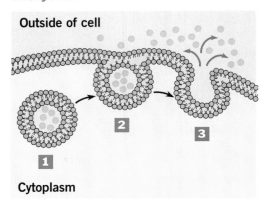

Outside of cell

Cytoplasm

1 2 3

Endocytosis

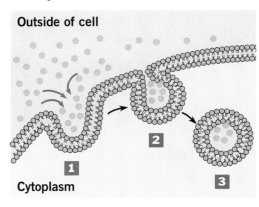

Outside of cell

Cytoplasm

1 2 3

During **exocytosis,** wastes and cell products are packaged by the Golgi apparatus in sacs called Golgi vesicles. The Golgi vesicles then fuse with the cell membrane, and the materials in the vesicles are secreted out of the cell. When you cry, tear gland cells use exocytosis to excrete a salty solution containing proteins.

During **endocytosis,** a portion of the cell membrane surrounds desirable macromolecules that are outside the cell. The cell pinches off a saclike portion of its outer membrane to form a tiny new vesicle. The membranous vesicle moves into the cell, where it can fuse with other organelles or release its contents into the cytoplasm. You can see this process in *Figure* 3.22.

Pinocytosis and phagocytosis are forms of endocytosis. During pinocytosis (sometimes called cellular drinking), the cell membrane encloses a droplet of fluid and its solutes and brings the droplet into the cell.

Phagocytosis is similar to pinocytosis. However, in phagocytosis, the cell engulfs a food particle or

other solid substance, rather than a liquid. The vesicle containing food can then fuse with a lysosome carrying digestive enzymes. Many unicellular organisms, such as amebas, obtain food by phagocytosis. Human white blood cells, such as the one shown in *Figure 3.23,* are phagocytes that engulf and destroy bacteria. How is phagocytosis by white blood cells beneficial for both the white blood cells and the body?

CHECKPOINT 3.5

1. Describe the process of osmosis, and explain its significance.

2. Explain how active transport and bulk movement differ.

3. Critical Thinking Meat can spoil if bacteria grow on it. One way to preserve meat is to soak it in a strong salt solution. Use what you have learned about cells in different solutions to explain how salt in meat would stop bacteria from growing.

Build on What You Know

4. How does active transport contribute to homeostasis? *(Need to jog your memory? Revisit relevant concepts in Chapter 2, Section 2.5.)*

FIGURE 3.23
In this picture three tumor cells are engulfed by a white blood cell. What form of bulk transport is this process?

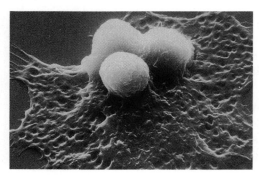

How do cells and their environment interact?

Chapter 3 Review

THE BIG IDEA!

3.1–3.3 Cell structures of living organisms perform life functions.

3.4 Cells of major groups of organisms can be distinguished by their structural differences.

3.5 Cells exchange materials with their environment by chemical and physical processes.

Sum It Up

Use the following summary to review the main content of this chapter.

3.1 A Look at Cells

- Cells may be complete organisms or components of multicellular organisms. Cells vary in size and shape.
- Cells were discovered after the invention of the microscope, an instrument that produces an enlarged image.
- According to the cell theory, cells are the basic units of life, all organisms are made of one or more cells, and all cells arise from existing cells.

3.2 Basic Cell Structures

- The cell membrane separates a cell's contents from its environment. The membrane consists of a bilayer of phospholipids with embedded proteins.
- The semifluid cytoplasm contains specialized organelles plus a cytoskeleton, which provides structure and allows for movement.
- The cell nucleus contains the chromosomes of the cell, which store genetic information, and the nucleolus, which makes ribosomes.
- Cells of prokaryotes do not have a definite nucleus. Cells of eukaryotes have a nucleus.

3.3 Cell Organelles

- Ribosomes assemble proteins from amino acids.
- The endoplasmic reticulum transports material.
- Mitochondria generate energy from food.
- The Golgi apparatus packages and transports proteins.
- Lysomes contain enzymes that digest food.
- Cilia and flagella move cells or substances.

3.4 Cell Diversity

- In plant cells, cell walls provide protection and shape; chloroplasts produce sugar; vacuoles store substances such as water and wastes.
- Cells can differ in their components, and their relationship to other cells.

3.5 Cells and Their Environment

- In diffusion and osmosis, substances move passively from areas of higher concentration to areas of lower concentration.
- In active transport, energy is used to move substances against the concentration gradient.
- During endocytosis and exocytosis, materials are packaged in sacs and moved in bulk.

Use Terms and Concepts

Use each of the following words or terms in a complete sentence. If you need to review a meaning, turn to the page indicated.

cell theory (p. 60)
cell membrane (p. 62)
phospholipid (p. 62)
cytoplasm (p. 63)
cytoskeleton (p. 64)
nucleus (p. 64)
chromosomes (p. 64)

nucleolus (p. 64)
prokaryotes (p. 64)
eukaryotes (p. 64)
ribosomes (p. 66)
endoplasmic reticulum (p. 66)
Golgi apparatus (p. 66)

mitochondria (p. 66)
lysosomes (p. 66)
cilia (p. 68)
flagella (p. 68)
cell wall (p. 69)
chloroplasts (p. 69)
vacuole (p. 70)

semipermeable (p. 72)
passive transport (p. 72)
active transport (p. 72)
diffusion (p. 72)
osmosis (p. 73)
endocytosis (p. 76)
exocytosis (p. 76)

Use Your Word Power

COMPLETION **Write the word or phrase that best completes each statement.**

1. _____ are organelles that enable plants to make sugars.

2. The diffusion of water across a semipermeable membrane is called _____ .

3. _____ is the material between the cell membrane and the nucleus.

4. Two structures that some cells use for movement are _____ and _____ .

5. The _____ is an extensive network of smooth or rough membranes that transport materials through cells.

6. A _____ is a thin layer of lipids and proteins that separates a cell's contents from its surroundings.

MULTIPLE CHOICE **Choose the letter of the word or phrase that best completes each statement.**

7. A structure that contains a cell's genetic information is called a (a) nucleolus; (b) chromosome; (c) ribosome; (d) lysosome.

8. Energy from ATP is needed for (a) diffusion; (b) osmosis; (c) facilitated diffusion; (d) active transport.

9. Animal cells contain (a) chlorophyll; (b) chloroplasts; (c) cell membranes; (d) cell walls.

10. Which of the following processes is NOT a form of bulk transport? (a) endocytosis (b) phagocytosis (c) exocytosis (d) osmosis.

Show What You Know

11. Compare the capabilities of a light microscope and an electron microscope.

12. Describe the contributions of Matthias Schleiden and Theodore Schwan to the cell theory.

13. List the organelles, and describe their functions.

14. Explain why the modern view of cell membrane structure is called the fluid mosaic model.

15. What is a concentration gradient?

16. What are differences between prokaryotes and eukaryotes?

17. What is a semipermeable membrane?

18. Name and describe two forms of passive transport.

19. Compare endocytosis and exocytosis.

20. **Make a Concept Map** Complete the concept map below by adding the following terms: Golgi apparatus, energy, chromosomes, organelles, proteins, ribosomes, endoplasmic reticulum, mitochondria, lysosome, genetic material.

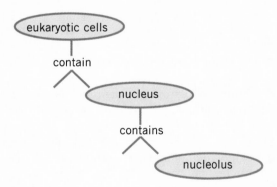

For help making a concept map, see Appendix E.

Take It Further

21. **Making a Generalization** Based on what you have learned, tell why you agree or disagree with the following statement: *Membranes are the most important structures in cells.* If you agree, provide specific evidence to support the statement. If you disagree, offer an alternative proposal and explain your reasoning.

22. **Making a Prediction** What would happen to your cells if a hypotonic solution were placed directly into your bloodstream? Explain your answer.

23. Interpreting a Graph The graph shows the sizes of several molecules that can diffuse across a lipid bilayer. Which substances do you think will diffuse most quickly? Which substances will diffuse most slowly? Which substances will diffuse at about the same rate? Explain your answers for each group of substances.

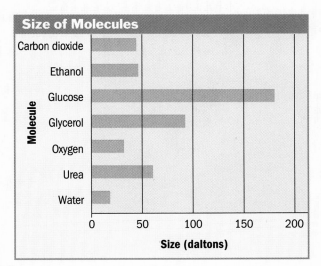

Size of Molecules

Molecule (y-axis): Carbon dioxide, Ethanol, Glucose, Glycerol, Oxygen, Urea, Water

Size (daltons) (x-axis): 0, 50, 100, 150, 200

24. Designing an Experiment Do you think that the rate of diffusion increases or decreases with temperature? Design an experiment to test your hypothesis.

25. Analyzing Data The table shows data for three different cells. Figure out whether each cell is prokaryotic or eukaryotic. If the cell is eukaryotic, is it from an animal or a plant? List the reasons for the decisions you made about each cell.

Structure	Cell A	Cell B	Cell C
Cell wall	Yes	Yes	No
Cell membrane	Yes	Yes	Yes
Chloroplasts	Yes	No	No
Mitochondria	Yes	No	Yes
Nucleus	Yes	No	Yes

Consider the Issues

26. What's the Solution? Different beverages have different concentrations of solutes. Some beverages have low solute concentrations and can be a source of water for body cells. Other beverages have high solute concentrations and can actually dehydrate your body cells. Should companies that market high-solute beverages be able to say these drinks quench your thirst? What information should consumers be given about the concentration of beverages?

Make New Connections

27. Biology and Art Choose either a plant or an animal cell. Prepare either a two-dimensional color poster with labels or a three-dimensional model.

28. Biology and Journalism Imagine that you are Rudolph Virchow. The year is 1858. You have just reached some exciting conclusions about the origins of plant cells, and you wish to share your conclusions with the general public. Write a short description of your theory for publication. Assume that your audience has not studied biology.

29. Biology and Medicine Interview a nurse or doctor about the use of intravenous (IV) solutions. Find out why patients might be placed on an IV drip. Who prepares the solutions? How does the concentration of solutes differ for different patients?

FAST-FORWARD TO CHAPTER 4

Cells could not function without energy. The next chapter describes the two major processes involved in storing and releasing energy—photosynthesis and cellular respiration.

Photosynthesis and Cellular Respiration

bioSURF

You can find out more about photosynthesis and cellular respiration by exploring the following Internet address:
http://basis_of_life.biosurf.com

In this chapter . . .

FEATURES

Everyday Biology
• The Foundation of a Healthful Diet
• Warming Up
• Future Fuel
• Feeling Dead?

In the Community
Breads Around Town

 Frontiers in Biology
Artificial Chloroplasts

LAB ZONES

Discover It!
• Seeing a Leaf "Breathe"

Do It!
• How Does Light Affect Chlorophyll Development?
• How Does Iodine React with Starch?

Think About It!
• Examining Patterns of Food Consumption

Investigate It!
• Measuring CO_2 Produced by Yeast

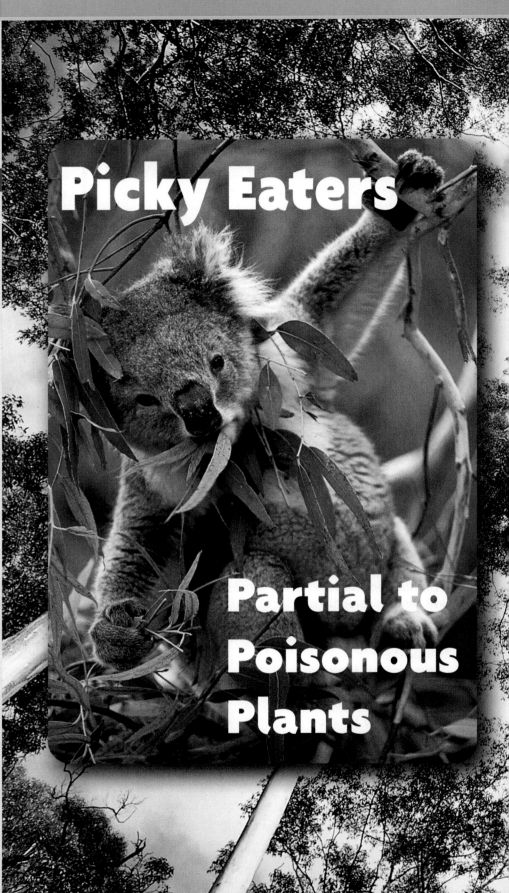

Picky Eaters

Partial to Poisonous Plants

Seeing a Leaf "Breathe"

You need *a freshly picked leaf, a bowl or other container large enough to hold the leaf, water*

1. Fill the bowl with water and submerge the leaf in it.
2. Wait 30 minutes. Observe the surface of the leaf.

The bubbles that have formed on the surface of the leaf are oxygen. After the leaf is separated from the plant, for a time it continues to manufacture food from the sunlight it has absorbed. This process releases a waste product, oxygen, which must be eliminated by the leaf.

WRITE ABOUT IT!

Plants take sunlight and water and turn them into food and the waste product oxygen. In your science journal, describe a project that you have done—it might be cooking, carpentry, or homework. What materials did you use? What waste products did you create in the process?

Many animals, such as the koalas of Australia, depend directly on plants for their food. Koalas are small, slow-moving mammals that rear their young in pouches. Koalas take a diet of plants to the extreme— they satisfy all but a few of their nutritional requirements by dining on the leaves of eucalyptus trees, supplemented with an occasional helping of soil. Koalas may prefer the flavor of leaves from certain species of the eucalyptus, or even from a single tree—and their tastes can change frequently!

Koalas are food specialists, animals that subsist primarily on one food, which makes them difficult to raise in captivity. The San Francisco Zoo has been successful in keeping koalas, aided by the eucalyptus that thrives in California's moderate climate. Zoo workers traverse the city daily, gathering fresh eucalyptus leaves to tempt the animals.

All animals ultimately depend on plants for food, but few benefit from the eucalyptus—the oils in its leaves are poisonous to most animals. A specialized digestive system allows the koala to survive on this unusual food source.

4.1 Energy and ATP

What you'll learn

IDEAS

- To explain how energy is stored and released during the ATP cycle
- To contrast the ways autotrophs and heterotrophs obtain food

WORDS

ATP, autotrophs, heterotrophs

Stockpiling energy

All animals get the energy they need to perform life functions by eating other organisms. Energy that is not used immediately can be stored and released later. This grizzly bear obtains energy from a varied diet of salmon, deer, leaves, tubers, berries, and insects.

THE ATP CYCLE

Molecules recycled and reused

Life depends on energy. But where does this energy come from? Energy for life's activities is stored in the chemical bonds of energy-storing compounds. These compounds release energy when certain chemical bonds are broken.

Compounds that store energy include ATP, NADH, NADPH, and $FADH_2$. (These letters are abbreviations for the complex names of the compounds.) In this chapter you will see how energy-storing compounds take part in the chemical reactions that are vital for life processes.

One of the most important energy-storing compounds is shown in *Figure 4.1*. This molecule, called adenosine triphosphate (uh-DEN-uh-seen try-PHOS-fayt), or **ATP,** is the chief energy-storing molecule used by organisms. An ATP molecule consists of three parts: ribose (a 5 carbon sugar), adenine, and phosphates. Ribose and adenine are chemically bonded to form a molecule called adenosine. A chain of three phosphates—the triphosphate group ("tri-" means "three")—is bonded to adenosine.

An ATP molecule releases chemical energy whenever a bond holding a phosphate group to the molecule is broken. This chemical reaction—the release of the end phosphate from ATP—creates a new molecule: ADP, or adenosine diphosphate ("di-" means "two"). Compare ATP and ADP in *Figure 4.1*. How are they similar? How are they different?

The chemical energy released by the breaking of a phosphate bond in ATP can be used by a cell to do work. ATP is involved in three main types of biological work. First, ATP provides energy for the mechanical functions of cells. For example, cells need energy for the movement of cilia and flagella. Muscle cells require energy to contract during movement. Second, ATP is used for the active transport of ions and molecules across cell membranes. Third, ATP is used during synthesis and breakdown of large molecules.

Because cells are constantly at work, they need a constant supply of ATP. Cells generate a continuous supply of ATP by attaching a phosphate to an ADP molecule. Forming this chemical bond requires energy. You may be wondering where the energy needed to make ATP

FIGURE 4.1
ATP and ADP are very similar. ADP is formed by breaking the bond holding the last phosphate on ATP. What is released when ADP is formed?

Adenosine Triphosphate ATP

Adenine
Ribose
Phosphates
Adenosine   Triphosphate group

Adenosine Diphosphate ADP

Adenine
Ribose
Phosphates
Adenosine   Diphosphate group

FIGURE 4.2

The ATP Cycle

1 **Stored energy**
Energy is stored in chemical bonds. The phosphate bonds in ATP are especially useful for storing energy.

2 **Releasing energy**
Energy that is released by breaking chemical bonds between phosphate groups in ATP is used to power cell activities.

ATP

Energy for cells

Energy from food

4 **Making ATP**
Energy released by other chemical reactions and processes can be used to bond a phosphate group to ADP, making ATP.

3 **Energy depleted**
ADP has less chemical energy than ATP. ADP also has one less phosphate group than ATP.

ADP

+ P

comes from. Stay tuned. The chemical reactions that make ATP will be described later in this chapter.

The cycle of making and breaking down ATP occurs continuously in cells. This cycle is summarized in *Figure 4.2*. The cycle turns very rapidly—10 million new ATP molecules are made in each cell every second.

SOURCES OF ENERGY

Choices from the menu of life

You may recall that all cells need energy to carry out the functions of life. This energy comes from food—substances containing organic compounds. Organisms break down organic compounds and use the energy stored in the chemical bonds. Organisms are classified into two groups, according to their method of obtaining food.

Autotrophs Organisms that can make food from carbon dioxide and an energy source such as sunlight are called **autotrophs** (AH-toh-trohfs). Plants, algae, and some bacteria are

autotrophs. The foods made by autotrophs are mainly carbohydrates such as glucose, a six-carbon sugar.

Because autotrophs can produce food for their own use as well as provide food for other organisms, they are known as producers. Producers are vitally important to all life on Earth. Without them, other life could not exist. But despite the huge role that producers play in sustaining life on this planet, they account for only about 17–20 percent of the 5 million species alive today.

In addition to making food for immediate use, autotrophs store food for future use—an autotroph's stored food is sometimes used by other organisms. Each year, autotrophs make enough sugar to fill a string of boxcars reaching to the moon and back 50 times! Much of the food stored by autotrophs is used by organisms that cannot make their own food.

Not all autotrophs depend on sunlight for energy to make food. In the 1970s, scientists discovered bacteria living near volcanic thermal vents in the deep sea. The thermal-vent bacteria

Examining Patterns of Food Consumption

Most humans obtain energy by consuming autotrophs and other heterotrophs. Human patterns of consumption change over time. The table below shows the percentage change over a decade (late 1970s–late 1980s) in the consumption of some foods.

Analyzing the Table

1 Which food sources come from autotrophs? Which sources come from heterotrophs?

2 According to the chart, were humans eating more or less food from autotrophs at the end of the decade? More or less from heterotrophs? What factors might explain the trends?

3 How have your own eating habits changed over the past five years? To what do you attribute the changes?

Patterns of Food Consumption
(Percentage Change Over a Decade)

Type of Food	% Increase	% Decrease
Meat, poultry, fish	9	
Beef		45
Pork		37
Milk, milk products		7
Whole milk		32
Low-fat/skim milk	112	
Eggs		33
Grain products	20	
Vegetables		10
Potatoes		5
Fruit	6	

FIGURE 4.3
Some heterotrophs are such voracious consumers that they deplete other organisms' food sources. Grasshoppers, such as the ones shown here, can ravage crops.

that eats corn, gets its food directly from autotrophs. Other heterotrophs, such as birds that eat grasshoppers, obtain food from autotrophs indirectly through other autotrophs.

When a heterotroph eats, what happens to food's stored energy? Some of the energy is lost with expelled waste. Cellular processes use some energy. The remaining energy is stored by the heterotroph for future use. This stored energy can also be passed on when the heterotroph is eaten.

CHECKPOINT 4.1

1. Summarize the steps of the ATP cycle by making a drawing with labels.

2. Contrast the food sources for autotrophs and heterotrophs.

3. Critical Thinking Compare ATP with a rechargeable battery. What are some other systems that store, transfer, and regain energy?

Build on What You Know

4. Write the conversion of ATP to ADP as a chemical equation. What are the reactants and products? *(Need to jog your memory? Revisit relevant concepts in Chapter 2, Section 2.3.)*

use energy obtained from inorganic compounds to produce food. These bacteria are producers for vast communities of worms, clams, and other organisms that inhabit a deep-sea world without sunlight.

Heterotrophs Organisms that cannot make their own food are called **heterotrophs** (HET-uh-roh-trohfs). Heterotrophs, which include animals, fungi, and many unicellular organisms, depend on autotrophs or other heterotrophs for food. Because heterotrophs must consume other organisms to obtain food, they are also referred to as consumers.

Food may be passed from autotrophs to heterotrophs directly or indirectly. A heterotroph, such as a grasshopper

4.2 Photosynthesis

From sun, life

Famine has been a threat to humans and other animals throughout history, but some organisms do not rely on others for food. About 3 billion years ago, organisms developed the ability to utilize an inexhaustible energy source: the sun. How do organisms use sunlight to form sugars?

What you'll learn

IDEAS
• To identify the substances and structures involved in photosynthesis
• To compare the steps in photosynthesis that require light with those that do not

WORDS
photosynthesis, pigment, chlorophyll, chloroplast, Calvin cycle

ENERGY FROM SUNLIGHT

Plants find sun enlightening

Without the energy of sunlight, life as we know it could not exist. Perhaps you have experienced one of the painful effects of the sun's energy—sunburn. Sunburn happens, in part, because your cells cannot directly use the sun's abundant energy. As you have learned, most autotrophs can use the sun's energy. The process by which autotrophs convert sunlight to a usable form of energy is **photosynthesis** (FOH-toh-SIN-thuh-sis). Organisms capable of photosynthesis evolved about 3 billion years ago. Today, photosynthesis supports most of the life on Earth.

Only a small percentage of the sun's energy is in the form of visible light. Although visible light appears as white light, it is actually a combination of different colors. Each color has a different wavelength and different energy.

Autotrophs that perform photosynthesis contain chemicals called pigments. A **pigment** is a molecule that absorbs certain wavelengths of light and reflects others. The reflected wavelengths determine what color you perceive an object to be. For example, notice the apple in *Figure 4.4*. If the pigments of the apple absorb all wavelengths of light except red, the red

wavelength is reflected to your eye, and the apple appears to be red. The combination of pigments in an object determines the wavelengths that are absorbed and reflected—in other words, its color. What wavelengths are reflected by a carrot?

Certain pigments in autotrophs are essential for photosynthesis. The most common and important of these photosynthetic pigments is called **chlorophyll** (KLOR-uh-fil). Chlorophyll absorbs violet, blue, and red light—the wavelengths that provide energy for photosynthesis. Because chlorophyll does not absorb green light but rather reflects it, most plants look green. In *Figure 4.5* you can see a graph of the wavelengths of light that are absorbed by chlorophyll.

FIGURE 4.4

You see many colored objects because of their pigments. Why does this apple look red?

Absorption

400 500 600 700
Wavelength (nm)

——— Chlorophyll *a*
- - - - Chlorophyll *b*
· · · · · · Beta-carotene

FIGURE 4.5
This graph shows you the wavelengths of light that are absorbed by chlorophyll and two kinds of accessory pigments. What colors are not absorbed?

Chlorophyll *a* is the primary pigment for photosynthesis in all plants and algae. Other pigments, called accessory pigments, absorb some colors of light that are not absorbed by chlorophyll. These pigments release energy to chlorophyll molecules for photosynthesis.

CHLOROPLASTS

Sunbathing organelles

In many autotrophs, the chlorophyll and other pigments are located in specialized organelles called chloroplasts. A **chloroplast** is an organelle that performs photosynthesis. A photosynthetic cell contains anywhere from one to several thousand chloroplasts. Just one square millimeter of a castor bean leaf, for example, contains about 500,000 chloroplasts.

The structure of the chloroplast is shown in *Figure 4.6*. Notice the stacks of disc-shaped structures inside the chloroplast. These stacks are called grana, and they are surrounded by a material called stroma. The individual disc-shaped structures in the grana are called thylakoids. In the thylakoid space is chlorophyll and all of the other pigments necessary for photosynthesis.

Each chloroplast may contain a hundred or more grana. Inside the thylakoids, hundreds of chlorophyll molecules and other pigments are organized into units called photosystems. Photosystems are the light-collecting units of the chloroplast. Inside chloroplasts, the sun's energy is captured and converted into chemical energy.

FIGURE 4.6

The Structures for Photosynthesis

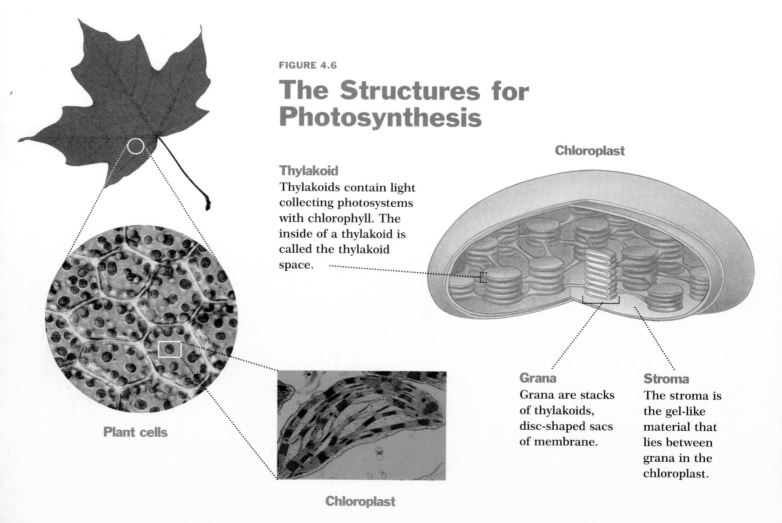

Thylakoid
Thylakoids contain light collecting photosystems with chlorophyll. The inside of a thylakoid is called the thylakoid space.

Chloroplast

Grana
Grana are stacks of thylakoids, disc-shaped sacs of membrane.

Stroma
The stroma is the gel-like material that lies between grana in the chloroplast.

Plant cells

Chloroplast

OVERVIEW OF PHOTOSYNTHESIS

The big picture

During photosynthesis, autotrophs use the sun's energy to make carbohydrate molecules from water and carbon dioxide, releasing oxygen as a byproduct. The process of photosynthesis can be summed up in the following chemical equation:

Light energy

$$6CO_2 + 6H_2O \longrightarrow C_6H_{12}O_6 + 6O_2$$

In this chemical equation the six-carbon sugar glucose is a product. The energy stored in glucose and other carbohydrates can be used later to produce ATP.

The process of photosynthesis does not happen all at once; rather, it occurs in two stages. The reactions in these stages are summarized in *Figure 4.7*. Photosynthesis begins when light is absorbed in the grana of the chloroplast. This starts the first stage, called the light-dependent reactions (shown in the left part of *Figure 4.7*). During the light-dependent reactions, water is split into hydrogen ions, electrons, and oxygen (O_2). The O_2 diffuses out of the chloroplast and NADPH and ATP are produced.

The Calvin cycle (shown in the right part of *Figure 4.7*) follows the light-dependent reactions. The products of the light-dependent reactions, ATP and NADPH, are used in the Calvin cycle. The Calvin cycle also requires an input of carbon dioxide (CO_2) to produce sugars.

FIGURE 4.7
Photosynthesis has two stages: the light-dependent reactions and the Calvin cycle. Which stage releases oxygen? Which stage produces sugars?

Do It!

How Does Light Affect Chlorophyll Development?

You can find out which wavelengths of light are needed for chlorophyll development in plants if you . . .

Try This

1 Place a damp paper towel in the bottom of each of five small glass jars and put two bean seeds on the towel in each jar. Cap the jars tightly.
2 Cover the five jars with red, blue, green, yellow, or clear cellophane. Label the lids with the color of the cellophane.
3 Place the jars in a sunny place for seven days.
4 After seven days, remove the cellophane from the jars and observe the color of the seedlings. Record your observations.

Analyze Your Results

1 Why is it important to wrap one jar in clear cellophane?
2 What color of light was reflected from each jar wrapped in cellophane? What colors passed through to the seedlings?
3 What substance is missing in the white seedlings and why?
4 What color of light is required for chlorophyll development?
5 What do you think would happen if you exposed the uncovered seedlings to the sun?

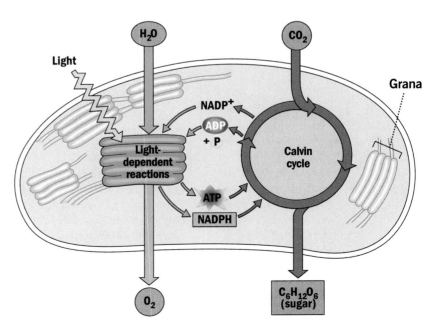

Chapter 4 Photosynthesis and Cellular Respiration **87**

LIGHT-DEPENDENT REACTIONS

ATP and O₂ too

The first stage of photosynthesis consists of the light-dependent reactions, so named because they depend on sunlight. These reactions occur in different areas of the thylakoid, called Photosystem I and Photosystem II. Recall that a photosystem is a light-collecting unit of the chloroplast.

The light-dependent reactions require water and sunlight. In this first stage, a water molecule is split in Photosystem II. Splitting a water molecule releases O_2, hydrogen ions (H^+) and energized electrons (e^-). Most of the O_2 diffuses out of the plant to become part of the air you breathe.

Follow the pathway of the electrons in *Figure 4.8*. Energized electrons moving from Photosystem II to Photosystem I provide energy for the active transport of H^+ from the stroma to the thylakoid space. What role does the resulting H^+ concentration gradient play in ATP production?

FIGURE 4.8

Light-dependent Reactions

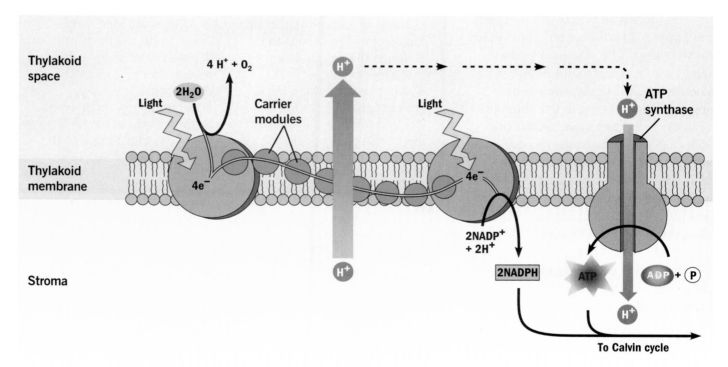

Photosystem II
Photosystem II uses sunlight to split water molecules into hydrogen ions (H^+), oxygen (O_2) and energized electrons (e^-). Most of the O_2 diffuses into the air. The electrons enter the electron transport chain.

Electron transport
Energized electrons are shuttled from Photosystem II across carrier molecules. The carrier molecules use the electrons' energy to actively transport H^+ from the stroma into the thylakoid space.

Photosystem I
Using the sun's energy, energy-depleted electrons are reenergized in Photosystem I. The energized electrons are used to produce NADPH, a molecule that will later be used to make glucose.

ATP synthesis
The high H^+ concentration in the thylakoid space creates a concentration gradient. H^+ diffuse back into the stroma through a membrane protein, ATP synthase. The energy released by the flow of H^+ converts ADP to ATP.

CALVIN CYCLE
The price of sugar

The next series of reactions require the products of the light-dependent reactions, as well as the input of carbon dioxide. The carbon dioxide is used to build carbohydrates. The process of constructing carbohydrates from carbon dioxide—the second stage of photosynthesis—occurs in the **Calvin cycle.** You can follow this cycle, named after its discoverer, Melvin Calvin, in *Figure 4.9.* The Calvin cycle takes place in the stroma, the gel-like material inside the chloroplast.

In the Calvin cycle, ATP and NADPH made in the light-dependent reactions are used for energy and hydrogen. By investing energy and hydrogen in several stages of synthesis, carbohydrates are built. Overall, one glucose molecule is produced for every six molecules of CO_2 that enter the cycle.

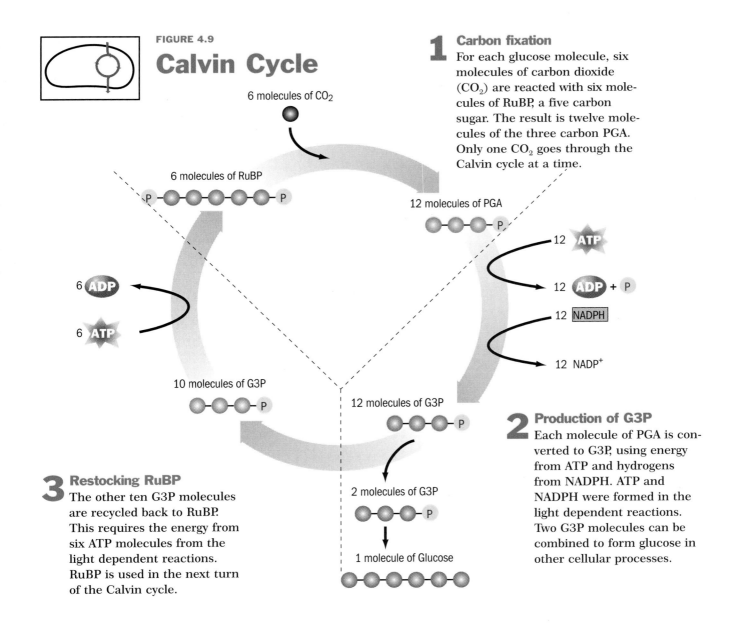

FIGURE 4.9

Calvin Cycle

6 molecules of CO_2

6 molecules of RuBP

P

12 molecules of PGA

P

12 ATP

12 ADP + P

12 NADPH

12 NADP⁺

6 ADP

6 ATP

10 molecules of G3P

P

12 molecules of G3P

P

2 molecules of G3P

P

1 molecule of Glucose

1 Carbon fixation
For each glucose molecule, six molecules of carbon dioxide (CO_2) are reacted with six molecules of RuBP, a five carbon sugar. The result is twelve molecules of the three carbon PGA. Only one CO_2 goes through the Calvin cycle at a time.

2 Production of G3P
Each molecule of PGA is converted to G3P, using energy from ATP and hydrogens from NADPH. ATP and NADPH were formed in the light dependent reactions. Two G3P molecules can be combined to form glucose in other cellular processes.

3 Restocking RuBP
The other ten G3P molecules are recycled back to RuBP. This requires the energy from six ATP molecules from the light dependent reactions. RuBP is used in the next turn of the Calvin cycle.

How Does Iodine React with Starch?

Chemists use iodine to test for the presence of starch. You can identify the chemical reaction between iodine and starch if you . . .

Try This

1 Obtain small samples of two unidentified carbohydrates from your instructor. Label them *1* and *2*. Are there any differences in the appearance of the two substances?
2 Apply one drop of iodine solution to each of your samples.
Caution: Iodine is poisonous. Clean up any spills promptly and wash your hands thoroughly at the end of the lab.

Analyze Your Results

1 Describe the reaction. Based on the results of the iodine test, which sample is a starch?
2 If the other substance is a carbohydrate but did not test positive for starch, what type of carbohydrate could it be?
3 Do you think a leaf would test positive for starch in the iodine test? Why or why not?

The Foundation of a Healthful Diet

Complex carbohydrates, found in grains, are an important source of energy for humans. Rice, bread, and pasta are examples of foods rich in complex carbohydrates.

THE FATE OF SUGARS

Molecules of power

What happens to all the sugar molecules formed during photosynthesis? Autotrophs—as well as heterotrophs—need energy to carry out their own life processes, such as growth and reproduction. Autotrophs and heterotrophs convert glucose to ATP and use this energy to power all of their functions.

Having worked to make the sugar molecules, autotrophs are the first to use them. Large autotrophs such as plants need to make energy available to all of their cells. Large plants have fluid-carrying tissues that transport the energy-rich glucose molecules from the leaves to the other cells of the plant.

Plants use some glucose for growth. For example, plants form structural molecules such as cellulose by linking many glucose molecules into long chains. Cellulose is the most abundant substance produced by living things. It provides strength and rigidity to plant structures. Only a few organisms can use cellulose as an energy source. Bacteria that inhabit the digestive tracts of cows are one example of organisms that can utilize this substance.

Most plants store as starches the energy rich glucose that they do not immediately use for energy or structural use. Like cellulose, starches are made of chains of glucose molecules, but bonded together in a different way. Starches are found in plant foods such as corn, potatoes, and wheat.

Plants and other autotrophs are consumed by heterotrophs, providing them with starches. Heterotrophs break down starches to glucose and use the stored energy in glucose for their own energy and structural needs. Any energy-rich glucose that is not used can be stored again as starch by the heterotrophs.

CHECKPOINT 4.2

1. Identify three substances or structures involved in photosynthesis, and describe their roles.
2. Summarize the main steps of photosynthesis.
3. Critical Thinking The Calvin cycle is sometimes described as the light-independent reactions. Look at Figure 4.9 and give evidence to refute or support the idea that the Calvin cycle is independent of light.

Build on What You Know

4. Some autotrophs do not store excess energy in starch. What other chemical compounds might they use to store energy? Explain your answer. *(Need to jog your memory? Revisit relevant concepts in Chapter 2, Section 2.1.)*

4.3 Cellular Respiration

The universal hunger

Your body cells share one important feature with the cells of all other living things: the need for chemical energy. Whether a diatom, a pine tree, a monitor lizard, or a cat—all organisms rely on cellular respiration for the energy they need to carry out life functions. The cells of all organisms, with the exception of bacteria, generate energy in "factories" called mitochondria, shown at right.

What you'll learn

IDEAS
• To explain how cellular respiration releases energy from food
• To compare aerobic and anaerobic respiration

WORDS
cellular respiration, glycolysis, Krebs cycle, electron transport, fermentation, calorie

BREAKING DOWN FOOD

Chemical bonds are a mouthful

You have learned that both autotrophs and heterotrophs use the organic compounds in food for energy sources. Complex carbohydrates are a major source of energy for most organisms. Before the energy in complex carbohydrates can be used by cells, the carbohydrates are broken down into simple sugars such as glucose ($C_6H_{12}O_6$).

The process by which glucose molecules are broken down to release energy is cellular respiration. Cellular respiration is a series of chemical reactions which produces ATP. Most cellular processes use ATP for energy. There are two types of cellular respiration. One is aerobic meaning that it requires oxygen. The other is anaerobic, meaning it can take place without oxygen ("an-" means "without").

Aerobic respiration produces 36 ATP molecules from each glucose molecule, as illustrated in *Figure 4.10*. Anaerobic respiration produces only 2 ATP molecules. Some organisms are only capable of anaerobic respiration. Other organisms are capable of both types of cellular respiration. Which type of cellular respiration occurs most commonly in your body cells?

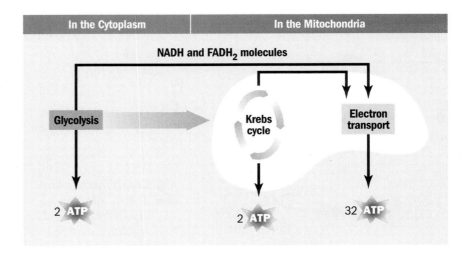

Compare the reactants and products of photosynthesis and cellular respiration in *Figure 4.11*. Cellular respiration appears to be the reverse of photosynthesis: The reactants of one process are the products of the other. However, the steps of cellular respiration are not simply the reverse of photosynthesis.

FIGURE 4.10

In most organisms, cellular respiration begins in the cytoplasm of the cell and continues in the mitochondria. ATP is produced in several steps. At which step is the most ATP produced?

FIGURE 4.11

Compare the overall process of cellular respiration with photosynthesis. How are the reactants and the products of the two processes related?

FIGURE 4.12

Glycolysis

To split glucose into pyruvate, a cell must first use the energy of two ATP molecules. What is the net yield of energy-storing molecules from glycolysis?

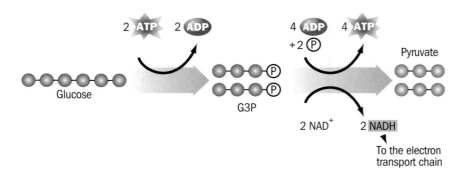

FIGURE 4.13

Krebs Cycle

1 Pyruvate change
Pyruvate is transformed into acetyl-CoA, losing a carbon in the form of CO_2. Acetyl-CoA enters the cycle.

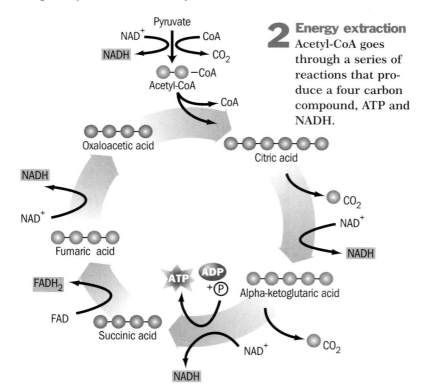

2 Energy extraction
Acetyl-CoA goes through a series of reactions that produce a four carbon compound, ATP and NADH.

3 Completing the cycle
A four-carbon compound is recycled into a compound that can react with acetyl-CoA. $FADH_2$ and NADH are formed.

THREE PHASES OF AEROBIC RESPIRATION

Oxygen for dinner

Aerobic respiration can be divided into three stages: glycolysis, the Krebs cycle, and electron transport.

Glycolysis Both aerobic and anaerobic respiration begin with a step called glycolysis. **Glycolysis** (gly-KOL-uh-sis) is the process by which glucose is converted to pyruvate and energy is released. Pyruvate is a three-carbon molecule that enters the Krebs cycle.

Glycolysis occurs in the cytoplasm of the cell. *Figure 4.12* shows only two steps of the process. Glycolysis is actually a ten-step process, with intermediate products made at each step.

A single glucose molecule that has undergone glycolysis will produce a net yield of two NADH, two ATP, and two pyruvate molecules. You may recall from section 4.1 that NADH is an energy-storing compound. Only about 2 percent of the chemical energy contained in each glucose molecule is released by glycolysis. Most of the remaining chemical energy is in the pyruvate molecules. This energy is released in the next stage, the Krebs cycle.

Krebs cycle The pyruvate molecules produced by glycolysis are transformed into acetyl-CoA, which enters the Krebs cycle. The **Krebs cycle**, named after its discoverer Hans Krebs, is a set of reactions that breaks down acetyl-CoA to form CO_2, ATP, NADH, and $FADH_2$. This cycle is also called the citric acid cycle because the first reaction forms citric acid. Notice in *Figure 4.13* that one ATP is formed from each pyruvate molecule. Because glycolysis forms two pyruvate molecules from every glucose molecule, the result of the Krebs cycle is two ATP for each glucose molecule. The energy in NADH and $FADH_2$ will be used to make more ATP.

Electron transport So far you have seen that glycolysis yields two molecules of ATP per molecule of glucose. The Krebs cycle produces another two. However, there is still more energy from the glucose molecule available for use by the cell.

The rest of the energy is contained in electrons carried by NADH and $FADH_2$. Before it can be used by the cell, the electrons' energy must be converted to ATP. **Electron transport** is the process by which energy is transferred from NADH and $FADH_2$ to ATP. This phase of aerobic respiration requires oxygen.

The movement of electrons from NADH and $FADH_2$ occurs along an electron transport chain in the inner membrane of the mitochondrion. Follow the path of the electrons in

Figure 4.14. Where do the electrons end up?

The electron transport chain generates 32 of the 36 ATP molecules produced from each glucose molecule. Due to some energy loss in the form of heat, aerobic respiration is relatively inefficient. The 36 ATP molecules represent less than half of the chemical energy in one glucose molecule. Yet this is still enough energy for humans and all other aerobic organisms to live.

As cells release energy through cellular respiration, they produce waste products. These waste products are carbon dioxide, water, and heat. High levels of carbon dioxide can kill cells, and for this reason all organisms have specialized mechanisms for removing this waste product.

Cross section of a mitochondrion

Outer membrane

Intermembrane space

Inner membrane

Matrix

FIGURE 4.14

Electron Transport

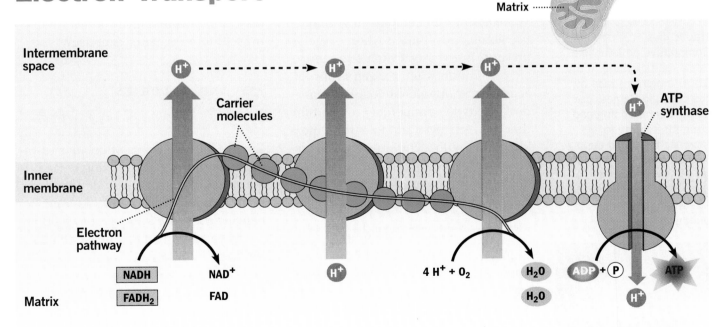

From the carriers . . .
Electrons (e⁻) are released from NADH and $FADH_2$ and start on the electron transport chain.

down the chain . . .
As the electrons pass across carrier molecules, their energy is used to pump H⁺ across the inner membrane, creating a concentration gradient.

and into water.
The final electron acceptor is oxygen, which then forms a water molecule with free H⁺.

Go with the flow.
As in photosynthesis, ATP synthase uses the diffusion of H⁺ down the concentration gradient to form ATP molecules.

FIGURE 4.15
Competitive athletes like these, participating in the 1500-meter (m) race at the Olympic Games, use aerobic conditioning and strength training to increase the blood supply to their muscles. Why do you think these types of training help minimize the effects of lactic acid buildup?

ANAEROBIC RESPIRATION

No O_2 at the fermentation station

As you know, you cannot survive without oxygen. However, certain cells in your body—namely, your muscle cells—can produce energy without oxygen. Some unicellular organisms such as yeast can also break down carbohydrates without oxygen. Anaerobic respiration is the process that releases energy from food molecules in the absence of oxygen. Through fermentation, anaerobic organisms and cells can exist without oxygen by using the small amount of energy supplied by glycolysis.

Fermentation is the extraction of energy from pyruvate in the absence of oxygen. There are two types of fermentation: alcoholic fermentation and lactic acid fermentation. In both types of fermentation, only two ATP molecules are formed from each molecule of glucose.

Yeasts are unicellular fungi that use aerobic respiration when oxygen is present. But yeasts switch to anaerobic respiration when oxygen is absent. Yeasts carry out alcoholic fermentation, the type of anaerobic respiration that converts pyruvate to carbon dioxide and ethanol. The process, shown below, gets its name from the fact that one of its products, ethanol, is an alcohol.

$$Pyruvate + NADH \longrightarrow Ethanol + NAD^+ + CO_2$$

Alcoholic fermentation is an important economic resource. Bakers use the alcoholic fermentation of yeast to make breads. As yeasts break down the carbohydrates in dough, CO_2 is produced and trapped in the dough. The bubbles of trapped CO_2 cause the dough to rise and are visible as the small holes in baked bread. As the dough bakes, the yeasts die, and the alcohol evaporates. Alcoholic fermentation is also used to make wine, beer, and the ethanol that is added to gasoline to make gasohol.

Animal cells cannot perform alcoholic fermentation. However, some cells, such as your muscle cells, can convert pyruvate to lactic acid. Anaerobic respiration in which pyruvate is converted to lactic acid is called lactic acid fermentation. During strenuous exercise, your breathing cannot provide you with all of the oxygen that your cells need. When muscle cells run out of oxygen, they switch from aerobic respiration to lactic acid fermentation. The process is shown below:

$$Pyruvate + NADH \longrightarrow Lactic\ acid + NAD^+$$

The athletes shown in *Figure 4.15* may soon experience the muscle fatigue and soreness caused by the buildup of lactic acid. Most of the lactic acid made in the muscles diffuses into the bloodstream and then into the liver, where it will be converted back to pyruvate. Have you ever felt muscle soreness after exercise?

ATP AND CALORIES

In the heat of the food

You share the process of cellular respiration with most other living organisms. Using this process, all organisms break down glucose molecules and convert the stored energy into ATP.

As you may recall, glucose that is not used immediately can be stored by organisms in different substances. Plants store excess glucose in starch molecules. Some animals store glucose in glycogen or fat. When the organism needs energy, these storage molecules can be broken down to yield ATP.

The energy contained in these substances can be measured and expressed in units called calories. A

Breads Around Town

Bread comes in a great variety of shapes, sizes, and textures, from fluffy challah to the flat, stretchy Ethiopian bread, *injera*. Some breads are leavened (made to rise) with yeast, baking powder, or sourdough; breads such as tortillas have no leavening. Talk to relatives and neighbors about breads served in their homes now and when they were growing up. Did any of their bread recipes originate in other countries? What leavening, if any, is used in the breads? You may also want to speak with a cook or baker at a local ethnic restaurant. What breads are traditionally served in the culture featured at the restaurant? Are the breads leavened or unleavened? Make a class chart of types of bread and their leavening, if any.

calorie is the amount of heat energy needed to raise the temperature of 1 gram (g) of water 1 degree Celsius. Although a calorie is expressed as a unit of heat energy, the energy can be used for all of the countless functions of the cell.

You may be familiar with Calorie values on food items that you buy in the store. When Calorie is spelled with a capital "C," it actually represents a kilocalorie (kcal), or 1000 calories. To measure the energy value of food, a small sample of the food is burned. The amount of heat the burning food gives off is measured using an instrument called a calorimeter. This process is used to determine the number of Calories a particular kind of food contains.

Your body is constantly balancing the calories you take in with the calories you use. People "counting Calories" are actually keeping track of the amount of energy in the food they consume. If people consume food containing more energy than they need, the excess energy is stored by the body. What do you think happens if the situation is reversed, and you do not consume enough energy for the cells' needs?

CHECKPOINT 4.3

1. Explain how cellular respiration releases energy from food.
2. Compare the processes of aerobic and anaerobic respiration. What are the reactants and products of each process? How much ATP does each process yield?
3. **Critical Thinking** Certain bacteria can remain alive in food canned in airtight but improperly prepared containers. What can you conclude about the bacteria's cellular respiration?

Build on What You Know

4. How is cellular respiration related to metabolism? *(Need to jog your memory? Revisit relevant concepts in Chapter 2, Section 2.4.)*

EVERYDAY BIOLOGY

Feeling Dead?

If you read mystery novels, you are probably aware of the use of arsenic as a poison. Arsenic accumulates in mitochondria, where it disables cellular respiration and paralyzes energy production. How would the action of arsenic in mitochondria harm an organism?

How do organisms get energy?

Measuring CO₂ Produced by Yeast

WHAT YOU WILL DO Carry out an experiment to test a hypothesis about the effects of sweeteners on carbon dioxide production by yeast

SKILLS YOU WILL USE Measuring, calculating, observing, collecting and recording data

WHAT YOU WILL NEED Yeast, warm water, scale, beakers, various sweeteners, funnel, balloons, permanent marker, tape measure

Propose a Hypothesis

In this lab, you will test the rates of alcoholic fermentation by yeast when combined with different types and amounts of sweeteners, such as table sugar, corn syrup, molasses, honey, fruit juice concentrate (with no added sugar), saccharine, and aspartame. Propose a hypothesis about how different sweeteners will affect the amount of CO_2 production by yeast.

Conduct Your Experiment

1 Choose two sweeteners to use in your experiment. Label them *1* and *2*.

2 Mix the yeast and the warm water to make a yeast solution. How much yeast will you use? How much water will you use?

3 Decide on the amount of sweetener and yeast solution for all samples. You will also need a control with no sweetener added.

4 Label three balloons as follows: *Control, Sweetener 1,* and *Sweetener 2.* Also label

each balloon with your name. Record the types of sweeteners you will place in two of the balloons.

5 Using a separate beaker for each sample, mix the sweeteners with the yeast solution in the amounts you determined in your plan.

6 Pour the mixtures and the control into the designated balloons and tie them. They should be as airtight as possible. Place the balloons in a warm area.

7 Observe the balloons 24 hours after completing step 6. Use a measuring tape to determine the diameter of each balloon, and record your measurements.

Analyze Your Data

1 What caused some of the balloons to inflate?

2 Which of the sweeteners that you used caused the yeast to produce more CO_2?

3 What characteristics of the sweeteners might be responsible for the difference in CO_2 production?

Draw Conclusions

1 Was your hypothesis supported by your results? Why or why not?

2 What can you conclude from your experiment about how different sweeteners affect alcoholic fermentation?

Design a Related Experiment

Design a lab to test the effects of other variables—such as the amount of sweetener, the amount of yeast, or the temperature—on the rate of CO_2 production by yeast.

4.4 Energy Flow in the Biosphere

The power of photosynthesis

The green layer floating on top of this pond is algae, millions of tiny photosynthetic organisms. In a typical pond ecosystem, algae provide food for other unicellular organisms, which provide food for fishes, which in turn feed birds and mammals. Photosynthesizers form the base of many food chains, and they supply nearly all the energy in the biosphere.

What you'll learn

IDEAS

• To summarize the flow of food and energy in the biosphere

• To infer the importance of photosynthesis and cellular respiration for living things

MAKING FOOD

"Cooking" for billions

By now you have probably gained a new respect for photosynthetic organisms. After all, it is no small task to provide food for the entire planet.

Plants, algae, and photosynthetic bacteria use energy from the sun to make sugars and other compounds. The sugars are used as food to fuel the reactions of cellular respiration. Through the chemical reactions of photosynthesis and cellular respiration, living organisms capture and harness energy. The flow of food and the flow of energy run parallel courses.

In the biosphere there is a continuous flow of energy from the sun, through a series of organisms, and back to the environment. Consider, for example, *Figure 4.16,* which shows chimpanzees eating bamboo. As an autotroph, the bamboo plant uses CO_2 and the energy from the sun to make sugars. This process, as you have learned, is photosynthesis. Cellular respiration enables the plant to utilize the energy in the sugars for growth and other cellular activities.

Most photosynthetic organisms, including bamboo plants, produce more sugars than they need. They often store the excess sugars by making larger molecules such as starches. The starches and other compounds made by autotrophs are important food sources for heterotrophs such as the chimpanzee.

When the chimp digests the bamboo, the plant's stored carbohydrates become available to the chimp's body cells. By the process of cellular respiration, the chimp's cells obtain energy from the carbohydrates. This energy powers all of the chimp's activities, including picking, eating, and digesting the bamboo plant. If the chimp consumes more carbohydrates than it

FIGURE 4.16

Chimpanzees get carbohydrates by eating bamboo and other plants, fruits, and seeds. What happens to the carbohydrates in the foods that you eat?

needs to survive, it stores the extra energy by converting the unused carbohydrates into glycogen and fats.

When the chimp dies and its body decomposes, all the energy stored in the body in the form of sugars, fats, proteins, and other molecules is released into the environment. Bacteria and other organisms use these organic molecules as food.

The flow of food from the bamboo plant to the chimp to the bacteria is called a food chain. Along the same path energy flows from the sun, to the bamboo plant, to the chimp, to the bacteria, and to the environment.

FIGURE 4.17

This plantation on a rural road near Recife, Brazil, grows sugarcane. The crop is used to make ethanol, a fuel for vehicles, as well as sugar and molasses.

FRONTIERS IN BIOLOGY

Artificial chloroplasts

Plants are expert at producing energy cleanly—a task that humans, so far, have found challenging. Someday scientists may overcome this challenge by unraveling the mechanisms of photosynthesis.

The Italian chemist Giacomo Ciamician referred to the process of photosynthesis as "the guarded secret of the plant." In 1912 Ciamician envisioned a time when the energy needs of entire cities would be provided by plants. In some areas Ciamician's vision has been partly realized. In Brazil, for example, many farmers grow sugarcane that is chemically converted into ethanol, a type of alcohol used to power cars.

Although we can observe and describe the processes of photosynthesis, synthesizing new molecules that can harness solar energy as chloroplasts do is another matter. Laboratory scientists have created artificial molecules that perform photosynthesis in solution. Molecular structures that perform photosynthesis in solids would offer much more useful and practical applications. However these structures have proven difficult to produce. In addition to providing power as solar cells do, artificial photosynthesis cells might be able to generate clean-burning fuels, such as hydrogen gas, from carbon dioxide, water, and sunlight. What are other potential applications and advantages of photosynthetic power?

CHECKPOINT 4.4

1. Summarize the flow of food and energy in the biosphere.

2. What is the importance of photosynthesis and cellular respiration for living things?

3. Critical Thinking Describe a food chain involving four organisms.

Build on What You Know

4. What cell organelles are involved in energy transfer and release? *(Need to jog your memory? Revisit relevant concepts in Chapter 3, Sections 3.3. and 3.4)*

 How does energy move through the biosphere?

Chapter 4 Review

4.1–4.3 All organisms get energy by breaking down the chemical compounds in food and making ATP and other molecules.
4.4 Energy from sunlight passes through a series of living organisms.

Sum It Up

Use the following summary to review the main concepts in this chapter.

4.1 Energy and ATP

- Organisms require a steady supply of energy, which they obtain by breaking chemical bonds of chemical compounds in food.
- Autotrophs are organisms that can make their own food; heterotrophs are organisms that cannot make their own food.
- Both autotrophs and heterotrophs store the energy they obtain from food in ATP and other compounds.
- In cells, ATP is repeatedly built up and broken down in a cyclical process.

4.2 Photosynthesis

- During photosynthesis, sunlight is converted into chemical energy, which is stored in food.
- Photosynthetic pigments such as chlorophyll are contained in chloroplasts.
- The first stage of photosynthesis consists of light-dependent reactions in which light energy is used to split water into oxygen, hydrogen ions, and energized electrons. The flow of electrons helps generate ATP.

- In the second stage of photosynthesis, called the Calvin cycle, carbon dioxide is converted into a three carbon molecule used in glucose synthesis.

4.3 Cellular Respiration

- During cellular respiration, energy is released from food molecules.
- Aerobic respiration, which requires oxygen, has three phases: glycolysis, the Krebs cycle, and electron transport.
- Anaerobic respiration, which takes place without oxygen, involves only glycolysis and fermentation.

4.4 Energy Flow in the Biosphere

- The sun provides a continuous supply of energy to the biosphere.
- Food flows along a food chain from producers to consumers to decomposers. Energy also flows along the same path.

Use Terms and Concepts

Use each of the following words or terms in a complete sentence. If you need to review a meaning, turn to the page indicated.

ATP (p. 82)
autotrophs (p. 83)
heterotrophs (p. 84)
photosynthesis (p. 85)
pigment (p. 85)

chlorophyll (p. 85)
chloroplast (p. 86)
Calvin cycle (p. 89)
cellular respiration (p. 91)

glycolysis (p. 92)
Krebs cycle (p. 92)
electron transport (p. 93)
fermentation (p. 94)
calorie (p. 95)

Use Your Word Power

TRUE-FALSE Write true if the statement is true. If the statement is false, replace the underlined word(s) to make the statement true.

1. Autotrophs are organisms that cannot make their own food.

2. During photosynthesis, food molecules are broken down to release energy.

3. A calorie is the amount of heat energy needed to raise the temperature of 1 gram of water 1 degree Celsius.

4. Chlorophyll is the chief energy-storing molecule used by organisms.

5. Many autotrophs contain chloroplasts, specialized organelles that contain chlorophyll and other pigments involved in photosynthesis.

COMPLETION Write the word or phrase that best completes each statement.

6. The process of getting energy from pyruvate in the absence of oxygen is called _____ .

7. _____ is the series of reactions that breaks down pyruvate during aerobic respiration.

8. The second stage of photosynthesis, the _____ , is the process of making carbohydrates from carbon dioxide.

9. The process by which glucose is converted to pyruvate and energy is released is called _____ .

10. Energy is transferred from NADH and $FADH_2$ to ATP during _____ .

Show What You Know

11. Which is the larger molecule, ATP or ADP? How are these two molecules different?

12. Explain the structure of chloroplasts.

13. Define autotrophs, heterotrophs, producers, and consumers in relation to each other.

14. What are the two main stages of photosynthesis? Which stage uses water and produces oxygen? Which stage produces glucose?

15. Summarize what happens during the light-dependent reactions of photosynthesis.

16. Which compounds are recycled during the Calvin cycle?

17. What are the main stages of aerobic respiration?

18. Contrast alcoholic fermentation and lactic acid fermentation.

19. **Make a Concept Map** Complete the concept map below by adding the following terms: pigments, Calvin cycle, chlorophyll, chloroplasts, heterotrophs, light-dependent reactions, food, ATP, ADP, light, water, carbon dioxide.

For help making concept maps, see Appendix E.

Take It Further

20. **Interpreting a Graph** The graph below shows the absorption of light by a particular pigment. What wavelengths of light does the pigment absorb? What color would you expect the pigment to be? Refer to Figure 4.5 on page 86.

Light Absorption by a Pigment

21. Designing an Experiment How could you demonstrate the effects of different amounts of light on plant growth? Formulate a hypothesis, and then design an experiment to test your hypothesis.

22. Making an Analogy Suppose you and five friends represent the six carbons of a glucose molecule. Describe the events and changes that happen to you and your friends as the molecule of glucose is broken down by aerobic respiration.

23. Analyzing Data The table below shows the amount of energy released from chemical compounds by three different processes. How does the release of energy compare in the three processes? What happens to the energy that is "lost"?

Comparing Energy Efficiency			
Fuel	**Conditions of Fuel Use**	**New Form of Converted Energy**	**% Energy**
glucose	burned during laboratory experiment	heat, light	100%
glucose	"burned" during cellular respiration	ATP	40%
gasoline	burned in auto engine	kinetic (motion)	25%

Consider the Issues

24. Plants for Fuel The world supply of fossil fuels such as oil and natural gas is being used up. Some scientists have proposed using plants to produce compounds such as ethanol that could be used as fuel. What questions should be considered in deciding whether the proposed use of plants is worth trying? How could some of these questions be answered?

Make New Connections

25. Biology and Art: A Local Field Trip Find an area near your school with several varieties of plants. Without disturbing any organisms, identify heterotrophic and autotrophic relationships between plants and other organisms. Create a poster showing some of the food chains present in your community.

26. Biology and Food Production Yeasts ferment sugars by anaerobic respiration. The byproducts of this process give many foods their unique qualities. Identify foods that are made with yeast, and find out how yeasts are used in various food-making processes.

27. Biology and Math Chemical equations are shown on pages 87 and 91. You can determine the number of atoms involved in a chemical equation by multiplying the number of atoms in each molecule by the number of molecules. For example, $4H_2O$ includes 8 hydrogen atoms (4 molecules $\times$ 2 atoms per molecule) and 4 oxygen atoms (4 molecules $\times$ 1 atom per molecule). Calculate the number of atoms involved in the chemical equations shown in this chapter.

FAST-FORWARD TO CHAPTER 5

Cells require energy for all their life processes, including making new cells. In the next chapter you will learn how cells reproduce, as well as the results of cellular reproduction.

You can find out more about the process of cell division by exploring the following Internet address:
http://basis_of_life.biosurf.com

Earning Your Stripes

A female zebra with a swollen belly stands apart from the herd, awaiting the birth of her foal. Birth can be a dangerous time for animals on the grasslands. A laboring mother or a newborn baby is more vulnerable to predators such as hyenas and lions. To protect them, the herd stallion stands guard a short distance away.

When the foal is born, it weighs about 30 kilograms (kg) and stands about 1 meter (m) tall. Eleven minutes after birth, the foal is standing. An hour after birth, the foal confidently runs and plays. The young zebra will grow quickly during its first few weeks of life. The herd is always on the move, and the foal must be strong enough to keep up. Its mother's milk provides calories and nutrients for growth. After the first week or two, the foal will also nibble grass, which eventually becomes its main food. Fully grown, the young zebra will stand about 1.37 m tall.

At birth the foal's stripes are brown. The color of the stripes will deepen to black as the foal grows. Color, size, and number of stripes are similar among members of a species of zebra. But, similar to human fingerprints, no two patterns of zebra stripes are exactly alike.

Zebras and humans, as well as most organisms, grow through a similar process. How does growth occur? What makes the size of our bodies increase?

LAB ZONE **Discover It!**

Observing a Plant Cutting

You need a plant, scissors, a small clear glass or plastic container, water

1. What do you think will happen when you cut off part of a plant and place it in water? Propose a hypothesis.
2. Use scissors to cut a small piece, including leaves and stem, from the tip of the plant. Place the cut end into a container filled with water.
3. Observe the cutting for a week.

What happened to the cut end of the plant? Plant parts have the ability to grow from a piece into a whole organism, unlike most animals. Although plants and most animals differ in this respect, their growth processes at the cellular level are much the same. You will read about these processes in this chapter.

WRITE ABOUT IT!

Have you ever grown plants from seeds or cuttings, raised baby animals, or observed a younger sibling or cousin? Describe what it is like to watch plants, animals, or humans grow. What stages do they go through? How does their appearance change?

5.1 When Do Cells Divide?

What you'll learn

IDEAS
• To analyze the limits on cell size
• To identify the roles of cell division in reproduction, growth, and repair

WORDS
asexual reproduction, sexual reproduction

Divide and grow!
All living things are made of cells. Cells must divide in order to reproduce, grow, and repair themselves. The trillions of cells that make up an elephant come from just one original cell: a fertilized egg. Each time this cell reproduces, the new cells that are formed contain all the essential cytoplasm, organelles, and chromosomes needed for the elephant to develop, survive, and function.

FIGURE 5.1
With the exception of muscle and nerve cells, cell size is not determined by the overall size of an organism. Most cells of this giraffe and this mouse are about the same size.

CELL SIZE
Bigger is not better

If you compare cells from a giraffe with cells from a mouse, you might be surprised to find that the cells are structurally alike. Although the animals themselves are vastly different in size and shape, their cells are not. In fact, the diameter of most eukaryotic cells falls within the fairly narrow range of 10-100 micrometers (μm).

One of the most important factors affecting cell size is the size of the cell membrane. Cells obtain nutrients and eliminate wastes through the cell membrane.

Eukaryotic cell

A cell must have a membrane surface large enough for all of the needed exchanges to take place with the environment. As cells increase in size, their need for nutrients increases, as does their production of wastes. Therefore, larger cells require a larger membrane surface area for survival.

Can cells continue to increase in size without limit? To answer this question, consider the models of cells in the activity on page 105. How do their surface areas compare? How do the volumes of the cells compare?

Smaller cells, similar to the model with 1-centimeter (cm) sides, have larger surface area to volume ratios. Larger cells, similar to the model with 4-cm sides, have smaller surface area to volume ratios. As cells increase in size, their volume increases more rapidly than their surface area does. It is more difficult for cells with a larger volume to transport needed nutrients in and harmful wastes out. Therefore, cells need to remain relatively small to survive.

The nucleus, as you have learned, controls many of the cell's activities. It also has an effect on cell size. Control is vital to cell functions, and the nucleus can control only a limited amount of living, active cytoplasm. The scope of nuclear control, therefore, can limit the size of cells.

GROWTH, REPAIR, AND REPRODUCTION

The great divide

When a cell reaches its maximum size, the nucleus initiates cell divison. Cell division is the splitting of a single cell into two cells. This process accounts for three essential life processes: growth, repair, and reproduction.

Growth You know from experience that living things grow, or increase in size. Growth is a result of cells producing new cells through cell division. The number of cells making up the organism increases, and the organism grows.

When some cells divide and then enlarge, they also develop specialized shapes and functions. The changes that take place in cells as they develop are called differentiation. As an organism develops, new cells differentiate into particular forms for particular functions. A nerve cell, for example, differentiates into a form that can conduct electric impulses. An intestinal cell differentiates into a form that can aid in digestion. Can you name some other types of specialized cells in your body?

Repair Cell division is also crucial for repairing tissues. Organisms vary in their ability to repair tissues by cell division. For example, when a sea star loses one of its five arms (*Figure 5.2*), the cells surrounding the injury are stimulated to divide repeatedly until they form a new arm. This level of repair, which replaces a missing body part, is called regeneration.

Regeneration to the extent seen in sea stars is not possible in humans. However, cell division is responsible for repairs that your body requires—

mending of skin, blood vessels, and bone, for example. Repairs are accomplished by cell regeneration at the site of an injury. Regeneration also replaces cells that die. Your skin cells are replaced by regeneration every 28 days!

Reproduction When the sea star loses its arm, it grows a new one. The lost arm's cells can also divide to form a whole new sea star. When an offspring is produced by only one parent, the process is called **asexual reproduction.** Asexual reproduction is a result of cell division.

Asexual reproduction is common among many

LAB ZONE ? Think About It!

Calculating Surface Area to Volume Ratio

The limits to cell size are governed by the surface area to volume ratio. Learn how to calculate the surface area to volume ratio of a cube by using the diagram and the formulas below.

Analyzing the Diagram

1 The formula for surface area is 6 × height × width (because a cube has six sides). The formula for volume is height × width × depth.
2 Calculate the surface area and volume for the two single cubes below. (The measurements are shown in centimeters.)
3 Place your answers in a ratio, with the surface area first. Reduce the ratio to simplest terms, if necessary.
4 How does the surface area to volume ratio change for the large cube when it is divided into 64 small cubes?

FIGURE 5.2
Cellular division has regenerated the lost arm of this sea star. What other organisms are capable of limb regeneration?

IN THE COMMUNITY

Healing Cuts

When we injure ourselves, our bodies generate new cells to replace the cells that were damaged or lost. We use many procedures and products to enhance the healing of injuries. Investigate products available at your pharmacy or grocery store that claim to promote healing of injuries. How do they claim to work? Do they affect cell division? Or prevent infection? Arrange to speak with a pharmacist, school nurse, or physician about the methods of treating a cut. What products and procedures do they recommend? How do the products and procedures work?

FIGURE 5.3
The unicellular eukaryote *Paramecium* can reproduce asexually. After replicating its genetic material, a *Paramecium* divides, producing two identical offspring. How does asexual reproduction differ from sexual reproduction?

types of organisms, including bacteria, protists fungi, plants, and some animals. During asexual reproduction cell division replicates the chromosomes of one parent cell. Asexual reproduction, therefore, produces offspring that are genetically identical to their parent.

Many plants and animals, including humans, are the result of a different kind of reproduction—sexual reproduction. **Sexual reproduction** produces offspring that have a combination of genetic material from two parent organisms. The recombination of chromosomes requires meiosis—a specialized form of cell division which you will learn about later in this chapter. After chromosomes combine in sexual reproduction, cell division results in growth of a new organism.

FRONTIERS IN BIOLOGY
Multiplying division

In humans, the rate of cell division, and therefore growth, is controlled by growth hormone, which is produced in the pituitary gland. During puberty, a large amount of growth hormone is produced, causing rapid gains in height and development. At the peak of their growth spurt, young adults increase in height by 8–9 cm a year.

When the pituitary gland malfunctions and does not produce enough growth hormone, dwarfism may result. Dwarfism is a condition in which a person never attains a height within the normal adult range. (Dwarfism can be caused by factors other than growth hormone deficiency.)

Researchers discovered that injections of human growth hormone could help stimulate growth. But the original method of obtaining growth hormone—from the pituitary glands of human cadavers—had several disadvantages. Only minute quantities could be obtained, and the hormone had the potential to transmit disease to the patients receiving it. In 1985 researchers discovered a way to use genetic engineering to produce a safe and plentiful supply of human growth hormone.

CHECKPOINT 5.1

1. Describe the factors that limit cell size.
2. Identify the roles of cell division in growth, repair, and reproduction.
3. **Critical Thinking** Which process do you think requires the greatest number of cell divisions in humans: growth, repair, or reproduction?

Build on What You Know

4. Choose two organelles and describe how their functions would be impaired in a cell that is too large. *(Need to jog your memory? Revisit relevant concepts in Chapter 3, Section 3.3.)*

5.2 How Do Cells Divide?

One nucleus is not enough

Cells divide in stages. In most cells the nucleus divides first, followed by division of the cytoplasm. A few types of cells do not undergo this final stage. For example, in the cells of skeletal muscles, which attach to bones and move them, the nucleus divides, but the cytoplasm does not. Skeletal muscle cells grow by enlarging, not dividing, and can end up with many nuclei.

What you'll learn

IDEAS
• To describe the characteristics of a cell in interphase
• To distinguish the steps of mitosis and cytokinesis

WORDS
interphase, replication, chromatin, sister chromatids, centromere, mitosis, cytokinesis, prophase, metaphase, anaphase, telophase

INTERPHASE: PREPARATION FOR DIVISION

Getting ready to split

Has anyone ever told you that you were "going through a phase"? A phase is a defined period within a cycle of change. Cells go through phases, too. The sequence of phases in the life cycle of a cell is called the cell cycle. The cell cycle is the period from the beginning of one cell division to the beginning of the next cell division. The cell cycle has two parts: growth and preparation (interphase) and cell division. Cell division in turn is divided into two stages—mitosis (nuclear division) and cytokinesis (cytoplasm division).

Interphase is the part of the cell cycle that occurs between divisions. At one time, biologists thought that interphase was simply a resting period. When they looked through a light microscope, cells seemed to be relatively inactive and unchanging during interphase.

Biologists now know that cells are very active during interphase, producing all of the materials necessary for cell growth and preparing for cell division. As you can see in *Figure 5.4,* interphase is by far the longest part of the cell cycle—typically about 90 percent of the total time. Can you explain why?

Interphase can be divided into three stages based on the metabolic activity taking place in the cell. The first stage, G1, or gap 1, is a period of activity characterized by growth and development. The second stage, during which the cell becomes committed to cell division, is called synthesis, or the S stage. During the S stage the chromosomes in the nucleus replicate. **Replication** occurs when material makes copies of itself.

The third and final stage of interphase is G2, or gap 2. During G2, the cell synthesizes organelles and other materials, many of which will play

FIGURE 5.4

This figure shows the amount of time spent by a typical cell in each stage of the cell cycle. How do the phases compare?

FIGURE 5.5

DNA in Cell Division

Cell division

Chromatin
During interphase, chromosomes are in the form of long, thin strands called chromatin. Chromosomes are replicated during the S stage of interphase.

Chromatids
Each replicated chromosome consists of two sister chromatids. During cell division, the DNA condenses into short, thick strands.

Chromosomes
After cell division, each daughter cell receives a full set of chromosomes—one chromatid from each pair.

Centromere   Chromatid

FIGURE 5.6
In a replicated chromosome, the chromatids—two identical strands of DNA—are joined at the centromere. How do chromatids compare with chromatin?

specific roles in cell division. In animal cells, a pair of organelles called centrioles replicate to form two pairs.

If you used a microscope to observe a cell nucleus at the beginning of interphase, you would see what looked like a tangled bundle of threads, as illustrated in *Figure 5.5*. **Chromatin** is a thin, fibrous form of the DNA and proteins that make up a chromosome. A cell's chromosomes are in chromatin form throughout interphase.

During the S stage of interphase, each chromosome is replicated. **Sister chromatids** are the two identical structures that result from chromosome replication. As cell division begins, the chromosomes coil and condense and the sister chromatids are clearly visible under a light microscope.

You can see what condensed sister chromatids look like under an electron microscope in *Figure 5.6*. The coiled chromatin makes each chromatid look hairy. A **centromere** is the point where sister chromatids are joined together. Centromeres are located at different points on different chromosomes. Biologists use characteristics such as centromere location to identify particular chromosome during mitosis.

CELL DIVISION

Nuclear fission

After interphase, chromosomes condense into a form visible under the light microscope, and changes occur in the nuclear envelope. These events signal the beginning of **mitosis**—the process during which a cell's nucleus divides into two identical nuclei.

In most cells, mitosis is followed by **cytokinesis,** the process in which a cell's cytoplasm divides to make two daughter cells. Each daughter cell forms around one of the two nuclei produced during mitosis. Daughter cells can continue the cell cycle by proceeding through interphase and another division, or they can differentiate structurally for specialized functions.

Both mitosis and cytokinesis proceed differently in plant and animal cells. These differences probably stem from the fact that plant cells—unlike animal cells—are surrounded by a rigid cell wall. In animals, formation of new cell membranes creates the two distinct daughter cells. In plants, both a new cell membrane and a new cell wall are needed to divide the parent cell into distinct daughter cells.

When cells divide

Mitosis is a continuous process that replicates the chromosomes and forms two new nuclei. Mitosis begins after interphase and ends before cytokinesis. In the late 1800s biologists defined four phases of mitosis. You can follow interphase and the phases of mitosis in *Figure 5.7* on pages 110–111.

Prophase The first phase of mitosis is called **prophase.** During this stage, the chromosomes in the nucleus condense. The sister chromatids of the condensed chromosomes are visible under a light microscope. In the cytoplasm, a bridge of proteins begins to assemble into microtubules, forming a fibrous structure called the mitotic spindle.

By late prophase the mitotic spindle stretches out between the opposite poles of the cell. The nuclear envelope and nucleolus break into fragments and then disappear. A part of each chromosome's centromere attaches to a spindle fiber, and the spindle fibers begin to move the sister chromatids toward the center of the cell.

Metaphase During the next phase, **metaphase,** the chromosomes are pulled to the center of the cell, where they line up on an imaginary line called the metaphase plate. At the end of metaphase, each chromosome is lined up an equal distance from the ends of the cell.

Anaphase As metaphase ends, anaphase, the third phase of mitosis, begins. During **anaphase,** the centromeres divide, the spindle fibers pull one set of chromatids toward one pole and the other set toward the opposite pole. Once separated the chromatids are two identical sets of daughter chromosomes.

Anaphase ends when the two sets of daughter chromosomes are located

Modeling the Phases of Mitosis

Building a model of a process may help you visualize and understand it better. You can find a way to represent the phases of mitosis if you . . .

Try This

1 Working in groups, assess the materials you have available. (Pipe cleaners, string, glue, paper clips, modeling clay, and toothpicks may be helpful.)
2 Make a sketch of each phase of mitosis and describe a plan for how you will construct a model of each phase.
3 Build the models.

Analyze Your Results

1 Test the accuracy of your group's models by asking other classmates to identify the stages represented. What responses did you get?
2 If any stages prove hard to identify from the models, how could you revise the models to make them clearer?

at opposite ends of the cell. The precise alignment of sister chromatids during metaphase is critical. When properly aligned, complete sets of daughter chromosomes move to opposite ends of the cell during anaphase. This ensures that each daughter nucleus receives a set of chromosomes identical to that of the parent cell.

Telophase In the last phase of mitosis, or **telophase,** two daughter nuclei are formed. The process is the reverse of what occurs during prophase. Nuclear envelopes form around each set of chromosomes. The chromosomes uncoil to form a loose mass of chromatin. By the end of telophase, the mitotic spindle has disassembled. In animal cells, each new nucleus has a pair of centrioles outside of its nuclear envelope. The centrioles remain in the cytoplasm of the new cells.

Cytokinesis, or cytoplasm division, begins during telophase as the daughter nuclei form. In animal cells, the cell membrane at the center of the parent cell folds inward to form a cleavage furrow. As the furrow deepens, the cell is pinched in half until the membrane meets and forms a division in the middle. When this happens, two distinct cells with complete cell membranes are formed.

FIGURE 5.7

The Phases of the Cell Cycle

1 Interphase
The cell spends most of the cell cycle in interphase, the phase between cellular divisions. Initially, the cell is in a period of growth. DNA is replicated and structures for mitosis are produced during this phase.

Nucleolus
Nucleus
Chromatin

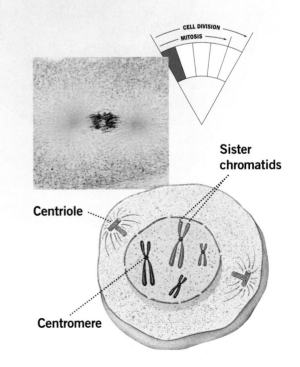

2 Prophase
The cell's chromosomes condense. In animal cells, a pair of centrioles migrates to each pole of the cell. The mitotic spindle forms and attaches to the centromeres of the chromosomes. The nuclear membrane and the nucleolus disappear.

Sister chromatids
Centriole
Centromere

CELL DIVISION
MITOSIS

5 **Telophase and Cytokinesis**
A nuclear membrane forms around each set of chromosomes, two nucleolus form, and the chromosomes uncoil into chromatin. The cytoplasm is divided and two daughter cells are formed.

Cleavage furrow

CELL DIVISION
MITOSIS

4 **Anaphase**
As the centromeres divide, the spindle disassembles, pulling the sister chromatids apart. In this manner an identical set of daughter chromosomes is pulled to each end of the cell.

CELL DIVISION
MITOSIS

Spindle fibers

3 **Metaphase**
The spindle arranges the chromosomes in the middle of the cell along an imaginary line called the metaphase plate.

Metaphase plate

FIGURE 5.8

Cytokinesis in Plant and Animal Cells

Daughter cells

Cell plate

Plant cell
A cell wall is being formed between two plant cells. The cell plate forms a new cell membrane and cell wall between two daughter cells.

Animal cell
An animal cell completes cytokinesis by "pinching off" its membrane to form two new cells. The cleavage furrow is clearly visible in this human embryo (right), about 24 hours after fertilization.

In plants, membrane-bound fragments begin to accumulate along the metaphase plate during late anaphase. The fragments fuse to form a double membrane, or cell plate, that extends the length of the cell between the two new nuclei. A new cell wall forms between the membranes of the cell plate. Eventually, a complete cell wall that divides the two daughter cells is formed. The double membrane remains and forms part of the cell membrane inside the wall. Compare the dividing plant cells with the animal cells in *Figure 5.8*. How do the differences in cytokinesis reflect the structural differences in plant and animal cells?

CHECKPOINT 5.2

1. How does the cell prepare for mitosis while in interphase?
2. Briefly summarize the steps of mitosis and cytokinesis.
3. **Critical Thinking** The cancer drug colchicine interferes with mitosis by dissolving proteins that form the spindles in cells. What effect would this drug have on cell division? Why?

Build on What You Know

4. Describe the differences between plant and animal cells. How do these differences affect cell division? *(Need to jog your memory? Revisit relevant concepts in Chapter 3, Section 3.4.)*

What process enables organisms to reproduce and develop?

Observing Mitosis

WHAT YOU WILL DO Observe cell division in an onion root tip, identify the places in an onion root tip where mitosis is occurring, and estimate the percentage of dividing cells

SKILLS YOU WILL USE Hypothesizing, observing, recording data, calculating

WHAT YOU WILL NEED Microscope, prepared slide of mitosis in onion root tip

Propose a Hypothesis

Propose a hypothesis about which parts of onion root tips have the highest rate of cell division.

Conduct Your Experiment

1 Place the prepared slide on the stage of the microscope, and focus with low power.
2 Scan the onion root tip for a region in which cells are in various phases of cell division and switch to high power.
3 Find a cell that is in one of the phases of mitosis and draw it. Label visible parts and record which phase it is in.
4 Try to find examples of cells in all the phases of mitosis. Repeat steps 2 and 3 for each.
5 Switch to low power and choose one region of the root tip. Count the number of cells undergoing mitosis and the number of cells that are not undergoing mitosis. Record the numbers.
6 Repeat step 5 for three additional regions of the root tip. Draw a simple sketch of the root tip, and shade in the areas you observed.

Analyze Your Data

1 Are cells undergoing mitosis in every part of the onion root tip? If not, in which part(s) is mitosis occurring?
2 Are all the mitotic cells in the same phase of mitosis? If not, which phases of mitosis are occurring, and in which parts of the root tip?
3 Is the number of cells undergoing mitosis the same in every region of the onion root tip? If not, how do the regions differ?
4 For each of the four regions you observed, calculate the percentage of mitotic cells compared with the total number of cells.

5 Based on your samples of the four regions, estimate the percentage of mitotic cells in the entire root tip.

Draw Conclusions

Summarize the pattern of mitosis in onion root tips. Why would mitosis occur in such a pattern?

Design a Related Experiment

Design a lab to compare mitosis in the cells of different organisms.

Lab: Observing Mitosis

Sample cell 1: metaphase

cell wall
chromosome
spindle
cytoplasm

5.3 What Is Meiosis?

What you'll learn

IDEAS

• To show how the reduction in numbers of chromosomes relates to the process of sexual reproduction

• To summarize the phases of meiosis

WORDS

diploid, haploid, meiosis, homologous pair

Froggy went a-courting

In most eukaryotic species, offspring are produced by the union of two specialized cells that contain the genetic instructions for creating a new organism. In this section you will learn about the process through which those cells are produced. Here you see *Agalychnis* tree frogs in development—the result of the union of two of those specialized cells. What familiar features are already visible?

REDUCING CHROMOSOME NUMBERS

When less is more

Earlier in this chapter you learned that organisms can reproduce asexually (with DNA contributed by one parent) or sexually (with DNA contributed by two parents). Some organisms, such as the sea star, can reproduce either asexually or sexually. Other organisms, such as mammals, can produce offspring only through sexual reproduction. In sexual reproduction, the genetic information of one parent is combined with that of the other parent to produce a genetically distinct offspring.

The life cycles of organisms that reproduce sexually vary considerably. In most organisms, however, sexual reproduction includes a special form of cell division in which the number of chromosomes is reduced.

You may recall that the body cells of every species have a characteristic number of chromosomes. Humans have 46 chromosomes (23 pairs) in each body cell. Any cell that contains two complete sets of

chromosomes is called a **diploid** (DI-ployd) cell ($2n$). Almost all of the cells in your body are diploid cells. Human sex cells—the egg and sperm that combine to produce offspring—contain only 23 chromosomes, half the number of a diploid cell. A cell with only one complete set of chromosomes is called a **haploid** (HA-ployd) cell (n). Haploid reproductive cells are called gametes, or sex cells.

Why is it important that gametes be haploid cells? If human gametes, like human body cells, were produced through mitosis, each gamete would have 46 chromosomes ($2n$). When the gametes (sperm and egg) of two parents fused, the offspring's cells would have 92 chromosomes ($4n$)! If this offspring could survive and reproduce, it would produce gametes with 92 chromosomes. How many chromosomes would the third generation have?

To keep the number of chromosomes stable from generation to generation, haploid cells are produced by a process called meiosis. **Meiosis** is a type of cellular reproduction in which the number of chromosomes is reduced by half, so that the daughter cells are haploid (n). Over generations, meiosis maintains a stable number of

FIGURE 5.9

In sexual reproduction, haploid cells are formed by the process of meiosis. Two haploid cells are then able to fuse to produce diploid cells.

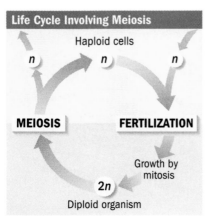

Life Cycle Involving Meiosis
Haploid cells
n n n
MEIOSIS   FERTILIZATION
Growth by mitosis
$2n$
Diploid organism

The buddy system

You already know that all human cells, except for sex cells, contain 46 chromosomes. These 46 chromosomes are arranged in 23 pairs. Each of the 23 pairs is called a **homologous pair.** With one exception, each pair (of the 23 pairs) contains chromosomes that are exactly alike in size, location of the centromere, and the dark-and-light banding pattern seen after staining with dyes. See *Figure 5.10.* Only one pair can differ. In females, this pair is alike and is called XX. In males, this pair is dissimilar in appearance and is called XY.

During meiosis, chromosomes in each homologous pair replicate and a single copy from each pair is distributed to each daughter nucleus. In humans, a cell with 46 chromosomes

FIGURE 5.10
The pair of homologous chromosomes in the micrograph above look identical.

chromosomes by producing gametes that have one set of chromosomes instead of two sets.

In some organisms, such as plants, two kinds of haploid cells are formed by meiosis. Gametes are formed at one stage of a plant's life cycle and special haploid cells called spores are formed at another stage. Spores give rise to a haploid organism. In other organisms, such as animals, only gametes are formed by meiosis. In all organisms, meiosis keeps the number of chromosomes stable over generations.

As you can see in *Figure 5.9,* the fusion of haploid gametes ($n + n$) creates offspring with diploid cells ($2n$). As the offspring develops into an adult, diploid body cells are produced through repeated rounds of mitotic cell division. Mitotic cell division maintains the diploid chromosome number ($2n$). Eventually, a diploid reproductive cell undergoes meiosis to form the next generation of haploid gametes (n).

Organisms that reproduce sexually typically have both diploid and haploid cells during some stage of their life cycle. However, the timing of meiosis and mitosis can vary among different types of organisms.

EVERYDAY BIOLOGY

The Chicken and the Egg

Eggs, the gametes produced by hens and other fowl, are a common part of the human diet. Most eggs produced for human consumption are not fertilized and therefore cannot develop into offspring.

LAB ZONE Think About It!

Calculating Haploid and Diploid Numbers

Haploid and diploid are designated by the algebraic notations *n* and *2n*, respectively. Either number can be calculated when the other number is known. For example, if the haploid number (*n*) is 3, the diploid number (*2n*) is 2 x 3, or 6. If the diploid number (*2n*) is 12, the haploid number (*n*) is 12 ÷ 2, or 6. The table below shows the haploid or diploid numbers of a variety of organisms. Copy the table onto a separate sheet of paper and complete it. Then use the table to answer the following questions.

Analyzing the Table

1 What are the haploid numbers for the two plants listed in the table?
2 In the table, which organisms' diploid numbers are closest to that of a human?
3 Explain why a diploid number is always even.
4 Which organism's haploid and diploid numbers do you find most surprising? Why?

Organism	Haploid Number	Diploid Number
ameba	25	
chimpanzee	24	
earthworm	18	
fern		1010
hamster	22	
honeybee		56
human		46
onion		16

FIGURE 5.11

The Phases of Meiosis

Meiosis I

Homologous pair of
chromosomes

Prophase I
The replicated pairs of
homologous chromosomes
condense and attach to
each other.

Metaphase I
The spindle fibers arrange
the homologous chromo-
some pairs in the middle of
the cell.

Anaphase I
The spindle fibers separate
the homologous pairs and
pull them to opposite poles
of the cell.

Telophase I
Cytokinesis takes place,
resulting in two haploid
cells. Each chromosome in
the haploid cells consists of
two sister chromatids.

undergoes meiosis to yield four haploid
cells with 23 chromosomes.

The process that determines which
chromosomes of a homologous pair
move to a specific daughter cell is
random. For example, in the first cell
shown in *Figure 5.11,* a given chromosome from the top homologous pair in
prophase I could end up in a haploid
cell with either of the homologous
chromosomes from the bottom pair.

THE PHASES OF MEIOSIS

One becomes four

Before meiosis, a diploid cell replicates
its chromosomes, so that each
chromosome consists of two sister
chromatids joined at a centromere.
The cell is then ready to start meiosis.
Meiosis consists of two stages: meiosis
I and meiosis II. Each stage can be
divided into four phases. You can
follow the phases in the process of
meiosis in *Figure 5.11*.

In the first phase of meiosis—
prophase I—the chromosomes
condense and each homologous pair
becomes attached to one another.
Each homologous pair of
chromosomes contains four sister
chromatids, two per replicated
chromosome. This grouping is called
a tetrad. The word *tetrad* means
"four."

The tetrad formation of
homologous chromosomes during
prophase I ensures that each pair will
separate during meiosis. Recall that
tetrad formation does not occur
during mitosis, where homologous
pairs do not separate.

During metaphase I, anaphase I,
and telophase I, movements of chromosomes similar to those in mitosis
take place. The chromosomes move to
the center of the cell and are then
pulled along spindle fibers to the cell
poles, where daughter nuclei form.
After meiosis I, each daughter-cell

Meiosis II

Prophase II
Spindle fibers form again, and chromosomes condense once more.

Metaphase II
Spindle fibers align chromosomes along the center of the cell.

Anaphase II
Sister chromatids are separated and pulled to opposite poles of the cell.

Haploid cells
Cytokinesis produces four haploid cells.

nucleus contains one member of each homologous pair (*n*). Each member still consists of two sister chromatids joined at the centromere.

The two haploid daughter cells from meiosis I then undergo a second division. In meiosis II, the sister chromatids move to the center of the cell. The centromeres split, separating the chromatids. The individual chromosomes are then pulled to the cell poles, where daughter nuclei form. As you can see in *Figure 5.11,* each of the four resulting daughter-cell nuclei contains one copy of one complete set of chromosomes (*n*).

Depending on the species and the sex of the individual, the cytokinesis that follows each meiotic division proceeds differently. In human males, all four haploid nuclei form sperm cells. In human females, only one of the four haploid nuclei forms an egg cell. The other three nuclei receive almost no cytoplasm and do not

form gametes. Do you think males or females produce the greater number of gametes?

CHECKPOINT 5.3

1. What is the importance of meiosis to sexual reproduction?
2. Explain the difference between a haploid cell and a diploid cell.
3. Write a summary of each phase of meiosis.
4. **Critical Thinking** Compare the chromosomes of a diploid cell to a collection of shoes in a closet. How are they similar? What would make the shoe collection comparable to the chromosomes of a haploid cell?

Build on What You Know

5. Cells are specialized in structure to match their function. Compare cell specialization in gametes with other examples of cell specialization. *(Need to jog your memory? Revisit relevant concepts in Chapter 3, Section 3.4.)*

5.4 New Chromosome Combinations

What you'll learn

IDEAS
- To compare meiosis and mitosis
- To explain the significance of genetic variation

WORD
variation

Variety is the spice of life

Like begets like: Human offspring are always human, cats give birth to kittens, and dogs produce puppies. Do the kittens (right) look like their mother? While offspring produced through sexual reproduction may resemble their parents, meiosis ensures that they will not be identical to them.

COMPARING MEIOSIS AND MITOSIS

Different ways to split

Mitosis and meiosis are similar in many ways. They are both forms of cell division. Both involve similar steps, including replication, the disappearance of the nucleus and nucleolus, and movement of chromosomes to opposite ends of the cell.

What other similarities do you see in *Figure 5.12*?

Notice that there are three main differences between mitosis and meiosis. First, meiosis produces daughter cells that have half the number of chromosomes found in the parent cell. This reduction in the amount of DNA produces haploid gametes. In sexual reproduction, haploid gametes fuse, genetic information is combined,

FIGURE 5.12

Two Types of Cell Division

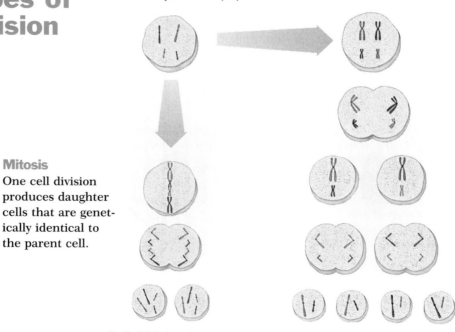

Parent diploid cell (*2n*)

Meiosis I
The chromosomes replicate, and the cell divides once.

Mitosis
One cell division produces daughter cells that are genetically identical to the parent cell.

Meiosis II
Each new cell divides, producing daughter cells that are genetically different from the parent cell.

2 diploid daughter cells
2 (*2n*)

4 haploid daughter cells
4 (*n*)

and diploid offspring are produced. Mitosis, on the other hand, produces daughter cells with the same number of chromosomes as the parent cell. These daughter cells enable organisms to grow, repair damaged tissues, and replace dying cells.

A second difference between mitosis and meiosis is that the daughter cells produced by meiosis are not genetically identical to each other. The separation of homologous chromosomes during meiosis is random, so each daughter cell has a new mix of chromosomes. In contrast, the daughter cells produced by mitosis have exact copies of the parent cell's chromosomes.

The third difference is that in meiosis, cell division takes place twice, producing four daughter cells. How many daughter cells are produced by mitosis? How do the number of daughter cells and the number of chromosomes compare?

THE VALUE OF VARIATION

Mixing it up

You may ask yourself, "Why do some organisms (such as the sea star discussed in Section 5.1) usually reproduce sexually if they can do so more easily through asexual reproduction?" Scientists do not know the complete answer to this question, but they do know that sexual reproduction has long-term advantages—it produces differences between organisms.

The differences between members of a population are collectively called **variation.** Variation results, in part, from the recombination of DNA that occurs during meiosis and fertilization. Compare the gametes in *Figure 5.13*. In this example, the species has a diploid number of four chromosomes ($2n=4$); the two red chromosomes were contributed by the mother, and the two blue

Combination 1   Combination 2   Combination 3   Combination 4

chromosomes by the father. As you can see, the combination of red and blue chromosomes in each gamete is determined by the way the homologous pairs line up in the metaphase of meiosis I. Meiosis results in a random separation of chromosomes in the gametes.

Because each parent can produce a variety of gametes, two parents can produce a variety of offspring. Each kitten in the litter pictured at the beginning of this section was produced by the same two parents, yet each offspring is very different-looking. Such variation is possible because the gametes combine randomly during fertilization.

To appreciate the effects of the random combination of gametes, consider the fusion (joining) of gametes from two parents. When male and female gametes fuse during fertilization, the DNA from both gametes becomes the genetic material for the new diploid cell. Suppose that the four combinations of gametes shown in *Figure 5.13* were produced by a female cat. Assume that a male cat also produces the same gametes. How many different combinations of chromosomes would be possible in their offspring?

Random separation of homologous pairs of chromosomes and random combination of haploid gametes are sources of variation associated with

FIGURE 5.13
The same parent cell can produce different combinations of chromosomes. How are the gametes different from one another?

LAB ZONE Do It!

Modeling the Phases of Meiosis

Learn the phases of meiosis "inside-out" when you . . .

Try This

1 Reappraise the models you made to illustrate the stages of mitosis. Make a sketch of the phases of meiosis, and plan how you would change your models to represent meiosis.
2 Using the same materials (pipe cleaners, string, glue, paper clips, modeling clay, toothpicks, etc.), redesign the models to show meiosis.

Analyze Your Results

1 Compare and contrast the processes of mitosis and meiosis.
2 What did you need to change in order to convert the mitosis model to a representation of meiosis?
3 Which model had a more complex construction?

sexual reproduction. In the next unit you will learn about a related process that also produces recombination.

In a changing environment, variation resulting from new chromosome combinations can be key to a population's survival. If a significant environmental change occurs, a trait that was once beneficial can become a disadvantage, and a trait that was not helpful can become an advantage. As the degree of variation in a population increases, so does the likelihood that individuals will survive environmental changes. For example, a population of diverse sea stars produced by sexual reproduction has a better chance of surviving a new disease than a population with less variation. The population with greater

variation has more genetic resources, and it has a better chance of responding successfully to any changes in the environment.

How does the enormous variation in organisms that reproduce sexually compare with the variation in organisms that reproduce asexually? Offspring produced through asexual reproduction do not have a recombination of chromosomes. They have the same chromosomes and therefore the same traits as their parent. In such organisms, genetic variation rarely occurs from generation to generation. A change in the environment that destroys one individual, such as the arrival of a new disease, could destroy the entire population. Variation is thought to be the reason that sexual reproduction is the dominant form of reproduction for so many species.

CHECKPOINT 5.4

1. What are three differences between mitosis and meiosis? Explain.
2. What is the advantage of sexual reproduction to a population whose environment changes?
3. Critical Thinking Organisms such as certain plants, fungi, and algae have the ability to reproduce either sexually or asexually. What would be the advantage of having both abilities?

Build on What You Know

4. How are organisms that reproduce asexually similar to autotrophic organisms? How are organisms that reproduce sexually similar to heterotrophic organisms? *(Need to jog your memory? Revisit relevant concepts in Chapter 4, Section 4.1.)*

What effect does meiosis have on chromosome number?

Chapter 5 Review

 5.1–5.2 Cell division is the basis of reproduction and development.
5.3–5.4 Chromosome number is reduced in meiosis.

Sum It Up

Use the following summary to review the main concepts in this chapter.

5.1 When Do Cells Divide?

- The ratio of cell membrane surface area to cell volume is a factor that limits cell size. When a cell reaches its optimum size, the nucleus initiates cell division.
- Cell division is the mechanism for growth and differentiation in multicellular organisms; for the replacement of old cells and the regeneration of injured cells; and for asexual reproduction and the growth that follows sexual reproduction.

5.2 How Do Cells Divide?

- The two parts of a cell's life cycle are interphase and cell division. Cell division involves mitosis and cytokinesis.
- During interphase, cells grow, chromosomes replicate, and cells prepare for cell division.
- During mitosis, the nucleus divides into daughter nuclei containing identical sets of chromosomes. For most cells, the final stage of cell division is the division of cytoplasm during cytokinesis.

5.3 What Is Meiosis?

- Almost all cells in an organism contain two complete sets of chromosomes. Reproductive cells contain only one set.
- Cells produced by mitosis are diploid; cells produced by meiosis are haploid.
- Meiosis keeps the number of chromosomes constant from generation to generation. During meiosis, homologous pairs of chromosomes separate to form four haploid daughter-cell nuclei.

5.4 New Chromosome Combinations

- Offspring produced asexually are exact copies of the parent cells.
- Offspring produced sexually differ genetically from their parent cells.
- The variation in offspring produced through meiosis can be the key factor in the survival of a population faced with environmental change.

Use Terms and Concepts

Use each of the following words or terms in a complete sentence. If you need to review a meaning, turn to the page indicated.

asexual reproduction (p. 105)

sexual reproduction (p. 106)

interphase (p. 107)

replication (p. 107)

chromatin (p. 108)

sister chromatids (p. 108)

centromere (p. 108)

mitosis (p. 108)

cytokinesis (p. 108)

prophase (p. 109)

metaphase (p. 109)

anaphase (p. 109)

telophase (p. 109)

diploid (p. 114)

haploid (p. 114)

meiosis (p. 114)

homologous pair (p. 115)

variation (p. 119)

Use Your Word Power

COMPLETION Write the word or phrase that best completes each statement.

1. Variation in a population results from _____ reproduction.

2. During interphase, the DNA in the nucleus is present in the form of thin strands called _____ .

3. Chromatids line up at the center of the cell during _____ .

4. Growth, regeneration, and _____ reproduction use the same method of cell division.

5. The structure at which sister chromatids are joined together is called the _____ .

6. The process of copying chromosomes is called _____ .

7. Differences between members of a population are collectively referred to as _____ .

MULTIPLE CHOICE Choose the letter of the word or phrase that best completes each statement.

8. Copies of chromosomes are made during (a) anaphase; (b) interphase; (c) telophase; (d) prophase.

9. Cells with two complete sets of chromosomes are (a) haploid; (b) reproductive cells; (c) gametes; (d) diploid.

10. Two identical daughter nuclei are produced during (a) meiosis; (b) endocytosis; (c) interphase; (d) mitosis.

11. Two sets of chromosomes are located at opposite ends of a cell at the end of (a) anaphase; (b) cytokinesis; (c) endocytosis; (d) interphase.

12. The mitotic spindle first makes its appearance during (a) cell plate formation; (b) exocytosis; (c) prophase; (d) metaphase.

Show What You Know

13. Name and describe the three stages of interphase.

14. Explain why a large animal and a tiny animal have cells that are about the same size.

15. What are the functions of the mitotic spindle in mitosis?

16. Explain why it is necessary for gametes to be haploid rather than diploid.

17. What are the major differences between mitosis and meiosis?

18. How do the chromosomes of an offspring produced by sexual reproduction compare with the chromosomes of its parents?

19. How does cytokinesis in animal cells differ from cytokinesis in plant cells?

20. Is there any difference between sister chromatids and homologous pairs? Explain your answer.

21. Briefly describe what happens inside the cell during telophase.

22. **Make a Concept Map** Complete the concept map below by adding the following terms: meiosis, haploid cells, diploid cells, sexual reproduction, asexual reproduction.

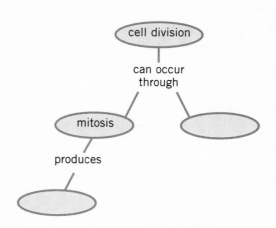

Take It Further

23. Developing a Hypothesis If sexual reproduction helps a population survive in a changing environment, what advantage(s) could a population that reproduces asexually have?

24. Designing an Experiment Design an experiment to test the hypothesis that mitosis in plants is affected by temperature.

25. Interpreting a Graph The graph below shows the typical time segments for mitosis in many mammal cells. Which stage of mitosis is the longest? Which is the shortest? What do you think is happening to the chromosomes when the cell is 55 minutes into mitosis?

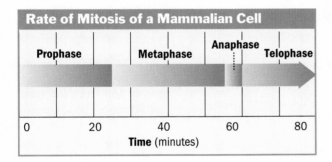

Rate of Mitosis of a Mammalian Cell

Prophase   Metaphase   Anaphase   Telophase

Time (minutes)
0   20   40   60   80

26. Analyzing Data Use the table below to answer the questions about mitosis.

Growth Rate of Rapidly Dividing Eukaryotic Cells	
Time (hours)	Number of Cells
0	1
10	2
20	4
30	8
40	16
50	32

A) Assuming that no cells die, how many cells will there be in one week?

B) Assuming that the original cell is diploid and divides mitotically, how many copies of each chromosome will there be in 60 hours?

Consider the Issues

27. Spinal Injury Research When the spinal cord is damaged, the nerve cells do not regenerate. Some recent studies with rodents suggest that nerve regeneration might be possible. What factors should society consider when allocating funds for spinal cord research or for educational programs on the prevention of spinal cord injuries?

Make New Connections

28. Biology and Art Mitosis is divided into phases for ease of discussion. To show how the action flows from one phase to the next, prepare a flip-book to show an animated version of mitosis. Focus on what happens to the chromosomes during each phase.

29. Biology and Community: A Project Find out what familiar food plants, such as apples or tomatoes, are grown in your community. Talk to gardeners, use the library, consult catalogs, or visit greenhouses to determine at what time of year cell growth from mitosis occurs most rapidly in these plants.

FAST-FORWARD TO CHAPTER 6

In Chapter 6 you will use your knowledge of meiosis to track the inheritance of chromosomes and traits in offspring.

Unit 1 Review

THE BIG IDEA! Answering the following questions will help you to link ideas and grasp the core concepts.

Connect the Chapters

1. How do cell structures and processes demonstrate that life depends on water?
2. Which process is more likely to involve chemical reactions—passive transport or active transport? Explain.
3. Explain how mitosis in animal cells, as an energy-dependent cellular process, is dependent on photosynthesis in other organisms.
4. Phosphate groups contain phosphorous atoms. What role does phosphorous play in mitosis, photosynthesis, and cellular respiration?
5. How can you tell if the solutions on both sides of a semipermeable membrane are identical in concentration?
6. What scientific experiments might be done to determine if a newly discovered life-form has chromosomes and grows by cell division?

Connect the Units

7. Use what you have learned about cell division and chromosome number to argue against the idea of spontaneous generation.
8. What is the difference between a large, adult multicellular organism and the cell from which it developed?

Connect to Themes

9. **Unity and Diversity** How do the number and characteristics of organic compounds demonstrate the basic unity of all living things?
10. **Stability and Equilibrium** How do organelles contribute to homeostasis?
11. **Energy** Summarize the process of cellular respiration. What are the reactants and products? How is energy used by living things?

project plans

1 Write a report on one of the scientists mentioned in this unit. When the scientist began doing research, what was already known about the topic? What contribution did the scientist make? What questions were left unanswered?

2 Pigments are important to art as well as photosynthesis. The availability of pigments in prepared paints is a relatively recent development. In the past, what materials have artists used to prepare pigments? How do art experts use their knowledge of pigments to expose art forgeries?

3 As a class, design a method of testing the pH of soil from different locations in your community. Note which plants thrive in which type of soil. If you test soil from landscaped yards, find out whether chemicals were added to the soil to change the pH. Plot the data on a map of your community.

CRITIC'S CORNER

A CD-ROM REVIEW BY CARLOS CONTRERAS EDINBURG, TEXAS

SimEarth, a simulation game by Maxis, allows you to control nearly every aspect of Earth. You can create your own planet or use one of the existing planets to create a whole new civilization, based on your decisions alone. You also learn how civilizations develop and how Earth is affected by our decisions. I would recommend this game to anyone who likes to use his or her imagination, as well as to anyone who enjoys simulation games. You can have hours of fun creating worlds you never thought were possible.

ANTHONY LAROSE
Cheese maker and team leader
at Franklin County Cheese
EDUCATION: High school diploma
and on-the-job training

"Cream cheese is made of butterfat and other nonfat solids like gums and proteins. Making it is a matter of getting the right percentages of each and reaching the proper pH level. One way to make cheese is with cultures. We use another method, called direct set, which means we use natural chemicals and machinery. First, we measure the fat content of the cream. Then we add other solids according to a formula. We pasteurize and homogenize the mix and adjust the pH level. Then you have cream cheese, and you're ready to pack. You have to do a lot of tasting during the process. When you taste the mix for flavor and texture, you can tell if you're doing it right."

bioSURF You can visit the Internet address *http://basis_of_life.biosurf.com* to find out more about jobs that involve organic compounds and biochemical processes.

DR. CHARLES S. CRAIK
Professor of biochemistry, biophysics, and pharmacology at the University of California, San Francisco, School of Pharmacy
EDUCATION: Ph.D. in chemistry

"I work with enzymes called proteases. One critical role enzymes play is in digesting food. . . . In the past, most proteases were thought of as digestive enzymes, but now we know they can also play a much more sophisticated role. . . . When a virus is replicating in the cell, it creates proteins that will eventually become part of the new virus. The protease enzyme serves as a pair of molecular scissors, trimming the viral proteins into the right shapes, like pieces of a jigsaw puzzle. Blocking that event can block viral assembly and replication of the virus. By designing molecules that can do this, we can help stop viral infections like AIDS that require a protease for survival."

bioSURF Look up the UCSF School of Pharmacy at *http://basis_of_life.biosurf.com* to learn more about Dr. Craik and other career-related information.

"It's risky to hope your research will actually lead to an application, but when you succeed, it is a very rewarding experience."

— DR. CHARLES S. CRAIK

Which of these amazing statements about genetics are fact and which are fiction?

Hit *or* Myth?

You can grow a **square** watermelon.

(Fiction. However, biotechnology researchers are attempting to produce fruits and vegetables that are easier to stack.)

Taste is inherited.

(Fact. While your "taste" in clothing, art, and music is not inherited, your ability to taste certain flavors is inherited.)

mmm...

eww!

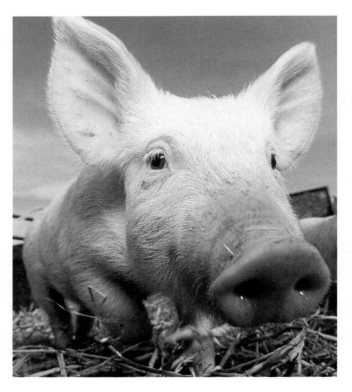

You may someday get **body parts** from a pig.

(Fact. Scientists are working to breed pigs with organs that can be safely transplanted into humans. These pig organs will not carry diseases—a stumbling block of today's experimental pig-to-human organ transplants.)

Pete

Re-Pete

Clones exist only in science fiction stories.

(Fiction. These two sheep are clones produced through genetic engineering techniques. Their genes are exactly alike.)

When you **lick a stamp,** you leave behind enough information to be identified.

(Fact. Like every cell in your body, cells in your saliva contain genetic information unique to you. If the genetic information on the back of a stamp matches yours, then you licked it!)

hobby: stamp collecting
best friend: "Buddy"
favorite pizza: Hawaiian
first job: grocery bagger
favorite tune: "Science Rocks"

In **all** organisms, sex is determined by genetics.

(Fiction. The sex of the map turtle is influenced by the eggs' incubation temperature. The hotter the temperature, the greater the percentage of female offspring.)

Fundamentals of Genetics

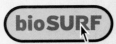

You can find out more about genetics by visiting the following Internet site: *http://genetics.biosurf.com*

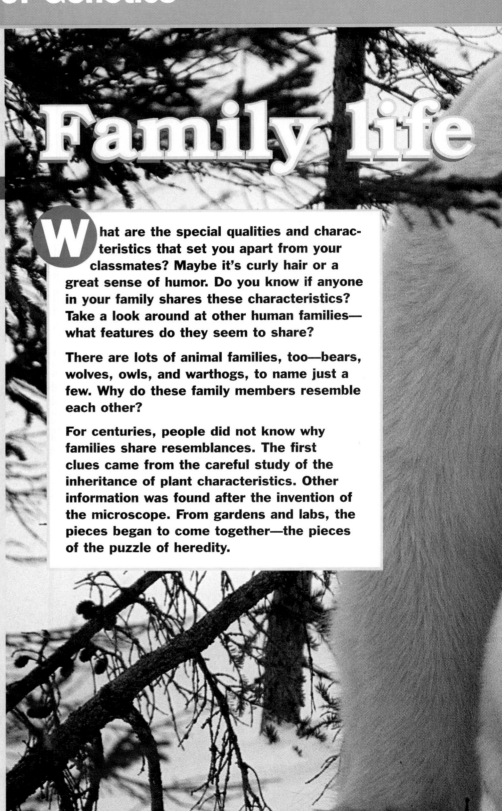

Family life

What are the special qualities and characteristics that set you apart from your classmates? Maybe it's curly hair or a great sense of humor. Do you know if anyone in your family shares these characteristics? Take a look around at other human families—what features do they seem to share?

There are lots of animal families, too—bears, wolves, owls, and warthogs, to name just a few. Why do these family members resemble each other?

For centuries, people did not know why families share resemblances. The first clues came from the careful study of the inheritance of plant characteristics. Other information was found after the invention of the microscope. From gardens and labs, the pieces began to come together—the pieces of the puzzle of heredity.

Discover It!

Find Characteristics That Are Inherited

You need pencil, paper, and graph paper

1. Make sure you can identify each characteristic. Make a chart to use in surveying your family or friends.
2. Survey as many people as you can for each characteristic. Tally your findings. Make a bar graph of your findings. Which is the most common characteristic?

Here are some questions to consider for your survey: Which human characteristics are easily observed? Can you roll your tongue into a U shape? Do you have attached ear lobes or free ear lobes? Do you have hair between your second and third knuckle? How about dimples?

WRITE ABOUT IT!

In your science journal, describe the results of your survey. For each characteristic, use fractions or percentages to describe how many surveyed people had the characteristic. If you add the fractions or percentages for those having dimples, for example, and for those who do not have dimples, what fraction or percent do you get? Explain why.

6.1 Patterns of Inheritance

What you'll learn

IDEAS

• To distinguish between dominant traits and recessive traits

• To analyze the results of Mendel's experiments with three generations of garden peas

WORDS

genetics, trait, purebred, hybrid, genes, allele, dominant allele, recessive allele

EVERYDAY BIOLOGY

Bloodlines

A popular myth about inheritance is that traits are passed from parents to offspring through the blood. The term "bloodline," used by animal breeders, reflects this myth. In this term, "blood" refers to lineage, or inheritance of traits.

Can a wallflower grow?
Are you ever too shy to talk to someone you really want to meet or too bashful to deliver a speech? Most people are shy at times. Scientists have used genetics to predict shyness in toddlers. As you may know, many toddlers are shy. Just how shy they are is partially determined by genetics. This shyness generally diminishes as individuals reach adulthood.

THE HISTORY OF GENETICS

Prehistoric pooches

Some people call dogs our best friends, but when did this friendship start? Dogs and humans have been companions for thousands of years. The domestication of dogs may have been one of the earliest human experiences with genetics. **Genetics** is the scientific study of heredity.

Millions of years ago there were no dogs. Today's domestic dogs are descended from a wild, wolfish ancestor. How did the snarling, dangerous wolf of millions of years ago become the loyal lapdog of today? Although we have no record of dog domestication, it seems certain that ancient peoples selected certain wolves to mate and thereby affected the traits that were passed from the parents to the pups.

A **trait** is a characteristic that can be passed from parent to offspring. With each generation, the traits of the wolves living with humans became more distinct from the traits of the wild wolves. Eventually, this process led to a new breed—the domestic dog. What wolf traits might our ancestors have prized most when breeding the domestic dog?

We have known for centuries that traits are passed from parents to offspring. What has not always been understood is how traits are determined. One explanation that appealed to scientists for many centuries was that traits of parents were blended, or mixed, in offspring. The blending hypothesis accounted for many observable traits and was widely accepted for many years. However, the idea of blending could not account for the appearance of unexpected traits in some offspring. It was not until scientists discovered the cellular basis of life that the inheritance of traits was better understood.

FIGURE 6.1

This artwork from the year 510 B.C. shows a Greek teenager playing with a domesticated cat and dog.

In Chapter 5 you learned about chromosomes and cell division. During cell division, chromosomes are replicated and then distributed to daughter cells. Reproduction requires cell division and chromosome replication. We now know that traits are passed from parents to offspring in these chromosomes. But the relationship between chromosomes and traits was not always understood.

The first clues to understanding inheritance came from Gregor Mendel, one of the most outstanding scientists in the field of genetics. Mendel, an Austrian monk, began his work in the 1860s. He used garden pea plants to study how traits were passed from one generation to another.

Most biologists in the 1860s did not use mathematics in their studies. However, Mendel recognized the importance of statistics in experimentation. After gathering detailed information on more than 20,000 pea plants, Mendel applied mathematics to his observations and found that the statistics did not support the blending hypothesis. Instead, the statistics led him to suggest several new hypotheses to explain inheritance of traits.

Like peas in a pod

Analyzing statistics was just one of the requirements of Mendel's work. Another was patience. Mendel worked for more than eight years on his pea plant experiments. Mendel chose the garden pea plant for three reasons: the structure of the pea flowers, the presence of distinctive traits, and the rapid reproduction cycle. These characteristics enabled Mendel to isolate and control variables and to produce observable results that he could duplicate.

The anthers are cut from the purple flower, which is then fertilized by pollen from the white flower.

The structure of the pea flower enabled Mendel to isolate an important variable—fertilization. In fertilization, the male plant gamete, located in pollen produced by the anther, is transferred to the female plant gamete, located at the base of the pistil. The relatively closed structure of the pea flower petals makes it very easy for pollen from the anther to fertilize the pistil of the same flower. This process is called self-fertilization. If a plant or any organism receives the same genetic traits from both of its parents, it is called **purebred.** Self-fertilization produces purebred pea plants.

As you can see in *Figure 6.2*, Mendel also altered plants and transferred pollen by hand. By controlling pollination and preventing self-fertilization, Mendel crossbred plants, producing hybrids. A **hybrid** is an organism that receives different forms of a genetic trait from each parent.

Garden pea plants have some traits that are easy to see, which made it possible for Mendel to produce observable results. Mendel studied seven traits. Each of these traits is unusual in that it has only two distinct forms. For example, the pea pods are either yellow or green. There is no intermediate, or blended, color. The height of the plant is either tall or

FIGURE 6.2
How did the shape of pea plants allow Mendel to manipulate pollination and control his experiments?

FIGURE 6.3
Gregor Mendel (1822–1884) is known as the father of genetics.

short, never medium. Distinct traits like this are rare in nature, as you will see later in this unit. The distinct traits in pea plants allowed Mendel to see his results without guesswork.

Another important feature of pea plants is that most plants reproduce in about 90 days. The short reproductive cycle gave Mendel results relatively quickly and allowed him to repeat the experiments many times to test his results.

MENDEL'S OBSERVATIONS

Chartreuse pea soup?

Mendel began his experiments using two different groups of purebred plants, as you can see in *Figure 6.4.* He called this generation the parental,

or P, generation. He called the first generation of offspring the first filial generation, because "filial" refers to offspring. He gave this generation the notation F_1. Mendel allowed F_1 plants to self-fertilize, producing the second filial, or F_2 generation. *Figure 6.4* shows Mendel's pea plant crosses and results using pea plants with either yellow or green peas.

What results did Mendel expect? According to the blending hypothesis, the green and yellow peas of Mendel's plants in the P generation should have blended to produce chartreuse offspring. Instead, Mendel found that all of the F_1 hybrid plants had yellow peas. There were neither green nor chartreuse peas in the first generation of pea plants, even though one of the parent plants had green peas.

When Mendel let the F_1 hybrid plants self-fertilize, he found green peas in the F_2 generation. About 75 percent of the plants in the F_2 generation had yellow peas and 25 percent of the plants had green peas. In other words, there was a ratio of three pea plants with yellow peas to one with green peas, or 3:1. Again, there were no chartreuse peas.

Mendel repeated his experiments for the other six traits. For each trait, he observed the same results in the F_1 generation–all of the F_1 plants were only one form of the trait. Mendel defined each form of the trait as either dominant or recessive. A dominant form appeared in the F_1 generation. A recessive form did not appear in the F_1 generation. For pea color, yellow is the dominant form and green is the recessive. According to *Figure 6.5*, which other six forms are dominant?

In the F_2 generation of his experiments, Mendel found that there were always two types of plants. About 75 percent of the F_2 plants showed the dominant form of the trait. About 25 percent of the F_2 plants showed the

FIGURE 6.4
Mendel's Crosses

Mendel crossed pea plants and observed the traits that appeared in the offspring. This cross examines the trait of pea color. Which color is dominant, yellow or green?

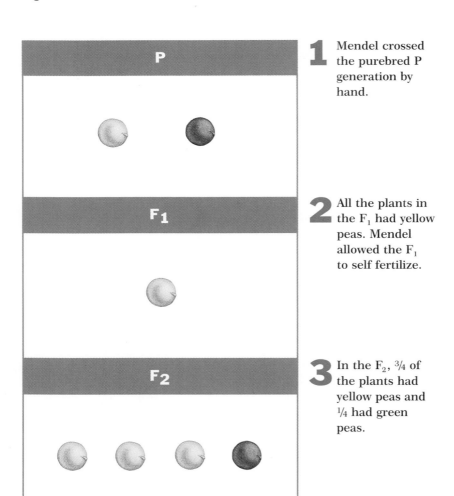

1 Mendel crossed the purebred P generation by hand.

2 All the plants in the F_1 had yellow peas. Mendel allowed the F_1 to self fertilize.

3 In the F_2, ¾ of the plants had yellow peas and ¼ had green peas.

FIGURE 6. 5
Mendel's Seven Traits

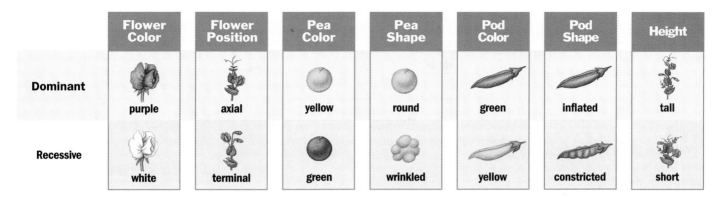

	Flower Color	Flower Position	Pea Color	Pea Shape	Pod Color	Pod Shape	Height
Dominant	purple	axial	yellow	round	green	inflated	tall
Recessive	white	terminal	green	wrinkled	yellow	constricted	short

Mendel studied seven distinct traits of pea plants. Which flower—purple or white—has the dominant trait?

recessive form of the trait. How did these results disprove the blending hypothesis?

MENDEL'S CONCLUSIONS

Factor in the evidence

Mendel's experiments showed that the blending hypothesis was wrong. He never observed pea plants with mixtures of two forms of a trait, such as chartreuse pea color. Mendel reasoned that forms of a trait must remain separate in offspring.

Mendel hypothesized that each trait is controlled by a distinct "factor." Since there were two forms of each trait, Mendel realized that there must be at least two forms of each factor.

Mendel was surprised that recessive forms of traits disappeared in the F_1 generation but reappeared in the F_2. He reasoned that, for every trait, a pea plant must carry a pair of factors which could affect each other. When a trait is inherited, Mendel concluded, the offspring receives one factor from each parent.

We now know that the Mendel's "factors" are genes. **Genes** are sections of a chromosome that code for a trait. Most organisms have two copies of every gene and chromosome, one from each parent.

We refer to the different forms of Mendel's factors as alleles. An **allele** is a distinct form of a gene. If an organism has two different alleles for a trait, only one is expressed, or visible. A **dominant allele** is a form of a gene that is fully expressed when two different alleles are present. A **recessive allele** is a form of a gene that is not expressed when paired with a dominant allele.

Mendel published an account of his experiments in 1866. At that time, the scientific community was focused on the work of another scientist, Charles Darwin, whom you will read about in Chapter 10. Mendel's published work went unrecognized for 37 years. As you will learn in the next chapter, the rediscovery of Mendel's work led to the formulation of the basic principles of inheritance.

CHECKPOINT 6.1

1. Explain the difference between a dominant trait and a recessive trait.
2. What result would you predict for Mendel's cross of a short pea plant with a tall one in the P generation?
3. **Critical Thinking** If the blending hypothesis were true, how would Mendel's results have been different?

Build on What You Know

4. Compare self-fertilization with asexual reproduction. *(Need to jog your memory? Revisit relevant concepts in Chapter 5, Section 5.3.)*

6.2 Principles of Inheritance

What you'll learn

IDEAS
- To explain the chromosome theory of heredity
- To summarize Mendel's laws

WORDS
chromosome theory of heredity, genotype, phenotype, homozygous, heterozygous

Good stains
Most of the time stains are bad news. But in the late 1800s a new technique called staining was developed that made chromosomes visible for the first time. The new staining technique allowed researchers to observe the chromosome changes during stages of mitosis and meiosis.

THE CELLULAR BASIS OF INHERITANCE

Dominant alleles call the shots

Soon after the rediscovery of Mendel's work, the American biologist Walter S. Sutton was observing stained cells through a microscope. He noticed that chromosomes acted like Mendel's factors. By 1903 Sutton had outlined the **chromosome theory of heredity.** This theory states that the material of inheritance is carried by the genes in chromosomes. You can use *Figure 6.6* to compare Mendel's conclusions with Sutton's. As Sutton was formulating his theory, a German biologist named Theodor Boveri independently reached the same conclusion—specific genes are located on specific chromosomes.

Representing alleles In order to explain the new chromosome theory of heredity, biologists came up with several terms and symbols. You are already familiar with some of these terms. Genes are sections of chromosomes that code for traits. Alleles are different forms of a gene. Pea color in pea plants is controlled by a single gene with two alleles—one for green, one for yellow.

As you work with traits and inheritance, you may use letters to represent alleles. The allele for yellow peas, the dominant trait, is represented by an uppercase letter Y. The allele for green peas, a recessive trait, can be represented by a lowercase y. We use the uppercase and lowercase forms of the same letter because the alleles for yellow and green peas are two versions of the same gene. As a rule, an uppercase letter represents a dominant allele. A lowercase letter represents a recessive allele.

Genes affect traits The genetic makeup of an organism is called its **genotype.** The genotype includes both genes in a homologous pair of chromosomes. The genotype of a pea plant that is purebred for yellow peas is written YY. A hybrid is written Yy. How would you write the genotype of

---

FIGURE 6.6

Mendel's Hypothesis

Mendel hypothesized the existence of chromosomes 37 years before Sutton observed them. Compare Mendel's factors with Sutton's chromosomes.

1866
Mendel used statistics to hypothesize the action of trait carriers, which he called factors.

1903
Sutton used a microscope and observed that chromosomes behaved like Mendel's factors.

Mendel's Factors	Chromosomes
Occur in pairs	Occur in pairs
Segregate in gamete production	Separate during meiosis
Pairs sort independently	Pairs sort independently

a purebred pea plant with green peas?

The **phenotype** of an organism is the outward expression of the trait. For example, the phenotype of Mendel's F_1 hybrid is yellow peas. Because Y is the dominant allele, both the YY and the Yy genotypes produce yellow peas. The genotype yy produces the green pea phenotype.

Scientists use two terms—homozygous and heterozygous—to describe genotypes. An organism in which the two alleles in a gene pair are identical is called **homozygous** (HOH-moh-ZY-gus) for that trait. YY and yy are both homozygous genotypes. Mendel's P generation, the purebred plants, were also homozygous.

In contrast, an organism in which the two alleles for a particular trait are different is **heterozygous** (HET-er-oh-ZY-gus). Yy is an example of a heterozygous genotype. The plants in Mendel's F_1 generation were heterozygous for the alleles being studied. Using the letters P and p for the color of pea flowers, what is the genotype of a pea plant that is heterozygous for flower color? What is its phenotype?

MENDEL'S LAWS

Law-abiding genes

The basic rules of inheritance are referred to as Mendel's laws. Like many of the laws that govern scientific processes, Mendel's laws have exceptions. You will read about these exceptions later in this chapter. However, many traits do follow Mendel's laws and are called Mendelian traits. Keep in mind the steps of meiosis as you read about Mendelian inheritance.

The Law of Segregation

Mendel hypothesized that gene pairs separate when gametes form. This idea is now known as the Law of Segregation. This law states that each

Think About It!

Predicting Parakeet Color

Parakeets are most often light green with a yellow head and black markings. One variation is blue with a white head and black markings. How are colors determined?

Analyzing the Diagram

1 A purebred green-and-yellow parakeet and a purebred blue-and-white parakeet are P generations in an experiment. All of the F_1 generation is green and yellow. Which trait is dominant?

2 Describe the genotypes and phenotypes in each generation.

3 Using your answers to the previous question, identify which genotypes are homozygous and which are heterozygous.

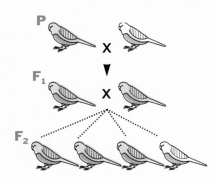

pair of genes segregates, or separates, during meiosis. Because of segregation, half of an organism's gametes contain one gene from a homologous pair, and half of the gametes contain the other gene.

The Law of Independent Assortment Mendel also studied the inheritance of two traits at the same time. In one study he crossed pea plants that had yellow, round peas (YYRR) with plants that had green, wrinkled peas (yyrr). In the F_1 generation, all the peas were yellow and round (YyRr). The F_1 plants were allowed to self-fertilize. All possible combinations of the pea colors and shapes appeared in the F_2 generation. The association of traits in a parent did not seem to matter. From this

FIGURE 6.7

Mendel's Laws at Work

Mendel's three laws correspond with events during meiosis and fertilization. What is the result of meiosis?

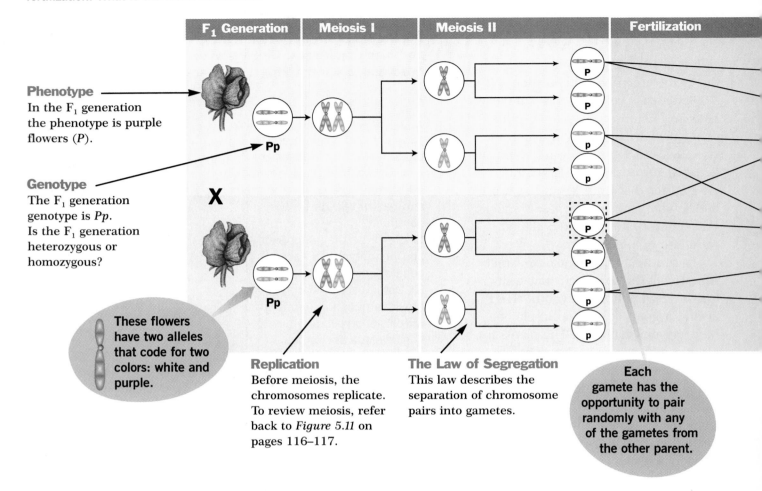

Phenotype
In the F_1 generation the phenotype is purple flowers (P).

Genotype
The F_1 generation genotype is Pp. Is the F_1 generation heterozygous or homozygous?

These flowers have two alleles that code for two colors: white and purple.

Replication
Before meiosis, the chromosomes replicate. To review meiosis, refer back to *Figure 5.11* on pages 116–117.

The Law of Segregation
This law describes the separation of chromosome pairs into gametes.

Each gamete has the opportunity to pair randomly with any of the gametes from the other parent.

information, Mendel concluded that traits are inherited independently.

Geneticists now recognize Mendel's idea of independent assortment as a law, called the Law of Independent Assortment. This law states that gene pairs segregate into gametes randomly and independently of each other.

Compare the Law of Independent Assortment with the behavior of chromosomes during meiosis, as shown in *Figure 6.7*. The separation of chromosome pairs occurs randomly and produces all possible combinations of chromosomes in the gametes. If the chromosome pairs did not separate

randomly, offspring would have the same combination of traits as one of the parents. In other words, without the Law of Independent Assortment, you could not have your father's eyes and your mother's smile!

The Law of Dominance
According to the Law of Dominance, the dominant allele is expressed and the recessive allele can be hidden. Recall that the letter representing the dominant trait is capitalized to represent the dominant allele. The same letter in lowercase is used to represent the recessive allele. In pea plants heterozygous for flower color (Pp), the purple-flower allele (P) controls

F₂ Generation

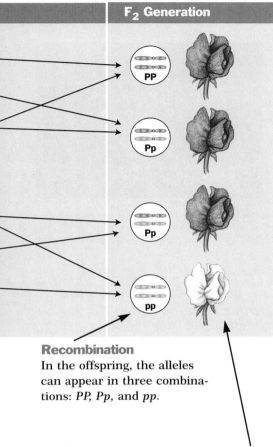

PP

Pp

Pp

pp

Recombination
In the offspring, the alleles can appear in three combinations: *PP, Pp,* and *pp.*

The Law of Dominance
If the dominant allele is in the genotype, then that trait is expressed.

the phenotype, and the flowers are purple. The other allele in the pair, the allele for white flowers (*p*), does not affect phenotype. A recessive allele is expressed only when the organism has no copy of the corresponding dominant allele. Is the Law of Dominance more useful when describing heterozygous organisms or homozygous organisms?

Do It!

Can You Illustrate the Law of Dominance?

Each offspring gets one gene from each parent. You can model the offspring if you . . .

Try This

1 Use four buttons, two of one color and two of another color, to represent two alleles. Select a color as the dominant trait; the other color is the recessive trait. Make a model to represent two parents, each of whom is heterozygous for the trait.
2 Each parent will give the offspring one allele for this trait. What are the possible combinations? Move the buttons to model each combination. Be sure to return the buttons to their original parent model. Record each of your offspring models.
3 Repeat until you have made all possible models.

Analyze Your Results

1 How many different arrangements of alleles can occur in the offspring of these parents?
2 How many ways can an offspring receive the same alleles (one of each color) as the parent?
3 How are two of Mendel's laws represented in this activity?

CHECKPOINT 6.2

1. What is the chromosome theory of heredity?
2. Describe and give examples of Mendel's laws.
3. Critical Thinking Using Mendel's laws, explain why his F₂ generation contained more pea plants with dominant traits than with recessive traits.

Build on What You Know

4. What phase of meiosis is described by Mendel's Law of Segregation? *(Need to jog your memory? Revisit relevant concepts in Chapter 5, Section 5.3.)*

What are traits, and how do scientists know they are inherited?

6.3 Genetics and Predictions

What you'll learn

IDEAS
• To explain how probability is used in genetic predictions
• To construct a Punnett square for monohybrid and dihybrid crosses
• To infer genotype by using a test cross

WORDS
Punnett square, test cross

Sunny with a chance of clouds
What will the weather be tomorrow? Meteorologists use Doppler radar and other tools to predict the weather. But even if you know the forecast, you won't actually know the weather until tomorrow. Geneticists also have tools to predict probable offspring phenotypes. You will learn about one such tool in this section.

PREDICTIONS FOR ONE TRAIT

In all probability

What comes to mind when you hear "there's a fifty-fifty chance" or "chances are one in ten"? When you use fractions, percentages, or ratios to predict the likelihood of an event or outcome, you are measuring probability. Probability is symbolized by the letter P.

When you flip a coin, you can get either heads or tails. The probability of getting heads on any one flip is $P = \frac{1}{2}$. If you flipped the coin ten times, you would expect heads to appear about five times, or 50 percent of the time. Probability can be

FIGURE 6.8
How to Make a Punnett Square

Punnett squares allow geneticists to predict the possible genotypes and phenotypes of offspring.

In this example, both parents are heterozygous for yellow-pea allele (*Yy*).

1 Make the grid
Place the alleles of the gametes of one parent along the top of a grid and those of the other parent along the left-hand side.

Parent 1

Parent 2

	Y	y
Y		
y		

2 Fill in the grid
Combine the parent alleles inside the boxes. The letters show the genotypes of the offspring.

	Y	y
Y	YY	Yy
y	Yy	yy

The genotype ratio is 1:2:1, meaning 1 YY, 2 *Yy*, 1 *yy*.

3 Fill in the offspring
Use the Law of Dominance to determine the phenotypes and phenotype ratio of the offspring.

	Y	y
Y	YY	Yy
y	Yy	yy

The phenotype ratio is 3:1, meaning 3 yellow peas to 1 green pea.

represented as a fraction ($\frac{1}{2}$), a percentage (50%), or a ratio (1:1).

Probability is useful in biology. Scientists often use probability to predict the phenotypes and genotypes of offspring in breeding experiments. They can even predict the numbers of kinds of offspring before fertilization takes place.

Scientists use a tool to make predictions about genetics—a Punnett square. A **Punnett square,** like the one in *Figure 6.8,* is a grid for organizing genetic information. A Punnett square shows probabilities, not actual results.

You can use Punnett squares to predict the offspring of crosses between pea plants. Consider the inheritance of pea color in pea plants, ignoring all of the plant's other traits. When you study the inheritance of only one trait at a time, you are studying a monohybrid cross. (The prefix "mono-" means "one.")

A Punnett square can be used to make predictions about a cross between two organisms. Consider, for example, a cross between two pea plants. Both plants are heterozygous for the yellow-pea trait (*Yy*). The cross is written *Yy* × *Yy*. Each parent can contribute two types of gametes. Half of the gametes carry the Y allele, and half carry the *y* allele.

Follow *Figure 6.8* to see how to complete a Punnett square for this cross. To fill in the square, write the alleles that one parent can contribute along the top and the alleles that the other parent can contribute along the side of the Punnett square. Then combine the alleles from both parents inside each box.

The combinations of alleles inside the boxes are the possible genotypes of the offspring. As you can see in the figure, there are three different offspring genotypes that are possible as a result of the F$_1$ cross. They are YY, *Yy,*

How Is Genetics Related to Probability?

You can use a Punnett square and two coins to learn more about probability if you . . .

Try This

1 Toss a coin 20 times. Record your results, heads (*H*) and tails (*T*).
2 Draw a Punnett square like the one shown here.
3 With a partner, toss two coins at the same time. Repeat 49 times and record each toss (*HH, HT, TH, TT*). Make sure that you note when you get heads and your partner gets tails *separately* from when you get tails and your partner gets heads. Add up the number of times you get each combination and fill in your Punnett square.

Your Toss

	H	T
H	HH	HT
T	TH	TT

Partner's Toss

H: heads
T: tails

Analyze Your Results

1 How does tossing one coin relate to gamete separation?
2 Based on your 50 tosses of two coins, what is the probability of one coin coming up heads and the other coming up tails?

and *yy*. What are the phenotypes of each of these genotypes? As you see from the Punnett square in *Figure 6.8,* the probable ratio of the offspring genotypes is 1:2:1. As you have learned, probability can also be shown as a percentage—25 percent YY, 50 percent *Yy,* and 25 percent *yy.* Again, keep in mind that a Punnett square tells you the probable proportion of offspring genotypes, not the guaranteed outcome.

Now that you have seen how to predict the outcome of a monohybrid cross using a Punnett square, you can go back to section 6.1 and predict the outcomes of other monohybrid crosses using Mendel's pea plant crosses. What would be the results of a cross between a purebred tall pea plant (*TT*) and a hybrid tall pea plant (*Tt*)?

PREDICTIONS FOR TWO TRAITS

Two traits are better than one

You just learned how to predict the results of a monohybrid cross. But why stop there? Predicting two traits with Punnett squares is like tossing two coins at the same time. Because the coins are not attached in any way, the outcome of one flip does not influence the outcome of the other. What is the chance that both coins show heads? You can find out by multiplying their separate probabilities. The chance of one coming up heads is $P = \frac{1}{2}$. The probability that both coins will show heads is $\frac{1}{2} \times \frac{1}{2}$, or $P = \frac{1}{4}$.

To study the inheritance of two traits at a time, you apply the same rules of probability as you do when you flip two coins. You can predict two traits by making a dihybrid cross. As you might guess, "di-" means "two."

The steps in predicting the results of a dihybrid cross are shown in *Figure 6.9*. The example cross is written $RrYy \times RrYy$. As you have learned, Mendel's Law of Independent Assortment states that alleles will sort into all possible combinations. Thus, there are four possible combinations of alleles in the gametes of the parent plants: RY, Ry, rY, and ry.

To predict the results of the dihybrid cross, you set up a 4 × 4 Punnett square. List the alleles in the gametes of one parent along the top of the square and the alleles in the gametes of the other parent along the side. Combine the alleles inside the boxes.

The phenotypes in the Punnett square in *Figure 6.9* include 9 round

---

FIGURE 6.9

How to Predict the Results of a Dihybrid Cross

Dihybrid crosses allow geneticists to predict the possible genotypes and phenotypes for two traits.

In this example, both parents are heterozygous for round yellow-pea alleles (*RrYy*).

1 Make the grid
Place all four combinations of alleles for one parent along the top of a grid and those of the other parent along the side.

2 Fill in the grid
Combine the parent alleles inside the boxes. The letters show possible genotypes of the offspring.

3 Fill in the offspring
Determine the offspring's phenotypes for both traits.

Parent 1 [RrYy]

Parent 2 [RrYy]

	RY	Ry	rY	ry
RY				
Ry				
rY				
ry				

	RY	Ry	rY	ry
RY	RRYY	RRYy	RrYY	RrYy
Ry	RRYy	RRyy	RrYy	Rryy
rY	RrYY	RrYy	rrYY	rrYy
ry	RrYy	Rryy	rrYy	rryy

There are 9 different genotypes: *RRYY, RRYy, RrYY, RRyy, RrYy, Rryy, rrYY, rrYy,* and *rryy.* Which genotype is most numerous?

	RY	Ry	rY	ry
RY	RRYY	RRYy	RrYY	RrYy
Ry	RRYy	RRyy	RrYy	Rryy
rY	RrYY	RrYy	rrYY	rrYy
ry	RrYy	Rryy	rrYy	rryy

The phenotype ratio is 9:3:3:1, meaning 9 round yellow peas, 3 wrinkled yellow peas, 3 round green peas, and 1 wrinkled green pea.

yellow peas, 3 wrinkled yellow peas, 3 round green peas, and 1 wrinkled green pea. The phenotype ratio is 9:3:3:1. Recall that this result can be written in many ways. For example, the probability of getting an offspring plant with wrinkled green peas is $P=\frac{1}{16}$. What is the probable percentage of offspring with round green peas? Notice that the offspring have combinations of traits that were not present in the parents. For example, neither parent had round green or wrinkled yellow peas. This outcome is a result of Mendel's Law of Independent Assortment and has some important implications that you will learn about in Chapter 7.

TEST CROSS
Seeing the invisible

As you just discovered, it is essential to know the genotypes of the parent generation of pea plants to make a Punnett square. How do geneticists know the genotype of a pea plant, or of any organism? The phenotype is often easy to determine by observation. But if an organism has the dominant phenotype, how can you tell if it is homozygous or heterozygous for this allele?

Scientists can distinguish between homozygous dominant and heterozygous organisms by doing test crosses. In a **test cross,** geneticists breed the organism whose genotype is unknown with a homozygous recessive organism. As you learned in section 6.2, the recessive allele is expressed only if the organism is homozygous for that allele. For this reason, the genotype of a recessive organism is always known. A test cross is the crossing of a known recessive genotype and an unknown dominant genotype, resulting in offspring with observable phenotypes.

If the unknown genotype is heterozygous, about half the offspring should show the recessive phenotype.

FIGURE 6.10
Using a Test Cross to Determine Genotype

A plant with yellow peas could be homozygous (*YY*) or heterozygous (*Yy*) for pea color. If a test cross results in 1 green pea: 1 yellow pea, what is the genotype?

Test Cross

The genotype of the green pea plant (*yy*) is always known because it is recessive.

If the pea plant being tested is homozygous dominant (*YY*), then all offspring will be yellow (*Yy*).

If the pea plant is heterozygous (*Yy*), then half of the offspring will be yellow (*Yy*) and half will be green (*yy*).

If the unknown genotype is homozygous dominant, all the offspring will show the dominant phenotype.

To demonstrate how a test cross is done, consider pea color in the test cross in *Figure 6.10*. Both YY and *Yy* genotypes produce yellow peas, because yellow color is the dominant allele. In a test cross, the unknown plant (Y?) is crossed with a homozygous recessive (*yy*) plant. What would the unknown genotype be if all of the offspring had yellow peas?

CHECKPOINT 6.3
1. How do geneticists use probability to predict genotype and phenotype?
2. Compare and contrast a monohybrid cross and a dihybrid cross.
3. **Critical Thinking** Use Punnett squares to show the results of the following crosses:
a) *Dd* × *dd* b) *QQ* × *qq* c) *MM* × *Mm*

Build on What You Know
4. In what step of the scientific method would you use a Punnett square? *(Need to jog your memory? Revisit relevant concepts in Chapter 1, Section 1.3.)*

6.4 Predictions and People

What you'll learn

IDEAS
• To interpret pedigrees and understand their purpose
• To contrast dominant and recessive genetic disorders
• To identify some methods used to determine the likelihood of a genetic disorder occurring in offspring

WORDS
pedigree, carrier

The dimple life

Do your cheeks dimple when you smile? Do you know a dimpled family? Dimples are controlled by a dominant allele. If the dominant allele is inherited, then it will be expressed. However, just because an allele is dominant does not mean it will be a common trait. How many people with dimples do you know?

PEDIGREE STUDIES

All in the family

Unlike Mendel's pea plants, which produced seeds every 90 days, patterns of human inheritance are not easy to study. Humans mature slowly, and many years pass between one generation and the next. Compared to other organisms, humans have few offspring. What we do have to aid the study of human inheritance are family trees and family histories.

Recently, researchers have developed techniques that enable them to study human genes directly. But most of our knowledge of human genetics still comes from studying the patterns of heredity in human populations and families.

Geneticists study family trees, or pedigrees, to learn about human inheritance patterns. A **pedigree** is a chart that shows how a trait and the genes that control it are inherited within a family. Pedigrees are used to

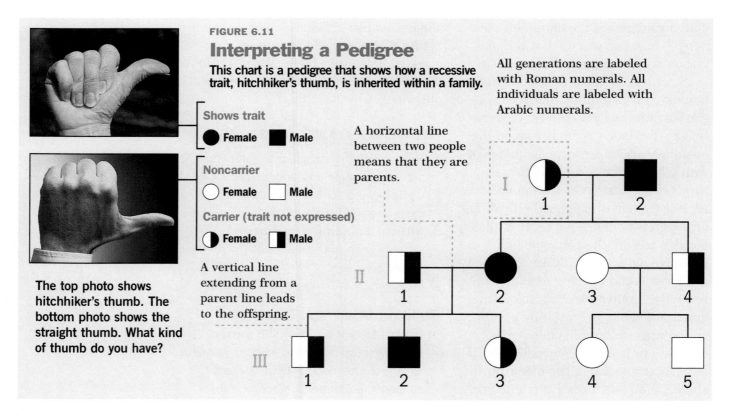

FIGURE 6.11

Interpreting a Pedigree

This chart is a pedigree that shows how a recessive trait, hitchhiker's thumb, is inherited within a family.

Shows trait
● Female ■ Male

Noncarrier
○ Female □ Male

Carrier (trait not expressed)
◐ Female ◧ Male

A horizontal line between two people means that they are parents.

A vertical line extending from a parent line leads to the offspring.

All generations are labeled with Roman numerals. All individuals are labeled with Arabic numerals.

The top photo shows hitchhiker's thumb. The bottom photo shows the straight thumb. What kind of thumb do you have?

study all sorts of families, from human families to fruit fly families. To develop a human pedigree, geneticists interview family members and friends of the family to collect as much information as they can about a family's genetic history and traits.

The pedigree in *Figure 6.11* traces a trait called hitchhiker's thumb through three generations of a family. Hitchhiker's thumb is a recessive trait. Compare the two thumbs shown in *Figure 6.11*. Do you have this trait?

As you now know, recessive alleles are not expressed in the presence of the dominant allele. If a pedigree is tracking a recessive trait, there may be heterozygous individuals who have one allele for the trait but do not express the trait because the dominant allele is also present. An individual who carries a recessive trait that is not expressed is called a **carrier.** What are the symbols for a carrier according to *Figure 6.11*?

Pedigrees help to determine the inheritance of some alleles and predict them in offspring. You will now learn about two kinds of genetic traits: those caused by recessive alleles and those caused by dominant alleles.

RECESSIVE TRAITS

It takes two

You know that a trait caused by recessive alleles is not expressed in a heterozygous person. While a recessive allele that can produce a genetic disorder does not affect a carrier's health, a carrier can pass the recessive allele on to offspring. Passed from generation to generation, the allele remains in the population.

Tay-Sachs disease, a fatal genetic disorder, is caused by a recessive allele. A person who is homozygous for the Tay-Sachs allele is not able to metabolize (break down) a particular

FIGURE 6.12
The gene for cystic fibrosis is located on this region of chromosome 7. The image at top left is of a normal lung. The top right image is of the lung of a person with cystic fibrosis.

type of lipid, so the lipid accumulates in the brain. This lipid accumulation eventually results in blindness and brain damage. Individuals with Tay-Sachs disease do not usually survive more than a few years. Carriers of this disease, however, do not show any effects of Tay-Sachs, and thus the allele is preserved in the population.

Cystic fibrosis (SIS-tik fy-BROH-sis) is another disease caused by recessive alleles. The gene for cystic fibrosis is located on a region of chromosome 7, as shown in *Figure 6.12*. Cystic fibrosis is a genetic disorder that results in an excessive secretion of thick mucus. This secretion accumulates in the digestive tract and in the lungs. Left untreated, children with cystic fibrosis die at a very young age. However, current treatments are prolonging life into young adulthood and beyond.

Albinism is another example of a condition caused by a recessive allele. True albinos have no skin pigment. You may have seen albino rabbits, which have completely white fur and pink eyes. A person who is homozygous for the albino trait cannot produce the skin pigment melanin. People with albinism typically have very pale skin and whitish-blond hair, and can be of any racial background.

FIGURE 6.13
Albinism is a recessive trait that affects humans of all races.

Like other recessive traits, a single copy of a gene for albinism results in the normal, pigmented phenotype. Without a pedigree or information on family history, a person would be unaware that he or she was a carrier of the trait. Unlike many recessive traits, however, albinism can be caused by several different alleles on different chromosomes. Two parents could have the albinism trait, but if the trait in each parent were caused by different alleles, the children of such parents would have the normal, pigmented phenotype.

DOMINANT TRAITS

Some alleles are more expressive than others

Dominant alleles control many human traits, including the inheritance of freckles, widow's peak, farsightedness, broad lips, and polydactyly—extra fingers and toes. You will recall that a dominant allele is always expressed in a person's phenotype. In many cases, a person who has inherited a dominant allele that produces a fatal disorder is likely to die before passing the allele on to offspring.

If a disorder caused by dominant alleles results in early death, then it cannot be passed on. For this reason,

disorders caused by dominant alleles are much less common than those caused by recessive alleles. A few dominant genetic disorders, however, do not show up until years after sexual maturity. In such cases the dominant allele may be passed on to offspring.

One example of a dominant allele disorder is Huntington disease. This disease is a fatal genetic disorder that results in deterioration of the nervous system, particularly the brain. Although a dominant allele causes Huntington disease, people typically do not develop symptoms until they are in their late thirties or early forties. By that time they may have already passed the allele on to their offspring. Huntington disease can now be identified before onset with a test that involves analysis of the genetic material.

FRONTIERS IN BIOLOGY

Genetic counseling

A couple aware of genetic disorders in their family histories and who are planning to have children may seek genetic counseling. A genetic counselor provides prospective parents with information about the probabilities of passing genetic disorders on to their offspring.

FIGURE 6.14
The gene for Huntington disease is located in this region on chromosome 4. The image on the left shows the brain of a Huntington patient. The image on the right shows the brain of a nonaffected person.

Key			
	Shows trait	Noncarrier	Carrier
Male	■	□	◧
Female	●	○	◑

FIGURE 6.15
The pedigree (left) is for PKU. Genetic counselors prepare pedigrees for prospective parents to assess the risk of passing on disease alleles. Which individual in the pedigree has PKU?

Genetic counselors begin their work by tracing the histories of both families. They then look for inherited disorders. A pedigree is developed, showing the probability of one or both parents carrying certain alleles. The probability that certain disorders will occur in the offspring can then be determined. With this information, the couple can consider the risk of passing a particular allele on to their children.

In addition to pedigrees, molecular techniques are used to identify genetic problems including the presence of abnormal genes. For example, a test for the amount of a specific protein in the mother's body early in pregnancy can reveal if the fetus has an extra copy of a chromosome, a condition that can cause Down syndrome.

Another test, which is now conducted on almost all newborn babies, identifies a genetic disorder called phenylketonuria (FEN-il-KEE-toh-NYOO-ree-uh), or PKU. A person with PKU lacks the enzymes needed to break down the amino acid phenylalanine, which is found in milk and many other foods. Without these enzymes, the amino acid accumulates in the body and begins to damage nerve cells. Untreated, PKU can lead to severe developmental disabilities and death. Sometimes, giving birth to a child with PKU is the first indication to parents that they are carriers for the allele.

PKU can be treated when diagnosed early. A special diet lacking phenylalanine prevents damage to the nerve cells. The child can grow normally and adopt a normal diet during adulthood. Thanks to genetic counselors, PKU and other disorders can be detected and treated early in life.

CHECKPOINT 6.4

1. What does a pedigree show?
2. Describe recessive and dominant alleles in humans.
3. Critical Thinking What steps can parents take to determine the likelihood of passing certain genes on to their offspring? Cite specific examples.

Build on What You Know

4. Suppose two parents are both carriers for a recessive disorder. Make a diagram showing all the possible pairings of their gametes after meiosis. *(Need to jog your memory? Revisit relevant concepts in Chapter 5, Section 5.2.)*

EVERYDAY BIOLOGY

Ears to You!

You have learned about traits in pea plants, but did you know that the laws of inheritance decide what kind of ear wax you have? There are two types of ear wax: sticky/wet (W) and dry (w). What kind do you have?

Using a Pedigree

WHAT YOU WILL DO Use a pedigree chart to determine parents' genotypes

SKILLS YOU WILL USE Observing, recording data, predicting

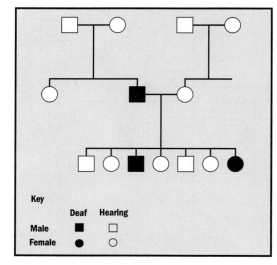

Key

	Deaf	**Hearing**
Male	■	☐
Female	●	○

Propose a Hypothesis

Based on the pedigree shown here, form a hypothesis concerning whether the allele for deafness is dominant or recessive.

Conduct Your Experiment

1 Copy the pedigree and the key onto a piece of paper and study it. Label each individual in the pedigree with their phenotype: hearing or deaf.
2 Analyze the pattern in the inheritance of the deafness trait. Does the trait skip generations or show up in every generation? Does it affect all the members of any generation?
3 Use your analysis and what you know about patterns of inheritance to infer the genotype of each individual. Write

the genotypes on your pedigree. It is possible that you will not be able to infer the complete genotype of every individual.

Analyze Your Data

1 What is the genotype of an individual with deafness? Can a deaf family member have more than one genotype?
2 What is the genotype of a hearing individual? Can a hearing family member have more than one genotype? Are any hearing individuals carriers?
3 Is the allele for deafness dominant or recessive?

Draw Conclusions

Describe what you have concluded about the dominant or

recessive inheritance of deafness in this family. Write a paragraph discussing what you learned in this activity. Support your conclusion with your observations.

Design a Related Experiment

Prepare a pedigree for three generations of an imaginary family that has another trait.

Using a Pedigree

6.5 Difficult Predictions

Caterpillar camouflage capers
Certain caterpillars may vary their appearance to resemble either a twig or a flower. The caterpillar's phenotype is determined by its diet. If the caterpillar eats oak twigs, then it appears as shown at the left. If it eats oak flowers, it appears as shown at the right. This relationship between diet and appearance is the basis for the caterpillar's camouflage.

What you'll learn

IDEAS
• To compare and contrast patterns of inheritance that do not follow Mendel's laws
• To explain how traits are influenced by the environment

WORDS
incomplete dominance, codominance, polygenic trait, multiple alleles, pleiotropy

INTERMEDIATE INHERITANCE
Genes in between

For the pea plant traits that Mendel studied, one allele was always dominant over the other. However, traits with two distinct forms are rare in nature. Many genes do not have purely dominant and recessive alleles. Instead, these genes show a form of intermediate inheritance.

In intermediate inheritance, the heterozygous offspring have a trait that is not exactly like the trait of either purebred parent. The phenotype of the heterozygous offspring shows the effects of more than one allele. You will now read about three forms of intermediate inheritance—incomplete dominance, codominance, and polygenic inheritance.

Incomplete dominance When two different alleles for the same trait combine, but neither allele "wins" expression over the other, the offspring have a form of intermediate

FIGURE 6.16
Incomplete Dominance in Snapdragons

Incomplete dominance occurs when the allele of neither parent is fully expressed and the offspring's phenotype is intermediate between that of the two parents. In this example, white and red flowers produce pink flowers.

P Generation	F₁ Generation	F₂ Generation

RR

rr

The P generation is purebred.

RR × rr
The red and white purebred plants are crossed.

Rr
The hybrid F₁ generation shows a unique phenotype. The flowers express both alleles.

Rr × Rr
Pink hybrid plants are self-fertilized.

	R	r
R	RR	Rr
r	Rr	rr

The parents' traits reappear in the F₂ generation.

Hold the Eggs

Diet can affect your blood cholesterol level whether you are HH, Hh, or hh. Saturated fats in your diet increase blood cholesterol, whereas polyunsaturated or monounsaturated fatty acids lower blood cholesterol. Eggs are a food high in saturated fats. Do eggs increase your cholesterol level?

inheritance called incomplete dominance. In **incomplete dominance,** heterozygous offspring show a phenotype that is in between the phenotypes of the two homozygous parents. Neither allele is fully expressed.

One example of incomplete dominance is flower color in snapdragons, such as those shown in *Figure 6.16* on page 147. If a snapdragon plant with red flowers is crossed with a white-flowered snapdragon plant, the offspring will have pink flowers. The alleles have not blended to make pink alleles. The red and white alleles remain separate in the snapdragon cells. Only the phenotype is intermediate, giving the appearance of pink flowers. Half the gametes of a pink snapdragon plant carry the allele for red flowers, and half carry the allele for white flowers.

Incomplete dominance is also responsible for the coat colors of many animals. Roan cows, whose coats are primarily red with white hairs, are offspring of red cows and white cows. A palomino—a creamy-golden horse with a pale mane and tail—is the offspring of a chestnut-colored horse and a white horse.

An example of a human trait that shows incomplete dominance is

hypercholesterolemia (HI-per-coh-LESS-ter-ruh-LEE-mee-ah). People with this disorder have too much ("hyper-") cholesterol in their blood. Cholesterol is a steroid produced by our bodies and used to make and repair cell membranes.

People with normal cholesterol levels have the homozygous dominant genotype (*HH*). People with this genotype generally can maintain healthy blood cholesterol levels with a low-fat diet and exercise. About one in 500 people are heterozygous (*Hh*) for the trait, and their cholesterol levels are twice as high as normal. Diet, exercise, and medical treatments can help to reduce their cholesterol levels. About one in a million people are homozygous recessive (*hh*) for the trait. Their cholesterol levels are about five times greater than normal. This rare homozygous recessive condition is very serious—it has even caused heart attacks in two-year-old children.

Codominance As you just learned, incomplete dominance occurs when two alleles are partially expressed and the offspring have a phenotype that is intermediate, or in-between, two parent phenotypes. In

The blood supply in your community, your state, and the entire country is a valuable commodity. When people are hurt in a disaster, emergency aid organizations put out a call for blood donors. Before donors give blood, a physician or nurse finds out about their general health and tests their blood. Then a technician takes one pint of blood from the donor. The donor then rests and perhaps has juice or a snack. Find out about blood drives in your community. How often do they occur? What are the requirements for donors? For more information about the national blood supply, visit *http://genetics.biosurf.com.*

IN THE COMMUNITY
Blood Drive

FIGURE 6.17

The Eyes Have It

Human eye color is a polygenic trait — many genes control the pigment melanin in the eye. What differences can you see between these two eyes?

Tone of pigment
The tone, or color of the eye pigment differs for each eye.

Amount of pigment
Blue eyes have less pigment than brown eyes.

Position of pigment
Eye pigment is not distributed evenly, creating patterns.

codominance, both alleles in the heterozygote express themselves fully. Because both of the alleles are fully expressed, both alleles are equally emphasized in the notation.

An example of a codominant trait in humans is blood type. The letters *A* and *B* that identify blood types refer to the two different carbohydrates that coat the surface of red blood cells. If you have type A blood, you have type A carbohydrate on your red blood cells. If you have type B blood, you have type B carbohydrate on your red blood cells. And if you have blood type AB, you have both carbohydrate types. People who have neither carbohydrate on their red blood cells have type O.

These alleles are represented by an *I*, and a superscript *A* or *B* to indicate whether the allele codes for type A or type B blood. The two alleles are I^A and I^B. If you received the blood type A allele (I^A) from one parent and the blood type B allele (I^B) from the other, your genotype is $I^A I^B$, and your phenotype is AB blood. You will find out more about blood types later in this section.

Polygenic traits Most traits are affected by more than one gene. A trait controlled by two or more genes

is called a **polygenic trait** (the prefix "poly-" means "many"). Your eye color is an example of a polygenic trait. As you can see in *Figure 6.17*, the tone, amount, and distribution of the pigment melanin all play a role in determining eye color. These characteristics are determined by many different gene pairs. And, like Mendel's pea plant genes, each gene pair for eye color might be inherited independently. Human skin color is also a polygenic trait. Many genes control the amount of the melanin in the skin.

MULTIPLE ALLELES AND PLEIOTROPY

Many alleles and traits

Most genes have more than two alleles. If three or more alleles are found in the population, we say these genes have **multiple alleles**. Human blood type genes are an example of a codominant trait and of a trait with multiple alleles. Blood types are phenotypes that can be produced by three different alleles—I^A, I^B, and *i*. Each person has only two of these alleles, one from each parent.

As you already learned, the alleles for A and B blood types are codominant. If you have blood type O, then

FIGURE 6.18
This table shows the different blood genotypes and phenotypes. How do blood types show codominance?

Blood Groups	
Phenotypes	**Genotypes**
A	$I^A I^A$ or $I^A i$
B	$I^B I^B$ or $I^B i$
AB	$I^A I^B$
O	ii

FIGURE 6.19
Sickled red blood cells stick together, jamming the circulatory system. What is the difference between the sickled cell (left) and the normal red blood cell (right)?

you have neither type A nor type B carbohydrates coating your red blood cells. O blood type is recessive, so the allele for O blood type is *i*. Thus, there are four blood types—A, B, AB, and O—and three blood type alleles—I^A, I^B, and *i*. *Figure 6.18* shows the phenotypes and genotypes for blood.

Another variation on the simple patterns of inheritance seen in Mendel's pea plants is called pleiotropy (plee-AH-troh-pee). **Pleiotropy** occurs when a single gene affects more than one trait.

Sickle-cell disease is an example of pleiotropy in humans. The allele that causes sickle-cell disease affects the shape of red blood cells. As you can see in *Figure 6.19,* blood cells in people with sickle-cell disease have a bent, or sickled, shape. The sickled cells do not flow well through the body and tend to clump together, blocking and damaging parts of the circulatory system. Damage to the circulatory system can have many phenotypic results. People with sickle-cell disease can experience weakness, anemia, brain damage, spleen damage and heart damage. Because of its numerous effects on the body, this allele is an example of pleiotropy.

ENVIRONMENTAL EFFECTS
Fair-weather genes

As you have discovered, many factors—including the activity of other genes—can influence the way a gene is expressed. Genes can also be affected by the environment—both the external environment and the environment inside an organism. In fact, phenotype is a combination of genetic and environmental influences.

Climate conditions are an outside environmental factor that can influence the expression of alleles. An

FIGURE 6.20
The Himalayan rabbit's fur color is affected by temperature. Why are the tips of the rabbit's ears darker than its body?

unusual effect of temperature is seen in the Himalayan rabbit, as you can see in *Figure 6.20*. This rabbit is normally covered with white fur, whereas its ears, nose, and feet are black. This pattern occurs because most of the rabbit's body is generally warmer than its extremities. Body temperature affects the expression of genes that code for fur color. When researchers remove a patch of hair from the body and cool the skin as new fur grows back, the new fur is black. When they shave hair from the feet or ears and keep those areas warm, the fur that grows back is white.

Environmental temperature also affects wing coloration patterns of the western white butterfly, found in the west of North America. These butterflies need their body temperature to be between 28°C and 40°C to take off in flight. Researchers have found that butterflies reaching adulthood in the spring exhibit darker wing coloration patterns than butterflies that mature in the summer. As you may know, dark colors absorb more heat. As a result of their darker wing patterns, the butterflies that live during the cooler spring weather will be able to reach a warm enough temperature to fly. In this case, the expression of the wing color genes is affected by day length, which varies from season to season.

Another example of environmental influence on gene expression is flower color in hydrangeas. Hydrangea flowers are either blue or pink, depending on soil acidity. If the soil is rather acidic, the hydrangeas have blue flowers. If the soil is neutral or somewhat basic, then the blooms are pink.

Changes in the social environment of an organism can also affect gene expression. The Japanese goby fish can change its sex back and forth in response to changes in its social environment. If a large male goby leaves a population, a female goby will become

Springtime

Temperature Table

Required for Takeoff	Average Spring	Average Summer
28–40°C	26.5°C	34.8°C

Summertime

FIGURE 6.21
Western white butterflies have darker wing patterns if they hatch in the spring. The dark wing color regulates temperature, a vital adaptation because the butterflies need to reach a certain temperature to fly. What is the temperature difference between a flying springtime butterfly and the air?

male. If another large male enters that goby population, this new male turns back into a female.

Gene expression can be influenced by the environment inside an organism's body. Although human height is determined by a form of polygenic inheritance, it is also affected by the nutrients in your diet. As you read earlier in this chapter, shyness can also be affected by genes. But, as individuals mature, the effect of genes on shyness diminishes, and the effect of the environment increases.

It is important to realize that the inheritance of shyness, height, and many other human traits is affected by genetics and also by the environment. In Chapter 8, you will learn more about effects of the environment on gene expression, particularly in the development of cancer.

FIGURE 6.22
These teenage twins share a love for roller coasters. What other characteristics do they have in common?

ISSUES IN BIOLOGY

The genetics of behavior

How can you determine if the inheritance of a trait is affected more by genetics or by the environment? This question—commonly expressed as "nature or nurture?"—is difficult to answer, especially for human traits. To find answers, some scientists study identical twins—people with the same genes—that have been separated at birth. Twins separated at birth or at a very young age and brought up by different families have different environments. These twins offer scientists an opportunity to study genetic and environmental influences.

Twin studies have shown some surprising results. For example, when one set of identical twin sisters met for the first time, each sister was wearing seven rings, three bracelets and a watch. Another set of identical twins were both named Jim by their adoptive parents. Both had dogs named Toy, married women named Linda, and named their sons James. Surveys of reunited twins found that, in addition to their shared habits, they also shared many opinions.

Although studies of identical twins separated at birth suggest some links between heredity and behavior, identical twins do not lead identical lives. Despite having similarities that could be explained by their identical genes, these separated twins also exhibited differences as a result of the different environments in which each grew up. This fascinating mix of similarities and differences gives researchers a unique opportunity to explore the effects of heredity and environment.

CHECKPOINT 6.5

1. Name and describe the forms of intermediate inheritance.
2. Describe a trait that is affected by the environment.
3. **Critical Thinking** When geneticist Lucien Cuénot attempted to produce a strain of mice homozygous for the dominant yellow-fur allele, all of the homozygous offspring died. This is an example of what kind of intermediate inheritance?

Build on What You Know

4. When scientists study identical twins, what variable is controlled?
   (Need to jog your memory? Revisit relevant concepts in Chapter 1, Section 1.3.)

What are some patterns of inheritance that make traits predictable?

Chapter 6 Review

Sum It Up

Use the following summary to review the main concepts in this chapter.

6.1   Patterns of Inheritance

- Genetics is the study of heritable characteristics, or traits.
- Gregor Mendel used mathematics to study the inheritance of traits.
- Alleles are alternate forms of a gene. In a hybrid organism, the dominant allele is expressed.

6.2   Principles of Inheritance

- The chromosome theory of heredity states that the inheritance of traits is controlled by genes, which are located on chromosomes.
- The genotype of an organism is all the alleles for a trait; the phenotype is the trait.
- The Law of Segregation describes how chromosome pairs separate during meiosis.
- The Law of Independent Assortment states that gene pairs separate independently of each other.
- The Law of Dominance states that the dominant allele, if present, will be expressed.

6.3   Genetics and Predictions

- Scientists use probability to predict traits in offspring.
- A Punnett square organizes information in order to make genetic predictions.

6.4   Predictions and People

- Pedigrees are used to trace the history of traits among relatives.
- Genetic counselors help identify the likelihood of a trait being passed to offspring.

6.5   Difficult Predictions

- Incomplete dominance, codominance, and multiple alleles can result in intermediate phenotypes.
- Genes can have more than two alleles.
- Alleles can have many phenotypic effects.

Use Terms and Concepts

Use each of the following words or terms in a complete sentence. If you need to review a meaning, turn to the page indicated.

genetics (p. 130)
trait (p. 130)
purebred (p. 131)
hybrid (p. 131)
genes (p. 133)
allele (p. 133)

dominant allele (p. 133)
recessive allele (p. 133)
chromosome theory of heredity (p. 134)
genotype (p. 134)
phenotype (p. 135)
homozygous (p. 135)

heterozygous (p. 135)
Punnett square (p. 139)
test cross (p. 141)
pedigree (p. 142)
carrier (p. 143)
incomplete dominance (p. 148)

codominance (p. 149)
polygenic trait (p. 149)
multiple alleles (p. 149)
pleiotropy (p. 150)

Use Your Word Power

COMPLETION **Write the word or phrase that best completes each statement.**

1. The _____ of an organism is the trait that is observed.

2. In _____ , both alleles are fully expressed in the heterozygous condition.

3. The study of the inheritance of traits is called _____ .

4. Similarities between Mendel's factors and the behavior of chromosomes led Sutton to propose the _____ .

5. The _____ describes how a dominant trait is expressed if the allele is present.

TRUE-FALSE **Write true if the statement is true. If the statement is false, replace the underlined word(s) to make the statement true.**

6. A <u>carrier</u> of a trait does not express the allele for that trait.

7. In Mendel's experiments, the F_1 generation was always <u>homozygous</u> for the studied trait.

8. The hidden <u>recessive</u> <u>trait</u> of the F_1 generation always appears in the F_2 generation.

9. Both of the alleles of a gene pair make up an organism's <u>genotype</u>.

10. A <u>test</u> <u>cross</u> can be used to show all possible outcomes for genetic crosses.

Show What You Know

11. What patterns of inheritance do not follow Mendel's laws?

12. What is the difference between a purebred organism and a hybrid organism?

13. How is a test cross used to distinguish the homozygous dominant genotype from the heterozygous phenotype?

14. Summarize the evidence that led to the chromosome theory of heredity.

15. What qualities of pea plants made them a good choice for Mendel's experiments?

16. How do genetic counselors use pedigrees?

17. What is the difference between incomplete dominance and codominance?

18. Why are twin studies performed in genetics?

19. **Make a Concept Map** Complete the concept map below by adding the following terms: alleles, genes, chromosomes, dominant.

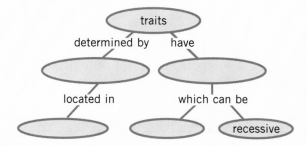

Take It Further

20. **Applying Concepts** In pea plants, round seed shape is dominant over wrinkled seed shape. Gray seed coat color is dominant over white seed coat color. Use a Punnett square to show a cross between a purebred plant with round seeds and gray seed coats and a purebred plant with wrinkled seeds and white coats. What traits are seen in the F_1 generation?

21. **Making a Prediction** Suppose Mendel had studied the inheritance of flower color in snapdragons instead of pea plants. How might his results have affected the laws that he developed?

22. **Analyzing Data** A man with blood type AB marries a woman with blood type O. Is it possible for them to have children with the same blood type as either of the parents? Use a Punnett square to explain your answer.

23. **Designing an Experiment** Petunias come in many different colors. Design an experiment to determine if purple or pink flower color is a dominant trait, or if there is an intermediate mode of inheritance.

24. Interpreting a Graph This graph shows the traits of 1355 butterflies. Which traits are dominant? Which are recessive? Explain your answer.

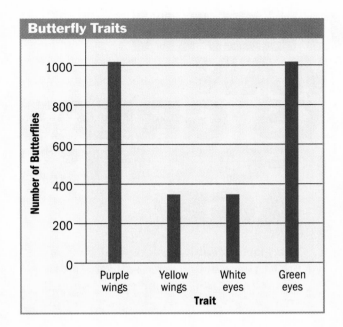

Butterfly Traits

(Bar graph: y-axis "Number of Butterflies" from 0 to 1000; x-axis "Trait" with categories: Purple wings ≈1000, Yellow wings ≈350, White eyes ≈350, Green eyes ≈1000)

25. Analyzing Data What form or forms of inheritance are indicated by the table below? Use the data to create a graph.

Average Height for Italian Males	
Year	Average Height (meters)
1938	1.66
1958	1.68
1970	1.70
1976	1.72
1982	1.73

Consider the Issues

26. Separated at Birth Twin studies are most reliable when comparing twins separated since birth. Sometimes the participants are not told that they are participating in a twin study nor that they have a twin. What are the pros and cons of this process?

Make New Connections

27. Biology and Art Many artists, such as Charles Neal, have painted landscapes and gardens. What traits could Mendel have studied in this painting? What traits can scientists study in portraits of people? Make your own drawing or painting of a garden. Identify traits that can be determined by genetics.

28. Biology and Community Go to a local greenhouse or flower store and investigate the inheritance of traits in different plants. Find out about new hybrids. What traits in the parent plants were crossed? What traits appear in the offspring?

29. Biology and History: A Project Mendel's work went unnoticed for 35 years. Investigate some other scientific discoveries that took place in the middle to late 1800s. Why was Mendel's work ignored? Make a time line, using the results of your investigation.

FAST-FORWARD TO CHAPTER 7

Mendel put together the first pieces of the heredity puzzle. In the next chapter, you will read about experiments that established the molecular basis of heredity.

bioSURF

You can find out more about DNA, genes, and chromosomes by exploring the following Internet address:
http://genetics.biosurf.com

In this chapter . . .

FEATURES

Everyday Biology
• DNA Duplicates
• A Cat Called Calico Carl

In the Community
On-ramp to Biology

 Issues in Biology
The Human Genome Project

LAB ZONES

Discover It!
• Making a Model of
  Genetic Material

Do It!
• What Is a Twisted Ladder?
• What Does Recombination
  Look Like?

Think About It!
• Gene Linkage in Imaginary
  Aliens

Investigate It!
• Extracting DNA

TYROLEAN ICE MAN LOOKS GREAT FOR HIS AGE

The glacier that had entombed him for 5000 years had preserved him almost perfectly. A little *too* perfectly, thought some scientists. Had hikers in the Swiss Alps found a Stone Age resident of the area, or was he a South American mummy that had been placed there as a hoax?

To resolve these questions about the "Tyrolean Ice Man," researchers analyzed his genetic material. Analyses of genetic material are often used to solve mysteries such as this one. As it turned out, the Tyrolean Ice Man's genetic material matched the genetic material of modern inhabitants of the Swiss Alps. This finding indicates that he did, indeed, live in the Alps 5000 years ago. But what is the genetic material, and how can it be used to identify relationships?

Making a Model of Genetic Material

You need one piece of yarn about 6 centimeters (cm) long, scissors, tweezers

1. Use the piece of yarn to represent a chromosome. Cut the yarn into segments. Each segment represents a gene. Caution: Use care when handling scissors.
2. Describe the relationship between the segments of yarn and your original piece of yarn.
3. Use the tweezers to pull apart the strings that make up the yarn. These strings represent molecules of DNA.
4. Describe the relationship between the strings and the "genes," and the relationship between the strings and the "chromosome."

The units of chromosomes have a great effect on how traits are inherited and expressed.

WRITE ABOUT IT!

In your science journal write about the genetic material and what you think its importance might be. Use your knowledge about the inheritance of traits.

7.1 Molecule of Heredity

What you'll learn

IDEAS

• To describe the experiments that led to the discovery of DNA as the genetic material in cells

• To appraise the use of the scientific method in these experiments

Pus proves a valuable research tool!
In 1874 Friedrich Miescher discovered acid molecules in the nuclei of pus cells. Miescher's discovery became known as deoxyribonucleic acid, or DNA. Once the DNA molecule was discovered, it took more than 50 years to determine its role in cell function.

GENETIC MATERIAL TRANSFORMS CELLS

"Living dead" bacteria?

Discoveries in the late 1800s and early 1900s helped put together many pieces of the heredity puzzle. As you learned in Chapter 6, Sutton and Boveri formulated the chromosome theory of heredity in 1903. But many questions remained, including, what are genes made of?

In 1928 British researcher Frederick Griffith took the first steps toward determining whether genes are composed of DNA or protein. You can follow his experiments in *Figure 7.1*. Griffith worked with bacteria called *Streptococcus pneumoniae*. One variety, strain S, looks smooth and causes pneumonia in mice. Another variety, called strain R because of its rough appearance, does not cause pneumonia in mice.

1 S bacteria caused pneumonia and death when injected into mice.

2 R bacteria had no visible effect when injected into mice.

FIGURE 7.1

Griffith's Experiments

Griffith injected bacteria into mice and observed the effects in four separate experiments. How did his research help answer the "DNA or protein" question?

3 S bacteria were killed by heating. Heat-killed S bacteria did not harm mice.

4 Griffith grew live R bacteria after mixing with heat-killed S bacteria. Mice injected with the mixture died of pneumonia.

Griffith found that strain S bacteria were coated with mucus but strain R bacteria were not. He also found that heating strain S bacteria killed them and that injections of the heat-killed S bacteria did not harm mice.

Griffith then injected a mixture of heat-killed S bacteria and living R bacteria into mice. Griffith hypothesized that the mice would not be affected by the mixture. To his surprise, however, the mice died of pneumonia. To find out what killed the mice, Griffith allowed bacteria from the dead mice to reproduce. The offspring bacteria had the mucous coats characteristic of S bacteria.

Griffith reasoned that somehow a transforming material had passed from heat-killed S bacteria to living R bacteria changing R bacteria into S bacteria. He concluded that the transforming material was genetic material, since new inherited traits were observed in the offspring. Other scientists observed that many proteins are harmed by heat, and proposed that DNA, not protein, was the genetic material.

In 1944 American biologist Oswald Avery and his colleagues discovered that only DNA from strain S bacteria was necessary to transform strain R bacteria into the S strain. These findings supported the theory that DNA is the molecule of heredity. This additional evidence still did not convince everyone. More information was needed.

DNA OR PROTEIN?

Phage factor

In 1952 American geneticists Martha Chase and Alfred Hershey found the final missing piece of the "DNA or protein?" puzzle. Their experiments used viruses called bacteriophages (bak-TEER-ee-oh-FAY-juz), or phages

for short. You will learn how phages infect bacterial cells in Chapter 14.

A phage has only two components: DNA and protein. You can see in *Figure 7.2* that when phages infect bacteria, they attach to the bacterium's surface and inject material into the bacterium. The rest of the phage remains outside the bacterium. The injected material controls the metabolism and characteristics of the bacterial cell, as genes do. Hershey and Chase reasoned that the injected substance must be the genetic material, but they still had to determine whether the substance was DNA or protein.

To find out, they mixed phages containing radioactive DNA with bacterial cells. They also mixed phages containing radioactive protein with other bacterial cells. The phages attached themselves to bacteria and injected their genetic material. After the material was injected, the bacteria began producing new phage viruses.

As you can see in *Figure 7.2,* only the radioactive DNA entered the bacteria, indicating that the phages had injected their DNA into the bacteria. The scientists concluded that DNA, and not protein, must be the genetic material.

CHECKPOINT 7.1

1. How did Griffith, Hershey, and Chase establish DNA as the genetic material in cells?
2. **Critical Thinking** Identify the steps of the scientific method in an experiment described in this section.

Build on What You Know

3. What nucleic acid, in addition to DNA, was responsible for the transformation of R bacteria into S bacteria in Griffith's experiments? *(Need to jog your memory? Revisit relevant concepts in Chapter 2, Section 2.1.)*

FIGURE 7.2

Hershey and Chase's Experiments

Is DNA or protein the genetic material?

Cell culture 1
When phages with radioactive (green) DNA infected bacteria, the bacteria became radioactive. The DNA, therefore, was the material that entered the bacteria.

Cell culture 2
When phages with radioactive (green) protein infected bacteria, the bacteria did not become radioactive. Protein, therefore, did not enter the bacteria.

Chapter 7 DNA, Genes, and Chromosomes **159**

7.2 DNA Structure and Replication

What you'll learn

IDEAS

- To describe the structure of DNA
- To explain the process of DNA replication

WORDS

adenine, guanine, cytosine, thymine, double helix, replication

What is it?
The top picture at right is of an everyday object photographed to show features that you cannot ordinarily see. What is it? When scientists were modeling the structure of DNA, they produced images by bouncing X rays off the DNA molecule. X-ray photos, such as the bottom one shown at right, helped scientists discover the structure of DNA.

NUCLEOTIDES AND BASES

Bases go hand in hand

After researchers had pinpointed DNA as the genetic material, they needed to solve the next part of the heredity puzzle: the structure of the DNA molecule. Like many great achievements, the modeling of DNA resulted from the work of many researchers.

You may be wondering why knowing the structure of DNA is so important. The structure of a molecule is related to its function, so knowing what a molecule looks like gives researchers insight into how the molecule works.

Before DNA was modeled, scientists already knew that it was made up of nucleotides. A DNA nucleotide has three components: a five-carbon sugar called deoxyribose; a

FIGURE 7.3

The DNA Double Helix

The shape of DNA, which looks like a twisted ladder, is commonly referred to as a double helix.

Where is DNA?
In eukaryotes, chromosomes contain DNA and are located in the cell nucleus.

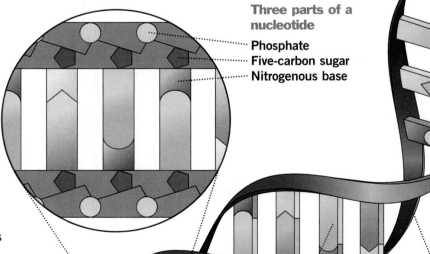

Three parts of a nucleotide
- Phosphate
- Five-carbon sugar
- Nitrogenous base

Helix backbone
Sugars and phosphates bind together to form the backbone of DNA, or the sides of the twisted ladder.

Nitrogenous-base pair

Nucleus

Chromosome

Cell

Purines	Pyrimidines
Guanine (G)	Cytosine (C)
Adenine (A)	Thymine (T)

FIGURE 7.4

The four nitrogenous bases pair up to form the rungs of the DNA twisted ladder.

phosphate group; and one of four nitrogenous bases.

The four nitrogenous bases in DNA are **adenine** (A), **guanine** (G), **cytosine** (C), and **thymine** (T). Two of these four nitrogenous bases—adenine and guanine—are purines (PYOOR-eenz). The other two bases—thymine and cytosine—are pyrimidines (pi-RIM-ih-DEENZ). One difference between purines and pyrimidines is that purine molecules are larger than pyrimidine molecules.

In the early 1950s American scientist Edwin Chargaff made an important discovery about the four nitrogenous bases. When he analyzed the amounts of the four bases in different species, Chargaff discovered that the amount of adenine is always equal to the amount of thymine, and that the amount of cytosine is always equal to the amount of guanine. These findings, called Chargaff's rules, proved to be an important clue in later investigations into the structure of DNA.

DOUBLE HELIX

The twisted ladder

Soon after Chargaff reported his findings, a new piece was placed in the DNA puzzle. Maurice Wilkins and Rosalind Franklin photographed DNA using X rays. Their images showed a wide, tightly coiled molecule with a spiral shape.

Rosalind Franklin showed one of her DNA images to the American scientist James Watson. Watson and his partner, Francis Crick, realized that the DNA molecule was too thick to be a single strand. After trying several models, they made one in which two strands were wrapped around each other. According to this model, which is now accepted as the correct structure for DNA, the DNA molecule is shaped like a twisted ladder. This shape is called a **double helix.** As shown in *Figure 7.3,* the DNA double helix is formed by two strands of nucleotides.

Watson and Crick found that two components of nucleotides, the sugar and the phosphate, bind to each other with a strong chemical bond to form a "backbone." The backbone forms the sides of the twisted ladder. The third component of nucleotides, the nitrogenous base, attaches to the sugar. Two bases bind together with weak chemical bonds to form the "rungs" of the ladder. In this way, the nucleotides form the DNA double helix.

Each rung, or base pair, of DNA consists of a purine and a pyrimidine. *Figure 7.4* shows that adenine pairs with thymine, and cytosine pairs with guanine. Because they always pair with each other, scientists say that adenine is complementary to thymine, and cytosine is complementary to guanine. How do Chargaff's rules support this part of Watson and Crick's model?

FIGURE 7.5

A Short History of Genetics

1866 Gregor Mendel experiments with pea plants.

1868 Friedrich Miescher extracts DNA from pus cell nuclei.

1900 Mendel's work is rediscovered.

1903 Walter Sutton and Theodor Boveri develop the chromosome theory of inheritance.

1910 Thomas Morgan (right) verifies Sutton's theory with fruit fly experiments.

1928 Frederick Griffith explores genetic material with mouse experiments.

1944 Oswald Avery's work indicates that DNA is most likely the genetic material.

1952 Edwin Chargaff determines rules that govern the proportion of DNA bases.

1952 Maurice Wilkins and Rosalind Franklin (left) photograph DNA using X-ray crystallography.

1952 Alfred Hershey and Martha Chase confirm that DNA is the genetic material.

1953 James Watson (below left) and Francis Crick (below right) model DNA.

FIGURE 7.6

DNA Replication

This diagram represents a snapshot of replication. At the moment pictured, the top of the strand is in the first step of replication, unzipping; the middle of the strand is building new rungs and a new backbone; and the bottom is already copied. How does the DNA strand serve as a template, or pattern, for its replication?

1 DNA unzips
Enzymes split apart base pairs and unwind the DNA double helix.

2 Bases pair up
Free nucleotides in the cell find their complementary bases along the new strands.

3 Backbone bonds
The sugar-phosphate backbone is assembled to complete the DNA strand.

TEM of DNA replicating
This transmission electron micrograph (TEM) shows the "replication fork" of DNA.

Replication

Replication

And DNA multiplies
One DNA molecule replicates, producing two DNA molecules. Each replicated molecule has a strand of parent DNA and a strand of new DNA.

Because the bases are complementary, each base has a tight and unique fit with only one other base. This description can be applied to the entire DNA strand. If you know the bases on one strand, you can determine the bases on the other strand through complementary-base pairing.

DNA REPLICATION

Unzip the blueprints

With one discovery, Watson and Crick revealed the structure of DNA and gained insight into its function. One of the important functions of genetic material is the ability to copy itself. The process by which DNA is copied is called **replication.** As you may recall from Chapter 5, DNA replicates prior to cell division. You can follow the steps of replication in *Figure* 7.6.

At the beginning of replication, the DNA double helix unwinds, or unzips. An enzyme breaks the weak bonds between the base pairs, separating the two strands of the DNA molecule. Each parent strand of DNA serves as a pattern, or template, for a new complementary strand.

The new strands are assembled from lone nucleotides in the nucleus, called free nucleotides. An enzyme called DNA polymerase (POL-ih-meh-RAYZ) matches the bases on the parent strand one by one with new bases of free nucleotides. Strong sugar-phosphate bonds form between nucleotides that are next to one another, creating a new backbone. Eventually, two new double helixes are formed. How do the new molecules compare with the parent DNA?

 Do It!

What Is a Twisted Ladder?

DNA is described as a twisted ladder. You can build a model of a double helix if you . . .

Clothing hanger

Nylon string

Toothpick

Twist

Try This

1 Get one meter (m) of thick string and 20 toothpicks.
2 Loop the string over a hanger. The string represents the sugar-phosphate backbone of a DNA molecule.
3 Insert the ends of the toothpicks into the two sides of the string. Space them about 4 cm apart. The toothpicks represent the complementary-base pairs.
4 Tie the two ends of the string together. Twist the knot a few times, and watch the shape of a double helix form.

Analyze Your Results

1 Why is DNA described as a twisted ladder?
2 How could this twisted-ladder model more accurately represent DNA?

CHECKPOINT 7.2

1. Describe the discoveries that led to the modeling of DNA.
2. What are the components of a nucleotide?
3. Why are the base pairs in DNA considered complementary?
4. Critical Thinking How is the structure of DNA related to its function?

Build on What You Know

5. How does mitosis result in two daughter cells that contain the same genetic information? *(Need to jog your memory? Revisit relevant concepts in Chapter 5, Section 5.4.)*

DNA Duplicates
As you may know, a photocopier makes exact copies of documents. In what way is DNA replication similar to this duplicating process? How is DNA replication different from the duplicating process used by copying machines?

How does the structure of DNA allow the molecule to copy itself?

Extracting DNA

WHAT YOU WILL DO Extract DNA from liver

SKILLS YOU WILL USE Measuring, predicting, collecting and recording data, observing

WHAT YOU WILL NEED Fresh beef or pork liver, scalpel or dissecting scissors, blender, 25-milliliter (mL) graduated cylinder, saline solution (0.9% NaCl), cheesecloth, 250-mL beaker, eyedropper, liquid soap, 95% ethanol, glass stirring rod

Propose a Hypothesis

You know that DNA is located in the cell nucleus. Propose a hypothesis about why the materials for this lab can extract the DNA in the liver cells.

Conduct Your Experiment

1 Cut a piece of liver about 2 cm long. Put 10 mL of saline solution and the liver into the blender. Blend until the mixture is uniform.
Caution: Use care when handling scissors and using the blender.

2 Fold two pieces of cheese-cloth in half. Use the cheese-cloth to strain the liver mixture into a beaker.
3 Use an eyedropper to add approximately 10 mL of liquid soap to the mixture. Mix thoroughly with the glass stirring rod.
4 Measure and record the volume of the soap-liver mixture in the beaker. Multiply this number by 2 and record your result. Add this volume of ethanol to the mixture.
5 Slowly stir the mixture with the glass stirring rod. A white substance will form where the ethanol and liver mixture meet.

6 Watch as the DNA precipitates up through the ethanol. The DNA will appear to be fibrous strands. Small bubbles will attach to these strands as they move up through the ethanol. Twirl the glass rod slowly in the mixture. Precipitated DNA strands will accumulate and clump together on the rod, forming a visible mass. Record your results.

Draw Conclusions

1 What does the DNA that you have extracted look like?
2 Now that you have performed this lab, how do you think Miescher first discovered DNA?

Design a Related Experiment

Design a lab to extract DNA from another substance, such as onions, dried peas, or yeast.

Lab: Extracting DNA

Step 4.)

I observed 25 mL of liquid in the beaker.
25 x 2 = 50 mL.

I added 50 mL of ethanol to the mixture, carefully pouring it along the side of the beaker.

7.3 Linked Genes

The stickleback mystery

To study inheritance among stickleback fishes, scientists crossbred a short, slender, small-mouthed stickleback with a long, fat, wide-mouthed stickleback. They found that the offspring were either all short, slender, and small-mouthed, or long, fat, and wide-mouthed. These particular traits were inherited together because of a special mode of inheritance.

LINKAGE

Trait show

How can organisms have hundreds of traits, yet not have hundreds of chromosomes? To answer this question, biologists hypothesized that a single chromosome must contain many different genes that control many different traits.

DNA, genes, and chromosomes are related to each other in much the same way as the parts of a city. Nucleotides, which are the components of DNA, can be thought of as individual people who all work together in a building. Each section of a DNA molecule is comparable to one building where people work. Each section of DNA is a gene, so a gene, too, is comparable to a building, each with its own function. Each chromosome with thousands of genes is like a city, with many different functions in many different buildings.

As you learned in Chapter 6, Walter Sutton developed the chromosome theory of heredity. The principle

What you'll learn

IDEAS

• To relate genes, traits, chromosomes, and DNA
• To contrast gene linkage with Mendelian inheritance
• To define recombination and mapping

WORDS

linked genes, crossing over

FIGURE 7.7

Chromosome Structure

What is the relationship between chromosomes and DNA?

A chromosome contains very tightly wound DNA.

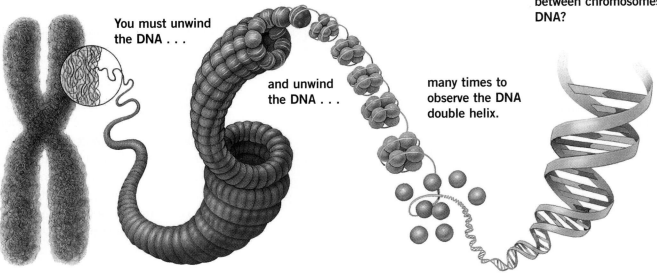

You must unwind the DNA . . .

and unwind the DNA . . .

many times to observe the DNA double helix.

FIGURE 7.8

Refining Mendel's Laws

Bateson and Punnett studied two traits in sweet pea plants: flower color and pollen shape. What was their hypothesis?

1 In the P generation, purebred plants with purple flowers and long pollen (*PPLL*) were crossed with purebred plants with red flowers and round pollen (*ppll*).

2 All of the F₁ generation had purple flowers and long pollen, as predicted by Mendel's laws. Which traits are dominant?

3 When the F₁ generation self-fertilized, the offspring did not have a 9:3:3:1 ratio. A greater number than expected had the same phenotype as the P generation.

4 Thomas Morgan hypothesized that the traits for flower color and pollen shape were linked on the same chromosome. Notice that this Punnett square does not account for the "Purple, round" or "Red, long" phenotypes from the table.

P Generation

PPLL × ppll

F₁ Generation

PpLl × PpLl

Phenotypes	Observed Offspring	Prediction with Independent Assortment
Purple, long	284	216
Purple, round	21	72
Red, long	21	72
Red, round	55	24

F₂ Generation

Punnett square for linked genes

	PL	pl
PL	Purple, long **PPLL**	Purple, long **PpLl**
pl	Purple, long **PpLl**	Red, rounded **ppll**

behind this theory is that specific genes controlling specific traits are located on specific chromosomes.

Sutton's theory helped to explain the results of an experiment conducted by geneticists William Bateson and R. C. Punnett (the man who developed the Punnett square). You can better understand their dilemma by following their experiment, shown in *Figure 7.8*.

These two researchers bred sweet pea plants. In sweet pea plants, purple flower color (*P*) is dominant over red flower color (*p*), and long pollen shape (*L*) is dominant over round pollen shape (*l*). Bateson and Punnett crossed purebred plants in their parent generation—*PPLL* × *ppll*. As expected, the F₁ generation was heterozygous for purple flowers and long pollen (*PpLl*).

Bateson and Punnett allowed the F₁ plants to self-fertilize. They expected flower color and pollen shape to sort independently. According to Mendel's Law of Independent Assortment, which you also learned about in Chapter 6, there are four different phenotypes possible as a result of a dihybrid cross. These four phenotypes should occur in a ratio of 9:3:3:1.

Bateson and Punnett's results differed from the expected ratio. The two parental phenotypes (purple flowers with long pollen, red flowers with short pollen) showed up more often than expected. It appeared that the traits of flower color and pollen shape did not sort independently. Did these results mean that Mendel's Law of Independent Assortment was incorrect?

The scientists suspected that the genes for the two traits were somehow connected and did not sort independently. Without independent assortment, the offspring should have the same combination of traits as the parents.

In 1910, the American geneticist Thomas Morgan conducted a similar experiment. Instead of sweet peas, Morgan used the fruit fly *Drosophila* (droh-SOF-ih-luh) in his experiment.

When Morgan bred fruit flies, he found that the traits of body color and wing shape did not sort independently. Aware of Sutton's chromosome theory of heredity, Morgan hypothesized that the genes for these traits were located on the same chromosome. During meiosis and gamete formation, the two traits would stay together.

The work of Sutton, Bateson and Punnett, and Morgan expanded Mendel's laws of inheritance. The chromosome theory of inheritance hypothesizes that each chromosome has many genes. When genes for two traits are located on the same chromosome, the two genes travel together into the same gamete. The two traits are inherited together, instead of sorting independently. **Linked genes** are genes that are located on the same chromosome.

Are Bateson and Punnett's results explained by the concept of linked genes? If the genes for flower color and pollen size are linked, the F_1 generation produces two kinds of gametes (PL and pl), instead of the four that would be predicted by the Law of Independent Assortment (PL, Pl, pL, pl). The Punnett square in *Figure 7.8* predicts that the F_2 generation will only have the same phenotypes as the P generation–plants with purple flowers and long pollen or red flowers and short pollen.

Remember that Bateson and Punnett also got two other phenotypes in the F_2: purple flowers with short pollen and red flowers with long pollen. Since the genes are linked, the Law of Independent Assortment cannot explain these combinations of traits. Thomas Morgan hypothesized

LAB ZONE — Think About It!

Gene Linkage in Imaginary Aliens

Imagine that a breed of space aliens has two alleles for the eye color gene: Magenta (*M*) is dominant and chartreuse (*m*) is recessive. They also have two alleles for the antenna shape gene: Bent (*B*) is dominant and curly (*b*) is recessive. Geneticists determined whether or not these two genes are linked. You can rediscover their findings if you make a Punnett square for the following parental cross: *BbMm* × *bbmm*. Then compare the results of your Punnett square with the offspring genotypes in the accompanying table.

Analyzing the Table

1 What are the phenotypes of the parents? What are the four possible offspring genotypes?
2 In what ratio should the offspring genotypes occur if the genes are on separate chromosomes?

Phenotype of Offspring	Genotype of Offspring	Observed
Bent, magenta	BbMm	2
Curly, chartreuse	bbmm	4
Bent, chartreuse	Bbmm	1
Curly, magenta	bbMm	1

3 What does the comparison of the Punnett square to the actual findings of the geneticists tell you about these genes? Are they linked? Explain your answer.

that there must be another reason to account for the new phenotypes.

RECOMBINATION

Do the gene shuffle

When Morgan performed his experiments with fruit flies, he concluded that the genes for body color and wing shape were linked and did not sort independently. However, like Bateson and Punnett, Morgan would get some offspring with a combination of traits that differed from the parental phenotypes. Since the genes for body color and wing shape were linked, the Law of Independent Assortment could not explain this result. Morgan decided that there must be a different explanation.

FIGURE 7.9

Crossing Over

Neighboring segments of these tetrads crossed over, or switched with each other. How does this process cause recombination?

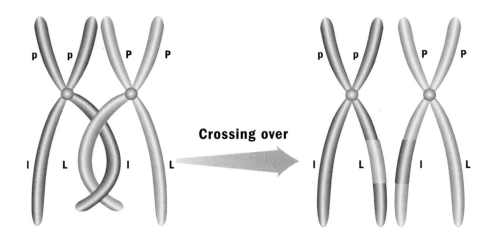

Crossing over

The new combination of traits was the result of a change in the position of alleles. When there are new combinations of alleles in offspring, the process is called recombination, and the offspring are referred to as recombinant.

Recombination can occur during meiosis, as you can see in *Figure 7.9.* As you learned in Chapter 5, homologous replicated chromosomes pair up in a set of four chromatids, or tetrads, during prophase I. Recombination occurs when the DNA strands in a tetrad cross over during prophase I.

Crossing over refers to the recombining of alleles that occurs when neighboring segments of tetrads break off where they meet and exchange genetic material.

In Bateson and Punnett's experiment, crossing over sometimes occurred during meiosis in the F_1 generation. The alleles for pollen shape switched, producing the gametes Pl and pL in addition to PL and pl. When the F_1 self-fertilized, the F_2 included recombinant offspring: purple flowers with round pollen and red flowers with long pollen.

Crossing over is only one type of recombination. In Chapter 9, you will learn about recombinant DNA technology, where scientists insert the genes of one organism into a second organism. The recombinant organism has a combination of genes that is different from its parents.

MAPPING

Go two blocks on chromosome 16 . . .

Scientists use data on recombination to determine the location of certain genes. Knowing the location of genes and whether they are linked can help genetic counselors. As you learned in Chapter 6, genetic counselors help people to determine if they will pass a

---

LAB ZONE Do It!

What Does Recombination Look Like?

You can model recombination if you . . .

Try This

1 Obtain two different colors of modeling clay.
2 Make one chromosome out of each color of clay. The chromosome should look like duplicated chromosomes at the beginning of meiosis.
3 Using your two clay chromosomes, model the steps of meiosis as shown in Figure 5.11, pages 116–117.
4 Repeat step 3, including crossing over in prophase I.

Analyze Your Results

1 Why did Bateson and Punnett see recombined traits in sweet pea plants?
2 How could recombination help geneticists locate genes on chromosomes?

harmful gene to their children. Linked genes can serve as guideposts for identifying genes associated with diseases.

To prepare gene maps, which show where genes are located on chromosomes, geneticists work with two traits (from two genes) at a time. For simplicity, we will assume that both genes have only two alleles. Alleles are the options available for a certain trait.

Once geneticists have identified two traits to study, they collect statistics on the inheritance of these two traits. If these traits are inherited independently, the geneticists can assume they are not located on the same chromosome. If the traits are not inherited independently, the traits are linked on the same chromosome.

After determining whether traits are linked, geneticists can pinpoint the location of genes by counting the number of recombinant offspring. The number of recombinant offspring indicates the number of times crossing over has occurred between two genes. Since crossing over can occur at any point between two genes, the amount of crossing over is related to the distance between two genes.

If two genes recombine often, they are located far apart. If you locate *s* and *n* in *Figure 7.10,* you can see how easily these two genes might be separated by crossing over.

If traits do not recombine often, they are more likely to be located close together on a chromosome. As genes get closer on the same chromosome, they recombine less frequently because there is less opportunity for crossing over. Do you see *b* and *r* in *Figure 7.10*? The *b* and *r* genes are not very likely to separate during crossing over. In this situation, very few offspring are recombinant. When fewer than one percent of offspring have a trait combination that differs from both parents, researchers assume that the two genes responsible for

Drosophila
(actual size 2.5–4.5 mm)

Chromosome 2
(actual size 0.5 μm)

those traits are located next to each other on the same chromosome.

Geneticists can approximate the distance between two genes on a chromosome by calculating the fraction of offspring that recombine two traits from their parents. Keep in mind, however, that this method of gene mapping does not give the exact location of a gene on a chromosome; it only indicates the relative distance between the two genes being studied. To locate genes, geneticists use molecular mapping techniques, which you will learn about in Chapter 8.

FIGURE 7.10
In this illustration, the labeled genes are all located on chromosome 2 of the fruit fly *Drosophila*. Which genes are likely to recombine?

CHECKPOINT 7.3

1. How are DNA, genes, and chromosomes related?
2. How does recombination enable scientists to map genes on chromosomes?
3. Critical Thinking How did Bateson and Punnett's experiment with sweet pea plants support the chromosome theory of heredity?

Build on What You Know

4. Rewrite the Law of Independent Assortment to include your knowledge of linked genes. *(Need to jog your memory? Revisit relevant concepts in Chapter 6, Section 6.2.)*

7.4 Sex Linkage

Color my world
If you can distinguish between the
colored dots in this image, you may be
able to make out a number. People who
do not see the number may have a form
of red-green color blindness. This common trait, as well as others that you will
learn about in this section, has a unique
pattern of inheritance.

SEX CHROMOSOMES
Y they're X-cellent

You have learned that chromosomes
come in homologous pairs. As is often
the case in science, there are exceptions to the rule. In this instance, the
exceptions are the sex chromosomes.

In some species, it is the **sex
chromosomes** that determine
whether the offspring are male or
female. Some plants and animals have
sex chromosomes; others do not. All
of the non-sex chromosomes are
called **autosomes.** Humans and
other mammals have two sex chromosomes—X and Y. Females have two X
chromosomes (*XX*), and males have
an X and a Y chromosome (*XY*).

During meiosis, sex chromosomes
behave like other chromosome pairs.
In humans, for example, sex chromosomes segregate with the autosome
pairs during meiosis. Because females
have two X chromosomes (*XX*), all
eggs have a single X chromosome. In
males (*XY*), half of the sperm carry a
Y chromosome and half carry an X
chromosome. Which gamete—egg
or sperm—determines the sex of
the offspring? Study *Figure 7.11* to
find the answer.

SEX-LINKED TRAITS
The flies have it

As you have just read, X and Y chromosomes are not homologous—they
do not contain matching genes. Genes
found only in the X chromosome are
X-linked, and genes found only in the
Y chromosome are Y-linked. Together,
the X-linked and Y-linked genes are
sex-linked genes.

Morgan's experiments The
first scientist to study sex-linked
genes was Thomas Morgan. Morgan,
you may recall, worked with the
fruit fly *Drosophila*. *Drosophila* is
used in many genetics experiments.
Fruit flies are easy to feed and maintain, they reproduce quickly, and
each generation has huge numbers of
offspring, enabling researchers to
gather large quantities of data in a
short time. In addition, *Drosophila*
has only four pairs of chromosomes.

FIGURE 7.11
The sex of humans is
determined by X and Y
chromosomes (below).
What percentage of the
offspring will be female?

Mother's chromosomes

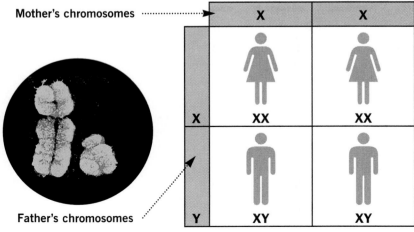

Father's chromosomes

	X	X
X	XX	XX
Y	XY	XY

In 1910 Morgan noticed a mutation in one of his fruit flies—a male fly was born with white eyes instead of the usual red eyes. Morgan crossed a red-eyed female with the white-eyed male. The F_1 offspring all had red eyes. Next, Morgan bred males and females of the F_1 generation to produce an F_2 generation. He expected to find a 3:1 ratio of red-eyed to white-eyed flies. As expected, Morgan got a 3:1 ratio of red-eyed to white-eyed flies. But the white-eyed flies were all males! The surprising result of this experiment is shown in *Figure 7.12*. Nothing in Mendel's hypotheses could explain a trait that was somehow tied to the sex of the organism.

Morgan hypothesized that the white-eye allele was recessive and the red-eye allele was dominant. Furthermore, he reasoned, the eye-color gene in *Drosophila* must be located only in the X chromosome. In other words, there was no eye-color gene in the Y chromosome. If this hypothesis were true, a male fly (*XY*) would have white eyes if his X chromosome contained that allele. Females (*XX*), which carry eye-color genes in both X chromosomes, would not express a single white-eye gene because that allele is recessive. Morgan tested his hypothesis by crossing white-eyed males with red-eyed females from the F_1 generation. About half of the female offspring had white eyes.

Morgan's results confirmed his hypothesis. His fruit fly experiments were the first to locate a specific gene in a specific chromosome. His results supported the chromosome theory of heredity.

Sex-linked traits in humans

Many more sex-linked genes were discovered in the years following Morgan's breakthrough experiments. Color blindness is a sex-linked trait in humans. Red-green color blindness is caused by an X-linked recessive allele,

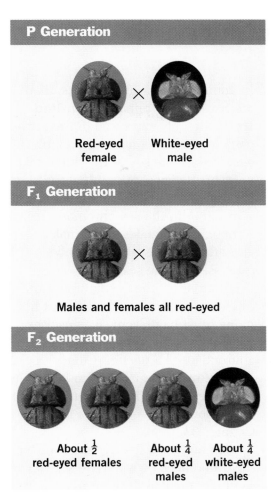

P Generation

Red-eyed female × White-eyed male

F₁ Generation

Males and females all red-eyed ×

F₂ Generation

About $\frac{1}{2}$ red-eyed females | About $\frac{1}{4}$ red-eyed males | About $\frac{1}{4}$ white-eyed males

FIGURE 7.12

Morgan was surprised when only the males had white eyes. Why did he expect a 3:1 ratio of red eyes to white eyes in the F_2 generation?

X^c. The allele for normal color vision, X^C, is dominant. A color-blind male has the genotype X^cY. A female who is color-blind has the genotype X^cX^c. What can you infer about the genotype of the mother of a color-blind boy?

Hemophilia is another example of an X-linked disorder in humans. This disorder results in excessive bleeding after even a minor injury. The heavy bleeding is due to the absence of a blood chemical needed for normal clotting. Hemophilia is treated with concentrated doses of this chemical extracted from normal blood.

Because males receive their X chromosome from their mother, they inherit color blindness and other X-linked traits only from their mothers. Females expressing X-linked traits inherit them from both parents, because they receive an X chromosome from each parent.

SEX-LIMITED AND SEX-INFLUENCED TRAITS

Just add hormones

In addition to sex-linked traits, there are sex-limited traits. **Sex-limited traits** are only expressed in the presence of sex hormones and are only observed in one sex or the other. Like most phenotypes, sex-limited traits are controlled by genes located in autosomes, not in the sex chromosomes. Although both males and females carry these genes, they are only expressed by one sex.

In order for the sex-limited trait to be expressed, the appropriate sex hormone must be present. Because sex hormones are not produced in large amounts until a person reaches puberty, most human sex-limited traits are not expressed in children. You will learn more about hormones in Chapter 33.

Sex-limited traits explain many of the differences between the sexes. For example, male birds often have more colorful plumage than female birds. How does this sex-limited trait enable some bird populations to survive? Human traits that are sex-limited include beard growth in men and milk production in women.

FIGURE 7.14

Sex-influenced traits, such as baldness, are expressed differently in each sex. Is the allele for baldness dominant or recessive in these people?

Traits controlled by other autosomal genes are sex-influenced. **Sex-influenced traits** are expressed in both sexes, but they are expressed differently. For example, the allele for baldness is sex-influenced. In the presence of male sex hormones, this allele is dominant. Female sex hormones, however, cause the allele to be recessive. Thus, a woman may lose hair if she has two alleles for baldness.

CHECKPOINT 7.4

1. What is the difference between autosomes and sex chromosomes?
2. What is the difference between sex-linked traits, sex-limited traits, and sex-influenced traits?
3. **Critical Thinking** What results would you expect from a cross between a white-eyed female and a white-eyed male *Drosophila*? Use a Punnett square.

Build on What You Know

4. How would you revise the Law of Dominance to accommodate sex-linked traits? *(Need to jog your memory? Revisit relevant concepts in Chapter 6, Section 6.2.)*

FIGURE 7.13

Sex-limited traits are observed in only one sex. In the photos below, the male cardinal is on the left, and the female is on the right. What sex-limited trait can you spot in these cardinals?

7.5 The Human Gene Map

What you and bread have in common

Did you know that you share about one quarter of your genes with baker's yeast, the microorganism that makes bread rise? These genetic similarities have given scientists insight into several human diseases, including cancer. Scientists discovered these similarities by studying the bases that make up the 16 chromosomes of the yeast cell.

What you'll learn

IDEAS
• To explain genomes and current genome research
• To compare monosomy and trisomy and their effects

WORDS
karyotype, genome, nondisjunction, monosomy, trisomy, polyploidy

GENOMES

No place like genome

Scientists have developed several different tools and techniques for studying chromosomes, genes, and base pairs in humans and other organisms. These techniques help doctors diagnose and treat genetic disorders. They have also provided great insight into the characteristics of all living things.

Figure 7.15 shows a karyotype, one tool scientists use to learn more about chromosomes. A **karyotype** is a photograph of all of an organism's chromosomes. To make a karyotype, scientists use chemicals to freeze cells at the metaphase stage of cell division. At this stage, chromosomes are easy to isolate and stain. Karyotypes allow researchers to study differences in chromosome shape, structure, and size. The chromosomes in the karyotype shown in *Figure 7.15* are arranged so that homologous pairs are grouped together. Can you find the sex chromosomes in this karyotype? Remember, sex chromosomes are not always homologous.

Using modern molecular techniques, scientists can also study genes and base pair sequences directly. These types of analyses are called genome studies. A **genome** (JEE-nohm) is the base sequence of all of the DNA in an organism. Nitrogenous bases, as you may recall, include adenine, guanine, cytosine, and thymine.

Genome size varies greatly from organism to organism. For example, the yeast genome includes 12.5 million bases, whereas the human genome includes 3 billion bases. However, many genes are similar in all organisms, such as the genes that control the production of common substances in eukaryotic cells.

FIGURE 7.15

Karyotypes, like the human karyotype below, are photographs of chromosomes.

The Human Genome Project

Researchers are very interested in sequencing all of the DNA in the human body. A worldwide effort—the Human Genome Project—is working toward this goal. The project was officially established in 1988 by scientists from thirteen nations. The Human Genome Project will not be completed until at least 2005 because the human genome is so large. To complete the project, scientists will have to sequence the 23 human chromosome pairs, which contain approximately 90,000 genes with more than 3 billion bases! As new information regarding the human genome is discovered, disease-causing genes—as well as genes for other traits—are being identified. For example, the genes responsible for cystic fibrosis, Duchenne muscular dystrophy, and Huntington disease have already been identified.

Supporters of the Human Genome Project expect that it will provide a wealth of information about human genes and how they might be manipulated. While the potential for new information is exciting, the project also raises some concerns.

Those who oppose the Human Genome Project question how useful the information will actually be. Eukaryotes have long stretches of DNA with no apparent function. In contrast, prokaryotes "use" all of their DNA sequence. Because so much of the DNA of humans and other eukaryotes appears to be unused, many people question whether the time and money spent on the project will be worthwhile.

Despite objections, the Human Genome Project continues. Other endeavors are underway as well, including projects to sequence the entire genomes of mice, cats, dogs, and the fruit fly *Drosophila*. In addition to the yeast genome, researchers have sequenced the genomes of the common bacterium *Escherichia coli*, the ulcer-causing bacterium *Helicobacter pylori*, and some viruses.

CHANGES IN THE GENOME

Two's company

Karyotypes and genome studies can reveal many characteristics of an organism. Because genome studies are difficult and take so much time, they are not used for genetic counseling. Genetic counselors do use karyotypes, however.

A karyotype can be used to find certain types of chromosomal abnormalities. For example, a karyotype may show too many or too few chromosomes. Changes in chromosome number occur when pairs of chromosomes fail to separate correctly during mitosis or meiosis. The failure of chromosomes to separate during cell division is called **nondisjunction,** which means "not separating." When nondisjunction occurs in mitosis, the individual cell may die, but the organism as a whole is not usually harmed. In contrast, nondisjunction during

FIGURE 7.16
These two high school students are researching genes for the Human Genome Project. According to the graph (below), how has the Human Genome Project progressed?

Progress of the Human Genome Project*

Number of Disease Genes Located vs. Year (1989–1996)

*Information provided by National Center for for Human Genome Research, NIH

Meiosis I

Prophase I

Anaphase I

Meiosis II

Anaphase II
In nondisjunction (bottom), chromatids do not separate at anaphase II.

In this model normal gametes have one chromosome in each cell.

These gametes have an incorrect number of chromosomes.

anaphase I or II of meiosis causes a pair of chromosomes to remain together. Because both chromosomes are located in one daughter cell, the other daughter cell does not receive a copy of the chromosome. As a result, abnormal gametes—which can produce abnormal offspring—are formed.

As you can see in *Figure 7.17*, one gamete has too many chromosomes, while another has too few. If an abnormal gamete joins with a normal gamete, the zygote will have an abnormal number of chromosomes. In **monosomy** (MON-oh-SOH-mee), the zygote has only one copy of a particular chromosome. In **trisomy** (try-SOH-mee), the zygote has three copies of a chromosome. Which gamete in *Figure 7.17* would produce a zygote with monosomy? Trisomy?

In humans, monosomy or trisomy of most chromosomes is so disruptive that it kills the embryo. When it occurs in certain chromosomes, however, the embryo survives but has developmental difficulties. Nondisjunction can involve both autosomes and sex chromosomes. Such specific

changes in the genome cause specific, recognizable disorders.

Down syndrome is a disorder caused by trisomy of chromosome 21 (trisomy 21). How would the karyotype in *Figure 7.15* on page 173 differ for individuals with this disorder? People with Down syndrome can be mildly or severely developmentally challenged.

Abnormalities in the number of sex chromosomes can also occur. These disorders include trisomy of the sex chromosomes, resulting in XXX or XXY. Monosomy of the sex chromosomes, XO, also occurs.

FIGURE 7.17
This diagram shows nondisjunction during meiosis II, resulting in abnormal gametes. How would the diagram look if nondisjunction occurred in meiosis I?

FIGURE 7.18
The child in the center has Down syndrome, a condition arising from trisomy of chromosome 21.

EVERYDAY
BIOLOGY

A Cat Called Calico Carl

Chances are you have never seen a male calico cat. Male calicoes are very rare because calico-patterned fur requires two X chromosomes. A male calico cat has trisomy of the sex chromosomes: XXY.

In **polyploidy** (POL-ee-PLOY-dee), nondisjunction occurs in all chromosome pairs. In many cases of polyploidy, nondisjunction occurs during the process of gamete production. Some of the resulting gametes will have more than one set of chromosomes. These gametes may then fuse with normal gametes or other polyploid gametes. For this reason, a polyploid organism has more than two entire sets of chromosomes. If polyploidy occurred in parent organisms with two chromosomes, for example, the resulting offspring would have four chromosomes.

In animals, polyploidy almost always results in death. However, in plants, polyploidy can actually produce a more robust plant. Because they often combine the hardiest characteristics of their parent species, polyploid plants are frequently healthier with larger flowers or fruit than plants with normal genomes.

Polyploidy in plants results when nondisjunction occurs during meiosis.

Some of the gametes produced from nondisjunction contain two complete sets of chromosomes. (Consequently, some of the other gametes produced do not contain a complete genome.) The plants then self-fertilize with diploid gametes or haploid gametes.

Polyploidy also occurs when a polyploid gamete of one species cross-fertilizes with a normal gamete from another species. In addition, because plants produced by polyploid gametes are often larger and hardier, plant breeders artificially produce polyploid plants with chemicals that prevent the separation of chromosomes.

About 25 to 50 percent of all plant varieties are polyploids, including many of the plants you eat. The wheat used to make bread is a polyploid that has 42 chromosomes. This wheat plant was an accidental hybrid of a cultivated wheat that had 28 chromosomes, and a wild grass that had 14 chromosomes. Potatoes, oats, bananas, peanuts, barley, plums, apples, sugarcane, coffee, and cotton also are polyploid plants.

CHECKPOINT 7.5

1. What is a genome?
2. Explain the difference between monosomy and trisomy.
3. **Critical Thinking** Make a sketch that shows how the chromosomal abnormality leading to Down syndrome is produced.

Build on What You Know

4. How does polyploidy emphasize the difference between mitosis and meiosis? *(Need to jog your memory? Revisit relevant concepts in Chapter 5, Section 5.4.)*

Where are genes located?

Chapter 7 Review

7.1–7.2 The structure of DNA, the molecule of heredity, enables the molecule to copy itself.

7.3–7.5 Genes, sections of DNA that code for a specific trait, are linked together on chromosomes.

Sum It Up

Use the following summary to review the main concepts in this chapter.

7.1 Molecule of Heredity

- Frederick Griffith's experiments showed that genetic material transformed cells.
- Martha Chase and Alfred Hershey proved that DNA is the genetic material of cells.

7.2 DNA Structure and Replication

- DNA is composed of nucleotides and is shaped like a double helix.
- A nucleotide has three parts: a sugar, a phosphate, and a nitrogenous base.
- Bases always form complementary base pairs: adenine binds with thymine, and cytosine binds with guanine.
- Complementary base pairing enables DNA to replicate, or copy itself.

7.3 Linked Genes

- Linked genes are located in the same chromosome and do not sort independently.
- Chromosomes sometimes cross over during meiosis, resulting in recombination of alelles.

7.4 Sex Linkage

- Sex chromosomes determine the sex of offspring. All other chromosomes are autosomes.
- The human sex chromosomes are the X chromosome and the Y chromosome.
- Genes located on sex chromosomes are sex-linked genes.
- Sex-limited and sex-influenced traits are controlled by genes located on autosomes, but these traits are affected by sex hormones.

7.5 The Human Gene Map

- A karyotype is an image showing all of an organism's chromosomes.
- A genome is the base sequence of all of the DNA in an organism.
- The Human Genome Project is the effort to sequence the entire human genome.
- Nondisjunction occurs when chromosomes fail to separate during cell division.

Use Terms and Concepts

Use each of the following words or terms in a complete sentence. If you need to review a meaning, turn to the page indicated.

adenine (p. 161)
guanine (p. 161)
cytosine (p. 161)
thymine (p. 161)
double helix (p. 161)
replication (p. 163)

linked genes (p. 167)
crossing over (p. 168)
autosomes (p. 170)
sex chromosomes (p. 170)
sex-linked genes (p. 170)

sex-limited traits (p. 172)
sex-influenced traits (p. 172)
karyotype (p. 173)
genome (p. 173)

nondisjunction (p. 174)
monosomy (p. 175)
trisomy (p. 175)
polyploidy (p. 176)

Use Your Word Power

COMPLETION **Write the word or phrase that best completes each statement.**

1. _____ or _____ can result from nondisjunction during meiosis.

2. _____ and thymine are complementary bases.

3. The shape of DNA is described as a twisted ladder, or a(n) _____ .

4. A(n) _____ is the base pair sequence of all of the DNA of an organism.

5. Recombination can occur during _____ of chromosomes.

6. _____ do not follow Mendel's Law of Independent Assortment.

TRUE-FALSE **Write true if the statement is true. If the statement is false, replace the underlined word(s) to make the statement true.**

7. <u>Sex chromosomes</u> are responsible for sex-influenced traits.

8. Sex-limited traits are controlled by genes on <u>autosomes</u>.

9. <u>Nondisjunction</u> occurs when chromatids fail to separate.

10. An image of all of an organism's chromosomes is called a <u>genome</u>.

11. The process by which DNA copies itself is called <u>replication</u>.

Show What You Know

12. How can researchers map genes?

13. Using words or drawings, describe how DNA replicates.

14. How did the results of Bateson and Punnett's experiments differ from their hypothesis? How did they explain the difference?

15. How does recombination of linked genes occur? Explain.

16. Why can nondisjunction be harmful when it occurs during meiosis?

17. Why do human males always exhibit recessive traits located in X chromosomes?

18. What is polyploidy? What are two ways that polyploidy can occur in plants?

19. What two major concepts did Morgan discover when working with the fruit fly *Drosophila*?

20. What is the Human Genome Project?

21. **Make a Concept Map** Complete the concept map below by adding the following terms: adenine, thymine, cytosine, guanine, sugar, phosphates, chromosomes, autosome, sex chromosome.

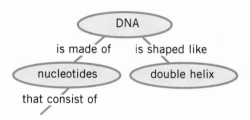

Take It Further

22. **Applying Concepts** Use sketches to show that the farther apart linked genes are, the more likely they are to be separated during crossing over.

23. **Identifying Cause and Effect** Suppose a man with hemophilia marries a woman who is a carrier of the disorder. Determine the probability that any son or daughter will have the disorder.

24. **Making a Prediction** How would survival be affected if everyone had the same genome?

25. **Analyzing Data** Chargaff measured the distance between DNA's sugar-phosphate backbones. Using your knowledge of purines and pyrimidines, describe how this knowledge helped Watson and Crick model DNA.

26. Interpreting a Graph An imaginary kind of beetle has two alleles each for color and pattern: maroon or ochre, spotted or solid. Two beetles heterozygous for both traits are crossed. This graph shows the observed phenotypes of the offspring. Are these traits linked? Which traits are dominant?

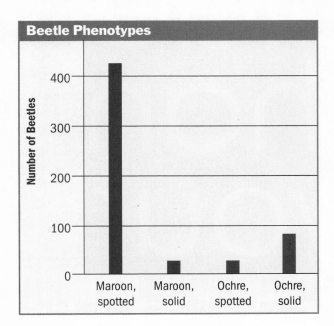

27. Analyzing Data Which strands are complementary pairs? Which strand doesn't have a pair? Graph the data to determine the answer.

Some Common Elements				
	Base Percentages			
	A	T	C	G
DNA Strand #1	23.6	24.8	29.2	22.4
DNA Strand #2	23.2	19.4	29.8	27.6
DNA Strand #3	19.6	26.8	26.3	27.3
DNA Strand #4	27.1	19.2	26.9	26.8
DNA Strand #5	25.2	23.1	22.7	29.0

28. Designing an Experiment Researchers suspect that a certain disease is caused by a recessive allele in a gene located in the X chromosome in fruit flies. Design an experiment to test this hypothesis.

Consider the Issues

29. Genome Money Matters The United States Congress contributed $53 million to begin the Human Genome Project. The final cost of the project is expected to be in the billions of dollars, with much of the money coming from government and private grants. Write a speech to deliver to Congress defending or opposing funding for the project. Support your argument.

Make New Connections

30. Biology and Physics Research and report on the characteristics of X rays. Describe how X rays produced the images used to research DNA structure.

31. Biology and Community Investigate the production of polyploid plants in your state. What methods and chemicals are used to produce the polyploid plants?

32. Biology and Design Use different materials than those in the Do It! activity to plan and construct a model of DNA. Use your model to show how DNA replicates.

FAST-FORWARD TO CHAPTER 8

DNA was established as the genetic material in cells because it transfers information from parents to offspring. The next chapter explains how DNA affects traits.

Protein Synthesis

bioSURF

You can find out more about protein synthesis by exploring the following Internet address:
http://genetics.biosurf.com

In this chapter . . .

FEATURES

Everyday Biology
- Tidy Proteins
- Feeling the Burn?

In the Community
Where There's Smoke . . .

 Frontiers in Biology
Eat Your Vegetables

LAB ZONES

Discover It!
- Identifying Ways to Prevent Skin Cancer

Do It!
- What Is Your Codon Count?

Think About It!
- From Milk to Wasp: Modeling Mutations

Investigate It!
- Modeling Protein Synthesis

Older than your years

Do you sometimes wish you looked a little older? The ultraviolet rays of the sun can grant that wish. Scientists have found that exposure to sunlight without protection—either from clothing or a sunscreen lotion—damages the skin, causing wrinkles and skin cancer.

You may think that skin cancer and wrinkles do not occur until old age. But the ultraviolet rays of the sun may already be changing the genetic material in your skin cells, so that new cells are not as healthy as their parent cells. By combining magnification and lighting to view a person's skin, doctors are able to detect skin damage, as shown in the photo.

But exactly what cellular changes are initiated by ultraviolet radiation? In this chapter, you will learn about how cellular processes work and what causes some of those processes to go awry—leading to the development of skin cancer and wrinkles. But you have the power right now to help prevent skin cancer—put on some sunscreen and a hat!

LAB ZONE Discover It!

Identifying Ways to Prevent Skin Cancer

You need *an old photograph or painting showing people participating in outdoor activities*

1. Look at the people in the image and observe any precautions they have taken to avoid the sun.
2. Write down your observations.

Fashion in many sunny climates has often included head coverings, long sleeves, and umbrellas to block the sun, even though the dangers of skin cancer may have been unknown at the time. How do you protect yourself from the sun? How do others around you protect themselves? How can you improve your sun-safety habits?

WRITE ABOUT IT!

In your science journal, write about a sunny day you spent outdoors. Did you and your companions wear sunscreen or protective clothing? If not, rewrite the story of your sunny day and include details of the preventive measures you could have taken.

THE BIG IDEA!

Genes are sequences of DNA bases that can be translated into proteins or parts of proteins when they are activated.
8.1–8.2

8.1 From Genotype to Phenotype

What you'll learn

IDEAS

• To describe the process of transcription of DNA to mRNA
• To demonstrate the process of translation of mRNA to build proteins

WORDS

protein synthesis, RNA, transcription, translation, introns, exons, codon, anticodon

Special diet creates super ants!
Most larvae of the ant species *Pheidole pallidula* develop into docile worker ants. But during times of danger the ants produce many more larvae that develop into large, aggressive soldier ants. Research indicates that the ants change their food supply when under threat. The change in diet alters their hormonal balance which, in turn, affects their genes. If genes are inherited, how do you think their effects can be changed?

FIGURE 8.1
Both DNA and RNA are nucleic acids, but they differ in structure. What are the differences?

RNA

RNA and DNA: Structural Differences

RNA	DNA
Single-stranded	Double-stranded
Base pairs: C–G, A–U	Base pairs: C–G, A–T
(Cytosine–Guanine	(Cytosine–Guanine
Adenine–Uracil)	Adenine–Thymine)
Ribose sugar group	Deoxyribose sugar group

DNA

GENE EXPRESSION

Protein rules

Protein has a role in virtually every activity of every organism, from the respiration of a bacterium to the blink of an elephant's eye. Organisms make the proteins they need through a process called protein synthesis. **Protein synthesis** is the process by which an organism's genotype (the genetic makeup) is translated into its phenotype (the traits). An organism's phenotype depends on the formation of specific structural proteins based on its genotype.

Genes code for the sequence of amino acids that make up proteins. A gene is made of DNA. The sequence of DNA bases in a gene determines the composition of one or more proteins. You can think of DNA as a template, or pattern, for making proteins.

Some genes code for proteins that regulate the expression of other genes; that is, they determine which genes are expressed at a given moment and which are not expressed. A gene is "expressed" when the protein that it codes for is synthesized.

DNA works with another nucleic acid—ribonucleic (RY-boh-noo-KLAY-ik) acid, or RNA. The structural differences between DNA and RNA are shown in *Figure 8.1*. **RNA** is a single-stranded nucleic acid that is involved in protein synthesis. There are three types of RNA—messenger RNA (mRNA), transfer RNA (tRNA), and ribosomal RNA (rRNA). Each type has a specific function.

Protein synthesis occurs in two stages. During the first stage—called **transcription**—the genetic information from a strand of DNA is copied into a strand of mRNA. The word "transcribe" means "to copy." You can see the steps of transcription in *Figure 8.2*.

FIGURE 8.2

Transcription

RNA polymerase

DNA

mRNA

mRNA

RNA polymerase

1 Transcription begins
The enzyme RNA polymerase separates, or "unzips," a section of DNA.

2 mRNA synthesis begins
RNA polymerase binds unattached RNA bases to their complementary bases on the DNA strand and link the RNA nucleotides to form a molecule of mRNA.

3 Transcription ends
After a section of DNA is transcribed, the next section is exposed. The process repeats until DNA signals mRNA synthesis to end.

Use this locator diagram of a eukaryotic cell to identify where the stages of protein synthesis take place.

RNA polymerase

Unattached RNA nucleotides

mRNA strand

DNA strands

Direction of transcription ⟶

The second stage of protein synthesis is called translation. You may be familiar with this word. Translation in cells is similar to translation in speech or writing. In cells, **translation** is a process by which the "language" of nucleic acids (bases) is changed into the "language" of proteins (amino acids).

In order for genes to be expressed, the DNA in chromosomes has to be made accessible. Recall from *Figure 7.7* that DNA is coiled and wound in chromosomes. Inactive DNA is tightly coiled, whereas active DNA is loosely coiled. The coiling and uncoiling of DNA is one way of controlling gene expression. Scientists hypothesize that chemicals such as growth factors and hormones cause chromosomes to tighten or loosen their coils.

BUILDING RNA

Making the messenger

Transcription is the process of transferring genetic information from a strand of DNA to a strand of mRNA. Once the chromosome coils loosen, transcription can begin with RNA polymerase (POL-ih-meh-rayz). This enzyme separates the two strands of a DNA double helix, exposing the base pairs of a gene. Unattached RNA bases are present in the nucleus. RNA polymerase matches RNA bases with the complimentary bases on one strand of the DNA template. As you see in *Figure 8.2,* RNA bases (U, A, G, and C) bind with complimentary DNA bases (A, T, C, and G). Note that in RNA it is uracil, not thymine, that binds with adenine. Because of these specific binding

Intron Exon Intron Exon

DNA

Transcription

RNA

Introns removed

Exons spliced together

spliced
mRNA

NUCLEUS

TRANSCRIPTION | DNA

RNA SPLICING | mRNA

Spliced mRNA

TRANSLATION

CYTOPLASM

FIGURE 8.3
Before mRNA leaves the nucleus of a eukaryotic cell, it undergoes RNA splicing. What happens to exons during mRNA splicing?

patterns, the precise code is copied, or transcribed, from DNA to mRNA.

In prokaryotic cells, which have no nuclei, mRNA travels directly to a ribosome. In fact, both transcription and translation can proceed simultaneously in prokaryotes. Because proteins are made quickly, prokaryotes can multiply rapidly. This rapid reproduction is one reason you get sick so quickly when infected by some disease-causing prokaryotes, such as the bacterium that causes strep throat.

In eukaryotic cells, or cells with nuclei, mRNA must go through an additional step before it reaches a ribosome. This additional step, shown in *Figure 8.3,* is called RNA splicing. DNA in eukaryotic cells contains regions that do not code for proteins. These noncoding regions of DNA or RNA are called **introns.** The sections of DNA or RNA that do contain codes for proteins are called **exons.**

DNA introns and exons are both transcribed into mRNA. Before the mRNA leaves the nucleus, enzymes remove the introns and join the exons to one another. In this way, mRNA is

spliced, or cut and rejoined, and the mRNA that leaves the nucleus includes only exons.

RNA splicing is an important step in protein synthesis in eukaryotes. It controls the genetic information that leaves the nucleus. Once the introns are removed, mRNA leaves the nucleus and moves to a ribosome in the cytoplasm, where translation occurs.

BUILDING PROTEINS

A new "language"

During translation, genetic information carried by mRNA is translated to form proteins. As you learned in Chapter 2, proteins are made of specific sequences of amino acids. Translation involves linking amino acids together into these sequences.

In the cytoplasm, mRNA attaches to a ribosome, a tiny organelle that can be found either floating freely in the cytoplasm or attached to endoplasmic reticulum. The ribosome, with its attached mRNA, is now ready to synthesize a protein. *Figure 8.4* shows the interactions of mRNA and ribosomes during the second stage of protein synthesis, translation.

During translation, a tRNA molecule transfers an amino acid to the ribosome. The tRNA's main function is to transport amino acids. As shown in *Figure 8.4* each new amino acid links with the previous amino acid, forming an amino acid chain. As more and more tRNAs arrive, each with an amino acid, the chain grows longer. The lengthening of the amino acid chain is called elongation.

You might wonder how tRNA delivers the amino acids in the correct order. This sequencing is done through a system of complementary codons and anticodons. A **codon** is a three-base section of mRNA. Most codons carry a code for a specific amino acid. For example, the codon

FIGURE 8.4
Translation

Making proteins

In the cytoplasm, one kind of amino acid is attached to each tRNA. An mRNA is attached to a ribosome. During elongation, tRNAs bring amino acids to the ribosome. Amino acids are added one at a time to the growing amino acid chain. Each tRNA anticodon pairs with a complementary mRNA codon, making sure that amino acids are added in the coded sequence.

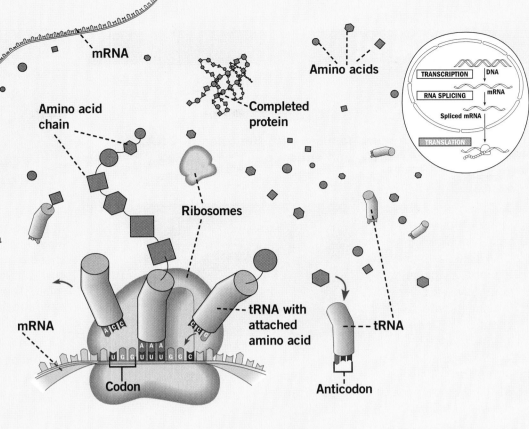

mRNA

Amino acid chain

Amino acids

Completed protein

Ribosomes

tRNA with attached amino acid

tRNA

mRNA

Codon

Anticodon

Elongation cycle: step 1
During elongation, the ribosome has two tRNAs bound to the mRNA. One tRNA (left) is attached to the growing amino acid chain. A new tRNA (right) brings a new amino acid.

Elongation cycle: step 2
The growing amino acid chain is bonded to the new amino acid on the new tRNA. The chain is now one amino acid longer.

Elongation cycle: step 3
The tRNA that released the growing chain leaves the ribosome. The mRNA moves down the ribosome, and the elongation cycle begins again.

GCU (guanine, cytosine, uracil) codes for the amino acid known as alanine (AL-uh-neen).

An **anticodon** is a sequence of three bases found on tRNA. Each tRNA carries only one anticodon, in contrast to the many codons in an mRNA molecule. Each tRNA anti-codon complements a specific mRNA codon. For example, the mRNA codon AGU is complemented by the tRNA anticodon UCA. Based on what you know about complementary base pairs, what is the tRNA anticodon for the mRNA codon GCU? For the mRNA codon GCA?

LAB ZONE Do It!

What Is Your Codon Count?

You can become more familiar with the roles of DNA, mRNA, codons, tRNA, and anticodons if you . . .

Try This

1 Take four sheets of paper of four different colors, and assign a DNA base (adenine, thymine, cytosine, guanine) to each color. Cut the sheets into squares about 3 × 3 cm. Mix all the squares.

2 On a table or the floor, place 30 squares in a left-to-right line. Group the squares by threes to represent DNA codons.

3 In your notebook, list the base sequences for these DNA codons, recording from left to right.

Analyze Your Results

1 What are the base sequences for the complementary mRNA codons? List them in your notebook.

2 What would the base sequences be for tRNA anticodons? List them.

3 The universal mRNA start codon is AUG. The three possible mRNA stop codons are UAA, UAG, and UGA. Are there any start or stop sequences among your codons? If so, record them.

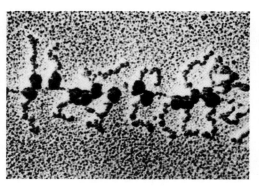

FIGURE 8.5
In this SEM photograph, you can see that many ribosomes have translated a single strand of mRNA, and the amino acid chains have begun forming at each ribosome. When do the ribosomes stop translating?

Anticodons and codons fit together in much the same way as plugs fit into sockets. The codons and anticodons ensure that the amino acids are linked in the proper order. Because a specific amino acid attaches only to a tRNA with a specific anticodon, the tRNA carries the appropriate amino acid when it plugs into its complementary mRNA codon.

Several codons on mRNA have a different purpose. These codons do not code for an amino acid; they are the "start" and "stop" codons. The start and stop codons do exactly what their names suggest. They signal a ribosome to either start or stop translation. As

you would expect, these codons are located at the beginning and end of a mRNA code for a particular protein.

The codes for amino acids, as well as the start and stop codons, are universal. In humans, mice, bacteria, or viruses, GGG translates to the same amino acid: glycine (GLY-seen). The universal start codon is AUG, which codes for methionine. UAA, UAG, and UGA are the three universal stop codons. You can see all the codons and the amino acids they code for in the table on page 187. The fact that all viruses and organisms share the same codons demonstrates the basic unity of life on Earth.

CHECKPOINT 8.1

1. During transcription, what is the relationship of mRNA to DNA ?

2. Explain the role of tRNA in protein synthesis.

3. Critical Thinking Translating the mRNA message into a protein can be compared to translating a language. Create an analogy for gene splicing.

Build On What You Know

4. Compare and contrast DNA replication and protein synthesis. *(Need to jog your memory? Revisit relevant concepts in Chapter 7, Section 7.2.)*

Modeling Protein Synthesis

WHAT YOU WILL DO Make a model to show the two processes of protein synthesis

SKILLS YOU WILL USE Modeling, collecting and recording data, analyzing, classifying

WHAT YOU WILL NEED 36 pushpins (5 different colors), metric ruler, 3 strips of corrugated cardboard (18 cm × 3 cm), marker

mRNA Codons and Amino Acids				
	2nd BASE			
	U	**C**	**A**	**G**	
U	UUU UUC — Phenylalanine / UUA UUG — Leucine	UCU UCC UCA UCG — Serine	UAU UAC — Tyrosine / UAA [Stop] / UAG [Stop]	UGU UGC — Cysteine / UGA [Stop] / UCG Tryptophan	U C A G
C	CUU CUC CUA CUG — Leucine	CCU CCC CCA CCG — Proline	CAU CAC — Histidine / CAA CAG — Glutamine	CGU CGC CGA CGG — Arginine	U C A G
A	AUU AUC — Isoleucine / AUA / AUG Methionine [Start]	ACU ACC ACA ACG — Threonine	AAU AAC — Asparagine / AAA AAG — Lysine	AGU AGC — Serine / AGA AGG — Arginine	U C A G
G	GUU GUC GUA GUG — Valine	GCU GCC GCA GCG — Alanine	GAU GAC — Aspartic acid / GAA GAG — Glutamic acid	GGU GGC GGA GGG — Glycine	U C A G

(1st BASE labeled along the left column)

Propose a Hypothesis

Propose a hypothesis about the relationship between bases in nucleic acids and amino acids in a model of protein synthesis.

Conduct Your Experiment

1 Group the pushpins by color to represent the five bases in DNA and RNA. Use the ruler and marker to divide each cardboard strip into six equal sections. Label the strips "DNA," "mRNA," and "tRNA." **Caution:** Pushpins are sharp.

2 Using the color pushpin you have chosen for each base, create the base sequence CCGAGTTAACCGACGTAA on the DNA cardboard strip. Put one codon in each section. Record your results.

3 Align the mRNA strip and the DNA strip. Use pushpins to model the complementary base sequence on the mRNA strip. Record the sequences.

4 Align the tRNA strip and the mRNA strip. Use pushpins to model the anticodons on the tRNA strip. Record these base sequences.

5 Use the table above to determine the names of the amino acids coded for by the mRNA base sequences. Record this information.

Analyze Your Data

1 Which parts of the activity represented transcription?

2 Which parts represented translation? Explain.

3 How would you change your model to show RNA splicing?

Draw Conclusions

How was your model similar to protein synthesis? How is the sequence of bases in nucleic acids related to the sequence of amino acids in proteins?

Design a Related Experiment

Design an experiment to show how a small change to a DNA or RNA base sequence can change the amino acids synthesized. Consider at least two different types of changes.

Modeling Protein Synthesis

Objective
Make a model to show the two processes of protein synthesis: transcription and translation.

8.2 Protein and Phenotype

What you'll learn

IDEAS

• To describe the control of gene expression in prokaryotes
• To appraise the effects of gene control in eukaryotic cells

WORDS

repressor, promoter

A chicken with duck feet?
Ducks have webbed feet. Chickens do not. Why? In part, because a molecular signal in the form of a protein called BMP (bone morphogenetic protein) helps control the normal development of a chicken's foot. A mutant gene that blocks cell receptors for BMP was introduced into this chicken embryo's right foot. What was the result?

Tidy Proteins

Do you like your laundry folded just so? The chains of amino acids that form proteins need to be folded just so, too. Scientists think that the way proteins are folded may be a key to understanding many traits.

PROTEINS AND CELL FUNCTIONS

What's your function?

Your body contains more than 50,000 different proteins. In fact, each individual cell can contain hundreds of different proteins. Proteins are the products of genes. When genes are changed, the proteins they code for may change. Changed proteins can affect cell structure and function and can result in an altered phenotype, as you can see in *Figure 8.6*.

As you know, all of your cells contain the same genes. But not all of your cells produce the same proteins. What, then, happens inside each cell to cause the same genes to produce different proteins? The answer is that genes in each of your cells—and in the cells of all living things—have control

mechanisms. These control mechanisms "turn on" or "turn off" genes, depending on specific environmental factors.

When a gene is "turned on," it is activated. Gene activation means that its product, a specific protein, is being synthesized by the cell. Protein synthesis indicates that a gene is being expressed. When a gene is "turned off," it is deactivated, and no protein synthesis (or gene expression) takes place.

The control of gene expression—that is, protein synthesis—differs in prokaryotes and eukaryotes. In prokaryotes, genes turn on and off primarily in response to changes in environmental factors. In multicellular eukaryotes, gene regulation often involves several rather complex systems.

FIGURE 8.6
A change in this person's DNA caused a change in protein synthesis in the cells of his fingers. The result is a phenotype that includes webbing and extra digits.

FIGURE 8.7

A Prokaryotic Control Mechanism

1 The genes are off

The regulatory gene codes for the production of the repressor. The repressor binds to DNA, preventing RNA polymerase from binding to the promoter. Protein synthesis of the digestive enzymes cannot occur.

Regulatory gene — Promoter — Repressor binding site — Genes that code for digestive enzymes

mRNA — Repressor — RNA polymerase — DNA

2 The repressor is inactivated

Lactose binds to the repressor, changing its shape, so that the repressor cannot bind to the DNA. RNA polymerase is free to bind to the promoter. Production of the enzymes can begin.

Lactose — Inactive repressor

3 The genes are on

As RNA polymerase moves along DNA, mRNA is translated to produce the digestive enzymes. When all the lactose is digested, the repressors take their original shape and bind to DNA again.

mRNA — Digestive enzymes

CONTROL IN PROKARYOTES

On again, off again

In a bacterial cell, some proteins are needed all the time, whereas other proteins are needed only under certain environmental conditions. Bacteria have mechanisms that turn the genes for such proteins on and off as needed. In 1961, French biochemists François Jacob and Jacques Monod proposed a hypothesis to explain this control of gene expression in bacteria. Their hypothesis describes how some proteins, once produced, turn off genes.

One example of the mechanism Jacob and Monod proposed is shown in *Figure 8.7*. The bacterium *E. coli* needs three enzymes to digest the sugar lactose. These enzymes are needed only when lactose is present. The genes that code for these enzymes are grouped on the *E. coli* chromosome. The relative amounts of lactose and enzymes in the cell are part of the mechanism that turns the genes for the digestive enzymes on and off.

Study *Figure 8.7* to see how the mechanism works: Inside an *E. coli* cell, a regulatory gene codes for the production of a specific protein called a repressor. A **repressor** is a protein that binds to DNA, turning off the genes that code for the digestive enzymes (step 1). The regulatory gene is continuously transcribed to make

FIGURE 8.8

Gene Control: An Analogy

You can compare the way lactose turns genes on and off to the way cold air signals a furnace to turn on.

1 Furnace "gene" on
In the presence of cold air, the thermostat signals the furnace to produce heat.

2 Furnace "gene" off
Once the cold air is warmed, the furnace is signaled to shut off.

mRNA, which is translated to make the repressor.

Near the digestive enzyme genes is the **promoter,** a section of DNA that serves as the binding site for the enzyme RNA polymerase. RNA polymerase is the enzyme that transcribes the DNA. The repressor blocks RNA polymerase from binding to the promoter. Because RNA polymerase is essential for transcription, the repressor prevents protein synthesis of the digestive enzymes. As you can see in step 1 of *Figure 8.7,* on page 189, no digestive enzymes are being produced.

So what turns the genes on? This is where lactose comes into the picture. When *E. coli* enters an environment high in lactose (step 2), lactose binds to the repressor, changing its shape. The changed repressor is inactivated and can no longer bind to DNA. Now RNA polymerase can bind to the promoter and move along the DNA, transcribing the genes that code for the digestive enzymes (step 3). The mRNA is translated and the digestive enzymes are synthesized— the genes that code for digestive enzymes are on.

Now look at *Figure 8.8*. Compare the concentration of lactose with the cold air (step 1). The furnace represents the digestive-enzyme genes, and the heat produced by the furnace represents the digestive enzymes coded by those genes. A high concentration of lactose turns on the digestive-enzyme genes, and the level of digestive enzymes increases.

A high temperature (less cold air) shuts the furnace off (step 2). Similarly, a high concentration of digestive enzymes causes lactose levels to fall, shutting off the genes.

The digestive enzymes are produced until all lactose is removed. In the absence of lactose, repressors are once again active, free to bind to

DNA, and the digestive-enzyme genes are switched off.

You have just read how the presence or absence of an environmental factor—lactose—determines whether certain genes are on or off. This is only one model of control. Sometimes the amount of the protein produced by a gene controls that gene's expression. How does this happen? The repressors are normally inactive (not bound to DNA), so the genes are on (producing their protein product). But high levels of the protein product activate the repressors, causing them to bind to the DNA. The repressor then prevents protein synthesis, and the genes are off. Once levels of the protein drop to normal, the repressors are inactivated and the genes are again on.

CONTROL IN EUKARYOTES

New cell, new control

Almost all types of cells in your body have the same set of chromosomes. Yet each type of cell has a different structure and function. You can see a few of these specialized cells in *Figure 8.9*. Specialized cells result from differences in the control of gene expression.

In humans and other eukaryotes, the control of gene expression is more complex than in prokaryotes such as bacteria. Most prokaryotes are unicellular. Eukaryotes are often multicellular. The development of specialized cells and tissues in eukaryotes requires complex systems of gene control.

One way the specialization of eukaryotic cells can be controlled is through selective gene expression. In other words, only some of the genes on a eukaryote's chromosomes actually function; the rest are turned off permanently. The genes that do function may be turned on or off, depending on the organism's stage of development or on environmental factors.

In *Figure 8.7* you saw how an environmental factor can turn genes on or off in prokaryotes. Research indicates that genes in eukaryotes also have regulatory proteins to turn the genes on or off. However, unlike the digestive enzyme genes in *E. coli*, the eukaryotic genes for related proteins are not linked together. Related genes can be far apart or on different chromosomes. Therefore, a single promoter or repressor cannot always control protein synthesis.

Another method for controlling eukaryotic gene expression is by controlling RNA splicing. Recall that mRNA in the cytoplasm contains only exons. In some cases, the splicing of RNA from a single gene varies according to cell type. The result is that each cell type produces a mRNA with a different combination of exons. Regulation of RNA splicing means that one gene produces different proteins in different cell types.

Sometimes the control mechanisms fail. A change in the expression of a gene can result in proteins being made at the wrong time. This can alter the development, structure and function of a cell. Sometimes this can cause a cell to become cancerous. A cancer cell lacks the genetic controls that normally limit its ability to grow and divide.

Nerve cells found in the brain

Skin cells and shaved hairs

Lung tissue

Colon tissue in the digestive system

Muscle cells like those found in the arms and legs

FIGURE 8.9
This athlete's body contains about 300 different cells with different functions. Almost all of these cells contain exactly the same DNA. The genes that are activated in specific cells determine their specialized functions.

CHECKPOINT 8.2

1. How is gene expression controlled in prokaryotes?

2. What is meant by the term *cell specialization?* How is cell specialization controlled?

3. Critical Thinking Suppose the first intron in a gene was not removed but was treated as an exon. How might mRNA's protein product be affected?

Build on What You Know

4. Using your knowledge of cell organelles and their functions, describe an imaginary defect in a cell's DNA and its effect on one organelle. (*Need to jog your memory? Revisit relevant concepts in Chapter 3, Section 3.3, and Chapter 7, Section 7.2.*)

What is a gene? What is the result of gene translation? **?**

8.3 Changes in Chromosomes

What you'll learn

IDEAS

• To explain how mutations can affect proteins and protein synthesis
• To distinguish between chromosomal mutations and gene mutations

WORDS

mutation, deletion, duplication, translocation, inversion, frameshift mutation, point mutation

Bald cats have mutant gene
The hairless Sphinx is a rare breed of cat. Its hairlessness results from a change in a chromosome—a recessive mutation of a gene. Some people think these cats are good pets for people who suffer from allergies. Others think that breeding cats for this trait is cruel because it leaves the cats unprotected from the cold.

FIGURE 8.10

Deletion

The notched wing on this fruit fly (bottom) results from a deletion mutation.

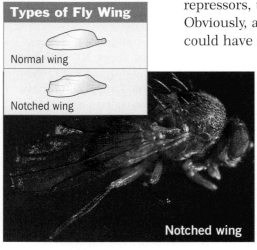

Types of Fly Wing

Normal wing

Notched wing

Notched wing

a b c d e f

Deletion

a c d e f

PROTEINS AND MUTATIONS

Small changes, big results

You know that proteins are an important part of an organism's structure and ability to function. Some proteins carry out functions within the cells of an organism. Others are exported from cells for other purposes. Still other proteins act as activators or repressors, turning genes on or off. Obviously, a change in a cell's proteins could have dramatic effects on the cell's structure or function. How can the composition of a cell's proteins change?

Changes in DNA can change the proteins that a cell synthesizes. A random change in the sequence of nucleotides in DNA is called a **mutation.** Many factors can cause mutations. You will learn about some of these factors in the next section. Some mutations have little or no effect on

an organism, others are harmful or fatal, and a very few are beneficial. There are two categories of mutations: chromosomal mutations and gene mutations. Chromosomal mutations involve entire chromosomes. Gene mutations involve individual genes.

CHROMOSOMAL MUTATIONS

Chaotic rearrangements

Chromosomal mutations are changes in the structure of a chromosome. There are four types of chromosomal mutations: deletion, duplication, translocation, and inversion.

A **deletion** occurs when a chromosome breaks and a piece of the chromosome is lost. If you use a computer, you probably know that the delete key can be used to remove letters or words from a document. Deleting words or letters changes the document. As you can see in the diagram in *Figure 8.10,* gene *b* has been deleted from the chromosome. How do you think this change affects the original chromosome?

Compare the two types of fruit fly wings shown in *Figure 8.10.* The

FIGURE 8.11

Duplication

In fruit flies, the bar eye mutation (bottom) is the result of a duplication. Which gene in the diagram was duplicated?

Normal eye

Bar eye

Duplication

notched-wing phenotype results from a deletion. This mutation is not especially harmful to the fly. Most deletions, however, are lethal, killing the organism.

A **duplication** occurs when part of a chromosome breaks off and is incorporated into its homologous chromosome. The homologous chromosome then has an extra copy of one of its parts. In Chapter 7 you learned about crossing over during meiosis. Duplication can result from an unequal crossover of chromosomes. Look at the diagrams of the chromosome in *Figure 8.11.* How did duplication change the chromosome? Now take a look at the photographs in *Figure 8.11.* The fly's bar eyes are the result of a duplication in the X chromosome.

In **translocation,** a chromosome part breaks off and attaches to a different, nonhomologous chromosome.

Translocation is illustrated in *Figure 8.12.* Translocation may result in too many or too few genes in a chromosome and can affect organisms in several ways. As in deletion and duplication, a change in the number of genes can harm or kill an organism. Changing the order of genes can also affect the control of gene expression.

An unusual series of translocations can occur in all seven chromosomes of a flower called the evening primrose. Although the results of the translocations are not visible, the mutation limits the plant's fertility, or ability to reproduce.

Invert means to "turn upside down" or "reverse the order of." When part of a chromosome breaks off, turns around, and reattaches in the reverse order, it has undergone **inversion.** *Figure 8.13* illustrates inversion. Inversions generally cause less harm than deletions or duplications, primarily because an inversion changes the order of genes in a chromosome but not the number of genes it contains.

GENE MUTATIONS

A little off base

Gene mutations are errors that occur within individual genes in a chromosome. Gene mutations can involve a single nucleotide or they can affect sections of DNA that include many nucleotides.

Frameshift mutations The deletion or addition of nucleotides that disrupts codons is called a **frameshift mutation.** Because mRNA is read in codons (three-base sections) during translation, an addition or deletion of nucleotides can alter the sequence of bases, or reading frame, of the genetic message.

Compare a frameshift mutation to a sentence composed of three-letter

FIGURE 8.12

Translocation

One type of evening primrose commonly undergoes translocation. Note that the original chromosomes are nonhomologous—they have different types and arrangements of genes. How are the chromosomes changed?

Translocation

FIGURE 8.13

Inversion

In an inversion, part of a chromosome is broken off and reattached in reverse order, but no genes are lost. How have the genes changed?

Inversion

Chapter 8 Protein Synthesis **193**

words: *Pat the bad cat.* Each word in this sentence can be compared to a codon in a DNA sequence. If a letter is deleted, for example *a* in *pat,* the sentence changes into *Ptt heb adc at.* As you can see, the sentence becomes nonsense. Analyze the frameshift mutation in *Figure 8.14.* What are the codons in the original reading frame? What are the codons in the shifted reading frame?

Recall what happens when a strand of mRNA is transcribed from DNA. Using that information, predict what might happen if one base is deleted from the DNA. You are right if you said the transcribed mRNA would also be affected. Unlike the sentence analogy, however, a frameshift mutation does not create nonsense. It can still be translated. Because each codon corresponds to an amino acid, altering the codons may alter the amino acid sequence. As you can see in *Figure 8.14,* the end result may be an entirely different protein product.

The amount of genetic material that is lost or gained during frameshift mutations is much smaller than the amount lost or gained in chromosomal mutations. However, because frameshift mutations affect the sequence of amino acids, they can have an enormous impact on an organism's structure and function.

Point mutations A change that occurs in only one nucleotide is a **point mutation.** A point mutation can result from a base-pair substitution in which just one pair of bases is replaced in a gene.

Because a point mutation affects a single codon, it tends to be far less disruptive than a frameshift mutation. Some amino acids are coded for by more than one codon, and substitution may simply change one codon to another codon for the same amino acid. For example, look at the table of codons on page 187. You can see that any substitution of the third base of a codon for arginine will still result in arginine. About 30 percent of all substitution mutations produce no changes in proteins.

In the remaining 70 percent of substitutions, changed nucleotides cause a different amino acid to be incorporated into a protein. The resulting protein may function normally or may be defective. *Figure 8.15* shows how the substitution of asingle base in the gene for hemoglobin can produce the gene for sickle-cell hemoglobin, which in turn causes sickle-cell disease. When oxygen is low, sickle-cell hemoglobin causes the blood cells to change into the sickle shape that characterizes the disease.

A third and very common point mutation occurs when a codon in the middle of a gene is

FIGURE 8.14
A frameshift mutation begins when DNA is changed and then transcribed. The resulting mRNA is missing a uracil base. Compare the amino acids normally coded for by mRNA with those it codes for after the mutation.

Before mutation

After mutation

Normal hemoglobin

Normal DNA

mRNA

Protein synthesized

Leu — Glu — Glu

Sickle-cell hemoglobin

Mutant DNA

mRNA

Protein synthesized

Leu — Val — Glu

FIGURE 8.15
Sickle-cell disease is a result of abnormal hemoglobin production caused by a point mutation. How does the DNA sequence change? The mRNA sequence? The amino acid sequence?

LAB ZONE **Think About It!**

From Milk to Wasp: Modeling Mutations

Small mutations in DNA can cause huge changes in the protein synthesized. Similarly, small changes in a word can drastically alter its meaning. Look at the following sequence of words:

milk mile wile wise wisp wasp

Note that each word differs from the previous word by only one letter and none of the words is meaningless. Consider these changes as "point mutations" affecting word meaning.

Try This

1 Think of a word. Then change the word letter by letter as modeled above. Make sure each word you create is an actual word. What word did you end up with?
2 Think of a way to use words to model frameshift mutations. Hint: You might take one sentence and make only one change in one word.
3 Model jumping gene mutation by inserting one sentence into another. Does the new sentence make sense?

changed to a stop codon. When genes with this mutation go through protein synthesis, translation is halted before the amino acid chain is completed.

Jumping genes A gene mutation can also occur when large stretches of DNA are inserted into the gene. American geneticist Barbara McClintock studied kernel color in maize (corn). Her research revealed that some genes "jump" from one location to another–they are called jumping genes. A jumping gene sometimes inserts itself into another gene, disrupting the DNA sequence of that gene.

McClintock proposed her theory in 1947, but her ideas were not acknowledged for years. In 1983, almost three decades after her first publication on

the subject, McClintock won the Nobel prize for her discovery.

CHECKPOINT 8.3

1. How do DNA mutations affect proteins?
2. Compare and contrast chromosomal mutations and gene mutations.
3. Critical Thinking The effects of a mutation are not always visible. How might a researcher determine whether a mutation has occurred and, if so, what type of mutation it is?

Build on What You Know

4. In Chapter 7 you learned about some changes in the human genome. Compare and contrast those types of genetic changes with chromosomal and gene mutations. *(Need to jog your memory? Revisit relevant concepts in Chapter 7, Section 7.5.)*

8.4 Genes and Cancer

What you'll learn

IDEAS
• To summarize the role of oncogenes in the development of cancer
• To identify environmental causes of mutation

WORDS
oncogene, mutagen, carcinogen

Handle with care
Wilhelm Roentgen discovered X rays in 1895. One of his first photographs was of his wife's hand. Almost overnight doctors put X rays to widespread use, but later experiments showed that X rays trigger mutations that can cause cancer. Today, the careful use of X rays can help diagnose and treat cancer, reveal living bones and teeth, and aid in medical research.

MUTATIONS AND CONTROL

Mutant genes let cells grow out of control

As you learned in section 8.3, mutations are random events with unpredictable results. Most mutations have little or no effect on an organism's function. Such mutations are a source of genetic variation. Genetic variations in a population can contribute to the adaptation of a species to a changing environment.

Some mutations, however, are harmful or even lethal. When mutations change the genes that control cell growth and specialization, cancer may result. In Chapter 5 you learned that cancer is uncontrolled, abnormal cell division. There are many different types of cancer, because any of the hundreds of types of cells in the human body can become cancerous.

Cancer cells can also migrate from one part of an organism to another part.

The causes of cancer vary. Some cancers, such as the one causing the eye tumors shown in *Figure 8.16,* can be inherited. Other cancers result from environmental factors. Still others are a result of combination of genetic and environmental factors. Regardless of their cause, all cancers share one feature: The genes that control production of new cells do not shut off as they should.

A gene that causes a cell to become cancerous is called an **oncogene** (ON-koh-jeen). Researchers have found that some oncogenes in viruses have been linked to certain types of cancer. Other oncogenes in human chromosomes appear to be mutated forms of genes that code for proteins called growth factors. These growth factors help control cell division and differentiation.

As you can see in *Figure 8.17,* there are three basic ways a gene can become an oncogene. First, a mutation may occur in a growth-factor gene. The mutation can result in production of normal amounts of growth factor, but the protein may be altered to a "super" growth factor, causing rapid and uncontrolled cell division.

Second, an error in DNA replication can result in multiple copies of a

FIGURE 8.16

These MRI (magnetic resonance imaging) photographs show cross sections of two skulls; the patients' eyes are at the top of each image. Compare the healthy patient's eyes (right) with those of the patient with the eye cancer retinoblastoma (left). Retinoblastoma results from the mutation of a gene that normally prevents tumor growth.

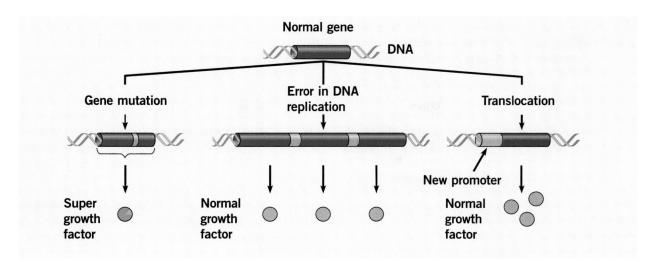

Normal gene

DNA

Gene mutation

Error in DNA
replication

Translocation

New promoter

Super
growth
factor

Normal
growth
factor

Normal
growth
factor

FIGURE 8.17
Here are three ways onco-
genes may arise from a
normal gene. The effects of
the mutations are similar.
How do the types of muta-
tions differ?

FIGURE 8.18
A tumor-suppressor gene in
chromosome 13 normally
prevents the growth of
retinoblastoma tumors.
Any deletion of a tumor-
suppressor gene can result
in cancer.

single growth-factor gene. Where one gene would normally be transcribed to produce growth factor, now several are transcribed, and the amount of growth factor in the cell increases. In this case, the replicated genes are acting together as oncogenes.

Third, a change in a gene's location can create an oncogene. As you learned in section 8.3, translocation can change a gene's position in a chromosome. In some cases, the translocated gene comes under the control of a new promoter that permits more frequent transcription of the gene. As a result, the growth factor is produced much more often.

Cancers may also arise because of changes in genes responsible for preventing uncontrolled cell growth, called tumor suppressor genes. You can think of tumor suppressors as "anti-oncogenes" because they help prevent the growth of tumors. A gene mutation can make a tumor suppressor non-functional. If a tumor suppressor gene is mutated or deleted, the result can be uncontrolled cell reproduction.

The rare, life-threatening cancer retinoblastoma (REH-tin-oh-blas-TOH-muh) was one of the first heritable cancers to be identified. Retinoblastoma results in tumors of the eyes. One form of the disorder was traced to changes in a tumor-suppressor gene on chromosome 13.

The inherited form of this cancer is caused by a recessive mutation in the tumor-suppressor gene. Recall that a recessive mutation is expressed only when both chromosomes in a homologous pair have the mutation. Patients with the recessive mutation in only one chromosome are said to be predisposed to the cancer. Tumors are almost certain to appear when there is a second, noninherited change on the homologous chromosome.

Another form of retinoblastoma is not inherited. Scientists have determined that the noninherited form is caused by deletions in both copies of chromosome 13, within immature cells of the eye. You can see the site of the tumor-suppressor gene and the deletions that affect the gene in *Figure 8.18.*

By identifying the sites of genes linked to cancers, geneticists can predict whether someone is predisposed to or almost certain to develop a cancer. This knowledge enables doctors to treat the disease more effectively. Work on the Human Genome Project, as well as research on organisms such as yeast and the *Drosophila* fruit fly, has helped identify heritable cancers

Deletion
site

Deletion
site

Location
of tumor-
suppressor
gene

Cancers Linked to Deletion Mutations	
Site of Cancer	Chromosome Affected
Breast	17
Colon	5, 17
Eye (retinoblastoma)	13
Kidney (Wilms tumor)	11

FIGURE 8.19

Some cancers at the sites listed above have been linked to deletions in specific chromosomes. Other cancers, however, have not been linked to genetic factors. To what other factors have cancers been linked?

FIGURE 8.20

In 1986, an accident at the Chernobyl nuclear power plant in Ukraine (then part of the Soviet Union) released a large amount of radiation. Since then, scientists have observed an extremely high mutation rate in the mitochondria of Siberian voles living in the area. What environmental factor probably caused the mutations?

such as those listed in *Figure 8.19*. It is important to keep in mind, however, that the development of cancer depends on environmental factors as well as genetic factors.

CAUSES OF GENE MUTATIONS

Environment comes into play

Environmental factors can play a major role in the development of cancer. A person with only a predisposition to a type of cancer will, under certain environmental conditions, almost certainly develop the disease. The same person can reduce his or her risk of developing cancer by controlling environmental conditions, because environmental factors can contribute to the formation of unfavorable gene mutations.

A factor in the environment that can cause mutations in DNA is called a **mutagen** (MYOO-tuh-jen). Well-known mutagens include some forms of radiation—such as the type released from nuclear accidents—and a variety of chemicals, including many found in tobacco products.

Some—but not all—mutagens cause cancer. An agent that causes or tends to cause cancer is called a **carcinogen** (kar-SIN-oh-jen). Examples

include the tars in cigarette smoke, some drugs, certain chemicals in smoked meats, coal tars in some hair dyes, viruses that have been linked to cancers, and some types of radiation.

Ultraviolet (UV) radiation is a mutagen and a carcinogen—UV rays cause DNA in cells to mutate, and exposure to UV radiation has been linked to skin cancer. Like other mutagens, UV rays cause changes in the DNA message that can be passed on to daughter cells when a cell divides.

A layer of ozone in the upper atmosphere normally protects us from some UV rays. However, the ozone layer has been damaged in recent decades, most likely by chemical pollutants called chlorofluorocarbons. These chemicals were once widely used in aerosol sprays and refrigerants. Many countries have passed laws to limit the use of chlorofluorocarbons.

How do carcinogens change DNA? The answer varies with the type of mutagen. Carcinogens can cause cancer by either replacing or changing DNA bases. Some carcinogens are chemically similar to the bases of DNA. These carcinogens are called base analogs (*analog* means "parallel"). Base analogs can be incorporated into a DNA molecule. Because they are not exactly the same as DNA

IN THE COMMUNITY

Where There's Smoke...

Research has shown that tobacco smoke can cause cancer. To protect the public health, many communities have regulated smoking in public places. For example, some communities do not allow smoking in restaurants; others require that restaurants have separate smoking and nonsmoking areas. Find out about the regulations that are in effect in your community and how they are enforced. Then survey community members to find out their opinion of local regulations. What do residents, business owners, and local officials think of the regulations? Compile your results and write a summary of your conclusions. Are the smoking regulations in your community appropriate? Should they be stricter or more lenient?

bases, these analogs form abnormal base pairs and confuse the genetic message. Other carcinogens react with the DNA bases, changing them. Then, when the cell divides, the changed DNA messages are passed on to daughter cells.

The ability of chemicals to cause cancer is linked to their ability to cause mutations. Scientists have devised a test for possible carcinogens called the Ames test. In the Ames test, bacteria are treated with the chemical that is a suspected carcinogen. If mutations are detected in the bacteria, it is assumed that the chemical may produce cancer-causing mutations in humans. Researchers then perform different tests to see if the substance poses a substantial risk to humans. If it does, measures may be taken to control or ban its use.

FRONTIERS IN BIOLOGY

Eat your vegetables

The information scientists have gathered about cancer, genes, and the environment may seem pretty grim. But there is good news—as scientists

learn more about cancer, they also learn more about how to prevent it and how best to treat it.

Scientists are using the ever-growing body of knowledge about the genetics of cancer to develop new approaches to treatment. Gene therapy—replacing mutated genes with normal ones—has already been attempted for some cancers and may become commonplace. Through genetic engineering, scientists are using viruses to help treat cancers. More conventional cancer treatments, such as radiation and chemotherapy, as well as methods of early detection, continue to be developed and refined.

As you have just read, environmental factors can increase a person's risk of developing cancer. But by controlling certain environmental factors, an individual can reduce his or her risk.

Screening to detect early-stage cancers is also an important preventive measure. The best times for screenings depend on a person's age, sex, and family history. Preventive screenings include tests for testicular and prostate cancer in men and the Pap test for cervical cancer in women.

EVERYDAY BIOLOGY

Feeling the Burn?

Why is skin cancer on the rise? For one reason, a lot of people think a tan looks good. Another reason may be the damaged ozone layer, which allows more UV rays to reach Earth's surface. The longer your exposure to UV rays, the greater your risk of developing skin cancer.

FIGURE 8.21
Because of the work of researchers, more and more people are surviving cancer. Angus Bradshaw survived Hodgkin disease and is now a healthy teenager leading an active life.

FIGURE 8.22
Healthy behaviors, such as wearing sunscreen, can help you reduce your risk of developing certain types of cancer.

Some doctors, as well as the American Cancer Society, recommend that beginning at age 40 women have regular mammograms to screen for breast cancer. Some experts urge that women with a family history of breast cancer begin having mammograms at an earlier age and have them more often than women without such a family history. Self-examinations for breast, skin, or testicular cancers are also helpful when combined with regularly scheduled screenings.

Because tobacco is a carcinogen, avoiding it is a healthy behavior that can lower your risk of developing lung and mouth cancers. About a third of all cases of cancer in the United States can be linked to cigarette smoking. As you will learn in Chapter 31, smoking can also lead to heart disease and lung disorders.

There are other healthy behaviors you can follow. Eat a diet low in fat and high in fiber and the vitamin source called beta-carotene. Such a diet includes lots of whole-grain breads, fruits, and vegetables (especially carrots, broccoli, cauliflower, and spinach), all of which can reduce your risk of developing certain digestive cancers. A diet rich in certain vitamins (A, C, and E) is also thought to reduce the risk of cancer in general. You can reduce your risk of developing skin cancer by using a sunscreen with a high sun-protection factor (SPF) and by wearing clothing and a hat that blocks the sun.

New discoveries in cancer research are being made all the time, and scientists are continually reviewing and refining their viewpoints as new data are collected. Advances in science, combined with the preventive steps people can take themselves, increase the chances for winning the fight against cancer.

CHECKPOINT 8.4

1. Describe the role of oncogenes in the development of cancer.
2. Name three environmental factors that can cause cancer and three factors that reduce the risk of developing it.
3. **Critical Thinking** Why would a recessive mutation—a mutation in only one of the chromosomes of a homologous pair—not necessarily result in cancer?

Build on What You Know

4. Describe the relationship between cell division and cancer. *(Need to jog your memory? Revisit relevant concepts in Chapter 5, Section 5.1.)*

What types of changes can occur in DNA? What are some results caused by changes in DNA?

Chapter 8 Review

 THE BIG IDEA! 8.1–8.2 Genes are sequences of DNA bases that can be translated into proteins or parts of proteins when they are activated.

8.3–8.4 Changes in DNA can cause changes in phenotype.

Sum It Up

Use the following summary to review the main concepts in this chapter.

8.1 From Genotype to Phenotype

- Protein synthesis occurs in two stages: transcription and translation.
- Transcription is the process by which information is copied from DNA into a strand of messenger RNA (mRNA).
- Translation is the process by which the information from nucleic acids is coded for amino acids.
- mRNA splicing occurs between transcription and translation in eukaryotes.

8.2 Protein and Phenotype

- The function and structure of a cell is determined by the kinds of protein it makes.
- The control of gene expression is different in prokaryotic and eukaryotic cells.
- Repressor proteins can block transcription when they bind to promotor regions of DNA.

8.3 Changes in Chromosomes

- A change in an organism's DNA is a mutation. A mutation can be beneficial, but it is usually harmful to or has no effect on the organism.
- Four types of chromosomal mutation are deletion, duplication, translocation, and inversion.
- Two kinds of gene mutation, or change in base sequence, are frameshift mutation and point mutation.

8.4 Genes and Cancer

- Oncogenes change a normal cell into a cancerous cell—one that reproduces abnormally.
- Mutagens are environmental factors that cause DNA mutations. Mutagens that cause cancer are carcinogens.

Use Terms and Concepts

Use each of the following words or terms in a complete sentence. If you need to review a meaning, turn to the page indicated.

protein synthesis (p. 182)
RNA (p. 182)
transcription (p. 182)
translation (p. 183)
introns (p. 184)
exons (p. 184)
codon (p. 184)

anticodon (p. 185)
repressor (p. 189)
promoter (p. 190)
mutation (p. 192)
deletion (p. 192)
duplication (p. 193)
translocation (p. 193)

inversion (p. 193)
frameshift mutation (p. 193)
point mutation (p. 194)
oncogene (p. 196)
mutagen (p. 198)
carcinogen (p. 198)

Use Your Word Power

COMPLETION Write the word or phrase that best completes each statement.

1. _____ are located in DNA and signal RNA polymerase to begin transcribing.

2. During transcription, DNA serves as a template for producing _____, which then leaves the nucleus to begin translation.

3. A(n) _____ involves the replacement of a single base in a codon.

4. A(n) _____ is a three-base section of mRNA.

5. The assembly of proteins is called _____ .

6. During protein synthesis in prokaryotes and eukaryotes, the process of _____ occurs before translation.

MATCHING Write the letter corresponding to the definition of each word.

7. Frameshift mutation ____

8. Deletion ____

9. Duplication ____

10. Translocation ____

11. Inversion ____

12. Oncogene ____

13. Carcinogen ____

14. Mutagen ____

a. When part of a chromosome breaks off and joins with its homologous chromosome

b. A mutagen that causes cancer

c. A mutation-causing agent

d. A gene mutation that affects the series of codons

e. When part of a chromosome breaks off and joins with a nonhomologous chromosome

f. A mutation in which part of the chromosome breaks off and is lost to the genome

g. A gene that changes a normal cell into a cancerous cell

h. When part of a chromosome breaks off, reverses order, and rejoins the chromosome

Show What You Know

15. What are codons and anticodons? How are they similar? How are they different?

16. How do repressors affect promoters? How do repressors affect protein synthesis?

17. Explain the process of transcription.

18. What is translation, and where in a eukaryotic cell does it occur?

19. Distinguish between introns and exons. Why is mRNA splicing necessary?

20. Name and describe the two types of gene mutations.

21. What role do mutagens play in cancer?

22. **Make a Concept Map** Complete the concept map below by adding the following terms: protein synthesis, mRNA, tRNA, translation, codon, elongation, anticodon.

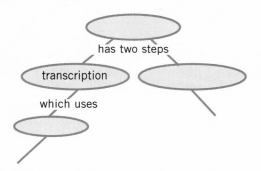

Take It Further

23. **Identifying Cause and Effect** To determine the codons for specific amino acids, scientists add mRNA molecules of one base (i.e. UUUUUU) to a test tube mixture capable of synthesizing proteins. What result will researchers then look for?

24. **Applying Concepts** About 30 percent of substitution mutations result in no change in the genetic code. Use the table on page 187 to explain why.

25. **Developing a Hypothesis** Many hormones are proteins. How might the production of a hormone affect the activation of genes in eukaryotic cells? (Hint: Use promoters in your hypothesis.)

26. Designing an Experiment You suspect that a certain substance is a mutagen. Design an experiment to test your hypothesis.

27. Interpreting a Graph The Ames test determines mutation rates by measuring the effects of substances on bacterial cell growth under special conditions. According to the graph, which of these imaginary substances are likely to be mutagens?

Ames Test Results

28. Analyzing Data The table below shows the percentage of bases in both strands of DNA and in the mRNA of an imaginary citizen from Atlantis, the lost city. Which DNA strand is the mRNA template? Explain your answer.

Base Percentages	A	G	C	T	U
DNA Strand 1	28.2	22.3	22.6	27.9	0
DNA Strand 2	27.9	22.6	22.3	28.2	0
mRNA	28.2	22.3	22.6	0	27.9

29. Making Analogies Working with a two-letter alphabet (*A* and *B*), devise a coding system using only *A*'s and *B*'s to give names to the colors *red, blue, yellow,* and *green*. Now write this sequence, using your code: *red, yellow, blue, red, red, green, yellow, blue.* How is your system similar to protein synthesis?

Consider the Issues

30. Regulating Cancer You have read about healthy behaviors that can help people reduce the risk of getting cancer. How do you think local and federal governments should regulate the production of carcinogenic substances?

Make New Connections

31. Biology and Music Some composers have created music based on gene sequences. Research the sequence of the gene that codes for a specific protein, such as insulin. Assign four notes to the four nitrogenous bases and play or sing your piece.

32. Biology and Community Contact a local chapter of the American Cancer Society or a local hospital. Volunteer to help at a cancer-awareness program or a fund-raiser for cancer research. Report your activities by telling what you have learned to the class.

33. Biology and Literature Write a skit about protein synthesis. Include characters such as ribosomes, amino acids, proteins, DNA, and RNA.

FAST-FORWARD TO CHAPTER 9

Using information discovered by geneticists, genetic engineers can now manipulate genes. In the next chapter, you will learn about genetic engineering and consider some of its applications.

The Biotechnology Revolution

You can find out more about genetic engineering by exploring the following Internet address:
http://genetics.biosurf.com

FEATURES

Everyday Biology
• The Ugliest Fruit
• Little Clues of You

In the Community
Biotech Bulletin

 Environmental Awareness
Seed Banks

Issues in Biology
Ethical Questions

LAB ZONES

Discover It!
• Discovering What Makes Fingerprints Unique

Do It!
• How Big Is the Human Genome?
• How Can Ethical Questions Be Answered?

Think About It!
• Analyzing Gel Electrophoresis Results

Investigate It!
• Modeling DNA Probes

ROYALTY WAS IN THEIR BONES

Discovering What Makes Fingerprints Unique

You need an ink pad, plain paper, tracing paper, and a thin black marker

1. Use the ink pad and paper to obtain the prints of all the fingers on one of your hands.
2. Place the tracing paper over your fingerprints. Trace the major patterns in your fingerprints with the black marker.

Fingerprints have been used for identification purposes for many years. Compare your traced fingerprints with those of your classmates. How are they unique?

Fingerprints have their shortcomings as an identification tool, however. Based on this exercise, what might the shortcomings be? Recently, scientists have used DNA fingerprints for identification purposes. Compared to your real fingerprints, your DNA fingerprint is more reliable.

WRITE ABOUT IT!

In your science journal, write about the similarities and differences you have seen between fingerprints. Then use what you know about DNA structure to hypothesize what might be unique about DNA to "fingerprint."

The location of the skeletons was known for almost 15 years before political changes permitted the remains to be examined. But in 1991 the time was right to uncover the 73-year-old bones and confirm their identity. The bones were scattered (as shown above) in a shallow pit. Were the skeletons the remains of Russia's last royal family, the Romanovs?

Although the bones' shapes and sizes seemed to match descriptions of the Romanovs, scientists needed more conclusive evidence. So they studied the DNA contained in the bones. Genetics researchers used a technique called DNA fingerprinting to confirm familial relationships among the skeletons. They also compared the DNA fingerprints with those of living relatives of the Romanov family—including Prince Philip of Great Britain—to prove that they had indeed found the skeletons of the royal family. By examining the sequence of bases in DNA, genetic engineers had solved one of Russia's great mysteries: the location of the final resting place of the royal Romanovs. But what is DNA fingerprinting, and how can it be used for identification?

9.1 Breeding

What you'll learn

IDEAS

- To compare inbreeding and outbreeding
- To identify the benefits and dangers of selective breeding

WORDS

selective breeding, inbreeding, outbreeding

Basic instincts

Not only do different dog breeds look different, they also exhibit different behaviors. For what unique traits do you think retrievers like this one were bred? Of course, it took many generations to establish these traits. In this chapter you will learn about faster ways to establish traits within a breed.

SELECTIVE BREEDING

The first biotechnology

The breeding of organisms to produce certain desired traits in their offspring is called **selective breeding.** Our ancestors were actually using laws of genetics when they selectively bred dogs and other animals. Selective breeding is one example of biotechnology. Biotechnology is the use of living organisms to make products, such as medicines and improved crops, or to benefit humans.

Humans used basic principles of genetics long before they understood those principles very well. For example, ancient peoples native to North and South America used selective breeding to develop corn and potatoes from wild plants. How does the wild grass teosinte, shown in *Figure 9.1,* differ from modern domestic corn? Today, farmers still use selective breeding to develop new crops.

In order for a new breed with a desired trait to be established, only the offspring that inherit the desired trait are selected to reproduce. This selection process is then repeated for subsequent generations until the trait has been successfully established in the population.

To maintain a desirable set of traits, breeders use a type of selection called inbreeding. **Inbreeding** is the crossing of organisms that have a similar genotype. For example, an animal breeder may mate two closely related animals that possess desirable traits.

FIGURE 9.1

Teosinte (left) was selectively bred to produce many varieties of corn, including modern domestic corn (right). The center photograph shows how a small teosinte cob compares to a modern corn kernel. What traits do teosinte and modern domestic corn share?

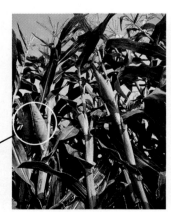

FIGURE 9.2

Inbreeding and Animal Health

Inbreeding can result in health problems. These problems are sometimes due to harmful recessive alleles.

A Persian cat's flat face is a trait often associated with breathing problems.

The shar-pei was bred for its huge rolls of skin—a trait that can lead to skin diseases.

A basset hound's characteristic droopy, baggy eyes are prone to infection.

As its population has diminished, the Florida panther has been forced to inbreed, resulting in heart defects and fertility problems.

After several generations, the offspring are probably purebred, or homozygous, for most of the desired traits. Certain crops and breeds of dogs, horses, and other animals are maintained by inbreeding.

Although inbreeding can produce and maintain desirable traits, it can also result in problems. Inbred organisms can carry recessive alleles that produce harmful traits when homozygous. As long as the recessive alleles for undesirable traits are paired with normal, dominant alleles, they cause little or no harm. However, close relatives are more likely to carry the same harmful recessive allele than are distant relatives. Therefore, the offspring of closely related parents are more likely than offspring of unrelated parents to be homozygous for undesirable traits. Review the information given in *Figure 9.2*. What types of health problems can arise through inbreeding?

HYBRIDIZATION

Mixing it up

Another type of selective breeding is called outbreeding, or hybridization. **Outbreeding** is the crossing of distantly related organisms. Such organisms may come from different species and be very different genetically from each other. More often, outbreeding involves individuals from two breeds of the same species—for example, a shar-pei and a basset hound. Animal and plant breeders often use outbreeding to combine the desirable qualities from two different parents.

Outbreeding is an important tool in efforts to conserve endangered species. For example, the Florida panther is one of the most endangered land animals in the world, with fewer than 100 members of this species left. Inbreeding among Florida panthers has led to health problems such as heart disease. In an effort to save the Florida panthers from total extinction and to bolster the panthers' genetic variation, Florida state officials have introduced Texas cougars into the panther population.

In some cases, outbreeding produces larger, healthier offspring—an effect called hybrid vigor. A mule, the result of crossing a male donkey and a female horse, is hardier than a horse but more docile than a donkey. Another example of a hybrid is shown in *Figure 9.3* on page 208. The "liger" is a large, strong hybrid produced by crossing a

FIGURE 9.3
A liger is the offspring of a male lion and female tiger.
Why is the liger an example of hybrid vigor?

The Ugliest Fruit

The Uglifruit is a type of tangelo that comes from the West Indies. Tangelos are hybrids produced by crossing tangerine trees with grapefruit trees. The name tangelo comes from TANGerine and pomELO, another name for grapefruit.

male lion with a female tiger. Hybrids that have parents from different species, such as mules and ligers, are usually sterile. Because the chromosomes of parents from different species do not usually match up in homologous pairs, they cannot undergo meiosis, and the hybrid offspring cannot produce normal gametes.

ENVIRONMENTAL AWARENESS

Seed banks

One of the most important banks in the world does not store gold, money, or jewels. This bank has the awesome task of preserving life as we know it. The bank contains seeds.

The National Seed Storage Laboratory (NSSL) is located in Colorado and has hundreds of thousands of seed samples. The majority of these samples are seeds for food crops from all over the world. Perhaps you are wondering why this facility exists. The answer to this question lies in our discussion of selective breeding. The NSSL is a storehouse of genetic material that allows breeders access to all kinds of plant varieties.

Suppose you wanted to grow corn that could be easily dried and made into cornmeal. You could acquire seeds that would produce that kind of corn. But what if you then discovered that the corn would not grow well in your field's dry soil? Thanks to the NSSL, you might be able to solve the problem by obtaining seeds for corn that would grow well in dry soils. Using outbreeding, you could then produce a hybrid of the two corn varieties. Eventually you could grow corn that was easily dried for cornmeal and that grew well in dry soil. Without the seed bank, producing such a hybrid would be difficult, if not impossible, in one person's lifetime.

Today the role of the NSSL is more important than ever. Farmers tend to grow large fields of crops using only one variety of a plant. Many other varieties of the same plant are therefore in danger of dying out. Should a blight ever strike the present-day crops, the NSSL could provide genetic material with which to start new, blight-resistant crop varieties. The NSSL also is a valuable source of plant genes for genetic engineers.

CHECKPOINT 9.1

1. Compare and contrast inbreeding and outbreeding.
2. What are the benefits of selective breeding?
3. **Critical Thinking** Suppose you are trying to develop a new food crop. A desirable trait and an undesirable trait are both determined by recessive alleles. Develop a pedigree to determine the advantages and disadvantages of selective breeding.

Build on What You Know

4. How did Mendel use inbreeding and outbreeding in his experiment? *(Need to jog your memory? Revisit relevant concepts in Chapter 6, Section 6.1.)*

9.2 Genetic Engineering

Pests from the past

Could researchers remove the DNA from a prehistoric mosquito trapped in amber and re-create this ancient organism in a laboratory? Although DNA from these organisms can be extracted, the organisms themselves cannot be re-created. For that to happen, the DNA would have to be in a dormant state, like that of a seed.

What you'll learn

IDEAS
• To analyze the process of gel electrophoresis
• To explain the process of gene cloning

WORDS
genetic engineering, restriction enzymes, DNA fingerprint, recombinant DNA, vector, plasmids

IDENTIFYING GENES

The little DNA that could

Countless science fiction stories have been written about genetics experiments gone awry, or about human clones taking over the planet. In more positive stories, people dream of an era when gene manipulation rids the world of disease. What is genetic engineering? And what possible effects might it have on our lives?

Genetic engineering refers to any technique used to identify or change genes at the molecular level. When genes are manipulated, an organism's characteristics are changed. In selective breeding, a genome is changed slowly and deliberately, over many generations. In contrast, genetic engineering can change genes in a shorter period of time. These techniques also enable scientists to identify a person from a strand of hair, to find out if a person carries the gene for a particular disorder, and to determine the basepair sequences of an organism's DNA.

One technique of genetic engineering is called gel electrophoresis. Gel electrophoresis is a process used by researchers to sort large molecules by size. DNA is usually cut into fragments before gel electrophoresis.

To do this, laboratory scientists mix the DNA sample with a restriction enzyme. **Restriction enzymes** are proteins that break DNA bonds in specific ways at precise base pairs sequences.

There are many different restriction enzymes, and each one recognizes a different short sequence of a DNA molecule, usually four, six, or eight bases in length. When a restriction enzyme is added to a DNA sample, it breaks the DNA bonds wherever the specific base pair sequence is located. In this way, the DNA sample is digested into fragments, as shown in *Figure 9.4*. The ends of the "cut" DNA include several unpaired nucleotides. These

FIGURE 9.4

In the example shown here, a restriction enzyme recognizes the six-base sequence GAATTC. Where does it "cut" the sequence?

Restriction enzyme recognition sequences

DNA

GAATTC
CTTAAG

GAATTC
CTTAAG

Restriction enzyme cuts the DNA into fragments.

AATTC
G

G
CTTAA

AATTC
G

G
CTTAA

Sticky end

ends are called sticky ends because they are open to new bonds.

During gel electrophoresis the DNA fragments are dropped into thin slits that have been cut in a track of gel. The gel tracks have a positive charge at one end and a negative charge at the other end. Because DNA has a negative charge, the DNA fragments move toward the positive end of the gel tracks. The smallest fragments move farthest along the tracks, whereas the larger DNA fragments do not travel as far.

Next, the fragments are dyed so they are visible as bands in the gel. You can see a gel electrophoresis photograph in step 4 of *Figure 9.5*. Why do the different fragments spread out?

The results of gel electrophoresis can yield a wealth of important information. For example, a strand of hair can be identified as from a person if restriction enzyme digestion and gel electrophoresis is performed on the DNA from the hair sample and DNA from that person's cells. If DNA fragments from both samples are the same, then it is likely that the samples came from the same person. For this reason, the pattern of bands obtained from gel electrophoresis is called a **DNA fingerprint.** Every person's DNA has a unique pattern that can be used for identification.

Gel electrophoresis can also be used to determine if a person carries a gene associated with a genetic disorder. The person's pattern of DNA bands is compared with the pattern known to be associated with the disease. If the two patterns match, that person may someday develop the disorder.

Another application of gel electrophoresis is finding the base-pair sequence of DNA strands. As you may recall from Chapter 7, the Human Genome Project is the effort to identify the nitrogenous base sequence of all of the DNA in every human chromosome. In one DNA sequencing method, scientists use four different special chemicals to recognize and

FIGURE 9.5

Gel Electrophoresis

Gel electrophoresis allows researchers to separate DNA fragments according to size.

Cut-up DNA

Power source

Gel tracks

Longer fragment

Shorter fragment

1 **Make DNA fragments**
A restriction enzyme cuts DNA at specific base sequences.

2 **Place DNA in gel tracks**
Because DNA is negatively charged, the DNA fragments move toward the positive end of the gel tracks.

3 **Allow DNA to travel**
As DNA fragments travel along the tracks, the shortest fragments travel the fastest and farthest.

cut four samples of the same DNA at each of the four bases of DNA. The samples are then poured into four gel electrophoresis tracks. Computers can "read" the order of the bases by analyzing the bands in the tracks.

CHANGING GENOMES

Wheel of DNA fortune

Genetic engineers do more than identify genes. Using modern techniques, scientists alter genomes by combining DNA from the genes of different organisms. DNA with components from different organisms is called **recombinant DNA** (ree-KAHM-bih-nuhnt).

With recombinant DNA technology, scientists can transfer genes from one organism into the cells of another organism. For example, genetic engineers have transferred specific human genes into bacteria or yeast. The yeast or bacteria can use the human gene to mass-produce human proteins. When genes are transferred into

such organisms, the genes are copied by the organism's cells along with the organism's chromosomes. Exact copies are called clones. Gene cloning is the process of using genetic engineering to make copies of genes.

To transfer DNA into a cell, genetic engineers use a carrier of genetic material called a **vector.** Bacteria contain vectors called plasmids. **Plasmids** are small circular pieces of DNA separate from the bacterial chromosome. Scientists also use viruses as vectors to transfer DNA into cells.

4 **Look at the results**
A dye is added to the gel. DNA fragments are visible as bands. The gel can be photographed.

| 1 | 2 | 3 | 4 | 5 | 6 | 7 | 8 | 9 | 10 | 11 | 12 | 13 | 14 |

Analyzing Gel Electrophoresis Results

Researchers can compare DNA samples using restriction enzymes and gel electrophoresis to produce band patterns like those shown above. Similar band patterns indicate similar base sequeneces. The above results were obtained by cutting twelve DNA samples into fragments with a restriction enzyme. Each sample was put into a separate track of a gel, where the fragments separated according to size. The fragments were visualized as bands using a dye. Tracks 2–13 contain the twelve samples.

Analyze the Results

1. Study and compare the gel electrophoresis results. Which tracks contain matching band patterns? What conclusion can you draw about the DNA samples in these tracks?

2. Which track does not contain any matching bands? What conclusion can you draw about the DNA sample in this track?

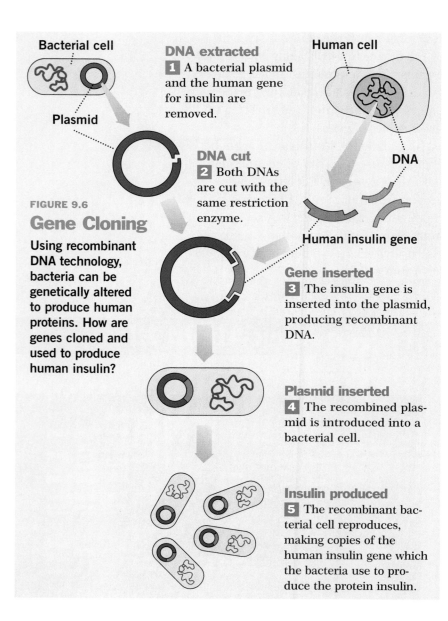

Bacterial cell

Plasmid

DNA extracted
1 A bacterial plasmid and the human gene for insulin are removed.

DNA cut
2 Both DNAs are cut with the same restriction enzyme.

Human cell

DNA

Human insulin gene

Gene inserted
3 The insulin gene is inserted into the plasmid, producing recombinant DNA.

Plasmid inserted
4 The recombined plasmid is introduced into a bacterial cell.

Insulin produced
5 The recombinant bacterial cell reproduces, making copies of the human insulin gene which the bacteria use to produce the protein insulin.

FIGURE 9.6

Gene Cloning

Using recombinant DNA technology, bacteria can be genetically altered to produce human proteins. How are genes cloned and used to produce human insulin?

Let us follow an example of recombinant DNA technology used to clone genes: the process of adding a human insulin gene to a bacterium. Insulin, a hormone that is normally produced by the pancreas, regulates the amount of glucose (a type of sugar) in the blood. Insulin is used to treat people with diabetes. The human insulin gene can be inserted into a bacterial plasmid. As the bacterium reproduces, the growing bacterial population produces insulin, which can then be harvested from the bacterial cells.

Before genes can be transferred from humans to bacteria, however, restriction enzymes must cut the DNA of the human insulin gene and the DNA of the plasmid. Recall that restriction enzymes cut DNA at specific locations. As you can see in step 2 of *Figure 9.6,* the DNA fragments have unmatched bases at each end.

The sticky ends of the human DNA fragment and plasmid DNA fragment are complementary. In other words, the sequence of bases at the ends of the piece of human DNA will bond with the sticky ends of the plasmid DNA fragment. Through this bonding process, the human DNA fragments combine with the plasmid.

Once the genes have recombined, the plasmid is inserted into a bacterial cell. As the bacterium reproduces, the resulting bacterial colony produces clones of the protein human insulin.

CHECKPOINT 9.2

1. What is gel electrophoresis and how is it performed?

2. What is gene cloning? What are the steps involved in gene cloning?

3. Critical Thinking Bacteria and humans are very different organisms. How is it possible to combine their DNA to make a human protein?

Build on What You Know

4. How might a person find out if he or she carries the gene for Huntington disease? *(Need to jog your memory? Revisit relevant concepts in Chapter 6, Section 6.4.)*

How can genotypes be changed?

9.3 Applications of Genetic Engineering

A little DNA to make it better
How about some genetic engineering for that boo-boo? The Genetically Engineered Biological Bandage (GEBB) may someday heal cuts. The GEBB contains genetically engineered human skin cells that produce a protein that stimulates growth. Using genetically engineered products can be as easy as putting on a bandage.

What you'll learn

IDEAS
• To describe applications of genetic engineering
• To compare the techniques used in these applications

WORDS
transgenic organisms

AGRICULTURE AND INDUSTRY

Bumper crop

You are now living in the midst of a revolution—the application of genetic engineering to almost every aspect of life. One goal of genetic engineers is to improve the quantity and quality of food. Genetic engineering can improve crops in many ways, as you can see in *Figure 9.7*. New genetic engineering techniques can make plants resistant to pests and weed killers and produce fruits and vegetables that are better suited for shipping and storage. Plants or other organisms that have been altered by adding a gene from a different species are called **transgenic organisms.**

One transgenic vegetable has already arrived in supermarkets—a tomato genetically engineered to ripen more slowly, thus preventing spoilage. Genetic engineers have changed and cloned the gene that codes for ripening in tomatoes. To date, the genetically engineered tomato has received mixed reviews from the public because it is rather expensive and has a slightly different taste. However, the

FIGURE 9.7
Engineering a Tomato
Tomatoes and other crops are the targets of many genetic engineering innovations.

Crops may be engineered to resist destructive pests.

Genetic engineers may make produce easier to ship.

Biotechnology may produce roots that resist drying.

tomato is just one example of the genetic engineering revolution in produce farming.

Genetic engineers are also studying ways to improve livestock. Transgenic animals can be produced by inserting DNA strands directly into an animal's egg, as shown in *Figure 9.8*. Genes for animals that produce more meat or are resistant to disease may someday be inserted into the reproductive cells of livestock to create these desirable characteristics in their offspring.

Research has revealed how to genetically engineer bacteria that can produce a milk-stimulating hormone for cattle. If you eat cheese, chances are you have already consumed a genetically engineered food. Most of the cheese produced in the United States has a genetically engineered component, called chymosin. Chymosin can replace rennin, a substance obtained from the stomach lining of slaughtered cattle. Both rennin and chymosin coagulate (clot) milk to make cheese.

Chymosin is made by transferring the cow genes that code for rennin into bacteria. The bacterial cells are then cloned to make chymosin. Genetically engineered chymosin makes smoother cheese, and it also has been marketed by some companies as "vegetarian." Do you think genetically engineered cheese is vegetarian? Why or why not?

In addition to these examples, transgenic organisms are used to process sewage, change cellulose in plant cell walls into fuel oil, and clean up oil spills and toxic waste dumps. Bacteria are the most common organisms used for genetic engineering. You

will read more about how bacteria are used in biotechnology in Chapter 14.

MEDICINE

Cures found in DNA codes

The area in which genetic engineering has had the greatest effect on our lives is medicine. Genetic engineering techniques have been used to develop gene therapy, to improve and develop vaccines and medicines, and to diagnose disorders.

Gene therapy Gene therapy is one of the fastest-growing areas in genetic engineering. Gene therapy differs from vaccines and medicines in that the treatment involves actually changing the genes that cause a genetic disorder.

Another form of gene therapy, designed to control the symptoms of cystic fibrosis, has already met with some success. One of the symptoms of cystic fibrosis is secretion of excess mucus, which can accumulate in the lungs and other organs. The excess mucus secretion is caused by a malfunctioning gene. In gene therapy, healthy genes that have recombined with certain viruses or carrier cells can be delivered to lung cells via a nasal spray. The healthy genes can then replace the malfunctioning genes, correcting the genetic defect.

Gene therapy provides researchers with a new tool to treat some human disorders, many of which had previously been untreatable or incurable. Such research may lead to a cure for hemophilia, a disease characterized by the inability of blood to clot. People who have hemophilia lack a protein that is necessary for blood clotting.

The search for a cure highlights one of the major stumbling blocks in gene therapy: How much is enough? The first step in developing a cure for

FIGURE 9.8
Scientists produce transgenic animals by using a microneedle (top) to inject DNA into an animal egg. How does this process differ from the development of transgenic bacteria?

FIGURE 9.9

Cleaning Out Clots

This SEM shows a large blood clot obstructing blood flow in an artery. How can genetically engineered bacteria clear the artery?

1 The blood clot in this artery restricts blood flow. When arteries that supply the heart muscle are blocked, heart tissue can be damaged, and a heart attack can result.

2 Protein from genetically engineered bacteria can dissolve blood clots, restoring blood flow to heart tissue.

■ Blood clot
■ Red blood cells
◄ Genetically engineered protein

hemophilia is finding a way to make the protein needed for clotting. The next and hardest step is controlling production of the protein. Too much protein could harm the patient just as much as the disease itself.

Vaccines and medicines

Researchers have used genetic engineering to produce vaccines and medicines. Products now available include veterinary vaccines; a vaccine for hepatitis B, a serious liver infection; human growth hormone; and a cell growth factor for patients with low blood-cell counts. Recombinant DNA technology is now being used to slow the progression of multiple sclerosis. In addition, genetically engineered bacteria can help dissolve blood clots in arteries of heart attack patients, as shown in *Figure 9.9*. A protein produced by the bacteria can clear the clogged arteries, allowing blood to flow freely again.

Scientists have used genetic engineering to design a protein that binds to a specific type of cell. The protein carries a radioactive tracer or a small amount of medicine. Because the protein binds to specific cells, abnormal cells can be targeted and treated while normal cells are unaffected. This technique may prove useful for cancer treatment.

LAB ZONE Do It!

How Big Is the Human Genome?

The Human Genome Project is possible only through cooperative efforts of many scientists worldwide. You can find out just how much information researchers need to complete the project if you . . .

Try This

1 Choose a page from one of your textbooks that has only text, no illustrations.
2 Count the number of characters (all letters, numbers, punctuation, and spaces) in five lines of text. Divide this number by 5; your result is the average number of characters per line.
3 Count the number of lines on the page. Multiply the number of lines by the average number of characters per line. Your result is the average number of characters on a page.
4 Each character represents a DNA base. Divide the average number of characters per page by 2 in order to represent the number of "base pairs" per page.
5 Determine the number of pages in your textbook, and multiply that number by the number of base pairs per page. How many base pairs are in the textbook?
6 The human genome has about 3 million base pairs. How many books would you need to store all of that information?

Analyze Your Results

1 If you stacked all the textbooks you would need to "store" the Human Genome Project, how tall would the stack be?
2 Research the number of stars in the Milky Way. How does this number compare with the number of base pairs in the human genome?

As you read in the previous section, insulin was one of the first medicines to be manufactured using genetic engineering. From 1921 until the early 1990s, diabetes was treated with insulin extracted from pigs or cows.

This insulin, however, caused allergic reactions in some patients. Today, genetic engineers mass-produce insulin by inserting the human insulin gene into bacteria. The transgenic bacteria make insulin that is identical to human insulin but does not cause allergic reactions. A sample of this insulin is shown in *Figure 9.10*.

Diagnosing disorders

Genetic engineering has enabled doctors to diagnose hundreds of disorders. Recently, genetic researchers developed a test that detects the gene for Huntington's disease. As you may recall from Chapter 6, Huntington's disease is a fatal genetic disorder that involves the deterioration of the brain and nervous system. Huntington's disease is caused by a dominant gene. The test for the gene is a search for a section of DNA called a marker. The DNA marker is on the same chromosome as the Huntington's gene and is present only if the Huntington's gene is on that chromosome. If the test detects the marker, then the person being tested probably carries the gene for Huntington's disease.

Another test detects the gene that causes retinoblastoma, an eye cancer. If the gene causing retinoblastoma is detected, doctors can begin treatment to eradicate the cancer early, potentially saving a person's eyesight.

Research Scientists use bacteria and other types of cells to clone and study defective human genes. In this way, scientists can better understand genetic disorders. Do you recall learning about the Human Genome Project in Chapter 7? Using genetic engineering, researchers aim to sequence all of the DNA in the 46 human chromosomes. With that knowledge, they hope to discover the function of every human gene, from the genes that determine eye color to those that cause disorders. This enormous project has already enhanced our understanding of human genetics and will do so in the years ahead.

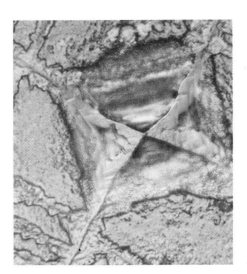

FIGURE 9.10
Human insulin, like the magnified sample above, is produced by recombinant DNA technology. What are the steps in the insulin production process?

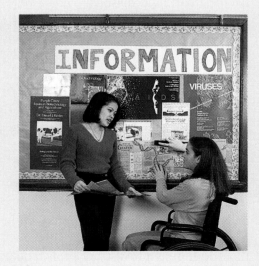

Misconception and mystery surround genetic engineering. Now that you have learned about this topic, inform your community about it as well. Ask your teacher or local librarian for a bulletin board where you and your classmates can create a genetic engineering information center. To gather information, you can find articles in magazines and newspapers, ask for literature from biotech companies, and check out genetic engineering homepages. Visit *http://genetics.biosurf.com* for links to these homepages. You also may want to survey your friends and neighbors about their hopes and fears regarding genetic engineering and make an effort to address these concerns in your information center.

IN THE COMMUNITY
Biotech Bulletin

FIGURE 9.11
After years of separation, this family (left) was reunited through DNA fingerprinting. The DNA fingerprints (right) show the patterns of a mother (M), father (F), and two children (C). What similarities among the parental and offspring DNA fingerprints can you see?

FORENSICS

Crime still doesn't pay

Sherlock Holmes had his magnifying glass. Today's detectives use more sophisticated tools as they search for courtroom evidence. Like Sherlock Holmes, modern detectives practice forensics, the use of the scientific method to solve crimes.

As always, someone's guilt or innocence can hang on analyzing the precise sequence of events occurring on the day of a crime. Today, with the advances of DNA fingerprinting, guilt or innocence can also hinge on determining the precise sequence of bases in a microscopic fragment of DNA. With the exception of identical twins, no two people have identical DNA. Because DNA fingerprints are unique, they can help solve crimes.

DNA fingerprints can even help unravel mysteries that have remained unsolved for decades. In 1991, a grave site that was thought to contain the remains of Butch Cassidy and the Sundance Kid was examined. A comparison of DNA fingerprints from the skeletons with DNA fingerprints from known relatives of the famous outlaws proved conclusively that neither Butch Cassidy nor the Sundance Kid was buried at the site.

DNA fingerprints can also be used to establish family relationships and reunite relatives. Parts of the patterns of both the mother and the father will be present in the DNA fingerprints of their offspring. The family in *Figure 9.11* was reunited through DNA fingerprints. Why do the offspring's DNA fingerprints have parts of their parents' patterns?

The applications you have just read about are only a few of many possible uses of genetic engineering principles. As researchers learn more about the exact mechanisms of genes, genetic engineering will become an even more significant part of everyday life.

CHECKPOINT 9.3

1. Name and describe three applications of genetic engineering.

2. How is recombinant DNA technology used in medicine?

3. Critical Thinking Would you want to find out if you carried a gene for an incurable disease? Why or why not?

Build on What You Know

4. How did investigators establish that the Tyrolean Ice Man was an inhabitant of the Swiss Alps? *(Need to jog your memory? Revisit relevant concepts in Chapter 7, page 156.)*

Little Clues of You

Have you brushed your hair, bathed with a washcloth, or trimmed your nails today? If so, you've left behind all the evidence forensics experts would need to obtain a DNA fingerprint.

Modeling DNA Probes

WHAT YOU WILL DO Use DNA sequences to identify individuals

SKILLS YOU WILL USE Making models, classifying, organizing

WHAT YOU WILL NEED Graph paper, scissors, a partner

Individual 1	ATCTCGAGACTGATTGGCCATAAGCTCGAG
Individual 2	ATTGGCCACTCGAGACGTTGGCCAAGTCCG
Individual 3	ATGACCATGGCCAGGCTCGAGCTGATGACG
Individual 4	ATATGGCCATTGCTCGAGTGGCCAGATCCG
Individual 5	ACTCGAGGTCCCTCGAGTGATGGCCATACG

Background

Scientists often use a probe to identify DNA. A probe is a short, single stranded DNA molecule that is labeled. Because the probe is single stranded, it can bind to other DNA that has a complementary sequence. For example, a probe with the sequence AGCT can bind to DNA containing the sequence TCGA. Scientists mix a probe with an unknown DNA sample. The probe will only bind to a DNA sample that has a complementary sequence.

Propose a Hypothesis

Propose a hypothesis regarding the uniqueness of DNA sequences in individuals.

Conduct Your Experiment

1 The DNA sequences for five individuals are shown in the figure. Copy the DNA sequences onto graph paper, putting one letter from the DNA sequence into each square.

2 Look for DNA sequences in each individual that are complementary to this six-base DNA probe: TCCGAG.

3 Circle any DNA sequence in each individual that is complementary to the sequence of the DNA probe.

4 Record the numbers of the individuals who were identified by the DNA probe.

5 Choose one of the five individuals, and construct a new DNA probe that will identify only that individual. Write out the DNA sequence of the probe, and exchange it with a new sequence written by your partner.

6 Repeat steps 2 and 3 to identify the unknown individual, using the DNA probe that your partner constructed.

Analyze Your Data

1 What DNA sequence is the complement of the DNA probe shown in step 2?

2 Which individual(s) was identified by the DNA probe given in step 2?

3 What is the complementary DNA sequence of the DNA probe from your partner (step 5)?

4 Which individual was identified by the DNA probe from your partner?

Draw Conclusions

Explain how a person can be identified by DNA probes. Is it possible for more than one individual to be identified by a DNA probe? Would DNA probes with longer or shorter sequences be more likely to identify only one individual? Write a paragraph discussing the answers to these questions.

Design a Related Experiment

Design an experiment to model how restriction enzymes could be used to create DNA fingerprints for the five individuals shown. Before writing your experiment, consider the fact that restriction enzymes cut DNA at specific base sequences.

9.4 Safety and Ethics in Biotechnology

If you make it, you own it
How would you like to patent your own virus? These mice (left) are patented. According to the United States Supreme Court, if you create a new virus or organism through genetic engineering, then you can get a patent for it. The ethics of an individual owning an entire genome is one of many concerns raised by biotechnological advances.

What you'll learn

IDEAS
• To appraise the safety issues and precautions taken in biotechnology
• To contrast the benefits and concerns associated with genetic engineering

SAFETY ISSUES

A new challenge

Life has existed on Earth for billions of years, but only recently have scientists acquired the knowledge to change the genes of living things. Biotechnology has already proven to be a method of creating products of great benefit to humans. But biotechnology also has a dark side—potential abuse and accidents.

Some people worry that genetic engineers might accidentally create deadly bacteria or viruses. What would happen if a modified bacterium or virus spread from a laboratory into the environment? How can you guard against the release of a dangerous bacterium?

In response to these fears, scientists adhere to strict laboratory regulations, as shown in *Figure 9.12*. Although no procedure is foolproof, precautions such as protective gear help guard genetic researchers from infection by a newly engineered organism. As another safety measure, genetically engineered organisms can be altered so that they cannot survive outside the laboratory.

Some organisms, however, are specifically designed for release into the environment. Bacteria that protect crops from frost damage are one example. Although these bacteria are helpful, will their release have any harmful, long-term effects? Could such organisms change natural cycles or enter food chains and ultimately affect other organisms? These questions deserve careful consideration.

FIGURE 9.12

Safety Precautions

Scientists always use safety precautions. Procedures vary with the type of organism used and the potential health risks it may pose.

Protective clothing
A face mask, gloves, and lab coat protect the eyes and skin from contact with potentially harmful organisms.

Contamination precautions
Strict procedures help workers avoid touching, breathing, or ingesting experimental materials.

Safe disposal
The disposal of contaminated wastes is federally regulated by OSHA, the Occupational Safety and Health Administration.

LAB ZONE Do It!

How Can Ethical Questions Be Answered?

The ethical questions raised by biotechnology have no "right" or "wrong" answers but are decided by society as a whole. You can model the information-gathering process of government officials if you . . .

Try This

1 Choose three safety or ethical issues related to genetic engineering. Design a survey to ask people their opinions on the issues. Your questions may have a format similar to the sample question (right).
2 Find 15 people who will complete your survey. Collect the surveys and tabulate the answers.

I support keeping personal genome information private. (check one)

☐ *Strongly agree*

☐ *Agree somewhat*

☐ *Disagree somewhat*

☐ *Strongly disagree*

Analyze Your Results

1 Was there total agreement on any issue? If more people were surveyed, would there be more or less agreement in the responses?
2 How informed about biotechnology issues were the people you surveyed? If you were a politician or government official, how would you act upon the results of this survey?

ISSUES IN BIOLOGY S T S

Ethical questions

Because of its potential for modifying human genes, biotechnology also raises some ethical issues. For example, it may soon be possible to treat or correct genetic disorders before they are passed on to offspring. It follows that human genes for traits other than genetic disorders could also be altered. Parents might engineer their children's physical and intellectual traits. What would be the result? Who

should be able to judge whether a trait is desirable or not?

Another ethical issue concerns the Human Genome Project. If this project is completed, it might be possible to screen people for their genetic predisposition to many diseases. Some insurance companies already use genetic screening and have denied insurance on the basis of test results. For this reason, many people feel that personal genome information should be kept private. What are the benefits of genetic screening? Would you feel safer knowing, for example, that an airplane pilot or firefighter had no genetic predisposition to heart disease?

At this time many questions remain unanswered. Perhaps you will be one of the scientists who helps resolve these difficult ethical issues. If not, you will definitely be a voter. By being informed, you can make wise decisions about the biotechnology issues that will arise.

CHECKPOINT 9.4

1. What are some safety precautions scientists use when working with genetically engineered organisms?
2. Identify a benefit and a concern in connection with the alteration of human genes.
3. Critical Thinking What are the possible harmful, long-term effects of engineering a crop to resist weed killers?

Build on What You Know

4. How could the scientific method help resolve safety and ethical issues related to biotechnology? *(Need to jog your memory? Revisit relevant concepts in Chapter 1, Section 1.3.)*

How can technology be used to affect phenotype?

Chapter 9 Review

 THE BIG IDEA! 9.1–9.2 Genotypes can be changed through selective breeding and genetic engineering.
9.3–9.4 Technology enables us to find out about genotype and use this knowledge to affect phenotype.

Sum It Up

Use the following summary to review the main concepts in this chapter.

9.1 Breeding

- Humans have practiced selective breeding of plants and animals for centuries.
- Outbreeding is the crossing of two different breeds and can result in hybrid vigor.
- Biotechnology is the use of living organisms to make products.

9.2 Genetic Engineering

- Genetic engineering refers to any technique used to identify or change DNA sequences.
- Scientists use gel electrophoresis to determine the sequence of DNA bases and to obtain DNA fingerprints.
- Recombinant DNA is a combination of the genetic material of two different breeds.
- Genes can be cloned using recombinant technology.

9.3 Applications of Genetic Engineering

- Genetic engineering has current and potential applications in agriculture, industry, medicine, and forensics.
- Genetic engineering enables scientists to perform gene therapy, develop medicines, diagnose disorders, and study genomes.

9.4 Safety and Ethics in Biotechnology

- Scientists are addressing concerns about the safety of creating and releasing genetically engineered organisms.
- Potential applications of genetic engineering, such as the alteration of human genes, raise ethical questions for members of society to consider.

Use Terms and Concepts

Use each of the following words or terms in a complete sentence. If you need to review a meaning, turn to the page indicated.

selective breeding (p. 206)

inbreeding (p. 206)

outbreeding (p. 207)

genetic engineering (p. 209)

restriction enzymes (p. 209)

DNA fingerprint (p. 210)

recombinant DNA (p. 211)

vector (p. 211)

plasmids (p. 211)

transgenic organisms (p. 213)

Use Your Word Power

COMPLETION Write the word or phrase that best completes each statement.

1. Hybrid vigor can result from _____ .

2. To perform gel electrophoresis, scientists use _____ to "cut" DNA into fragments.

3. _____ are bacterial vectors.

4. A _____, obtained through gel electrophoresis, can be used for identification.

5. For centuries, humans have used _____ to produce crops and livestock.

6. _____ are genetically engineered lifeforms with the DNA of two different breeds.

TRUE-FALSE Write true if the statement is true. If the statement is false, replace the underlined word(s) to make the statement true.

7. A plasmid is a type of <u>vector</u>.

8. <u>Genetic engineering</u> has many potential benefits.

9. Transgenic organisms contain <u>recombinant DNA</u>.

10. <u>Inbreeding</u> produces hybrid organisms.

11. Everyone has a unique <u>DNA fingerprint</u>.

Show What You Know

12. What is selective breeding, and what are the applications of selective breeding?

13. What are the steps in gel electrophoresis?

14. How is recombinant DNA technology used to produce human insulin?

15. Why are recessive alleles more likely to be expressed in the offspring of close relatives?

16. Name and describe two applications of genetic engineering.

17. What are some safety precautions used by scientists involved in genetic engineering?

18. What is a transgenic organism?

19. What is forensics, and how can genetic engineering be used in forensics studies?

20. How are vectors and plasmids related?

21. **Make a Concept Map** Complete the concept map below by adding the following terms: recombinant DNA technology, vector, plasmid, gene cloning, biotechnology, restriction enzymes, DNA fragments, DNA fingerprint.

Take It Further

22. **Applying Concepts** What advantages does genetic engineering have over selective breeding?

23. **Making a Prediction** What might be a negative result of growing a crop that is genetically engineered to resist weed killer?

24. **Developing a Hypothesis** A genetically engineered medicine for heart attack patients, tPA, is being used on some stroke victims. A stroke is caused by a blood clot in the brain. Why might tPA effectively treat strokes?

25. **Designing an Experiment** The use of DNA fingerprints as legal evidence is sometimes contested. Design an experiment to test the accuracy of DNA fingerprints.

26. **Interpreting a Graph** The following graph shows death rates for infectious diseases (influenza, pneumonia, and tuberculosis) and noninfectious diseases (heart disease and cancer). How have antibiotics and vaccines affected death rates? How might further applications of genetic engineering to cancer and heart disease treatment change death rates in the future?

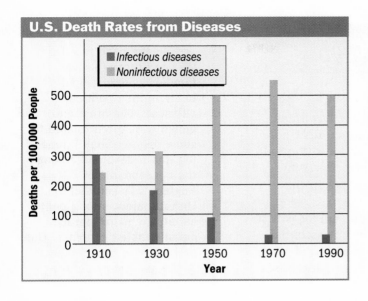

U.S. Death Rates from Diseases

- Infectious diseases
- Noninfectious diseases

Deaths per 100,000 People

Year: 1910, 1930, 1950, 1970, 1990

Drawing by Gahan Wilson; © 1996 The New Yorker Magazine, Inc.

"Looks like we grafted a few too many human genes into the kohlrabi."

27. Analyzing Data Review the table below. Then copy the following DNA sequence three times and include the complementary strand:

ATGAGATCTACGGAATTCTCAAGTTCGAATCG

Identify where each restriction enzyme will cut the strand.

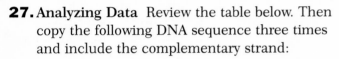

DNA Restriction Enzymes	
Enzyme	**Recognition Sequence**
*Bgl*II	A ▼GATCT TCTAG▲A
*Eco*RI	G ▼AATTC CTTAA▲G
*Hind*III	A ▼AGCTT TTCGA▲A

Consider the Issues

28. Make a New Organism If you could use genetic engineering to create a new organism or to mass-produce a product, what would it be? How would it affect the world? What safety precautions might you take? You may illustrate or create a model to accompany your answer.

Make New Connections

29. Biology and Cartoons What is the joke in the following cartoon? How is the cartoon

inaccurate? Critique the cartoon using your knowledge of genetic engineering.

30. Biology and Economics Find a genetically engineered product at the grocery store or pharmacy. Examples include engineered produce, cheese containing chymosine, or human insulin. Compare the price of the engineered product with that of the traditionally produced product. Is there a difference? Why or why not?

31. Biology and Community: A Project Interview someone who has been affected by genetic engineering—an employee in the field, a farmer, or a person treated with genetically engineered medicine. Ask about his or her experiences, both positive and negative, and inquire about any misconceptions he or she may have had or encountered.

FAST-FORWARD TO CHAPTER 10

People can change genomes through biotechnology. Other environmental influences can also affect genomes. In the next unit you will learn about theories that explain how traits of organisms have changed over time.

Unit 2 Review

Connect the Chapters

1. Compare recombination as it occurs in crossing over with the recombinant DNA technology used to produce insulin.
2. Explain why gene therapy for cystic fibrosis does not prevent the malfunctioning gene from being passed on to offspring.
3. Compare Mendel's breeding experiments with pea plants to biotechnology.
4. Contrast the use of test crosses and DNA markers to identify carriers of recessive genes.
5. How are chromosomes, genes, codons, anticondons, and proteins related?
6. Explain how Griffith's 1928 experiment with bacterial strains was an early example of genetic engineering.

Connect the Units

7. Cells do not need as much energy to produce RNA polymerase as they need to produce other proteins. Why?
8. Identify one event in the process of gene expression in a eukaryotic cell for which active transport is essential.
9. Explain the function of DNA polymerase during the interphase portion of the cell cycle.

Connect to Themes

10. **Unity and Diversity** How does eukaryotic gene expression show unity and diversity?
11. **Patterns and Changes** How do linked genes affect the Law of Independent Assortment?
12. **Systems and Interactions** How does the concentration of lactose control lactose digestion in *E.coli*?

project plans

1 In the past, marriages in European royal families were arranged to strengthen political alliances. The bride and groom were often related to some degree. Such inbreeding was widespread among the descendants of England's Queen Victoria. Unfortunately, strong political alliances did not lead to equally robust genomes. One problem was the incidence of the genetic disorder hemophilia. Make a poster displaying a pedigree of Queen Victoria's lineage. Identify the descendants who carried the hemophilia gene, and those who expressed the gene.

2 As a class, research and experiment with varieties of a flower or vegetable. For example, find out how many varieties of tomatoes can be grown in your area. Then design an experiment to find the variety best suited for local soil and weather conditions.

CRITIC'S CORNER

A BOOK REVIEW BY STACIE SIMMONS OF KANSAS CITY, MISSOURI

The Double Helix, by Nobel Prize winner James D. Watson, tells the story of scientists and their determination to discover the structure of DNA. The book describes a scientific team working together to decipher a mystery (with a little help from x-rayed molecules). Each scientist had his or her own job to do; each had a unique way of helping out. The unity of these scientists, and their often humorous relationships with each other, make this book a page-turner for students of all interests and backgrounds.

DR. KEITH BLACK
Neurosurgeon, UCLA Medical Center;
professor of neurosurgery at UCLA

EDUCATION: Neurological surgery residency;
general surgery internship; M.D.; B.S.

"I specialize in brain tumors. Most of these tumors are very complex, and about half of them are malignant. One part of my work is surgery, because malignant tumors cannot be cured without it. I also do research—I try to find ways of curing or improving the treatment of brain tumors. One of the newer treatments is gene therapy. We aim to develop a brain-tumor vaccine. We've learned that tumors release proteins that turn off the ability of immune cells to fight disease. We genetically modify tumor cells so that they no longer release these proteins, then we can take the modified cells and inject them back into the patient. That way, the person's immune system can recognize the tumor's cells and fight them."

bioSURF Learn more about Dr. Black's cancer research at UCLA Johnson Cancer Center by visiting *http://genetics.biosurf.com* for more information.

ANAMARIA CRAICI
College intern at the National Cancer Institute,
National Institutes of Health

EDUCATION: College junior majoring
in biochemistry and molecular biology;
high school diploma

"Science is a lot of fun. It's like solving a mystery, and you have to choose the way to find the answers."
—ANAMARIA CRAICI

"I have always known that science was where I wanted to go. You work with an unknown, a question. I study the systems plants have to defend themselves against all kinds of pathogens. A pathogen is an organism that can cause a disease—a bacterium, or a virus, for example. My professor, Dr. Craig Tepper, is looking for the genes that 'turn on' when a plant is attacked. My job is to do nonradioactive DNA sequencing. By studying how plants defend themselves, we hope to learn how to induce plants to grow in places where they normally wouldn't, or cure plants that are dying."

bioSURF Find out about internships at the National Cancer Institute at the National Institutes of Health by visiting the site *http://genetics.biosurf.com*.

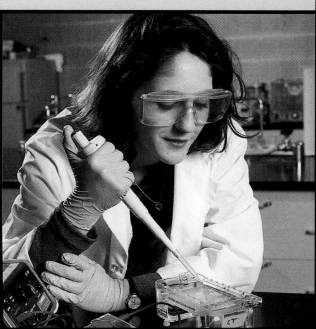

Which of these amazing statements about change and diversity are fact, and which are fiction?

Hit *or* Myth?

Life on Earth came from **Mars.**

(Fiction. No one knows how life on Earth began, but scientists are debating whether some meteorites from Mars contain bacterial fossils.)

Poodle puppies are born with **fancy haircuts.**

(Fiction. Poodle haircuts are not inherited. Poodles are groomed to achieve that look, and their offspring must also be groomed.)

Scientists **date** dinosaurs.

(Fact. Scientists can determine the age of dinosaur bones by measuring radioactivity.)

Lizards are more closely related to birds than to crocodiles.

(Fact. Researchers have found that looks are deceiving—a lizard is genetically more similar to a bird than to a crocodile.)

In a healthy population, everyone has the **same** genes.

(Fiction. Genetic variety is a source of beneficial mutations, which can be key to a population's survival.)

Panda bears are **not** bears.

(Fact and fiction. Most scientists classify the giant panda as a bear, but they consider the red panda to be a type of raccoon.)

Dragonflies were once as **large as pigeons.**

(Fact. Fossil evidence indicates that giant dragonflies cruised Earth 290 million years ago.)

CHAPTER 10
The Theory of Evolution

You can find out more about diversity and change in biology by exploring the following Internet address: *http://evolution.biosurf.com*

In this chapter . . .

FEATURES

Everyday Biology
- New Species with Many Niches
- The Bright Side of Motion Sickness

In the Community
The World in Their Eyes

 Environmental Awareness
The Story of the English Peppered Moth

LAB ZONES

Discover It!
- Observing the Variety of Life

Do It!
- How are Inventions Like Evolution?
- How Quickly Do Populations Decrease?

Think About It!
- Recording Observations

Investigate It!
- Modeling Coevolution

CHARLES DARWIN
Goes to Sea

After traveling to a foreign country or a different state, you may view the world in a new way. Travel certainly had that effect on Charles Darwin, who set sail from England in 1831 bound for the Galapagos Islands, located off the western coast of South America. During his five-year voyage aboard HMS *Beagle,* Darwin pursued his interest in the wildlife that inhabited the islands. Fascinated by the diversity of life-forms he observed, Darwin made copious notes in his diary and collected vast numbers of plant and animal specimens. He was most intrigued by the thirteen varieties of finches and countless types of beetles he observed.

Not content to merely observe, Darwin speculated about the variety of life-forms he saw. Why were there thirteen kinds of finches on the Galapagos? Did just one kind of finch inhabit the islands at one time? What advantages did a brightly colored beetle have? And why were some beetles tiny, compared with others? In answering these questions, Darwin developed one of the most revolutionary theories in the history of science: the theory of evolution.

A page from Darwin's journal.

 Discover It!

Observing the Variety of Life

1. Carefully observe the beetle collection shown on this page. Select five beetles.
2. Record all of the characteristics—similarities and differences—that you observe among the five beetles.
3. Based on your observations, predict the conditions in which each beetle lived. For example, a small, dull-colored beetle probably lived in a similarly colored environment, avoiding predators by blending with its surroundings.

Charles Darwin made observations similar to these when he sailed to the Galapagos Islands. Darwin developed his theory of natural selection to explain why beetles that live in different environments look different.

WRITE ABOUT IT!

In your science journal, write about the observations you made when you traveled to a different part of your town, state, or country. In what ways did you gain a different perspective about your surroundings?

10.1 Variation and Adaptation

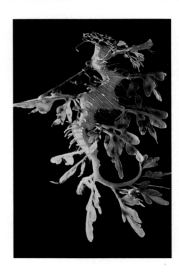

What you'll learn

IDEAS
- To distinguish between variation and adaptation
- To explain how fossils are used to study ancient life forms

WORDS
species, variation, adaptation, niche, fossils

Come into my parlor . . .
The organism in this photo may look like seaweed, but it is actually a sea horse. Through its camouflage, the sea horse remains hidden until its prey approaches close enough to be captured and eaten. Camouflage also hides the sea horse from its enemies. While all organisms do not show such amazing camouflage, they do fit into their environment in some way.

FIGURE 10.1
Members of a species can vary greatly. Red foxes can be red (top) or silver (bottom). What other differences can you see between the two foxes?

VARIATION

The spice of life

We often talk about an individual's unique characteristics and easily recognize the uniqueness of many species. A **species** consists of interbreeding populations of organisms that can produce healthy, fertile offspring. Within any species, an amazing amount of variation exists. **Variation** is defined as the differences between individual members of a population. The unique attributes of each animal—for example, the way it hunts and communicates, the color of its fur, and the shape of its teeth—distinguish it from its peers.

Variation can be dramatic, or it can be subtle. As you can see, the two foxes in *Figure 10.1* are very different in color. The foxes can also vary greatly in size. There are subtle differences, too. A fox may have many or few offspring. The size of a fox's

territory can vary, and different foxes might have slightly different diets.

Not all variations in organisms can be observed. Some differences are biochemical. Look again at the foxes in *Figure 10.1*. These two members of the same species may have different blood types or hormone levels. They certainly have slightly different genomes.

Many, though not all, variations are genetically determined. Inherited variation is the result of two random processes: mutation and recombination. As you may recall from Chapter 8, new alleles, or forms of a trait, can arise by random mutation. A mutation is a change in the sequence of a gene.

Most mutations are either neutral or harmful. Occasionally, a mutation will increase the chances of an organism's survival. When this happens, the mutation is beneficial. A mutation is more likely to be beneficial when the environment is in a state of change. Under changing conditions, mutations that were once neutral or harmful to the organism may become advantageous. For example, the mutation that produced the silver-colored red fox would have been harmful in the temperate habitat of the red-colored red fox. But in a snowy environment, the silver color is a beneficial mutation, as silver foxes have better camouflage.

Although mutation is important, most variation results from the recombination of existing alleles. During sexual reproduction, alleles recombine by three different mechanisms: independent assortment of chromosomes, crossing over during meiosis, and combination of genes from egg and sperm during fertilization.

ADAPTATION

To niche its own

Variation creates a population with diverse traits. The particular traits inherited by each individual organism determine whether or not an organism will survive in a particular environment. An **adaptation** is an inherited trait that increases a population's chances of survival and reproduction in a particular environment.

Adaptations are an advantage to a population, although sometimes that advantage is hard to measure. Notice the adaptations of the anteater shown in *Figure 10.2*. What advantages do these adaptations provide the species?

Through adaptations, populations often become suited to a specific niche. Broadly speaking, a **niche** (NICH) is a habitat and the role a population plays in that habitat. A niche includes where organisms live, what and how they eat, how they raise their offspring, and what their predators are. Conditions such as space, light, moisture, and temperature also define a population's niche.

Niches include all the environmental factors to which populations are adapted. The anteater and termite niches shown in *Figure 10.2* are examples. As you can see, the termites occupy a smaller area and have a

EVERYDAY BIOLOGY

New Species with Many Niches

A previously unknown animal, the Panay cloudrunner, was discovered in the Philippines in 1992. The cloudrunner resembles a squirrel and occupies niches in many habitats, including grasslands and forests.

FIGURE 10.2

The Anteater and Termite Niches

Anteaters and termites have adaptations that make them well suited for their roles in their habitat.

Snout
The anteater uses its long snout to explore the termite mound for food.

Tongue
Its long, sticky tongue can grab termites from deep within their nest.

Tail
The anteater uses its long tail for balance.

Termite nest
The structure of the termites' nest makes it difficult for most animals to attack them.

Termite defense
Thousands of soldier termites rush to the walls of the mound to defend their home.

FIGURE 10.3
Fossils can be formed and later discovered in very different environments.

2 When the animal died, its remains became embedded in sediments on the ocean floor.

1 An animal lived in an ocean environment millions of years ago.

3 Millions of years pass. Humans discover fossilized remains high above sea level. Over time, the ocean floor had become part of a mountain chain!

larger population than does the anteater. The size and nature of a niche can be quite different for different populations. When two populations attempt to occupy the same niche, fierce competition arises. Eventually, one population proves better adapted to the niche and drives out the competition.

BIODIVERSITY

Global village

You do not have to go far to appreciate the abundance and variety of life. A walk through the woods or along a city street is a walk through a biological community where many populations of organisms live together, interact, and often compete for natural resources. Such a community includes a collection of niches to which its members have adapted. The variety and abundance of species that make up a biological community are called its biodiversity.

In any community, change creates advantages for some species and disadvantages for others. Natural disasters, such as fires or floods, destroy some habitats and create others. During times of drastic change, populations whose members are better able to adapt to the new environment will fare better than those whose members are highly specialized. Populations with a broad variety of traits are better able to compete for natural resources in a changing environment.

Scientists estimate that Earth is currently home to between 5 million and 30 million different species. But today's biodiversity is a fraction of what has existed during Earth's history: 99 percent of all types of organisms that ever lived are now extinct. Earth's environments and the species that populate those environments have changed many times over the 4-billion-year history of life.

Much of Earth's history can be studied using **fossils,** the preserved remains or imprints of ancient organisms. When scientists speak of the fossil record, they are referring to the information that is stored in fossilized remains. Scientists who study ancient life through fossils are called paleontologists (PAY-lee-uhn-TAL-uh-jists).

Most fossils are found in the sedimentary rock formed when sand and silt settled to the bottom of a body of water. As *Figure 10.3* illustrates, organisms die, then settle into the sediment. The dead organisms and the sediment are compressed into rock. As Earth's surface shifts, layers of rock that were once at the bottom of a body of water become dry land.

Paleontologists do not have a complete fossil record of ancient life. By their very nature, fossils are hard to find and are vulnerable to weathering and erosion. In addition, the soft bodies of some animals do not fossilize well. Most living things do not leave any trace of their existence, as the conditions necessary for fossil formation are rarely present when an organism dies. However, a great deal of our knowledge about the history of life comes from fossils.

CHECKPOINT 10.1

1. How are adaptation and variation related?
2. How do paleontologists study ancient species?
3. **Critical Thinking** If a zebra was born with very thick fur, under what circumstances would that mutation lead to an adaptation?

Build on What You Know

4. Compare and contrast how variation arises in organisms that reproduce sexually and organisms that reproduce asexually. *(Need to jog your memory? Revisit relevant concepts in Chapter 5, Section 5.4.)*

10.2 Darwin and His Theory

Follow your dreams and write a theory
Charles Darwin had a love of nature from boyhood, but his father encouraged him to become a doctor. When Darwin lost interest in studying medicine, his father urged him to go into the clergy. Eventually Darwin found his career interest. He pursued his love of nature when he sailed to the Galapagos Islands. His observations there led to a theory that revolutionized biology.

What you'll learn

IDEAS
• To explain the theories that led to the theory of evolution
• To analyze Darwin's theory of evolution by natural selection

WORDS
evolution, natural selection, gradualism, punctuated equilibrium

THEORIES CHANGE OVER TIME

Evolution revolution

Many people have tried to explain Earth's biodiversity. Where do you think the diverse species of today came from? Explanations of the origin and diversity of life are not new. More than 2000 years ago, the topic of bio-diversity was discussed by Greek philosophers. They had many ideas, including the idea that the form, or shape, of an organism is related to its function.

In the mid-1700s, Swiss naturalist Charles Bonnet published a theory to explain biodiversity. He noticed that many fossilized remains bore no resemblance to modern organisms. He theorized that periodic catastrophes had affected the entire planet, and that after each catastrophe, life began anew. According to Bonnet, the fossils that remained represented the organisms that lived prior to these catastrophes. He first used the word *evolution* to describe the development of diverse life-forms. **Evolution** means change over time.

Bonnet's views were later challenged by Jean-Baptiste Lamarck, a French naturalist who reasoned that the fossils of extinct animals were the ancestors of those living today. Lamarck's hypothesis included three main ideas.

FIGURE 10.4

Time Line of Theories

People debated for thousands of years about how different life-forms developed.

1809
Lamarck hypothesizes that "simple" organisms emerge spontaneously and evolve to greater "complexity."

1844
Darwin writes his theory on the origin of the species.

1858
Wallace and Darwin publish their theories of evolution.

300 B.C.
Greeks theorize that an organism's form is related to its function.

1769
Bonnet observes that fossils do not resemble modern organisms and theorizes they are from a previous era.

1831
Darwin sets sail on HMS *Beagle*.

Chapter 10 The Theory of Evolution **233**

FIGURE 10.5
According to Lamarck, when short-necked giraffes stretched their necks to reach leaves high on a tree, their necks became longer. The longer neck was then passed on to the offspring. What principles of Lamarck's hypothesis are represented here?

First, Lamarck thought that organisms constantly strive to improve themselves. Second, he believed that the most-used body structures develop, whereas unused structures waste away. This idea was called the principle of use and disuse. Third, Lamarck thought that once a structure is modified by use or disuse, the modification is inherited by the organism's offspring. This third principle is called the inheritance of acquired characteristics. Study *Figure 10.5* to see how Lamarck's hypothesis explains the evolution of the giraffe's long neck.

Lamarck published some of his ideas on evolution in 1809, the same year Charles Darwin was born. His work had a strong influence on Darwin. Lamarck's hypothesis about the inheritance of acquired characteristics was later disproved by German biologist August Weismann. Through experiments with mice, Weismann concluded that changes in an individual during its lifetime do not affect its reproductive cells or its offspring.

INFLUENCES ON DARWIN

Interdisciplinary studies

In 1831 Charles Darwin joined an around-the-world trip on a ship called the HMS *Beagle*. As you read at the beginning of this chapter, Darwin used the trip as an opportunity to collect plant samples and study animal species from the shore.

Darwin was especially intrigued by the finches he observed, such as those shown in *Figure 10.6*. Darwin observed that each different group of finches had its own niche. This led Darwin to wonder whether each group of finches was a different species.

Darwin later learned that the 13 different finches he had studied were indeed separate species. Each species was suited to the environment of its niche. Darwin hypothesized that

the adaptations of animals to their environment and the emergence of new species were closely related processes.

Geology After Darwin returned home, he spent a great deal of time studying his notes, reading, and conversing with colleagues. From the books of his friend Charles Lyell, Darwin learned that geological change is an extremely slow, uniform process. Lyell reasoned that Earth must be very old. Using Lyell's hypothesis, Darwin concluded that gradual geological changes over long periods of time influence plant and animal life.

Artificial selection Darwin also studied the selective breeding of domestic animals and crops. By selecting a parental generation with the

FIGURE 10.6
Darwin studied finches as he sailed to the Galapagos Islands. What similarities and differences do you think Darwin might have observed in the finches below?

GALAPAGOS ISLANDS

Isabela Island

Fernandina Island

San Salvador Island

Santa Cruz Island

San Cristóbal Island

most desirable characteristics, farmers and animal breeders can raise more desirable offspring, such as cows that give more milk, or hardier horses. Any domesticated plant or animal bred to accentuate desirable characteristics is the result of artificial selection.

Because of artificial selection, domesticated organisms often bear little resemblance to their ancestors. For example, careful artificial selection for certain traits of the wild mustard plant resulted in the vegetables shown in *Figure 10.7*. Darwin suspected that a selection process also occurred in nature.

Population control Darwin was also influenced by the economist Thomas Malthus, who stated that the human population was growing so fast that the supply of resources could not keep up with demand. According to Malthus, when a population exceeds its resources, disasters such as war, starvation, or widespread disease limit the population's growth.

Darwin recognized that Malthus's principles applied not only to humans, but to all species. If all the offspring of a population survive, the population quickly outgrows its supply of resources. Therefore, not all offspring can survive. Darwin reasoned that there is always competition for food, water, and space in the environment. The individuals that survive the competition can then reproduce. Darwin proposed that the ability to reproduce and pass on traits that aid survival is as important as survival itself.

THE THEORY OF EVOLUTION

It's only natural

In 1844 Darwin wrote a paper explaining his theory of evolution. He based his theory on the observations and studies he had made over the previous 15 years. Because he knew his ideas would challenge popular beliefs,

FIGURE 10.7
Artificial Selection

Artificial selection led to the development of many vegetables from the wild mustard plant.

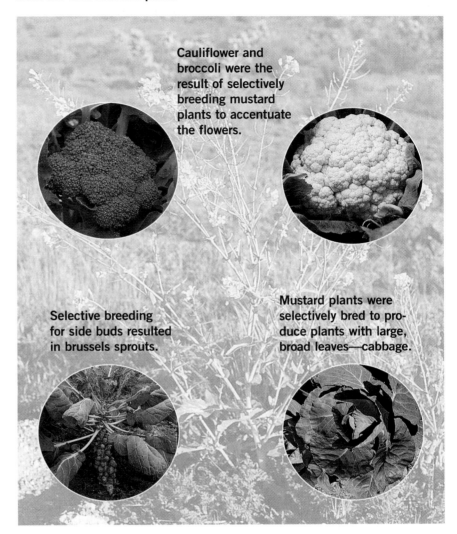

Cauliflower and broccoli were the result of selectively breeding mustard plants to accentuate the flowers.

Selective breeding for side buds resulted in brussels sprouts.

Mustard plants were selectively bred to produce plants with large, broad leaves—cabbage.

Darwin did not publish his work for more than ten years.

Meanwhile, another young English biologist named Alfred Wallace made a sea voyage to the West Indies. Wallace also observed and collected many plant and animal specimens. Not surprisingly, Wallace developed a theory similar to Darwin's. Eager to publish his conclusions, Wallace wrote to Darwin, explaining his theory.

In 1858 both men agreed to send their papers together to the same scientific organization. Wallace graciously gave Darwin credit for having

The Bright Side of Motion Sickness

Have you ever had motion sickness? Darwin was very prone to seasickness. For that reason, he spent a lot of time ashore during his five-year voyage and obtained important data for his research.

FIGURE 10.8
The fastest ostrich in a population has a favorable variation. How might this variation lead to natural selection?

developed the theory first. The theory was presented more fully in the book *On the Origin of Species by Means of Natural Selection*, which Darwin published a year later.

Natural selection Darwin observed an amazing variety of plants and animals on the Galapagos Islands. But what was the process that shaped their adaptations? Darwin called the process **natural selection,** a theory that consists of four main points:

There is variation within populations. Many variations are inherited, and such traits are passed from parent to offspring. Though little was known of genetics in Darwin's time, variation among species was well documented. Darwin's own work on the *Beagle* provided evidence of inherited variations.

Some variations are favorable. Darwin observed many examples of favorable variations on the Galapagos

FIGURE 10.9

This lion is about to eat an ostrich egg. Which point of natural selection does this photograph illustrate?

Islands. A favorable variation is one that improves an organism's ability to function and reproduce in its own particular environment. For example, some ostriches can run faster than the others. This favorable variation enables faster ostriches to escape predators more easily, making them more likely to live and reproduce.

Not all young produced in each generation can survive. Many die as a result of disease or starvation. As you can see in *Figure 10.9,* some off-spring are killed by predators. Consequently, only a few live long enough to reproduce.

Individuals that survive and reproduce are those with favorable variations. The offspring of the survivors will inherit the favorable variations. Therefore, with each new generation, a progressively larger proportion of offspring will have these variations. This idea is the main concept of natural selection.

Ostriches are probably a result of natural selection. They are the fastest birds on land, achieving running speeds of up to 65 kilometers per hour. Their speed is due to favorable traits such as long, powerful legs. Only the fastest ostriches have lived long enough to reproduce, and they have passed on the traits that enable them to run so quickly.

THE NATURE OF CHANGE

Stop and go

Evidence indicates that natural selection is the mechanism of evolution, or change over time. Natural selection can result in the evolution of new species. But at what rate does evolution take place?

According to some scientists, small genetic changes occur slowly within a population. This theory, known as **gradualism,** proposes that new species evolve as the genomes of two populations differentiate over enormous spans of time. Darwin originally proposed that evolution occurred at a slow, gradual rate.

In 1972 scientists Stephen Jay Gould and Niles Eldridge advanced another explanation about the rate of evolution. Their theory, known as **punctuated equilibrium,** suggests that populations remain genetically stable for long periods of time, interrupted by brief periods of rapid genetic change. This abrupt genetic change can be caused by sudden changes in the environment or by an increased mutation rate. Rapid genetic changes in a population can result in the evolution of new species.

What evidence supports or contradicts these theories? If gradualism is correct, the fossil record should show steady, gradual changes from ancient organisms to modern ancestors.

However, the fossil record lacks many of the intermediate life-forms Darwin and proponents of gradualism would expect to see. These scientists point out that many changes cannot be preserved in fossils. Darwin's explanation for the gaps in the fossil record was that the periods of change were far shorter than the periods of no change. However, Gould and Eldridge suggest that the gaps in the fossil record support punctuated equilibrium. Scientists on both sides of the debate continue to search for and find evidence supporting their theories. As in many areas of science, conflicting theories help drive scientific research about evolution.

Gradualism   **Punctuated Equilibrium**

Time

CHECKPOINT 10.2

1. Compare and contrast the three main points of Lamarck's theory with the four points of Darwin's theory of natural selection.
2. Describe two sources of information that Darwin used to formulate his theory of natural selection.
3. **Critical Thinking** Why do you think rapid evolution might occur when a small population becomes isolated from the main population?

Build on What You Know

4. How might Mendel have helped Darwin develop his theory? Write a letter from Mendel to Darwin. **(Need to jog your memory? Revisit relevant concepts in Chapter 6, Section 6.1.)**

FIGURE 10.10
Compare the theory of gradualism with that of punctuated equilibrium.

How do populations change over time? **?**

10.3 Tracking Changes

What you'll learn

IDEAS

- To explain how scientists reconstruct history through fossils
- To describe how scientists reconstruct evolutionary history through present-day organisms

WORDS

homologous structures, vestigial structures, analogous structures

Fossil firms up family history

Why are paleontologists excited when they discover a fossil? Fossils are rare, and finding a well-preserved fossil, such as the fish shown here, can be thrilling. Fossils can capture a moment in time—a moment so far removed that no human record exists of what life was like then.

CHANGES IN THE PAST

Fossils make history

According to evolutionary theory, all life originated from a common unicellular ancestor through natural selection. The fossil record reveals changes in populations over time, and supports the theory of evolution.

Using radiometric dating, scientists can often calculate a fossil's age. The oldest fossils are of ancient prokaryotes. By pinpointing the age of fossils, scientists can reconstruct an evolutionary time line.

Figure 10.11 shows fossils of different horselike species. The oldest fossils (far left) are the leg and tooth of the small animal. How do the older fossils compare with the more recent fossils? This fossil record provides information about the evolutionary history of today's horse. If you study only the fossils below, there appears to be a straight-line progression from the first horse ancestor to the modern horse species. Such a progression implies an evolutionary "goal," since there is a trend toward larger body size, fewer toes, and flat teeth.

FIGURE 10.11

The fossil record of the evolution of the horse is incomplete but informative. Compare the modern horse species (below, far right) with the older species to its left. How would you describe the apparent evolutionary trend shown here?

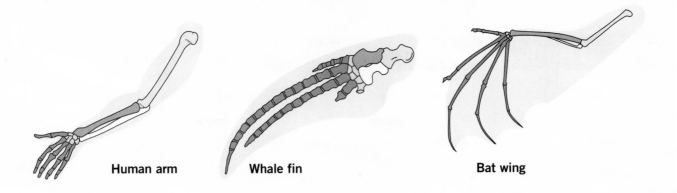

Human arm   **Whale fin**   **Bat wing**

However, evolution rarely follows a straight line to a goal. Scientists are careful to consider all known horse-related fossils—representing more than 20 species—when drawing conclusions about the evolution of the modern horse. Not all of the horselike species evolved with fewer toes or flatter teeth. There are no goals in evolution.

Reconstructing the evolutionary history of a species can be difficult. As you have learned, the fossil record can be incomplete. Despite these uncertainties, the fossil record reveals relationships between species and how their structures have changed over time.

STRUCTURES

Whale claws, snake legs

The degree of relatedness between two different species depends on how long ago they shared a common ancestor. In addition to using the fossil record, scientists compare the anatomy of living species to establish relatedness.

Homologous structures Traits that are similar in different species because the species share a common ancestor are referred to as **homologous** (hoh-MOL-uh-gus) **structures.** Compare the homologous structures in *Figure 10.12*. The arm, fin, and wing may have evolved from the forelimb of a common vertebrate ancestor. Their appearance differs

because these species are adapted to different niches.

Vestigial structures Pythons have leg and hip bones, as shown in *Figure 10.13*. **Vestigial structures** (veh-STIH-juhl) are inherited, but reduced in size and often unused. They suggest structures of the ancestors of modern organisms.

Although vestigial structures like the python's leg and hip bones are no longer used in locomotion, they are remnants of functional structures inherited from an ancestor. A python's vestigial structures are homologous to the leg and hip bones of other reptiles, evidence that pythons are related to legged reptiles. Humans have a vestigial structure—the appendix, a tiny, dead-end pouch on the intestine that may play a minor role in the immune system.

Analogous structures Distantly related organisms sometimes have characteristics that are similar in function but different in structure. For example, insect wings are quite unlike bird wings, even though they serve the same function—flight. Their structural differences indicate that insects and birds evolved independently. **Analogous** (an-AL-uh-guhs) **structures** are those

FIGURE 10.12
The homologous bones illustrated here are shown in the same color. How are the human arm, whale fin, and bat wing similar?

FIGURE 10.13
Pythons have vestigial hip and leg bones, evidence of a legged ancestor.

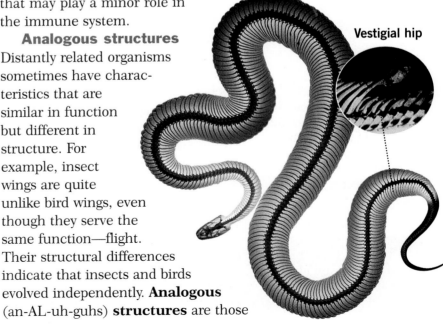

Vestigial hip

Recording Observations

Darwin carefully recorded his observations in journals. Recording accurate observations is an important part of the scientific method. How can you ensure that you record accurate observations?

Observe the weather over a five-day period. On the last day, record from memory each day's weather in as much detail as possible. Repeat the process for another five days, but record your observations at least once a day.

Analyze Your Results

1 Compare your records. How do they differ? Which record is more accurate?

2 If you were to propose a hypothesis about weather patterns in your area, what type of journal would help you form an accurate hypothesis? Why?

Gill pouch

FIGURE 10.14
Like the embryos of all animals with backbones, this human embryo has gill pouches. In humans, these pouches develop into inner ear tubes. In fishes, gill pouches become gill slits.

that are similar in function, but are not inherited from a common ancestor.

ADDITIONAL DATA

Living history

Scientists also rely on embryology and biochemistry to understand evolution. Embryology is the study of the early stages of an organism's development. Biochemists study and compare chemicals found in living things.

Embryos of related organisms develop in similar ways. For example, all vertebrate embryos have folds of tissue in the neck region called gill pouches. An example of gill pouches

is shown in *Figure 10.14*. These folds develop into gill slits in fishes. Mammals never develop gills, but the gill pouches appear in mammalian embryos. The gill pouches are thought to be inherited from a common ancestor.

In addition to embryo structures, living things share biochemical characteristics, such as a dependence on ATP. Perhaps the clearest biochemical evidence of the common origin of living things is the genetic code. The same four nitrogenous bases—adenine, thymine, guanine, and cytosine—exist in every form of life. In addition, the genetic code itself—the codons for the amino acids—is almost universal.

The exact sequence of nitrogenous bases is unique to each species. Closely related species share more base sequences than do distantly related species. In the 1990s, genes from fossils have been sequenced using new DNA technology. Molecular biologists use similar gene sequences to reconstruct evolutionary history and to identify closely related species.

CHECKPOINT 10.3

1. How do scientists learn about life's history through fossils?

2. What can scientists learn from the DNA of present-day organisms?

3. Critical Thinking A whale fin and a human hand are thought to be homologous. Do you think a whale would have vestigial hip and leg bones?

Build on What You Know

4. Why do you think all living things depend on water? *(Need to jog your memory? Revisit relevant concepts in Chapter 2, Section 2.5.)*

What evidence supports the theory of evolution?

10.4 Origin of Species

New niches

In 1883 the Krakatoa volcano blast destroyed most of the island and buried the rest under meters of hot ash, leaving the area lifeless. Separated from the nearest land life-forms by more than 40 km, Krakatoa today teems with new plants and animals. Destroyed niches are eventually replaced.

What you'll learn

IDEAS
• To identify the characteristics that define a species
• To compare the different modes of speciation

WORDS
speciation, divergent evolution, convergent evolution, coevolution, adaptive radiation

SPECIATION

My, how you've changed

Evolution is the process by which populations change in response to their environments. Sometimes these changes result in striking variation within populations of a species. In some cases, the changes are so great that members of the original population can no longer successfully breed with members of the changed population. In such circumstances, the changed population has become a new species. As you have learned, a species is interbreeding populations of organisms that can produce healthy, fertile offspring. **Speciation** is the evolution of one or more species from a single ancestor species.

Species can originate when members of a population become isolated from their original population. Such isolation often happens as a result of geographic change. For example, a mountain range or body of water may separate a group from its original population.

With the geographic barrier in place, the separated group may respond differently to the unique selection pressures of its new environment. If two populations stay apart long enough, they become reproductively isolated. In other words, the populations cannot or will not interbreed. Once two populations are reproductively isolated, the populations are considered to be separate species, and speciation will have occurred.

FIGURE 10.15

Speciation

Although these squirrels look very much alike, they cannot interbreed and are thus two different species. How were the two species isolated?

White-tailed antelope squirrel

Harris's antelope squirrel

FIGURE 10.16

Divergent Evolution

Fur color in polar bears is an adaptation to their environments. How could divergent evolution have resulted in these two bear species?

FIGURE 10.17

Convergent Evolution

Although this serval cat (left) and maned wolf (right) have similar traits, they have different ancestors from different continents. The two species are the result of convergent evolution.

MECHANISMS OF EVOLUTION

Constantly changing

As new species originate, they may go through different processes of evolution. Some of the different evolutionary processes are divergent evolution, convergent evolution, and coevolution. Convergent evolution differs from the other processes in that it occurs independently among members of different species.

Divergent evolution When isolated populations of a species evolve independently, the process is called **divergent evolution.** Divergent evolution often occurs when geographic barriers separate members of a population. But it may also occur when a small group leaves an original population to colonize a new area.

The ancestors of the polar bears, for example, migrated from land onto Arctic ice and became isolated from the ancestors of the brown bear. Because the two bear populations lived in different environments, different traits were advantageous. How would white fur in the polar bear ancestors help them to survive?

According to the theory of natural selection, individuals with the advantageous traits survived, reproduced, and passed on these traits to their offspring. As generations passed, the genomes of the two populations became so different that the new population of polar bears could no

Serval cat

Maned wolf

Both serval cats and maned wolves have very long ears, an adaptation that enables them to hear their prey move in tall grasslands.

Serval cats and maned wolves both eat rodents and lizards.

Serval cats and maned wolves both have long legs, useful characteristics for chasing their prey.

longer breed with the original population of brown bears.

Convergent evolution Sometimes, different species with different ancestors develop similar characteristics. When unrelated species display similar features, they may owe these likenesses to convergent evolution. **Convergent evolution** occurs when natural selection has produced analogous (similar) adaptations in response to similar environments. Darwin compared convergent evolution to two people coming up with the same invention independently.

Convergent evolution can sometimes mislead scientists into concluding that organisms are more closely related than they actually are. In these instances, scientists must rely on other methods of analysis, such as embryology or biochemistry.

You can see an example of convergent evolution—the African serval cat and the South American maned wolf—in *Figure 10.17*. In addition to their physical similarities, these two animals have similar niches. They both hunt rodents and lizards, live in tall, grassy areas, and count on their extraordinary hearing ability to catch their prey. Yet they are very different, unrelated species.

Coevolution A population's physical environment is not the only factor that shapes the adaptations that will be favored by natural selection. Sometimes, interactions with other plants or animals affect evolution. Over millions of years, species that interact closely often adapt to one another in a process called **coevolution.**

Many species of plants depend on a coevolutionary relationship to reproduce. The shape, smell, and color of their flowers have been naturally selected to attract certain pollinating insects, birds, or bats. These species of pollinators, in turn, have evolved specialized structures to reach the flowers'

nectar. Such an exclusive relationship benefits both the plant and the pollinator. Many flowers and hummingbirds, such as those shown in *Figure 10.18,* have coevolved in this manner.

Filling the vacuum

Populations cannot evolve and new species cannot survive unless there are resources to support them. You may remember from section 10.1 that a niche includes all the factors to which a population must adapt, including habitat, food supply, and temperature. An empty habitat does not stay empty very long, as populations will invariably evolve to fill it. As a result, many different species may evolve from one ancestral species. Each species will have a different niche.

Adaptive radiation is the evolution of many diversely adapted species from one common ancestor. Darwin observed the effects of

FIGURE 10.18
The hummingbird's long, thin beak enables it to harvest nectar from these flowers. How have hummingbirds and these flowers coevolved?

LAB ZONE Do It!

How Are Inventions Like Evolution?

Darwin compared convergent evolution to the independent invention of the same product by two different people. You can see how his analogy holds up if you. . .

Try This

1 With your class, select an aspect of life that you would like to change. One idea might be the classroom.
2 For 15 minutes, everyone in your class (alone or in small groups) should brainstorm inventions that would change that aspect of life. Be creative as you brainstorm.
3 Compare ideas with your classmates.

Analyze Your Results

1 Were any of your ideas the same as those of your classmates? How many ideas were similar, and in what ways?
2 How does this activity illustrate convergent evolution? How might you improve Darwin's analogy?

FIGURE 10.19
Adaptive Radiation

As populations of finches migrated to the different Galapagos Islands, they adapted to the different environments.

Insect eater
One of the few known cases of tool use by birds is an insect-eating finch.

Cactus eater
These finches have large, crushing beaks for eating cactus.

Seed eater
These finches have a beak size that matches the seeds they eat.

Common ancestor

adaptive radiation in the Galapagos Islands. Each of the thirteen different finches he collected belonged to a separate species. They were similar in many ways, but differed in beak size and feeding habits.

Evidence shows that the original species of Galapagos finch, an immigrant from South America, lived on one island. Then a few individuals migrated to neighboring islands, where they were exposed to new environments and isolated from the original population. Over time, the migrant finch populations adapted to their new environments and so became separate species.

While the unique demands of life on each island left each population of finches specifically adapted, they still retained enough common features to link them to the original species population. Adaptive radiation describes how a chain of islands like the

Galapagos becomes populated by diverse forms of life. Species migrate to these islands in unusual circumstances and then evolve in isolation.

CHECKPOINT 10.4

1. What is the difference between two different species and a single species in which there is a lot of variation?
2. Name and describe three processes of evolution.
3. **Critical Thinking** Scientists are not sure whether the American red wolf is a hybrid of a coyote and a grey wolf, or if it is a separate species. How might this question be resolved?

Build on What You Know

4. Compare and contrast selective breeding (artificial selection) and coevolution. *(Need to jog your memory? To revisit relevant concepts, see Chapter 9, Section 9.1.)*

Modeling Coevolution

WHAT YOU WILL DO Model coevolution

SKILLS YOU WILL USE Modeling, collecting and recording data, predicting

WHAT YOU WILL NEED Long tweezers, teaspoons, dried peas or beans, 25-milliliter (mL) graduated cylinders, 100-mL beakers, watch or clock

Propose a Hypothesis

Write a hypothesis about how using differently shaped objects to retrieve seeds from differently shaped containers models adaptations in species that have undergone coevolution.

Conduct Your Experiment

1 Divide your class into three teams—A, B, and C. Each team represents a bird species; each team member a single bird. For the experiment, "species" A will use tweezers, B will use their fingers, and C will use spoons. The tweezers, fingers, and spoons represent the different birds' beaks.

2 Fill the containers half full with dried peas or beans. The beakers and graduated cylinders represent two different species of flowers. The seeds represent the birds' food.

3 For one minute, each team member removes seeds, one at a time, from his or her own beaker. The beaker must remain stationary. Do not tip the beaker.

4 After one minute, count the number of seeds each team has "eaten." Record this data.

5 Assume that a flower was successfully pollinated each time a seed was successfully eaten. Record the number of successful pollinations for each one-minute trial.

6 Repeat steps 2 through 5, using the graduated cylinders.

Analyze Your Data

1 Which team retrieved the most seeds from the beakers? From the graduated cylinders?

2 From what type of flower was each team the most successful at obtaining food?

Draw Conclusions

1 From which flower would species A feed most effectively? From which flower would each species feed most often?

2 Which type of bird is the most likely pollinator of each flower?

3 For each bird and flower species, describe what would happen to the other populations if one species became extinct.

4 How does this activity model coevolution? (Hint: Use the terms *variation, competition,* and *natural selection* in your answer.)

5 How could you improve this model?

Design a Related Experiment

Design an experiment that models coevolution between flowers of different colors and pollinating insects attracted to specific colors.

Modeling Coevolution

Objective: To get an idea of how coevolution works
Team A: Birds species with tweezer "beaks"
Type of flower: Beaker with dried peas
Number of seeds removed after one minute:

10.5 Population Genetics

What you'll learn

IDEAS
- To describe the principles of population genetics
- To analyze the effects of changes in the environment on populations

WORDS
gene pool, allele frequency, genetic equilibrium, genetic drift, directional selection, disruptive selection

Night lights in the USA
This photo shows the United States at night. The light areas indicate where many people live, or where the population is the most dense. Can you identify the area where you live? How would you describe the population in that area? Researchers study populations of many different kinds of organisms and observe how the populations are evolving.

GENE POOL

Hardy populations

As you continue to study the diversity of life, remember that populations are the smallest unit in which evolution takes place. Each individual member of a population exhibits unique characteristics, but the effect of natural selection—evolution—can only be measured in terms of an entire population. The study of genetic traits and changes in populations is called population genetics.

You have read about some ways in which species may evolve. All mechanisms of evolution involve changes in the gene pool. A **gene pool** is the combined genetic material of all the members of a given population. The gene pool includes all the genes for every trait on every chromosome of every reproductive individual within that population.

In Chapter 6 you learned that genes often have two or more different forms, called alleles. In any gene pool, the number of each allele is a fraction of all the genes for a particular trait. These fractions are known as **allele frequencies.** In *Figure 10.20,* you can see an example of how a population's allele frequencies are determined. Evolution often begins with a change in allele frequencies over time within a population.

In 1908, two researchers studying population genetics independently came to the same conclusion: if a population is not evolving, the allele frequencies in the population remain stable. This idea is called the Hardy-Weinberg principle, named after the two researchers who developed it. This constant state of allele frequencies is called **genetic equilibrium** (ee-kwih-LIH-bree-um).

FIGURE 10.20
Allele Frequency

Given a population of **500** wildflowers that are either

pink or white

AA or *Aa*   *aa*

There are **1000** flower-color genes. The pink allele (*A*) is dominant over the white allele (*a*).

In this given population

20 are because they are homozygous (*aa*) for the recessive allele.

480 are because 320 are homozygous dominant (*AA*) and 160 are heterozygous (*Aa*).

There are **640 + 160 = 800** dominant (*A*) alleles.

There are **160 + 40 = 200** recessive (*a*) alleles.

800 alleles are dominant (*A*) and the allele frequency is 800/1000 = **80%**.

200 alleles are recessive (*a*) and the allele frequency is 200/1000 = **20%**.

80% pink alleles   **20%** white alleles

FIGURE 10.21

Genetic Equilibrium

How well do these puffins meet the requirements for genetic equilibrium?

Puffins with brighter bills may have better mating success.

Assume that there is no net change in alleles.

Migration is unlikely due to the specific habitat and poor mobility of puffins.

Natural selection favors birds that can catch more fish.

The Hardy-Weinberg principle states that, under specific conditions, allele frequencies in a population remain constant from generation to generation. If specific conditions are not met, the genetic equilibrium is disrupted, and the population may evolve. Four conditions are required to maintain genetic equilibrium: no natural selection, random mating, no migration, and no significant mutations. Review *Figure 10.21* to learn whether or not a puffin population meets the conditions of the Hardy-Weinberg principle.

For a population to remain in equilibrium, all alleles in the population must be equally favored. There must be no reason for one allele to have a selective advantage over another—in other words, no natural selection.

In most animal populations, mating is not completely random. In fact, many animal species put effort into selecting a specific mate. However, for a population to remain in genetic equilibrium, there must be no trait that makes some individuals more attractive as mates than others.

Because migrating individuals may bring new alleles into a population and change gene frequencies, there must be no migration into or out of a population for genetic equilibrium to be maintained. In other words, the population must be isolated from other populations of the same species. The mixing of genes as a result of migration is called gene flow.

Like migration, mutation can introduce new alleles into the population. But if the number of existing alleles mutating to new alleles equals the number of new alleles mutating back to old alleles, there is no net change in alleles. Genetic equilibrium is maintained.

In some populations, all four conditions may be met or nearly met for long periods of time. However, genetic equilibrium is often disrupted. Evolution is the result of a disruption in genetic equilibrium.

Population size is also an important factor in the Hardy-Weinberg principle. The smaller the population, the greater the impact of migration, mutation, and selection.

Genetic drift occurs when natural disasters, such as forest fires, kill large numbers of a population.

GENETIC DRIFT

A sea of changes

Even when all the Hardy-Weinberg conditions are met, genetic equilibrium can be affected by chance changes in allele frequencies. **Genetic drift** is the random change in allele frequencies in a population due to chance events.

 Do It!

How Quickly Do Populations Decrease?

You can calculate how long it takes for a population to decline to the size that it will be affected by genetic drift if you . . .

Try This

1 Imagine that a certain population in a South American rain forest currently numbers 200. The population is decreasing by 10 percent each year.
2 Calculate the projected population size for each of the next 10 years.
3 Graph your results. Place population numbers on the y-axis (vertically) and time on the x-axis (horizontally).

Analyze Your Results

1 How many years does it take the population to fall below 100?
2 Describe your graph. How would you describe the decline of the population?
3 How might the genetic variation in the original population of 200 compare to the genetic variation in the population of 100?
4 How could bottlenecking affect the population?

Chance events, such as migrations or natural disasters, can cause dramatic reductions in population size and create a new, small population from a larger one. The gene pool of the new population will often have a different allele frequency from the original gene pool. Genetic drift has a greater impact on smaller populations, groups with fewer than 100 individuals.

The term "bottlenecking" refers specifically to the genetic drift occurring after a random population-reducing event. The Florida panther is an example of a species that has undergone bottlenecking. Early Florida settlers hunted the panthers to protect their homes and livestock. Then, as homes and cities were built in panther habitats, the panther population was reduced further. Today, the Florida panthers number fewer than 100.

The resulting genetic drift means that today's Florida panther population has much less genetic variation than the original population. Populations with little genetic variation are vulnerable because they cannot easily adapt to environmental changes. Due to their lack of genetic variation, Florida panthers are more susceptible to genetic disorders, and the population is less likely to survive than more genetically diverse populations of panthers.

Recently, Texas cougars have been introduced into Florida to crossbreed with the Florida panther and increase the genetic variation. How do you think this action will affect the future of the Florida panther population?

DISTRIBUTION AND SELECTION

For whom the bell tolls

Populations are not static. Variation and adaptation allow populations to respond to the unique challenges of their environment. Scientists often study the effect of natural selection on the phenotypes of populations.

By graphing the number of individuals in a population with specific phenotypes, scientists can measure how much variation exists in a population. And by studying changes over time in the distribution of variations, scientists can evaluate evolutionary change.

Suppose a scientist determines the colors and numbers of all rabbits in a test area. A graph of these data might show a bell-shaped curve like the one in *Figure 10.23*. This pattern indicates that the largest number of individuals are a medium shade, and fewer individuals are very light or very dark. This bell-shaped curve is called a normal distribution.

Now suppose the environment changes and becomes more barren, exposing more dark soil. Rabbits with dark coats would be less visible against the darker background and would be more able to avoid predators. Light-colored rabbits would be more visible. In this darker environment, darker

individuals would survive to reproduce more often than lighter ones, and more offspring would tend to be dark.

After several generations, the distribution might shift in the direction of darker coat color. Such a shift in frequency to an extreme phenotype is called **directional selection.** A typical graph of directional selection is shown in *Figure 10.23* (center).

Selection can also act against the middle of a distribution pattern. A

IN THE COMMUNITY

The World in Their Eyes

Humans have a definite effect on the population genetics of many organisms. Take a stroll through your community and look for habitats that have been affected by humans. One example might be an area where a new road or housing development has displaced plants and animals.

Another might be a wildlife preserve or sanctuary. The Biosurf web site *http://evolution.biosurf.com* includes other examples. List the examples you find.

FIGURE 10.23

Distribution Curves

Environmental changes can affect the frequencies of the phenotypes that occur within a population.

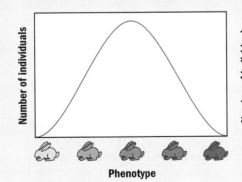

Normal distribution
This curve is called a normal distribution because it is so common in nature. What color are most of the rabbits?

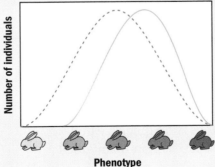

Directional selection
Directional selection occurs when a change in the environment favors an extreme phenotype. Which phenotype is favored now?

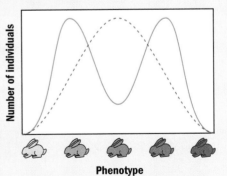

Disruptive selection
Disruptive selection occurs when an environmental change makes it unfavorable to have the medium phenotype. Describe the favored phenotype(s).

FIGURE 10.24
On dark tree trunks light moths are not a favored phenotype. Which of the moths shown above would best survive on dark tree trunks?

selection that does not favor the most common variation within a population is called **disruptive selection.** For example, if the environment changed to dark ground with light-colored sage brush, only very dark or very light rabbits would be safe from predators. A medium-colored coat would not be advantageous.

ENVIRONMENTAL AWARENESS

The story of the English peppered moth

Actions of humans can have a dramatic impact on other organisms' lives. Consider the English peppered moths, which inhabit forested areas. Before the Industrial Revolution, most peppered moths were a light color. Tree trunks in rural England were covered with light gray lichens, allowing light-colored moths to blend perfectly with the tree trunks. Darker moths were seen occasionally, probably due to mutations. But darker moths were easy for predators to spot, and they were quickly eaten by birds. Natural selection maintained a low number of dark moths.

When England became industrialized, soot and smoke from factories killed the lichen on trees, exposing darker bark. Within a few years, people noticed a change in the peppered moth population: most moths were now dark-colored. Industrial pollution had changed the background against which the moths rested; the light-colored trait had become a disadvantage. Natural selection now favored the darker moths. In only a few generations, directional selection caused a change in the color of the majority of peppered moths from light to dark.

In recent years, air pollution has decreased. Less soot is now released into the air. As a result, the lichen population has revived and some tree trunks are light-colored once again. How do you think the change in the lichen population has affected the peppered moths?

CHECKPOINT 10.5

1. Describe the following principles of population genetics: genetic equilibrium, genetic drift, directional selection, disruptive selection.
2. How do changes in the environment affect populations?
3. Critical Thinking Draw a normal distribution curve for dog size, assuming that medium-size dogs are most common and very small and very large dogs are least common.

Build on What You Know

4. How would a complex pattern of inheritance (such as codominance or multiple alleles) affect a population genetics study? *(Need to jog your memory? Revisit relevant concepts in Chapter 6, Section 6.5.)*

What factors can contribute to the formation of a new species?

Chapter 10 Review

10.1–10.2 Populations change over time through natural selection.
10.3 Scientific analysis of fossils and modern organisms supports the theory of evolution.
10.4–10.5 New species can originate through natural selection and other changes in a population's gene pool.

Sum It Up

Use the following summary to review the main concepts in this chapter.

10.1 Variation and Adaptation

- Most variation in a population results from mutation and recombination of existing alleles.
- Some variations are adaptations that increase a population's chances for survival and reproduction.
- Each species in an environment has its own niche. Niches are created and destroyed by environmental changes.

10.2 Darwin and His Theory

- Based on observations made during his voyage, Darwin concluded that adaptation and the evolution of species were related.
- Darwin drew analogies between biological change and geological change, and between artificial selection and natural selection.
- When organisms compete for limited resources, those with favorable traits survive and pass those traits along to the next generation.
- Some scientists, including Darwin, propose that evolution occurs gradually. Other scientists infer from gaps in the fossil record that evolution occurs in short periods of rapid change.

10.3 Tracking Changes

- To reconstruct evolutionary history, scientists examine fossils, compare structures of living and extinct species, study embryonic development, and analyze DNA.

10.4 Origin of Species

- New species can develop when populations become separated and isolated.
- Similar traits can develop in unrelated species occupying comparable niches.
- Interactions with other organisms affect evolution.
- Many diverse species can evolve from one ancestral species.

10.5 Population Genetics

- Evolution results from disruptions in genetic equilibrium.
- The normal distribution of variations in a population can be changed by natural selection.

Use Terms and Concepts

Use each of the following words or terms in a complete sentence. If you need to review a meaning, turn to the page indicated.

species (p. 230)
variation (p. 230)
adaptation (p. 231)
niche (p. 231)
fossils (p. 232)
evolution (p. 233)
natural selection (p. 236)
gradualism (p. 236)

punctuated equilibrium (p. 237)
homologous structures (p. 239)
vestigial structures (p. 239)
analogous structures (p. 239)
speciation (p. 241)

divergent evolution (p. 242)
convergent evolution (p. 243)
coevolution (p. 243)
adaptive radiation (p. 243)
gene pool (p. 246)

allele frequencies (p. 246)
genetic equilibrium (p. 246)
genetic drift (p. 248)
directional selection (p. 249)
disruptive selection (p. 250)

Use Your Word Power

COMPLETION Write the word or phrase that best completes each statement.

1. A(n) _____ is the combined genetic material of all individuals in a population.

2. Over millions of years, two interacting species may adapt to one another's needs through _____ .

3. The preserved remains or imprints of organisms are known as _____ .

4. A(n) _____ is a population's habitat and the role the population plays in the habitat.

5. Change over time is another description of _____ .

6. A(n) _____ is an interbreeding population that produces healthy, fertile offspring.

7. Darwin proposed that the adaptation of a species to its environment occurs through _____ .

MULTIPLE CHOICE Choose the letter of the word or phrase that best completes each statement.

8. Camouflage is an example of (a) variation; (b) adaptation; (c) speciation; (d) mutation.

9. Structures that are inherited but have no current function are (a) vestigial; (b) analogous; (c) divergent; (d) homologous.

10. A process that explains gaps in the fossil record is (a) genetic equilibrium; (b) gradualism; (c) punctuated equilibrium; (d) genetic drift.

11. The selection that favors an extreme phenotype is (a) natural selection; (b) directional selection; (c) artificial selection; (d) disruptive selection.

12. Species that have descended from different ancestors but have similar traits evolved through (a) divergent evolution; (b) adaptive radiation; (c) coevolution; (d) convergent evolution.

Show What You Know

13. How does migration affect the genetic equilibrium of a population?

14. What is the relationship between speciation and adaptive radiation?

15. What did Darwin learn from Malthus?

16. Is there a one-to-one relationship between species and niches? Explain your answer.

17. How does extinction affect adaptive radiation?

18. What aspect(s) of Lamarck's hypothesis contradicts what you have learned about genetics?

19. **Make a Concept Map** Complete the concept map below by adding the following terms: allele frequencies, genetic equilibrium, natural selection, migration, and mutation.

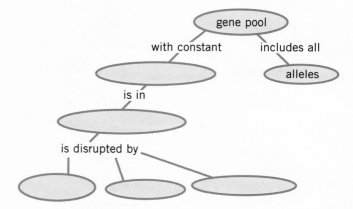

Take It Further

20. **Applying Concepts** The sea horse is a fish of the genus *Hippocampus*. Male sea horses carry developing eggs in a short, broad pouch. Kangaroos belong to the genus *Macropus*. Female kangaroos have a pouch for carrying newborns. Do you think the two pouches are homologous or analogous structures? Explain your answer.

21. **Making an Analogy** Was the development of Darwin's and Wallace's theories most like divergent evolution, convergent evolution, or coevolution? Give reasons for your answer.

22. Designing an Experiment If you want to graph distribution curves for length of adult trout, how would you collect the data? What drawback might there be to using data that has already been collected?

23. Interpreting a Graph Suppose you determined the number of species on seven islands of various sizes. The graph below summarizes your data. What can you conclude from the graph? How might this conclusion be applied to the reduction in size of tropical rain forests?

Number of Species Compared to Island Size

Island

Number of Species

100

10

0

2.5   25   250   2,500 25,000 250,000
Area of Island (km²)

Consider the Issues

24. Society and Evolution As medical technology has advanced through the centuries, some people believe natural selection for humans has been replaced by "Social Darwinism." Explain what is meant by Social Darwinism. Decide whether or not you believe Social Darwinism is a factor in human evolution.

25. Fine-tuning the Definition Wolves and dogs are classified as different species, but they interbreed and their offspring are fertile. However, a Saint Bernard weighing about 85,000 grams (g) and a Chihuahua weighing less than 435 g are both dogs, *Canis familiaris*, but are unlikely to mate. Should organisms be classified as separate species if they *cannot* interbreed, or when they *do not* interbreed?

Make New Connections

26. Biology and Art Some fossils are the original remains of an organism—a fly trapped in amber, for example. Other fossils form when an organism's remains are buried and decompose, leaving a hollow in the rock that serves as a mold. When a material similar to plaster of Paris fills the hole, a cast of the original organism forms. Ask your art instructor to help you create a mold and cast some "fossils" of your own.

27. Biology and History Darwin's theory was not well received when it was first proposed. The year after Darwin published his theory, a famous confrontation occurred between Bishop Samuel Wilberforce and Thomas Henry Huxley at a meeting of the British Association for the Advancement of Science. Work with a partner to present a reenactment of the debate.

28. Biology and Geography In developing a theory of natural selection, Darwin was strongly influenced by data he collected on the Galapagos Islands. The islands still provide valuable scientific data. Research and report on the islands. Where are they located? What political background do the islands have?

FAST-FORWARD TO CHAPTER 11

Chapter 10 has focused on how natural selection could have produced Earth's diverse species. In Chapter 11, you will learn how scientists have applied the theory of evolution to theories about the origin of life on Earth.

bioSURF

You can find out more about the history of life by exploring the following Internet address:
http://evolution.biosurf.com

In this chapter . . .

FEATURES

Everyday Biology
• Shooting Stars
• Mighty Mitochondria
• Strolling Across the Ocean

In the Community
Hometown History

 Issues in Biology
Mass Extinctions

LAB ZONES

Discover It!
• Describing Basic Requirements

Do It!
• How Did Plate Tectonics Result in Speciation?

Think About It!
• Determining the Age of a Fossil

Investigate It!
• Constructing Microspheres

AN ISLAND IS BORN

Named for the god of fire in Icelandic myths, Surtsey Island burst from the floor of the Atlantic Ocean in November of 1963. For the next three and a half years, the island continued to expand. Located off the southern coast of Iceland, Surtsey Island today measures 2.5 square kilometers.

Surtsey Island resulted from volcanic eruptions that steadily built up land from the ocean floor. As is the case with all volcanic eruptions, the birth of this island was accompanied by the release of steam, invisible gases, and ash. Although the beginning of Surtsey Island was dramatic, scientists know that events such as this one were commonplace during Earth's early history. The opportunity to observe the birth of Surtsey Island was a chance for scientists to study conditions similar to those on Earth before life existed—and to hypothesize how such conditions led to the first living cells. What were those conditions, and how did they lead to life on Earth?

Discover It!

Describing Basic Requirements

You need paper and pencil

1. Record as many as possible of the basic requirements for human life. One example is water.
2. Speculate on which of these requirements may not have been present when Earth first formed.

Earth was very different when it first formed. Frequent volcanic eruptions, intense lightning storms, and the absence of life were just some of the existing conditions. By using the scientific method, scientists from many fields have developed theories that explain the history of life.

WRITE ABOUT IT!

Imagine you could observe the formation and early history of Earth. In your science journal, describe the conditions you would see and the difficulty you would have living on Earth at that time.

11.1 Earth's Early History

What you'll learn

IDEAS

• To explain how the scientific method is used in studying Earth's early history
• To compare and contrast two hypotheses about how life began on Earth

WORD

microspheres

It's a bird! It's a plane! It's molecules! In 1984 scientists found pieces of a meteorite that had slammed into Antarctica about 13,000 years ago. Analysis showed that the meteorite contained complex organic molecules, leading scientists to wonder: Was life started by molecules from outer space? This idea is the basis for one of two hypotheses about the beginning of life on Earth.

FIGURE 11.1
Astronomers study the universe to learn more about the origin of Earth. What other scientists study Earth's origin?

STUDYING LIFE'S ORIGINS

Detecting life

Until a few hundred years ago, most people believed that life could arise from nonliving matter. This belief could explain how life originated on Earth. According to this belief, called spontaneous generation, living things can spring from nonliving materials when invisible "active principles" are present.

As you read in Chapter 1, living things do not come from nonliving material. According to the theory of biogenesis, life arises from living things. Even if life comes only from life, the question remains: Where did the first life-form come from? Many different answers to this question have been proposed.

Scientists have approached this question the same way they approach other questions—through the scientific method. The scientific method involves several steps, including formulating a hypothesis or possible explanation, gathering evidence through observation and experimentation, and drawing conclusions that support or refute the hypothesis.

A scientist studying the origin of life works like a detective. Detectives do not witness events. Instead, they must search for clues, try to reconstruct events, and formulate theories to explain the evidence. Like detectives, scientists cannot witness how life started on our planet. But scientists can use evidence and models to make and test hypotheses about the origin of life on Earth.

FIGURE 11.2
Geologists study rock samples to uncover Earth's early history.

3 The center of Earth was melted by great pressure and intense heat.

4.1 billion years ago
4 The surface of Earth cooled, forming the crust.

5 An atmosphere formed as Earth cooled.

4.5 billion years ago
2 Rocks in the solar system condensed to form Earth.

6 billion years ago
1 The solar system formed from swirling gases and dust.

FIGURE 11.3
Formation of Earth

Scientists have strong evidence indicating that the conditions on Earth today are very different from those that existed during Earth's formation and early history. Many scientists think that life could have arisen spontaneously under the conditions that existed on early Earth. To formulate theories about past conditions and life's origin on Earth, scientists have gathered information from many different scientific disciplines, including astronomy, geology, chemistry, and biology.

FORMATION OF EARTH

Hot dust collides

Scientists have hypothesized about conditions on Earth when life began. These conditions were the result of the planet's formation. According to most current theories, the solar system formed about 6 billion years ago from a swirling cloud of gas and dust. The process is summarized in *Figure 11.3*.

Scientists infer that most of this gas and dust condensed at the center of the solar system, producing the sun. Held by the gravity of the sun, pockets of dust and rocks around the cloud's edges then condensed to become planets, such as Earth; comets; and asteroids.

Gravity compressed Earth's basic materials, producing intense pressure. This pressure, along with radiation from certain elements, generated heat that melted the core material of the young planet. The heavier elements—such as nickel and iron—settled to the center and formed the planet's core. The lighter materials—such as hydrogen, helium, and other gases—rose to the surface and cooled to a solid crust about 4.1 billion years ago. Hydrogen gas, the lightest of materials, probably formed the outermost layer—Earth's first atmosphere.

After the planet's formation, frequent and violent volcanic eruptions shaped many landforms and emitted gases into the changing

A Comparison of Earth's Ancient and Modern Atmospheres		
Gas	Ancient (percent of atmosphere)	Modern (percent of atmosphere)
Carbon dioxide	92.2	0.03
Nitrogen	5.1	78.1
Sulfur dioxide	2.3	Trace
Hydrogen sulfide	0.2	Trace
Ammonia	0.1	Trace
Methane	0.1	Trace
Oxygen	0.0	20.9
Argon	0.0	0.9

FIGURE 11.4
How is today's atmosphere different from the atmosphere that probably existed about the time life appeared?

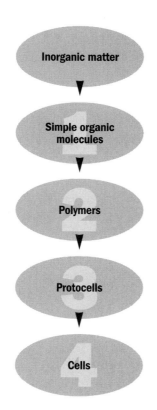

FIGURE 11.5
Most scientists agree that the formation of life had to follow these four steps.

atmosphere. Today, volcanoes still pour gases into the atmosphere. Geologists and astronomers have studied these gases, as well as the atmospheres of other planets, to identify gases that might have been present in Earth's ancient atmosphere. Their studies suggest that Earth's atmosphere 4 billion years ago probably consisted of gases such as ammonia (NH_3), methane (CH_4), carbon dioxide (CO_2), and nitrogen.

Evidence indicates that there was little or no oxygen (O_2) in the atmosphere when life appeared. Today, oxygen in the atmosphere is produced by photosynthetic organisms. The absence of oxygen, as you will see, was a key factor in the beginning of life on Earth. Using *Figure 11.4,* you can compare the composition of the ancient and modern atmospheres.

Scientists hypothesize that there was also water vapor in Earth's ancient atmosphere. The water vapor condensed to produce torrential rainstorms. Rainwater flowed from the land into basins in Earth's crust, forming seas. The rainwater carried dissolved gases and dissolved minerals such as phosphorous from rocks. These dissolved compounds formed a rich mixture in the seas.

Some energy sources present on the surface of early Earth are absent or reduced today. For example, the atmosphere lacked an ozone layer

such as the one that now surrounds Earth and shields us from the sun's harmful ultraviolet radiation. Without an ozone layer, enormous amounts of energy in the form of ultraviolet radiation reached Earth's surface. In addition, intense lightning storms may have contributed great amounts of electrical energy.

THE FIRST ORGANIC COMPOUNDS

Sparking to life

Evidence indicates that Earth was lifeless for as long as a half-billion years after it formed. Scientists may never know exactly when and how life originated, but they have formed several hypotheses based on what they know of life today. This information indicates that certain events had to occur before life could begin. Taking these events into account, scientists infer that life originated in four steps, as summarized in *Figure 11.5.*

In the first step, nonliving, or inorganic, matter was transformed into simple organic molecules. Organic molecules were then bonded to form chains of molecules, or polymers. Polymers began to develop characteristics of living cells, becoming "protocells." Finally, protocells evolved into true living cells, with the ability to replicate and pass on traits. With this overview, you can now review in more detail the steps leading to the formation of life.

Organic molecules The first step toward life may have been the formation of organic molecules. One of the theories that explains how these molecules formed was proposed by Russian biochemist Alexander Oparin in 1924. Oparin hypothesized that energy in ultraviolet radiation and lightning stimulated chemical reactions in the ancient atmosphere. These random chemical reactions, occurring over millions of years, produced organic molecules. This hypothesis is called chemical evolution.

American scientists Stanley Miller and Harold Urey performed a test of Oparin's hypothesis in 1953. Using the apparatus depicted in *Figure 11.6,* Miller and Urey modeled the ancient atmosphere by mixing water vapor, methane, ammonia, and hydrogen gases in a reacting chamber. Electrodes produced sparks to simulate lightning. After one week, Miller analyzed the liquid produced by the experiment and found that it contained amino acids and other organic molecules.

In keeping with the scientific method, Miller performed control experiments to verify his results. The first control experiment was a repeat of the experiment without the use of electrodes. Since no organic molecules were formed, this experiment confirmed the requirement of an energy source.

In another control experiment, Miller checked for contaminants. He sterilized the apparatus by heating it to 130°C for 18 hours, insuring that no organic molecules remained in the apparatus. The experiment still produced many organic molecules. What questions were answered by the two control experiments?

Miller and Urey's results demonstrated that chemical evolution could have occurred under the conditions modeled by their experiments. Other scientists have tested the chemical evolution hypothesis using different mixtures of gases that might model the atmosphere of early Earth. These scientists have also tried using different energy sources, including ultraviolet light, to stimulate the chemical reactions. Their experiments have produced not only amino acids, but also ATP and the nitrogenous bases of DNA and RNA.

FIGURE 11.6

Miller-Urey Apparatus

These gases represent Earth's early atmosphere.

Electrodes simulate lightning storms.

Water vapor

This cooling chamber forces "rainfall."

The flask collects samples from the "sea" for chemical analysis.

A Bunsen burner heats the water in the flask to produce water vapor.

A second hypothesis about the origin of organic molecules was proposed by Francis Crick, one of the scientists who discovered the structure of DNA. His hypothesis stated that organic molecules came from outer space. Geologists have found traces of amino acids and other compounds in meteorites, such as the one shown in *Figure 11.7.* Crick hypothesized that meteorites might have been the source of organic molecules in ancient seas.

Polymers In the second step in the formation of living cells, the newly formed organic molecules may have undergone a chemical change that led to the formation of polymers, which are chains of monomers. Each monomer is a small organic molecule, such as an amino acid, that acts as a building block for a larger molecule. For example, protein molecules are

FIGURE 11.7

Some scientists hypothesize that life originated from complex molecules found in meteorites.

polymers composed of chains of amino acids.

Two events must occur for monomers to form polymers. First, the monomers must come close enough to react with each other. Second, the monomers must chemically bond. In modern cells, enzymes initiate and speed up these two reactions. There were no enzymes when the first polymers formed, so the conditions under which the reactions occurred must have initiated polymer formation. There are several theories as to what those conditions were, most of which focus on where the organic molecules accumulated.

Some scientists propose that, in Earth's early seas, chance encounters of monomers occurred frequently enough to enable polymer formation. Other scientists hypothesize that polymers formed in evaporating puddles of sea water. Ocean waves may have splashed water onto rocks, forming puddles. Heat from the prehistoric sun or the volcanic rock could have heated the water. As the puddles dried, the solution left behind would become very concentrated; therefore, organic molecules could be close enough to react with each other. Over time, the material deposited on the rocks may have formed long polymers.

A third hypothesis about polymer formation involves common clay. Many organic molecules are attracted to the surface of particles found in clay. On early Earth, amino acids and other monomers may have collected on clay particles. There the monomers could have become concentrated, and polymer formation could have occurred.

THE FIRST CELLS

Shape of things to come

The formation of a cell membrane was probably the third step in the origin of life. Because of its membrane, a cell's internal environment is separate and different from its surroundings. This separation allows the chemical reactions of life to occur inside the cell.

Protocells The first cell membranes probably formed when polymers, large organic molecules, chemically interacted with their surroundings. Researchers have discovered that if certain protein molecules are mixed with water, tiny bubble-like structures will form. These protein and water bubbles, called **microspheres,** look and behave somewhat like cell membranes.

While microspheres are not cells, they may resemble early protocells that probably formed in the ancient seas. Early protocells may have absorbed nutrient molecules from their surroundings, enlarged, and then divided. When the protocells divided, however, they could not pass on traits to their offspring. This situation would not change until the evolution of the nucleic acids RNA and DNA.

Cells At some point in Earth's history, protocells absorbed nucleic acids from the environment. Once

FIGURE 11.8

What does lava flow do to ocean water? How might this have affected polymer formation on early Earth?

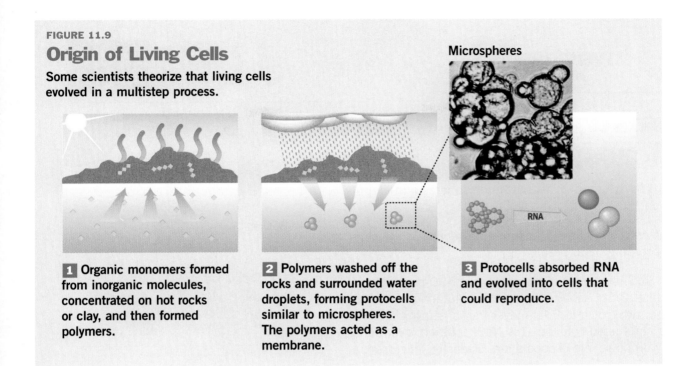

FIGURE 11.9

Origin of Living Cells

Some scientists theorize that living cells evolved in a multistep process.

Microspheres

RNA

1 Organic monomers formed from inorganic molecules, concentrated on hot rocks or clay, and then formed polymers.

2 Polymers washed off the rocks and surrounded water droplets, forming protocells similar to microspheres. The polymers acted as a membrane.

3 Protocells absorbed RNA and evolved into cells that could reproduce.

they contained DNA or RNA, the early cells could reproduce and transfer genetic information to offspring. Which nucleic acid was first present in early cells? The answer to this question lies in the replication process.

As you may recall from Chapter 7, replication of DNA and RNA in cells requires enzymes. However, RNA replication can occur in a test tube without the help of enzymes. When free RNA is mixed with RNA nucleotides, new segments of complementary RNA are formed. Therefore, scientists theorize that RNA was the first molecule to evolve with the ability to self-replicate, and that early cells probably contained RNA.

Once RNA was enclosed in a protocell membrane, the membrane would allow organic compounds to concentrate in the protocell. The increased concentration of organic compounds would enable essential

chemical reactions and energy production similar to cellular metabolism. If this newly formed structure were capable of reproduction and metabolism, it could truly be called a living thing—the first cell.

CHECKPOINT 11.1

1. How do researchers use the scientific method to discover the origins of life on Earth?

2. Describe a theory that explains the origin of cells.

3. Critical Thinking Compare and contrast the environment of early Earth with that of modern Earth.

Build on What You Know

4. Why were protocells unable to inherit traits until DNA or RNA evolved? *(Need to jog your memory? Revisit relevant concepts in Chapter 7, Section 7.2, and Chapter 8, Section 8.1.)*

How did the first organic molecules and cells probably form on Earth?

?

Constructing Microspheres

WHAT YOU WILL DO Construct microspheres and identify their parts

SKILLS YOU WILL USE Measuring, observing, collecting and recording data, predicting

WHAT YOU WILL NEED Safety goggles, 500-mL beaker, hot plate, 0.5 g aspartic acid, 0.5 g glutamic acid, 0.5 g glycine, two 250-mL Erlenmeyer flasks, stirring rod, ring stand, graduated cylinder, 1% NaCl solution, oven mitts, tongs, dropper, microscope slide, coverslip, microscope

Propose a Hypothesis

Propose a hypothesis about the composition and appearance of microspheres.

Conduct Your Experiment

Caution: Wear your lab coat and safety goggles for protection.
1 Fill a 500-milliliter (mL) beaker half full of water. Place the beaker on a hot plate and bring the water to a boil.
Caution: Be careful of the hot plate and boiling H_2O.
2 Add 0.5 gram (g) each of aspartic acid, glutamic acid, and glycine to a 250-mL flask. Use a stirring rod to mix the amino acids well.

3 Clamp the flask to a ring stand and lower it into the beaker of boiling water, as shown above. Heat the amino acids for 20 minutes. Remove from heat.
Caution: The steam and the beaker will be hot.
4 Measure 5 mL of a 1% NaCl solution, and pour it into a clean flask. Place the flask on a hot plate, and heat the solution to boiling.
5 Put on a pair of oven mitts, and use tongs to pick up the flask of boiling NaCl solution. Slowly pour the solution into the flask of amino acids.
6 Loosen the clamp holding the flask of amino acids, and lift it out of the boiling water. Turn off the hot plate, and allow the flask to cool on the ring stand for 10 minutes.

7 Use a dropper to transfer a drop of the amino acid mixture to a microscope slide. Cover with a coverslip.
8 Examine the slide with a microscope under low and high power. Draw diagrams of what you observe.

Analyze Your Data

1 What did you observe with the microscope?
2 What does your model represent?
3 How are microspheres similar to cells? How are they different?

Draw Conclusions

Did your findings support your hypothesis? Revise your original hypothesis to reflect your observations and analysis.

Design a Related Experiment

Would you get the same results using the DNA bases cytosine, guanine, adenine, and thymine? Design an experiment to find out.

Lab: Constructing Microspheres

Objective: To construct microspheres and identify their parts

Hypothesis

11.2 The First Organisms

How old are you now?
You have read that Earth is about 4.5 billion years old and that the solar system is about 6 billion years old. Scientists discovered this information by studying rocks on Earth, moon rocks, and meteorites. By measuring the amount of radioactive elements such as uranium in the rocks, scientists could estimate the age of Earth and the solar system.

What you'll learn

IDEAS
• To describe how the age of fossils is determined
• To summarize the development of the first prokaryotic and eukaryotic cells

WORDS
half-life, stromatolites, endosymbiosis

READING THE FOSSIL RECORD

Dating isotopes

As you read in Chapter 10, biologists have developed a theory of evolution that explains the changes in living things over time. The appearance of cells marked the beginning of the amazing biodiversity that exists today.

Of the many methods scientists use to study life's history, the most well-known is analyzing fossil evidence. Scientists can estimate the relative age of fossils from their location in rock. The oldest fossils are found in lower rock layers. As time passes, layers of rock are deposited on top of the previous layer. The oldest rock layers are on the bottom, and the most recently formed layers are on the top. The comparison of rock layers does not provide the actual age of a fossil, but it can indicate that one fossil is older than another.

A fossil's real age can be estimated by analyzing the isotopes in the rock surrounding the fossil. Isotopes are single atoms of the same element that have different numbers of neutrons.

Some isotopes are radioactive and undergo a change called radioactive decay. During radioactive decay, the isotope gives off particles and energy, changing its identity to a different element. For example, radioactive potassium (^{40}K) decays to produce a gas called argon. Radioactive decay occurs at a constant rate, called a half-life. The **half-life** of an element is the time it takes for half of the atoms in a sample to undergo radioactive decay. The half-life of ^{40}K is 1.3 billion years.

By studying radioactive isotopes in rocks and fossils, paleontologists can use radioactive dating methods to determine the fossil's age. Two of the most frequently used methods are potassium-argon dating and radiocarbon dating.

Potassium-argon dating is used for rocks that are suspected to be billions of years old. Once certain types of rocks form, the ^{40}K in the rocks decays to form argon, which is trapped in the rock crystals. The amount of argon in the rock can be compared to the amount of ^{40}K in the

FIGURE 11.10
Scientists can infer the relative age of fossils from their location in rock. Which of the rock layers shown here is probably the oldest?

FIGURE 11.11

Radiocarbon Dating

Paleontologists use radiocarbon dating to determine the age of rocks and fossils.

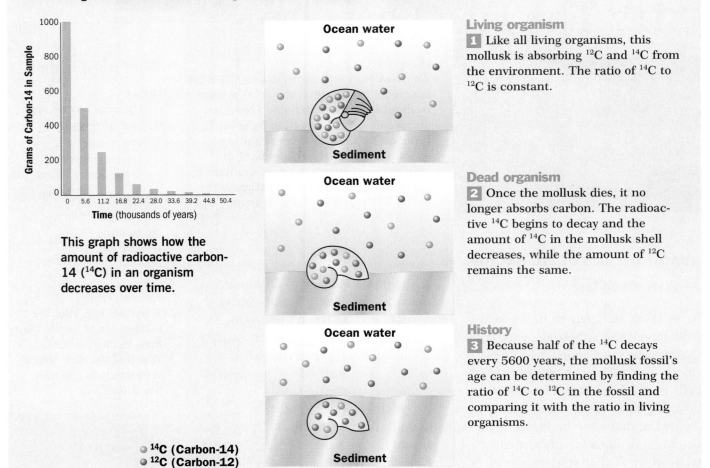

This graph shows how the amount of radioactive carbon-14 (^{14}C) in an organism decreases over time.

Ocean water

Sediment

Ocean water

Sediment

Ocean water

Sediment

^{14}C (Carbon-14)
^{12}C (Carbon-12)

Living organism

1 Like all living organisms, this mollusk is absorbing ^{12}C and ^{14}C from the environment. The ratio of ^{14}C to ^{12}C is constant.

Dead organism

2 Once the mollusk dies, it no longer absorbs carbon. The radioactive ^{14}C begins to decay and the amount of ^{14}C in the mollusk shell decreases, while the amount of ^{12}C remains the same.

History

3 Because half of the ^{14}C decays every 5600 years, the mollusk fossil's age can be determined by finding the ratio of ^{14}C to ^{12}C in the fossil and comparing it with the ratio in living organisms.

rock. From this ratio, scientists can calculate how long ago the rock formed. In older rocks, the ratio of argon to ^{40}K will be higher than in younger rocks. Fossils found in or very near the rocks are assumed to be the same age as the rock.

Scientists use another method of dating, radiocarbon dating, on younger fossils. There are two isotopes of carbon: the radioactive isotope carbon-14 (^{14}C) and the more common, non-radioactive isotope carbon-12 (^{12}C). In the atmosphere, the two isotopes are found in a constant ratio. Since living organisms are continually taking in carbon compounds from the

atmosphere, the ratio of ^{14}C to ^{12}C (^{14}C:^{12}C) in living cells also remains constant.

After an organism dies, no new carbon compounds are taken in. The amount of ^{12}C does not change, but the amount of radioactive ^{14}C decreases as it decays to other compounds. As the amount of ^{14}C decreases, the ^{14}C:^{12}C ratio changes over time. The age of a fossil can be determined by measuring the ratio of ^{14}C to ^{12}C and comparing the ratio with that of a living organism.

Since the half-life of ^{14}C is 5600 years, every 5600 years one half of the ^{14}C in a fossil will decay. For example,

FIGURE 11.12

Finding the First Fossils

The fossilized prokaryote (left) is about 3.5 billion years old.

Fossilized remains of bacterial mats (above) are some of the oldest known fossils. Modern colonies of bacteria form similar mats (below).

suppose there are 8 g of ^{14}C in a fossilized snail shell and 16 g of ^{14}C in a living snail shell. The amount of ^{12}C in both shells is the same. Since the ^{14}C:^{12}C ratio in the fossil is one-half the ^{14}C:^{12}C ratio in the living snail shell, the fossil is approximately 5600 years old. How old is a fossilized snail shell containing 4 g of ^{14}C?

The radiocarbon dating method is accurate only for fossils younger than 50,000 years. About how many ^{14}C half-lives is that? Radiocarbon dating is useful for dating fossils of prehistoric humans, because such remains are less than 50,000 years old.

EARLY PROKARYOTES

How long has life lived?

The oldest fossil evidence of cells that scientists have found so far is 3.5 billion years old. Therefore, scientists know that life is at least that old, and probably older. These fossils, shown in *Figure 11.12,* are called stromatolites.

LAB ZONE Think About It!

Determining the Age of a Fossil

Scientists use radiocarbon dating to determine the age of fossils. You can find out how they arrive at their conclusions if you . . .

Try This

1 Imagine you found a fossil, such as the one shown here.
2 You are given the following data: The leaf originally contained 12 g of ^{14}C. The fossil contains 3 g of ^{14}C.
3 Find out how many half-lives the fossil has had. Knowing that the half-life of ^{14}C is 5600 years, calculate the age of the fossil.

Analyze Your Results

1 How old is your fossil?
2 How has the amount of ^{12}C changed since the fossil was formed?
3 How do scientists determine how much ^{14}C was originally in the fossil?

FIGURE 11.13

Changing Atmosphere

Heterotrophs consumed many organic molecules and released carbon dioxide.

Competition led to the evolution of autotrophs, which produced their own food and released oxygen.

Stromatolites are the fossilized remains of layered mats of prokaryotic cells and sediment. The prokaryotic cells are similar to modern bacteria.

Most scientists agree that the first living cells were heterotrophs, organisms that cannot make their own food. Autotrophs can make their own food. The first heterotrophs absorbed organic compounds from their environment and produced carbon dioxide. As these early cells reproduced and their numbers increased, they began to use up the available supply of organic compounds. Strong competition developed among the heterotrophs for the available nutrients. Which cells would survive?

Many genetic variations occurred in the first billion years of life. Some of these variations resulted in the emergence of autotrophs. Because Earth's first autotrophs did not need organic compounds for food, they were freed from competition with heterotrophs for nutrients.

In order to use solar energy to make food, the first autotrophs evolved with a system resembling photosynthesis. But these earliest autotrophs did not produce oxygen. You read in Chapter 4 that photosynthesis is the process in which plants use the energy in sunlight, carbon dioxide, and water to make food and produce oxygen. It was not until about 2.5 billion years ago that autotrophs evolved with a photosynthetic process similar to that of modern plants. It was then that oxygen was first released into the water, and eventually into the atmosphere, as diagrammed in *Figure 11.13*. The evolution of autotrophs had a dramatic effect on Earth's atmosphere.

Most modern cells, called aerobes, require oxygen for survival. Other modern cells, called anaerobes, cannot survive in the presence of oxygen. The earliest cells on Earth were probably anaerobes, and most were killed by the new, oxygen-containing atmosphere. However, some early anaerobes survived because they lived buried in places without oxygen, as some anaerobes do today. Other cells survived because they developed the ability to tolerate oxygen. Eventually, these cells also developed the ability to use oxygen to obtain energy from food. Thus the first aerobes—cells needing oxygen for survival—evolved.

THE FIRST EUKARYOTES

Organellegenesis

Evidence indicates that the first eukaryotic cells evolved about 1.5 billion years ago. How did eukaryotic cells evolve to have inner membranes, such as a nuclear membrane and membrane-bound organelles? Two widely accepted hypotheses explain this phase of evolution. You can compare these hypotheses in *Figure 11.14*.

Some scientists hypothesize that inner membranes originated from infolding of the outer cell membrane, in a process similar to modern endocytosis. As you may recall from

FIGURE 11.14
Two Hypotheses of Eukaryotic Origins

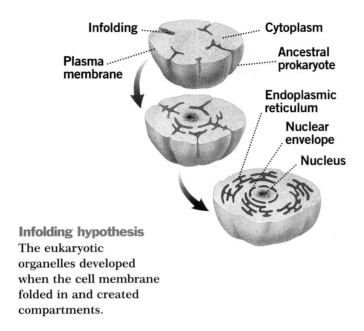

Infolding hypothesis
The eukaryotic organelles developed when the cell membrane folded in and created compartments.

Labels: Infolding, Plasma membrane, Cytoplasm, Ancestral prokaryote, Endoplasmic reticulum, Nuclear envelope, Nucleus

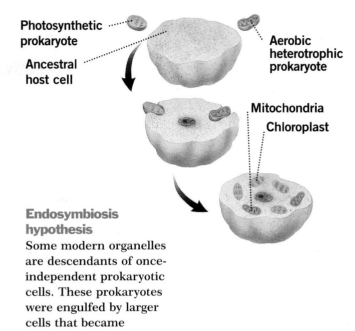

Endosymbiosis hypothesis
Some modern organelles are descendants of once-independent prokaryotic cells. These prokaryotes were engulfed by larger cells that became eukaryotic cells.

Labels: Photosynthetic prokaryote, Ancestral host cell, Aerobic heterotrophic prokaryote, Mitochondria, Chloroplast

Chapter 3, endocytosis occurs when the cell membrane folds into a pouch that encloses particles. According to the infolding hypothesis, organelles developed when cell membranes folded in, creating compartments where specialized functions were carried out. These compartments probably resembled the endoplasmic reticulum, Golgi apparatus, and vacuoles of modern cells.

American scientist Lynn Margulis developed a second hypothesis called **endosymbiosis.** According to this hypothesis, the ancestors of mitochondria and chloroplasts were independent aerobic prokaryotes that were engulfed by larger cells. The larger cells eventually depended on the engulfed prokaryotes, which took on the specialized roles of cellular organelles.

Some organelles contain their own DNA and ribosomes. These organelles make their own proteins and reproduce—an indication that they may have once been capable of an independent existence.

Regardless of the method by which organelles evolved in eukaryotic cells, a permanent partnership was established. With their specialized organelles, these early eukaryotic cells were ideally suited for the development and specialization of multicellular organisms.

CHECKPOINT 11.2

1. How do scientists establish the approximate age of fossils?

2. Explain one of the hypotheses about the formation of eukaryotic cells.

3. Critical Thinking Write a paragraph describing the cause-and-effect relationship between the atmospheric changes on early Earth and evolution of life forms.

Build on What You Know

4. Why were autotrophs so important in the evolution of life? *(Need to jog your memory? Revisit relevant concepts in Chapter 4, Section 4.1.)*

EVERYDAY BIOLOGY

Mighty Mitochondria

The evolution of organelles resulted in a valuable material for research: mitochondrial DNA, or mDNA, which mutates far less frequently than nuclear DNA. Mitochondrial DNA is used extensively in evolution studies and in DNA fingerprinting.

11.3 History of Living Things

What you'll learn

IDEAS

• To explain the emergence of multicellular organisms

• To evaluate the effect of plate tectonics and of mass extinctions on speciation

WORDS

eras, periods, epochs, plate tectonics

Earthdancing

Madagascar, a large island off the eastern coast of Africa, is home to many unique species, such as the black-and-white lemur (right). Like other land masses, Madagascar has drifted around Earth throughout geological history, hosting new species and isolating its existing ones. This land movement also explains why each continent has different species.

MEASURING TIME

From another era

Do you agree with the expression "Time flies when you're having fun"? No matter how much fun you are having, 250,000 years is a long time—unless you compare it with 4 billion years. As you can see in *Figure 11.15*, the time period that humans have been on Earth—just 250,000 years—is comparable to just seconds, when compared with the length of time that life has been on Earth.

In order to catalog the 4 billion years of life on Earth, scientists have created a geological time scale. This scale divides the history of life into large time spans called **eras.** Eras are subdivided into **periods,** and periods into **epochs.** You may be familiar with the names of many of these divisions, such as Mesozoic era, Jurassic period, and Pleistocene epoch.

The beginning and end of each time span is marked by the extinction of many life-forms and the appearance of new ones. *Figure 11.17* shows living things that characterize the different periods, as well as major changes that mark each period.

Scientists date the beginning and end of epochs, periods, and eras by studying the fossil record. They use radioactive dating of fossils to identify the time when a life-form became extinct or a new organism appeared. These milestones are integrated with evolutionary theory to create a geological time line tracing the history of life.

One of the most important milestones in this time line follows the end of the Precambrian era. Fossil evidence shows that the beginning of the Cambrian period was marked by an explosive increase in the number and diversity of living things. The lack of

FIGURE 11.15

Earth's Geological Clock

A clock can be used as a model of the geological time scale. The spiral represents the increasing number of species.

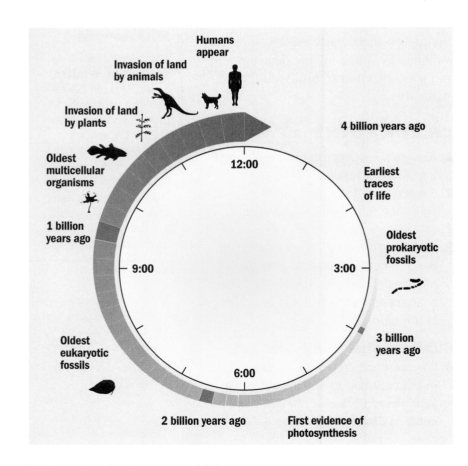

FIGURE 11.16
This table shows the different eras, periods, and epochs of Earth's history.

Geological Time Scale			
Age*	Era	Period	Epoch
0.01	CENOZOIC	Quaternary	Recent
1.8			Pleistocene
5		Tertiary	Pliocene
24			Miocene
38			Oligocene
54			Eocene
65			Paleocene
144	MESOZOIC	Cretaceous	
213		Jurassic	
248		Triassic	
286	PALEOZOIC	Permian	
360		Carboniferous	
408		Devonian	
438		Silurian	
505		Ordovician	
590		Cambrian	
	PRECAMBRIAN		

*Millions of years ago

fossils in the Precambrian era was once seen as evidence against Darwin's theory of evolution. However, in this century, microscopic fossils of prokaryotes have been found, filling in some holes in the Precambrian fossil record. After the appearance of the first living cells and the first eukaryotes in the Precambrian era, the next major event in the history of life was the appearance of multicellular organisms.

MULTICELLULAR ORGANISMS

A whole new dimension

As eukaryotic cells evolved, a variety of cells arose with different shapes and different combinations of organelles and membranes. The population of eukaryotic cells was more diverse than the population of prokaryotic cells. This variety of eukaryotes gave rise to a very important kind of life-form: the multicellular organism.

Eukaryotic cells did not automatically form multicellular organisms. Most scientists theorize that there was an intermediate, colony-forming stage. Colonies are formed when daughter cells remain attached to each other after cell division. Some modern green algae, such as the *Volvox* shown in *Figure 11.18,* exist as colonies that probably resemble early eukaryotic colonies.

Scientists propose that all of the cells in early colonies were identical and could move independently. Gradually the colonies became organized and some cells began to perform specialized functions. Groups of cells in the colonies became more specialized and formed tissues—cells that worked together to perform a function for the whole colony. As some cells became dependent on others for specialized functions, they lost their ability to

FIGURE 11.18
Some modern protists, such as these green algae, resemble the first colonial organisms.

FIGURE 11.17
Geological Time Line

Earth formed

Prokaryotic organisms evolved

Eukaryotic organisms evolved

Multicellular organisms evolved

Precambrian

IN THE COMMUNITY
Hometown History

move. This evolution of colonies gave rise to multicellular organisms with specialized, interdependent cells.

These early multicellular organisms probably inhabited the ancient seas, like their unicellular predecessors. The emergence of terrestrial organisms did not occur until 430 million years ago.

INVASIONS OF THE LAND
How life stayed wet

Clearly, the biggest difference between life in the ocean and life on land is that organisms on land are not surrounded by water. This difference was also the biggest challenge that the first land organisms faced.

Organisms living in water depend on their surroundings for many essential functions, including reproduction, respiration, excretion, and mobility. For example, the swimming sperm of aquatic organisms require water to

reach the egg and support development of offspring. This type of reproduction is not possible on dry land. In order to survive on land, organisms had to adapt to new, waterless surroundings. How could early land organisms conserve and replenish water?

As multicellular organisms adapted, some species gained the ability to overcome these obstacles. Plants were the first organisms to make the transition from water to land. Waxy coverings on most plant parts prevented excessive water loss. An internal transport system brought water and nutrients from the soil to all parts of the plant. Fossil evidence shows the earliest land plants to be about 450 million years old.

Fungi became land dwellers shortly after plants, followed by the arthropods, invertebrate animals such as insects. Insects and other arthropods evolved with hard body coverings, which prevented water loss. The oldest insect

FIGURE 11.17
(continued)

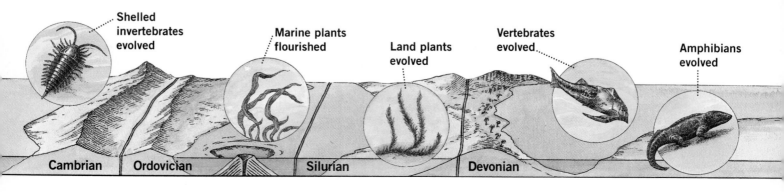

Shelled invertebrates evolved

Marine plants flourished

Land plants evolved

Vertebrates evolved

Amphibians evolved

Cambrian | Ordovician | Silurian | Devonian

fossils are 400 million years old. Amphibians were the last group to make the transition from sea to land. However, most groups of prehistoric amphibians eventually became extinct.

PLATE TECTONICS

Continental crash course

Paleontologists have found fossils of subtropical plants and animals in Alaska, a place known for its cold, harsh climate. You may be wondering how warm-weather organisms could have lived there.

According to geological evidence, at one time Alaska was connected to Asia by a land bridge. This entire region was much closer to the equator—and was therefore much warmer than it is today. But Alaska is not the only area that has moved during Earth's history.

The fossil evidence indicates that all modern continents have moved—together and apart as well as closer to and farther from the equator. Why do the continents move?

Earth consists of a molten core and a hard crust. The crust is broken into plates, which float on the molten core like rafts on water. Continents and other land masses move as the plates move. **Plate tectonics** is the movement of Earth's crustal plates over its molten core. Plate tectonics affect land, climate, and organisms.

Land changes There have been many different continent configurations in the past. Continents stay together if they are located on the same plate, and move apart if they are located on different plates. For example, most of Asia and Europe always remain together because these two continents are located on the same plate. In contrast, the distance between North America and Europe increases about 2 centimeters (cm) every year. North America and Europe are located on different plates.

If you look closely at a map, you may notice that some of the continents could fit together. The eastern coast of South America, for instance, looks as if it could fit together with the western coast of Africa. In fact, all the world's major continents once formed a supercontinent called Pangaea (pan-GEE-uh). *Figure 11.19* shows how the continents have moved over time. How do you think the movement of continents affected evolution?

Climate changes In addition to changes in land, there have been many climate changes during Earth's history. Some of these changes resulted from the movement of land masses. Other climate changes had different causes. Both global cooling and global warming, for example, can be explained by increased volcanic activity. Plate tectonics is responsible for volcanic activity, as you see in *Figure 11.20* on page 272.

Amphibian and reptile fossils on the barren antarctic desert indicate that there have been at least two

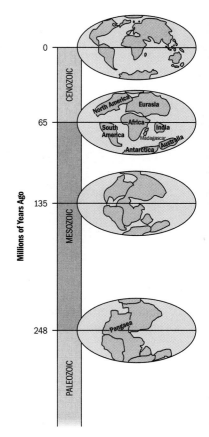

FIGURE 11.19
The continents are parts of floating pieces of Earth's crust called plates.

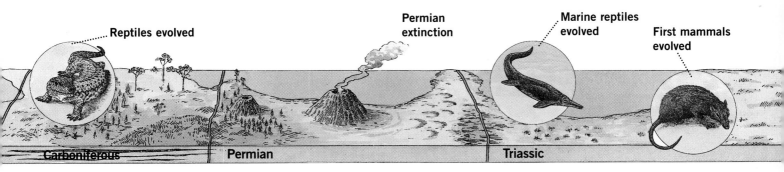

Reptiles evolved

Permian extinction

Marine reptiles evolved

First mammals evolved

Carboniferous   Permian   Triassic

FIGURE 11.20

Plate Tectonics

Volcanic eruptions, earthquakes, and mountain formations are caused by plate tectonics. These geological processes occur at plate boundaries.

Two plates collide and form mountains.

When a thick plate meets a thinner plate, the thicker plate falls beneath, resulting in earthquakes and volcanoes.

As two plates spread apart on the ocean floor, molten material surfaces, solidifies, and becomes new land.

EVERYDAY BIOLOGY

Strolling Across the Ocean

The land bridge that formed between Asia and Alaska was probably the route followed by the first human settlers of North and South America. Scientists think this crossing took place 50,000 years ago.

FIGURE 11.17
(continued)

instances of significant global warming in history. These changes made Antarctica subtropical in the past. In extreme contrast, Earth was much colder during an ice age just 15,000 years ago. At that time, glaciers containing an enormous amount of water covered much of the land. As a result, the seas were shallower and the coastlines around continents extended farther out than they do today.

Life changes Plate tectonics is one factor affecting the pattern of Earth's speciation—the evolution of one species into many separate species. The movement of continents would have isolated some species from others. For example, Australia has some of the most unique life-forms on the planet. It probably comes as no surprise that Australia is also the continent that has been isolated the

longest from other land masses on Earth.

The isolation of species was only one factor that affected evolution. Migration can also significantly affect a population's gene pool. Land bridges between Alaska and Asia and between North and South America allowed species to migrate. The camel is an example of a species that migrated across land bridges. The fossil record indicates that camels' ancestors first lived in North America and then spread to South America and Asia. In South America, the population evolved into the present-day llama. The camel's ancestors in Asia evolved into today's camel. In North America, the camel's ancestors eventually became extinct.

Climate changes and land movements are responsible for much of the speciation on Earth. Without the fossil record, however, this information would be difficult to obtain.

ISSUES IN BIOLOGY

Mass extinctions

The fossil record reveals the existence of many life-forms that are no longer with us. The dinosaurs are the most famous example, but many species have become extinct over time. Scientists have identified five mass extinctions, periods when a majority of species were eliminated.

These mass extinctions could have had different causes. One of the earliest—the Permian extinction at the

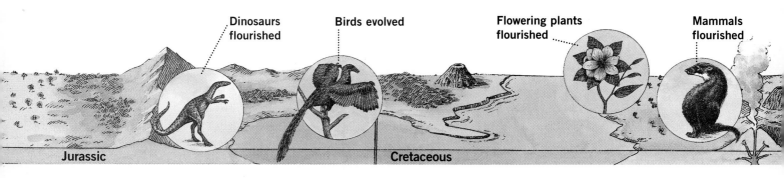

Dinosaurs flourished

Birds evolved

Flowering plants flourished

Mammals flourished

Jurassic   Cretaceous

end of the Permian period—occurred 250 million years ago. More than 90 percent of the ocean animal species were eliminated. Many land insects also perished. What could have caused this massive destruction?

One theory is based on the fact that the Permian extinction occurred at about the same time that the continents came together to form Pangaea. The combining of the continents eliminated many water habitats, accounting for the extinction of much of the sea life. At the same time, volcanoes were unusually active. The resulting changes in the atmosphere, such as cooling due to ash in the air, may have resulted in the extinction of many land organisms.

The Cretaceous mass extinction, 65 million years ago, is best known for the elimination of the dinosaurs. Many other species in the sea and on land also disappeared at this time.

An intriguing explanation for the Cretaceous mass extinction is that it was caused by a large comet or asteroid striking Earth. This hypothesis is supported by the existence of a layer of material in Earth's crust that is common in extraterrestrial debris but uncommon elsewhere. This layer is located at the same place in the fossil record as the Cretaceous extinction. In addition, an exceedingly large crater, possibly caused by the impact of a comet or asteroid, has been found that dates back to this time.

Many scientists hypothesize that the amount of dust released into the

Do It!

How Did Plate Tectonics Result in Speciation?

Because the continents move around on plates, many populations separated and evolved into different species. You can better understand how this occurred if you . . .

Try This

1 Review the relationship between Earth's plates and its molten core.
2 Design a model of the movement of plates on Earth's core. Your model should show how mountains form when plates collide.
3 Model a population located on two plates that are together. Then make the plates separate.

Analyze Your Results

1 How do colliding plates result in mountains? Based on your model, why do earthquakes occur at the boundary between plates?
2 Why does speciation occur when plates move, causing continents to move together or apart?

air from the impact of a comet or asteroid would be enough to darken the sky for years, drastically affecting photosynthetic organisms. As a result, the entire food chain would be disrupted, causing the extinction of many species, including dinosaurs.

Not all theories account for the dinosaurs' dying out so suddenly. Changes in the environment from increased volcanic activity and

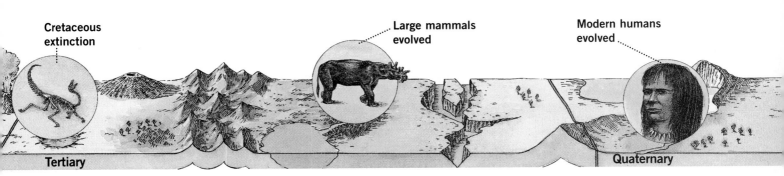

Cretaceous extinction

Large mammals evolved

Modern humans evolved

Tertiary

Quaternary

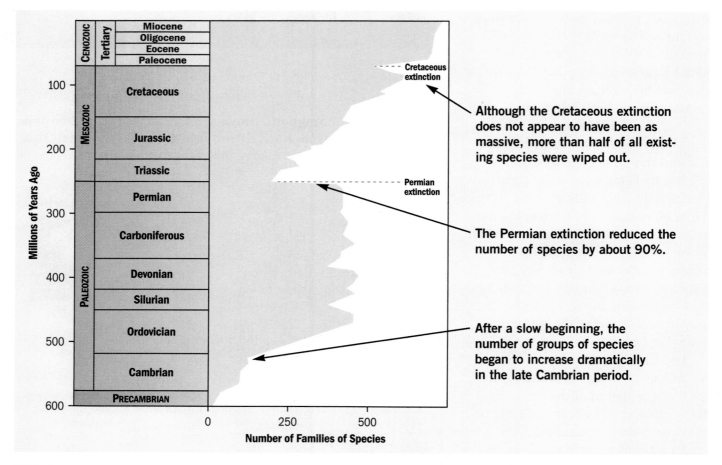

FIGURE 11.21

Over time, the number of species on Earth has changed and many species have become extinct. Which two mass exinctions are labeled?

Chart annotations:

Cretaceous extinction — Although the Cretaceous extinction does not appear to have been as massive, more than half of all existing species were wiped out.

Permian extinction — The Permian extinction reduced the number of species by about 90%.

After a slow beginning, the number of groups of species began to increase dramatically in the late Cambrian period.

continental movement could have radically changed the dinosaurs' ability to survive. Evidence to support one of these theories needs to come from a careful examination of the fossil record. If the dinosaurs disappeared quickly from the fossil record, then it is likely that a single catastrophic event, such as an asteroid crash, was responsible. If the fossil record indicates a slow decline of the dinosaurs, then climate changes were more likely the cause of extinction.

Whatever the cause, all mass extinctions resulted in the adaptive radiation of the species that survived. The species that survived a mass extinction faced much less competition. The availability of new niches

after mass extinctions probably sparked the evolution of many species, including primates.

CHECKPOINT 11.3

1. Explain how multicellular organisms emerged from unicellular life.
2. How did plate tectonics and mass extinctions result in speciation?
3. **Critical Thinking** Why was there increased volcanic activity during the Permian extinction?

Build on What You Know

4. Why can adaptive radiation occur after mass extinctions? *(Need to jog your memory? Revisit relevant concepts in Chapter 10, Section 10.4.)*

 How have our planet and the organisms that inhabit it changed over time?

Chapter 11 Review

Sum It Up

Use the following summary to review the main concepts in this chapter.

11.1 Earth's Early History

- Between 5 and 4.5 billion years ago, Earth formed when dust and rocks in the solar system condensed.
- Earth's early atmosphere differed from today's in many ways, such as the absence of both oxygen and a protective ozone layer.
- The seas that formed from condensed water vapor contained dissolved minerals and gases.
- Most scientists agree that the origin of life required the completion of four steps: simple organic molecules, polymers, protocells and cells.

11.2 The First Organisms

- Radioactive isotopes are used to determine the age of fossils.
- The oldest-known fossils are from bacteria that lived 3.5 billion years ago.
- As heterotrophs multiplied, they competed for a decreasing supply of organic nutrients. Around 2.5 billion years ago, autotrophs evolved that produced oxygen.

- Cells that could tolerate oxygen evolved into the first aerobes.
- The first eukaryotes evolved about 1.5 billion years ago.

11.3 History of Living Things

- Scientists theorize that multicellular organisms evolved from colonies of eukaryotic cells.
- Terrestrial organisms evolved about 450 million years ago. Adaptations for life on land included internal transport systems and methods to conserve water.
- The locations of Earth's continents have changed over time. Land movements and climate changes are major causes of speciation on Earth.
- Mass extinctions resulted in the adaptive radiation of surviving species.

Use Terms and Concepts

**Use each of the following words or terms in a complete sentence.
If you need to review a meaning, turn to the page indicated.**

microspheres (p. 260)
half-life (p. 263)
stromatolites (p. 266)
endosymbiosis (p. 267)

eras (p. 268)
periods (p. 268)
epochs (p. 268)
plate tectonics (p. 271)

Use Your Word Power

COMPLETION **Write the word or phrase that best completes each statement.**

1. When colonies of bacteria fossilize, they can form _____ .

2. On the geological time scale, periods are divided into _____ .

3. When certain protein molecules are mixed with water, they form _____ .

4. The movement of the Earth's continents over time is caused by _____ .

5. The longest time spans in the geologic time scale are called _____ .

6. The time it takes for half the isotopes in a sample to decay is called its _____ .

7. According to the _____ hypothesis, organelles were once independent prokaryotes.

TRUE-FALSE **Write true if the statement is true. If the statement is false, replace the underlined word(s) to make the statement true.**

8. <u>Microspheres</u> contain remains of the earliest known prokaryotes.

9. The <u>epoch</u> of potassium-40 is 1.3 billion years.

10. <u>Plate tectonics</u> causes earthquakes and volcanic eruptions.

11. <u>Stromatolites</u> provide a model for the evolution of a cell membrane.

12. The presence of DNA in some organelles supports the <u>endosymbiosis</u> hypothesis.

13. An explosive increase in biodiversity separates the Precambrian and Cambrian <u>periods</u>.

Show What You Know

14. Explain how clay crystals might have contributed to the formation of polymers.

15. How could the absence of an ozone layer have affected conditions on Earth billions of years ago?

16. What are some of the changes caused by plate tectonics?

17. Summarize the two scientific theories that explain the origin of Earth's organic molecules.

18. What role might colonies have played in the evolution of multicellular organisms?

19. How did atmospheric oxygen alter the evolution of primitive life?

20. **Make a Concept Map** Complete the concept map below by adding the following terms: periods, epochs, stromatolites, microspheres, monomers, polymers, protocells, prokaryotes.

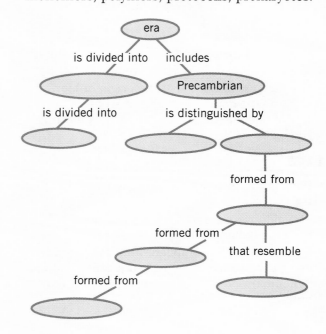

Take It Further

21. **Developing a Hypothesis** When Earth's atmosphere first began to form, hydrogen (H_2) was the most abundant element in the solar system. However, there is very little H_2 in the atmosphere today, and the element makes up less than 1 percent of Earth's mass. What might have happened to the H_2? **Hint:** Review Figure 11.4, and research the uses of H_2 and the chemical compounds in which H_2 can occur.

22. Analyzing Data In 1909 Charles Walcott found fossils on the Burgess Shale of the Canadian Rockies. Explain how fossils of bottom-dwelling sea creatures half a billion years old were found 2 kilometers above sea level.

23. Analyzing Data A meteorite contains evidence that life may have begun about 3.5 billion years ago. Explain how this data could support Crick's hypothesis about the origin of life. Suggest an alternate interpretation of the data that could support Oparin's hypothesis about the chemical origin of life.

24. Identifying Cause and Effect Could the first aerobes have evolved before the first autotrophs? Explain your answer.

25. Applying Concepts Could radiocarbon dating be used to accurately determine the age of dinosaur fossils? Explain your answer.

26. Designing an Experiment Describe an experiment to test one of the hypotheses explaining how polymers formed. What differences between modern and ancient Earth environments would you need to address?

27. Interpreting a Graph The graph below summarizes changes in the amount of atmospheric oxygen since life first appeared on Earth. What evolutionary events occurred at the arrows? Explain your answer.

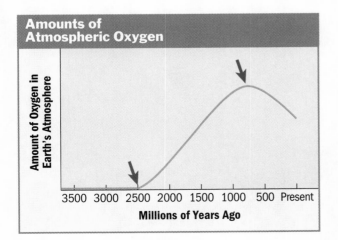

Amounts of Atmospheric Oxygen

Amount of Oxygen in Earth's Atmosphere

3500 3000 2500 2000 1500 1000 500 Present

Millions of Years Ago

Consider the Issues

28. New Model Resisted In 1915 the German meteorologist Alfred Wegener proposed a theory of continental drift. He concluded that fossils of certain reptiles found only in South Africa and Brazil (see below) supported his theory. His idea was rejected until the 1960s, when evidence of sea-floor spreading was found. Consult Figure 11.22. Why was Wegener's model rejected? Research Wegener's work and decide whether or not his theory was criticized fairly. Present your decision in the form of a "news report."

Brazil ---------- South Africa

Make New Connections

29. Biology and Art Refer to Figure 11.17 and make a large geological time line for your classroom. As you study Units 3–7, add evolutionary events to the time line.

30. Biology and Creative Writing Imagine the world as it might be if autotrophs had not evolved. What would Earth be like? What types of organisms would exist? Would humans have evolved?

FAST-FORWARD TO CHAPTER 12

In Chapter 11, you learned about the history of life on Earth. In Chapter 12, you will focus on the evolution of the primates, including monkeys, apes, and humans.

You can find out more about human evolution by exploring the following Internet address:
http://evolution.biosurf.com

In this chapter . . .

FEATURES

Everyday Biology
- Big Ape!
- What Is Race?

In the Community
The Big Dig

 Issues in Biology
Difficulties in Interpretation

LAB ZONES

Discover It!
- Analyzing Adaptations

Do It!
- Modeling Archaeological Activity

Think About It!
- Hominid Origins

Investigate It!
- Comparing Genetic Relationships

First steps

Analyzing Adaptations

You need pennies

1. Place a few pennies on your desk. Try to pick up the pennies with your hand closed into a fist.
2. Pick up the pennies as you usually would. Observe how you use your thumb when picking up the pennies. Record your observations.

Walking on two legs freed the ancestors of humans to use their hands and eventually to fashion and use tools. In what other ways might the use of hands have affected human evolution? What other animals have thumbs that are similar to those of humans? What can these animals do that cannot be done by animals lacking this type of thumb?

Three and a half million years ago a few ancestors of modern humans crossed a grassland in what is now Laetoli (LYE-toh-lee), Tanzania. The soil was damp, and a light volcanic ash was falling. Soon after, a nearby volcano erupted, blanketing the ground with more ash and filling the walkers' footprints. When the ash hardened, the footprints were preserved.

In 1978 archaeologist Mary Leakey discovered these footprints, which were considered a major find by paleontologists. Although skeletons and other fossil remains of human ancestors had been found, paleontologists had no conclusive evidence of our ancestors' walking upright on two feet— one of the most important events in human evolution. The Laetoli footprints provided that evidence and established the time period of this milestone in human evolution. How did humans evolve, and who were our ancestors?

Dr. Leakey (left) and her crew worked under hot, backbreaking conditions.

WRITE ABOUT IT!

Imagine that your footprints are discovered 3.5 million years from now. In your science journal, describe the conclusions that archaeologists might draw, based on your footprints. What additional information would enable future archaeologists to reconstruct accurately a typical day of your life?

12.1 Primates

What you'll learn

IDEAS
• To summarize the evolutionary history of primates
• To compare the characteristic traits of the different types of primates

WORDS
primates, prosimian, anthropoids, opposable thumb, binocular vision, prehensile tail

Small mammal makes good
While dinosaurs roamed Earth, small mammals were creeping around the dinosaurs. The first primates may have resembled the small, insect-eating tree shrew (right) currently found in Southeast Asia and India. Weighing less than half a kilogram, the primate's small size and nocturnal habits help keep it out of harm's way.

FIGURE 12.1
All modern primates evolved from a common ancestor between 65 and 55 million years ago. Which primates are prosimians? Which are anthropoids?

THE EVOLUTION OF PRIMATES

A chip off the old block

The oldest mammal fossils date back to the Triassic period (220 million years ago). Mammals are thought to have evolved from small, active, meat-eating reptiles. Fossil evidence linking the reptiles to mammals includes similarities in their skulls, jaws, and teeth.

The mass extinctions at the end of the Cretaceous period mark the beginning of a surge of adaptive radiation in many species. About 65 million years ago, following the dinosaur extinctions, the number of mammal species increased greatly. The oldest primate fossils date from about this time. The **primates** (PRY-mayts) are a group of mammals that includes all monkeys, apes, and humans.

According to the fossil evidence, the earliest primates were similar to the tree shrew shown above. Although

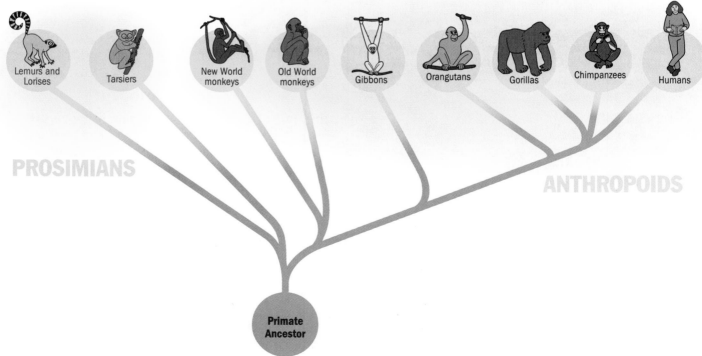

Lemurs and Lorises | Tarsiers | New World monkeys | Old World monkeys | Gibbons | Orangutans | Gorillas | Chimpanzees | Humans

PROSIMIANS | ANTHROPOIDS

Primate Ancestor

the early primates' overall anatomy resembles that of a shrew, fossil evidence also shows some characteristics common to later primates.

Early primates are thought to have evolved into two groups, the prosimians and the anthropoids. A **prosimian** (proh-SIM-ee-un) is a small, monkey-like primate with large, forward-facing eyes. Prosimian means "pre-monkey." Modern prosimians probably resemble the primates' earliest ancestors. **Anthropoids** (AN-thruh-poydz) are humanlike primates, and include monkeys, apes, and humans. Anthropoid means "humanlike." Scientists use these terms to describe both modern and extinct primates.

There are nine groups of primates living today, as you can see in *Figure 12.1*. Evidence indicates that the two types of prosimians first evolved about 55 million years ago. The ancestral anthropoids, however, evolved into many different groups. Most scientists agree that the earliest anthropoids evolved from a common prosimian ancestor some 50 million years ago. However, which prosimians evolved into the anthropoids is still under debate.

Adaptive radiation may have resulted in the formation of separate anthropoid groups. One group, the New World monkeys, evolved on the American continents. The other groups, including the Old World monkeys and the apes, evolved on the African, Asian, and European continents. Because large bodies of water isolated these populations, these two primate groups evolved separately.

Chimpanzees, gorillas, orangutans, and gibbons are modern examples of apes. Evidence indicates that the gibbons have been on Earth the longest, around 35 million years. The most recent primates—orangutans, gorillas, chimpanzees, and humans—are thought to have evolved from a common ancestor between 8 and 5 million years ago. Because of their shared evolutionary histories, all primates share some common traits.

Most of our knowledge about primate evolution comes from the fossil record. But the fossil record is incomplete, leaving gaps in our knowledge. One reason for the incomplete fossil record of primates is that many primate ancestors lived in tropical forests, and fossils are not readily preserved in acidic tropical soils.

Genetic research has helped fill in some gaps. As you read in Chapter 10, scientists can analyze genetic material to clarify relationships between species. Scientists can compare differences between specific base sequences to infer how long ago two organisms split from a common ancestor. For example, through genetic similarities, scientists know much about the evolutionary relationship between humans and chimpanzees. As more is learned about the genes of primates, the picture of their evolution becomes more complete.

FIGURE 12.2
What adaptation to primate environments is visible here?

FIGURE 12.3
With an opposable thumb and long flexible fingers, primates have a strong, secure grip. Why might this be important?

CHARACTERISTICS OF PRIMATES

Mammals swing!

Scientists agree that the first primates lived in trees, because most modern primates have adaptations to such an environment. *Figures 12.2* through *12.5* show several of these adaptations. Although humans do not spend their lives in trees, we have many features associated with a tree-dwelling life.

Make a fist and observe the directions your fingers point. Like other primates, you have an **opposable thumb,** a digit that can be placed in the opposite direction from the other

FIGURE 12.4
Primates like this slender loris have binocular vision, an adaptation that allows for accurate judging of distance and depth.

FIGURE 12.5
Prolonged and close care of offspring is a primate trait exhibited by orangutans. Young primates other than humans may spend as long as three to five years with their mothers before living on their own.

FIGURE 12.6
Like many species of New World monkeys, this capuchin monkey has a prehensile tail. What other primate characteristics does this animal have?

four fingers. Look at the ends of your fingers. Like many primates, you have sensitive finger pads and protective nails, not claws. These structures enable primates to grip objects firmly, and to move and manipulate tiny objects. Like other primates, your arms move freely around the shoulder joint, an adaptation that allows swinging from hand-to-hand. All of these adaptations enable primates to move easily and securely in trees.

Most primates have excellent hand-eye coordination, which is enhanced by their binocular vision. With **binocular vision,** both eyes are used at once in overlapping fields, so that objects appear to have depth. Through the course of evolution, the long snout of the early primates flat-tened and the eyes migrated to the front of the face. The resulting binocular vision increased depth perception and allowed primates to judge distances accurately, an important adaptation when moving high above ground.

Primates share other traits as well. They have relatively large brains when compared to other mammals. Like humans, a few other species of primates have been observed making and using simple tools. For example, some chimpanzees know how to fashion a probe from a twig and use it to "fish" for termites. Others have been seen using a crumpled leaf as a simple sponge to retrieve drinking water from a deep hollow in a tree.

Many primates have complex social behaviors and strong family relationships. Typically primates attentively care for their young for a long time after birth. Extended parental care may also be an adaptation to life in the trees. Without the constant attention of a family member, a newborn that cannot swing or climb well would not survive long in the treetops.

DIVERSITY OF PRIMATES

More than a barrelful

Despite their common origin and similar traits, the primates are quite different from one another. The two primate groups—prosimian and anthropoid—are divided further according to physical traits and evolutionary relationships. Each type of primate, whether living or extinct, is characterized by specific traits.

Prosimians Like the loris shown in *Figure 12.4,* many prosimians are nocturnal, or active mostly at night. Their large eyes are an adaptation to their nighttime activities. Because fossils of the earliest primate ancestors also have large eye sockets, scientists suspect that they, too, were nocturnal.

Some prosimians are insect-eaters, as the first primates probably were. Other modern prosimians eat plants or fruit. Most prosimians are agile tree-climbers.

Today there are about 35 species of prosimians, including lemurs, lorises, and tarsiers. These primates live in the tropical forests of southeast Asia, India, Africa, and Madagascar. Of all modern prosimians, the lemurs of Madagascar most closely resemble the common primate ancestor, possibly because of their isolation from other primates on their island home. Habitat destruction threatens prosimians.

Anthropoids There are about 113 different species of anthropoids, including New World monkeys, Old World monkeys such as the Celebes macaques shown in *Figure 12.7,* and the apes. The terms Old World and New World were used by the first Europeans who came to the Americas. To them, the American continents were new. The terms are still used to describe these groups of primates, which show distinct differences.

The New World monkeys of Central and South America have broad, flat noses. A common trait of most New World monkeys is a long, prehensile tail. A **prehensile tail** (pree-HEN-sil) is composed of many muscles and can be used to grip branches while climbing. The tail acts as an extra hand as the animals move through the trees. Almost all New World monkeys are tree-dwelling and are active during the day. They are social animals, usually living in family groups of various sizes.

Old World monkeys can be found in Africa, southeast Asia, and the Philippines. They usually have long, prominent noses and short tails. Many Old World monkeys have brightly patterned fur, or brightly colored patches of skin on their face or rump. Although members of this group typically spend most of their time on the ground, many are good climbers. Most are active during the day and live in groups. Compare the features of the Old World monkey shown in *Figure 12.7* to those of the New World monkey in *Figure 12.6.* How are they alike? How are they different?

Species of apes live in tropical forests of Africa, southeast Asia, Java, and Borneo. Almost all apes move about on the ground, although they are good tree climbers. Apes are different from other primates. Most apes are larger and more powerful than monkeys, with larger brains and no visible tails. Apes can spend more time upright than other primates, but like many primates, tend to move on four limbs when on the ground. Apes are typically vegetarians, although chimpanzees sometimes eat insects and small mammals.

Of all the anthropoids, the apes are most similar to humans. As you can see in *Figure 12.8,* some proteins in humans and chimpanzees are very similar. Biochemical analysis indicates that chimpanzees and gorillas are more closely related to us than they are to the other apes, the orangutans and the gibbons. In fact, the DNA of humans and chimpanzees differs by less than 3 percent, compelling evidence of an evolutionary connection.

FIGURE 12.7
Old World monkeys include baboons, langurs, and macaques like these Celebes macaques of Indonesia. Macaques are social animals that live in family troops of various sizes.

Comparison of Human and Chimpanzee Proteins		
Protein	Number of Amino Acids	Amino Acid Differences
Hemoglobin	579	1
Myoglobin	153	1
Cytochrome c	104	0
Serum albumin	580	7

FIGURE 12.8
Biochemically, there are very few differences between chimpanzees and humans, indicating a close evolutionary relationship.

Common langur

Japanese Macaque

coldest   **hottest**

Chimpanzee

Squirrel Monkey

FIGURE 12.9
Most primates inhabit tropical areas, but can be found in a variety of environments on most continents. Which primate can live in almost any habitat on Earth?

EVERYDAY BIOLOGY

Big Ape!

The smallest ape, the gibbon, weighs about 5 kg. In contrast, the largest gorilla weighs about 270 kg. How do humans compare? The high end of the normal range for an adult male is about 125 kg.

Primates are a diverse group—physical appearance, behaviors, and habitats vary among species. Some of this diversity is shown in *Figure 12.9*. Most primates live in tropical areas of the world, although some species of Old World monkeys can tolerate mild winters. One primate—humans—can live in just about any region of the world. This is because of our ability to adjust to different environments and to change environments to fit our needs. Humans are the most adaptable of the primates. Despite these differences, all primates share some common characteristics which indicate common evolutionary origin.

CHECKPOINT 12.1

1. List the nine primate groups and the approximate time of their evolution.
2. What do most primates have in common?
3. **Critical Thinking** The gibbon least resembles the other apes. It is smaller and lives mostly in trees. What factors account for these differences? Why are gibbons still considered apes?

Build on What You Know

4. Humans have 46 chromosomes and chimpanzees have 48. Do these numbers indicate a close genetic relationship? Why or why not? *(Need to jog your memory? Revisit relevant concepts in Chapter 5, Section 5.3 and in Chapter 7, Section 7.5.)*

? **What traits do all primates have in common? Why is a human considered a primate?**

Comparing Genetic Relationships

WHAT YOU WILL DO You will model how gene sequences can be used to determine evolutionary relationships.

SKILLS YOU WILL USE Predicting, observing, collecting and recording data

WHAT YOU WILL NEED Graph paper

Human
GCAGAGGAACCGCTACAAGAGCATACGCAAGAGCGGGT AGTAAAACCATACCTTAAATGGGGGGGGCCACCTTCGGCG GATACTCTTTCAA
Gorilla
GAGGAGGAACCGCTACAAGAGCATACGCAAGAACGCG TAGTAAAACCATACCTTAAATGGGGGGGGCCACCTTCGG CGGATACTCTTTCAA
Horse
GCAGAGGAACCGCTACAAGAGCGGGAGCAAGAACGCG CAGTAAAACCTTACCTAAAATGCGGGCTTGACCTTCGAAG TATACTCTTTCAT

Propose a Hypothesis

Write a hypothesis comparing the genetic relationships of a horse, a gorilla, and a human. Which two do you think are more closely related?

Conduct Your Experiment

1 Answer the following questions before you begin. What are the base pairs in DNA? In RNA? By what processes are proteins produced in a cell? What is a codon? An anticodon?

2 The illustration shows partial DNA sequences of the hemoglobin gene in a human, a horse, and a gorilla. "Transcribe" the DNA into mRNA. Record each mRNA sequence on graph paper.

3 Refer to the chart on page 185 and "translate" the mRNA sequences into amino acid sequences. Record each amino acid beneath its mRNA codon.

4 Circle and count the number of bases in the horse mRNA sequence that differ from bases in the same location in the human mRNA sequence. Record your data.

5 Circle and count the number of amino acids in the horse amino acid sequence that differ from the human amino acid sequence. Record your findings.

6 Count and record the number of bases in the horse mRNA sequence that differ from the human mRNA sequence but do not code for a different amino acid.

7 Repeat steps 3, 4, and 5, but compare the gorilla and human sequences.

Analyze Your Data

1 Which mRNA sequence—the horse's or the gorilla's—is most similar to the human mRNA sequence?

2 Which amino acid sequence—the horse's or the gorilla's—is more similar to the human amino acid sequence?

Draw Conclusions

Based on your results, which two organisms are more closely related? Write a paragraph in which you support your conclusion with your observations. Was your hypothesis supported or disproved?

Design a Related Experiment

Plan an experiment in which you determine evolutionary relationships based on a physical characteristic. For example, choose several different plants and compare their flowers. Based on this trait, how would you describe their evolutionary relationships? How accurate is this method?

Comparing Genetic Relationships

1. Objective
Model how gene sequences can determine evolutionary relationships: DNA: GGG AAA
RNA: CCC UUU   Protein: Pro Phe.

12.2 Hominids

What you'll learn

IDEAS

• To identify various hominid species and the time periods in which they existed

• To compare the characteristics of major hominid groups

WORDS

hominids, bipedal

Primates in the sky?

In 1974 a team led by Donald Johanson found a skeleton of what appeared to be a small female hominid. The skeleton was nicknamed "Lucy" because the Beatles' song "Lucy in the Sky with Diamonds" was playing in the camp as the crew celebrated the discovery. Ironically, recent studies of Lucy's pelvis indicate "she" might have been male—"*Luke* in the Sky with Diamonds"?**

COMPARISON OF HOMINIDS

Stand by your hominid

As you read in the last section, apes and humans evolved between 8 and 5 million years ago. The anthropoids that evolved to become the human family are called **hominids** (HAH-mih-nidz). Hominids are the human-like anthropoids.

Evidence of the hominids' appearance and way of life is provided by the hominid fossil record. For example, a comparison of modern and fossil teeth can yield information about the ancient hominid diet. By comparing fossil bones with those of modern primates, scientists can infer whether an ancient hominid was bipedal or walked in an apelike manner, using its hands. **Bipedal** refers to the ability to walk on two legs. Since humans are bipedal, an early bipedal hominid may be more closely related to humans than to the early, apelike hominids. In *Figure 12.10* you can see some examples of the skeletal structures that scientists compare.

According to the fossil record, several hominid species coexisted at various times during the past 5 million years. Today, modern humans, known scientifically as *Homo sapiens,* are the only surviving hominid species. Why the ancient hominids became extinct is still a matter of scientific debate. One theory is that competition among hominid species may have led to their extinction.

It is not known which of the hominids shown in *Figure 12.11* are our distant relatives and which, if any, are our direct ancestors. Scientists have not yet identified the very first hominid ancestor, nor have they identified a direct line of descent from the earliest known hominid to modern humans. Some of the older species may be evolutionary

FIGURE 12.10

A bipedal hominid walks on two legs. What skeletal features promote this type of movement?

Comparison of Gorilla and Human Skeletons	
Modern Gorilla	**Modern Human**
C-shaped spine	S-shaped spine
Spinal cord exits near back of skull	Spinal cord exits at bottom of skull
Arms are longer than legs, used when walking	Arms are shorter than legs, not used when walking
Pelvis is long and narrow	Pelvis is bowl-shaped

Modern gorilla   Modern human

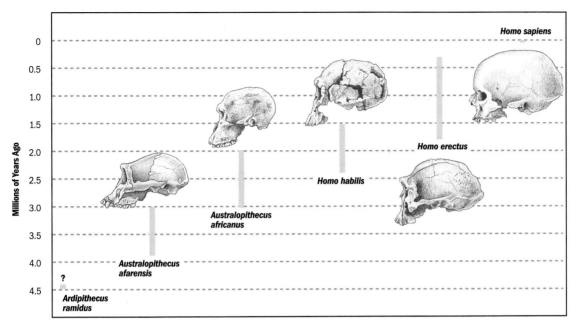

FIGURE 12.11

This illustration identifies some important hominid species. Each vertical bar indicates the time period in which a particular hominid group existed. How does the modern human skull (far right) compare with the other hominid skulls?

(Chart labels: Millions of Years Ago; Homo sapiens; Homo erectus; Homo habilis; Australopithecus africanus; Australopithecus afarensis; Ardipithecus ramidus; ?)

branches became extinct and did not lead to a modern species. However, many scientists conclude that at least some of these hominids are part of the evolutionary line that led to humans.

THE EARLY HOMINIDS

Can you dig it?

Fossils of the oldest known hominid date from about 4.4 million years ago. This hominid, *Ardipithecus ramidus* (ahr-deh-PITH-uh-kus RAM-eh-dus), was discovered in 1994 in Ethiopia by Dr. Gen Suwa. In the language of that area, *ramid* means "root." The hominid's name implies that it is a "root species," one from which other species may have evolved.

Ardipithecus ramidus (abbreviated *A. ramidus*) is the most apelike fossil hominid. The fossil evidence of *A. ramidus* is not complete. Scientists have not found fossils of the pelvis, knee, and foot bones, which would reveal whether or not *A. ramidus* was bipedal. However, some fossil evidence indicates that *A. ramidus* could carry an infant in its arms, and so might have been bipedal. From fossilized wood and seeds found at the site, we know that *A. ramidus* probably lived in forests.

The next four species of hominids share the same first name—*Australopithecus* (ah-stray-loh-PITH-uh-kus). *Australopithecus* means "southern ape," referring to the sites south of the equator where most of the fossils of these hominids were found. The oldest species, *Australopithecus anamensis* (ah-nah-MEN-sis), is between 4.2 and 3.9 million years old. *A. anamensis* weighed about 55 kg (121 lb) and lived in lakeside forests. In some ways this hominid was apelike—it had large teeth and small ear openings. Its leg bones, however, resemble human leg bones—strong evidence that *A. anamensis* was bipedal.

The next oldest hominid is *Australopithecus afarensis* (ah-far-EHN-sis). "Lucy," the hominid described at the beginning of this section, belongs to this group. Because of Lucy's remarkably complete skeleton, we know a great deal about *A. afarensis*. *Figure 12.12* shows what Lucy might have looked like.

Lucy lived between 4 and 3 million years ago. She had a low forehead, a flat nose, and no chin. Lucy's skull is

FIGURE 12.12

Hypotheses about the physical appearance and lifestyle of *Australopithecus* are based on fossil evidence. How does "Lucy" differ from modern humans?

like that of a chimpanzee, but her teeth are more like those of a human. From her pelvis and leg bones we know that Lucy was bipedal. She stood only about 130 centimeters (cm) tall (a little over 4 feet), but was quite strong.

The jaw of *A. afarensis* protruded and had large back teeth. These hominids probably ate whatever they could find—seeds, fruits, and any small animals they could catch or scavenge. *A. afarensis* probably spent most of the time on the ground, but its long fingers and toes may have helped it climb trees.

In 1924, Raymond Dart discovered the first member of the hominid group known as *Australopithecus africanus* (ah-freh-KAHN-us), or *A. africanus*. *A. africanus* lived between 3 and 2 million years ago. Like *A. afarensis*, *A. africanus* was bipedal and had some apelike features. However, *A. africanus* had a slightly larger body and brain. The teeth of *A. africanus* more closely resemble human teeth than those of apes. Because *A. africanus* lived later than *A. afarensis*, and because the two species had similar features, many scientists hypothesize that *A. africanus* evolved from *A. afarensis*.

About 2 million years ago, *Australopithecus boisei* (BOY-see-eye) and *Australopithecus robustus* (roh-BUS-tus) evolved. Many scientists agree that *A. boisei* and *A. robustus* are not our direct ancestors. This conclusion is based on the thick, heavy bones and other differences between these two species and modern humans. Some scientists call them *Paranthropus* (PAR-uhn-throh-pus) instead of *Australopithecus*. These species are thought to represent branches of the human family tree that became extinct more than 1 million years ago.

HOMO HABILIS AND HOMO ERECTUS

Handy hominids take a stand

In 1964, the famous archaeology team of Louis and Mary Leakey announced the discovery of what appeared to be the first hominids to make and use tools and weapons. Because of this unique ability, the new species was named *Homo habilis* (HO-mo HAH-beh-lus), or "handy man." *H. habilis* probably existed between 2.4 and 1.5 million years ago.

Scientists generally agree that *Homo habilis* is a direct ancestor of our modern human species, *Homo sapiens*. The name *Homo* indicates that a fossil is more like *Homo sapiens* than any earlier hominid. As you can see in *Figure 12.13*, *H. habilis* was bipedal. The *H. habilis* brain was much larger than that of any species of *Australopithecus*, but it was still only about half the size of a modern human brain. *H. habilis* may also

LAB ZONE Think About It!

Hominid Origins

About nine different hominid species have been described. Where did these different hominids first evolve? What might account for the existence of different hominid species and their distribution?

- Australopithecus
- Homo habilis
- Homo erectus

Analyzing the Map

1 The map above shows where various hominid fossils have been found. How would you describe the distribution and location of the sites?
2 Note where the oldest fossils have been discovered. How does their distribution and location compare with that of the more recent fossils?
3 Develop a hypothesis explaining the difference in distribution between the oldest and the most recent fossils.
4 What additional information would you need to support your hypothesis?

have had some form of simple speech and probably hunted and collected seeds, fruits, and vegetables.

For almost 1 million years, *H. habilis* coexisted in Africa with various species of *Australopithecus*. The evolutionary relationship between *Australopithecus* and *H. habilis* is unclear, but they do have some common characteristics. What are some of the similarities between these two hominid groups? At some point, *H. habilis* may have evolved into a new species with an even larger brain—*Homo erectus* (uh-REK-tus), or "upright man."

H. erectus was probably the first hominid to migrate out of Africa, into Asia and Europe. Compared to earlier hominids, *H. erectus* most closely resembles modern humans. In general, *H. erectus* was taller and had a larger brain than *H. habilis*. *H. erectus* built fires, wore animal skin clothing, lived in caves, and made relatively refined stone tools.

The oldest *H. erectus* fossil is about 1.8 million years old. The *H. erectus* fossil known as Java Man was found in 1891 in Java, Indonesia. *H. erectus* remains found in China became known as Peking Man.

Most *H. erectus* populations probably died out 300,000 years ago. In 1996, scientists dated some *H. erectus* fossils as only 50,000 years old. Did *H. erectus* live at the same time as *H. sapiens*? New discoveries, techniques, and debates are needed to answer this question.

CHECKPOINT 12.2

1. What is the earliest hominid? What is the next-oldest fossil hominid?
2. Compare and contrast the groups *Homo* and *Australopithecus*. How are they similar? How do they differ?
3. **Critical Thinking** Suppose you find a 1 million-year-old hominid fossil with humanlike traits. Which hominid species might it be? Which hominids can you eliminate? Why?

Build on What You Know

4. At least three types of hominids could have lived at the same time, in the same area. What does this coexistence mean in terms of available niches? *(Need to jog your memory? Revisit relevant concepts in Chapter 10, Section 10.1.)*

FIGURE 12.13
Evidence indicates that *H. erectus* (above right) had a larger body and brain than *H. habilis* (above left), used a wider variety of tools, and knew how to make fire. In what other ways do these two hominids differ?

FIGURE 12.14
***Homo erectus* used tools to make tools. The hand ax (left) and cleaver (right) were formed using specially selected stones as shaping tools.**

12.3 *Homo sapiens*

Cave men had culture
Popular myth is that the "cave men," the first modern *Homo sapiens*, were primitive brutes. However, archaeological evidence, such as paintings from France's Cro-Magnon cave and Spain's Altamira cave (right), suggests that these humans thought about matters beyond their next meal, or who had the biggest and best shelter.

THE NEANDERTHALS

Something old

The earliest *Homo sapiens* may have evolved from *H. erectus* between 300,000 and 200,000 years ago. Two of the best known groups of *H. sapiens* in the fossil record are the older Neanderthals (nee-AN-der-tholz) and the more recent Cro-Magnons (kro-MAG-nuhnz).

In 1856, three years before the publication of Darwin's *On the Origin of Species by Means of Natural Selection,* the first Neanderthal fossils were found in the Neander Valley of Germany. Some scientists refer to the Neanderthals as *Homo neanderthalensis*, a dead-end branch of our family tree. Other scientists consider the Neanderthals early humans—*H. sapiens*—and possible direct ancestors of modern humans.

In this textbook we group the Neanderthals with *H. sapiens*. We know that the Neanderthals lived throughout Europe, Asia, and the Middle East between 230,000 and 30,000 years ago. Although they are related to modern humans, the Neanderthals have some unique characteristics.

Physical characteristics As you can see in *Figure 12.15,* Neanderthals were short and solid, with short arms and legs. Their thick, heavy bones indicate that they were quite strong.

Based on reconstructions, the Neanderthal face was similar to ours, but with a heavier brow, larger nose, and smaller chin.

Neanderthal brains were slightly larger than those of modern humans, perhaps because of their overall larger and heavier body size. The Neanderthal skull was longer than that of both modern humans and Cro-Magnons, and it had a bulge at the back. Compare the three skulls in *Figure 12.16.* What other differences can you see?

Tools and culture The entrances of Neanderthal caves often had a fire at the center. The ground around the hearth was cleared of debris, and animal bones were typically thrown to the back of the cave. Flint chips found around the hearths are evidence that Neanderthals fashioned stone tools while sitting around a fire. Such evidence has led scientists to conclude that Neanderthals had a simple but organized social structure.

Although the number of animal bones at campsites indicates that Neanderthals were good hunters, they also probably made plants an important part of their diet. A specific pattern of wear on Neanderthal teeth and some of their stone tools indicates that Neanderthals used to scrape hides for clothing or shelter.

Scientists have found many Neanderthal tools made of bone and stone.

FIGURE 12.15
Like modern humans, the Neanderthals are classified as *Homo sapiens*. However, they are distinguished by their short, solid build and distinctive facial features.

Neanderthal

Cro-Magnon

Modern human

FIGURE 12.16
Note the differences and similarities between these human skulls.

One researcher claims to have identified over 60 different types of stone flake tools and 20 types of hand axes. Only a few examples of decorated tools and jewelry (ivory rings and pierced animal teeth) have been discovered in Neanderthal cave sites.

Neanderthal skeletons have been found in arranged positions and with food, weapons, and even flowers. This evidence suggests that Neanderthals were the first hominids to participate in ritual burials.

Neanderthals apparently lived at the same time as modern hominids for at least 10,000 years. Scientists do not know why the Neanderthals disappeared. Some think modern hominids may have driven the Neanderthals to extinction through competition. The Neanderthals may have relied on foods that were harder to find and eat. If modern hominids were more efficient at finding and eating food, they may have been able to specialize—some remaining with their children in a protected area, while others collected food. Such advantages may have given modern hominids an evolutionary edge.

THE CRO-MAGNONS

Something new

The first fossils of a fully modern *H. sapiens*, found in Africa, appear to be about 120,000 years old. However, the Cro-Magnons, dating back about 40,000 years, are the best known example of modern *H. sapiens*.

Physical characteristics

Physically the Cro-Magnons were nearly identical to modern humans. Cro-Magnon skulls, like those of modern humans, have a vertical rather than a sloping forehead. Unlike Neanderthals, Cro-Magnons have small or no eyebrow ridges, and their lighter jaw has a prominent chin and smaller molars. Overall, Cro-Magnons were taller and lighter than Neanderthals; their build is typical of many modern humans. In fact, if you were to pass a Cro-Magnon on the street, you would probably never know it!

LAB ZONE Do It!

Modeling Archaeological Activity

Although fossils are scarce, archaeologists can infer much information from such evidence. You, too, can get the big picture, if you . . .

Try This

1 Obtain 25 pieces from a 250-piece jigsaw puzzle. (Do not assemble the puzzle or look at the puzzle box.)
2 Study the pieces carefully. Record your observations.
3 Based on your observations, infer how the whole picture looks. Try to infer the size and shape of the puzzle as well.
4 Confirm your inference by completing the puzzle or by looking at the box.

Analyze Your Results

1 How accurate was your inference?
2 What is your estimate of the smallest percentage of the puzzle needed to make an accurate inference?
3 Which inference would be more accurate: one based on 10 percent of a 1000-piece puzzle or one based on 10 percent of a 250-piece puzzle?

Tools and culture The Cro-Magnon culture appears to have been more complex than that of Neanderthals. Archaeological evidence reveals that 30,000 years ago, these humans had well-designed dwellings, language, art, trade, and even class distinctions. In some ways, their culture was similar to today's cultures.

Cro-Magnon sites provide evidence of an organized social structure. Their settlements show separate areas for butchering, for cooking, and for dumping garbage. Areas were also set aside for tool and blade making. Tools were finely crafted from materials including bone, antler, wood, and various types of stone. Cro-Magnon artwork includes decorated tools, ivory carvings, clay figures, musical instruments, and extensive cave paintings.

Cro-Magnon burials suggest complicated rituals and perhaps a developed spiritual life. Elaborate items were placed with the bodies, which were often richly decorated.

DISTRIBUTION OF *HOMO SAPIENS*

Where is home, sweet home?

Scientists are currently debating the origin and subsequent distribution of *H. sapiens*. Two main hypotheses are the multiregional hypothesis and the "Out of Africa" hypothesis, both illustrated in *Figure 12.18*.

According to the multiregional hypothesis, various *H. sapiens* populations evolved from different *H. erectus* populations in different parts of the world. If this is true, modern *H. sapiens* date back 1 to 2 million years, when groups of *H. erectus* first left Africa and became established elsewhere. Interbreeding of these groups would account for the genetic similarity found in all humans.

The "Out of Africa" hypothesis states that modern *H. sapiens* evolved in Africa from ancient populations of *H. erectus* before spreading to other continents. In this scenario, humans left Africa as fully modern *H. sapiens*, and later replaced older *H. sapiens* populations, such as the Neanderthals. If this hypothesis is correct, such a migration from Africa would have occurred relatively recently, and modern human diversity would date back only 100,000 years. Scientists point out that Africa is the only continent where human fossils chronicle a relatively uninterrupted evolutionary path.

Do other types of data support the "Out of Africa" hypothesis? Geneticists Rebecca Cann and Alan Wilson, from the University of California at Berkeley, analyzed the mitochondrial DNA of a broad range of people. They found that mitochondrial DNA in

FIGURE 12.17

Compare the Neanderthal stone tools (below left) to the Cro-Magnon tool and sewing needle (below right).

Sewing needle

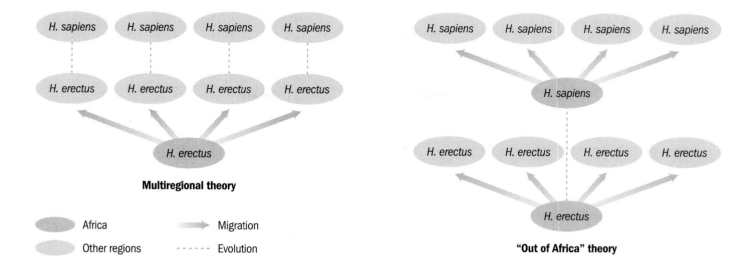

Multiregional theory

Africa | Migration
Other regions | ----- Evolution

"Out of Africa" theory

today's population is nearly uniform. As you know, the greater the difference between two individual's DNA, the longer ago they diverged from a common ancestor.

From their results, Cann and Wilson concluded that the various modern human populations split from a common source relatively recently. They also traced the modern DNA to an African source. Many scientists propose that these data support the "Out of Africa" hypothesis.

However, other scientists interpret the evidence differently. According to these scientists, the data support the multiregional hypothesis because small populations—like those first established by *H. erectus*—lose genetic diversity over time due to genetic drift. When these different populations interbreed, mitochondrial DNA among them becomes more uniform. Scientists propose that even 2 million years is not enough time for *H. sapiens* to have evolved significant genetic differences.

Meanwhile, researchers are trying to recover DNA from Neanderthal and other extinct human fossils. They hope to identify the similarities in DNA between ancient humans and modern humans and then compare those to the similarities in DNA among different populations of modern humans. The results could help to resolve this question.

FIGURE 12.18
The two models of the origin and distribution of *Homo sapiens* are the multiregional hypothesis and the "Out of Africa" hypothesis. Scientists have data to support both hypotheses.

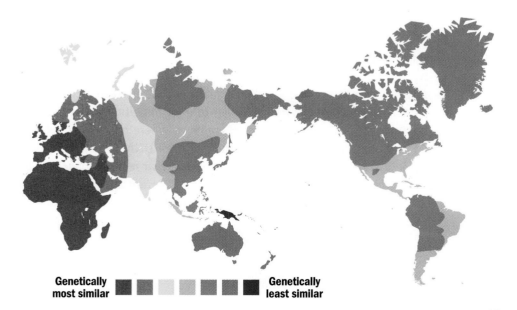

Genetically most similar   Genetically least similar

FIGURE 12.19
This map shows the degree of relatedness among populations of modern humans, based on analysis of mitochondrial DNA. Which hypothesis do these data support?

The Big Dig

Archaeologists of the future might draw conclusions about today's society by looking at our trash. Consider the items in your trash can, or in your community garbage dump. How would an archaeologist use these items to form hypotheses about today's society? Archaeologists use remnants of items used by ancient hominids, such as tools, cooking utensils, or jewelry. The ancient trash gives archaeologists a picture of the lives of ancient hominids and helps them answer questions about human evolution. You can visit *http://evolution.biosurf.com* to find more information about this work.

FIGURE 12.20
The Piltdown skull was a hoax, consisting of a modern human skull cap and an orangutan jaw. Scientists debated the bones for more than 40 years, until new dating techniques proved the "fossil" was modern.

ISSUES IN BIOLOGY

Difficulties in interpretation

With new fossil discoveries and scientific advances, scientists revise the explanations of human evolution. Even for experienced paleontologists, interpreting fossils can be difficult. For example, it can be difficult to tell whether two slightly different fossils represent different species, or only different sexes of the same species. Differences between species may not be apparent in bones and teeth, but in soft tissues, which do not fossilize. Injury and disease can change the structure of bones, making identification and reconstruction difficult.

Because of conflicting interpretations of fossils and the need to revise hypotheses with each new discovery, the public can misinterpret archeological findings. The debate among scientists has also led to misconceptions about human evolution. For example, some people assume that humans evolved from modern apes. Instead our close genetic relationship implies that apes and humans evolved from a common ancestor; humans did not evolve from apes. Likewise, human evolution did not occur in a linear fashion, with less advanced hominids evolving directly to modern *Homo sapiens*. Instead, there have been many hominid groups in the family tree, with several human species co-existing during various times.

Keep in mind that archaeologists make interpretations by comparing their fossil findings with known data. Like all scientific hypotheses, archeological hypotheses are based on reason and supported by data. When the data are wrong or are interpreted incorrectly, an incorrect hypothesis can be formed. Continuous research and debate are needed to yield the most accurate picture of human evolution.

CHECKPOINT 12.3

1. Name three members of the group *Homo sapiens*. What traits characterize each group?
2. Compare and contrast the "Out of Africa" and the multiregional hypotheses. What evidence supports each?
3. **Critical Thinking** Review Figure 12.19. How might you use arrows on a map to draw migration routes based on the information shown?

Build on What You Know

4. Geneticists have used mitochondrial DNA to infer migration patterns of *H. sapiens*. Where could they obtain other forms of DNA? *(Need to jog your memory? Revisit relevant concepts in Chapter 3, Section 3.2.)*

 What different hominid species have been identified?

Chapter 12 Review

12.1 Primates are mammals with binocular vision and dexterous hands and arms.
12.2–12.3 There have been many different hominid species over time, each species with its own unique characteristics.

Sum It Up

Use the following summary to review the main concepts in this chapter.

12.1 Primates

- After the Cretaceous extinction, the number of mammal species increased dramatically.
- Modern primates evolved from a common ancestor between 65 and 55 million years ago.
- The earliest primates were tree-dwellers with grasping hands, swinging arms, and enhanced depth perception. They evolved into two groups, the prosimians and the anthropoids.
- Many primates have relatively large brains and complex social behaviors and relationships.
- The main groups of modern primates are the prosimians, New World monkeys, Old World monkeys, and apes.
- DNA analysis shows that chimpanzees and humans are closely related.

12.2 Hominids

- The oldest hominid fossil is about 4.4 million years old. About nine different hominid species have been identified. *Homo sapiens* is the only surviving hominid species.
- Archaeologists use fossils of primates' teeth and leg and pelvic bones to infer their diet and mode of locomotion.

- *Homo habilis* coexisted with *Australopithecus* species. *Australopithecus* died out, but *Homo habilis* gave rise to *Homo erectus*—a direct ancestor of modern humans.
- *Homo erectus* migrated from Africa to Europe and Asia.

12.3 *Homo sapiens*

- Neanderthals lived in Europe, Asia, and the Middle East as recently as 30,000 years ago.
- Neanderthals were shorter than modern humans, with heavier bones and larger brains. They made tools from stone and bone.
- Some scientists think that competition with Cro-Magnons caused the extinction of Neanderthals.
- Cro-Magnons are physically identical to modern humans. They had a complex culture with an organized social structure.
- Explanations for the origin of *Homo sapiens* include the multiregional and "Out of Africa" hypotheses.

Use Terms and Concepts

Use each of the following words or terms in a complete sentence. If you need to review a meaning, turn to the page indicated.

primates (p. 280)
prosimian (p. 281)
anthropoids (p. 281)

opposable thumb (p. 281)
binocular vision (p. 282)

prehensile tail (p. 283)
hominids (p. 286)
bipedal (p. 286)

Use Your Word Power

COMPLETION Write the word or phrase that best completes each statement.

1. _____ is an adaptation that results in increased depth perception.

2. A monkeylike creature with large, forward-facing eyes is a(n) _____ .

3. _____ include lemurs, gibbons, and humans.

4. The muscular _____ acts as an extra hand for some primates.

5. The _____ allows humans to grip objects firmly.

6. _____ is the term used to describe the ability to walk on two legs.

TRUE-FALSE Write true if the statement is true. If the statement is false, replace the underlined word(s) to make the statement true.

7. Binocular vision produces overlapping fields of vision.

8. Most primates living in tropical forests eat insects.

9. Anthropoids probably evolved from a common hominid ancestor.

10. Pelvic, knee, and foot bones can reveal whether a fossil is bipedal.

11. Primates evolved from a small tree-dwelling ancestor.

12. A prehensile tail is a common trait of New World monkeys.

13. New World monkeys, Old World monkeys, and apes are all prosimians.

Show What You Know

14. Why do scientists think that *Australopithecus robustus* and *A. boisei* are not ancestors of *Homo sapiens*?

15. Explain why the fossil record of primates is relatively incomplete.

16. What are the advantages of binocular vision?

17. Explain why scientists think that the earliest primate ancestors were nocturnal.

18. For which traits were *Homo habilis* and *H. erectus* named?

19. What is the major difference between Old World and New World monkeys?

20. Compare the tools of Neanderthals and Cro-Magnons.

21. **Make a Concept Map** Complete the concept map below by adding the following terms: monkeys, apes, hominids, chimpanzees, prosimians, anthropoids, gorillas.

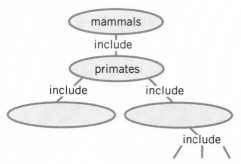

Take It Further

22. **Developing a Hypothesis** Neanderthals often camped at the entrances of caves, in which evidence of fires has been preserved. Suggest at least three reasons why Neanderthals might have built fires at their campsites.

23. **Making an Analogy** Primates are adapted to a tree-dwelling environment. What events in gymnastic competitions remind you of this adaptation?

24. **Making an Analogy** Genealogists specialize in researching and constructing family trees. How is the work of genealogists and archaeologists similar? How do they differ?

25. **Developing a Hypothesis** What might have happened differently in the evolution of anthropoids had North America and Eurasia been connected?

26. Analyzing Data Compare the skulls in this sketch. Which skull might belong to an *Australopithecus* species? Which to another hominid species? Explain your answer.

A   B

27. Interpreting a Graph Suppose the graph below shows the average difference between the DNA of humans and other anthropoids. Based on this analysis, which group is most closely related to humans? Which large group is missing? Explain your answer.

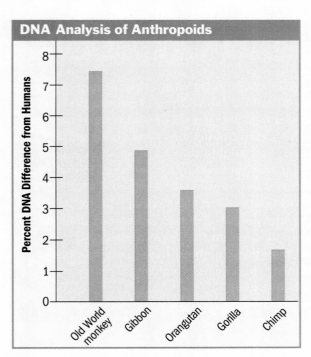

DNA Analysis of Anthropoids

Percent DNA Difference from Humans

Old World monkey — Gibbon — Orangutan — Gorilla — Chimp

28. Designing an Experiment Suppose you found a site containing hominid bones. Propose at least one method (other than studying teeth) for determining the hominids' diet.

Consider the Issues

29. Burying the Bones In 1996, hikers found a skeleton on Federal land in Washington State. Radiocarbon dating indicated an age of 9400 years, among the oldest human remains found in North America. The Oregon Umatilla tribe claimed the skeleton. According to law, Native American remains found on federal lands must be returned to the appropriate tribe for reburial. According to scientists, the evidence is insufficient to support the Umatilla claim, and the skeleton requires further study to determine its ancestry. If you were the judge, what would you decide? Why?

Make New Connections

30. Biology and Language One of the defining characteristics of *Homo sapiens* is the use of language. Linguistics, from the Latin *lingua,* meaning "tongue," is the study of languages. Like species, languages are classified and studied to determine if and how they are related. How are relationships between languages determined? How many languages do you and your classmates know? Create a linguistic family tree including those languages.

31. Biology and Art Learn more about the prehistoric cave paintings in Europe. When and how were they discovered? What tools and supplies did the artists use? What explanations have been proposed for why the paintings were made?

FAST-FORWARD TO CHAPTER 13

In Chapter 13, you will learn about the system for grouping species. You will also learn how species are named and how they can be identified.

CHAPTER 13
Classification

You can find out more about classification by exploring the following
Internet address:
http://evolution.biosurf.com

WHERE IS THE GIANT SQUID?

If you ever see a giant squid in its natural environment, be
sure to take plenty of notes, for you might be the first person
to observe such a sight! In the words of one researcher,
more is known about extinct dinosaurs than about giant
squids. Of the many giant squids that have washed ashore
(top left), the longest was more than 18 meters. These ocean
dwellers have appeared in countless legends and stories. Yet
researchers have little data about the habitat, eating habits,
and mechanisms of movement of these enormous animals
and other organisms that live in the open ocean.

Researchers can hypothesize about how giant squids live,
but they cannot identify the closest relatives of these mysterious marine animals. Are giant
squids more closely related to
the *Idiosepius* squid, just
2.5 centimeters long, or to the
3.5-meter-long Humboldt squid?
Researchers need direct observation of the giant squids in their
environment in order to discover
how squids are related to each-
other. What types of information
could researchers use to classify
the giant squid? And what other
strange living things inhabit the
ocean? Why is the classification
of organisms vital to the study of
life on Earth?

This eye of a Humboldt
squid is much smaller than
the average giant squid eye.

Discovering a Reason for Classification

You need *a photograph of an organism that is unfamiliar to you*

1. Your teacher will display the photograph to your class.
2. Everyone in your class should write down one name they would assign to the organism. What other species might this organism be related to? Why?
3. Compare the different names that you and your classmates gave the unfamiliar organism. What criteria were used in naming the organism?

Although classification may be difficult under certain circumstances, it serves an important purpose. Classification eliminates confusion caused by name differences, organizes vast amounts of information into manageable levels, and reveals evolutionary relationships among organisms.

WRITE ABOUT IT!

In your science journal, write about how your name identifies you. Do you have a common name that leads to confusion, or a name that is difficult to spell? Write about any nicknames you may have and explain how you got them.

13.1 Classification

What you'll learn

IDEAS

- To describe the system for classifying organisms
- To distinguish between different classification systems

WORDS

taxonomy, kingdom, phylum, classes, orders, family, genus, divisions, binomial nomenclature

Classified information

Can you imagine shopping in a store that did not organize its stock? It would be chaos! Most hardware stores first sort items into general categories, such as electrical and plumbing supplies. Then they create smaller categories—for example, metal and plastic pipes in the plumbing section. Scientists have a similar method for categorizing organisms.

FIGURE 13.1

Classifying Life

Trace the taxonomy of house cats, from kingdom to species. Which of the animals shown is most closely related to the house cat?

GROUPING ORGANISMS

Sorting life is a taxing business

Biologists study an enormous variety of organisms. Imagine trying to identify relationships between whales, bacteria, sponges, and redwood trees. Just sorting out species of ants can be challenging. Biologists organize living things into categories. The field of biology that identifies and classifies organisms is called **taxonomy** (taks-ON-oh-mee). Taxonomists analyze shared characteristics to determine evolutionary relationships between species. These organisms are then grouped, or classified. The biological classification system groups the most closely related organisms together.

	Kingdom	Phylum	Class	Order	Family	Genus	Species
	Animalia	Chordata	Mammalia	Carnivora	Felidae	Felis	Sylvestris
House cat	🐱	🐱	🐱	🐱	🐱	🐱	🐱
Mountain lion	🐆	🐆	🐆	🐆	🐆		
African lion	🦁	🦁	🦁	🦁			
Horse	🐴	🐴	🐴				
Giant squid	🦑						

House cats are members of the kingdom Animalia. Their skeletal structure places them in the phylum Chordata.

Members of the class Mammalia have hair and nurse their offspring. Most members of the order Carnivora have sharp teeth and eat meat.

Members of the family Felidae have long, lithe bodies and are excellent hunters. The small, domesticated cat belongs to the genus *Felis* and the species *sylvestris*.

The classification system that biologists use today is based on a system developed by Carl von Linné, a Swedish biologist of the mid-1700s. Linné established a system of groups called taxa (singular: *taxon*). Each taxon is a category into which related organisms are placed. The system of classification Linné developed is a hierarchy of taxa. Linné ranked taxa from the broadest, most general groups to the smallest, most specific groups.

Linné's classification system originally included five levels; modern scientists have added two more. The broadest, most general group into which all organisms are divided is called a **kingdom.** Organisms that have similar characteristics such as cell structure, level of cell specialization, and method of obtaining nutrients are grouped together in a kingdom. Kingdoms are divided into phyla (singular: **phylum**). Within each phylum there are groups called **classes.** Classes are further divided into **orders.** The next level is **family,** which is divided into genera (singular: **genus**). A genus is further divided into species.

At each classification level, organisms that share the most characteristics are grouped together. Compare the organisms shown at each level in *Figure 13.1*. What characteristics do all of the organisms shown in the class Mammalia share? Species is the most specific level of the classification system because members of one species can interbreed and produce offspring. Typically, members of a genus and the taxa above cannot interbreed or produce offspring.

The seven categories apply to many, but not all, organisms. The plant kingdom is divided into categories called **divisions** instead of phyla. Bacterial species are often divided into groups called strains.

Do It!

How Do Taxonomists Classify Organisms?

Taxonomists categorize organisms based on their evolutionary relationships. You can model this process and assign objects to taxonomic categories if you . . .

Try This

1 Pick a place that contains a variety of objects, such as a closet, a locker, or the space underneath your bed.
2 Make a list of all of the objects in that place. Be sure to include any dust, crumbs, and scrap papers you find.
3 Divide the objects into several kingdoms. Continue to divide the objects into the other taxa: phyla, classes, orders, families, genera, and species. Record your results.

Analyze Your Results

1 What characteristics did you use to organize the objects? Could you have used other criteria?
2 Was there an object that had a kingdom of its own? What distinguished it from the objects in other kingdoms?

THE KINGDOMS

Kingdom borders

Linné classified all organisms into two kingdoms, Plantae and Animalia. A third kingdom, Protista, was added to the classification system in the 1800s. The kingdom Monera was added later. In 1969 a fifth kingdom, Fungi, was added. Although the number of kingdoms used by taxonomists is still a subject of debate, a five-kingdom system is commonly used today.

Monera All bacteria belong to the kingdom Monera. These unicellular prokaryotes do not have a nuclear membrane or any membrane-bound organelles. Most bacteria are heterotrophs, but some are autotrophs.

Protista The kingdom Protista includes unicellular and multicellular eukaryotes. Eukaryotic cells have nuclei and organelles that are surrounded by membranes. The cells of

Who Is K.P. Cofgs?

A mnemonic device helps you to remember something. You can memorize the seven taxa if you come up with a sentence in which the first letter of each word represents a taxon. Here is one example: Kings Play Chess On Fuzzy Green Stools.

FIGURE 13.2

The Five Kingdoms

The five kingdoms are arranged according to their evolutionary relationships (right). In the diagram below, the size of the circle indicates the number of species. Which kingdom has the most species?

Plantae
Plants are multicellular, autotrophic eukaryotes. Their cells have cell walls.

Fungi
Members of the kingdom Fungi are heterotrophic eukaryotes whose cells have cell walls.

Animalia
An animal is a multicellular heterotroph whose eukaryotic cells lack cell walls.

Protista
Protists are eukaryotes. Most are unicellular, but some are multicellular with little cell specialization.

Monera
Monerans are unicellular prokaryotes; there are both heterotrophic and autotrophic monerans.

most multicellular protists are not specialized. Some protists are autotrophs, but others are heterotrophs. Protists include amebas, as well as algae such as kelp.

Fungi Fungi are eukaryotes. Most are multicellular, with cells that have cell walls. Fungi are also heterotrophs. They obtain nutrition by releasing digestive enzymes into a food source and absorbing the digested nutrients. Fungi include molds, mildews, mushrooms, and yeasts.

Plantae Plants are multicellular eukaryotes. The cells of plants have cell walls and are specialized to form tissues, which are organized into distinct organs. Most plants are autotrophs. They carry out photosynthesis to obtain nutrition for life processes. The kingdom Plantae includes mosses, ferns, cone-bearing plants, and flowering plants.

Animalia Animals are multicellular, eukaryotic, and heterotrophic. Animal cells do not have cell walls, but they do have cell membranes. Most members of the animal kingdom can move from place to place at some stage in their life cycle. In addition to the many familiar representatives, this kingdom includes sponges, jellyfish, worms, sea stars, and insects.

Kingdom battles

As in most scientific fields, technological advances have provided equipment and techniques—for example, the electron microscope and molecular analysis—that reveal new information about evolutionary relationships. As more is learned about different organisms, scientists debate and revise the way they classify them. In fact, there are several classification systems.

Bacteria are one example of organisms that are difficult to classify. Their evolutionary relationships are unclear. One reason is that bacteria do not fossilize easily, so their fossil record is incomplete. For many years, the classification of living bacteria was based on traits that can be easily observed.

Today, thanks to advances in molecular biology, scientists are able to compare RNA in bacterial ribosomes. The biochemical data are used to infer evolutionary relationships between bacteria. As a result, many scientists argue that the kingdom Monera should be divided into two separate kingdoms, for a total of six kingdoms.

As you can see in *Figure 13.3,* the six-kingdom system splits monerans into the kingdoms Eubacteria and Archaebacteria. Scientists base this distinction on the argument that these two groups are as different as prokaryotes and eukaryotes. Other scientists interpret recent biochemical findings differently and use an eight-kingdom system. As more information is discovered, the trend toward more kingdoms may continue.

In contrast, some taxonomists favor using an even more general category than kingdoms, which they call domains. According to this system, there are three domains: Bacteria, Archaea, and Eukarya. Domains are further divided into kingdoms. Which classification system do you support?

FIGURE 13.3

Some scientists prefer classification systems other than the five-kingdom system. How do these systems differ? How are they similar?

Five Kingdoms

| Monera | Protista | Plantae | Fungi | Animalia |

Six Kingdoms

| Eubacteria | Archae-bacteria | Protista | Plantae | Fungi | Animalia |

Eight Kingdoms

| Eubacteria | Archae-bacteria | Archezoa | Chromista | Protista | Plantae | Fungi | Animalia |

Three Domains

| Bacteria (eubacteria) | Archaea (archae-bacteria) | EUKARYA (eukaryotes) |

NAMING ORGANISMS

A rose is a rose is a rose

What do a crawdad, crayfish, mudbug, and rock lobster have in common? The answer is everything—these are all names for the same species of freshwater crustacean. Within a language, there are often several different words for the same object. And because there are hundreds of languages, hundreds of words can be used to describe the same thing.

Clear communication among scientists around the world requires an international system for naming organisms. Linné and the scientists of his time used Latin for the names of taxa. Because Latin was no longer a spoken language, the meanings of the words were not likely to change, as the meanings of words in modern language do. In English, for example, the word *cool* was once used only to describe a temperature. Today, *cool* can also mean "excellent." Linné was so enthusiastic about his new system that he changed his own name to a Latin version—Carolus Linnaeus (lih-NAY-us).

Before Linnaeus developed his system, scientists used very long Latin names to describe organisms. This system was not useful because the names became too long and complex. The scientific name for the common European honeybee, for example, consisted of 12 words describing the bee's shape and color.

Linnaeus proposed using a system called **binomial nomenclature,** meaning "two-name naming." In that system, an organism's scientific name consists of the genus name and the species name. For example, the crayfish shown in *Figure 13.4* is *Cambarus bartoni*. The genus name is first and

mudbug

crawdaddy

crayfish

rock lobster

FIGURE 13.4
Its scientific name is *Cambarus bartoni,* but you may know this crayfish by any of its four nicknames.

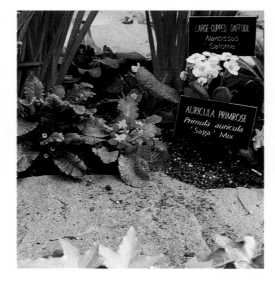

FIGURE 13.5
Binomial nomenclature ensures that biologists are referring to the same organism. What is the scientific name of this plant?

is capitalized; the species name is second and is not capitalized. Both words are printed in italics or underlined. The genus name can be abbreviated to a single letter, as in *C. bartoni.* Using binomial nomenclature, the honeybee's name is reduced from 12 words to 2: *Apis mellifera.* What other scientific names do you know?

CHECKPOINT 13.1

1. How are organisms classified? Describe the modern classification system.

2. What characteristics distinguish the five-kingdom classification system from other classification systems?

3. Critical Thinking What items are commonly found in a grocery store? Use Linnaeus' system to classify these items into groups.

Build on What You Know

4. The classification system organizes huge amounts of information into a usable form. What other ranking systems are used in science to organize large amounts of data? *(Need to jog your memory? Revisit relevant concepts in Chapter 1, Section 1.1, and Chapter 2, Section 2.2.)*

13.2 Basis for Classification

Not just for the birds
When is a Baltimore Oriole not a Baltimore Oriole? When it is a Northern Oriole! Bird specialists once considered the Baltimore Oriole (left) and Bullock's Oriole variations of a single species—the Northern Oriole. However, it has been discovered that the birds rarely interbreed, so now both birds are called by their original names. New data often lead researchers to reclassify organisms.

What you'll learn

IDEAS
• To relate phylogenetic trees and evolutionary relationships
• To explain the basis for classification and some problems in classifying organisms

WORDS
phylogenetic tree

EVOLUTIONARY RELATIONSHIPS
Taxa are branching out

A family tree illustrates relationships among individuals and includes ancestors as far back as records allow. The more distant ancestors appear at the base or on the trunk of the tree. Recent relatives make up the branches or the branch ends. Taxonomists use a diagram similar to a family tree. The diagram, called a **phylogenetic** (fy-loh-juh-NEH-tik) **tree,** shows the evolutionary relationships among organisms.

Family historians use family records and photographs to create a family tree. Scientists use the fossil record and structural and molecular comparisons to construct phylogenetic trees similar to the one in *Figure 13.6*. Like a family tree, a phylogenetic tree has a trunk and branches, but a phylogenetic tree illustrates relationships among species—not individuals.

According to the theory of evolution, all organisms are descendants of a common ancestor—the first cell. Therefore, all organisms, living or extinct, are related to some degree.

FIGURE 13.6
A Phylogenetic Tree
You can use a phylogenetic tree to compare evolutionary relationships among organisms. The number of branches indicate the degree to which two organisms are related. For example, a domestic cat is more closely related to a lion than it is to a horse. The boxes show milestones, or distinguishing characteristics of each branch.

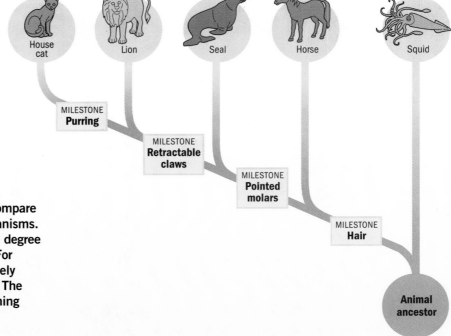

House cat   Lion   Seal   Horse   Squid

MILESTONE **Purring**

MILESTONE **Retractable claws**

MILESTONE **Pointed molars**

MILESTONE **Hair**

Animal ancestor

FIGURE 13.7

A Phylogenetic Tree of Major Groups

This phylogenetic tree illustrates the evolutionary relationships among major groups of modern organisms. The branch points of the tree represent common ancestors. Each time a branch divides into a smaller branch, it shows the emergence of a new group of organisms.

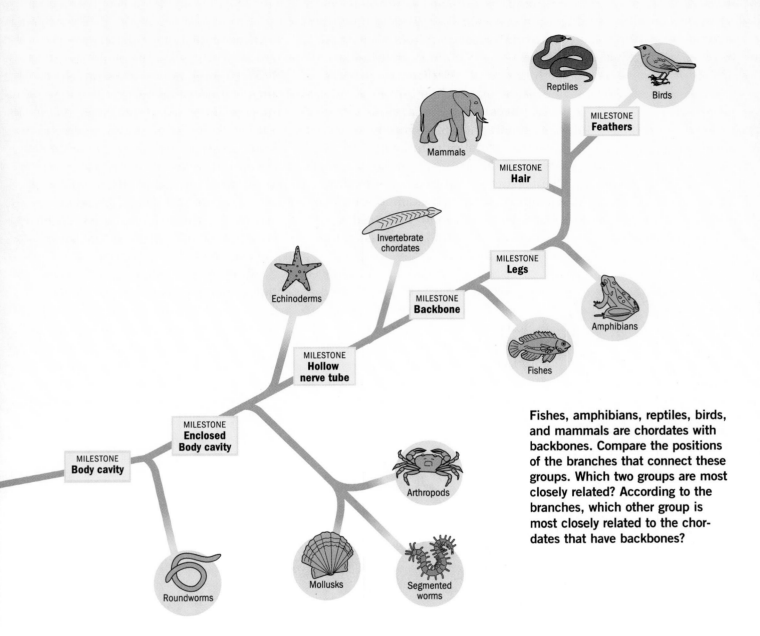

Fishes, amphibians, reptiles, birds, and mammals are chordates with backbones. Compare the positions of the branches that connect these groups. Which two groups are most closely related? According to the branches, which other group is most closely related to the chordates that have backbones?

Evolutionary relationships can be compared to relationships between family members. Brothers and sisters are very closely related. They share very recent common ancestors—their parents. Cousins are are less closely related than brothers and sisters because they share less recent common ancestors, grandparents.

In a similar manner, species are closely related if they share a recent ancestor, and are classifed to share more specific taxa such as Family or Order. For example, lions and domestic cats are both classified as belonging to the family Felidae.

Species whose shared ancestor is very distant are less closely related and are classified to share more general taxa such as Phylum or Kingdom. House cats and the giant squid only share the kingdom Animalia. How does the phylogenetic tree in *Figure 13.7* show these relationships?

Books and their covers

Linnaeus based his classification system on features that he could observe. Scientists still observe physical features of modern organisms to determine evolutionary relationships. As you now know, structures that are similar because they were inherited from a common ancestor are homologous structures. For example, lions and other big cats of the family Felidae share many obvious similarities, such as long, lithe bodies, powerful claws, and rounded ears.

Physical similarities do not always indicate a close evolutionary relationship. As you may recall, structures that look similar but evolved from different ancestors are called analogous structures. The fins on the dolphin and shark shown in *Figure 13.8* are analogous structures. By comparing the fins, scientists have concluded

FIGURE 13.8

The shark (top) and the dolphin (bottom) have fins that look similar. However, internal examination reveals that the shark fin contains cartilage and the dolphin fin contains bone. How does this difference indicate a distant evolutionary relationship?

FIGURE 13.9
The hyrax (above) is about the size of a rabbit. The inset (left) gives you an idea of the hyrax's size relative to the largest land mammal, the African elephant (far left). Yet the fossil record suggests that the elephant and the hyrax share a common ancestor.

that the two types of fins evolved separately. Therefore, they cannot be used as evidence of relatedness. To pinpoint true homologous structures that indicate common ancestry, scientists often study internal structures, such as cells and organs or developing embryos.

Like analogous structures, physical differences do not always prove that two organisms are not related. Do you think the elephant and hyrax, shown in *Figure 13.9*, are related? Structural comparisons from the fossil record show that these species evolved from a common ancestor.

BIOCHEMISTRY

Looks aren't everything

In addition to studying fossil evidence and comparing physical structures, scientists use other tools to classify organisms. Biochemical analyses of DNA, RNA, and proteins can provide evidence of evolutionary relationships.

In analyzing DNA, scientists infer that, after speciation, the mutations that occur in one new species will be different from those in the other new species. The more differences there are between the DNA sequences of

LAB ZONE Think About It!

Constructing a Phylogenetic Tree

Scientists compare the amino acid sequences of the same protein in different species. These data reveal degrees of relatedness between organisms, and can be used to create a phylogenetic tree. You, too, can use biochemical data to construct a phylogenetic tree if you . . .

Sequence of Amino Acids in Cytochrome *c* Protein	
Organism	**Sequence of First 25 Amino Acids**
Dog	G D V E K G K K I F V Q K C A Q C H T V E K G G K
Tuna	G D V A K G K K T F V Q K C A Q C H T V E N G G K
Moth	G N A D V G K K I F V Q R C A Q C H T V E A G G K
Wheat	G N P D A G A K I F K T K C A Q C H T V D A G A G

Try This

1 Letter by letter, compare the amino acid sequences for cytochrome *c* (a mitochondrial protein) in dogs and tuna. Record the number of amino acids that differ.
2 Repeat this process until you have compared each of the four sequences with the other three. You will have six numbers.
3 Use your results to sketch a phylogenetic tree.

Analyze Your Results

1 How does your tree indicate the relationships among the organisms? Which two organisms are most closely related? Which organisms are least closely related?
2 If you determined relationships based on external features, how would your phylogenetic tree look? Would it match the tree you created based on the amino acid sequences? Why or why not?

two organisms, the more distant the common ancestor, and the less closely the organisms are related.

Biochemists also study the proteins coded for by DNA. For example, cytochrome *c* is a protein in the mitochondria of almost all eukaryotes. Scientists use differences in the amino acid sequences of cytochrome *c* to determine relationships among species. The cytochrome *c* amino acid sequence in humans differs from the sequence in chickens by 14 amino acids. The human sequence differs from the sequence in fruit flies by 25 amino acids. Based on this data, with which species—chickens or fruit flies—do humans share a more recent common ancestor?

FIGURE 13.10
How Should Birds Be Classified?

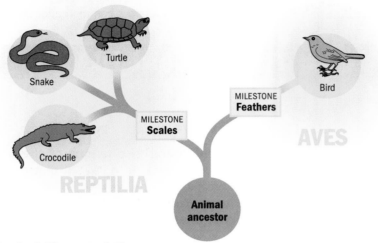

Physical Characteristics
Based on physical characteristics, crocodiles, snakes, and turtles are all classified as Reptilia. Birds are classified as Aves.

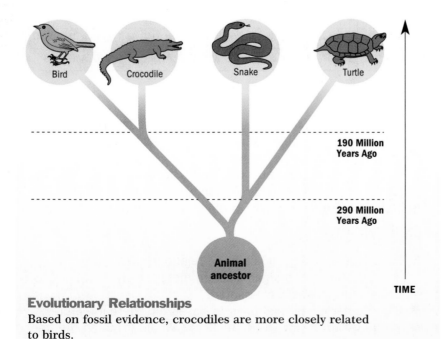

Evolutionary Relationships
Based on fossil evidence, crocodiles are more closely related to birds.

PROBLEMS IN CLASSIFICATION
Identity crisis

Despite the methods scientists have developed, it is still often difficult to classify organisms. Like every scientific field, taxonomy constantly changes as researchers discover new information and refine theories. As you have read, all taxonomists do not use the five-kingdom system. At each taxon below kingdom, the difficulty in classification tends to increase.

One example of a difficulty in classification involves the members of the class Reptilia. Older taxonomy methods placed snakes, turtles, and crocodiles together in the same class, based on shared traits such as scales and skull structure. Birds were assigned to their own class, Aves.

According to the most recent evidence, however, crocodiles and birds share a common dinosaur ancestor that lived about 190 million years ago. Snakes and turtles have a more distant common ancestor that lived almost 100 million years earlier. The fossil evidence indicates that crocodiles are actually more closely related to birds than they are to snakes or turtles.

Such evidence leads some taxonomists to conclude that birds should be reclassified as a type of reptile. Based on the information in *Figure 13.10*, how do you think birds should be classified? Additional information, such as the breeding habits of the

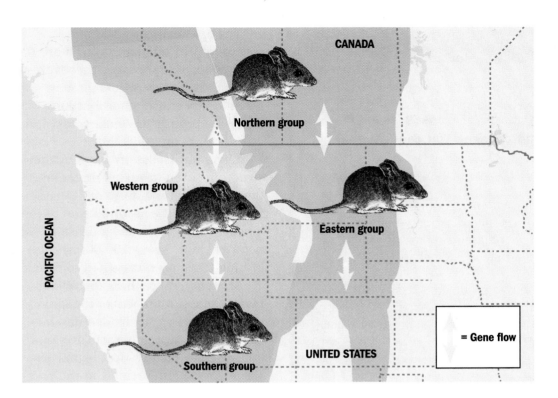

FIGURE 13.11

Two Species or Not Two Species?

THIS figure shows the range of four populations of the deer mouse *Peromyscus maniculatus.* What factors prevent the eastern and western populations from becoming genetically separate species?

CANADA

Northern group

Western group

Eastern group

PACIFIC OCEAN

= Gene flow

UNITED STATES

Southern group

extinct ancestors of birds and reptiles, would further clarify the relationships among members of the class Reptilia and the class Aves. Unfortunately, fossils contain few clues about organisms' breeding habits.

Species definitions can also be problematic. You may recall that a species is populations that can interbreed and produce fertile offspring. But this definition is difficult to apply to organisms that reproduce asexually. These organisms are classified based on their cell shape, organelles, and DNA.

It is also difficult to classify organisms that can reproduce sexually but do not live in the same area. An example of populations that are difficult to classify is four groups of deer mice in the Rocky Mountains, shown in *Figure 13.11.* The groups are physically similar but live in different regions. Interbreeding takes place where ranges overlap, except between the eastern and western groups. Yet, these two groups are considered the same species because gene flow occurs via the northern and southern groups.

Interbreeding among overlapping groups allows gene flow — the transfer of genetic information among all four mouse populations, even the two groups that never breed. However, some scientists speculate that all four mouse populations are evolving into different species. Someday perhaps none of the groups will interbreed.

Sometimes, classification proves so difficult that taxonomists need to propose new taxa. In 1995 the discovery of organisms living on the mouthparts of lobsters excited researchers worldwide. *Figure 13.12* shows one of these new organisms. The organism, *Symbion pandora*, has reproductive and structural characteristics that placed it in a newly proposed phylum—the Cycliophora.

The study of evolutionary relationships is an evolving field, as taxonomists attempt to construct more accurate phylogenetic trees. Perhaps you will be among the scientists who collect new data and debate their meaning.

FIGURE 13.12
Imagine researchers' surprise when they discovered members of a new phylum, Cycliophora, living on the mouthparts of lobsters.

Why Is Classification Difficult?

Phylogenetic trees grow and change. You can discover why if you . . .

Try This

1 Your teacher will give you an assortment of objects, such as rocks, preserved specimens, leaves, and classroom objects.
2 Classify the objects. Record your classifications, as well as the criteria for classification. Criteria may include shape, color, function, or size.
3 Your teacher will then give you a new object. Classify the new object according to your system.
4 Now swap your objects for those of a classmate. Devise a classification system for your classmate's objects.

Analyze Your Results

1 How do your systems compare with your classmate's? Using the practice of peer review in the scientific method, analyze both systems.
2 How did the new objects affect the classification system? Compare this activity to the process of scientific classification.

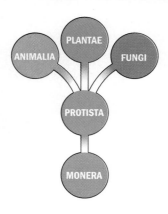

FIGURE 13.13

In the phylogenetic trees in this textbook, each of the five kingdoms has been assigned a different color.

STUDYING BIODIVERSITY

Kingdoms up close

In this textbook you will learn about many phyla and classes of the five kingdoms. As you have read, members of a kingdom also share evolutionary relationships. The phylogenetic tree shown in *Figure 13.13* will appear in many of the following chapters to remind you of the relationships between kingdoms.

Monerans are prokaryotes with few structures to study and compare. Until scientists could study their DNA, RNA, and proteins, monerans were difficult to classify. There are about 10,000 species in the kingdom Monera.

The approximately 100,000 species of the kingdom Protista are grouped together because they lack characteristics that would classify them in any of the other four kingdoms. All protists are eukaryotes, and most protists are unicellular.

Taxonomists classify fungi by the structures used in sexual reproduction. Because fungi were once classified as plants, the second taxon of the kingdom Fungi is called a division, not a phylum. About 100,000 species of fungi have been classified to date.

There are more than 260,000 plant species. Members of the kingdom Plantae can be divided into two broad categories: nonvascular plants and vascular plants. Most plants are vascular and differ widely in their physical characteristics.

Taxonomists estimate that there are at least 800,000, and perhaps as many as 12 million, species in the kingdom Animalia. Scientists have proposed more than 30 animal phyla. In this textbook, you will study 10 of the most abundant animal phyla.

CHECKPOINT 13.2

1. How do phylogenetic trees show evolutionary relationships among organisms?
2. What methods do scientists use to obtain data for phylogenetic trees?
3. Critical Thinking How is it possible for two different species to have similar physical characteristics yet be only distantly related?

Build on What You Know

4. How might taxonomists use the presence of vestigial structures to classify animals? *(Need to jog your memory? Review relevant concepts in Chapter 10, Section 10.3.)*

How do scientists organize the vast numbers of Earth's organisms?

13.3 Identifying Organisms

Lemur tricks

A German college student, Jutta Schmid, thought she had discovered a new species of primate when she saw this tiny lemur. However, records revealed that this species was discovered in the 1840s, but became confused later on with another species of lemur. Such events show the need for effective classification systems to catalog biodiversity.

What you'll learn

IDEAS
• To demonstrate the applications of a dichotomous key
• To explain the relationship of classification to biodiversity

WORDS
dichotomous key

DICHOTOMOUS KEYS

Your key to nature

Identifying organisms is not limited to the science of taxonomy. Many people are curious about organisms. Some people identify birds, trees, or other organisms as a hobby. Others use this information to plan gardens or to learn more about their surroundings. Have you ever seen a bird or a flower that you wanted to identify?

Have you ever wondered what type of bug just bit you? If so, then you would probably find a dichotomous (dy-KAH-toh-mus) key helpful. A **dichotomous key** is a tool used for identifying organisms. You can use a dichotomous key, such as the one in *Figure 13.14,* to identify insects.

A dichotomous key lists specific observable traits of many organisms. For each trait, the key lists two contrasting options. By picking the options that match an organism's features, you can identify the organism. Dichotomous keys are often found in field guides—books that identify many species of a certain phylum or class.

Most often, people who use field guides will notice an organism in their environment and want to identify it.

FIGURE 13.14

How to Use a Dichotomous Key

Suppose you want to identify the topmost insect shown here. Follow the steps starting at number 1 to learn the insect's name.

1
    a. Insect has wings .... go to 2.
    b. Insect has no wings .... go to 9.

Because the insect has wings, go to the choices numbered 2a and 2b. If your insect had no wings, you would go to the choices numbered 9a and 9b. The next set of choices reads:

2
    a. Insect has two wings .... go to 3.
    b. Insect has four wings .... go to 12.

Your insect has four wings, so you skip ahead to number 12, which gives the following choices:

12
    a. Wings are of equal size .... go to 13.
    b. Wings are of unequal size .... go to 18.

The insect has wings of unequal size, leading you to number 18 with the following choices:

18
    a. No projections in rear .... go to 21.
    b. Long thin projections in rear .... go to 25.

Eventually, you reach a choice that does not direct you to another set of choices. Instead, the key states the identity of the organism. In this case, number 25 identifies the insect as a mayfly.

Rather than looking through the entire field guide for a photograph of that organism, a person can use the field guide's dichotomous key to make an identification.

In order to use a dichotomous key, you need to have some information about the organism you are trying to identify. For example, you may need to know that the organism is a tree, not a bush. With this information, you can select the appropriate key in the field guide. The key will then present you with a series of options focused on the organism's distinguishing features. These options are not always based on evolutionary relationships; distantly related organisms with analogous structures may be in the same key. By choosing the options that match the features of an unknown organism, you can identify it.

 Do It!

How Do I Use a Field Guide?

Field guides often have taxonomy information and dichotomous keys to help users identify insects, flowers, birds, shells, fishes, mammals, and more. You too can learn to use a field guide if you . . .

Try This

1 Choose an organism common to your environment. Observe it closely or frequently. Record your observations.
2 Obtain a copy of an appropriate field guide from your local library.
3 Refer to your notes and follow the directions in the field guide to identify the organism you have observed. Then use the field guide while observing the organism in its environment.

Analyze Your Results

1 If your field guide included a dichotomous key, how did it help you identify the organism? What is the organism's name?
2 How do you know that you correctly identified your chosen organism? What could you do to confirm your identification?

Using classification

Taxonomists estimate that there are 1.5 to 12 million different species living on Earth today. The variety in living things is called biodiversity.

Thousands of researchers work in nearly every type of Earth's environment studying many different species. Their work can reveal unknown facts about a species, or show that a group of organisms should be considered two species, not one.

Researchers are also constantly searching for organisms that have not yet been classified. In 1994 researchers discovered a mammal—a type of Vietnamese ox—which they named *Pseudoryx nghetinhensis*. That same year a new species of tree kangaroo was discovered in New Guinea. And recently scientists found a previously unknown form of fungi, which will allow them to classify the form that produces the drug cyclosporin. Cyclosporin is used to prevent the rejection of transplanted organs in humans.

Without doubt, identifying and classifying the millions of species on Earth will be a difficult task for taxonomists. These researchers are constantly constructing and reconstructing phylogenetic trees. However, the biodiversity of life is not limitless.

Human existence has taken a huge toll on many other organisms. Habitat destruction and pollution have resulted in the extinction of thousands of species. In addition, scientists estimate that nearly 25,000 species are endangered, which means that they may face extinction if circumstances do not change. Extinction is a natural by-product of evolution. However, the rate of extinction has been higher in recent times than at almost any other time in Earth's history.

Looking for Diversity

Even a small community is biologically diverse. Observation will reveal representatives of most, if not all, of the five kingdoms. Walk through your community or the area around your school. Observe and record the organisms you see. Keep in mind that monerans and protists are not readily visible. How many different types of organisms can you find in your community?

Use a field guide or a dichotomous key to identify the different organisms. Check a local library to see if local organisms have been cataloged. A resource such as *http://evolution.biosurf.com* may also help you to classify the different organisms. Present your "biodiversity catalog" to your school or local library.

Biodiversity—the result of billions of years of evolutionary history—is the safeguard of natural selection and a nonrenewable resource. As you may recall from Chapter 10, the more variation there is within a population, the better that population can adapt to a changing environment. Biodiversity describes the variation among all species and is the reason why life has been able to adapt to changing environments on Earth for 3.5 billion years.

As classification efforts reveal more information about Earth's biodiversity, the importance of protecting all varieties of species is confirmed. In recent years, we have learned much about the importance of diversity and the interdependence of organisms. This knowledge has helped scientists and legislators formulate policies to preserve our biodiversity.

CHECKPOINT 13.3

1. What is a dichotomous key, and how is it used?
2. How does classification of organisms lead to a better understanding of biodiversity?
3. **Critical Thinking** Dichotomy is defined as a division into two parts. How does the word *dichotomy* relate to a dichotomous key?

Build on What You Know

4. How do mutations contribute to biodiversity? *(Need to jog your memory? Revisit relevant concepts in Chapter 8, Section 8.3.)*

EVERYDAY BIOLOGY

Guiding Life

If there is life, then there is a field guide for it. Guides about birds, trees, insects, and even nonliving stars and rocks are available to help you identify the natural wonders around you.

FIGURE 13.15
The *Pseudoryx*, a Vietnamese ox, was unclassified until 1994.

How is the classification of organisms useful?

Investigate It!

Designing a Key

WHAT YOU WILL DO Classify a group of leaves and design a dichotomous key that can be used to identify the leaves

SKILLS YOU WILL USE Observing, organizing, and classifying

WHAT YOU WILL NEED 6–10 different types of leaves, a ruler, hand lens

Make Some General Observations

1 Gather the leaves to be classified. If you wish to collect your own leaves, get permission from your teacher before you begin collecting. **Caution:** Avoid plants that are dangerous or harmful, such as poison ivy.

2 Count the number of different leaves.

3 Use the ruler and hand lens to examine each leaf carefully. What traits characterize each type of leaf? Record your observations.

Propose a Hypothesis

Propose a hypothesis about which characteristics can be used for classifying the leaves.

Plan Your Procedure and Conduct Your Experiment

1 Identify the characteristics you will use to classify your leaves. Will you use size, color, shape, or a combination of traits? Keep in mind that you will divide specimens based on two contrasting, or dichotomous, characteristics.

2 Design your dichotomous key and test it by using it to identify each specimen.

3 Revise your key as needed. Review a field guide or dichotomous key for ideas on how to make your key easier to use.

Analyze Your Data

1 How did you organize the specimens into groups?

2 How many different characteristics did you use to divide the groups?

3 Are there other ways in which you could have grouped the specimens? Describe the alternate ways.

Draw Conclusions

Was your hypothesis supported by the results of the experiment? Which characteristics were most useful when differentiating between two different leaves? Explain.

Design a Related Experiment

Suppose you wanted to design a dichotomous key for birds. What characteristics might you use to differentiate groups of birds? Propose a hypothesis and design an experiment to test it.

Designing a Key

Objective
Classify a group of leaves and design a dichotomous key.

General Observations
10 leaves total
Leaf 1: heart-shaped, dull green on top, lighter underneath, fuzzy, about 8 centimeters long, edges smooth
Leaf 2: many indentations along edge, very smooth both sides, bright green on top, whitish underneath

Chapter 13 Review

13.1–13.2 Scientists classify organisms into a hierarchy of groups based on evolutionary relationships.

13.3 Classification has numerous applications, including identifying species.

Sum It Up

Use the following summary to review the main concepts in this chapter.

13.1 Classification

- Biological classification systems group organisms into categories based on shared characteristics.
- The modern classification system has seven taxa and is modeled after the system developed by Linnaeus in the 18th century.
- Modern classification systems group organisms into kingdoms based on such characteristics as cell structure, level of cell specialization, and method of obtaining nutrients.
- Based on recent biochemical data, some scientists use classification systems with additional kingdoms; others use three overarching categories called domains.
- Linnaeus introduced the system of binomial nomenclature, in which an organism is identified by its genus and species.

13.2 Basis for Classification

- Taxonomists use phylogenetic trees to show degrees of relatedness among biological groups.
- When classifying organisms, Linnaeus was limited to features that he could observe. Today's scientists also use organisms' fossil record and biochemistry to clarify relationships.
- Scientists may change classifications or create new taxa as more data becomes available.

13.3 Identifying Organisms

- Naturalists can use dichotomous keys to identify organisms. A dichotomous key lists the observable traits of an organism.
- Some of the estimated 1.5 to 12 million species living on Earth have not been discovered and classified. The diversity of living things, or biodiversity, is a nonrenewable resource; nearly 25,000 species are endangered.

Use Terms and Concepts

Use each of the following words or terms in a complete sentence. If you need to review a meaning, turn to the page indicated.

taxonomy (p. 300)
kingdom (p. 301)
phylum (p. 301)
classes (p. 301)
orders (p. 301)

family (p. 301)
genus (p. 301)
divisions (p. 301)
binomial nomenclature (p. 304)

phylogenetic tree (p. 305)
dichotomous key (p. 313)

Use Your Word Power

COMPLETION Write the word or phrase that best completes each statement.

1. The two-word term that comprises the scientific name *Homo sapiens* is an example of _____ .

2. The field of biology that deals with classifying organisms is _____ .

3. Scientific names are made of a(n) _____ and a species.

4. A(n) _____ guides users to the identification of an organism.

5. Members of the _____ Aves are birds.

6. A(n) _____ is a diagram used by taxonomists to show relationships among organisms.

7. In most classification systems, _____ is the broadest taxon.

MULTIPLE CHOICE Choose the letter of the word or phrase that best completes each statement.

8. In a scientific name, the genus is never (a) italicized; (b) lowercase; (c) abbreviated; (d) capitalized.

9. The category in animals that is equivalent to a division in plants is a(n) (a) class; (b) order; (c) phylum; (d) family.

10. Phylogenetic trees (a) map relationships among individuals; (b) are used in field guides; (c) show evolutionary relationships; (d) are based on analogous structures.

11. Giant squids and cats belong to the same (a) order; (b) class; (c) phylum; (d) kingdom.

Show What You Know

12. What is an advantage of binomial nomenclature? Explain your answer.

13. In terms of number of species, which kingdom is the smallest? Which is the largest?

14. How do kingdoms and species differ?

15. Identify a difference between Linnaeus's taxonomic system and the one used in this textbook.

16. What evidence has caused some taxonomists to reconsider the classification of birds?

17. How have technological advances affected scientific classification?

18. What characteristic differentiates the kingdom Fungi from the kingdom Plantae?

19. Explain how using physical characteristics to classify organisms can be misleading. Give an example.

20. **Make a Concept Map** Complete the concept map below by adding the following terms: divisions, classes, orders, genera, species, Protista, Fungi, Plantae, Animalia, eukaryotes, prokaryotes, heterotrophs.

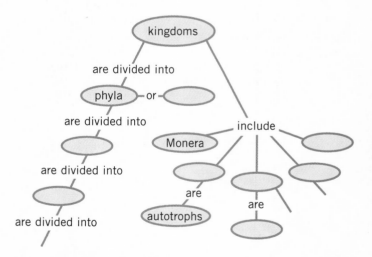

Take It Further

21. **Making an Analogy** What do first and last names have in common with binomial nomenclature?

22. **Organizing and Classifying** Imagine that you have discovered a new multicellular organism that has cells with nuclear membranes and cell walls. How could you classify this organism? What else would you need to know before placing it in an appropriate kingdom? Explain.

23. Making an Analogy The classification system for instruments in a symphony orchestra includes strings, woodwinds, brass, and percussion. What characteristics distinguish one category from another? How are the classification systems for instruments and species different?

24. Designing an Experiment Scientists are debating the classification of spotted skunks. Some taxonomists think that all spotted skunks belong to a single species. Other taxonomists would rather split the species into two groups, eastern spotted skunks and western spotted skunks. Design an experiment to determine how to classify these skunks.

25. Analyzing Data The table below shows the approximate number of species in each kingdom. Graph these data, indicating the number ranges as appropriate. Why are these numbers approximate? Research and graph the number of phyla in two kingdoms of your choice.

Species Number per Kingdom	
Kingdom	**Approximate Number of Species**
Monerans	10,000
Protists	65,000–200,000
Fungi	100,000
Plants	260,000
Animals	800,000–12,000,000

Consider the Issues

26. Politics and Classification The Endangered Species Act protects species in danger of extinction. The classification of a population as a separate species, therefore, can be an important decision politically. The red wolf, for example, is currently considered an endangered species. Some people argue that the red wolf is a hybrid between a coyote and a gray wolf. How could scientists determine whether or not the red wolf is a separate species? If it is a hybrid, should the dwindling red wolf population still be protected?

27. Computers Used for Classification Many organisms have not yet been classified. Even if a trained professional could classify 10 species per year—including time for field trips, analysis, and publication—it would take about one million years to classify an estimated 10 million species worldwide. With Statistical Analysis System (SAS) computer programs, researchers can integrate new data and compare large numbers of traits quickly. Why is classification important? What are some drawbacks of computerized classification?

Make New Connections

28. Biology and Art Imagine that you have to prepare a page in a field guide. Choose several related organisms. Pick an appropriate format, using field guides in the library as models. Then decide on the traits that would best identify the organisms you chose. Create the illustrations for your guide.

29. Biology and Library Science A library would be of little use if its collection was not catalogued. Most libraries use one of two systems—either the Dewey decimal system or a system devised by the Library of Congress. Investigate these two systems. What are the differences between them? Which system does your school library use? Your public library?

30. Biology and History Columbus and other early explorers collected many species of plants and animals. Research one of the early explorers. Find out what geographic and scientific discoveries the explorer made.

FAST-FORWARD TO CHAPTER 14

In Chapter 13 you learned about five kingdoms. In Chapter 14 you will study bacteria—members of the kingdom Monera—and viruses, which do not belong to any of the five kingdoms.

Unit 3 Review

Connect the Chapters

1. Explain how the key adaptations of primates provide clues about the niches in which they evolved.
2. What classification information is provided by the designation *Homo erectus* but not by the names Java Man or Peking Man?
3. Explain how adaptive radiation is reflected on a phylogenetic tree.
4. Use the emergence of the first autotrophs to illustrate the four main points of Darwin's theory of evolution.
5. What relationships would you expect between the gene pools of baboons, gibbons, and lemurs?
6. How was anthropoid evolution affected by the separation of North America from Eurasia? What geologic forces affected this separation?

Connect the Units

7. What are the key differences between carbon-12 and carbon-14?
8. Why are few of the mutations that occur in a parent passed along to offspring?
9. Could a normal distribution curve describe the offspring of red and white snapdragons? Why or why not?

Connect to Themes

10. **Unity and Diversity** Does the increase in taxa since the mid-1700s necessarily reflect an increase in biodiversity? Explain your answer.
11. **Patterns of Change/Cycles** Study the timeline and the graph in *Figure 11.21* that shows when mass extinctions occurred. Can you infer any patterns or cycles? Why or why not?
12. **Stability and Equilibrium** How might the concept of genetic drift support the theory of punctuated equilibrium?

project plans

1 Working individually or in small groups, study a primate other than humans. Report on the primate's habitat and observed behaviors. Are there similarities between primate behavior and human behavior?

2 As a class, create your own fossil "dig" and invite another class to excavate your "fossil bed." Select a suitable outdoor area and mark your site with a grid of string or tape so you can record the locations of the finds. Decide what "fossils" you will scatter at the site—for example, small objects such as coins or candy wrappers. Provide the "archeologists" with appropriate tools. Publish your findings in the form of a scientific report.

3 Plant a terrarium or garden with a collection of seeds. As the seeds sprout and the plants mature, observe and record how principles of natural selection are demonstrated.

CRITIC'S CORNER

A FILM REVIEW BY DANA DENSON, MARVELL, ARKANSAS

Filled with entertainment and suspense, *Inherit the Wind* is a film based on the true story of the John Scopes trial in Dayton, Tennessee. It focuses on the inability of a community to "hear about" anything that appears to contradict its religious beliefs. Henry Drummond, an energetic high-school teacher, believes that education is a growing process cultivated through open-mindedness. Drummond presents, explains, and discusses Darwin's Theory of Evolution to his science class. As a result, he is forced to defend himself and his convictions in court.

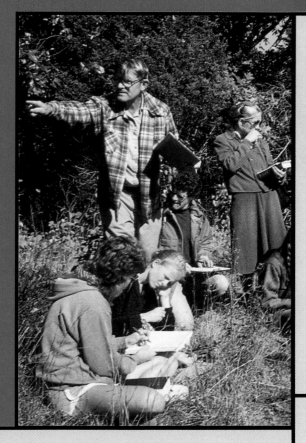

DR. WILLIAM NIERING
Professor of botany at Connecticut College,
Director of research at Connecticut College Arboretum
EDUCATION: B.A. and M.S.; Ph.D. in ecology

"Plant taxonomy is critical to the study of biodiversity, because most plant species haven't been identified yet. To study plants, you have to be able to identify what you are looking at, especially if you need to collect more of it. As a field ecologist, I determine how much of a species is in an ecosystem—a difficult task because different plants are found in different elevations within an area. To make matters worse, the difference between plants can be small, but critical. So, taxonomy helps me make sense out of chaos.

Taxonomy is also important to businesses. Some industries today are testing plants to see if they are medicinally useful. Somewhere there may be an unidentified plant that could cure a deadly disease."

bioSURF Visit the Internet site *http://evolution.biosurf.com* to explore taxonomy.

> Somewhere there may be an unidentified plant that could cure a deadly disease.
> — DR. WILLIAM NIERING

VERONICA ARREOLA
Intern and project leader,
Field Museum of Natural History
EDUCATION: College senior studying to become a science teacher

"My main project is about the locomotion of burrfish. We're trying to figure out exactly how burrfish move. Our work could help scientists compare burrfish to other fish in the same family, as well as to their ancestors. This comparison could help us classify burrfish more accurately, since it sheds light on the differences between fish.

We put burrfish into a flow tank, vary the water flow to different speeds, and videotape the fish to see which fins they use. Burrfish look something like puffer fish—they have hard spines all over their bodies, so they really can't move much. Most fish move only one or two fins at once, or just undulate. Burrfish use all of their fins at once."

bioSURF Search *http://evolution.biosurf.com* for more information about classification.

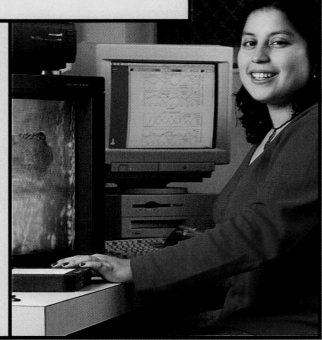

Which of these amazing statements about monerans (bacteria), protists, and fungi are fact, and which are fiction?

Hit *or* Myth?

Some termites are **gardeners.**

(Fact. Some types of termites prepare and tend underground fungus gardens. They eat the fungi, which enable their bodies to digest woody materials.)

Cows contribute to **global warming.**

(Fact. A type of bacterium in the digestive tracts of cows produces methane gas in the cows' intestines. When the methane is released by cows, it contributes to global warming.)

Bacteria **make gold.**

(Fiction, but close to fact. Bacteria are used as "miners" to leach minerals, including gold and copper, from ores.)

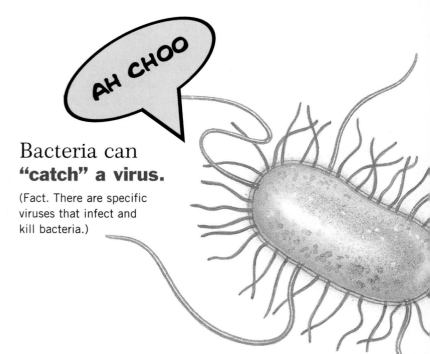

AH CHOO

Bacteria can **"catch" a virus.**

(Fact. There are specific viruses that infect and kill bacteria.)

There are **protists** in your pudding.

(Fact. A substance extracted from seaweed, a type of protist, is used as a thickener in pudding, ice cream, and many other foods.)

Bacteria-produced **headphones** can make music sound better.

(Fact. Headphones made of bacteria-produced cellulose have great acoustic qualities.)

Blue whales are the largest organisms.

(Fiction. Would you believe that a fungus growing in Michigan is one of the world's largest organisms, much larger than any whale?)

Your **jeans** are made with fungus.

(Fact. A type of fungus in soil is used to treat jeans to give them a "stone-washed" look.)

You can find out more about viruses and monerans by exploring the following Internet address: *http://microorganisms.biosurf.com*

Should we destroy a deadly virus?

In 1989, while renovating a church in London, workers opened a century-old crypt. To their horror they found themselves viewing the mummified remains of smallpox victims. Could the deadly virus escape the grave to infect the living? Scientists confirmed that the poxvirus that causes smallpox could survive about 100 years in mummified bodies buried in ground that was frozen year-round. London's temperate climate eliminated this possibility.

Fears and facts like these fuel a raging debate about whether or not humans should destroy the poxvirus. This virus killed about 20 percent of the people it infected in the centuries before immunization stopped its spread. The photo above shows the skin lesions of smallpox. Today it exists only in high-security laboratory containment. Many people want the contents of the containers destroyed because they fear the virus may escape. Others argue that the risk of the virus's escape is far outweighed by the wealth of scientific information the virus can provide.

LAB ZONE Discover It!

Imitating the Spread of a Virus

1. Your teacher whispers a statement about viruses to one student at the front of the classroom. That student whispers what he or she has heard to another student. Each student in turn passes on what he or she has heard until the statement has been whispered to everyone in the class.

2. The last student to hear the statement writes what he or she has heard on the chalkboard. Then the teacher writes the original statement on the chalkboard.

How different are the two statements? By comparing them, you can get an idea of how a virus can change as it spreads from one organism to another over time.

WRITE ABOUT IT!

In your science journal, write about any memorable experiences you have had with flu viruses that infected people in your family or school. How long did it take for the virus to spread from person to person? Describe your symptoms and how you felt while you were sick.

14.1 Characteristics of Viruses

What you'll learn

IDEAS
• To identify the structural characteristics of viruses
• To compare forms of viral replication

WORDS
virus, capsid, envelope, host, lytic cycle, lysogenic cycle, prophage

Avoiding an outbreak
Protective clothing and high-tech gear are a daily reality for scientists who work in a Level 4 laboratory at the Centers for Disease Control (CDC) in Atlanta, Georgia. There, biologists work in a science-fiction-like environment to control the potentially deadly viruses they are studying.

THE STRUCTURE OF VIRUSES

Trouble in a small package

If you ever had a cold or the flu, you probably hosted viruses. How well do you know these guests? A **virus** is an infectious agent made up of a core of nucleic acid and a protein coat.

Viruses are not cells. Unlike plant and animal cells, a virus particle does not have a nucleus, a membrane, or cellular organelles such as ribosomes, mitochondria, or chloroplasts. Although viruses are not cells, they do have organized structural parts.

Compared to even the smallest cell, a virus is tiny. The virus that causes polio, for example, measures only 20 nanometers (nm) in diameter. One

FIGURE 14.1
Appearing as tiny blue dots in this photo, AIDS viruses attack a human immune system cell (T-cell).

nanometer is one billionth (10^{-9}) of a meter. At that size, 3000 polioviruses could line up across the period at the end of this sentence. In *Figure 14.1* you can see the difference in size between a cell and a virus.

All viruses have at least two parts—a protective protein coat and a core of nucleic acid. The protein coat around the core of nucleic acid is called a **capsid.** Depending on the virus, the capsid may consist of one or several kinds of protein.The capsid protects the viral nucleic acid core from its environment.

As you learned in Chapter 2, nucleic acids include DNA and RNA. In cells, DNA is the hereditary material. Some viruses also contain DNA, while other viruses only contain RNA. In viruses containing RNA, the RNA functions as the hereditary material.

Compared to a cell, a virus has a relatively "simple" existence. Viruses do not eat, respire, or respond to environmental changes as cells do. It should not surprise you, therefore, to learn that viruses have fewer genes than cells have. While a human cell may contain about 100,000 genes and a bacterial cell about 1000, a virus may contain only 5 genes.

In *Figure 14.2* you can see the parts of an influenza (flu) virus: a core of RNA, a surrounding capsid, and an outer covering called an envelope. An **envelope** is an additional protective coating usually made of lipids, proteins, and carbohydrates. Envelopes are found only in viruses that infect animal cells. An envelope has spikelike projections that recognize and bind to complementary sites on the membrane of the cell being infected. Think about how a prickly burr sticks to objects. The small illustration below shows how the projections on a viral envelope help a virus cling to an animal cell in a similar manner.

VIRAL REPLICATION

Ticking time bombs

Viruses do not reproduce; they replicate. Reproduction, which is a characteristic of living things, involves cell division. Replication does not involve cell division.

Viruses cannot replicate on their own. In order to replicate, viruses require a host. A **host** is an organism that shelters and nourishes something.

FIGURE 14.2

An Influenza Virus

Envelope
An envelope is made of an outer lipid layer and an inner protein layer surrounding the capsid.

RNA
The influenza virus has a total of eight strands of RNA. Many viruses contain DNA rather than RNA.

Capsid
The proteins in a capsid are determined by the genes in the virus.

Influenza viruses (red) attack a host cell (yellow) in a tissue culture.

Projections
The spikelike projections on the viral envelope help the virus recognize and attach to a host cell.

Living cells host viruses. These host cells provide all the materials that viruses need to copy themselves.

When it enters a host cell, a virus may immediately begin to replicate, or it may remain relatively inactive. The viral replication process that rapidly kills a host cell is called the **lytic** (LIT-ik) **cycle.** You can follow the lytic cycle in *Figure 14.3*. The lytic cycle begins when a virus invades a host cell and begins to replicate immediately, producing many new viruses. Eventually the host cell lyses, or breaks apart, releasing the newly made viruses. The new viruses may then enter other cells and repeat the cycle.

As a child you may have had chicken pox, which is caused by a virus. While you were ill, most of the viruses were in the lytic cycle.

Because your cells were being destroyed by the chicken pox virus, you showed symptoms of the disease.

Sometimes a virus does not start the lytic cycle immediately. Instead, the virus enters the lysogenic cycle. The **lysogenic** (ly-soh-JEN-ik) **cycle** is a type of replication in which a virus does not immediately kill a host cell. The lysogenic cycle in a bacterial cell is shown on the right side of *Figure 14.3*. Which steps do the lytic and lysogenic cycles share?

During the lysogenic cycle, viral DNA inserts itself into a host cell's chromosome. A viral DNA segment that is inserted in a bacterial cell's chromosome is called a **prophage** (PROH-fayj). A host cell carrying a prophage may divide many times. The prophage is replicated every

FIGURE 14.3

Lytic and Lysogenic Cycles

Follow the replication cycles of a virus that has invaded a bacterium. In the lytic cycle, a virus immediately replicates after entering a cell. In the lysogenic cycle, viral DNA attaches itself to a host's chromosome, where it may exist as a harmless prophage for years. What part or parts of the virus enter the bacterial cell?

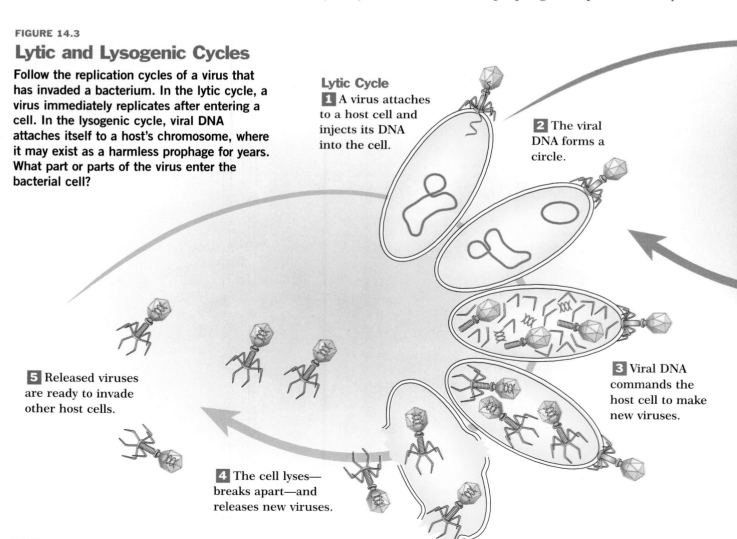

Lytic Cycle
1 A virus attaches to a host cell and injects its DNA into the cell.

2 The viral DNA forms a circle.

3 Viral DNA commands the host cell to make new viruses.

4 The cell lyses— breaks apart—and releases new viruses.

5 Released viruses are ready to invade other host cells.

time the host cell's chromosome replicates.

Some prophages remain in the lysogenic cycle indefinitely. Usually, however, some type of environmental stimulus eventually results in the separation of a prophage from the chromosome of its host cell. The viral DNA then enters the lytic cycle. The virus that causes cold sores in humans can go through the lysogenic cycle, for example. Cold sores erupt when these viruses enter the lytic cycle.

Lysogenic Cycle

1 After a virus injects its DNA into a bacterial cell, the viral DNA inserts itself into a host's chromosome.

Stimulus

No stimulus

2 The host cell divides, replicating viral DNA along with its own DNA.

3 A stimulus allows the viral DNA to separate from the cell's chromosome and enter the lytic cycle. Without a stimulus, the viral DNA stays in the cell's chromosome.

FIGURE 14.4
Many viruses are attacking this *E. coli* bacterial cell, which is defenseless against their onslaught. What happens once the cell is infected?

ALIVE OR NOT?

To be or not to be . . .

Do you think viruses are alive? To answer this question, ask yourself two additional questions. Which characteristics of living things do viruses share? Which do they not share?

When viruses are inside host cells, they share some of the characteristics of life with host cells. Viruses contain nucleic acid and protein. Viruses also change over time as a result of mutations in their DNA or RNA that affect the composition of their proteins.

Outside living cells, viruses are inactive; that is, they cannot grow or replicate. Viruses must be inside living cells to be active. After entering host cells, viruses act like parasites, organisms that harm or destroy the host as they use it for their own benefit.

CHECKPOINT 14.1

1. What are the structural characteristics of viruses?
2. Compare the lytic and lysogenic cycles.
3. **Critical Thinking** Make a diagram to show the lytic and lysogenic cycles in a eukaryotic host cell.

Build on What You Know

4. Make a chart to compare viruses with prokaryotes and eukaryotes. *(Need to jog your memory? Revisit relevant concepts in Chapter 3 Section 3.2.)*

EVERYDAY BIOLOGY

Sick Computers?

Computer viruses behave much like biological viruses. They attach themselves to files, then spread and multiply as the files move between disks, computers, and networks. They may cause odd system behavior or may damage data.

14.2 Origin and Diversity of Viruses

Where do warts come from?
Contrary to superstitious belief, warts—rough growths that most commonly appear on the skin of our hands and feet—are not caused by touching a toad or a frog. Viral infection is the real culprit. Although they are only slightly contagious, warts are more likely to spread if they are scratched open.

DISCOVERY AND ORIGIN OF VIRUSES

Finally found

Have you ever made a surprising discovery while searching for an ordinary object such as keys or a missing book? If so, was your surprise so great that you stopped your original search and turned your attention to your new discovery?

Like your discovery, the discovery of viruses was a scientific surprise. It happened while biologists were looking for something else—the cause of tobacco mosaic disease. Tobacco mosaic disease stunts the growth of tobacco plants and discolors their leaves. You can see the disease's effect on tobacco leaves in *Figure 14.5*.

The Russian biologist Dmitri Ivanovsky was one of the first scientists to look for the cause of tobacco mosaic disease. After a series of experiments in 1892, Ivanovsky concluded that unusually small bacteria or poisons from bacteria must cause tobacco mosaic disease.

Five years later the Dutch biologist Martinus Beijerinck discovered that the agent causing tobacco mosaic disease replicated in tobacco cells. Beijerinck hypothesized that tobacco mosaic disease was caused by something smaller than any known bacterium. He called the infectious agent a *virus*, a Latin word meaning "poison."

Nearly 40 years later, in 1935, the American biochemist Wendell Stanley isolated crystals of the infectious agent from diseased tobacco plants. Because bacterial cells do not form crystals,

FIGURE 14.5
Compare the healthy tobacco leaf on the left with the diseased leaf on the right. How do they differ?

Filovirus
Filoviruses do not have a distinct, uniform shape. Some of these Ebola viruses are threadlike, and some are looped at one end.

Stanley confirmed Beijerinck's conclusion: The infectious agent could not be a bacterium. Biologists suddenly had a new type of infectious agent, a virus, to study.

Although biologists have learned much about viruses since 1935, they still can only hypothesize about how viruses originated. One hypothesis is that viruses evolved from their host cells. At first, viruses may only have been short fragments of chromosomes in host cells. These fragments replicated along with host chromosomes as the host cell divided (just as they do in the lysogenic cycle). In time, these pieces evolved the ability to produce capsid proteins. You may notice that this hypothesis implies that a host cell is the closest relative of a virus. Is this hypothesis a good explanation of the origin of viruses? Why or why not?

DIVERSITY OF VIRUSES

An unending supply

Classifying viruses is difficult because they are so diverse. As a result, biologists have developed several different ways of organizing viruses. Sometimes they are organized by shape, sometimes by the host they infect. Viruses may also be classified according to the way they function inside a cell.

Shape You can see the four shapes of viruses in *Figure 14.6*. The arrangement of proteins in capsids determines the shape of the viruses.

Host Viruses can be organized according to the type of host they

FIGURE 14.6

Viral Shapes

Viruses have many different shapes. What characteristics do all the viruses you see here share?

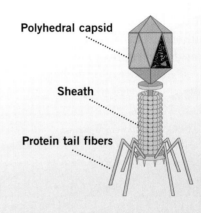

Polyhedral capsid

Sheath

Protein tail fibers

Binal virus
A binal virus consists of two distinct parts: a polyhedral capsid and a helical tail. Compare this virus with the one shown below.

Polyhedral virus
Polyhedral viruses have a multifaceted geometric appearance. The adenovirus shown here is one virus that causes colds.

DNA

Inner helical RNA

Protein molecules

Helical virus
Viral RNA or DNA coils tightly inside the long, narrow capsid of a helical virus.

infect. There are animal viruses, plant viruses, and bacterial viruses. Viruses that infect only bacterial cells are referred to as bacteriophages (bak-TEER-ee-oh-FAY-juhz).

Many but not all viruses invade only a specific type of organism. For example, the virus that causes polio replicates only inside human host cells. The virus that causes rabies infects only the cells of particular animal species, such as dogs and humans.

You may wonder how viruses can be so specific. In section 14.1 you learned that capsids and envelopes contain specific proteins. Receptor sites on host cells also contain specific proteins. If the outer proteins in a virus do not fit with the outer proteins of a cell, the virus will not attach to the cell. Without attachment, the viral nucleic acid cannot enter the host cell to replicate.

Function Some viruses, such as retroviruses, can also be classified based on how they function in a host. A **retrovirus** is a virus that contains

FIGURE 14.7

The Retrovirus

Notice how the enzyme reverse transcriptase is packaged in the core of the HIV shown below. If the enzyme did not enter the host along with the viral RNA, what step in replication could not occur?

Envelope

Capsid

Reverse transcriptase enzyme

Viral RNA

an RNA core that replicates by first transcribing its RNA into DNA. The prefix "retro-" means "reverse." What do you think might work in reverse in this group of viruses?

Most viruses and all organisms make RNA from DNA in the process of transcription. Retroviruses are able to make nucleic acids in reverse order from the usual process. In retroviruses DNA is made from RNA.

As you can see in *Figure 14.7*, retroviruses have an enzyme called reverse transcriptase, which transcribes viral RNA into viral DNA inside the host cell. You can study this figure to better understand the replication of a human immunodeficiency virus (HIV). This retrovirus causes acquired immunodeficiency syndrome (AIDS).

Retroviruses include tumor-producing viruses as well as HIV. Tumor-producing retroviruses and HIV follow a similar invasion pattern. Many tumor-producing viruses, however, enter the lysogenic cycle after step 3 in *Figure 14.7*. Tumors do not immediately appear, but the virus DNA replicates along with the host

Model a Bacteriophage

Building a model gives you an idea of structure. You can model a bacteriophage, which is a binal virus, if you . . .

Try This

1 Study the illustration of the binal virus on page 331.
2 Gather any materials that will help you to build your model. These might include toothpicks, pipe cleaners, string, and clear plastic food wrap.
3 Build your model, trying to keep the sizes of the parts in relative proportion.

Analyze Your Results

1 Name the bacteriophage parts on your model.
2 How is your model similar to or different from the models that other students have made? How could you improve yours?
3 What would you change to make a model of a different virus?

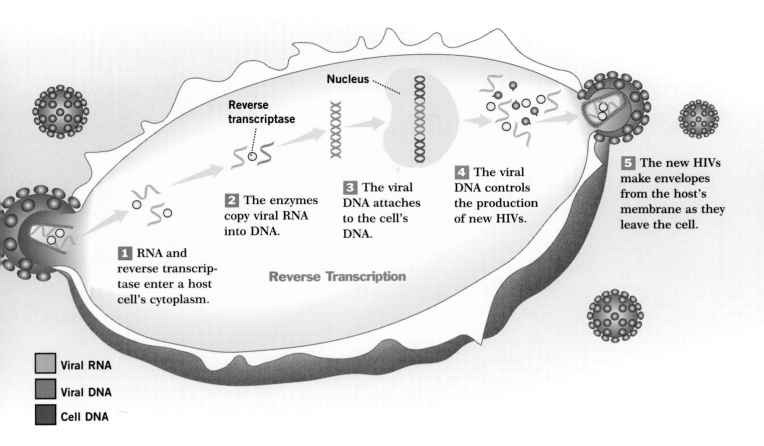

Nucleus

Reverse
transcriptase

1 RNA and
reverse transcrip-
tase enter a host
cell's cytoplasm.

2 The enzymes
copy viral RNA
into DNA.

3 The viral
DNA attaches
to the cell's
DNA.

4 The viral
DNA controls
the production
of new HIVs.

5 The new HIVs
make envelopes
from the host's
membrane as they
leave the cell.

Reverse Transcription

■ Viral RNA

■ Viral DNA

■ Cell DNA

cell DNA. Eventually, many host cells will contain tumor-producing viral DNA. Using what you have learned about the lysogenic cycle, predict what will happen next.

Nonviral particles Scientists have discovered two infectious agents that have simpler structures than viruses: viroids and prions. A **viroid** is a single strand of pure RNA. Viroids cause plant diseases. For example, viroids have killed many coconut palm trees in the Philippines. Other viroids affect the health of crops such as potatoes and tomatoes. Unlike viruses, viroids do not have capsids protecting their nucleic acids.

A **prion** is a protein molecule that can cause disease in animals. Prions are the only known infectious agents that do not contain DNA or RNA but can, nonetheless, spread throughout an organism.

A prion causes a fatal disease called scrapie in sheep. Prions have also been found in the brains of cows that died from the so-called mad cow disease. Other prions are found in humans who suffer from kuru or Creutzfeldt-Jakob disease. Both of these diseases affect the central nervous system. A cure has not yet been found for diseases caused by viroids or prions.

CHECKPOINT 14.2

1. What hypothesis did scientists develop to explain the origin of viruses?

2. In what ways are viruses diverse?

3. Critical Thinking Make a table to show the similarities and differences between viruses, viroids, and prions.

Build on What You Know

4. How were viruses used to answer the "DNA or protein" question? Why was this finding important? *(Need to jog your memory? Revisit relevant concepts in Chapter 7, Section 7.1.)*

The All-Too-Common Cold

Studies have shown that frigid weather and wet feet do not cause colds. Hundreds of different viruses and viral strains are the true culprits.

14.3 Viruses in the Biosphere

What you'll learn

IDEAS
• To describe the role of viruses in the environment
• To explain viral disease and uses of viruses

WORD
vaccination

Dog virus kills big cats

In 1994 scientists were puzzled when about one third of the lions in the Serengeti National Park died of a mutant strain of canine distemper virus (CDV). After extensive study, they concluded that dogs that had died of CDV had been eaten by jackals and hyenas. The infected jackals and hyenas then transmitted CDV to the lions through mucus exchanged during fights.

ECOLOGICAL ROLES

Hosting bad company

When you visit someone's home, you try to be on your best behavior. Viruses that invade a host cell are not always so polite. Some viruses can live in cells without harming them. Other viruses, however, cause specific diseases that develop as the viruses destroy host cells.

Viral diseases that infect humans include the common cold, measles, chicken pox, and mumps. Some viral diseases have dramatically decreased human populations. For example, an influenza virus outbreak after World War I killed more people than the war itself. Before the development of a polio vaccine in the 1950s, thousands of people died from or were permanently disabled by the poliovirus. More recently, the spread of HIV has resulted in a worldwide AIDS epidemic. Millions of humans have already been infected, and thousands more become infected with HIV each day.

Animals and plants are also susceptible to viruses. Viral diseases that can infect animals include distemper, rabies, and pneumonia. Viral diseases that affect plants may discolor leaves, stunt growth, or eventually kill a plant. These plant viruses are often spread from plant to plant by insects and air currents.

Viral diseases cannot be cured by antibiotics, which are effective only against bacterial cells. Although antiviral drug research continues, treatment of many viral diseases is often limited to relieving symptoms while the body's immune system battles the disease.

LAB ZONE Think About It!

Analyzing Disease Occurrence

The numbers of reported cases of some vaccine-preventable viral diseases appear in the table below.

Analyzing the Table

1 Which disease had the most dramatic decrease in number of cases between 1990 and 1994?
2 Why do you think these diseases continue to occur?
3 Make a graph that displays the information in the table.

Reported Cases of Viral Diseases in the United States, 1990–1994					
Viral Disease	**1990**	**1991**	**1992**	**1993**	**1994**
Rubeola (Measles)	27,786	9,643	2,237	312	963
Pertussis (Whooping cough)	4,570	2,719	4,083	6,586	4,617
Rubella (German measles)	1,125	1,401	160	192	227

Source: U.S. Dept. of Health and Human Services

Human uses

After reading about viral diseases, you might think that viruses serve no useful purposes. That is not true.

Vaccines Viruses can be used against themselves in the production of life-saving vaccines. **Vaccination** is the process of injecting a person with a harmless—weakened or dead—form of a virus. The vaccine stimulates the immune system to produce cells and proteins that will destroy that type of virus if it enters the body. The vaccination of large numbers of people helped to end epidemics of diseases such as smallpox, polio, and measles.

Genetic engineering Through ongoing research using viruses, virologists—scientists who study viruses—have learned more about basic cell processes and structures. Concentrating on the behavior of viral DNA in the host cell, virologists have applied their findings to the field of genetic engineering. You read about genetic engineering in Chapter 9.

Viruses sometimes pick up pieces of host cell genes and carry them into other cells. Under controlled conditions, genetic engineers can correct genetic defects by using viruses to carry desirable genes from one cell to another. For example, some children are born with a defect in the gene that produces an enzyme needed by a healthy immune system. These children can survive only in a germ-free "bubble" environment. Through genetic engineering, a virus can be used to insert a corrected gene into their body cells. This inserted gene makes the immune system function properly.

Agriculture Viruses are also used to control pests that destroy human food crops. The benefit of viral treatments for crops is that they eliminate harmful insects without creating pollution.

You may be surprised to learn that viruses can create natural beauty. For example, viral infections produce the stripes and bright color combinations in the petals of gladiolas and tulips.

FIGURE 14.8
Polio patients unable to breathe were placed in iron lungs, which "breathed" for them. Jonas Salk (above) developed a preventative vaccine from three strains of dead polioviruses.

CHECKPOINT 14.3

1. What populations can be altered by viruses in the environment?

2. Name three viral diseases that may infect humans.

3. Critical Thinking What factors would have to be considered before using a virus to kill insects?

Build on What You Know

4. What characteristics of viruses make them useful to genetic engineers? *(Need to jog your memory? Revisit relevant concepts in Chapter 9, Section 9.2.)*

What are viruses and how do they replicate?

14.4 Characteristics of Monerans

What you'll learn

IDEAS
- To identif / the structural characteristics of monerans
- To compare how monerans grow, reproduce, and survive

WORDS
plasmids, endospores, binary fission, conjugation

A universe of monerans

This photo shows the point of a pin magnified many times. Those microscopic organisms dotting the pin's surface are monerans. An amazing array of monerans can be found everywhere on Earth. In fact, they exist on most objects you touch every day, and there are trillions of them on and in your body. What exactly are monerans?

MONERAN STRUCTURE

Just the basics

The word *monera* (moh-NAYR-uh) may be unfamiliar, but you have probably heard the word *bacteria*. Most organisms in the kingdom Monera are bacteria (singular: *bacterium*). One characteristic that classifies an organism as a moneran is the lack of a membrane-bound nucleus. As you learned in Chapter 3, cells that lack a membrane-bound nucleus are called prokaryotic cells. Organisms that consist of prokaryotic cells are called prokaryotes. All of the 5000 known species of monerans are prokaryotes.

Monerans share other characteristics, as you can see in *Figure 14.9*. Most bacterial DNA is in a single, double-stranded, circular chromosome that attaches itself to the cell membrane. Some kinds of bacteria also contain smaller pieces of circular DNA called **plasmids.** As many as 80 plasmids may be found in a cell. You can compare chromosomes and plasmids in *Figure 14.10*.

LIFE CYCLE

Millions of multiplying monerans

When it has enough food and an efficient waste disposal system, some bacteria can reproduce every 20 minutes. At that rate, from 1 bacterium about 500 bacteria would be produced in three hours and about 16,000,000 in eight hours. Can you imagine how heavily populated Earth would be if every animal multiplied that quickly? Fortunately such unlimited growth does not occur. Lack of food and a buildup of waste keep populations of bacteria in check. Although their

FIGURE 14.9
Monerans share five characteristics. How do their characteristics compare with those of viruses?

Characteristics of Monerans
Monerans lack a membrane-bound nucleus.
Monerans have a cell membrane but do not have membrane-bound organelles such as mitochondria and chloroplasts.
Ribosomes in monerans are slightly different from the ribosomes in other organisms.
Monerans are smaller than almost all other organisms.
Most monerans are unicellular organisms.

FIGURE 14.10

A Typical Moneran

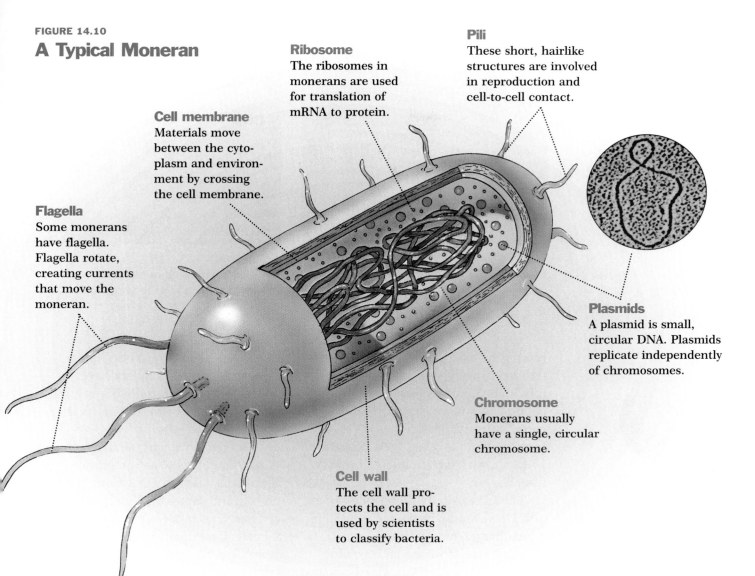

Ribosome
The ribosomes in monerans are used for translation of mRNA to protein.

Pili
These short, hairlike structures are involved in reproduction and cell-to-cell contact.

Cell membrane
Materials move between the cytoplasm and environment by crossing the cell membrane.

Flagella
Some monerans have flagella. Flagella rotate, creating currents that move the moneran.

Plasmids
A plasmid is small, circular DNA. Plasmids replicate independently of chromosomes.

Chromosome
Monerans usually have a single, circular chromosome.

Cell wall
The cell wall protects the cell and is used by scientists to classify bacteria.

growth may be limited by environmental factors, bacteria can adjust in order to survive harsh conditions.

Survival When living conditions become unfavorable, some monerans can form dehydrated cells known as **endospores.** You can see an illustration of an endospore in *Figure 14.11*. Endospores have thick walls and can resist heat, drought, and radiation.

Monerans that form endospores have an advantage for survival. Endospores can be alive but inactive for many years, possibly even for centuries. Then, when conditions are right, the endospores can break open and produce new bacterial

cells. Endospore formation allows some species of monerans to survive harsh conditions and to reproduce when conditions improve.

Reproduction Most monerans can reproduce either asexually or sexually. However, most monerans

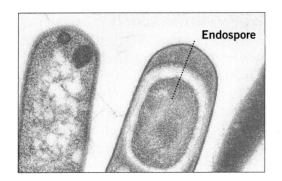

Endospore

FIGURE 14.11
This cell has replicated its chromosome and surrounded it with a strong wall, forming an endospore. Why might it be an advantage for a bacterium to form an endospore?

Chapter 14 Viruses and Monerans   **337**

FIGURE 14.12

Moneran Reproduction

Binary fission (left) is a form of asexual reproduction. Conjugation (right) is a form of sexual reproduction. What might be an advantage of conjugation over binary fission?

Binary fission
Binary fission means literally "division in half."

Pili form a bridge.

Conjugation
DNA from a plasmid or chromosome moves through the sex pili.

FIGURE 14.13
Binary fission can occur as rapidly as every 20 minutes. The photos above show bacterial reproduction over 5 hours.

reproduce asexually through binary fission. **Binary fission** is a process in which the chromosome of a unicellular organism is continually replicated, after which the cell divides forming two identical cells. *Figure 14.12* shows bacteria during binary fission.

Bacteria usually reproduce asexually. However, bacteria occasionally do exchange genetic information through a form of sexual reproduction called conjugation. **Conjugation** is the process of exchanging genetic material through cell-to-cell contact. During conjugation, some chromosomal DNA and plasmids may move from one bacterial cell to another.

You can see bacteria during conjugation in *Figure 14.12*. As conjugation begins, bacteria are attached together by special hairlike structures called pili (singular: *pilus*). During the later stages of conjugation, a bridge of cytoplasm forms between two bacterial cells, and the DNA passes from one cell to another.

Conjugation increases the genetic diversity of bacteria. Greater genetic diversity increases the chance that some bacteria will survive environmental change, such as the change

that takes place when antibiotics are introduced. Scientists have observed that bacterial DNA is occasionally altered by mutation, further increasing diversity.

Bacteria have additional methods of exchanging genes. Sometimes bacterial cells take up DNA from dead cells of the same or a closely related species. The process by which bacterial cells pick up and incorporate DNA from dead bacterial cells is called transformation. As you read in Chapter 7, this process helped Griffith discover some properties of DNA.

CHECKPOINT 14.4

1. What are the structural characteristics of monerans?
2. What adaptations enable monerans to survive and reproduce?
3. **Critical Thinking** How does the outcome of endospore formation differ from that of binary fission and conjugation?

Build on What You Know

4. What structures might you find in a eukaryotic cell but not in a prokaryotic cell? *(Need to jog your memory? Revisit relevant concepts in Chapter 3, Section 3.2.)*

Does Temperature Affect Bacterial Growth?

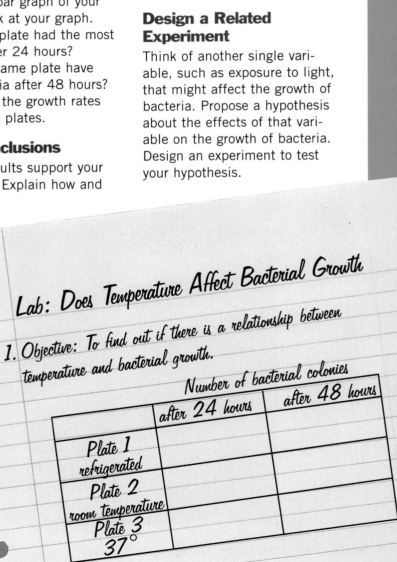

WHAT YOU WILL DO Observe and graph the growth of bacterial colonies at three different temperatures

SKILLS YOU WILL USE Observing, controlling variables, collecting and recording data

WHAT YOU WILL NEED Three sterile agar plates (per group of three students), a clock, a hand lens

Propose a Hypothesis

Propose a hypothesis about the effects of temperature on the growth of bacteria.

Conduct Your Experiment

1 Look at the sterile agar plates through the hand lens. They should appear clean with no bacterial growth. Number the plates from 1 to 3.
Caution: Wash your hands with warm water and soap before and after handling the agar plates.
2 Remove the covers from the three plates and expose them all to the air for 20 minutes. Replace the covers.
3 Refrigerate plate 1. Leave plate 2 at room temperature. Incubate plate 3 at 37°C. Make a table listing the plate numbers with their temperature conditions and intervals for observation.
4 After 24 hours examine each plate with a hand lens. Record the numbers of bacterial colonies at 24 hours for each plate number. Return the plates to the locations described in step 3.
5 Repeat step 4.

Analyze Your Results

1 Use the data on your table to create a bar graph of your results. Look at your graph. Which agar plate had the most bacteria after 24 hours?
2 Did the same plate have more bacteria after 48 hours?
3 Describe the growth rates on the three plates.

Draw Conclusions

Did your results support your hypothesis? Explain how and why temperature affected the growth of bacteria.

Design a Related Experiment

Think of another single variable, such as exposure to light, that might affect the growth of bacteria. Propose a hypothesis about the effects of that variable on the growth of bacteria. Design an experiment to test your hypothesis.

Lab: Does Temperature Affect Bacterial Growth

1. Objective: To find out if there is a relationship between temperature and bacterial growth.

	Number of bacterial colonies	
	after 24 hours	after 48 hours
Plate 1 refrigerated		
Plate 2 room temperature		
Plate 3 37°		

14.5 Origin and Diversity of Monerans

What you'll learn

IDEAS
- To analyze the evolution and classification of monerans
- To compare and contrast methods of classifying monerans

WORDS
archaebacteria, eubacteria, aerobes, anaerobes

Bacteria blinkers

The flashlight fish produces bright blue-green light with the aid of bacteria in the pouches below its eyes. To confuse its predators, the flashlight fish can swim one way with its lights on and then swim the other way with its lights off. This bright bacterium is only one of the millions of monerans that inhabit Earth.

CLASSIFICATION OF MONERANS

Ancient and true

Until recently it has been difficult to study the evolution of monerans because their fossils yield minimal information. The techniques of molecular biology, however, have helped scientists discover a lot about the evolution of monerans. Scientists have studied the DNA, RNA, and proteins of living monerans to infer their evolutionary relationships. Based on these studies, most microbiologists divide the kingdom Monera into two groups: archaebacteria (AR-kee-bak-TEER-ee-uh) and eubacteria (YOO-bak-TEER-ee-uh). These groups are so different that some scientists consider them to be separate kingdoms.

Archaebacteria The group of monerans that are often found living in harsh environments are the **archaebacteria.** Archaebacteria can live where no other organisms can survive—in acidic hot springs, near undersea volcanic vents, and in highly salty water.

Archaebacteria are considered ancient ("archae-" means "ancient") because they probably resemble the first forms of life on Earth. Scientists think that the harsh environments in which archaebacteria now live resemble conditions that existed on Earth when life appeared.

FIGURE 14.14

Archaebacteria thrive in the extremely hot environment of Morning Glory Pool in Yellowstone National Park, Wyoming.

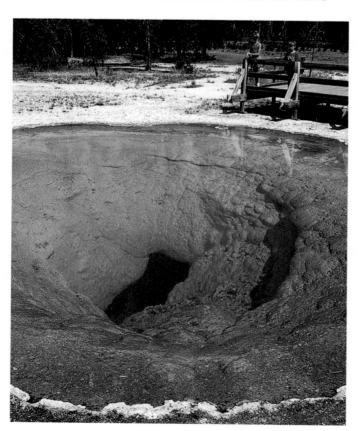

Archaebacteria can be divided into three groups, based on the environments in which they live: methanogens, thermophiles, and halophiles. Archaebacteria that live in oxygen-free environments and produce methane (CH_4) are called methanogens (METH-an-oh-jenz). Methanogens live in the digestive tracts of cows and other mammals, in swampy areas, and in sewage.

A second group of archaebacteria live in extremely hot water (60°C to 250°C). This group is called the thermophiles (THER-moh-fylz; "therm-" means "heat"). You can see one of the hot environments inhabited by thermophiles in the photo in *Figure 14.14*.

Archaebacteria that live in extremely salty conditions are called halophiles ("salt-lovers"). Halophiles have been found growing in the Great Salt Lake in Utah and in the Dead Sea—places where the water is up to ten times saltier than sea water!

Eubacteria The so-called true bacteria, **eubacteria,** include all other bacteria (the prefix "eu-" means "true"). Eubacteria live in environments much less harsh than those of archaebacteria. This group contains many types of organisms—so many, in fact, that they are difficult to classify. Using molecular biology comparisons taxonomists divide eubacteria into several subgroups, as shown in *Figure 14.16*.

FIGURE 14.15
Eubacteria are an extremely diverse group of monerans. Most Eubacteria are unicellular. *Nostoc,* a freshwater cyanobacterium, forms filaments.

FIGURE 14.16
Kingdom Monera

FIGURE 14.17
Examples of bacterial shapes: cocci are spherical, bacilli are rod-shaped, and spirilli are spirals.

OTHER WAYS TO IDENTIFY AND CLASSIFY MONERANS

Many fingerprints

Before the development of techniques in molecular biology, classification by molecular comparison was not possible. Instead, scientists classified and identified bacteria using different criteria. Among these criteria are cell shape, cell wall composition, nutrition, and respiration.

Cell shape Bacteria have various shapes. *Figure 14.17* illustrates three of the most common bacterial shapes: spheres (cocci), rods (bacilli), and spirals (spirilla). Bacteria may exist in chains (for example, streptococci) or clusters (staphylococci).

Cell wall composition The presence of a cell wall is a characteristic common to most monerans. However, the structure of that cell wall can differ. Scientists have developed a technique for identifying eubacteria based on cell wall differences. This technique, called Gram staining, was developed in 1884 by Hans Christian Gram, a Danish microbiologist. *Figure 14.18* shows how this technique reveals cell wall structure.

Gram staining identifies distinct groups of eubacteria: gram-positive and gram-negative eubacteria. Both of these groups include organisms that cause human diseases such as scarlet fever and toxic-shock syndrome. An extra lipid bilayer in gram-negative eubacteria prevents many antibiotics from entering the cell, thereby making the antibiotic ineffective. Therefore, Gram staining is important in both the identification and the treatment of infection.

Nutrition Another common method of moneran identification is based on how bacteria obtain nutrition. Organisms that cannot make their own food are known as heterotrophs. Most monerans are heterotrophs: they get energy by consuming organic molecules made by other organisms.

Organisms that can make their own food are known as autotrophs. Autotrophs that make food by using sunlight and carbon dioxide are called photoautotrophs. Many photoautotrophs, such as the cyanobacteria, contain chlorophyll, which gives them a green color. Autotrophs that make their own food by using chemicals such as ammonia or sulfur are called chemoautotrophs. The archaebacteria that inhabit the hot spring in *Figure 14.14* are chemoautotrophs.

Respiration Still another method of identifying bacteria is based on cellular respiration. Organisms that use oxygen during respiration are called

FIGURE 14.18

Gram Staining

In Gram staining, eubacteria are stained first with a purple dye, rinsed, and then stained with a red dye. Depending on the structure of their cell walls, eubacteria appear purple or red. What color are Gram-positive eubacteria after staining? Gram-negative?

Gram-positive eubacteria

Gram-negative eubacteria

FIGURE 14.19
These green cyanobacteria growing in mats (above) are photoautotrophs. An electron micrograph of a tooth (left) reveals heterotrophic bacteria.

FIGURE 14.20
Common Bacteria

1. *Methanosarcina barkeri*
2. *Desulfovibrio desulfuricans*
3. *Beggiatoa alba*
4. *Ancalochloris perfilievii*
5. *Escherichia coli*
6. *Aquaspirillum magnetotacticum*

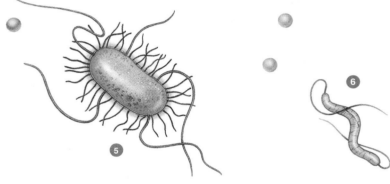

aerobes. The bacterium that causes tuberculosis is an aerobe that lives in human lungs, where it is bathed in the oxygen it needs for respiration.

Anaerobes are organisms that do not use oxygen during respiration. Anaerobes typically get energy through the process of fermentation, which you read about in Chapter 4. The anaerobic tetanus bacterium may grow in deep puncture wounds where oxygen is nearly absent.

CHECKPOINT 14.5

1. How are archaebacteria and eubacteria related?
2. Describe the different methods for identifying and classifying monerans.
3. **Critical Thinking** Where in your home would you most likely find archaebacteria?

Build on What You Know

4. According to the theory of evolution, what role did monerans play in the origin of life? *(Need to jog your memory? Revisit relevant concepts in Chapter 11, Section 11.2.)*

(Need to jog your memory? Revisit relevant concepts in Chapter 11, Section 11.2.)

LAB ZONE ## Do It!

Identify Shapes of Bacteria

You will identify the shapes of bacteria when you . . .

Try This

1 Examine under the microscope each of the three numbered slides your teacher has given you.
2 Make a rough sketch of each bacterium, and classify them as either cocci, bacilli, or spirilla.

Analyze Your Results

1 Uncover the slide labels and check to see that you identified the shapes correctly.
2 How did the appearance of the bacteria under the microscope differ? Did they vary much from the photos of cocci, bacilli, and spirilla in Figure 14.17?

14.6 Monerans in the Biosphere

What you'll learn

IDEAS
- To describe the ecological role of bacteria in the environment
- To explain how monerans affect humans

WORDS
decomposers, symbiosis

Bacteria's oil-eating debut
The Exxon *Valdez* oil spill in Alaska in 1989 yielded scientific proof that bacteria could be used to remove oil from contaminated beaches. Test plots of oil-covered beach were treated with liquid fertilizer containing bacteria; others were left untreated. Results: Oil in the treated areas degraded two to four times faster.

In the Bacteria Cafeteria

High-quality strains of fermenting bacteria are used to make Swiss cheese. The carbon dioxide emitted by the bacteria during fermentation forms the cheese's characteristic holes.

ECOLOGICAL ROLES

No life without bacteria

Although they are tiny, monerans are the most numerous individual organisms on Earth. This large kingdom has a significant impact on the biosphere. Imagine that dead organic material littered the Earth's surface and never decayed. This is just one example of what would occur without bacteria. In fact scientists say that, without bacteria, life as we know it would cease to exist in just a few weeks. Bacteria are vital to the well-being of all organisms because they recycle important chemicals in the environment.

Monerans and other organisms that break down dead organic materials are called **decomposers.** Monerans in soil and water help recycle carbon, nitrogen, and sulfur along with other chemicals needed by living things. Some species of bacteria live in the roots of plants and convert gaseous nitrogen from the air into useful nitrogen compounds. Plants and animals then use these compounds to make other nitrogen-containing compounds such as proteins. The recycling of organic materials is essential for the continuation of life on Earth.

In addition to recycling chemicals in the environment, bacteria interact closely with other organisms. Many bacteria live with organisms of other species in a type of relationship called symbiosis (SIM-bee-OH-sis). **Symbiosis** is a relationship involving direct contact between two organisms in which at least one of the partners benefits. The other partner may be helped, harmed, or remain unaffected. You share a symbiotic relationship with the bacteria in your mouth. The bacteria benefit from the environment of the mouth, but they may harm you by causing plaque and tooth decay.

The bacteria living in the rumen of a cow are also symbiotic monerans. These bacteria benefit from being provided with nutrients in a warm, protective environment. The cow also benefits because the bacteria in its digestive tract break down the cellulose in plants the cow has eaten. This process aids digestion and makes nutrients available to the cow.

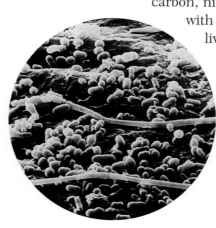

FIGURE 14.21
This scanning electron micrograph shows underarm bacteria. It is with you always, even right after a shower!

DISEASES CAUSED BY MONERANS

Bacteria can kill

Although bacteria play an important role in recycling chemicals, not all species of bacteria are helpful. Disease-causing bacteria do exist and can be deadly to humans and other organisms. Harmful bacteria may enter our bodies from the air, food, and water. They may also invade through body openings such as the nose or through breaks in the skin. Other bacteria live in our bodies and only cause illness when the body's defenses have been weakened.

Scientists began to understand the connection between bacteria and disease in the 1800s. Robert Koch, a German physician, was the first to connect diseases with specific bacteria when he identified two species of bacteria: one responsible for tuberculosis and one responsible for anthrax. Tuberculosis is a disease that usually affects humans; anthrax is a disease that usually affects livestock. The table in *Figure 14.22* provides facts about some other bacterial diseases. The symptoms of bacterial infection range from fevers and sore throats to stomach cramps and rashes.

Antibiotics that kill harmful bacteria can cure many bacterial diseases when the drugs are used as prescribed. Application of antibiotic ointment to any cuts in the skin is a good precaution against possible bacterial infection.

IN THE COMMUNITY
Beefing Up Inspections

Although beef and poultry are inspected for bacterial contamination, sometimes these foods are stored or cooked improperly at home or in restaurants. As a result, people can become sick after ingesting contaminated beef and poultry. Contact your local or state board of health to request information on safe food-handling techniques you can use at home. Ask specifically for information about Hazard Analysis Critical Control Point, or HACCP. Many restaurants use this system to monitor how they receive, prepare, and store foods. To learn about national inspection regulations for beef and poultry before they reach your home or a restaurant, contact the U.S. Department of Agriculture (USDA) or log on to *http://microorganisms.biosurf.com*. Ask about the newest methods being used to detect contamination—methods that do not rely on only surface inspection of meat.

FRONTIERS IN BIOLOGY
Employing bacteria

Scientists have found many ways in which to harness nature's microscopic army of bacteria. Bacteria serve several useful purposes, including helping us rid the environment of harmful substances. Bioremediation is the process of using microorganisms to help restore natural environmental conditions. For example, bacteria can be put to work at hazardous waste sites to break down harsh chemicals such as creosote and coal tar. In modern sewage treatment plants, such as the one shown in *Figure 14.23*, bacteria decompose solid and liquid waste

Some Bacterial Diseases		
Disease	**Mode of Transmission**	**Major Symptoms**
Lyme disease	through the bite of infected deer ticks	rash at bite site, headache, chills, and fatigue
Toxic strep	through mouth or skin lesions	sore throat, fever, sudden rash, or slow-healing wound
Cholera	by ingesting water contaminated by human feces	acute diarrhea, stomach cramps, and dehydration
Tetanus	through deep puncture wounds that close to air	neurological disturbances resulting in spastic paralysis

FIGURE 14.22
Lyme disease and toxic strep are readily treated with antibiotics such as penicillin and erythromycin. Both cholera and tetanus can be prevented by vaccination.

into harmless and sometimes helpful materials.

In addition to helping restore the environment, bacteria are used in the production of many foods. Bacteria ferment sugar in the making of cheese, yogurt, some beverages, and vinegar.

Bacteria can also be used in manufacturing products that we use. They can help extract minerals from mined ores, including gold and copper. Other bacteria are involved in making products such as flushless toilets, biodegradable plastics, and pharmaceuticals.

Bacteria also have many applications in medicine. Molecular biologists insert human genes into bacteria and use the altered bacteria to make important medical products. For example, a strain of *E. coli* bacteria has been genetically engineered to produce human insulin, which must be taken by people with some forms of diabetes. Scientists have genetically

FIGURE 14.24
Proteins extracted from *Pseudomonas syringae* bacteria are mixed with water, causing the water molecules to crystallize at higher temperatures, and aiding in snowmaking.

engineered bacteria to produce human proteins that can be used to treat growth defects, heart attacks, burns, ulcers, and possibly cancer.

CHECKPOINT 14.6

1. What roles do monerans play in the environment?
2. Describe five ways in which humans are affected by monerans.
3. **Critical Thinking** Compare the roles and effects of viruses and monerans in the environment.

Build on What You Know

4. Most monerans are decomposers, helping to recycle materials, including organic molecules. How are chemical reactions involved in the formation of organic molecules? *(Need to jog your memory? Revisit relevant concepts in Chapter 2, Section 2.3.)*

FIGURE 14.23
At water-treatement plants, such as the one in Oakland, California, (below, right) water being purified is sprayed over a rock bed coated with aerobic bacteria and fungi. As the water seeps through the treated rock bed, the bacteria help to cleanse it of harmful pollutants.

Rotating spray arm

Liquid wastes

Outflow

What are monerans?

Chapter 14 Review

14.1–14.3 Viruses are particles that depend on living things to replicate.
14.4–14.6 Monerans are microscopic organisms that lack a membrane-bound nucleus and membrane-bound organelles.

Sum It Up

Use the following summary to review the main concepts in this chapter.

14.1 Characteristics of Viruses

- A virus has a core of nucleic acid—either DNA or RNA (never both)—and a protective capsid.
- A virus can be active and replicate only inside a host cell.
- Viruses can replicate immediately (lytic cycle) or after a period of time (lysogenic cycle).

14.2 Origin and Diversity of Viruses

- Viruses probably appeared after cells evolved.
- Viruses can be divided into groups based on the type of nucleic acid they contain, their shape, and the type of host they infect.
- Retroviruses, unlike any other organisms, make DNA from RNA.

14.3 Viruses in the Biosphere

- Viruses can affect plants and animals, including humans.
- Viruses may invade and destroy host cells.
- Viruses are used in making vaccines, in genetic engineering, and in pest control.

14.4 Characteristics of Monerans

- Monerans are usually unicellular prokaryotes.
- Monerans reproduce by binary fission or conjugation.
- Monerans can survive harsh conditions by forming endospores.

14.5 Origin and Diversity of Monerans

- Monerans probably resemble the first life forms on Earth.
- The kingdom Monera is composed of archaebacteria and eubacteria.
- Monerans can be identified by cell wall structure, shape, metabolism, or respiration.

14.6 Monerans in the Biosphere

- Monerans are vital as decomposers.
- Many monerans live in symbiotic relationships.
- Some monerans cause disease.
- Humans use bacteria in many ways.

Use Terms and Concepts

Use each of the following words or terms in a complete sentence. If you need to review a meaning, turn to the page indicated.

virus (p. 326)
capsid (p. 326)
envelope (p. 327)
host (p. 327)
lytic cycle (p. 328)
lysogenic cycle (p. 328)
prophage (p. 328)

retrovirus (p. 332)
viroid (p. 333)
prion (p. 333)
vaccination (p. 335)
plasmids (p. 336)
endospores (p. 337)
binary fission (p. 338)

conjugation (p. 338)
archaebacteria (p. 340)
eubacteria (p. 341)
aerobes (p. 343)
anaerobes (p. 343)
decomposers (p. 344)
symbiosis (p. 344)

Use Your Word Power

COMPLETION Write the word or phrase that completes each statement.

1. A(n) _____ is the viral cover of animal viruses.

2. A(n) _____ is an organism whose organelles are used by a virus to replicate.

3. The _____ begins with the virus inserting its DNA into the host cell DNA.

4. A(n) _____ is a single strand of pure RNA.

5. Bacteria most commonly reproduce by _____ .

6. Small circular DNA molecules in bacteria are called _____ .

7. The dehydrated cells that enable bacteria to resist unfavorable conditions are called

    _____ .

8. _____ are monerans that usually live in harsh environments.

9. Organisms that need oxygen to respire are called _____ .

10. Organisms that do not use oxygen to respire are called _____ .

11. _____ are bacteria and other organisms that break down dead organic material.

12. A relationship called _____ may help, harm, or have no affect on an organism.

TRUE-FALSE Write true if the statement is true. If the statement is false, replace the underlined word(s) to make the statement true.

13. A prion is an infectious particle that is associated with mad cow disease.

14. A bacteriophage is a virus that infects bacteria.

15. A plasmid produces nucleic acid in the reverse of the usual process.

16. The protein coat around the core of a virus is a capsid.

17. During the lysogenic cycle of a viral infection, a host cell is destroyed.

18. A prophage is a segment of viral DNA that is inserted in the DNA of a bacterium.

19. Viruses _____ .

20. Binary fission is a means for some bacteria to exchange genetic material.

21. Eubacteria are monerans that live in conditions that most closely resemble ancient Earth.

Show What You Know

22. Compare the relative size and structure of a virus and a cell.

23. Why do biologists hypothesize that cells evolved before viruses?

24. Explain how vaccines prevent diseases.

25. Name and describe three disorders caused by a virus and three caused by a bacterium.

26. **Make a Concept Map** Complete the concept map by adding the following terms: viruses, bacteria, cell walls, replication, binary fission, conjugation.

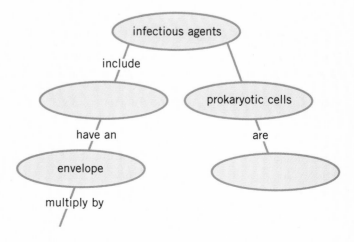

Take It Further

27. Making a Generalization If you were asked your view on whether or not viruses are alive, what would you reply, and how would you support your conclusion?

28. Analyzing Data Proteins in food are digested by enzymes and secretions in the stomach and small intestine. If you swallow a virus, which has a protein coat, what effect do you think the enzymes and secretions will have on the virus?

29. Designing an Experiment Develop an experiment to test the hypothesis that contact of an agar plate with a finger results in more bacterial growth than the exposure of the plate to classroom air.

30. Interpreting a Graph The graph below shows the result of an experiment with bacterial cells. At the start of the experiment, one group of bacterial cells was infected by a virus and the other group was not. The two curves on the graph indicate the number of living cells in each group. What effect did the virus have on the bacterial cells? Explain your answer.

Effect of Viral Infection on Bacterial Growth

Number of Living Bacterial Cells (millions) vs. Time (hours)

Infected
Not Infected

Consider the Issues

31. Who Gets the First Shot? How do you think new experimental vaccines should be tested? In some cases, people at high risk for contracting a certain disease, such as the flu, volunteer to be vaccinated with newly developed vaccines. Explain your ideas.

32. Releasing Altered Genes A bacterium that lives in the corn ear worm—a destructive crop pest—has been genetically altered to kill the worm. Many people think that altered bacteria should be sprayed on crops that are infested with the worm. Others argue that the altered organism should not be released into the environment. What reasons might they give?

Make New Connections

33. Biology and Art Assume that there has been a recent outbreak of rabies, which infects squirrels, skunks, and raccoons in your community. Create a poster to alert people to this virus and to show commonsense steps people can take to avoid infection.

34. Biology and the Community Investigate local resources for ensuring that people and pets receive adequate vaccinations. Find out what the medical guidelines are for vaccination.

FAST–FORWARD TO CHAPTER 15

Monerans are prokaryotes.
Protists, which you will read about in
Chapter 15, are eukaryotes.
Abundant and diverse, they range
from microscopic
amebas to giant
kelps.

You can find out more about protists by exploring the following Internet address:

http://microorganisms.biosurf.com

In this chapter . . .

FEATURES

Everyday Biology
- Don't Drink the Water!
- Is There Algae in Your Sundae?

In the Community
A Protist Investigation

 Frontiers in Biology
Medicine vs. Malaria

LAB ZONES

Discover It!
- The Protist Search

Do It!
- Can You Find Protists in Pond Water?

Think About It!
- Protozoan Excretion

Investigate It!
- Observing Protist Responses to Light

YELLOW BLOBS OOZE OVER SUBURBS

Discover It!

The Protist Search

You need an abrasive household cleaning product, a toothpaste carton, an empty ice cream container, and a dictionary

1. Examine the list of ingredients on each household product, carton, or container.
2. List the ingredients that contain any form of the words *diatom, silica, carrageenan, algin,* or *agar.* Look up the names of these ingredients in the dictionary. All of these words indicate the presence of a protist.

Protists exist nearly everywhere on Earth where there is moisture. As you read this chapter, you will find out more about slime molds such as the type in the story on this page. You will also learn about the sources of the protists that you discovered in household products.

In the heat of the summer of 1973, a weird phenomenon occurred in suburban backyards near Dallas, Boston, and on Long Island. Torn between alarm and fascination, residents watched in bewilderment as strange, slithering, yellow blobs moved across their lawns and sometimes onto their porches. Armed with their garden hoses, these suburbanites soon discovered that blasting the moving blobs with water broke them apart, but the pieces continued to crawl and grow. Were they alien invaders? Could they be stopped?

Scientists soon assured the panicked public that the mysterious yellow blobs were harmless plasmodia—slime molds in the crawling stage of their life cycle. Environmental conditions that included a rainy spring had created prime conditions for the slime molds to grow, and now they were moving in search of food. Slime molds are just one of the amazingly diverse types of living organisms called protists.

WRITE ABOUT IT!

In your science journal, describe an experience you have had that involved a seaweed or a mold. How did the seaweed or mold look and feel? Where did you find it— in a fish tank? In the bathroom? In a pool? At the beach? Use as many adjectives as you can to describe the seaweed or mold.

15.1 Characteristics of Protists

What you'll learn

IDEAS

• To compare prokaryotic and eukaryotic cells

• To explain how protists are classified

An undersea forest of protists

Like trees in a forest, giant kelp are large plantlike protists that form a fertile ecosystem in cold coastal waters. Kelp beds, which sometimes stretch from the seafloor to the water's surface, provide food and shelter for many marine plant and animal species.

THE STRUCTURE OF PROTISTS

Leftovers share few characteristics

Protists live wherever there is water—in oceans, ponds, mud puddles, on the surface of snow, and even inside other organisms. The variety of protists is amazing. Some are plantlike organisms, others are animal-like. Still others are decomposers. A few are even parasites. Protists range in size from microscopic algae to giant seaweeds. The shapes of protists include bells, stars, snowflakes, and pincushions.

The only characteristic common to protists is that they are all eukaryotic organisms. As you may recall from Chapter 3, eukaryotic cells have membrane-bound nuclei and membrane-bound organelles. *Figure 15.1* illustrates the main differences between a typical eukaryotic and prokaryotic cell.

FIGURE 15.1

Comparison of Prokaryotic and Eukaryotic Cells

How do the structure and size of this prokaryotic cell and eukaryotic cell compare?

Prokaryote (Moneran)
- Cell membrane
- Chromosome
- Ribosome

Eukaryote (Includes Protists)
- Mitochondrion
- Cell membrane
- Nucleus
- Nuclear membrane
- Endoplasmic reticulum with ribosomes

10 μm   100 μm (μm = micrometer)

FIGURE 15.2

Kingdom Protista

Protists can be organized into three groups based on their nutritional requirements: animal-like, plantlike, and funguslike.

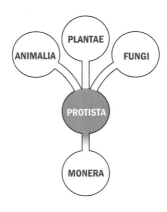

ORIGIN AND DIVERSITY OF PROTISTS

Very old and varied

The first eukaryotes are thought to have evolved about 1.5 billion years ago. As you learned in Chapter 11, eukaryotes may have formed from a symbiotic relationship among prokaryotes. The membrane-bound organelles in eukaryotic cells may have once been prokaryotic cells. Can you visualize how the organelles of the eukaryotic cell in *Figure 15.1* may have resulted from small prokaryotic cells living inside a larger prokaryotic cell? The early eukaryotes may be ancestors of the first unicellular protists.

Protists can also be multicellular. How, then, did multicellular protists arise? Scientists hypothesize that as the first eukaryotic cells increased in number, the cells may have assembled to form colonies. (A colony is a group of similar organisms living and growing together.) Over time, the cells of organisms in colonies may have developed specialized functions that increased the success of that colony. For example, some of the cells may have become specialized for reproduction, while others may have been useful in anchoring the colony at a single location. These specialized colonies may represent the ancestors of multicellular protists such as kelp.

EVERYDAY BIOLOGY

Don't Drink the Water!

When you are hiking, be sure not to quench your thirst in streams, ponds, or lakes—even if they look clear and clean. Unseen protists in the water can cause serious illness in humans.

Can You Find Protists in Pond Water?

Observing protists first-hand gives you a better idea of how they move and how plentiful and varied they are. You can do this when you . . .

Try This

1 Bring a small, fresh sample of pond water to class.
2 Use a toothpick to spread a circle of methyl cellulose on a slide, then place a drop of pond water on the slide. Use a coverslip.
3 Use a microscope to examine the pond water under low power. Sketch the organisms you see, and record how they move.

Analyze Your Results

1 How many different organisms did you observe?
2 Compare the organisms you observed with those in Figure 15.3. Are any of them similar? Are any of them different?

The diversity of protists reflects several significant evolutionary developments. As you can see in *Figure 15.3*, these developments include variety in the size, shape, and color of protists. This diversity has made it difficult for scientists to classify protists. Some biologists suggest that 20 new kingdoms would need to be created to account for the diversity among protists.

Although it is not based on evolutionary history, one popular classification system divides the protists into three groups based on the way they obtain nutrition—animal-like, plantlike, and funguslike protists. Animal-like protists are heterotrophs; plantlike protists are autotrophs; and funguslike protists are mostly decomposers, heterotrophs that feed on dead organic matter.

FIGURE 15.3
Note the variety of sizes and shapes among these protists found in drops of pond water.

CHECKPOINT 15.1

1. What are the differences between a prokaryotic and eukaryotic cell?
2. Explain the classification of protists.
3. Critical Thinking Why is it difficult to develop a system of classification for protists?

Build on What You Know

4. What is the difference between an autotroph and a heterotroph? *(Need to jog your memory? Revisit relevant concepts in Chapter 4, Section 4.1.)*

What are protists?

15.2 Animal-like Protists— Protozoans

Cliff-building protists?
It may be difficult to believe, but the enormous White Cliffs of Dover on the southeastern coast of England were made from animal-like protists. The deposits of lime-stone that form the cliffs are the hard outer shells of dead protists that have accumulated over many centuries.

What you'll learn

IDEAS
• To describe common characteristics of protozoans
• To compare diverse protozoans

WORDS
protozoan, pseudopods, flagella, cilia

CHARACTERISTICS AND DIVERSITY OF PROTOZOANS

Hop, skip, or jump

When you think about the characteristics that are common to animals, you may recognize that all animals are heterotrophs—they consume other organisms for food. A protist with the animal-like characteristic of heterotrophy is called a **protozoan.** Protozoans differ from animals in that they are unicellular and do not have specialized tissues, organs, or organ systems that carry out life functions.

Protozoans are a very diverse group of organisms. They are classified into four groups according to how they move. These groups are the sarcodinians, zooflagellates, ciliophorans, and sporozoans.

Sarcodinians You may have seen science fiction films in which an oozing blob engulfs everything in its path. Some protozoans move in a similar flowing manner and are called sarcodinians—organisms that move by extending lobes of cytoplasm.

Some sarcodinians are surrounded by hard shells. These sarcodinians move by extending lobes of cytoplasm through

holes in their shells. Two types of shelled sarcodinians are foraminiferans and radiolarians. These are shown in *Figure 15.4.* The shells of foraminiferans are part of White Cliffs of Dover, which you read about above.

FIGURE 15.4
The radiolarians (below) and the foraminiferan (right) are sarcodinians with hard shells made of calcium carbonate and silica.

Pseudopod
Ameba

FIGURE 15.5

The Movement of Protozoans

Sarcodinians

An ameba stretches its cell membrane into a lobe of cytoplasm and anchors the lobe at its tip. Cytoplasm then flows into the pseudopod, and the ameba "creeps forward."

Flagella
Trichonympha

Other sarcodinians, like the ameba, do not have shells. An ameba extends lobes of cytoplasm called **pseudopods** (SOO-doh-pahdz) to move and obtain food. "Pseudo-" means "false," and "-pod" means "foot." Because it constantly extends and retracts its pseudopods, an ameba has no definite shape. How many pseudopods do you see in the ameba shown in *Figure 15.5*?

An ameba, like many protists, has an adaptation that enables it to survive harsh conditions. When the environment is unfavorable, an

Zooflagellates

Zooflagellates move by means of flagella. How would the motion of these flagella affect the way the protozoan moves?

ameba becomes a hard cyst. In the cyst state, an ameba can withstand drought, heat, famine, or ingestion by other organisms. When people ingest food or water that contains amebic cysts, they may become infected with parasitic amebas. For example, amebic dysentery is a parasitic infection transmitted by contaminated water.

Zooflagellates Some protozoans use **flagella**—whiplike structures that aid in movement. Protozoans that use flagella are called zooflagellates.

Zooflagellates use flagella in a variety of ways. Some whip their flagella to move in a relatively straight path. Others use their flagella to create currents that spin them through the water.

LAB ZONE Think About It!

Protozoan Excretion

Water constantly enters many protozoan cells by osmosis. These protozoans have contractile vacuoles to get rid of excess water. Water is collected in the vacuole. When the vacuole reaches a certain size, it moves to the cell surface and contracts, expelling the water through a temporary opening in the cell membrane.

Analyze the Information

1 Most marine protozoans have no contractile vacuoles. Can you propose a hypothesis to explain why this is?

2 What would happen to a protozoan that was unable to expel excess water?

Ciliophorans

Ciliophorans are covered with short, hairlike projections called cilia. How do cilia differ from flagella?

Paramecium

Cilia

Power stroke: forward movement

Recovery stroke: no forward movement

Plasmodium in a blood cell

Sporozoans

The red blood cell above has been invaded by a sporozoan parasite.

Some zooflagellates inhabit other organisms in long-term, symbiotic relationships. In *Figure 15.5* you see *Trichonympha*, a zooflagellate that lives in the gut of a termite. *Trichonympha* digests the cellulose in the wood that the termite eats. In return, *Trichonympha* releases nutrients that the termite can use, allowing the termite to benefit from the relationship.

Ciliophorans The ciliophorans (sil-ee-oh-FOR-unz), or ciliates, are the most numerous and diverse group of protozoans. Ciliates are protozoans that are covered with cilia. **Cilia** are short, hairlike projections used for movement. Look carefully at *Figure 15.5* and notice the cilia of a *Paramecium*. A paramecium's cilia move in unison like boat oars as they propel the cell through water. In some other ciliates, the cilia may be shaped like teeth, paddles, or feet.

Most ciliates live in freshwater habitats and, like the majority of protozoans, can form cysts to survive unfavorable environments. Most ciliates are also harmless, but a few are parasitic and can harm their host.

Sporozoans Some parasitic protozoans are called sporozoans. Despite their name, sporozoans do not form true spores the way bacteria and some other protists do. Sporozoans are characterized by the absence of structures used for movement.

The life cycles of sporozoans are complex and include both sexual and asexual phases. Sporozoan life cycles often involve more than one host. For example, in section 15.5 you will see how the sporozoan *Plasmodium* infects both mosquitos and humans, causing human malaria.

CHECKPOINT 15.2

1. What characteristics are common to protozoans?

2. Describe the four groups of protozoans.

3. Critical Thinking How can parasitic sporozoans move from one host to another if they do not have structures for movement?

Build on What You Know

4. Compare endospores in monerans with cysts and spores in protists. *(Need to jog your memory? Revisit relevant concepts in Chapter 14, Section 14.4.)*

Kingdom: Protista

Category: Protozoa

Phyla:
Sarcodina
Zooflagellata
Ciliophora
Sporozoa

15.3 Plantlike Protists—Algae

What you'll learn

IDEAS

• To describe the characteristics of plantlike protists

• To compare unicellular and multicellular algae

WORDS

algae, alternation of generations

A long dark snake in the Pacific
When sailors reported seeing something that looked like a dark snake about 150 kilometers (km) north of the equator, people thought they had been at sea too long. But images taken from the space shuttle also showed it. In the photo at the right, the dark line under the shuttle's wing is dense algae growth along the boundary between two ocean currents.

CHARACTERISTICS OF ALGAE

Is it easy being green?

Did you see any green organisms when you looked at pond water through the microscope? Most of those green organisms were probably plantlike protists. Some protists are considered plantlike because they perform photosynthesis.

Protists that perform photosynthesis are called **algae** (singular: *alga*). Like most plants, algae contain chlorophyll and produce food and oxygen as a result of photosynthesis. Unlike plants, most algae do not contain specialized tissues or organs.

As with other protists, the evolutionary origins of algae are not very well documented in the fossil record. Consequently, algae have been classified based on differences in their structures. One way to organize algae for study is to divide them into two groups: unicellular and multicellular.

UNICELLULAR ALGAE

Making it on their own

Unicellular, or single-celled, algae include dinoflagellates, diatoms, and euglenoids. Important differences between these organisms include their outer covering and means of movement. Dinoflagellates are covered with cellulose plates, diatoms are covered with silica (glass) shells, and euglenoids have no rigid cell wall. Euglenoids and dinoflagellates use flagella for movement, while diatoms secrete substances for movement. Dinoflagellates and diatoms are among the most numerous algae in the oceans, whereas euglenoids are common in fresh water.

Dinoflagellates Algae with two flagella that beat to spin their cell in corkscrew fashion through the water are called dinoflagellates. With the exception of some that live with coral on reefs, all dinoflagellates have flagella. Cellulose plates that cover each dinoflagellate give the organism its unique shape.

FIGURE 15.6
Dinoflagellates
Gonyaulax (left) can form toxic "red tide." The eight organisms (below) are *Ceratium*, a colonial chain-forming dinoflagellate.

Flagellum

Gonyaulax

Ceratium

FIGURE 15.7
Diatoms

A bucket of water scooped from an ocean may contain millions of these microscopic algae. How does a diatom move material into and out of its cell?

Kingdom: Protista
Category: Algae
Phyla:
Dinoflagellata
Bacillariophyta
Euglenophyta
Chlorophyta
Rhodophyta
Phaeophyta

The majority of dinoflagellates grow in saltwater habitats. While most dinoflagellates are free-living, some have symbiotic relationships with jellyfish, sea anemones, coral, and other organisms that live near coral reefs. Symbiotic dinoflagellates, which lack flagella, supply nutrients to the animals in which they live.

Diatoms The snowflakelike organisms in *Figure 15.7* are unicellular algae called diatoms. Diatoms have glasslike cell walls containing silica. The walls have two parts that fit together like a box and lid. Pores in the cell walls allow material to pass into and out of the diatom. Diatoms have thousands of different shapes and patterns. Many diatoms float in water—probably because they contain oil, which is less dense than water. Diatoms are among the most abundant organisms in the oceans.

Euglenoids Organisms similar to the euglena shown in *Figure 15.8* are called euglenoids. Euglenoids are difficult to classify because they resemble both algae and protozoans. Some biologists classify organisms such as euglena as protozoans because they lack rigid cell walls and they move using

flagella. However, taxonomists have traditionally classified euglenoids as algae because they have chloroplasts and perform photosynthesis.

MULTICELLULAR ALGAE

A cooperative venture

Multicellular algae have specialized structures that resemble the parts of plants. Once considered plants because they have chloroplasts, multicellular algae are now classified as protists

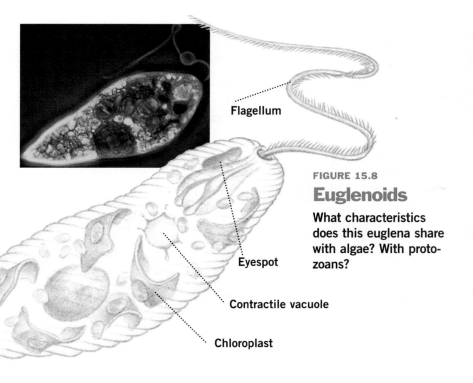

Flagellum

Eyespot

Contractile vacuole

Chloroplast

FIGURE 15.8
Euglenoids

What characteristics does this euglena share with algae? With protozoans?

Chlamydomonas

Volvox

Ulva

FIGURE 15.9

Green algae: unicellular (top), colonial (center), and multicellular (bottom)

because few of them have true tissues, and their reproductive methods are more like those of protists than of plants. Multicellular algae are classified by color, which is determined by the type of pigment in their cells.

Green algae Organisms classified as green algae, the Chlorophyta, are protists that have the pigment called chlorophyll *b* as a major component in their cells. The composition of the cell wall of green algae and the structure of their chloroplasts most closely resemble those of plants.

In *Figure 15*.9 you can see some diverse representatives of green algae. Some green algae are unicellular. One example is *Chlamydomonas*, which grows abundantly in ponds and moist soil. Other green algae, such as *Volvox*, live in colonies that may include several thousand cells. Some multicellular green algae, such as *Ulva*, are made of flat, leaflike sheets of cells. Other multicellular algae grow as filaments with cells linked end to end.

Most green algae live in fresh water or in moist soil. Some types of green algae, such as *Ulva*, live in the oceans. Many green algae live in symbiotic relationships with other organisms. For example, lichens result from symbiotic relationships between green algae and fungi.

Red algae Most red algae, called Rhodophyta, grow in warm, saltwater habitats. Although some red algae live near the ocean surface, others dwell as deep as 260 meters (m), nearly 26 stories beneath the surface. At these depths, few wavelengths of light are available for photosynthesis. However, red algae contain accessory pigments that enable them to use the available wavelengths of light to perform photosynthesis.

Red algae respond to reduced light by adjusting the ratio of the accessory pigments they produce. An accessory pigment that produces a reddish color gives members of this group their name. Depending on the presence of other pigments, red algae can also appear green, orange, or almost black.

Brown algae The Phaeophyta, or brown algae, are multicellular and grow mostly in cool saltwater habitats. This group includes the largest organisms in the kingdom Protista, the giant kelps. Giant kelps can grow up to

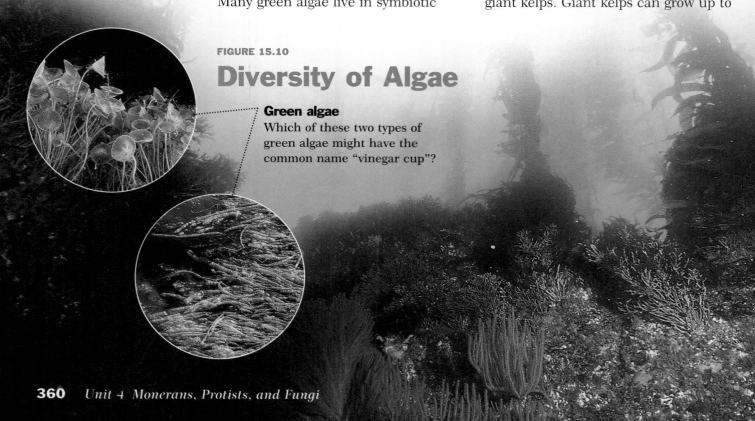

FIGURE 15.10

Diversity of Algae

Green algae
Which of these two types of green algae might have the common name "vinegar cup"?

FIGURE 15.11

Alternation of Generations

Some algae exhibit a complex life cycle, such as that of *Ulva.* Compare the gametophyte and sporophyte stages. How does the cycle alternate between haploid and diploid?

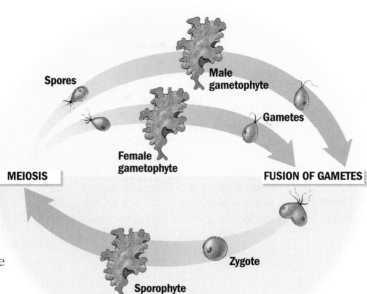

Haploid

Diploid

100 m long and are found in deep water beyond the intertidal zone. Like land plants, brown algae have some specialized parts. For example, the giant kelp has specialized air bladders, which act as life jackets and cause the leaflike portion of the kelp to float near the surface, where it can absorb sunlight for photosynthesis.

Some multicellular algae have complex life cycles that alternate between a spore-producing stage called the sporophyte generation and a gamete-producing stage called the gametophyte generation. This type of life cycle is called **alternation of generations.** You can see the steps in the life cycle of algae called *Ulva* in *Figure 15.11.* In *Ulva,* both the sporophyte and gametophyte generations look the same. In other algal life cycles, the sporophyte and gametophyte generations may look different.

CHECKPOINT 15.3

1. What are the characteristics of algae?

2. What are the differences and similarities between unicellular and multicellular algae?

3. Critical Thinking Make a chart to compare the characteristics of members of the algae phyla.

Build on What You Know

4. What are the reactants and products of photosynthesis? Where might algae get photosynthetic reactants? *(Need to jog your memory? Revisit relevant concepts, in Chapter 4, Section 4.2.)*

Red algae
This red alga is a frequent inhabitant of cool-water reef communities.

Brown algae
This common brown alga is *Macrocystis pyrifera.* Does its name seem to fit its appearance?

15.4 Funguslike Protists— Molds

IDEAS

• To describe the structural and functional characteristics of funguslike protists

• To distinguish between the three groups of funguslike protists

WORDS

mold, plasmodium

Kingdom: Protista
Category: Molds
Phyla:
Myxomycota
Acrasiomycota
Oomycota

Mold or movie star?
The oozing mass grows larger as it moves ever so silently and slowly along the ground, devouring every microorganism in its path. This may sound like a scene from a science fiction movie, but it is really a description of one of the most intriguing of the funguslike protists—the slime mold.

CHARACTERISTICS OF MOLDS

Nature's dustbusters

Most funguslike protists are small and live in damp or watery places, helping to break down dead organic matter. A protist that acts as a decomposer is known as a **mold.**

Most taxonomists divide the molds into three groups: plasmodial slime molds, cellular slime molds, and water molds. Slime molds are named for their most obvious characteristics—a shiny, wet appearance and a texture like gelatin. Water molds are funguslike protists that live mostly in the water.

Plasmodial slime molds The organism in *Figure 15.12* is a plasmodial slime mold. In the feeding stage of its life cycle it is called a **plasmodium.** A plasmodium can weigh as much as 50 grams (g) and grow as large as the palm of a human hand. However, regardless of its size, a plasmodium is a single cell with many nuclei.

When environmental conditions become unfavorable a plasmodium either creeps somewhere else, or it enters a different stage of its life cycle. The plasmodium does this by forming a structure called a fruiting body. The fruiting body produces spores, which are then distributed by wind and animals. Spores can remain dormant for many years. When conditions are favorable, the spore releases haploid gametes that fuse to form a diploid zygote. This diploid zygote then develops into a new plasmodium.

FIGURE 15.12
This plasmodium is unicellular but has many nuclei. It feeds on bacteria and other microorganisms as it creeps along a surface. How does this protist differ from protozoans?

Cellular slime molds Like the plasmodial slime mold, a cellular slime mold alternates between a spore-producing, fruiting body form and an amebalike feeding form. In *Figure 15.13* you can see the different forms of a cellular slime mold. The feeding stage of a cellular slime mold consists of small, single cells that move, engulf, and ingest food much as amebas do. These cells live in fresh water, in damp soil, or on decaying plant matter.

When food runs low or water becomes scarce, the cells secrete a chemical attractant that causes nearby mold cells to clump together to form a pseudoplasmodium. A pseudoplasmodium is a clump of cells that produces fruiting bodies. The fruiting bodies then produce spores. Unlike a true plasmodium, however, the cells of a pseudoplasmodium are independent entities. Also, the cells of a pseudoplasmodium are haploid; a true plasmodial cell is diploid.

Water molds You may have observed a scene like that shown in *Figure 15.14* in real life. The cottonlike fluff is actually an organism called a water mold. Water molds are decomposers in freshwater ecosystems. Some water molds are parasitic and attack the injured skin or gill tissues of fishes. A few water molds, such as white rusts and downy mildews, are parasites of certain land plants.

White rusts and downy mildews used to be classified as fungi but are now considered to be protists for several reasons. One reason is that true fungi have cell walls that contain chitin, whereas the water molds have cell walls that are mostly cellulose. Moreover, asexual reproduction in the water molds produces spores with flagella. True fungi produce spores without flagella.

FIGURE 15.14
This water mold is decomposing a salamander.

CHECKPOINT 15.4

1. How are funguslike protists structurally and functionally alike?

2. What are the differences between the three groups of funguslike protists?

3. Critical Thinking What advantages do slime molds gain by producing fruiting bodies when food is scarce?

Build on What You Know

4. Compare the roles of protists and monerans as decomposers. How do the two groups differ? *(Need to jog your memory? Revisit relevant concepts, in Chapter 14, Section 14.6.)*

FIGURE 15.13
What three life stages of a cellular slime mold are shown in these images of the slime mold *Dictyostelium*?

How are protists classified? **?**

Observing Protist Responses to Light

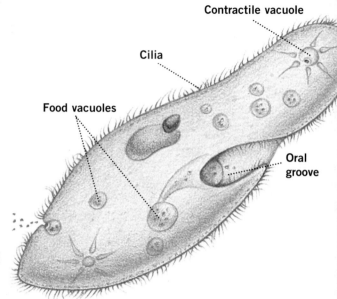

Contractile vacuole

Cilia

Food vacuoles

Oral groove

WHAT YOU WILL DO Observe and compare the responses of two different protists to light

SKILLS YOU WILL USE Predicting, observing, collecting and recording data

WHAT YOU WILL NEED Microscope, microscope slides, toothpick, methyl cellulose, *Paramecium* and *Euglena* cultures, forceps, metric ruler, index card

Propose a Hypothesis

Formulate a hypothesis about what you think will happen when two different protists—paramecia and euglena—are exposed to light.

Conduct Your Experiment

1 Use a toothpick to spread a small circle of methyl cellulose on the center of a slide. Place a drop of paramecium culture in the ring of methyl cellulose.

Using forceps, gently lower a coverslip over the culture.
2 Use the low power lens of a microscope to locate several paramecia. Focus on one paramecium with the high power lens. Examine its characteristics under high power. Record your observations and draw a paramecium.
3 Cut an index card to the same size as a microscope slide. In the center of this strip, cut a slit that is 1.5 centimeters (cm) long and 0.2 cm wide. Slip the strip under the slide on the microscope.

4 After 5 minutes, carefully remove the strip and locate the paramecia. Record your observations in your notebook.
5 Repeat steps 1–4 using the euglena.

Analyze Your Data

1 Describe the characteristics of the two types of protists you observed.
2 Compare the characteristics of both protists.
3 Compare the response of each type of protist to light.

Draw Conclusions

Was your hypothesis correct? If not, why not? If it was incorrect, rephrase it to reflect the results of your experiment.

Design a Related Experiment

Design an experiment to test how paramecia and euglenoids respond to the concentration of salt in a solution. Begin by proposing a hypothesis. Then write out the procedure you would follow to test your hypothesis.

Lab: Observing Protist Responses to Light

Objective : To find out how paramecia and euglena respond to light

Light Conditions

	Parmecium	Euglena
light		
dark		

15.5 Protists in the Biosphere

Algae in your tank?
Imagine pulling up to a gas pump and saying, "Fill it up with algae." Well, it could happen. Scientists have considered algae as a supplement to biodiesel fuels—those made from plant oils. In addition to being plentiful, algae would be cleaner than existing fuels. So someday, you may be pumping protists like the ones these swans are swimming through.

What you'll learn

IDEAS
- To describe the ecological roles of protists
- To explain diseases caused by protists and the importance of protists to humans

WORD
plankton

ECOLOGICAL ROLES

Can't live without you

Algae and protozoans are two of the most numerous types of organisms in the oceans. These two groups of protists play an essential role in the lives of other aquatic organisms.

As you know, all organisms need a source of energy. As the major component of plankton, protists provide an essential food base in aquatic food chains. **Plankton** are mostly microscopic organisms that float near the surface of oceans and lakes. In *Figure 15.15* you can see a whale, which is a water-dwelling heterotroph that obtains energy directly by eating plankton. Other heterotrophs obtain energy indirectly by eating organisms that may have eaten plankton.

The algal component of plankton is called phytoplankton because the algae perform photosynthesis. Green algae, dinoflagellates, and diatoms are phytoplankton found in the oceans and freshwater lakes.

In addition to serving as a food source in aquatic environments, phytoplankton carry out more than 70 percent of Earth's photosynthesis. Recall from Chapter 4 that photosynthesis results in the production of oxygen. Algae help to maintain Earth's oxygen and carbon dioxide levels.

Protozoans, too, play an important ecological role. Many protozoans are predators of bacteria and other organisms. In many environments, protozoans help keep the numbers of bacteria in balance with other organisms. Other protozoans and molds feed on dead organisms and thereby play an important role in recycling chemicals in the environment.

FIGURE 15.15
Some large mammals, such as baleen whales, feed on plankton. Imagine the tremendous amount of plankton it takes to feed one humpback whale.

DISEASES CAUSED BY PROTISTS

Not so nice

Not all protists are beneficial. Some protozoans, algae, and molds cause disease. Protists may cause disease either directly or indirectly.

A protozoan called *Trypanosoma* causes the fatal disease African sleeping sickness if it infects the central nervous system cells of humans or some other animals. Another protozoan called *Giardia* causes disease when humans ingest water containing giardia cysts. Each cyst releases giardia organisms that attach to a host's intestinal lining, causing diarrhea, nausea, and fatigue.

Figure 15.16 illustrates slicks of an alga called *Gonyaulax*, which produces a toxin (poison) that can paralyze and sometimes kill humans and other animals. A gonyaulax toxin can concentrate in the shellfish that live in the same waters. Humans or other consumers who eat the contaminated

FIGURE 15.16

Red tide results from periods of rapid reproduction among protists called *Gonyaulax*.

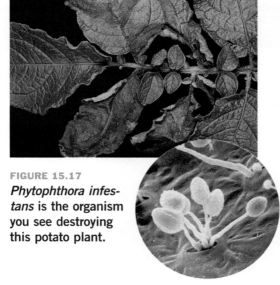

FIGURE 15.17

Phytophthora infestans is the organism you see destroying this potato plant.

shellfish may become ill from exposure to the toxin.

The funguslike protist *Phytophthora infestans* causes a potato disease called late blight, which makes potatoes inedible. Currently, the disease threatens potato crops around the world. Because the potato is a food staple in many countries, an outbreak of this disease can seriously affect a country's social, political, and economic stability. In Ireland in the mid 1800s, the disease devastated the potato crop and eventually forced more than one million Irish people to emigrate to other countries, including the United States.

Contact your state health officials to find out about illnesses in your state caused by protozoans, algae, or molds. Ask what steps, including water testing and purification, are taken by health officials to prevent the illnesses. Also contact state agricultural officials to determine if blights threaten food crops or other vegetation in your state. Find out if there are environmentally safe products that can prevent these plant diseases. Log on to *http://microorganisms.biosurf.com* to gather additional information. Design a presentation to share your investigation results with classmates.

IN THE COMMUNITY
A Protist Investigation

FIGURE 15.18

The Life Cycle of *Plasmodium*

The life cycle of the protozoan *Plasmodium* includes stages in both mosquitos and humans. *Plasmodium* protists cause malaria in humans.

Life cycle begins

1 An infected mosquito bites a healthy human. The protozoans, in the form of sporozoites, enter the body.

Inside the human

2a Inside liver cells, the sporozoites develop into cells called merozoites. Most merozoites enter red blood cells and reproduce asexually, rupturing the blood cells and causing chills and high fever.

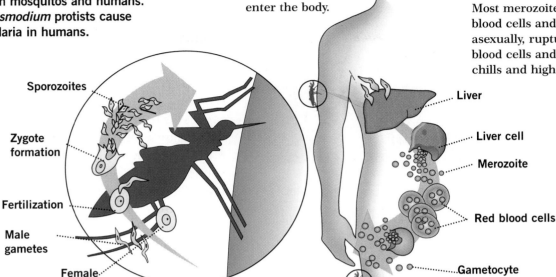

Sporozoites
Zygote formation
Fertilization
Male gametes
Female gametes

Liver
Liver cell
Merozoite
Red blood cells
Gametocyte

Inside a mosquito

4 In the digestive tract, gametocytes develop into gametes, which fuse to form a zygote. The zygote develops many sporozoites that travel to the mosquito's salivary glands.

Life cycle continues

3 A mosquito bites an infected human and picks up some gametocytes along with other blood components.

2b Some merozoites do not enter the blood cells, but remain in the blood as gametocytes.

FRONTIERS IN BIOLOGY S T S

Medicine vs. malaria

Malaria is a disease that kills several million people every year. It is spread by *Anopheles* mosquitoes. The organism that causes malaria is a parasitic protozoan called *Plasmodium*. One stage of a *Plasmodium's* life cycle occurs in the digestive tract of a mosquito. Another stage of its life cycle occurs in the liver and red blood cells of humans who have been bitten by an infected mosquito. *Figure 15.18* shows how both humans and mosquitoes host the *Plasmodium* parasite and thus spread malaria.

In spite of decades of scientific efforts to control it, malaria remains the leading cause of death worldwide for children under five. Why is it difficult to control? Part of the reason lies in the short reproductive cycle of *Anopheles*. In addition, this mosquito has acquired immunity to pesticides that were previously effective. Similarly, the *Plasmodium* protozoan multiplies rapidly in the human body and has developed a resistance to drugs. For example, the drug chloroquine is no longer effective in treating malaria. As the incidence of this disease increases, efforts to create a vaccine and new malaria-fighting drugs continue.

FIGURE 15.19

Seaweed salad (below) is just one of the foods that seaweed supplies humans. It is also harvested as a food source for animals, as well as for use in fertilizer, cosmetics, and pharmaceuticals.

HUMAN USES

Delicious protists!

How would you like a dish of seaweed for dessert? Perhaps you would prefer to drink a glass of seaweed with your meal. No? Actually you have been eating some form of algae all your life.

Three complex carbohydrates used in food products—carrageenan, agar, and algin—are extracted from seaweed. Carrageenan, a thickener and flavor-enhancer for foods, is added to many dairy products, such as milk shakes and chocolate milk. The agar taken from red algae is sometimes used to thicken soups, puddings, and cake frostings.

Some people eat seaweed for its mineral components, especially iodine. In Japan, sheets of a red algae called nori are used to wrap sushi. In *Figure 15.19* you can see farmers harvesting seaweed for use as livestock feed and crop fertilizer.

In addition to their role as a food source, protists are useful in other ways. When diatoms die, for example, their shells sink to the bottom of the sea. Over millions of years, geological processes have thrust these deposits upward to form new land. Land containing diatom shells—called diatomaceous earth—is mined and used in the manufacture of everyday products. The gritty texture of diatomaceous earth makes it useful in products such as insulation, filters, detergents and cleansers, abrasives, and polishing agents in toothpaste.

Protists are also useful as bioindicators. Their presence or absence gives some indication of the health of an ecosystem. For example, marine biologists—scientists who study ocean life—collect plankton. The kinds and numbers of protists present in the plankton are indicators of the general health of an ocean region.

CHECKPOINT 15.5

1. What is the ecological importance of protists?

2. Describe negative and positive ways in which protists affect humans.

3. Critical Thinking Do you think malaria could be transmitted by blood transfusion? Explain your answer.

Build on What You Know

4. How do parasitic protists display coevolution? *(Need to jog your memory? Revisit relevant concepts in Chapter 10, Section 10.4.)*

Is There Algae in Your Sundae?

Algin, a product extracted from brown algae, is often added to ice cream and frozen whipped toppings to make them smoother.

What impact do protists have on other organisms in their environment?

Chapter 15 Review

15.1 Protists are a diverse group of eukaryotes that include unicellular and multicellular organisms.

15.2–15.4 Protists can be classified into three groups—protozoans, algae, and molds.

15.5 Protists have a major ecological impact as food sources, decomposers, and infectious agents.

Sum It Up

Use the following summary to review the main concepts in this chapter.

15.1 Characteristics of Protists

- Protists have eukaryotic cells.
- Protists are diverse; they differ in size, shape, and manner of movement.

15.2 Animal-like Protists—Protozoans

- Animal-like protists are called protozoans.
- Protozoans are classified by how they move: sarcodinians move by extending lobes of cytoplasm; zooflagellates use flagella to move; ciliophorans live mostly in fresh water and use cilia to move; and sporozoans cannot move themselves.

15.3 Plantlike Protists—Algae

- Plantlike protists are called algae.
- Unicellular algae include dinoflagellates, diatoms, and euglenoids and some green algae.
- Multicellular algae include green algae, red algae, and brown algae.

15.4 Funguslike Protists—Molds

- Funguslike protists are classified as either plasmodial slime molds, cellular slime molds, or water molds.
- Plasmodial slime molds have single cells with multiple nuclei that can form spore-producing fruiting bodies.
- Cellular slime molds have single ameboid cells that can come together to form fruiting bodies and produce spores.
- Water molds include different freshwater and land protists that act as decomposers and sometimes as parasites.

15.5 Protists in the Biosphere

- Protists in plankton are important in the food chain and in oxygen production.
- Protists cause disease directly and indirectly.
- Protists have many commercial uses including food additives and other household products.

Use Terms and Concepts

Use each of the following words or terms in a complete sentence. If you need to review a meaning, turn to the page indicated.

protozoan (p. 355)
pseudopods (p. 356)
flagella (p. 356)
cilia (p. 357)
algae (p. 358)

alternation of
  generations (p. 361)
mold (p. 362)
plasmodium (p. 362)
plankton (p. 365)

Use Your Word Power

MATCHING **Look at the list of terms on the previous page and write the word or phrase that best matches each of the following phrases.**

1. The general name for an animal-like protist

2. A reproductive life cycle with both haploid and diploid stages

3. Whiplike structures that allow some animal-like protists to move

4. The general name for plantlike protists

5. Short, hairlike projections that some animal-like protists use to move

6. The feeding stage of a plasmodial slime mold

7. The "false feet" that sarcodinians use for movement

8. A collection of mostly microscopic organisms that float near the surface of oceans and lakes

9. The general name for a funguslike protist

MULTIPLE CHOICE **Choose the letter of the word or phrase that best completes each statement.**

10. Funguslike protists include (a) algae; (b) slime molds; (c) sporozoans; (d) sarcodinians.

11. All protists are (a) eukaryotes; (b) prokaryotes; (c) unicellular; (d) multicellular.

12. Among the five kingdoms, protists have (a) the fewest varieties; (b) the least diversity; (c) the most features in common; (d) the fewest features in common.

13. Amebas survive harsh environments by (a) extending pseudopods; (b) forming cysts; (c) ingesting other organisms; (d) releasing toxins.

14. Protists that lack structures for movement are (a) zooflagellates; (b) sporozoans; (c) sarcodinians; (d) ciliophorans.

15. The organisms that could NOT be classified as phytoplankton are (a) fungi; (b) green algae; (c) diatoms; (d) dinoflagellates.

16. A plasmodium is (a) multicellular; (b) dormant; (c) stationary; (d) multinucleated.

17. The type of organisms LEAST closely related to euglenoids are (a) dinoflagellates; (b) foraminiferans; (c) diatoms; (d) green algae.

Show What You Know

18. What is the major difference between prokaryotic and eukaryotic cells?

19. How do protozoans differ from animals?

20. Why does an ameba have no definite shape?

21. What characteristics distinguish algae from other protists?

22. Describe how protists are used indirectly in food products.

23. How do euglenoids differ from other algae?

24. How is it possible for red algae to grow at ocean depths of more than 250 meters?

25. **Make a Concept Map** Complete the concept map below by adding the following terms: molds, algae, plantlike, animal-like, funguslike, unicellular, multicellular.

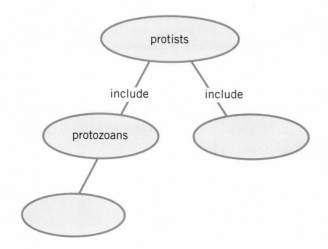

Take It Further

26. Developing a Hypothesis A paramecium can reproduce asexually about 700 times, after which it dies. However, it can reproduce many more times if it conjugates in addition to reproducing asexually. How might the ability for sexual reproduction affect the life span of *Paramecia*?

27. Interpreting a Graph The graph below shows reported cases of malaria in three regions of the world in selected years. Describe the trend exhibited by each of the three regions. Officials estimate that there are at least ten actual cases for each one reported. Based on this estimate, about how many actual cases of malaria were there in Africa in 1987?

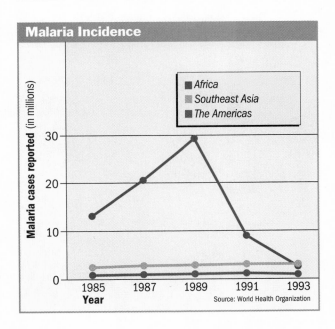

28. Analyzing Data In the graph above, notice the dramatic drop in reported cases of malaria in Africa after 1989. Is it likely that the actual incidence of malaria would have decreased so rapidly? What other factors could affect the number of cases reported? Explain your answer.

Consider the Issues

29. Toxic Plankton on the Rise Blooms of toxic plankton are increasing around the world, with serious consequences. For example, fish kills,—deaths of millions of fishes—have been linked to toxic plankton, and the dangers to humans are quite real as well. A major factor is increased coastal development and the resulting pollution. What should be done to decrease toxic plankton blooms? Should coastal development be stopped or should the scientific community come up with other options? What are your thoughts on this issue?

Make New Connections

30. Biology and History Research the causes and effects of the potato famine that began in 1845 in Ireland. As you research, answer these questions: How is the protist that causes late blight transmitted? To prevent the spread of late blight, what strategies do governments use today that were not available in 1845? Present your answers, along with any illustrations you find, on a class bulletin board.

31. Biology in the Community In this chapter you have read about various protists and their uses by humans. Go to a local food store, supermarket, or restaurant. Try to find some samples of protists. Describe the type of organisms you found and where you found them. If they were in a food or food product, describe how you were able to detect their presence.

FAST FORWARD TO CHAPTER 16

Protists are eukaryotes. Fungi, which you will read about in Chapter 16, are also eukaryotes. Like protists, fungi are diverse and abundant. They were once classified as plants because of their many plantlike features.

CHAPTER 16
Fungi

You can find out more about fungi by exploring the following Internet address:
http://microorganisms.biosurf.com

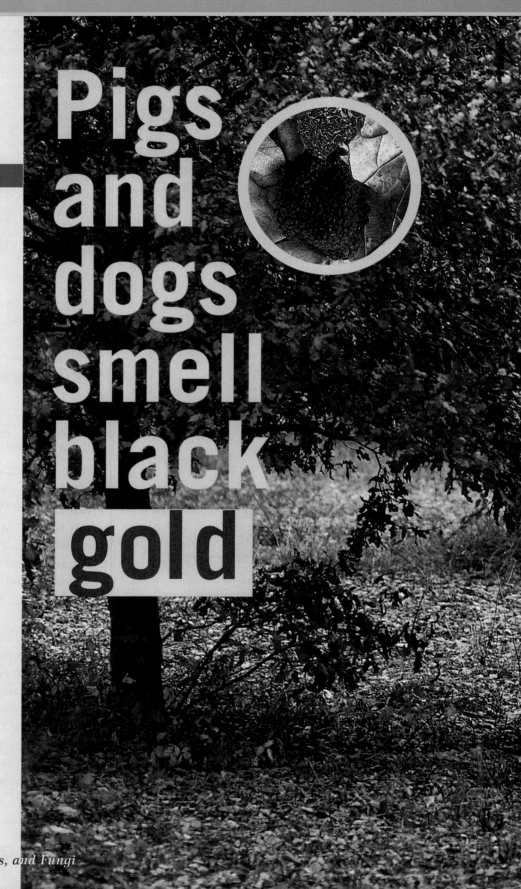

Pigs and dogs smell black gold

F rance, midwinter: An air of secrecy surrounds the small hunting party as a pig and his owner slip quietly into a grove of oak trees. The pig sniffs the ground as his owner looks anxiously behind him to be sure he is not being followed. Their quest: to find the valuable fungi called the black Perigord truffle—*Tuber melanosporum.* Why would a landowner guard the location of a bed of fungi so carefully? The answer lies in value: The wholesale price for a kilogram (kg) of Perigord truffles in the United States ranges from $550 to $750, and may increase depending on scarcity.

Pigs and dogs have been used as truffle hunters for centuries because those mammals are strongly attracted to the odor that truffles emit. In fact, pigs and dogs have detected the presence of truffles growing underground in the soil around tree roots from distances of more than 46 meters (m).

How do fungi such as the Perigord truffle grow? What exactly is a fungus anyway?

Grouping Mushrooms

You will need *several different varieties of fresh mushrooms*

1. Examine the mushrooms. Look for similarities and differences. Slice the mushrooms in half lengthwise and note their structures.
2. Devise your own system for classifying the mushrooms. Explain your reasons for grouping specific items together or separately.

WRITE ABOUT IT!

Go on a "mold patrol" and write about your findings in your journal. Look for any places outside or inside your home where mold is growing. As you write, describe the molds, their specific locations, and any physical characteristics that appear to be common to all of the locations.

16.1 Characteristics of Fungi

What you'll learn

IDEAS

- To identify the common characteristics of fungi
- To describe the structure, nutrition, and growth of typical fungi

WORDS

hyphae, septa, mycelium

A fungus to offend everyone

What attracts flies, makes your yard smell like rotting flesh, and appears almost overnight? The answer is the stinkhorn—one of the thousands of members of the kingdom Fungi. The characteristics of this smelly fungus definitely make it an unwelcome guest at picnics and outdoor parties. Other fungi, such as button mushrooms and yeasts, are important ingredients for food at those same picnics and parties.

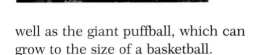

STRUCTURE OF FUNGI

Tangled webs

Imagine a pizza without crust and mushrooms, or a doctor without antibiotics. If you can imagine those things, then you are imagining a world without fungi. Fungi contribute to food, to medicine, and to the recycling process that returns nutrients from dead organisms to the environment.

Fungi come in many forms; two are shown in *Figure 16.1*. The kingdom Fungi includes microscopic yeast as well as the giant puffball, which can grow to the size of a basketball.

The cell walls of most fungi are made of chitin—a tough, flexible carbohydrate that also makes up the hard outer skeleton of insects. What advantage do cell walls made of chitin provide for fungi?

Yeasts are typical unicellular fungi. Yeast cells have a cell wall, a cell membrane, a nucleus, a large vacuole, and membrane-bound organelles. Like other eukaryotic organisms, yeasts undergo cell division.

There are no typical multicellular fungi. The mushrooms in *Figure 16.2* contain structures common to most multicellular fungi, however. For example, the mushrooms display above-ground reproductive structures—a stipe, an annulus, and a cap.

In contrast to the unicellular fungi, multicellular fungi are composed of a mass of tiny, individual filaments, barely visible to the unaided eye. The individual filaments, called **hyphae** (HY-fee), are tubules filled with cytoplasm and nuclei. Some hyphae may be divided into segments by walls

FIGURE 16.1

Brightly colored pink-capped mushrooms (right), photographed in the rain forest of Costa Rica, and filamentous coral fungus (below) give some indication of the wide variety of fungi.

FIGURE 16.2

Structure of a Mushroom

A mushroom displays characteristics common to all fungi. Its cells are eukaryotic, with cell walls made of chitin. Why do you think the reproductive structures of these mushrooms are above ground?

Cap
The cap protects the spores and aids in their dispersal.

Annulus
The annulus marks the site of attachment of the cap before it opens.

Stipe
A mushroom has a stipe, or stalk, that supports its cap.

Gills
Mushrooms have rows of gills on the underside of the cap. These gills contain cells called basidia, which produce spores.

Hyphae
Each hypha in this mushroom is a tubule filled with cytoplasm and nuclei.

Mycelium
Most fungi have a mass of tangled, interwoven hyphae that form the entire body of the fungus.

called **septa** (singular: *septum*), as shown in *Figure 16.3*. Septa have holes through which cytoplasm and organelles move. Some fungi do not have septa in their hyphae, and each hypha is one continuous filament containing cytoplasm and nuclei.

Hyphae are the living, growing parts of fungi. Hyphae can weave together in a variety of ways, thereby producing many different forms of fungi. Hyphae can grow quite quickly; certain fungi produce about 35 to 40 m of hyphae in only one hour!

Nuclei — Cell wall

Pore

Septum

Cell wall

Nuclei

FIGURE 16.3

Most groups of fungi have hyphae with septa (left). Some fungi have no septa (right). Their cytoplasm is continuous within hyphae.

The mass of tangled, interwoven hyphae that forms the body of a fungus is called a **mycelium** (my-SEE-lee-um) (plural: *mycelia*). In *Figure 16.2* you can see how hyphae interweave to form the mycelium of a mushroom.

Feeding a fungus

All fungi are heterotrophs; they obtain their nutrition from other organisms. However, nutrients must first be transported from the environment into the fungi. How do fungi accomplish this task?

Nutrition Fungi obtain food by absorbing it—that is, they take food in by the diffusion of small organic molecules from the environment. The environments that fungi inhabit usually contain only large organic molecules. Fungi have evolved an ability to produce enzymes in their hyphae, which they secrete directly into their environment. The enzymes break the large organic molecules into small organic molecules that the fungi can easily absorb. Fungi are capable of producing enzymes that break down large, complex organic molecules such as lignin, which is a major component of wood.

Although fungi are similar in the way they absorb nutrients from the environment, they differ in the types of organisms that they use as a source

FIGURE 16.4
When ants ingest spores of a certain tropical fungus, the spores develop a mycelium that feeds on the ant's body tissue until the ant dies. In the photo above, fungal fruiting bodies protrude from a dead ant's head. What is the function of the fruiting bodies?

of nutrition. Most fungi are saprophytes—organisms that digest and absorb nutrients from dead organisms. Where does the fungus in *Figure 16.4* get its nutrients? Is it a saprophyte?

Other fungi depend on living hosts for food. Fungi that obtain nutrients from living things can be parasites, mutualistic partners, or predators. Parasitic fungi absorb nutrients from living hosts, a process that often causes disease in, and sometimes the death of, the host. Still other fungi live in a mutualistic relationship with their host. Fungi in mutualistic relationships absorb nutrients from the host, but they reciprocate by providing the host with needed materials, such as minerals from the soil. A few fungi are predators—organisms that trap and kill their prey. What types of specialized structures would you expect to find in predatory fungi?

Growth Fungi use the nutrients they absorb primarily for growth. Fungi usually grow very rapidly, as nutrient transport to the actively growing areas of hyphae is extremely

Modeling Fungal Growth

You can model one day's growth of one hypha when you . . .

Try This

1 Draw a circle 2 centimeters in diameter to represent the size of a fungus.
2 If the 100,000 hyphae of a fungus grow a total of 1 kilometer a day, calculate the average growth of 1 hypha in one day.
3 Draw a second circle outside the first to represent the size of the fungus after one day's growth.

Analyze Your Results

1 How much did each hypha grow in one day?
2 What factors might affect this rate of growth?

FIGURE 16.5

Growth of Fungus

The photo (left) shows a *Penicillium* mycelium growing on an orange. If you used a microscope, you could see the hyphae of *Penicillium* penetrating orange cells, as shown in the drawing (right). What is the function of these penetrating hyphae?

efficient. Materials move quickly through a fungal mycelium because the hyphae of the mycelium share the same cytoplasm. So materials from the entire mycelium are available to all hyphae. The Think About It! activity on page 376 will help you understand just how quickly the mycelium of a fungus can grow.

FIGURE 16.6
A ring of mushrooms, popularly called a fairy ring, feeds on dead plant material. As the expanding mycelium consumes nutrients, what do you think happens to the grass under the mushrooms?

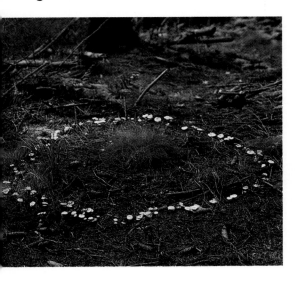

Growth in the hyphae occurs at the tips. The hyphae grow longer, but they remain very narrow. As a result of this growth pattern, the mycelium spreads outward quickly, occupying an increasingly large area. The many mushrooms you see in *Figure 16.6* may look like individual organisms, but they are all part of a single fungus. The visible mushrooms of a single, underground mycelium can spread to cover more than 1000 acres.

CHECKPOINT 16.1

1. What are the characteristics common to all fungi?
2. How do typical fungi grow?
3. How do fungi obtain nutrients?
4. Critical Thinking What characteristics would you expect to find in environments where saprophytes flourish? Explain your answer.

Build on What You Know

5. Make a chart to compare fungal cells with prokaryotes, animal cells, and plant cells. *(Need to jog your memory? Revisit relevant concepts in Chapter 3, Section 3.2 and Section 3.4.)*

16.2 Origin and Diversity of Fungi

Kingdom: Fungi
Four divisions:
Zygomycota
Ascomycota
Basidiomycota
Deuteromycota

How large is the fungus among us? Looking more like a mutant marshmallow than a fungus, *Lypcoperdon giganteum,* or the giant puffball, is certainly an armful. It is tiny, however, compared to the fungus *Armillaria bulbosa.* The mycelium of a single one of these fungi spreads out under many acres of forest floor in Michigan and is estimated to weigh at least 100 tons.

ORIGIN OF FUNGI

Fungus among us

You may wonder how fungi evolved. Well, so do mycologists—biologists who study fungi. The fossil record does not provide much information about fungi origins. Many mycologists hypothesize, however, that fungi evolved at least 400 million years ago from a protist ancestor.

Fungi were long classified as members of the plant kingdom because they appeared to be similar to plants. However, fungi differ from plants in several distinct ways. Compare what you have learned about cell wall composition in fungi and plants. The cell walls of plants are composed of cellulose, whereas the cell walls of almost all fungi contain chitin. In addition, plants are autotrophs, whereas fungi are heterotrophs—they cannot make their own food. Because of these and other differences, fungi are now classified in their own kingdom. However, because fungi were once classified as plants, the main groups of the kingdom Fungi are called divisions rather than phyla.

Fungi are grouped in one of four divisions based primarily on their method of reproduction. Three of these divisions—common molds, sac fungi, and club fungi—are classifications based on the structures used in sexual reproduction. The fourth division—the imperfect fungi—includes fungi that have been observed to reproduce only asexually.

Fungi in all four divisions are known to reproduce asexually. Asexual

Spores

FIGURE 16.7
The yeast cell (far left) is budding—a form of asexual reproduction in which a small budlike cell grows from a larger cell. Another form of asexual reproduction occurs as a puffball (near left) disperses its spores. Why are so many spores released at once?

reproduction can occur in three ways: budding, regeneration, and spore production. During budding, a parent cell divides and produces offspring by forming a small bud, which separates from the parent. Regeneration occurs when a piece of mycelium breaks off from a fungus and grows on its own. *Figure 16.7* illustrates two asexual reproductive forms.

Most fungi reproduce asexually by producing spores in a structure called a fruiting body. **Spores** are reproductive cells that can remain dormant or develop into a new organism. Fungi produce many spores. A typical mushroom, for example, makes 16 billion spores. Fruiting bodies are aboveground stalks that support the structures in which spores are made. You can see different types of fruiting bodies in *Figure 16.9*.

Common molds, sac fungi, and club fungi are the divisions of fungi that can reproduce sexually. As you learned in Chapter 5, sexual reproduction generally involves combining the genes from two different parents. In fungi there are no males or females.

FIGURE 16.8
Kingdom Fungi

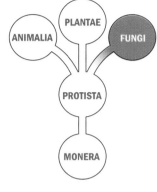

Instead, fungi have two different mating types of hyphae: plus (+) and minus (−). Sexual reproduction in fungi occurs by the fusion of two hyphae with different mating types and the resulting production of spores.

As you just learned, spore production occurs in both asexual and sexual reproduction. Although the spores produced by both methods of reproduction look the same, spores that are produced sexually contain a new combination of genetic information.

FIGURE 16.9
All fruiting bodies produce spores. How are these bodies adapted for dispersing spores? How could animals, wind, and water help to disperse spores?

EVERYDAY BIOLOGY

A Shower Smorgasbord

What feeds a bathroom fungal mold? Traces of soap and shampoo, which contain fatty acids, and your dead skin cells provide nourishment for the fungal mold growing on your shower curtain.

FIGURE 16.10

The Life Cycle of a Common Mold

Compare sexual and asexual reproduction in the common bread mold called *Rhizopus*. How do they differ?

Haploid (*n*)
Diploid (*2n*)

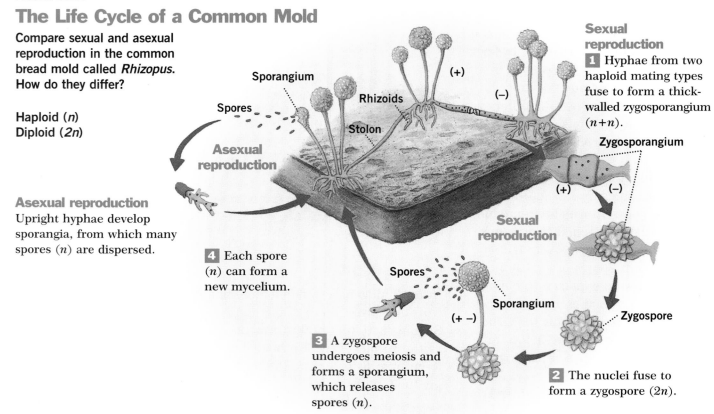

Asexual reproduction
Upright hyphae develop sporangia, from which many spores (*n*) are dispersed.

Sexual reproduction
1 Hyphae from two haploid mating types fuse to form a thick-walled zygosporangium (*n+n*).

4 Each spore (*n*) can form a new mycelium.

3 A zygospore undergoes meiosis and forms a sporangium, which releases spores (*n*).

2 The nuclei fuse to form a zygospore (*2n*).

Sporangium
Spores
Rhizoids
Stolon
Asexual reproduction
(+)
(−)
Sexual reproduction
Zygosporangium
(+)
(−)
Zygospore
Spores
Sporangium
(+ −)

COMMON MOLDS

A spore at the door

You have probably seen mold on bread or mildew on a shower curtain. These organisms are common molds. Scientists call this division of fungi Zygomycota (ZY-goh-my-KOH-tuh). Zygomycetes, as fungi in this group are called, are frequently found in soil or on dead animals or plants.

Common molds are structurally unique. Their hyphae lack septa, the walls that divide a hypha into segments. The hyphae of common molds also have some specialized functions.

There are three kinds of specialized hyphae in common molds—rhizoids, stolons, and sporangia. **Rhizoids** absorb nutrients and hold common molds to their food source like roots anchor plants to soil. **Stolons** connect groups of rhizoids to one another. Stolons transport cytoplasm containing nutrients and other materials through the body of the fungus. Sporangia (singular: *sporangium*) produce spores during reproduction. As you can see in *Figure 16.10,* sporangia

FIGURE 16.11

The mycelium of the bread mold *Rhizopus* has hyphae that produce sporangia. Why do sporangia grow upward?

produce haploid spores (n) during asexual reproduction. These spores bear genetically identical offspring.

During other stages in the life cycles of common molds, genetic material from two different mating types, a (+) mating type (n) and a (–) mating type (n), merge. Nuclei from the two mating types fuse to form a diploid ($2n$) structure called a **zygospore**. Division Zygomycota gets its name from these tough spores. Zygospores can survive for many years in harsh conditions. When conditions are right, the hard shell of the zygospore cracks open to produce a new sporangium. After the nuclei undergo meiosis, the sporangium bursts and thousands of new haploid (n) spores are released into the environment.

FIGURE 16.13
The Life Cycle of Sac Fungi

Sac fungi usually reproduce asexually. Under what environmental conditions might they reproduce sexually?

SAC FUNGI

A mixed bag

The sac fungi are a diverse division that includes unicellular yeasts, powdery mildews, the fungi in most lichens, and the flavorful morels. In fact, there are more than 60,000 species of sac fungi.

The characteristic that links the members of this group together is the production of saclike structures called **asci** (singular: *ascus*) during sexual reproduction. This characteristic gives the division its name—Ascomycota (AS-koh-my-KOH-tuh).

As you can see in *Figure 16.13*, the sexual reproduction cycle includes two mating types fusing to form a cell called an ascogonium. This structure produces hyphae that grow upward. Asci—the saclike reproductive structures—form at the tips of the ascogonium. The nuclei in asci go through several changes that eventually result in the formation of spores with

FIGURE 16.12
Morels (above) and bird's nest fungi (below) are both sac fungi. Morels, prized by gourmet cooks for their flavor, can be more expensive than caviar.

Spores

Asexual reproduction

Sexual reproduction
1 Hyphae (n) of two mating types fuse, forming an ascogonium.

Ascogonium

Ascus

Sexual reproduction

Asexual reproduction
Asexual spores (n) form at the ends of hyphae and are dispersed.

Ascospores

Ascus

2 The ascogonium produces many hyphae that become the fruiting body. The end of each hypha forms an ascus. Each ascus has two nuclei ($n+n$).

3 The two nuclei in each ascus fuse, forming diploid ($2n$) nuclei. Meiosis in each ascus produces haploid nuclei.

Ascogonium

4 The haploid nuclei (n) undergo mitosis to produce eight ascospores (n). Ascospores develop into new hyphae (n).

FIGURE 16.14

This green-headed jelly fungus is just one example of a species of club fungi.

CLUB FUNGI

Welcome to the club

When you think of fungi, you probably think of mushrooms. Mushrooms are club fungi. Club fungi are members of the division Basidiomycota (bay-SID-ee-oh-my-KOH-tuh).

One of the most distinguishing characteristics of club fungi is their tendency to reproduce sexually. Asexual reproduction is possible in club fungi but very rare. You can follow the most common life cycle of a club fungus in *Figure 16.15*, which shows a mushroom as a representative example.

The visible parts of the mushroom—stalk, cap, and gills—are made of tightly packed mycelia. These reproductive structures form a fruiting body that houses the tiny spore-producing **basidia** (singular: *basidium*).

Spores that are produced in basidia are released, and if environmental

new genetic combinations. In favorable environmental conditions, these spores grow into new fungal organisms.

Sexual reproduction in sac fungi is rare. In most cases, sac fungi reproduce asexually by producing haploid spores and releasing them into the environment. Unicellular sac fungi most often reproduce by cell division and budding, which you read about earlier.

FIGURE 16.15

The Life Cycle of a Club Fungus

Mushrooms usually reproduce sexually. Their spores develop in basidia on their gills.

Haploid (*n*)
Diploid (*2n*)

3 Basidia—each containing two haploid nuclei (*n+n*)—form in the tips of cells that line the gills.

4 The nuclei in a basidium fuse, forming diploid nuclei (*2n*). Meiosis occurs, producing haploid (*n*) nuclei.

5 The haploid nuclei mature into basidiospores (*n*), which are then dispersed.

Diploid nuclei

Basidia

Gills lined with basidia

Haploid basidiospores

2 Environmental changes can cause a mycelium (*n+n*) to compact and form a visible mushroom.

(+) Hyphae

(−) Hyphae

1 Hyphae of different mating types (*n*) fuse, producing hyphae whose cells contain two nuclei (*n+n*).

6 Basidiospores (*n*) germinate and form hyphae (*n*).

conditions are favorable, new mushrooms grow. As a result of the genetic recombination that occurred during the process of sexual reproduction, there is variation among these offspring fungi.

IMPERFECT FUNGI

Can't have it all

Some fungi apparently reproduce only asexually. These fungi are commonly called imperfect fungi and are grouped in the division Deuteromycota (DOO-ter-oh-my-KOH-tuh).

If you have ever had athlete's foot or ringworm, you have been a host for an imperfect fungus. Not all imperfect fungi are harmful, however. The imperfect fungus *Penicillium* produces the antibiotic penicillin, which you may have taken to help fight a bacterial infection.

Imperfect fungi reproduce asexually by producing spores called conidia in specialized hyphae called conidiophores. These asexually produced spores are released into the environment. If they land in a suitable place, they start growing. Most imperfect fungi are moldlike in appearance.

IN THE COMMUNITY
Pharmacies and Fungi

Visit a pharmacy in your community and locate the aisle containing antifungal medications. Look at the list of ingredients on the packages of these over-the-counter medications. Make a list of the ingredients used in each brand of medication. Be careful to note the "active ingredient" in each product. The active ingredient is the chemical that acts to prevent the growth of the particular fungus. Does the active ingredient vary from product to product? Carefully read the information on the product to see if it treats only certain types of fungi. Also note the indications or symptoms that are connected with certain fungal infections. Log on to *http://microorganisms.biosurf.com* to gather more information about fungi. Share your observations with the class.

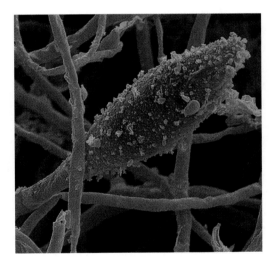

FIGURE 16.16
The imperfect fungus you see here causes athlete's foot, a condition easily transferred between humans in the humid environment of a locker room.

CHECKPOINT 16.2

1. What are some of the diverse characteristics of fungi?
2. How do the different groups of fungi reproduce?
3. Critical Thinking Why do you think most fungi have evolved the ability to produce spores through both sexual and asexual reproduction?

Build on What You Know

4. Compare the reproductive cycles of fungi with those of funguslike protists. How are they similar? Different? *(Need to jog your memory? Revisit relevant concepts in Chapter 15, Section 15.4)*

What are the major characteristics of fungi?

16.3 Fungi in the Biosphere

What you'll learn

IDEAS

• To describe the role of fungi in the environment and their relationships with other organisms

• To compare and contrast fungal diseases and appraise the importance of fungi to humans

WORDS

lichen, mycorrhizae

A good day's work
"It's a great harvest!" was the enthusiastic cry of the hunters who pull the treasured mushrooms from the pine and fir forests of central Oregon. One recent autumn, prized matsutake mushrooms gathered from these woods in only four hours sold for $1500.

ECOLOGICAL ROLES

Close associations

Fungi are key members of stable ecosystems. To feed, fungi break down organic materials, converting them into a form that can be used by the fungi and other living things. In this way fungi recycle the nutrients needed to keep communities alive.

In addition to their role in maintaining ecosystems, fungi often participate in symbiotic relationships with members of other species. Recall that symbiosis is a relationship between organisms of different species that live together in direct contact.

Lichens When a fungus and a photosynthetic organism "join forces," the entity that results from the symbiotic partnership is called a **lichen** (LY-ken). Among the lichens, the most common partnership is between a sac fungus and a green alga, or a cyanobacterium. The alga, or the cyanobacterium, provides food for the fungus through the process of photosynthesis. In this partnership, the photosynthetic organism provides the food, whereas the fungus provides the physical environment that contains the food producer. What kind of symbiosis would you call this relationship?

FIGURE 16.17
Below is a cross section of a lichen. Lichens like those shown in the photograph (left) can grow almost anywhere, including in caves and on rocks. What characteristics allow them to grow in such barren places?

Ascocarp of fungus

Algal layer

FIGURE 16.18

Which plant probably has mycorrhizae associated with its roots? The inset photo shows mycorrhizae growing densely around plant roots.

The ability to perform photosynthesis and absorb nutrients dissolved in rainwater and dew enables lichens to survive in extremely harsh environments. *Figure 16.17* shows one of the varied locations lichens inhabit. When lichens grow on bare rock they help break down the rock into soil particles. The large size of many lichens indicates that they are thousands of years old. In fact, lichens are some of the oldest individual organisms on Earth.

Mycorrhizae Fungi are not always "freeloaders" in symbiotic relationships. **Mycorrhizae** (my-kuh-RY-zee) result from mutually beneficial relationships between plants and fungi. Mycorrhizae form when the tiny hyphae of a fungus grow on and in the roots of a host plant. Over time, the mycorrhizae can account for as much as 15 percent of the total mass of the roots.

The fungus in mycorrhizae benefits from the relationship because it can absorb nutrients made by the plant— a photosynthetic organism. The plant also benefits. The hyphae of the fungus act as root extensions for the plant, increasing the ability of the roots to absorb water and nutrients from the soil. In addition, the fungus secretes digestive enzymes that help break down organic matter in the soil. The plant can then absorb the decomposed material as nutrients and minerals.

In their symbiotic relationship, the plant and the fungus can survive harsher conditions than either could individually. Plants with mycorrhizae also grow faster and are more disease resistant than those without mycorrhizae. Which plant in *Figure 16.18* might benefit from a mycorrhizal association?

Many biologists hypothesize that mycorrhizae were instrumental in the evolution of land plants. Today, more than 90 percent of tree species and 80 percent of all other plant species have mycorrhizae. Many trees and plants could not survive without their fungal partners.

DISEASES CAUSED BY FUNGI

Living rusts

As you have just read, fungi can be extremely beneficial to some plants. However, not all fungi have mutualistic relationships with plants. Some fungi act as parasites that cause disease. Fungal diseases can occur in both plants and humans, although their effect on plants is generally more deadly.

Plant disease In some parts of the world, disease-causing fungi destroy large amounts of harvested food crops each year. Parasitic fungi that attack grain crops include smuts and rusts, both of which are types of club fungi.

Dutch elm disease has killed millions of American elm trees. The fungus that causes Dutch elm disease was accidentally imported to the United States from Europe after World War I. The fungus, which is spread from tree to tree by bark beetles, is both a parasite and a decomposer. As a parasite,

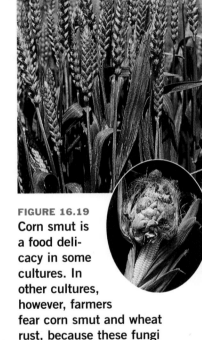

FIGURE 16.19
Corn smut is a food delicacy in some cultures. In other cultures, however, farmers fear corn smut and wheat rust, because these fungi devastate crops.

LAB ZONE Do It!

Does Moisture Affect Bread-Mold Growth?

You can compare conditions for growing bread mold when you . . .

Try This

1 You need two slices of bread. Moisten the surface of one slice with water, and leave both slices exposed to the classroom air for a few hours.
2 Put a little more water on the moistened slice and place the slices of bread in separate plastic bags. To keep the bags from touching the bread, insert plain, rounded toothpicks in the bread as needed. Seal the bags.
3 After four or five days, look for mold growing on the bread.

Analyze Your Results

1 Do you see mold? Is there more mold on one slice than on the other?
2 What conclusions can you draw about the effect of moisture on bread-mold growth?

the fungus feeds on and kills the elm tree. Then, as a decomposer, it digests the dead tree.

Human diseases Fungi also cause disease in humans. Like all fungi, fungal parasites obtain nutrition in order to live. Fungi that infect humans obtain nutrients from body tissues. As you now know, fungi secrete digestive enzymes into the environment and then absorb the nutrients the enzymes break down. When fungi release these enzymes into human tissues, the tissues often become irritated and inflamed. Irritation and inflammation are symptoms of infection.

Some of the more common fungal diseases in humans are athlete's foot, ringworm, and thrush, a painful mouth infection in infants. Scientists have not always known that these diseases are caused by fungi. What organisms might the scientists have originally suspected?

HUMAN USES
From cooking to cures

Versatile might not be the first word you would choose to describe fungi, but it is an appropriate adjective. The beneficial uses of fungi are so varied that one type might appear on your dinner plate and another type might save your life.

Want a treat? Many edible fungi, including the matsutake mushroom you read about at the beginning of this section, are considered delicacies. The common button mushroom, *Agaricus campestris,* is popular for making sauces and salads. You may see other mushrooms, both wild and cultured, for sale in your local supermarket.

Although some wild mushrooms are edible, many are poisonous, such as the one shown in *Figure 16.20.* If eaten, such mushrooms can cause severe illness and even death. For this reason, gathering and eating wild mushrooms should be left to experts who can distinguish the poisonous mushrooms from those that are harmless.

FIGURE 16.20
This *Amanita muscaria*, also known as the death-cap mushroom, is very common—and deadly.

Fungi provide many of the distinct aromas and tastes in our foods. The flavor of many cheeses results from the presence of fungal molds. An imperfect fungus, *Aspergillus*, is used in making citric acid and soy sauce. Perhaps the most widely used food-related fungi are yeasts. Yeast has been used around the world for centuries to make bread rise and to ferment beverages.

FRONTIERS IN BIOLOGY

Fungi in medicine

In 1928 an unexpected discovery involving *Penicillium*, a fungal mold that rots fruit, changed medical history. Scottish scientist Alexander Fleming was studying *Staphylococcus*, a type of bacteria that causes skin infections. He grew the bacteria in culture dishes containing agar and nutrients. One day he noticed that a *Penicillium* mold was growing in some of the culture dishes. In the area around the fungal mold there was a clear zone with no *Staphylococcus*.

Hypothesizing that the fungus had killed the bacteria, Fleming conducted more tests. His hypothesis proved correct. He had discovered a chemical that destroyed disease-causing bacteria. Fleming named his discovery penicillin, after the fungus that produces it. This important antibiotic has saved millions of lives. Penicillin prevents bacterial infection in wounds and promotes healing in burns.

Many other discoveries of antibiotics followed Fleming's discovery of penicillin. Today, most antibiotics are synthesized chemically in laboratories rather than isolated from living fungi and bacteria. The chemical structure of synthetic antibiotics is usually based on a natural chemical made by fungi or bacteria.

As you will recall from Chapter 9, yeasts are important tools in genetic engineering. Like their moneran counterparts, genetically altered yeasts are used to synthesize many important proteins. Moreover, yeasts are eukaryotes, so the proteins produced by genetically engineered yeasts may provide a better match for other eukaryotes—including you!

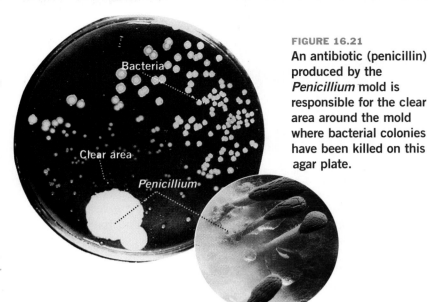

FIGURE 16.21

An antibiotic (penicillin) produced by the *Penicillium* mold is responsible for the clear area around the mold where bacterial colonies have been killed on this agar plate.

Bacteria

Clear area

Penicillium

CHECKPOINT 16.3

1. What is the role of fungi in the environment?

2. Compare the general effects of fungal diseases on plants and humans.

3. **Critical Thinking** How do you think the discovery of penicillin affected those who fought in World War II? Explain your answer.

Build on What You Know

4. What characteristics do bacteria and fungi share as decomposers? *(Need to jog your memory? Revisit relevant concepts in Chapter 14, Section 14.6.)*

EVERYDAY BIOLOGY

A Fungus for a Headache?

Believe it or not, a parasitic rye fungus, called ergot, is the source of a drug called ergotamine, which can relieve migraine headache symptoms.

How do fungi act as decomposers and symbiotic partners of other organisms?

LAB ZONE Investigate It!

Comparing Spores of Fungi and Green Plants

WHAT YOU WILL DO Examine and compare the external reproductive structures and spores of the mushroom and fern and design a related experiment

SKILLS YOU WILL USE Observing, collecting and recording data, predicting, experimenting

WHAT YOU WILL NEED A mushroom, a fern frond with spore cases, a single-edged razor blade, 2 pairs of forceps, a microscope, 2 microscope slides

Propose a Hypothesis
How do you think spores from plants compare with spores from fungi? Propose a hypothesis.

Conduct Your Experiment
1 Use a razor blade and forceps to cut a paper-thin section of a gill from the underside of a mushroom cap, as shown in the photograph above. **Caution:** Handle the razor blade with care.

2 Prepare a wet mount of the gill section. Examine the slide under a microscope set at low power.

3 Take notes on your observations of the mushroom gill and diagram what you see.

4 Remove a spore case from the fern frond and transfer it to a microscope slide. Examine it at low power.

5 Take notes on your observations of the fern spore case and record what you see.

6 Remove the slide. Using the other pair of forceps, gently pull open the fern's spore case.

7 Examine the slide again, and record your observations of the inside of the fern spore case.

Analyze Your Data
1 Describe any similarities you observed in the mushroom and fern spores.

2 Describe any differences you observed in the mushroom and fern spores.

Draw Conclusions
What characteristics were you able to compare in this experiment? From this experiment, what conclusions can you draw about the similarities and differences between the reproductive structures of fungi and ferns?

Design a Related Experiment
Suppose your teacher gives you another spore case and asks you to identify its source as either a mushroom or a fern. Propose a hypothesis, then design an experiment that will test your hypothesis.

Lab: Comparing Spores of Fungi and Green Plants

Objectives:
1. to examine the external reproduction structures and spores of a mushroom and a fern

2. to describe their similarities and differences

Observations: mushroom gill

Chapter 16 Review

16.1–16.2 Fungi are stationary organisms that live as heterotrophs.

16.3 Fungi act as decomposers and symbiotic partners of humans and many other organisms.

Sum It Up

Use the following summary to review the main concepts in this chapter.

16.1 Characteristics of Fungi

- Most fungi are multicellular organisms composed of individual filaments called hyphae.
- The bodies of most fungi are composed of interwoven hyphae called mycelia.
- Most fungi obtain nutrition by absorbing nutrients from dead organisms.
- Growth in fungi is usually very rapid because absorbed nutrients are efficiently transported to growing areas of hyphae; the hyphae of the mycelium share the same cytoplasm.

16.2 Origin and Diversity of Fungi

- Mycologists hypothesize that fungi evolved at least 400 million years ago from an ancestral protist.
- The four divisions of fungi are: Zygomycota (common molds); Ascomycota (sac fungi); Basidiomycota (club fungi); Deuteromycota (imperfect fungi).

- Some fungi are classified on the basis of structures used in reproduction: zygospore, ascus, and basidium.

16.3 Fungi in the Biosphere

- Many fungi are decomposers.
- Symbiotic relationships between certain fungi and algae result in lichens.
- Symbiotic relationships between fungi and plants can result in mycorrhizae.
- Fungal diseases in plants include smuts, rusts, and Dutch elm disease; fungal diseases in humans include athlete's foot, ringworm, and thrush.
- Some fungi are important to humans as a source of food, medicines, and eukaryotic cells for genetic engineering applications.

Use Terms and Concepts

Use each of the following words or terms in a complete sentence. If you need to review a meaning, turn to the page indicated.

hyphae (p. 374)

septa (p. 375)

mycelium (p. 375)

spores (p. 379)

rhizoids (p. 380)

stolons (p. 380)

zygospore (p. 381)

asci (p. 381)

basidia (p. 382)

lichen (p. 384)

mycorrhizae (p. 385)

Use Your Word Power

COMPLETION **Write the word or phrase that best completes each statement.**

1. Sac fungi reproduce sexually by means of a(n) _____ .

2. A(n) _____ is the diploid structure with strong walls produced during a common mold's sexual reproductive cycle.

3. The _____ are the parts of hyphae that anchor a fungus to its source of nutrients.

4. The hyphae that connect groups of rhizoids are called _____ .

5. The _____ is the body of a fungus.

6. The filaments of multicellular fungi are _____ .

7. Symbiotic relationships between plant roots and fungi result in _____ .

8. A(n) _____ is the result of a symbiotic relationship between a fungus and a green alga or cyanobacterium.

9. The reproductive cells produced in fruiting bodies are _____ .

10. Club fungi reproduce sexually by forming spores in a(n) _____ .

11. Some hyphae are divided into segments by _____ .

TRUE-FALSE **Write true if the statement is true. If the statement is false, replace the underlined word to make the statement true.**

12. The mycelium of a fungus consists of many <u>hyphae.</u>

13. Fungi digest their food by secreting <u>nutrients</u> into the food.

14. A mushroom's cells are <u>prokaryotic.</u>

15. A mushroom is <u>heterotrophic</u> because it depends on other organisms for its nutrition.

16. <u>Molds</u> are unicellular sac fungi that reproduce either sexually or asexually.

Show What You Know

17. Explain what septa are and how they differ among groups of fungi.

18. How do fungi obtain nutrition?

19. Explain how the process of hyphae growth makes fungi grow rapidly.

20. Why did scientists originally classify fungi as plants?

21. What is a common characteristic of sexual reproduction in fungi?

22. How do fruiting bodies function in fungal reproduction?

23. Describe the budding process in yeasts.

24. Why are the activities of fungi important in maintaining ecosystems?

25. Why might drought, cold, or lack of food trigger sexual reproduction in fungi?

26. **Make a Concept Map** Complete the concept map by adding the following terms: common molds, sac fungi, imperfect fungi, zygospore, basidia, asci, sexual reproduction, mycelium, septa, hyphae.

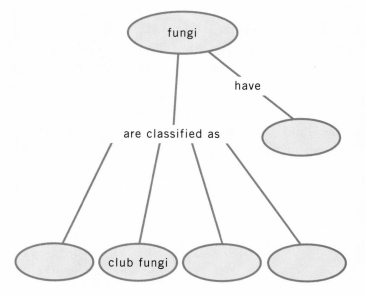

Take It Further

27. Applying Concepts In which of the four divisions of fungi would you classify the fungus in the photograph below? Give reasons for your answer. What would you examine to verify your answer?

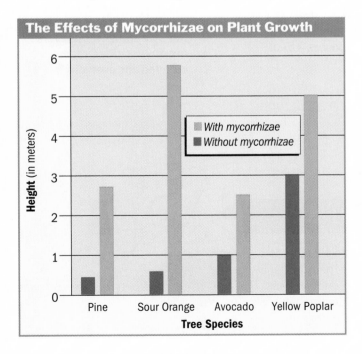

28. Interpreting a Graph The graph below illustrates the growth rates of four species of trees—two individuals of each. One tree of each species grew with mycorrhizae and one grew without mycorrhizae. For each species, how does the growth of the two plants compare? Make a generalization about the growth rate of plants with mycorrhizae.

The Effects of Mycorrhizae on Plant Growth

Height (in meters) — vertical axis: 0, 1, 2, 3, 4, 5, 6

Legend:
- With mycorrhizae
- Without mycorrhizae

Tree Species (horizontal axis): Pine, Sour Orange, Avocado, Yellow Poplar

29. Designing an Experiment Design an experiment to test the effect of mycorrhizae on plant growth. What variables would you control?

Consider the Issues

30. Mushroom Dilemma Suppose mushrooms of a poisonous species resemble mushrooms of a harmless, edible species. When people pick and eat the poisonous mushrooms, they become ill. Mycologists know of a chemical that kills the poisonous mushrooms, but its effect on plants and wildlife is unknown. Do you think the chemical should be used to eliminate the poisonous mushrooms? Explain your answer. Suggest some alternative solutions.

Make New Connections

31. Biology and History Ergotism is a disease caused by a fungus. Some historians have suggested that the Salem witchcraft trials in 1692 may have involved people with ergotism. Research and write a short story or skit about ergotism and the Salem witchcraft trials.

32. Biology and the Community What forms of fungi exist where you live? Find out if there is a mushroom farm in your community. Investigate fungi that harm crops grown in your state, and find out if the crops can be treated to prevent fungal diseases.

FAST-FORWARD TO CHAPTER 17

Fungi are heterotrophs assigned to their own kingdom. In the next unit you will learn about plants—autotrophs that form the base of many food chains.

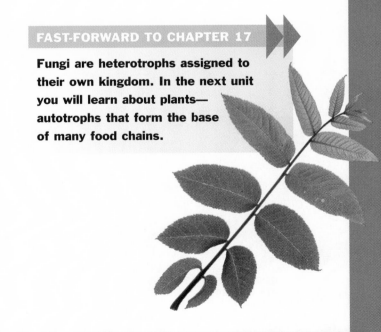

Unit 4 Review

THE BIG IDEA! Answering the following questions will help you to link ideas and grasp the core concepts.

Connect the Chapters

1. Some protozoans produce cysts. Some bacteria produce endospores. What do both structures have in common? How do these structures compare to the spores produced by fungi?

2. Which characteristics of slime molds or water molds characterize them as funguslike?

3. Compare the relationship between a virus and its host to that between a sac fungus and green alga in a lichen.

4. What characteristic do cyanobacteria and diatoms share? Would you expect any fungi to have this characteristic? Explain.

Connect the Units

5. What do meiosis and conjugation have in common? How do they differ?

6. Explain how the characteristics of viruses, monerans, and fungi enable them to be used in genetic engineering.

7. How might the niches that archaebacteria occupy have helped them to survive?

Connect to Themes

8. Unity and Diversity The kingdom Fungi is a highly diverse collection of species. What general traits unify this kingdom?

9. Systems and Interactions How does the addition of an enzyme change transcription in retroviruses?

10. Evolution What evidence supports the hypothesis that mycorrhizae evolved with plants?

11. Systems and Interactions How do bacterial, protist, and fungal decomposers affect ecosystems?

project plans

1 Plan a fungi hunt. See how many different fungi you can locate. Use reference materials to identify the types of fungi you find. Document the names of the fungi and where you found each of them. Be sure to wear protective gloves while collecting specimens. Do not eat any of the fungi you find.

2 To prevent outbreaks of influenza, health departments offer inexpensive or free flu vaccines each fall. As a class, design a study and collect data to answer the following questions: What percent of your study population became infected in a given time period? Were people who were vaccinated less likely to become infected than those who were not? If someone was vaccinated but still became infected with the flu, were the symptoms less severe? Are flu vaccines recommended for everyone?

CRITIC'S CORNER

A BOOK REVIEW BY NORA CANNICK HILTON HEAD, SOUTH CAROLINA

The Hot Zone, written by Richard Preston, is a work of serious nonfiction. It tells the horrifying tale of people infected with two sister viruses, Ebola and Marburg, and of the doctors who treat them. The deadliest of the two viruses is Ebola. Ebola attacks every organ and tissue in the human body except skeletal muscle and bone. I enjoyed reading this book and finding out about two dangerous viruses that I didn't know much about.

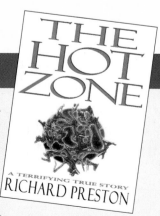

THE HOT ZONE

A TERRIFYING TRUE STORY
RICHARD PRESTON

DR. KIMBERLY HOLDING
Epidemic Intelligence Service Fellow,
Centers for Disease Control and Prevention

EDUCATION: M.D., B.A. in biology

❝ I travel all around the country and the world studying epidemics. Working in the field is exhilarating. I feel like I'm doing something that will help other people. When I'm not traveling on a case, I'm assigned to the Division of HIV/AIDS Patient Surveillance here in Atlanta. We look at the numbers of AIDS patients nationwide by category, in order to target people for prevention programs.

My first job after college was as a secretary at a lab, and I gradually started doing some lab work, too. I guess I went from the typewriter to the lab to medical school!

Biology is great because it is a never-ending field—as long as there are cells in the world, there will always be biology to study. In science, everyone benefits from everyone else's knowledge, and you're always learning.❞

bioSURF Log on to *http://microorganisms.biosurf.com* where you can connect to the Internet site for the Centers for Disease Control and Prevention in Atlanta, Georgia, to find out more about epidemiologists.

KAREN BROWN
Scuba diver, educator, and photographer;
owner, Ocean Adventure

EDUCATION: B.A. in sociology; self-taught in underwater biology, photography, and education

❝ We try to show the students what it would be like to go scuba diving with us. . . . We don't hammer them on the head about ecology. We feel it's more effective to educate people about what the underwater world is like and show them that it's very beautiful. Conservation comes naturally from there. . . . As a diver, I would like to have something to say about the way sewage is treated. Pollution from sewage makes sea urchins thrive. And sea urchins eat kelp. Usually, they just eat dead kelp, but if there are too many sea urchins, they will cut the living kelp off right at the roots.❞

bioSURF To find out more about careers in ecology, log on to the Internet site *http://microorganisms.biosurf.com.*

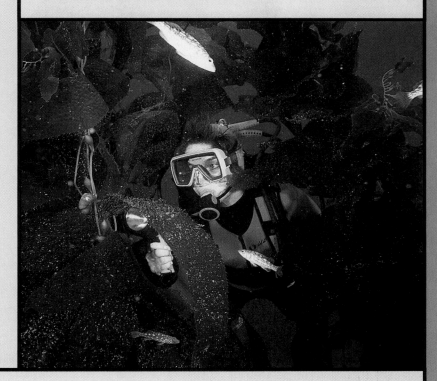

"If people can try to learn as much as they can about something as small as the kelp forest, they can't help but appreciate it." — KAREN BROWN

Which of these amazing statements about the world of plants are fact, and which are fiction?

Hit *or* Myth?

All flowers smell **sweet.**

(Fiction. When the titan arum at England's Royal Botanical Gardens bloomed in 1996, gardeners had to plan exits so that visitors could quickly escape from the flower's strong odor.)

Plants can get **sunburned.**

(Fact. During hot, dry, windy weather, plants can develop a condition called leaf scorch. The symptoms include withered, discolored leaves.)

You may find ferns on the menu at some **restaurants.**

(Fact. The tops of young fiddlehead ferns are considered a delicacy in some parts of the United States. If you see them on a menu and feel adventurous . . . *bon appétit!*)

Flowers never get bigger than about the size of a **dinner plate.**

(Fiction. The flowers of the rafflesia plant, which grows in Indonesia, can reach sizes of up to 1 meter across.)

A plant cannot control its **temperature.**

(Fact and fiction. Some plants can maintain a constant temperature while flowering. For example, the lotus flower keeps its temperature between 30° and 35° Celsius. Forty lotus blossoms produce about as much heat as one lightbulb.)

A **weed** inspired the invention of Velcro.

(Fact. Swiss engineer George de Mestral used a microscope to examine a cocklebur he removed from his dog. The pesky weed led to the idea for a fastener that uses tiny hooks and loops.)

Clothing can be made from trees.

(Fact. Viscose rayon is made of processed wood pulp, often from spruce or hemlock trees.)

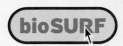

bioSURF

You can find out more about plants by exploring the following Internet address:
http://plants.biosurf.com

In this chapter . . .

FEATURES

Everyday Biology
- Leaves Fall in Autumn
- What's a Weed?
- You Say To-MAY-to, I Say To-MAH-to
- That Bread Is Really Stale!

In the Community
Leaves, Stems, Roots

 Environmental Awareness
Part-time Farmers

LAB ZONES

Discover It!
- Observing a Flowering Plant

Do It!
- Observing the Effects of Light on Plants
- Categorizing Plants

Think About It!
- What Parts of Plants Do We Eat?

Investigate It!
- Examining the Parts of a Plant

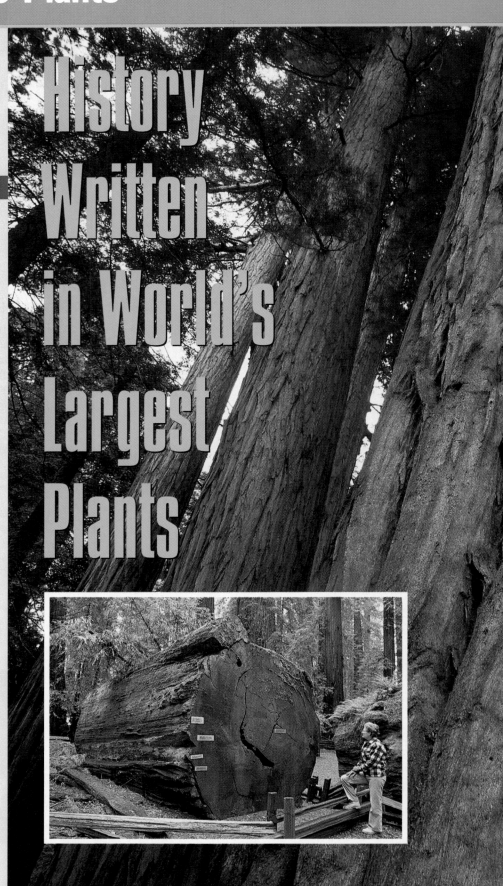

History Written in World's Largest Plants

LAB ZONE Discover It!

Observing a Flowering Plant

You need *a whole plant with a flower, a hand lens, black paper*

1. Observe the plant closely, and make a drawing of it. Label as many parts as you can.
2. Use the hand lens to observe the plant parts more closely. Make notes about their appearance and texture.
3. Tap the flower against the black paper. What happens? Observe the substance with the hand lens.

The substance that is released by the flower is pollen—small grains of protein that contain the male gametes for reproduction. All plants—including the giant redwoods shown here—produce pollen to reproduce sexually.

WRITE ABOUT IT!

In your science journal, write about how plants affect your life. Name the kinds of plants that are common in your neighborhood or community.

Thousands of tourists who visit California's Richardson Grove State Park each year peer into history inside the world's largest plant: the coastal redwood. These immense redwoods, called *Sequoia sempervirens*, or "evergreen" sequoias, are among the world's oldest trees.

Professor Emanuel Fritz of the University of California made an extensive study of a redwood. He had the trunk cut open to reveal the rings—a living record of the tree's history. In redwoods, each spring's growing season produces a ring of light-colored wood. Each summer adds a narrower band of dark wood. The number of light-dark rings provides an accurate record of the life of trees that may be as much as 3500 years old. Fritz found that the tree he studied had started to grow in about A.D. 730. Before falling to the ground in 1933, it stood 95 meters high and weighed almost half a million kilograms.

Scars inside a tree trunk can pinpoint the year a fire ravaged the forest or a disease struck the tree. By studying the scars, Fritz discovered the cause of his tree's death. Exactly 113 years earlier, a fire had so damaged the tree's trunk and roots that eventually the tree could no longer support its own weight.

Botanists learn about plants by carefully examining them . . . inside and out. What can botanists tell us about a plant's growth?

17.1 The Structure of Plants

What you'll learn

IDEAS

• To identify the main structures in leaves, stems, and roots

• To compare the key functions of leaves, stems, roots, and flowers

WORDS

blade, veins, petiole, taproot, fibrous root, flower, pollination, seed, fruit

Bee-ing a plant

Plants cover the continents in an incredible display of variety. Plants have many unusual adaptations that increase their chances for survival. The flower of the bee orchid (right) has the color, pattern, and scent of a female bee. These features attract male bees, which pollinate the flower. While plants may have unique adaptations, plant structures and their functions are generally similar.

INTRODUCTION TO PLANTS

Green all around you

Imagine walking through your favorite outdoor environment. What organisms do you see? In most places, the organisms you are most likely to see are plants. Plants grow almost anywhere on land—along city streets, on walls, in yards, and in forests. Where else do you see plants?

As a group, plants display amazing variety. Some, such as redwood trees, reach enormous heights. Others, such as the floating fern *Azolla*, are smaller than your fingernail. Some plants have colorful flowers, and others have none. The life spans of plants also vary. Some plants, such as marigolds, live for a single season. Others, such as bristlecone pines, live for thousands of years.

Even with this great variety, plants show remarkable similarities. Almost all plants have green parts. Many plants are woody. The majority of plants have flowers. Unlike animals, nearly all plants live their lives rooted to one place in the soil.

The differences among most plants are due to variations in a few basic parts: leaves, stems, roots,

flowers, and seeds. In this chapter you will learn about the various forms of these basic parts and how the structures of plants enable them to live and reproduce in different environments.

LEAVES

Busy blades

Leaves are often the most highly visible structures of a typical plant. Leaves are the organs where an essential life process, photosynthesis, occurs. Photosynthesis is the process of using sunlight, water, and carbon dioxide to make sugars. (Other green plant parts may also perform photosynthesis, but the leaves are the main sites for this process.) You can review the details of photosynthesis in Chapter 4.

Leaves, like other plant parts, share some common features. The largest part of most leaves consists of a flat, broad section called the **blade.** The blade contains cells that perform photosynthesis. Blades can be large and flat, like the leaves of a sycamore, or rounded and pointed, like the needles of a pine. Compare the leaf

Flower

Leaf

Stem

FIGURE 17.1

You probably know the names of the above-ground parts of a typical plant. What are the functions of those parts?

blades shown in *Figure 17.2*. Blades are not airtight structures. Tiny pores in the blades allow for water evaporation and the exchange of carbon dioxide and oxygen with the atmosphere.

Leaves contain tubelike structures called **veins,** which carry water, minerals, and sugars throughout the blades. As you can see in *Figure 17.2,* the veins may be arranged in different patterns. How would you describe these patterns? You can use the vein patterns to determine whether a flowering plant is a monocot or a dicot. Monocots and dicots are two important groups of flowering plants that have distinctive features. You will read more about monocots and dicots in Chapters 19 and 20.

Veins enter most leaves through the **petiole,** a short stalk that connects the leaf to the stem. In addition to providing support, a petiole enables the transport of fluids between leaves and stems.

Leaves may be classified as simple or compound. Simple leaves consist of one blade. Compound leaves have two or more small blades, called leaflets, that are linked to one main petiole.

Compound leaves can be classified as either pinnate or palmate. Pinnate leaves are like feathers, with smaller veins branching off a main central vein called the midrib. Examples of plants with pinnately compound leaves include coconut palms, ash and walnut trees, and rose shrubs. Palmate leaves resemble the fingers and palm of your hand, with several lobes radiating from a central point. Examples of plants with palmately compound leaves include castor bean plants, palmetto palms, and buckeye (horse chestnut) trees.

FIGURE 17.2

Characteristics of Leaves

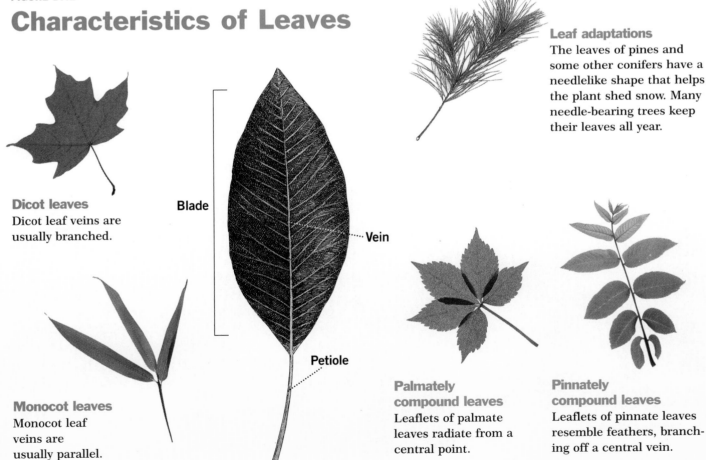

Dicot leaves
Dicot leaf veins are usually branched.

Monocot leaves
Monocot leaf veins are usually parallel.

Blade

Vein

Petiole

Leaf adaptations
The leaves of pines and some other conifers have a needlelike shape that helps the plant shed snow. Many needle-bearing trees keep their leaves all year.

Palmately compound leaves
Leaflets of palmate leaves radiate from a central point.

Pinnately compound leaves
Leaflets of pinnate leaves resemble feathers, branching off a central vein.

Chapter 17 Introduction to Plants   **399**

STEMS

Holding up the plant

Leaves do not function alone in a typical plant but are attached to structures called stems. Stems have two main functions: supporting leaves and flowers, and transporting water and nutrients within the plant.

Transport in stems is accomplished by some tubelike cells that carry sugars from leaves to other parts of the plant. Other tubelike cells transport water and minerals up from the soil into the veins of leaves and flowers. In a few plants, the stems also function as food storage places. A potato is an underground stem that stores a large amount of starch.

The arrangement of a plant's stems and leaves determines its overall shape. The size of a typical plant depends on the size of its stems. Based on their shape, size, and kind of stem, plants are traditionally grouped in one of four categories: herbaceous plant, shrub, vine, or tree. In *Figure 17.3* you can see examples of these.

Stems vary in strength. Herbaceous (her-BAY-shus) stems are nonwoody, composed of relatively soft tissue covered with a thin protective layer. The woody and strong stems of a tree or bush include its trunk, branches, and twigs. You can identify many trees and bushes by their stems even during seasons when the leaves have fallen. Vines have slender, woody stems that are usually supported by trees, posts, or other objects.

Leaves attach to stems at locations called nodes. The sections of stem between the nodes are called internodes ("inter-" means "between"). Compare the shapes and functions of the stems in *Figure 17.3*. How do they vary?

In most stems, growth begins in structures called buds, which may grow into leaves, branches, or flowers. Buds usually develop in regular patterns. For example, buds develop on opposite sides of a mint stem. On a sunflower stem, buds grow in a staggered pattern along the stem. The pattern of bud growth is an adaptation that provides a plant's leaves with the greatest exposure to light.

FIGURE 17.3

A Variety of Stems

Stem

Stem

Herbaceous plants

Stems

Trees and shrubs

Vines

Fibrous root   Tap root

FIGURE 17.4
Contrast these two types of roots. Describe their shapes. Which type grows more deeply into the soil?

ROOTS

Stuck in the mud

In a typical plant, the root is the portion of the plant that grows below the surface of the soil. The two main functions of roots are to absorb water and minerals and to anchor the plant firmly. Some roots also store food.

Roots absorb water and minerals from the soil, an essential activity for a plant. Most of the absorption of water and minerals takes place at the root tips, which are covered with root hairs. Root hairs are tiny narrow tubes growing from the cell membranes of some root cells. Root hairs greatly increase the surface area that is available for water absorption.

There are two common types of roots, as you can see in *Figure 17.4*. One type, a **taproot,** is a single large central root with much smaller side roots branching out from it. Taproots can grow deep below the ground and "tap" the groundwater. If you have ever tried to pull up a dandelion plant, you know that taproots make strong anchors. You can see an example of taproot strength in *Figure 17.5*. Some plants with taproots, such as

IN THE COMMUNITY

Leaves, Stems, Roots

Do field research near your home or school and find three or four examples of stems, leaves, and visible roots. Do not damage or remove the plants—record your findings with sketches and written descriptions. Record the names of the plants you know. In addition to houseplants and plants found outdoors, these basic plant structures may be no farther away than the pantry. Many of the foods that we eat are plants, and other kitchen staples such as spices are made from plants.

carrot and beet plants, store large amounts of food, which they use to produce flowers and fruits. Gardeners and farmers usually harvest these roots before flowering occurs.

Another type of root, a **fibrous root,** is in the form of a clump of short, threadlike divisions. Fibrous roots often grow only in the upper few centimeters of the soil. They collect water and minerals from a shallow but wide area. Because the numerous roots wrap tightly around soil particles, fibrous roots are efficient at preventing soil erosion. Grasses are typical plants with fibrous roots.

FIGURE 17.5
Despite the prevailing winds that have made these branches grow sideways, this tree's deep roots anchor it firmly in place.

FIGURE 17.6

Flowers and Fruits

FLOWERS, SEEDS, FRUITS
A flower's life story

Although many plants lack flowers, people usually describe a typical plant as having flowers. A **flower** is the reproductive organ of a flowering plant. The function of flowers is to produce male gametes (sperm) and female gametes (eggs) and to provide a structure for fertilization.

Unlike most animals, plants are usually fixed in one spot for their entire lives, making sexual reproduction difficult. Some of the structures of flowers are adaptations that enable plants to sexually reproduce while remaining stationary.

A plant's production of pollen is an example of such an adaptation. Sexual reproduction in flowering plants begins when pollen, a carrier of sperm, is transported to the parts of flowers that contain eggs. The process of transporting pollen from male to female flower parts is called **pollination.** Pollen can be transported by wind, water, insects, or other organisms. Plants produce large quantities of pollen, which helps ensure that pollination will occur.

Fertilization—the union of sperm with eggs—occurs after pollination. The result of fertilization is the development of a zygote, which grows into a plant embryo. Tissues develop around the embryo to nourish it. Together these structures develop into a seed. A **seed** is a reproductive structure consisting of a plant embryo and its stored food. The offspring of many plants grow from seeds. You will learn more about pollination and fertilization in Chapter 19.

Pollination and fertilization
Many flowers contain colorful petals and other structures adapted for pollination and fertilization, steps in the reproduction of flowering plants.

Protection and dispersal
Fruits protect one or more seeds, which contain the plant embryos. Fruits often play a role in dispersing the seeds to new locations.

Seeds

Plants have various ways of dispersing, or spreading, their seeds. The methods of seed dispersal cause the offspring of plants to be spread over wider areas from one generation to the next. Being spread over increasingly wide areas improves the chances that a species will survive.

In flowering plants the seeds develop in a structure called a **fruit.** Fruits house and protect seeds and may also help disperse them to new locations. A great variety of fruits exist. Some familiar fruits are peaches, tomatoes, walnuts, and cherries. You can see the various structures involved in the production of orange fruits and seeds in *Figure 17.6.* What other fruits and seeds are a part of your diet?

ENVIRONMENTAL AWARENESS

Part-time farmers

Would you expect that working in a garden on Saturdays could be both fun and profitable? In 1992 a high school science teacher in Los Angeles invited her students to earn extra credit by raising some vegetables to sell at a local farmers' market.

At the end of the first year of the project, the students had a net income of a few hundred dollars. After splitting the profits among three graduates, the group wondered how to increase their profits. The students decided to expand their product line by making a salad dressing.

A local business helped the students with finances and advice on putting together a nutritious salad dressing. A local foundation gave a grant of money. The students' first product, "Straight out 'the Garden," was a creamy Italian salad dressing. By 1995, the group was able to contribute thousands of dollars to a scholarship fund for fellow students.

FIGURE 17.7
These high school students converted a plot of weeds into a productive garden, which became the start of a new business. Their salad dressing was a financial success.

These students are part of a worldwide trend toward growing crops in small areas away from farming communities. More and more people are planting crops beside roads, on balconies, in urban lots, and anywhere else plants can thrive. A recent United Nations report estimates that one in three of the world's urban residents is growing some kind of food.

The motivation to grow crops varies. Some people grow food for their own families. Some sell their crops for profit. Some share part or all of their produce with food banks and those in need. Do you garden? If so, what do you do with your crops?

CHECKPOINT 17.1

1. Describe the main structures of leaves, stems, and roots.
2. Compare the main functions of leaves, stems, roots, and flowers.
3. **Critical Thinking** Suppose that a plant lacked stems. What kind of challenges would it face in competing with other plants?

Build on What You Know

4. In what structures of the leaf does photosynthesis take place? Briefly describe these structures. *(Need to jog your memory? Revisit relevant concepts in Chapter 4, Section 4.2.)*

Examining the Parts of a Plant

WHAT YOU WILL DO Identify and observe the parts of a tomato plant

SKILLS YOU WILL USE Observing, measuring, comparing and contrasting

WHAT YOU WILL NEED A whole tomato plant, hand lens, sharp knife, small brush, metric ruler

Propose a Hypothesis

A tomato is a typical flowering plant. Propose a hypothesis about which structures you will find in the tomato plant.

Conduct Your Experiment

1 Obtain a specimen of a whole tomato plant with fruit, stems, leaves, and roots. Sketch the plant.
2 Examine a leaf. Draw the leaf, labeling the blade and the petiole.
3 Examine the underside of the leaf with the hand lens. Record the pattern of leaf veins. Add the veins to your drawing.
4 Examine a stem from the plant. Using a sharp knife, cut a cross section and a lengthwise section. Record what you see. **CAUTION:** Use care when handling the knife.
5 Use a knife to loosen the soil around the edge of the plant container. Gently remove the plant and soil ball from the pot. Using a small brush, carefully remove the soil from the roots until you can see the overall root shape. Record what you see.
6 Cut a tomato fruit in half. Draw the inside of the fruit.

Observe and record the patterns of seeds.
7 Remove individual seeds. About how many are there? Count the seeds and record the data. Examine a seed with the hand lens.

Analyze Your Data

1 Is the stem nonwoody (herbaceous) or woody?
2 Does the tomato have a taproot or a fibrous root?
3 Do tomato plants have flowers? How do you know?
4 Describe the structure of the tomato fruit and seeds?

Draw Conclusions

Did your observations support your hypothesis? Explain why or why not. If not, what other observations would be needed?

Design a Related Experiment

Choose a small plant that you consider unusual. Design an investigation that enables you to make as many comparisons as possible between the unusual plant you choose and the tomato plant you examined in this investigation.

Lab: Examining the Parts of a Plant

Objective: To identify and observe the parts of a tomato plant

Procedure

1. Sketch the plant. Label the parts.
2. Examine a leaf with the hand lens.
3.

17.2 Plants in the Biosphere

Recycling weeds

Water hyacinth is an aquatic weed notorious around the globe because its rapid reproduction clogs waterways. In Nepal, just one of the places where water hyacinth is a nuisance, local inhabitants use the fibrous plant for making paper. The papermakers help keep ponds and streams clear and make a useful product from plant material that would otherwise be thrown away.

What you'll learn

IDEAS
• To explain the role of plants in food chains
• To summarize the variety of ways that people use plants

WORDS
cereals, cellulose

ECOLOGICAL ROLES

Energy, oxygen, and shelter

Without plants, land animals would cease to exist. Plants are autotrophs, organisms that can make their own food using simple chemicals and an energy source. As you may recall, plants are also called producers because they make food that other organisms can use.

In a food chain, energy flows from one organism to another. Because of their photosynthetic ability, plants are the first link in most land-based food chains. Imagine a food chain that consists of plants, insects, birds, and wildcats. Plants use the sun's energy to convert carbon dioxide and water into carbohydrates. Energy is stored in the chemical bonds of carbohydrates.

The energy in plant carbohydrates is passed on to consumers when insects eat the plants. The energy is transferred again when birds eat insects. The transfer of energy in this food chain continues when wildcats devour birds.

Through photosynthesis, plants give off a supply of oxygen to the atmosphere. Almost all organisms, including plants and animals, need oxygen to perform cellular respiration—that is, to obtain energy by

FIGURE 17.8

Plants provide daily meals for many kinds of animals, and they also replenish the oxygen in the atmosphere. In addition, animals like this raccoon find shelter in naturally occurring plant structures. Beavers are famous for using plants to build lodges and dams.

You Say To-MAY-to, I Say To-MAH-to

Some of the foods that most people call vegetables are classified as fruits by biologists. How does the general public's definition of a fruit differ from a biologist's definition?

chemically breaking down food. The waste products of cellular respiration are water and carbon dioxide. So consumers supply plants with an essential ingredient for photosynthesis: carbon dioxide.

In addition to supplying food and oxygen, plants also provide shelter for other organisms. Many species of insects live under loose bark or among the leaves and roots of plants. Many kinds of birds and mammals live in or among plants or use plant materials to build nests for their young. Through protective coloration, many animals avoid predators by blending in with the plants in their environment.

HUMAN USES

Countless uses of plants

As consumers and as inhabitants of the biosphere, humans use plants in many of the same ways other animals do. However, humans have developed some additional uses for plants. These uses often cause humans to change the local environment in order to increase production of certain plants.

Agriculture Archaeological evidence indicates that humans have been growing plants for food for thousands of years. For example, early farmers in the Americas probably

FIGURE 17.9

Five Important Agricultural Plants
Major Areas of World Production

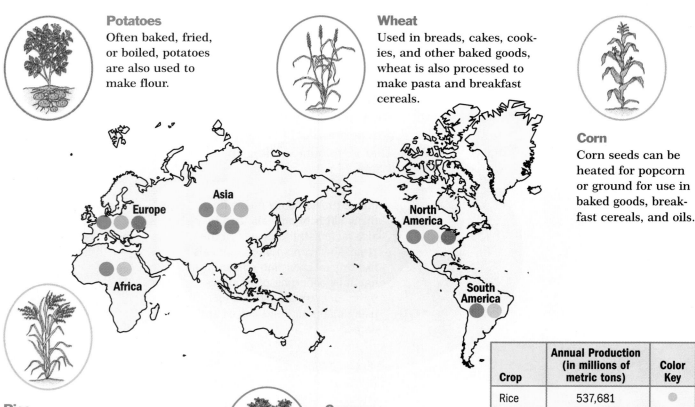

Potatoes
Often baked, fried, or boiled, potatoes are also used to make flour.

Wheat
Used in breads, cakes, cookies, and other baked goods, wheat is also processed to make pasta and breakfast cereals.

Corn
Corn seeds can be heated for popcorn or ground for use in baked goods, breakfast cereals, and oils.

Rice
Most rice is eaten in the form of white rice, but some is used to make flour, breakfast cereals, and snacks.

Cassava
These plant roots are boiled, roasted, and fried, and are also used to make flour and porridge.

Crop	Annual Production (in millions of metric tons)	Color Key
Rice	537,681	●
Wheat	534,822	●
Corn	505,978	●
Potato	270,621	●
Cassava	152,473	●

developed corn by breeding a plant called teosinte. Most ancient civilizations depended on plants as their main food source: rice in Asia; wheat and barley in the Middle East; and corn, squash, beans, and potatoes in various parts of the Americas.

Even now, the human diet is based overwhelmingly on plants. Almost 90 percent of the food you eat comes directly or indirectly from just 20 different kinds of cultivated plants. Rice, wheat, corn, potatoes, and cassava—the five most widely planted crops—feed a major portion of the world's population. Of these plants, rice, wheat, and corn are called cereals, cereal grains, or grains. The **cereals** are the edible fruits or seeds of grasses.

People get foods, flavorings, and spices from all parts of plants. You have probably eaten lettuce leaves, celery stems, and carrot roots. How many of the following food sources do you recognize? Sugar comes from the roots of sugar beets and from the stems of sugarcane. Olive oil comes from crushed fruit, and safflower oil from crushed seeds. Peppermint oil for flavoring is extracted from leaves and stems. Spices include gingerroot, cinnamon bark, and pepper fruits.

Medicines Many medicines are extracted from plants. For centuries, healers have used plant extracts to treat diseases. For example, Native Americans chewed willow bark to relieve pain. In the 1800s, chemists discovered that willow bark contained substances that could be used to make aspirin. Plants are the source of other medicines, such as digitalis and quinine.

New medicinal uses for plants are tested every year. The bark of the Pacific yew tree, which grows along the west coast of North America, contains taxol. Taxol appears to inhibit the growth of some cancers.

LAB ZONE — Think About It!

What Parts of Plants Do We Eat?

Humans eat a great variety of plant parts. The table below shows the plant foods a person ate each day for five days. Use this information to answer the following questions. Use your text or a botany reference source if you do not know what part of a particular plant is used for food.

Analyzing the Chart

1 On which days did the person eat seeds?
2 Name all the fruits the person ate over the five-day period.
3 Which foods are roots? Name three additional types of roots that humans eat.
4 Which plant part did the person eat most often: fruit, bark, seed, root, stem, leaf, or flower? Explain your answer.

Day	Food
Monday	lettuce, tomato, cucumber
Tuesday	oatmeal, cinnamon, raisins
Wednesday	rice, carrot
Thursday	apple, spearmint, sunflower
Friday	potato, broccoli

Industry Many useful products can be made from plants. Organic chemicals from plants are used in dyes, glues, perfumes, and car wax. Tannic acid in bark is used to tan, or stiffen and preserve, leather. Plant waxes and oils, such as lemon and tung oils, are used to polish wooden furniture.

In Chapter 2 you learned that a very common organic compound on Earth is the plant substance cellulose. **Cellulose** is a polysaccharide consisting of long chains of glucose molecules. Cellulose fibers make plants a suitable raw material for a number of products. For example, people process fibers from the cotton and flax plants into fabrics and rope. Wood is cut and shaped to form a variety of objects, from furniture and building lumber to bowling pins and musical instruments. Ground wood pulp is treated to make paper.

FIGURE 17.10
The black pepper used by many families to flavor foods comes from dried berries that are ground into tiny pieces.

Cork oak tree
(bulletin board)

Rubber tree
(Bunsen burner tubing)

Cotton plant
(pants)

Flax plant
(linen jacket)

Douglas fir
(cabinets)

FIGURE 17.11

The products of plants can be used in many ways: inside your body, in the clothing you wear, or in your environment. Which plant parts are used for the items in this photo?

Decomposed plants provide some heating fuels. Peats come from partly decayed plants. Coal, one of the "fossil fuels," was formed from plants that died between 280 and 360 million years ago.

"Problem" plants Plants are not always beneficial to humans. For example, some plants contain deadly poisons. Other plants, such as poison ivy, can cause allergic reactions and rashes in some people.

If you have ever worked in a garden, you know about the problems caused by weeds. Weeds can seriously harm food crops by competing for nutrients, water, and even sunlight. Even desirable plants can cause damage when they interfere with human activities. For example, the vinelike shoots of some plants can inhibit the growth of or even kill other plants. Tree roots can damage septic systems and water lines. Falling trees and limbs can damage homes and pull down power and telephone lines.

Despite the problems they can cause, plants sustain life—they play important roles in preventing erosion, providing food and shelter, and recycling water, carbon, oxygen, nitrogen, and minerals through an ecosystem. Without plants, life in all its amazing variety could not exist on Earth.

CHECKPOINT 17.2

1. Draw an example of a land-based food chain and label the producers and the consumers.

2. Summarize the ways humans use plants.

3. Critical Thinking Consider what you have learned about the uses of plants. Why do you think biologists are disturbed by the rapid extinction of plant species around the world?

Build on What You Know

4. What kinds of organisms typically are at the beginning of food chains in the ocean? *(Need to jog your memory? Revisit relevant concepts in Chapter 15, Section 15.5.)*

17.3 Characteristics of Plants

The blueprints of nature

When some architects and engineers look at trees, they see models of structural stability. Trees can bear more than four times their weight without breaking. Trees have even been used as the basis for certain designs. The architect of the Eiffel Tower in France took inspiration from the trunk of an oak tree when he designed the base of that landmark.

What you'll learn

IDEAS
• To describe the stationary existence of a plant
• To compare the three types of plant tissues
• To summarize the alternation of generations that occurs in plants

WORDS
xylem, phloem, alternation of generations

A TYPICAL PLANT

Is being green enough?

Do you know a plant when you see one? Which of the following organisms are plants: trees without leaves in winter, seaweed anchored to ocean-side rocks, green leaf-bearing organisms that trap and digest insects, water lilies living on the surface of a pond?

For biologists, the definition of the plant kingdom has changed over time. The plant kingdom used to include plants, fungi, and some protists. Today the kingdom is smaller. Plants can be characterized by contrasting them with organisms from the other kingdoms. Which properties of plants set them apart from other life forms, such as the praying mantis in *Figure 17.12*? Which properties of plants are characteristic of only the plant kingdom?

Plants are multicellular eukaryotes. These two characteristics make them different from the prokaryotic monerans and unicellular protists. Plants differ from multicellular protists in that plants contain specialized structures that multicellular protists lack. Plant cells contain cell walls; animal cells do not. And almost all plants are autotrophs, whereas animals, fungi, and most monerans are heterotrophs.

According to these criteria, all the organisms you were just asked about are plants—except seaweed. Seaweed is classified as a multicellular protist.

MULTICELLULAR ORGANIZATION

Specialized cells distribute the work

All plants are multicellular; composed of thousands or even billions of cells. Plant cells are specialized. Cell specialization means that the cells have structural modifications that enable them to perform a specific function. Specialized cells are interdependent; they require resources that are supplied by other cells in order to live. How would a group of specialized cells be more efficient than a colony of unspecialized, independent cells?

FIGURE 17.12
Despite its green color, this praying mantis is very different from the green plant on which it hides in order to catch insects. How many differences can you describe?

Plant cells Even though they are specialized for various functions, plant cells do share some common characteristics with many other types of cells. For example, most plant cells have a nucleus embedded in cytoplasm. All have organelles such as mitochondria and ribosomes.

A few characteristics of plant cells make them very different from animal cells. First, most plant cells contain chloroplasts, the organelles that make photosynthesis possible. The photosynthetic pigment chlorophyll and other pigments are located inside chloroplasts.

Second, a rigid cell wall encloses a plant cell, giving it a shape. The cell wall is composed of cellulose and other substances. Cell walls enable a plant to grow and obtain materials from the environment. In addition, plant cells are connected to one another by shared cytoplasm. These cytoplasm extensions can pass through pores in the cell walls of adjacent cells so that materials in the cytoplasm can be shared. Most plant cells have large, central vacuoles.

Plant tissues Groups of cells that are similar in structure and are arranged so that they can perform a specialized function are called tissues. Scientists classify plant tissues into three types: dermal, vascular, and ground. The location of these tissues in various plant structures is shown in *Figure 17.13*.

Dermal tissue (sometimes called protective or surface tissue) forms the outermost tissue layer on leaves and stems. On leaves, the dermal tissue can be covered with a waxy substance that makes the leaves waterproof. On stems, dermal tissue may be in the form of thick bark, spongy cork, or a tight sheath. Protection is one function of dermal cells. Some dermal cells also contain chloroplasts and perform photosynthesis.

There are two types of vascular tissue (also called transporting or conducting tissue). **Xylem** is vascular tissue that transports water and minerals in a plant. It is made mostly of dead cells with thick cell walls stacked end to end to form a continuous tube shaped like a drinking straw. **Phloem** is vascular tissue that transports the sugars produced by photosynthesis throughout a plant. It is composed of living cells.

All the remaining plant cells are part of ground tissue, or fundamental tissue. Some cells of ground tissue, called parenchyma cells, perform photosynthesis and store organic compounds. Other ground tissue cells provide support, especially for young and herbaceous plants.

FIGURE 17.13

Plant Tissues

The majority of plants have three types of tissues. What do the cross-sections of a leaf, stem, and root show you about the location of those tissues?

Dermal tissue
Vascular tissue
Ground tissue

FIGURE 17.14
Unlike animals, most of which move around looking for food and water, plants usually grow in one location. How do they obtain the materials they need?

STATIONARY EXISTENCE

Life's challenges on the spot

When you think of plants, what is the first characteristic that occurs to you? Perhaps it is that plants do not move from place to place as animals do. Plants are stationary organisms. They do not have tissues that are specialized for movement.

Plants can grow in a variety of locations. Most plants grow in soil. A few plants grow attached to the trunks or branches of trees. A very few plants live on the surface of water.

Regardless of where they live, plants must obtain the energy and materials they need without moving to a new location. Sunlight is an abundant source of energy for all but a few parasitic plants. Air and soil supply the essential materials for plants to grow. The carbon dioxide that plants need for photosynthesis comes from the air.

LAB ZONE Do It!

Observing the Effects of Light on Plants

How do different levels of light affect plants? Find out when you . . .

Try This

1 Use six plants of the same species and age. Divide the plants among three pots.
2 Label the pots *High Light, Low Light,* and *No Light.* Record the appearance of the plants right after potting, and then place the pots in their appropriate locations.
3 Over the next week, observe the plants every other day and record their appearance. Water them according to the needs of their species. Be sure to give each set of plants the same amount of water.

Analyze Your Results

1 Which plants changed the most during the week? Which changed the least?
2 What conclusions can you draw from the changes in the appearance of the plants? Explain.
3 What recommendations would you make regarding the ideal amount of light for this plant species?

The water and other minerals that plants require come from the soil. (Dissolved gases and minerals supply the needs of plants that live in water.)

Because plants cannot move from place to place, sexual reproduction is a complicated process. Sexual reproduction cannot occur unless a sperm and egg unite. As you have learned, plants have special structures that enable them to reproduce sexually.

FIGURE 17.15
Just as sunflowers "follow" (continuously face) the sun, many plants respond to environmental changes.

Animals

Plants

FIGURE 17.16
Unlike animals, plants have an intermediate stage between diploid parent and diploid offspring. This stage involves the formation of haploid spores that grow into haploid organisms. How is the production of haploid cells different in animals?

TWO-PHASE LIFE CYCLE

From haploid to diploid and back again

All plants undergo **alternation of generations,** in which they switch from diploid (2n) generations to haploid (n) generations. During each of these two stages, the plant has unique structures and functions. It is not certain what benefits a two-phase life cycle may have for plants, but it is clear that plants reproduce very differently from animals.

The diploid plant has two complete sets of chromosomes (2n). However, instead of producing gametes, the diploid plant undergoes meiosis to produce haploid spores (n). Plant spores divide by mitosis to form a plant structure in which each cell is haploid (n). This is very different from animals, in which meiosis only produces gametes for sexual reproduction. You can compare the two processes in *Figure 17.16*.

The haploid plant produces gametes in specialized structures by further mitotic divisions. During fertilization, some of the haploid (n) gametes will fuse with other haploid (n) gametes, forming a zygote, which develops into a new diploid (2n) organism. The new diploid (2n) plant has two sets of chromosomes, one from each haploid (n) parent.

CHECKPOINT 17.3

1. How does a plant's stationary existence affect carrying out essential functions?

2. Identify and describe the three types of tissues that plant cells can form.

3. Briefly compare the stages of the plant life cycle and the animal life cycle.

4. Critical Thinking Plants do not move but animals can. How does this difference affect their life functions?

Build on What You Know

5. What are the differences between mitotic division and meiotic division? Contrast the roles of mitosis and meiosis in plant and animal reproduction. *(Need to jog your memory? Revisit relevant concepts in Chapter 5, Section 5.4.)*

What are the main structures that enable plants to survive on land and produce food?

17.4 Overview of Plant Diversity

Social climbers

The bromeliad shown here is an example of an epiphyte—a plant that lives on another plant without harming it. Bromeliads, common in rainforests, are relatively large plants that flower and produce seeds. The seeds take hold in patches of windborn soil and decaying vegetation on tree limbs. Size and method of reproduction are among the characteristics used to classify plants.

What you'll learn

IDEAS
• To contrast the diversity of plant size, woodiness, reproduction, and lifespans
• To identify some features used to classify plants

WORDS
vascular plant, nonvascular plant, gymnosperm, angiosperm, annual, biennial, perennial

SIZE

Pining for the sky

One of the easiest ways to appreciate the great diversity of plant species is to look at their size. Plants can range in size from towering pine trees to the tiny mosses that grow on their bark. Plants can also differ greatly in other structures and functions. How did the diversity in the plant kingdom arise?

The great diversification of plant characteristics is the result of several key adaptations that arose during their evolution. Taxonomists use these key characteristics to classify plants, as you will learn in Chapter 20. Some important adaptations are the presence of an internal transport system, the production of seeds, and the enclosure of seeds in a protective covering.

Which of these characteristics is related to the size of a moss or a tree? The answer is the presence or absence of an internal transport system. Vascular tissue transports water and dissolved materials through a plant. A plant that has vascular tissue is called a **vascular plant.** All trees, vines, and flowering plants are vascular

plants. A plant without vascular tissue is called a **nonvascular plant.** Nonvascular plants tend to be smaller than vascular plants. Mosses are common nonvascular plants.

Have you ever seen the cross-section of a tree trunk and noticed the series of rings of increasing size radiating outward from the center? These concentric rings represent layers of vascular tissue. If you cut across a moss stem, you would see that this pattern is absent. Mosses have no vascular tissue and therefore lack the extensive internal transport system of trees.

How is the size of a plant related to the presence or absence of vascular tissue? Vascular plants grow larger and taller than nonvascular plants because they can transport water and nutrients a greater distance. Larger plants have more vascular tissue.

FIGURE 17.17
The presence of vascular tissue is one factor that allows this tree to grow much larger than the moss living on its bark.

Categorizing Plants

In order to categorize plants, botanists examine and compare plants. You can categorize types of plants when you . . .

Try This

1 Collect samples of wood and wood products—for example, sticks, children's blocks, or kitchen spoons. Collect photographs or illustrations of plants.
2 For each wood sample or wood product, decide if it came from a tree, shrub, or vine. Record your categorizations.
3 Estimate the actual size of the plants shown in each photograph or illustration. Record your estimates.
4 If the plants have stems, note their appearance and diameter. Record your observations about the stems of all specimens, leaving room under each entry for further data.

Analyze Your Results

1 Sort all the photos and illustrations into two groups: woody and nonwoody plants.
2 Test this hypothesis: Woody shrubs and trees tend to be bigger than nonwoody plants.
3 Use the categories you devised in step 2 to compare the sizes of plants to their kinds of wood products. Explain your findings.

WOODINESS

Some plants are harder than others

Vascular plants can be subdivided into various groups according to the characteristics of their stems. One of the most important and noticeable stem characteristics is woodiness. Wood is a substance composed primarily of layers of xylem cells. The cellulose in the cell walls of vascular tissue provides structure for the plant. However, cellulose is just one of the many structural components of wood. Other wood components include lignin and polysaccharides called pectic substances.

Woody plants are often described as trees, shrubs, or vines. Shrubs are typically smaller than trees, and vines have stems that are relatively flimsy. Examples of woody vines are grapes, blackberries, and climbing roses. Examples of shrubs include blueberry, rhododendron, dwarf spruce, boxwood, and roses.

Plant stems that are smooth and nonwoody are characteristic of the second group of vascular plants. Plants with nonwoody stems are called herbaceous plants. Herbaceous plants do not produce wood as they grow. Examples of herbaceous plants are ferns, zinnias, tomatoes, petunias, daisies, and birds-of-paradise.

REPRODUCTION

Flowers are just one way to reproduce

A plant's reproductive system is another characteristic used for classification. Based on their mechanism for sexual reproduction, there are two main groups of plants. One group, the seed plants, form seeds for protection and nourishment of the plant embryo. This group can be further divided according to whether the seeds are formed in a cone or fruit. A second group, the seedless plants, do not form seeds.

Mosses and ferns are examples of seedless plants. Plants of their haploid generation form gametes. Fertilization occurs in specialized structures in a haploid parent. The fused gametes develop immediately into growing embryos. The moss or fern embryo develops into a diploid offspring within the structure of a parent plant. For this reason, the embryo does not need to await favorable conditions before developing. What are some of the advantages and disadvantages of plant reproduction without seeds?

As you just read, there are two categories of seed plants. A vascular plant that produces seeds enclosed in cones is a **gymnosperm.** Gymnosperms include pines, firs, spruces, cypresses, and redwoods. After fertilization occurs, the seeds of gymnosperms develop within cones and are released when the cones open. You will learn more about the life cycle of gymnosperms in Chapter 20.

A vascular plant that produces seeds enclosed in fruit is called an **angiosperm.** A fruit is a structure that provides a means for protecting and spreading seeds. Seeds usually do not sprout and grow until the fruit that encloses them has been removed from the parent plant.

Fruit exists as two types: fleshy and dry. Fleshy fruits, including apples, cherries, grapes, strawberries, tomatoes, and cucumbers, have a high moisture content. (Some of the foods we think of as vegetables are considered to be fruits by scientists.) Dry fruits include walnuts, acorns, wheat kernels, and the tiny parachute structures of dandelions.

You may wonder about reproduction in grasses, which are common herbaceous plants. Grasses are flowering plants that produce seeds. To maintain their lawns, most people cut the grass before it can "go to seed." Actually, mowing prevents the grass plants from developing any seed producing flowers.

FIGURE 17.18

Shopping for Plants

In nurseries across the country, people select plants to grow as houseplants or in home gardens. What traits might be important in determining the types of plants to purchase?

LIFE SPAN

A day or a century . . .

The fourth feature used to classify plants is the length of time they live—their life span. Plants vary greatly in life spans. Some plants live for a matter of days, whereas others live for centuries. There are three general categories of plant life spans.

An **annual** is a plant that lives, reproduces, and dies in one year or in one growing season. Most vegetables and garden flowers are annuals. Most annuals are herbaceous plants.

A **biennial,** less common than an annual, is a plant that completes its life cycle in two years. Biennials usually do not flower until their second year. Biennials include garden flowers such as pansies and foxglove. Two other familiar biennials, carrots and beets, are usually harvested for their stems and roots during the first growing season.

A **perennial** is a plant that lives, reproduces, and continues to grow year after year. Perennials may be either herbaceous or woody. Some of the most familiar woody plants—trees—are perennials.

The life span of plants is determined by a combination of genetic and environmental factors. Many long-lived plants continue growing despite yearly environmental fluctuations. However, harsh environmental conditions can shorten the life of other plants. What kinds of weather conditions do you think adversely affect plant life? Have you had any experience with situations in which environmental conditions caused the early death of plants?

That Bread Is Really Stale!

4000-year-old loaves of bread were found in ancient Egyptian tombs. Analysis of the bread shows that the Egyptians baked with emmer, a tough-hulled type of wheat. When the grain was allowed to sprout before it was dried and ground, it produced a more nutritious flour.

FIGURE 17.19

Bristlecone pines have one of the longest known life spans. Some of them are more than 5000 years old.

CHECKPOINT 17.4

1. Summarize the diversity found in plants' size, woodiness, reproduction, and life span.
2. Give examples of the way plants are classified, based on specific features.
3. **Critical Thinking** Propose a hypothesis to explain why angiosperms have become the dominant type of plant.

Build on What You Know

4. Annual, biennial, and perennial plants all have different lifespans. What types of niches do each of the three groups of plants occupy? Would the niches be different in different environments? Explain your answers. *(Need to jog your memory? Revisit relevant concepts in Chapter 10, Section 10.1.)*

 What are four key features used to classify plants?

Chapter 17 Review

THE BIG IDEA! 17.1–17.3 Most plants have structures that enable them to survive on land and produce food.
17.4 Key features can be used to classify plants.

Sum It Up

Use the following summary to review the main concepts in this chapter.

17.1 The Structure of Plants

- The basic structures of a leaf—blades, veins, and petioles—enable the leaf to function as an organ of photosynthesis.
- Leaves can be classified as simple or compound. Compound leaves can be further classified as pinnate or palmate.
- Stems support leaves and flowers. Stems also transport water and nutrients within the plant.
- Roots absorb water and minerals and anchor plants. Plants can have either a single large, taproot or numerous small, diffuse roots.
- Flowering plants reproduce by means of flowers, seeds, and fruits.

17.2 Plants in the Biosphere

- Carbohydrates produced by plants begin most food chains on land. Plants are also a source of oxygen for cellular respiration.
- Humans obtain 90 percent of their food directly or indirectly from 20 kinds of cultivated plants.
- Many plant extracts are used as medicines.
- Wood and cellulose are used for fuel, construction, and fabrics.

17.3 Characteristics of Plants

- Most plants have dermal tissues for protection, vascular tissues for transport, and ground tissues for all other functions.
- Plants are stationary; they depend on gases in the air and nutrients from the soil dissolved in water to survive.
- Plant life cycles alternate between haploid and diploid generations.

17.4 Overview of Plant Diversity

- The size of a plant is related to the presence or absence of vascular tissue.
- Trees and shrubs have woody stems. Herbaceous plants such as ferns and many flowering plants have nonwoody stems.
- Plants can be classified by whether or not they have seeds and whether or not they have flowers.
- Plants can be classified by whether they live one year, two years, or many years.

Use Terms and Concepts

**Use each of the following words or terms in a complete sentence.
If you need to review a meaning, turn to the page indicated.**

blade (p. 398)
veins (p. 399)
petiole (p. 399)
taproot (p. 401)
fibrous root (p. 401)
flower (p. 402)

pollination (p. 402)
seed (p. 402)
fruit (p. 403)
cereals (p. 407)
cellulose (p. 407)
xylem (p. 410)

phloem (p. 410)
alternation of
   generations (p. 412)
vascular plant (p. 413)
nonvascular plant
   (p. 413)

gymnosperm (p. 415)
angiosperm (p. 415)
annual (p. 416)
biennial (p. 416)
perennial (p. 416)

Use Your Word Power

COMPLETION **Write the word or phrase that best completes each statement below.**

1. The life cycle of plants is called _____ .

2. The _____ is the flat part of the leaf that contains the cells for photosynthesis.

3. _____ is a compound in cell walls that is made of long chains of glucose molecules.

4. _____ are the edible fruits or seeds of grasses.

5. Plants that have an extensive transport system are called _____ .

6. During _____ , pollen from male flower parts is transported to female flower parts.

MULTIPLE CHOICE **Choose the letter of the word or phrase that best completes each statement.**

7. Veins transport fluids between leaves and stems through (a) fibrous roots; (b) blades; (c) petioles; (d) taproots.

8. The plant reproductive structure that consists of an embryo and its food is a (a) flower; (b) cereal; (c) gamete; (d) seed.

9. The tubelike vessels in leaves that carry water, minerals, and sugar are (a) taproots; (b) veins; (c) vascular plants; (d) blades.

10. Plants that lack transport tissues are (a) vascular plants; (b) nonvascular plants; (c) perennials; (d) flowering plants.

11. The reproductive organs of flowering plants are (a) flowers; (b) cones; (c) fruits; (d) petioles.

Show What You Know

12. How do the patterns of veins differ in monocot and dicot leaves? Draw examples.

13. What kind of tissue is xylem? How does it differ from phloem?

14. Describe the structure and function of fruit.

15. Compare annuals, biennials, and perennials.

16. What are the relative advantages of taproots and fibrous roots?

17. What reproductive structure do angiosperms and gymnosperms have that mosses and ferns lack? What advantage is there to having such a structure?

18. What are the similarities and differences between the two stages of a plant's life cycle?

19. **Make a Concept Map** Complete the concept map below by adding the following terms: flower, xylem, phloem, gymnosperms, angiosperms, cones.

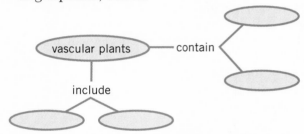

Take It Further

20. **Making an Analogy** What do short-distance runners, middle-distance runners, and long-distance runners have in common with annuals, biennials, and perennials?

21. **Organizing and Classifying** Imagine that you are serving on a committee for economic development in your area. Research some businesses and industries related to plants that the committee might want to bring into the area to promote economic growth. Take into account the area's climate, soil type, and available resources when making your recommendations.

22. **Designing an Experiment** Suppose you find some flower seeds in an envelope that has no identifying label. Design an experiment to show whether or not the seeds are those of an annual plant.

23. Interpreting a Graph Many gardeners spread a layer of mulch—pine bark, wood chips, straw, or other organic matter—on the soil around plants. This graph shows one effect that mulch has on soil. Describe that effect. What conditions might have produced the changes shown in the graph?

Changes in Soil Moisture

Relative Amount of Moisture (%)

Time (number of days)

■ Soil covered with mulch
■ Soil without mulch

24. Analyzing Data Examine these leaves and write a description of each. Classify each leaf according to its structure.

a   b

Consider the Issues

25. Production Versus Population Scientists are trying to develop new varieties of food crops that will increase the amount of food produced on a given plot of land. At the same time, the world population keeps increasing. Do you think it is possible to solve the problem of world hunger by increasing agricultural production? Explain your answer.

Make New Connections

26. Biology and Art Notice how one sixteenth-century artist used plant forms in a portrait. Consult art history books to find other works that use plants in fanciful ways, and then create your own "plant art."

Emperor Rudolph II (1590), painted by Guiseppi Arcimboldo

27. Biology and Economics Research how much wheat, rice, and corn are produced by the world's four leading nations for each crop. Why are there different production patterns?

28. Biology and Community: A Project Find out about the most important kinds of plants grown in your county or state, and investigate the ways these plants are used. Report your findings.

FAST-FORWARD TO CHAPTER 18

Chapter 18 will explore three topics that were introduced in this chapter: how plants obtain energy, how plants transport water and other nutrients, and how plants grow.

bioSURF

You can find out more about life processes in plants by exploring the following Internet address:
http://plants.biosurf.com

In this chapter . . .

FEATURES

Everyday Biology
- Drowning Plants
- Where Does Maple Syrup Come From?
- Steady as a . . . Hammock?

In the Community
Trimming Trees

 Environmental Awareness
Too Much CO_2?

LAB ZONES

Discover It!
- Experimenting with Leaves

Do It!
- Observing Stomata and Guard Cells
- Observing Plant Transport
- Measuring Root and Stem Growth

Think About It!
- Analyzing Tree Rings

Investigate It!
- Observing Leaves, Stems, and Roots

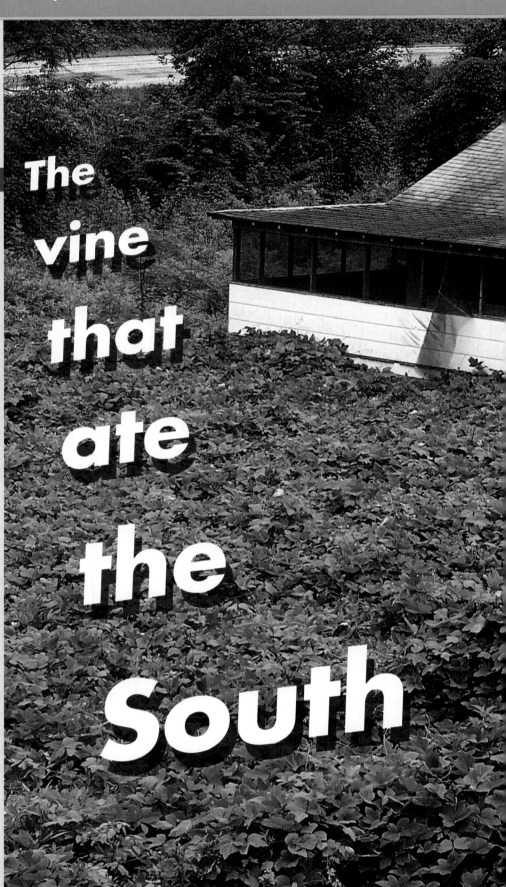

The vine that ate the South

T he "mile-a-minute vine"—that's what people from the southern United States sometimes call kudzu (KUHD-zoo). Kudzu can grow about one foot per day; it is one of the fastest-growing plants that we know.

Native to parts of Asia, kudzu arrived in 1876, when it was displayed in the Japanese pavilion at the United States Centennial Exhibition. Americans liked its attractive, fragrant flowers and began planting the vine. During the Great Depression of the 1930s, farmers controlled soil erosion by cultivating acres of kudzu. In the warm, damp climate of the South, removed from its natural insect enemies, kudzu flourished—too well. It covered fences and buildings, choked trees, and toppled utility poles. In just a few years, kudzu came to be regarded as an annoying, destructive weed. Kudzu is difficult to kill, and one herbicide even increases its growth! Kudzu now covers more than 7 million acres of the South.

In Japan, where kudzu does not grow as well, it is used for a variety of products, including a cornstarchlike substance, herbal remedies, baskets, fabrics, and paper. The demand for these products in Japan could make kudzu a cash crop for southern farmers in the United States. It seems that the weed's new uses may gain it some respect again.

Although kudzu's growth rate is unusual, its life processes are the same as those of other plants. What are the life processes of plants?

Experimenting with Leaves

You need *a potted plant and petroleum jelly*

1. Coat the top of several leaves with a heavy layer of petroleum jelly.
2. Coat the underside of several different leaves with a heavy layer of petroleum jelly.
3. Observe the leaves daily for one week. Record your observations.

In Chapters 4 and 17 you read about photosynthesis. What changes, if any, did you observe in the two sets of leaves you used in your experiment? How do you think coating the leaves with petroleum jelly affected the plant's ability to perform photosynthesis?

WRITE ABOUT IT!
In your science journal, write what you know about plant growth and reproduction. If possible, include examples from your own observations of your yard or community. Or, ask gardeners or people who grow houseplants about their experience with plants. Record what you learn.

18.1 Photosynthesis in Plants

What you'll learn

IDEAS
- To describe the structure of a leaf and identify where photosynthesis occurs
- To explain the roles of sunlight, water, and carbon dioxide in photosynthesis

WORDS
cuticle, stomata, mesophyll, compensation point

Making the best of it

Several adaptations for maximizing photosynthesis have evolved in plants. For example, in some plants, such as the one shown here, the undersides of the leaves have pigments that reflect escaping light back into the leaves for a second harvest. In other plants, transparent patches on each leaf's surface act as lenses to concentrate the light on the chlorophyll inside the leaf.

LEAVES: SITES OF PHOTOSYNTHESIS

Secrets of leaves

As you learned in Chapter 17, plants can make their own food from molecules of carbon dioxide and water, provided they have the right source of energy—light. During photosynthesis, plants transform light energy into the chemical bonds in glucose and other compounds.

Photosynthesis occurs primarily inside the green leaves of plants. (In mosses, photosynthesis occurs in the green leaflike structures.) Although photosynthesis is the main function of leaves, it is not their only function. In some plants, leaves also store food.

Figure 18.1 includes a micrograph and a drawing that show a typical leaf. Recall that a leaf consists of a flat, broad blade and a stemlike petiole that

FIGURE 18.1

Leaf Structure

Petiole

Vein   Blade

Mesophyll (ground tissue)

Cuticle

Upper epidermis (dermal tissue)

Vein (vascular tissue)

Chloroplast in mesophyll cell

Lower epidermis (dermal tissue)

Stoma

Guard cells

attaches the blade to the stem. Internally, leaves contain the same three types of tissue—dermal, ground, and vascular—as stems and roots.

A leaf epidermis has two specialized structures that are adaptations for photosynthesis on land: the waxy cuticle and the stomata (stoh-MAH-tuh). The **cuticle** is a waterproof layer that coats the parts of the plant exposed to the air. This waxy covering helps conserve water by slowing evaporation. You can use your fingernail to scrape off the thick cuticle of some plants, such as the wax palm. The cuticle from the wax palm is called carnauba wax and is used to make polishes, candles, and lipstick.

The **stomata** (singular: *stoma*) are pores, or holes, in the epidermis that allow gas exchange. In the leaf shown in *Figure 18.1,* the stomata are on the underside. Stomata allow carbon dioxide to enter a leaf, and water vapor and oxygen to diffuse out. Guard cells like those shown in *Figure 18.2* surround each stoma. The guard cells open or close the stomata, depending on environmental conditions and the needs of the plant. In general, stomata are open during the day and closed at night.

FIGURE 18.2

When a pair of guard cells open to form a pore, or stoma, water vapor and oxygen diffuse from the leaf. What substance enters the leaf through the stoma?

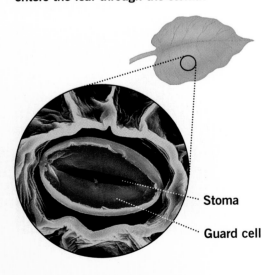

Stoma

Guard cell

LAB ZONE **Do It!**

Observing Stomata and Guard Cells

Some of the raw materials and products of photosynthesis enter and exit through stomata in leaves. Guard cells open or close the stomata depending on environmental conditions. Watch how guard cells work when you . . .

Try This

1 Cut a small leaf from a plant. (Plants with smooth leaves work best.) Place it on a slide. Examine the underside of the leaf with the microscope on low and high power.
2 Identify and sketch a stoma and its guard cells.
3 What conditions could you manipulate to change the size of the stoma? Design an experiment that involves changing one environmental condition.
4 Record the appearance of the stoma and guard cells again. Then implement your idea for altering the leaf's environmental conditions. Record any changes you observe.

Analyze Your Results

1 What happened when you changed the leaf's environmental conditions? Why?
2 If the guard cells did not react, how might you change your procedure to produce a response?

If you look more closely at the cutaway section in *Figure 18.1,* you will see that there is a region of ground tissue between the two layers of epidermis. This region, called the **mesophyll,** is a tissue made of parenchyma cells (pah-REN-kih-muh). Parenchyma cells are the most abundant and least specialized type of plant cells. Air spaces make up 20 to 70 percent of the volume of the mesophyll. The air spaces allow carbon dioxide and oxygen gases to be exchanged inside the leaf.

The mesophyll is the part of the leaf where most photosynthesis takes place. Cells in the mesophyll contain hundreds of tiny green structures called chloroplasts. Inside each chloroplast are thousands of chlorophyll molecules that capture the sun's energy.

As you learned in Chapter 17, leaves have a network of tubelike structures called veins. Veins are made of vascular tissue arranged in bundles. Like other vascular tissue, veins in leaves transport water and food. Water moves from the veins to the mesophyll cells, which transport sugar to back to the veins. Veins have an outer layer of cells called the bundle sheath. In some plants, photosynthesis occurs in the bundle sheath as well as in the mesophyll.

FACTORS AFFECTING PHOTOSYNTHESIS

A simple threesome

As you learned in Chapter 4, in nature photosynthesis requires three key factors: energy from the sun, water, and carbon dioxide.

Light Photosynthesis takes place in two stages. It begins with a light-trapping stage that occurs only when the sun or artificial light shines on the plant. Chlorophyll and other photosynthetic pigments in the plant act as "light antennas," absorbing light energy and transforming it into chemical energy. Oxygen is given off during the light-trapping stage.

The second stage, called the Calvin cycle, does not need light to proceed. The Calvin cycle uses stored energy and certain compounds made during the light reactions to convert carbon dioxide into simple sugars such as glucose.

In addition to carrying out photosynthesis, plants also respire. Cellular respiration is the breakdown of molecules such as glucose into simpler molecules such as carbon dioxide and water. Cellular respiration provides energy for plants. Plants use the energy released from breaking down glucose to grow, reproduce, and synthesize essential compounds. The waste products of cellular respiration in plants are the same as those in animals—carbon dioxide and water.

As you may have guessed, plants perform both processes simultaneously: they make glucose by photosynthesis and utilize the glucose for energy at the same time. The net amount of sugar made by a plant depends on several factors, including the plant's rate of

FIGURE 18.3

Sugar cane (left), a tropical grass, requires lots of sunlight. How would the light requirements of the plants that grow under redwood trees compare to the light requirements of sugar cane?

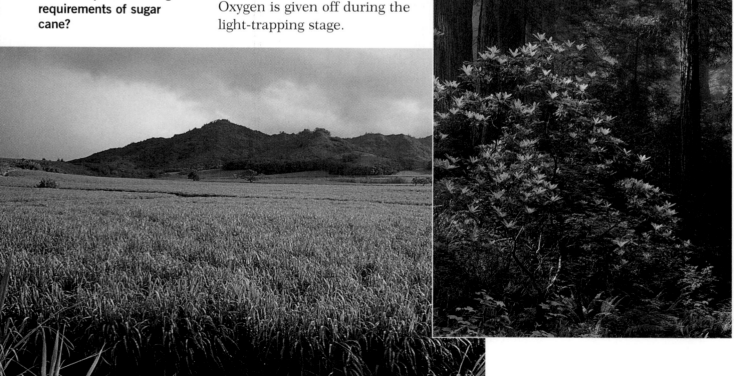

cellular respiration. One factor that affects the production of sugar is the amount of available light. The **compensation point** is the amount of light energy, captured through photosynthesis, that will just keep a plant alive.

You can think of the compensation point as the amount of light energy needed by a plant to balance its energy needs. If the sugar made by photosynthesis just balances the sugar used by the plant to stay alive, there is no net energy gain or loss. If a plant makes more sugar than it uses, the plant gains energy. Plants can store this excess energy or use it for growth. If a plant uses more sugar than it makes, there is a net energy loss for the plant. What do you think happens if a plant receives less sunlight than its compensation point over a long period of time?

The amount of sunlight required for specific plants to reach their compensation point varies. Some plants, such as sugar cane and other tropical grasses, need a great deal of light and grow best in full sunlight. Other plants, such as ivy and azaleas, need only a moderate amount of sunlight. They can grow in the shade. Some garden plants are designated shade-loving plants.

Many shade plants grow beneath the larger trees of a mature forest, along with younger trees. Shade plants and young trees grow relatively slowly when light is scarce. However, after old trees fall or are cut down, more light can reach the forest floor. Smaller shade plants may then grow more quickly, reaching their full height and width. Young trees may also begin to approach their full potential size.

Water As mentioned previously, water is a key ingredient for photosynthesis. Plants need water to complete the first stage of photosynthesis—the light-trapping reactions.

FIGURE 18.4
Van Helmont's Experiment

Year one
Van Helmont planted a 2-kg willow tree in about 90 kg of soil.

Year five
After five years, the tree gained 75 kg, and the soil lost about 55 g.

In 1630 Jan Baptista van Helmont, a Belgian physician, performed a classic experiment that helped scientists understand the role of water in photosynthesis. As illustrated in *Figure 18.4*, van Helmont planted a 2-kilogram (kg) willow tree in a tub containing about 90 kg of soil. He watered the tree with rainwater for five years, and then he weighed the tree and the dried-out soil. The tree had gained about 75 kg, whereas the soil had lost only about 55 grams (g). (Recall that 1000 g make up 1 kg, so the loss in the soil's weight was extremely small.)

Van Helmont concluded that the tree's growth was due almost exclusively to the water that had been added to the soil. But he was only partly right. Van Helmont had neglected to consider that a substance from the air (carbon dioxide) might also affect the plant's weight. However, van Helmont did show that soil does not contribute very much to the new material of a growing plant.

Van Helmont's experiment illustrates the way scientific knowledge is sometimes gained. When researchers investigate an unknown event, they may discover the explanation a step at a time. Today, scientists know that about 90 percent of the water taken in

FIGURE 18.5

When water (H$_2$O) enters the guard cells of a leaf, they swell, opening the stoma, or pore. When guard cells lose water, they become limp, closing the stoma. What is the role of the stoma?

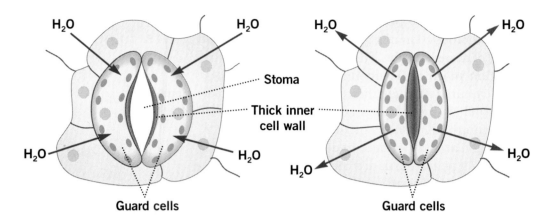

H$_2$O   H$_2$O   H$_2$O   H$_2$O

Stoma

Thick inner cell wall

H$_2$O   H$_2$O   H$_2$O   H$_2$O

Guard cells   Guard cells

FIGURE 18.6
In 1782 Jean Senebier used an experiment like the one illustrated here to show that photosynthesis requires carbon dioxide (CO$_2$).

Without CO$_2$
Leaves placed in water that does not contain CO$_2$ give off no O$_2$ when exposed to sunlight.

O$_2$

With CO$_2$
Leaves placed in water that contains CO$_2$ give off O$_2$ when exposed to sunlight.

by plants is lost through evaporation and is not used in photosynthesis. Consequently, most of the water absorbed by the plant does not add to the plant's mass.

Scientists also now know that the amount of water in a plant is controlled by the opening and closing of the stomata through the action of guard cells. Exactly how does this occur?

Look at the pair of guard cells surrounding each stoma, or pore, shown in *Figure 18.5*. As you can see, the cell walls nearest the pore are thicker than the cell walls on the opposite side. When water is abundant in a plant, the two guard cells expand and their thin outer walls are forced into a curved shape. This action causes the thick inner walls to be pulled away from each other, and the stoma opens wider. When water is scarce in the plant, the guard cells shrink. The thick inner walls are not pulled away from each other, and the stoma becomes smaller or closes.

Overall, the availability of water affects photosynthesis in two ways. First, water is needed as a raw material for the reactions that trap light energy. Second, enough water must be available to keep the guard cells full so the stomata in the leaves will stay open. When the stomata close, carbon dioxide cannot enter the leaves, and the plant is rapidly depleted of

another key ingredient for photosynthesis: carbon dioxide.

Carbon dioxide Carbon dioxide (CO$_2$) is the third key factor for photosynthesis. As you may recall, CO$_2$ is used to make simple sugars during the Calvin cycle.

Although many scientists have studied the role of CO$_2$ in photosynthesis, French scientist Jean Senebier performed a crucial experiment in 1782. As shown in *Figure 18.6,* he placed cut leaves in a solution of carbonated water (water mixed with CO$_2$). When the leaves were exposed to sunlight, they produced what Senebier called "pure air." We now know that Senebier observed oxygen (O$_2$). However, when Senebier put cut leaves into water without CO$_2$ and exposed those leaves to sunlight, they did not produce O$_2$. From this experiment and others he performed, Senebier concluded that leaves use CO$_2$ in a process that requires sunlight and produces O$_2$.

ENVIRONMENTAL AWARENESS

Too much CO$_2$?

There is more carbon dioxide (CO$_2$) in the air today than there was in the late 1800s. In 1870, CO$_2$ concentration in the air was about 270 parts per million (ppm); now the concentration is about 360 ppm. Much of the additional CO_2 is from the burning of wood and fossil fuels. We use the energy in these fuels for nearly all of our present-day activities.

The CO_2 in the atmosphere traps heat in almost the same way that the glass roof and sides of a greenhouse do. The heat-trapping action of CO_2 in the atmosphere is called the greenhouse effect. The greenhouse effect is natural. Without it the temperature of the surface of Earth would average only −18°C. But if the level of CO_2 in the atmosphere increases, the greenhouse effect intensifies.

An intensified greenhouse effect may lead to global warming. Global warming is an increase in Earth's temperature from the rapid buildup of CO_2 and other greenhouse gases. What do you think might result from global warming? Although all scientists do not agree that the problem is serious, many are concerned. Some researchers are asking whether we should try to restore the balance of oxygen and CO_2 in the atmosphere, and if so, how.

To more fully understand the impact of the greenhouse effect, some scientists are investigating the capacity of plants to take in more CO_2 than is currently in the air. If plants can take in more CO_2 than the current amounts and remain healthy, then these plants may be able to reduce the amount of CO_2 in the atmosphere.

Researchers have already discovered that some plants, including certain crops, do appear to grow larger and produce more leaves and fruit when they are exposed to higher levels of CO_2 than are now present in the air. During tests performed in Arizona with sour orange trees and cotton plants, high CO_2 levels increased the crop yields 10 to 15 percent. Some researchers think that exposure to higher CO_2 levels will cause major

crops such as wheat and rice to produce more grain.

The question of whether plants in natural ecosystems will benefit from higher CO_2 levels has not yet been resolved. Scientists are testing an area of trees and shrubs in North Carolina by exposing the area to additional amounts of CO_2. Although the scientists expect the trees and shrubs to grow more, they have not yet determined how the rest of the ecosystem will be affected. In the long term, it is uncertain whether natural ecosystems will benefit from higher levels of CO_2 in the air.

FIGURE 18.7
Researchers use pipes to pump extra CO_2 into an area of forest, where they can study the effects of CO_2 on the ecosystem. The concentration of CO_2 in the experimental plot is 550 ppm, a level that will be reached in Earth's atmosphere sometime in the next century.

CHECKPOINT 18.1

1. Describe the structure of a leaf.
2. Explain the roles of light, carbon dioxide, and water in photosynthesis.
3. **Critical Thinking** Design an experiment to measure a plant's rate of photosynthesis. Keep in mind the reactants and products of photosynthesis.

Build on What You Know

4. During photosynthesis, carbon dioxide and water move by diffusion and osmosis. Under what circumstances would each process occur? *(Need to jog your memory? Revisit relevant concepts in Chapter 3, Section 3.5.)*

18.2 Transport in Plants

What you'll learn

IDEAS

• To describe the structure and function of vascular tissue in plants

• To explain the mechanisms of water and sugar transport in plants

WORDS

turgor, transpiration, pressure-flow hypothesis

Some plants play possum

You brush against a plant. Within a few seconds, the plant's leaves fold and become limp. The sensitive mimosa plant, shown here, responds to touch by imitating the appearance of a wilted plant. This response may make the plant less likely to be an herbivore's next meal.

TRANSPORT IN ROOTS

Roots absorb their surroundings

Have you ever left celery out of water until it wilted? Next time that happens, try putting the celery in a container of water for a few hours and observe how it regains its rigidity. The celery wilted because it lost water to the air. The cells in the celery are said to have lost their turgor. **Turgor** is the rigidity of a cell caused by osmotic pressure of the cell's membrane on the cell's wall.

Turgor depends on water. When the central vacuoles in plant cells are full of water, they exert pressure on the cell walls in the same way that air keeps a balloon inflated. When the central vacuoles are not full, plant cells deflate like a balloon without air.

How does a plant obtain the water necessary to maintain turgor? Vascular plants absorb water through their roots. Once water is absorbed, plants transport water and nutrients through vascular tissue, which extends from the roots to the stems and the leaves.

There are two types of vascular tissue: xylem and phloem, shown in *Figure 18.8*. Both contain specialized conducting cells. Xylem is the vascular tissue that carries water and minerals upward in a plant. Water always moves through xylem in one direction: from roots to stems to leaves. Water finally evaporates into the surrounding air through the stomata.

Phloem is the vascular tissue that transports sugar dissolved in a solution called sap. Unlike water in the xylem, sap can flow in two directions in a plant. Sap flows from the places where sugars are made (usually the leaves) to the areas where sugars are used or stored (usually stems and roots). Sap also flows from the places where

FIGURE 18.8

Root Structure

Epidermis
These cells, covered with root hairs, absorb water and nutrients.

Root hair
These tiny projections provide more surface area for absorption.

Cortex
Active transport of ions in this layer draws water into these cells.

Endodermis
Water diffuses from this layer into vascular tissue.

Xylem
Xylem transports water upward to all parts of the plant.

Phloem
Phloem transports sugars to all parts of the plant.

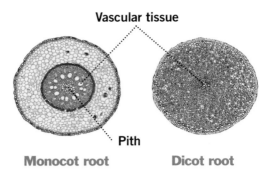

Vascular tissue

Pith

Monocot root   **Dicot root**

FIGURE 18.9
Vascular tissue in monocot and dicot roots is arranged differently.

sugars are stored to the places where the sugars are being used.

Xylem and phloem are both located in the center of a root. Notice in *Figure 18.9* that the arrangement of the vascular tissue differs in monocots and dicots. In dicots, the vascular tissue forms a solid core at the center of the root. In monocots, the vascular tissue forms a ring that surrounds a central region of cells called the pith. Despite the difference in arrangement, the vascular tissue in monocots and dicots transports materials in the same way to and from the stem and the rest of the plant.

Water Plants use their roots to absorb water from the soil. The water enters the roots primarily through osmosis. You can see the root structures that absorb water in *Figure 18.8*. Water enters the outer layer of the

root, or epidermis, through root hairs. Next, water moves by osmosis into cells in the cortex, because these cells have high concentrations of mineral ions. Then, water moves through the endodermis into the xylem.

The amount of water absorbed by a root depends on the moisture content of the soil. When soil contains a large amount of water, more water can be taken up by the roots. During a drought or in an ecosystem with low rainfall, the soil is drier, and less water is absorbed.

Minerals Plants also need minerals from the soil to carry out life processes. These minerals are water-soluble (can dissolve in water). Some minerals diffuse into the roots in solution along a concentration gradient. Others are carried into the roots by active transport.

Two important factors affect a plant's ability to obtain minerals. These factors are the amount of water in the soil and the amount of oxygen available to the roots. Most roots need oxygen to provide energy for active transport and other activities.

To obtain minerals from the soil, plants get help from other organisms. Decomposers such as fungi are important to plants because they release organic compounds and minerals from the bodies of dead organisms, making these substances available for absorption by plants. Mycorrhizae are special fungi that live in symbiotic relationships with the roots of some plants. The mycorrhizae secrete digestive enzymes that help break down organic material in the soil and release minerals, which plants can then absorb.

FIGURE 18.11
If a plant does not receive adequate minerals, such as nitrogen-containing nitrates, its growth will be stunted and its leaves discolored (bottom photo).

EVERYDAY BIOLOGY

Drowning Plants

Overwatering can be just as bad for plants as not giving them enough water. When soil is filled with water, oxygen may not reach the roots. If root cells do not have enough oxygen for cellular respiration, they cannot produce the energy needed for cell activities.

FIGURE 18.10
The red mangrove survives in salty ocean water that would kill most other plants. The mangrove's network of roots supports the leafy branches above the water and silt.

A plant's nutrition superhighway

Stems typically have two main functions: supporting leaves and flowers, and transporting water and food between roots and leaves. In a few plants, stems have additional functions, such as food storage. White potatoes, for example, are underground stems that store large amounts of food as starch.

Xylem After water and minerals are absorbed by the roots of a plant, these substances are transported up to the plant's stems and leaves. As you probably recall, xylem is the tissue that carries water and dissolved minerals from roots to other parts of a plant. Two kinds of conducting cells are present in xylem: tracheids (TRAY-kee-idz) and vessel elements. These cells do not conduct water until they are dead and empty of cytoplasm. Because these cells have thick walls, they form hollow cylinders through which water flows easily.

As you can see in *Figure 18.12*, tracheids are long, narrow xylem cells with thin separations between them. Vessel elements are short, wide xylem cells with no end walls, and thus no separations between them. Vessel elements are arranged end to end like barrels stacked on top of one another. Because of their width, vessel elements allow greater water flow than tracheids, just as more water flows through a wide pipe than through a narrow pipe.

Flowering plants, or angiosperms, contain tracheids and vessel elements. Cone-bearing seed plants, however, contain only tracheids. Because vessel elements move water more efficiently than tracheids, vessel elements enable flowering plants to transport water more easily than cone-bearing plants. This difference may help to explain why angiosperms dominate many landscapes.

Phloem Sugars made in the leaves of a plant by photosynthesis must be transported throughout the plant. You have learned that phloem carries sap upward and downward in a plant.

Phloem has two types of cells: sieve tube elements and companion cells. Can you locate these cells in

FIGURE 18.12

Vascular Tissue

Xylem
Tracheids and vessel elements are dead, hollow cells through which water flows.

Tracheid

Vessel element

Phloem
The movement of sugars through sieve tube elements is controlled by companion cells.

Sieve tube element

Companion cell

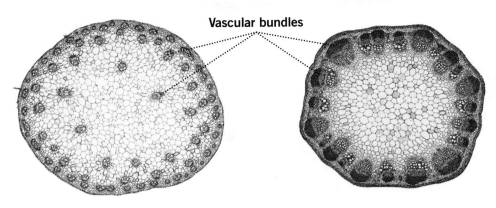

Vascular bundles

Monocot stem

Dicot stem

Figure 18.12? Unlike the cells in xylem, phloem cells are alive when they transport materials. Sieve tube elements are stacked end to end to form long tubes called sieve tubes. Like a sieve or strainer, their end walls have holes through which the sap moves. Sieve tube elements do not have ribosomes and nuclei, and they depend on companion cells for their basic needs. Companion cells enable the sieve tube elements to function, thereby controlling the movement of substances through the sieve tubes.

Although vascular tissue is found throughout the plant, its arrangement is different in stems and roots. In roots, the vascular tissue forms a central cylinder. In stems, it is arranged in vascular bundles. The arrangement of these vascular bundles differs in monocots and dicots, as shown in *Figure 18.13*. In dicots, the vascular bundles form a ring that divides the ground tissue into cortex and pith. In monocots, the bundles are scattered throughout the ground tissue.

Water transport The theory that best explains water movement in plants was proposed more than a century ago and is known today as the transpiration-cohesion theory. According to this theory, water movement in plants is driven by **transpiration,** the evaporation of water from the parts of a plant exposed to air. This evaporation takes place through open stomata.

How does transpiration cause water to move up a plant? Substances tend to move from areas of higher pressure to areas of lower pressure. As water evaporates from a leaf stomata, the pressure lowers in the xylem of the leaf. To equalize the pressure, water in the xylem moves upward from the stem to the leaf. This in turn causes lower pressure in the stem xylem, and water moves there from

LAB ZONE Do It!

Observing Plant Transport

Stems transport water to the leaves and flowers of a plant. What happens when the water is mixed with food coloring? You can find out if you . . .

Try This

1 Use two different shades of food coloring to dye water in two containers. Use the same amounts of food coloring and water in each container. Cover the containers with plastic wrap, and poke a small hole in the center.
2 Without cutting off the flower, split the stem of a white flower (carnations work well) lengthwise in two.
3 Insert one of the stem halves into each cup through the hole in the plastic wrap.
4 Let the flower sit undisturbed for 1 to 24 hours.

Analyze Your Results

1 Record the results of the experiment in a sketch.
2 Did the two colors affect all parts of the flower equally? If the colored parts are unequal, how do you account for this? What does this effect tell you about the relationship between the stem and the flower?

the root xylem.

Transpiration in plants creates a strong force, or pull. In order for water to be pulled up a plant, this force must move through a continuous chain of water molecules in the xylem, from the leaves to the roots. The water molecules in the xylem are linked together by another force called cohesion. As you learned in Chapter 2, cohesion is an attractive force between water molecules that causes water molecules to stick together. You can compare the results of the forces of transpiration and cohesion to moving while holding hands with someone. When you move, you pull the person with you.

Water movement through plants is very rapid because of the large amounts of water lost through transpiration. A maple tree can lose as much as 200 liters of water per hour. In fact, water can travel up a plant as fast as 75 centimeters per minute.

TRANSPORT IN LEAVES

Sugars are forced to "leave" their source

As you know, leaves also have vascular tissue for transport of materials. The vascular bundles in leaves are called veins. Veins contain xylem and phloem for transportation of water and food.

The structure of leaves is very important for water transport in plants. Water is transported from the roots to the leaves through the xylem. You have just learned that water is pulled upward in a plant by transpiration and cohesion. Most transpiration occurs through the stomata cells in leaves, releasing enormous amounts of water to the atmosphere.

The movement of sugars is best explained by the **pressure-flow hypothesis.** You can follow the steps described by this hypothesis in *Figure 18.14.* Sugars are transported from a

FIGURE 18.14
Pressure Flow

1. Sugars are actively transported from source cells into sieve tube elements.

2. Because of the high sugar concentration in the phloem, H_2O diffuses into the sieve tube elements, raising the H_2O pressure.

3. Pressure cause the sap–sugar water–to flow through the phloem.

4. Sugars are transported out of the phloem into sink cells; water diffuses into the xylem, reducing the H_2O pressure in the phloem.

$\longrightarrow$ Sugar

$\longrightarrow$ H_2O

region of the plant called a source to a region called a sink. A source is any part of the plant where sugars are produced by photosynthesis or the breakdown of starch. A sink is part of the plant where sugars are utilized or stored. Leaves are typical sources, and roots are typical sinks. However, roots in which sugars have been stored can also function as sources. Where are the sinks in a potato plant?

At the start of the process, sugars are pumped by active transport from the source into sieve tubes. Then, water enters the sieve tube elements from the xylem by osmosis, raising the water pressure. Both water and sugar move down a pressure gradient. Finally, at the sink, the sugars are removed from the sieve tubes by active transport and water leaves by osmosis.

Energy is required to pump sugars into sieve tubes and sometimes to pump sugars out of the sieve tubes. Sieve tube elements in phloem must be alive to function, because only living cells can provide the energy needed for active transport.

Sugars move through plants more slowly than water does. The fastest rate of phloem transport is a little more than 2 meters per hour. At that speed, how long would it take for sugars to travel down a 30-meter tree trunk?

FIGURE 18.15
Plant Transport System

Leaves
Source cells in the leaves move sugars into the phloem for transport to the rest of the plant, while receiving water and nutrients from the xylem. Water evaporates through stoma in the leaf.

Stems
Water, minerals, and sugars move through vascular tissue in the stems to all parts of the plant.

Roots
Xylem in the roots absorbs water for the plant. Roots use and often store sugars delivered by the phloem.

CHECKPOINT 18.2

1. Identify the two types of vascular tissue in plants. Briefly discuss their structure and how they work.
2. Describe the mechanisms plants use to obtain water and nutrients and to transport sugars.
3. **Critical Thinking** Why is the transport of water fastest at midday and slowest at night? What environmental factors might be involved?

Build on What You Know

4. How do concentration gradients affect osmosis? **(Need to jog your memory? Revisit relevant concepts in Chapter 3, Section 3.5.)**

What are the main structures of plants? What is the function of each?

Observing Leaves, Stems, and Roots

WHAT YOU WILL DO Observe cross sections of a bean leaf, stem, and root; identify the parts of each section

SKILLS YOU WILL USE Observing, recording data, comparing and contrasting

WHAT YOU WILL NEED Live bean plant, microscope slides, scalpel, dropper, coverslips, microscope, safranine stain, paper towel

Propose a Hypothesis

Based on what you know about plant structures, propose a hypothesis about the similarities and differences in the organization of leaf, stem, and root tissue.

Conduct Your Experiment

1 Remove a leaf from the bean plant. Place it on a slide. Holding the scalpel at a slight angle, slice thin cross sections from the leaf. **Caution:** Be careful when using a scalpel.
2 Prepare a wet mount of a cross section.

3 Focus the microscope on low power. Switch to high. Draw what you see, and label epidermis, vascular bundle, guard cells, and stomata.
4 Add a drop of safranine stain to one edge of the coverslip. Place a paper towel on the other edge to draw the stain under the coverslip.
5 Repeat step 3.
6 Cut a piece from the stem below the first leaves. Repeat steps 2–5, labeling pith, vascular bundle, and cortex.
7 Cut a piece from the largest root. Repeat steps 2–5, labeling xylem, phloem, endodermis, cortex, and epidermis.

Analyze Your Data

1 Describe the internal structure you observed in the leaf stem and root, before the stain was added.
2 Where is the xylem located in the leaf? In the root? In the stem?
3 What structure is in the stem and root but not in the leaf? Suggest a function for this structure based on its location.

Draw Conclusions

Did you hypothesize correctly? If not, write a paragraph summarizing the similarities and differences among the tissues in leaves, stems, and roots.

Design a Related Experiment

Write a procedure for comparing and contrasting the leaves, stems, and roots of a monocot and a dicot.

Lab: Observing Leaves, Stems, and Roots

Objective: To observe cross sections of a bean leaf, stem, and root and to identify the parts of each section.
Hypothesis: Roots, stems, and leaves are made of three types of tissue: dermal, ground, and vascular. The arrangement of the tissues is different in the different plant structures.

18.3 Plant Growth

Little gems
In the Japanese art of bonsai, people create miniature potted trees by training the tree limbs into graceful shapes with wire and by pruning. Bonsai trees are not dwarf species. Gardeners control the size by planting trees in small, shallow pots (which limit root growth) and by pruning the roots and shoots regularly.

What you'll learn

IDEAS
• To explain where cells and tissues develop in plants
• To compare two patterns of plant growth

WORDS
meristems, primary growth, secondary growth, cambium

MERISTEMS: SITES OF GROWTH

Take it from the top

Do you know how humans grow in height? As the length of certain bones, primarily the leg and spinal bones, increases, we grow taller. Plants grow taller by increasing in length at the tips of roots and stems. If humans grew taller in the same way as plants, they would grow at the tips of their toes and at the top of their heads.

The growing tissues of plants are called **meristems.** Meristems are located at the tips of stems and branches, at the tips of roots, and in buds in the joints where leaves attach to stems. In woody plants, meristems are also located between the xylem and phloem of the vascular system and near stem surfaces.

The function of meristems is to produce new cells by mitosis. As is common in mitosis, the new cells that are produced are all alike at first. However, the cells eventually specialize, or differentiate, to form one of three types of tissues—vascular tissue, dermal tissue, or ground tissue. As you have learned, these three tissues make up a plant.

The growing tissues at the tips of roots and stems are called apical meristems. (*Apex* means "tip," and *apical* means "at the tip.") Apical meristems cause the tips of roots and stems to grow longer. Because of the activity of apical meristems, plants grow taller and their roots grow deeper into the soil.

Axillary meristems occur in buds that arise in the the joints, called axils, between leaves and stems. Axillary meristems cause side branches to grow on stems. You can see where apical and axillary meristems are located in *Figure 18.16*.

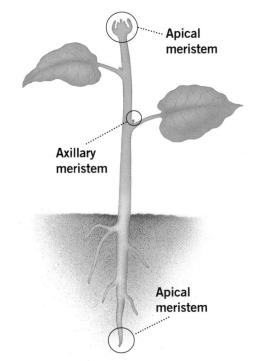

Apical meristem

Axillary meristem

Apical meristem

FIGURE 18.16
Meristems are regions of fast-growing areas, such as the tips of the roots and the stems.

Growing up

There are two patterns of growth in seed plants. During one kind of growth, all plants grow taller and deeper; in the other type, woody plants grow thicker. The first process—the elongation of stems and roots—is called **primary growth.** All plants exhibit primary growth. Primary growth occurs when a plant's stem gets longer and its roots grow deeper. You will learn more about the second growth pattern, which makes woody plants thicker, later in this section.

The first stem that emerges from a seed is called the primary shoot. The primary shoot forms the stems and leaves. Primary shoots have two types of meristems: apical meristems and axillary buds. Can you locate both types of meristems in *Figure 18.17*? Apical meristems, which are located at the tips of all stems, have cells that form the stem and leaves. Axillary buds form at the base of each leaf. Axillary buds can form either a branch or a flower. Because they can form side branches from the stem, axillary buds are also called lateral buds. (*Lateral* means "sideways.")

In most plants, the axillary buds are kept inactive by hormones produced in the meristem at the tip of the shoot. If this tip is damaged or removed, hormone production will stop and the axillary bud will begin to grow. You may have seen gardeners take advantage of this phenomenon.

FIGURE 18.17

Primary Growth

All plants exhibit primary growth, in which the stems grow longer and the roots grow deeper.

Apical meristem

Axillary bud

Zone of differentiation

Zone of elongation

Zone of cell division

Apical meristem

In order to make plants grow bushier, gardeners often clip off the tops. This technique is used to create hedges. Cutting off the tops removes the hormonal inactivation and the axillary buds start to sprout side branches.

The primary growth of roots and stems involves three steps: cell division, elongation, and differentiation. In the first step, cell division in the apical meristem forms new cells. In the second step, cells grow longer in a region of the root called the zone of elongation. The elongation of cells pushes the root through the soil.

In the third step, cells become specialized in the zone of differentiation. In this zone, cells undergo changes to become part of the vascular tissue (xylem or phloem), dermal tissue, or ground tissue (parenchyma and supporting cells). In *Figure 18.17,* where are the cells in each of the three steps located in a root?

SECONDARY GROWTH

Putting on width

If you observe the growth of a tree over a long period of time, you will probably notice that the tree grows wider as it grows taller. During **secondary growth,** the roots, stems, and branches of certain seed plants grow wider. The widening of a tree trunk is an example of secondary growth.

Secondary growth does not occur in all plants. Most herbaceous plants have only primary growth. Secondary growth is usually only seen in woody vines, shrubs, and trees. For example, most gymnosperms show secondary growth, Secondary growth creates the layers of dead cell tissue called wood.

Secondary growth is an adaptation that enables some woody plants to survive in certain environments. As a plant's stem grows thicker, it becomes

LAB ZONE Do It!

Measuring Root and Stem Growth

You can observe and measure the rate of root and stem growth when you . . .

Try This

1 For this activity, choose seeds for plants such as radishes, corn, or peas.
2 Fill a clear plastic or glass container loosely with crumpled paper towels. Dampen the towels with water.
3 Place a seed between the towels and the wall of the container so that the seed is easy to view and the roots have room to grow.
4 Keep the paper towels damp and make observations at the same time each day for one week. Record the date and your observations of the roots.
5 Once growth appears, remove the seedling from the container during each observation, and use a ruler and permanent marker to mark 1-centimeter increments on a root and the stem. Record the length of the root and the stem at each observation.

Analyze Your Results

1 Describe the rate of root growth in your seed. Did growth occur at a steady rate or did it occur at varying rates?
2 From your observations of the marks on the root and stem, where did growth occur in the seedling? Explain.

stronger. A stronger stem allows a plant to grow taller. Plants that grow taller have an increased chance of reaching light. Because plants compete for light, tall plants are more likely to obtain vital sunlight and to reproduce successfully. Secondary growth is an adaptation that has contributed to the dominance of woody plants in many ecosystems.

Lateral meristems Secondary growth is caused by cell division in structures called lateral meristems. Unlike apical meristems, which are located at the tips of roots and stems, lateral meristems are located within and parallel to the sides of roots and stems. Generally, lateral meristems are shaped like a hollow cylinder inside a root or stem.

FIGURE 18.18
Secondary Growth of a Woody Stem

After year 1
The young tree's vascular cambium lies between primary xylem and phloem. The epidermis forms the outer layer.

After year 2
The vascular cambium produces new layers of secondary xylem and phloem, and the cork cambium produces cork.

After year 3
Old layers of xylem become heartwood, while old layers of phloem and accumulated cork thicken the bark.

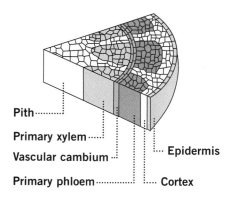

Pith
Primary xylem
Vascular cambium
Primary phloem
Epidermis
Cortex

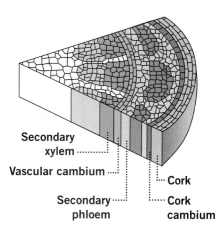

Secondary xylem
Vascular cambium
Secondary phloem
Cork
Cork cambium

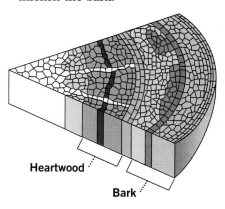

Heartwood
Bark

Lateral meristems are also called cambium. **Cambium** is the meristem in woody plants that produces new cells for lateral growth. There are two common types of cambium: vascular cambium and cork cambium. Find each type in the cross section of a tree trunk shown in *Figure 18.18.* Which cambium is part of the bark of the tree?

Vascular cambium One type of cambium, vascular cambium, is located between the xylem and phloem. Cell divisions in the vascular cambium produce new xylem toward the inside of the cambium, and new phloem toward the outside of the cambium. The growth of new xylem and phloem occurs in a cycle. Each year the vascular cambium produces new xylem and new phloem during a plant's growing season.

Starting in a woody plant's second year of growth, the new xylem that the vascular cambium produces each year is called secondary xylem. Secondary xylem is familiar to you as wood. Similarly, the new phloem formed by the vascular cambium each year is called secondary phloem. Secondary phloem has no common name. As the stems and roots grow thicker year by year, secondary xylem carries water and secondary phloem carries sugars through the plant.

Cork cambium The other type of cambium, cork cambium, is the lateral meristem between the phloem

IN THE COMMUNITY
Trimming Trees

Sometimes plant growth causes problems, as when a tree grows into power lines or onto a neighbor's property. Trees on town or city streets are generally cared for by municipal workers. Call your local government and find out what to do if you notice a tree on public property that needs attention. Trees on private property are the responsibility of the property owner, who will generally hire a private service to assist. Arrange to speak with someone at a private tree-trimming service in your community. How are trees cut back or removed? What equipment is needed? Ask for some examples of situations that necessitate tree removal.

and the epidermis. Cell divisions in the cork cambium replace the cortex layer and the epidermis, or skin of the plant, with cork, which protects the tree. You are probably familiar with natural cork—the material used for some types of bulletin boards. The secondary phloem, cork cambium, and cork combine to form the bark that surrounds the trunk of a tree.

Many trees have several layers of cork that are dead and cannot expand. As a result, continued expansion of the tree trunk splits the outer layers. As the layers of cork split, they cause the bark to split. Trees such as oaks have split bark because of the growth of the cork cambium.

Certain trees are grown and maintained so that their cork can be harvested. Cork oak trees in Portugal produce about 60 percent of the world's supply of natural cork. Cork can be removed from cork oaks every 7 to 10 years, starting when the trees are about 25 years old. Trees up to 200 years old can still produce usable cork. Cork harvesters must be careful not to damage the vascular cambium layer when they remove cork from a tree. If this layer is damaged, the tree will die.

The structure of wood Xylem accumulates yearly, but only the newer outer layers continue to transport water. The outer light-colored layers of secondary xylem are sapwood.

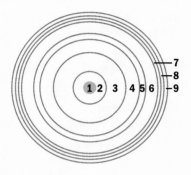
Eventually, older xylem cells get clogged and can no longer carry water. The clogged dark-colored layers of xylem at the center of the tree are heartwood. Heartwood typically contains substances such as oils, gums, resins, and tannins that are not present in sapwood. These substances can be extracted from lumber and used to produce valuable products such as acetone, lacquer, photographic film, and turpentine. Heartwood is stronger and more resistant to decay than sapwood.

You see the structure of wood in *Figure 18.19.* Notice the series of concentric rings, which are called growth rings. How do growth rings form? Xylem that grows in the spring is called

Spring wood   **Summer wood**

FIGURE 18.19
Compare the spring wood and the summer wood in this stained stem (left). Why is the spring wood wider?

FIGURE 18.20

A Tale of a Tree

This redwood lived for 1204 years, from 729 to 1933. One scientist identified some of the major events that occurred during the tree's life.

1932 Last growth ring. The tree fell the following year.

1776 Declaration of Independence signed

1492 Europeans discover America

1215 Magna Carta signed

1066 Norman conquest of England

729 Seedling sprouts

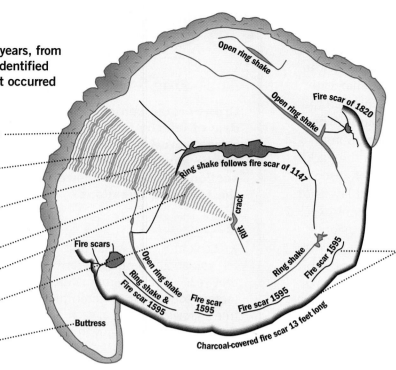

Fire scars

This tree cross section shows evidence of at least nine fires, including a blaze in 1820 that burned through almost half of its bark, cambium, and heartwood.

Buttress

Before the 1820 fire, this tree had begun to grow a buttress, or support column, which grew even more rapidly after the fire. The buttress kept the tree standing for more than one hundred years.

spring wood. Spring wood consists of large, wide xylem cells that can transport large amounts of water.

During the summer, when conditions are often drier, the vascular cambium produces thick-walled, narrow xylem cells. This summer wood carries less water than spring wood. The alternating production of spring wood and summer wood produces growth rings in tree trunks.

Growth rings also form in roots. In both stems and roots, each ring represents one year's growth. Growth rings vary in width. When environmental conditions such as rainfall and temperature are favorable, more growth occurs, resulting in wider growth rings. There is less growth during a drought. Growth rings are narrower when conditions are unfavorable for growth. Why can you determine the age of a tree by counting its growth rings?

Sometimes a tree trunk tells an even more dramatic story, as you can see in *Figure 18.20*. This ancient tree was burned extensively in a fire in 1820, but it did not fall until more than 100 years later.

CHECKPOINT 18.3

1. Where do new cells and tissues develop in plants?

2. Describe two common patterns of plant growth. What kinds of plants exhibit each pattern of growth?

3. Critical Thinking Would you expect most monocots to produce cork? Explain your answer.

Build on What You Know

4. How does mitosis enable a growing plant to preserve the genetic message encoded in most of its cells? (*Need to jog your memory? Revisit relevant concepts in Chapter 5, Section 5.1.*)

What specialized tissues enable plants to grow?

Chapter 18 Review

THE BIG IDEA!

18.1–18.2 Plants perform life processes using specialized structures.

18.3 The parts of most plants grow from specialized tissues.

Sum It Up

Use the following summary to review the main concepts in this chapter.

18.1 Photosynthesis in Plants

- In the layer of mesophyll cells between the upper and lower epidermis of a leaf, chloroplasts capture light energy.
- The epidermis of a leaf has a waterproof covering called a cuticle.
- Plants exchange oxygen and carbon dioxide and lose water through pores called stomata. Guard cells affect the size of stomata.
- For a plant to store energy or grow, it must produce more glucose than it needs for cellular respiration.
- Most of the water taken up by plants is lost through evaporation.

18.2 Transport in Plants

- Water in plant vacuoles maintains the rigidity, or turgor, of plant cells.
- Water enters roots from soil mainly by osmosis.
- Some minerals enter roots by diffusion; others, through active transport. All roots need oxygen to provide energy for active transport.

- In vascular plants, xylem transports water and dissolved minerals; phloem transports sap containing dissolved sugars.
- Xylem cells that transport water and minerals are dead and hollow. As water evaporates through leaves, replacement water is pulled up through the hollow tubes by cohesion.
- Living phloem cells use energy to actively transport sugars from source cells into sieve tubes, and from sieve tubes into sink cells.

18.3 Plant Growth

- Primary growth occurs only in apical meristems —at the tips of stems, branches, and roots, and in the joints where leaves attach to stems.
- All plants have primary growth. Woody plants can also grow thicker through secondary growth.
- Wood is layers of secondary xylem. Bark is formed from layers of cork, cork cambium, and phloem.
- The thickness of spring and summer xylem layers provides clues about climatic change.

Use Terms and Concepts

Use each of the following words or terms in a complete sentence. If you need to review a meaning, turn to the page indicated.

cuticle (p. 423)

stomata (p. 423)

mesophyll (p. 423)

compensation point (p. 425)

turgor (p. 428)

transpiration (p. 431)

pressure-flow hypothesis (p. 432)

meristems (p. 435)

primary growth (p. 436)

secondary growth (p. 437)

cambium (p. 438)

Use Your Word Power

COMPLETION **Write the word or phrase that best completes each statement.**

1. The _____ is the region of the leaf in which photosynthesis takes place.

2. When vacuoles in plant cells are filled with water, the plant has _____ .

3. Pores in the epidermis that allow for gas exchange are called _____ .

4. Tissues of plants that provide new growth are called _____ .

5. The widening of a tree trunk is an example of _____ growth.

TRUE-FALSE **Write true if the statement is true. If the statement is false, replace the underlined word(s) to make the statement true.**

6. The amount of light required for a plant to reach its compensation point is <u>constant</u> from plant to plant.

7. The <u>pressure-flow hypothesis</u> explains the movement of sugars through phloem.

8. <u>Transpiration</u> provides the initial force that moves water from the roots to the leaves.

9. <u>Secondary growth</u> causes the elongation of stems and roots.

10. <u>Cambium</u> is a meristem that produces new cells for growth in woody plants.

Show What You Know

11. Describe the key differences between the structure of xylem and phloem tissue.

12. Explain why it is advantageous for plants to have 20 to 70 percent of the mesophyll volume composed of air spaces.

13. Use a diagram to compare the location and function of apical and lateral meristems.

14. What role does vascular cambium play in the growth of a woody stem?

15. How do guard cells control the exchange of oxygen, carbon dioxide, and water through stomata?

16. Explain how gardeners use axillary buds to control the growth of shrubs.

17. What is the cuticle? What is the cuticle's function?

18. What plant substances are responsible for converting light energy into chemical energy?

19. Describe what happens when a plant wilts. What causes wilting?

20. **Make a Concept Map** Complete the concept map below by adding the following terms: xylem, phloem, source cell, sieve tube, living, nonliving, sink cell, vessel element, transpiration, cohesion, tracheid.

Take It Further

21. **Developing a Hypothesis** Many plants have stomata only on the underside of their leaves. The leaves of water lilies float on the surface of the water. Where would you expect their stomata to be? Explain your answer.

22. **Applying Concepts** Calculate the time it would take for water to travel to the top of the trunk of a 105-meter redwood tree. Assume that the water is traveling at its maximum rate.

23. **Designing an Experiment** Plan an experiment to determine whether the rate of transpiration is affected by wind. Hint: Include a method to measure the water that each plant absorbs.

24. **Applying Concepts** Sap for maple syrup is "tapped" from sugar maples in autumn.

Propose a hypothesis to explain why sap rises in the spring rather than in autumn.

25. Designing an Experiment What relationship would you expect between the length of a plant's life and its ability to undergo secondary growth? What data could you collect and compare to test your hypothesis? Describe an experiment to collect this data.

26. Interpreting a Graph The graph below shows the result of an investigation about the percentage of dividing cells in a root tip. What do the data indicate about cell division in roots?

Cell Division in a Root Tip

27. Analyzing Data Examine this cross section of a root and determine whether the plant is a monocot or a dicot. Explain your answer.

Consider the Issues

28. Urban-dwelling Plants It can be difficult for trees to survive in a city. Urban trees are exposed to air pollution from vehicles. Salt from icy roads and oil from poorly maintained engines are washed into the trees' water supply. Their roots are often buried under cement. What benefits do trees provide to a community? What actions can you take to increase the number of trees in your community and to increase their chances of survival?

Make New Connections

29. Biology and Art Make a three-dimensional model of one of the following: the layers in a plant leaf; the structure of a plant root; the structure of a woody plant stem with secondary growth.

30. Biology and Physics Find out about experiments NASA has done to investigate how plants grow in zero gravity. What is the long-term purpose of these experiments?

31. Biology and Community What kinds of plant-growing conditions are characteristic of your county or state? Consider the length of the growing season, the typical temperature range, the type of soil, and the usual amount of rainfall. How do these conditions support the crops that grow best in your area? What kind of outdoor ornamental plants thrive there? Consider using images and maps in the report of your findings.

FAST-FORWARD TO CHAPTER 19

In Chapter 19 you will study two important aspects of plant survival: how plants respond to and change their environments, and the strategies plants use for reproduction.

You can find out more about response and reproduction in plants by exploring the following Internet address: *http://plants.biosurf.com*

In this chapter . . .

FEATURES

Everyday Biology
- Flowers for All Seasons
- Apple a Day, Every Day

In the Community
Irritating Plants

 Environmental Awareness
Computers on Farms

LAB ZONES

Discover It!
- Ripening Green Bananas

Do It!
- How Do Plants Respond to Light?
- Observing Asexual Reproduction in Plants

Think About It!
- Analyzing Germination Conditions

Investigate It!
- Observing Seedlings

Snowbells blossom in the high mountain air of the Alps, below snow-covered peaks. Far to the north, in the heart of Alaska, a woolly lousewort pokes through the early summer snow on the permanently frozen earth. How do these plants survive in polar regions that are often dark, usually racked by wind, and nearly always cold? How do they reproduce in the thin air and frigid temperatures of a mountaintop? The answers to these questions are often astounding.

Some plants secrete alcohol, which acts as an antifreeze. Others, like the pasqueflower, have highly reflective petals that cup to catch the sun's rays. Inside the blossom it may be up to 10 degrees Celsius warmer than the surrounding air. These cold-weather, seed-bearing plants will slow down reproduction, taking two or three years to accomplish what a warm-air plant does in one growing season. Their buds form in one summer, lie dormant over the long winter, and flower with the first warm days of the next growing season. Many arctic plants reproduce underground, sending out rhizomes, or underground stems, in the protected earth to start new plants.

In the cold, some plants conserve heat and energy, protecting their internal fluids from freezing. But in severe cold, plants become dormant. What are other ways that plants respond to their surroundings as they grow and reproduce?

Ripening Green Bananas

You need 3 green bananas, 1 apple, 2 resealable plastic bags

1. Place 1 banana with an apple in a tightly sealed plastic bag. Place 1 banana by itself in a tightly sealed plastic bag. Place 1 banana in the open air, away from any other fruit.
2. For each of the next 3–5 days, take notes on the changes, if any, in the three bananas.

Plants, like many other living things, produce hormones. A hormone called ethylene controls the rate of ripening in fruit. The banana sealed in the bag with the apple tends to ripen fastest because it is exposed to the ethylene produced by the apple.

WRITE ABOUT IT!

In your science journal, write a brief description of a visit to a garden, orchard, or greenhouse where fruits or vegetables are growing. Base your account on personal experience, or use your imagination. What sights, sounds, and smells would you encounter?

19.1 Plants Respond to the Environment

What you'll learn

IDEAS

• To give examples of environmental stimuli and plant responses

• To explain what hormones are and to give an example of a plant hormone

WORDS

stimulus, tropism, hormone, auxin, photoperiodism, dormancy

The shady side of the street

Plants can respond to many different stimuli in their environments. Can you imagine why a plant would grow away from the light? The ivy-leaved toadflax grows on walls and rock faces. Its seeds need darkness to germinate. The stems carrying the seeds grow toward the shadowy cracks where new seeds can sprout.

FIGURE 19.1

What stimulus is causing this plant to grow in one direction? What is the name for this type of growth?

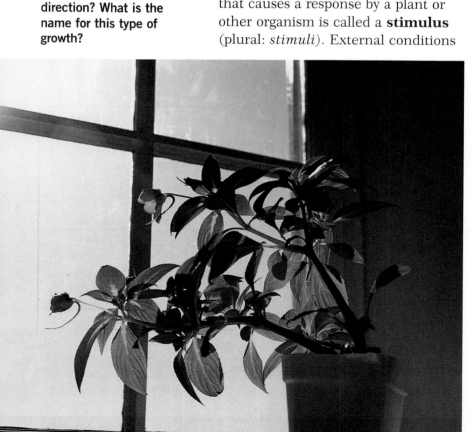

TYPICAL PLANT RESPONSES

Fitting into the scene

Plants, like all other living organisms, respond to conditions in their environment. In most cases, they respond to specific environmental changes. Any environmental condition or change that causes a response by a plant or other organism is called a **stimulus** (plural: *stimuli*). External conditions such as gravity, day length, temperature, light, moisture, and physical contact can act as stimuli. Plants also respond to changes in their internal, or cellular, environment.

Plants respond to stimuli in various ways. For example, plants can change the direction of their growth, move individual parts, and undergo seasonal cycles of growth, flowering, and dormancy.

Tropisms The growth of a plant in a certain direction in response to a stimulus is called a **tropism** (TROH-piz-uhm). A tropism may be positive, with growth toward a stimulus, or it may be negative, with growth away from a stimulus. What type of tropism do you see in *Figure 19.1*?

Phototropism is the response of plants to light. Positive phototropism, growth toward light, enables many growing embryos and new growth of mature plants to absorb the sunlight they need for photosynthesis.

A second type of tropism, gravitropism, is growth in response to gravity. Roots are positively gravitropic, meaning that root tips grow downward. Gravitropism is adaptive because roots grow where they are more likely to get water and nutrients. New growth on plant stems is negatively gravitropic, meaning that the tips grow upward toward a light source.

A third type of growth response is called thigmotropism, or response to touch. An example of thigmotropism is the coiling of the stems of a plant such as the morning glory. Thigmotropism enables a plant to grow on a surface that can support it. Wherever the stem touches the support, the cells on the opposite side of the stem grow longer, causing the stem to coil around, or grasp hold of, the support.

Nastic movements Sometimes parts of plants will move slightly in response to any stimulus. Nastic movements are responses that occur in the same way, regardless of the stimulus. Nastic movements are usually short-term, reversible changes.

One of the most fascinating nastic movements is the opening and closing of the carnivorous Venus's flytrap leaves. When an insect brushes against their trigger hairs, the leaves close and capture it. What do you think happens to the insect?

LAB ZONE **Do It!**

How Do Plants Respond to Light?

Can plants find their way through a maze? Find out when you . . .

Try This

1 Set up a maze by cutting a hole in a cardboard carton with dividers, as shown in the photograph. **Caution:** Use care when handling scissors.
2 Plant four bean seeds in a small flower pot. Place the pot in a corner of the carton as far away from the outside hole as possible. Close the sides of the carton so that the only light in the box comes from the hole that you cut.

3 Over the next two weeks, open the carton every two to three days to water the seeds and observe the seedlings.

Analyze Your Results

1 Summarize what happened to the bean seeds.
2 What caused the bean plants to grow the way they did?

PLANT HORMONES

Chemicals in control

Nervous systems enable humans and other animals to respond to stimuli in their environment. Plants, however, do not have nervous systems. How, then, do they respond to changing environmental conditions? Plants respond by producing chemicals called hormones, which control plant growth and responses. A **hormone** is an organic compound that is produced in small amounts and released by one part of an organism to affect another part. Sometimes, plant hormones also affect the tissues that produce them.

Each plant hormone can have several effects, depending on the nature

EVERYDAY BIOLOGY

Flowers for All Seasons

Growers force plants to bloom out of season by altering the light stimulus. Growers use artificial light to control day lengths in greenhouses. With this technique, we can have flowering chrysanthemums and poinsettias throughout the year.

FIGURE 19.2
When this Venus's flytrap leaf quickly closes its two lobes, it can capture an insect, a source of nitrogen for the plant.

FIGURE 19.3

Some of the effects of five plant hormones are listed here. Which one promotes the ripening of fruit? Which ones stimulate flowering?

FIGURE 19.4

The Darwins' Experiments

Charles and Francis Darwin demonstrated that coleoptile tips will grow toward light, unless they are shielded from it.

Coleoptile

Control　Tip removed　Tip covered by opaque cap　Tip covered by transparent cap　Base covered by opaque shield

of the hormone, the sensitivity of its target cells, and the amount of hormone present. Hormones in plants affect their growth and their ability to respond to changes in the environment. Some plant hormones and their various effects are listed in the table in *Figure 19.3*.

If you have ever grown a plant on a windowsill, you have probably observed an example of phototropism—the tendency of plant stems to grow toward sunlight. In the 1880s Charles Darwin and his son Francis studied the growth of plants toward light. *Figure 19.4* summarizes the results of their experiments. The Darwins studied the coleoptiles (KOH-lee-AWP-tulz) of oat seedlings. A coleoptile is a sheath covering the first leaves that emerge from the seeds of grasses.

The Darwins observed that the coleoptiles would curve toward the light only if the tip of the coleoptile remained intact. If the tip was cut off, the coleoptile did not curve toward the light.

The Darwins also discovered that if the coleoptile tip was covered with an opaque cap, which did not transmit light, the coleoptile did not curve as it grew. However, if the cap was transparent, the coleoptile curved toward the light as it grew. The coleoptile also turned to the light when its base was covered with an opaque shield.

From these experiments, the Darwins concluded that the tip of the coleoptile, rather than the curving region, was sensitive to light. The coleoptile response did not occur in the tip where the light was sensed, but in a different place. In some way, the tip was transmitting a signal to the rest of the plant.

In 1926 Dutch botanist Fritz Went continued the experiments of the Darwins. His experiments are summarized in *Figure 19.5*. Went cut off the tips of oat coleoptiles and placed the tips upright on blocks of agar. (Agar is a gelatinlike substance made from seaweed.) After an hour, Went put the same agar blocks onto coleoptiles with cut-off tips that were growing in the dark. Went placed the agar blocks so that they covered only part of the tip of the coleoptile. Much to Went's surprise, the coleoptiles curved away from the agar.

Went concluded that the agar blocks had absorbed from the coleoptile tips a substance that caused cells to grow longer. When this substance was applied to one side of a coleoptile, it stimulated the growth of cells on that side, causing the coleoptile to curve.

Went observed that the substance causing the growth was made in the tip of the coleoptile but caused growth below the tip. He concluded that the substance causing the growth was a hormone, because a hormone is produced in one part of an organism but affects another. Went named the hormone auxin, from the Greek word meaning "to grow." **Auxin** is a plant hormone that causes plant cells to grow longer, which results in plant growth.

Other scientists showed that light influences the diffusion of auxin through a plant. When a plant is exposed to light, the auxin diffuses from cells on the lighted side of the plant to cells on the shaded side of the plant. The auxin causes the cells on the shaded side of the plant to grow longer. The result is that the plant curves toward light as it grows.

Auxin has other effects on plants. It promotes the new root growth in cuttings and causes fruit to develop. You can study the table in *Figure 19.3* to learn about other plant hormones. What are some of the different effects of other plant hormones?

DAY-LENGTH RESPONSES

Plants take measure

Many plant species respond to changes in light. The flowers of some plants, such as daylilies and morning glories, close during the night and open again each morning. Many plants also respond to the seasons, forming flowers and growing buds only during a particular time of the year.

One way plants respond to seasonal conditons is by detecting changes in the length of daylight—shorter daylight in winter, longer in summer. In many plants, flowering time is linked to the lengths of daylight and darkness. Any response of a plant to daylight length is called **photoperiodism.**

Botanists divide plants into three groups, based on their response to specific photoperiods: long-day plants, short-day plants, and day-neutral plants. Long-day plants tend to bloom in late spring or early summer, when days are long and nights are short. Long-day plants include some irises, wheat, lettuce, radishes, and corn. Short-day plants bloom in late summer, autumn, or winter, when days grow short. Short-day plants include ragweed, soybeans, asters, and chrysanthemums. Day-neutral plants do not respond to changes in day length. Day-neutral plants include roses, snapdragons, sunflowers, and tomatoes.

You may be surprised to learn that long-day and short-day plants do

Apple a Day, Every Day

In nature, apples ripen during the fall. To provide ripe apples in other seasons, growers store apples in refrigerated warehouses with high levels of carbon dioxide. Carbon dioxide postpones the production of ethylene that causes ripening until the fruit is sent to the market.

FIGURE 19.5
Went's Experiment

Fritz Went showed that a substance from a coleoptile tip could diffuse into an agar block and then into another coleoptile, causing growth. He concluded that the substance was a hormone.

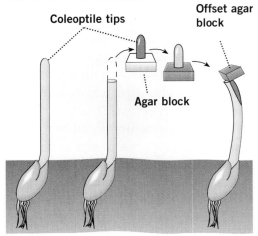

Coleoptile tips

Offset agar block

Agar block

| Control | Auxin from the coleoptile tip diffused into the agar block. | Auxin in the agar block caused the coleoptile to bend. |

not actually respond to the hours of sunlight, but rather to the hours of continuous darkness. So these plants could also be called short-night and long-night plants! *Figure 19.6* illustrates how short-day and long-day plants differ. Look for the presence or absence of flowers to see how night length affects each type of plant.

A brief flash of light during the night is enough to disrupt the flowering cycle of short-day (long-night) plants. In one practical application of the plant response to day length, growers use flashes of light in greenhouses to control flowering. How did a flash of light affect the plants illustrated in *Figure 19.6*?

There is much about photoperiodism that scientists do not yet understand. However, they do know that photoperiodism and some other plant responses to light are controlled by a blue pigment called phytochrome (FY-toh-krohm). Phytochrome changes its structure in response to different light colors. It controls plant responses such as flowering, seed germination, and seasonal inactivity. Scientists actively continue to investigate phytochrome to learn more about how it functions.

Plants nod off, too

Some plants respond to the changing seasons by becoming dormant. **Dormancy** is a period of decreased activity that results from structural and chemical changes in a plant. Plants may undergo dormancy in climates that are extremely cold or very hot and dry. A dormant period may be needed before some seeds and bulbs will start to grow.

You can probably name some trees that lose their leaves and become dormant in the fall. Dormancy is common among deciduous plants that live in cold winter climates. It reduces the chance that plants will be damaged by freezing temperatures.

During autumn, longer nights stimulate the leaves of deciduous plants to loosen and drop. A leaf scar forms on the stem after a leaf drops. The remaining cells secrete wax, which seals the stem from pathogens, organisms that cause disease. Deciduous plants also respond to longer autumn nights by forming bud scales. Bud scales protect developing buds from cold and infection. You can usually see leaf scars and bud scales if you look at a dormant stem during winter.

Seasonal dry periods can also stimulate plant dormancy. The dormancy responses resulting from lack of water are similar to those resulting from cold. Plants lose their leaves and form drought-resistant buds.

Have you ever wondered how seeds that have been stored in a package for a long time can start to grow when planted in a garden? Many varieties of seeds and bulbs have a dormant period before they sprout. When mature seeds are released from the parent plant, they remain dormant until the right growth conditions exist. Packaged seeds remain dormant until they are planted because in a package

FIGURE 19.6
Short-day plants flower only when the nights are long enough—longer than the critical night length. If the critical night length is interrupted by a flash of light, no flowering occurs.

The Reaction of Certain Plants to Night Length and Light		
Night Length: Three Variations	Short-Day Plants (long-night)	Long-Day Plants (short-night)

FIGURE 19.7
Crocus bulbs require a period of cold before they begin to grow. How can you use that information to force crocuses to bloom ahead of schedule?

LAB ZONE **Think About It!**

Analyzing Germination Conditions

The table at right lists types of plants and the conditions required for their seeds to germinate.

Analyzing the Table

1 How do the conditions listed help each type of seed to germinate?

2 Using what you have read about plant responses, suggest another possible condition that could stimulate a seed to germinate. How would the signal and the timing of germination benefit the plant?

Plant	Condition or Mechanism
Apple	Exposure to temperatures below 10°C
Guanacaste	Seedpod weakened by the digestive acids in an animal's stomach
Hakea	Exposure to fire, which breaks the seed coat
Shadscale	Exposure to heavy rain that washes salt from the seed
White sweet clover	Agitation, such as shaking by wind, that causes a pluglike structure to fall from the seed

the seeds do not have the right conditions for growth.

Sometimes the period of dormancy is caused by growth inhibitors—chemicals that stop growth. Growth inhibitors must be removed before any new growth can occur. The seeds of many plants that are planted in autumn will not sprout until spring, after the moisture in the soil has washed growth inhibitors from the seeds.

A cold period is sometimes necessary to destroy the growth inhibitors in bulbs. If you wish to force a crocus or paper-white narcissus to flower before spring arrives, refrigerate the bulbs for about a month. You can then plant the bulbs in containers, and they will bloom indoors.

The dormancy of a few types of seeds is broken by intense heat. The loblolly-pine is the best-known example; its cones fly open during forest fires, and its seedlings are the first to grow when the scorched land begins to recover. Other examples of seeds that require heat to sprout include

Australian bush plants that have woody fruits with seeds inside. These fruits may stay attached to the trees for years until a fire causes the seeds to burst from the fruit. In this way, the land can be reseeded quickly as the new seeds begin to sprout.

CHECKPOINT 19.1

1. Name three types of stimuli that affect the growth of plants.
2. Explain what a hormone is, and give an example of a plant hormone and its effects.
3. **Critical Thinking** Why is it important that the flowers of a particular species open at the same time?

Build on What You Know

4. How might dormancy help a plant maintain homeostasis during dry, hot weather? *(Need to jog your memory? Revisit relevant concepts in Chapter 2, Section 2.4.)*

19.2 Plants Change the Environment

What you'll learn

IDEAS
• To describe how plants change the environment
• To explain how plants are essential for animal survival

WORDS
colonizers

Seafaring seeds

Earth is always changing. New land appears in the form of volcanic islands and coral reefs. Gradually, these empty lots in the ocean acquire plant life. How do plants cross the water? Some seeds, like those of the coconut, float. Other seeds travel on and in animals, including humans. Wherever plants spring up, they cause many changes in the soil, the animal population, and even the climate.

PLANT COLONIZERS

Plants take turns

You have seen that plants interact with the environment in several ways. Plants also change the environment. If you observe a vacant lot or a natural meadow over a period of time, you will notice many changes. Some changes happen within one growing season; others occur over many years.

Plants appear soon after a tract of land is cleared. Although the land may seem to be composed of only dirt, plant seeds are often buried in soil or carried on wind or water currents, or by animals passing through the area. For plants, essential factors for growth are adequate moisture, nutrients in the soil, and sunlight. If the essential factors are present, some seeds will grow.

The first organisms to dwell in an uninhabited area are called **colonizers.** Plant colonizers often include mosses, which can grow even in rocky and barren areas. As mosses die and decay, they provide soil for other plants. Other colonizers, often called weeds, are hardy plants that can grow in harsh conditions. Most colonizers are short plants with dense, fibrous root systems. These plants are followed by small flowering plants and shrubs whose seeds soon spread through the area and germinate.

As colonizers inhabit an area for several years, there is a gradual change in the type of plants living in that area. The small pioneer plants

FIGURE 19.8
Plant Succession

1 Valley glaciers sometimes shrink, revealing large areas of barren earth.

2 Only hardy plants can live in the soil exposed by a retreating glacier.

3 Over the years, the soil becomes richer and new plants take root.

present at the beginning would decrease in number, while the larger plants would become more abundant. With time, the dominant plant species in the ecosystem—grasses, shrubs, or trees—would replace the pioneer species. This progression of different plant species over time is called succession. You will learn more about succession in Chapter 37.

As plants live and eventually die in an area, they cause changes in the soil. Plants' roots give off carbon dioxide that forms carbonic acid in the soil. This acid helps break down rocks. As roots grow, they exert pressure, which cracks pebbles and rocks around them.

Some plants enrich the soil through the symbiotic relationships they form with certain bacteria. Legumes, which are members of the pea family, form root sacs in which nitrogen-fixing bacteria live. The bacteria convert nitrogen gas into compounds the plants can use. When the legumes die, some of the nitrogen compounds released into the soil from the roots of legumes are used by other plants.

When leaves drop from plants and when plants die, the dead plant material starts to decay, forming a substance in the soil called humus.

Humus provides nutrients for plants, helps the soil hold water, and helps keep the soil open to air. All of these effects of humus help plants to grow.

Plants can also modify the local climate and landforms in many ways. For example, plants can act as windbreaks and prevent erosion; they can change the air temperature and raise the humidity. When plants are removed from an area, the local climate and soil also may be dramatically changed. The loss of plants through intentional deforestation or natural disaster can lead to increased erosion from water and wind and can alter the temperature and humidity.

A remarkable example of the effect of plants on the environment began in the 1950s in China when the government planted 300 million trees along its famous Great Wall. One goal of the planting was to slow the winds that blew from the desert regions of China, causing terrible dust storms. Chinese weather data showed that between 1950 and 1960 there were 10 to 20 dust storms per year. By the 1980s and 1990s, there were only 2 to 3 dust storms per year. Other factors may have affected the weather pattern, but it seems that as the trees matured, they helped change the environment.

Computers on farms

You might be surprised to see a farmer on a tractor or a combine working with a laptop computer. But high-tech farming, also called precision or site-specific farming, could be the wave of the future. In an effort to reduce costs and increase crop yields, high-tech farmers use computer and satellite technology.

This technology enables farmers to analyze variations in soil type and quality in each of their fields. The farmers are then able to customize the amount of fertilizers and pesticides they need to apply to different fields or even to different areas of one field. Using this technology, farmers often reduce the total amount of fertilizers and pesticides they use. Precision farming helps farmers grow better crops and save money, and it also is good for the environment.

FIGURE 19.9
Ants living in the thorns of acacia trees protect the trees from insects that would eat the leaves and branches. The trees provide a home for the ants and a sugar solution that nourishes them.

INTERACTION WITH ANIMALS

Consumers on scene

As you have learned, plants are necessary for the survival of land-dwelling animals. Plants provide food, protection, and shelter for animals. One or another species of animals eats the fruits, stems, or seeds of almost every plant. Animals that do not themselves eat plants consume animals that do. Trees and shrubs provide shelter from storms and sunlight. Their boughs or larger stems offer nesting sites for birds and other small animals, homes for insects, and dense shelter for larger animals such as deer.

As the types of plants change during the process of succession, so do the animals living in that area. For example, suppose an untended field undergoes succession to become a forest. When small plants start to grow in an open field, many insects can obtain food and shelter. Soon, grasses fill in the field and more insects, lizards, and burrowing rodents may arrive. Woody shrubs may eventually replace the grasses, allowing birds and larger mammals to inhabit the area. As trees replace the woody shrubs, many birds and other animals find food and shelter among the plants.

CHECKPOINT 19.2

1. Describe several ways in which plants can change the environment.
2. List three ways in which plants sustain animal life.
3. Critical Thinking Choose one of these environments: a plowed field, the mossy slope of a mountain, a vacant lot. What succession of plants would you anticipate finding there?

Build on What You Know

4. Roots give off substances into the soil that become acids. What kind of ions do acids release? What happens to the pH of the soil? **(Need to jog your memory? Revisit relevant concepts in Chapter 2, Section 2.5.)**

? **What are some ways that plants respond to the environment and some ways that they influence the environment?**

19.3 Asexual Reproduction in Plants

How to clone a plant
When meristems are cut from a plant, placed in nutrient solution and shaken, the cells in the meristem tissue divide and the tissue grows. Then the tissue samples can be cut apart and grown again in fresh nutrient solutions. If grown in separate containers they will develop into whole plants. The plants shown here were cloned using this method of asexual reproduction.

What you'll learn

IDEAS
• To explain the process of asexual reproduction in plants
• To identify the methods and uses of artificial propagation in plants

WORDS
vegetative reproduction, artificial propagation

VEGETATIVE REPRODUCTION

Send in the clones

Sexual reproduction in plants, as in all organisms, combines genes from two individuals, thereby producing genetic variation. By contrast, asexual reproduction does not involve fertilization and therefore produces offspring that are genetically identical to the parent. As you may recall, genetically identical offspring are referred to as clones.

You can see examples of plant clones in *Figure 19.10.* Most clumps of cattails are clones of a single plant, as

are many groves of aspen trees. Probably the oldest plant clones on Earth are the creosote bushes that grow in the Mojave Desert. These plants are about 12,000 years old. One of the largest clones of plants consists of aspen trees in the Rocky Mountains, which cover 43 hectares and weigh 5447 metric tons.

Although most plants reproduce asexually only at certain times during their lives, others use this means most often. Being able to reproduce both sexually and asexually has definite advantages. In a stable environment with abundant resources, asexual reproduction is faster than sexual reproduction and produces offspring that are well adapted to the existing

FIGURE 19.10
Naturally occurring plant clones include clumps of cattails (left) and groves of aspens (right). All of the plants in a group of clones are genetically identical and developed from one original plant.

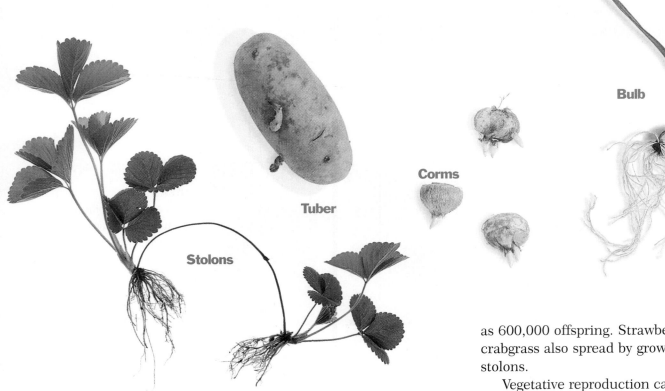

Bulb

Tuber

Stolons

Corms

FIGURE 19.11
Stolons, tubers, corms, and bulbs are structures that can produce new plants by asexual reproduction. How do these structures differ?

environment. In a changing environment, sexual reproduction can produce plants with new combinations of traits that may increase their chances of survival.

Asexual reproduction that takes place naturally in plants is called **vegetative reproduction.** Plants that reproduce by vegetative reproduction can duplicate themselves very rapidly, often crowding out other plants. Vegetative reproduction can occur in several ways.

The aspen trees you just read about are clones produced by stolons, also called runners. Stolons are stems that grow along the surface of the ground and produce several buds. Each bud grows into a new plant. The water hyacinth, an aquatic weed that clogs the canals and rivers in Florida, also uses stolons for vegetative reproduction. Reproduction in water hyacinths is so rapid that in one year, just ten plants can produce as many

as 600,000 offspring. Strawberries and crabgrass also spread by growing stolons.

Vegetative reproduction can also result from rhizomes, specialized stems that grow underground. A stand of bamboo trees may actually spring from the rhizomes of a single bamboo plant. Some plants, such as potatoes, form tubers—swollen tips of rhizomes—which are specialized for storing food. Tubers can also give rise to new plants.

Corms and bulbs are two more types of modified underground stems. Like tubers, corms are modified for food storage, but unlike tubers corms grow upright. Crocuses and gladioli produce corms. Bulbs are underground stems bearing modified fleshy leaves that store food. Onion plants and lilies form bulbs. You can compare several of the structures involved in vegetative reproduction in *Figure 19.11.*

ARTIFICIAL PROPAGATION

Trees get cultured

If you have ever eaten seedless grapes or navel oranges, you have tasted the products of artificial propagation. **Artificial propagation** occurs when people use vegetative reproduction to produce new plants. The methods of artificial propagation include cutting, grafting, and growing tissue cultures. People frequently grow plants by artificial propagation because it is often faster than growing plants from seeds, and it produces a genetically identical crop. Bananas, apples, grapefruits, grapes, potatoes, and pears are crops often grown using artificial propagation.

Artificial propagation is the by-product of a plant's ability to regenerate lost parts. After a plant is injured, its parenchyma cells begin to divide, covering the wound with new tissue. Eventually, a plant can produce a bud in the new tissue. The bud may then develop into a whole new plant.

Plants such as grapes, ivy, raspberries, apples, blackberries, and potatoes are easily propagated by using cuttings. To make a cutting, gardeners or farmers remove a piece of the stem or leaf from a plant and place it in soil. Cuttings are so easy to establish that when farmers in tropical regions cut branches of some plants to make fences, the cut pieces often begin to grow. Soon, there is not just a fence but a living, growing hedge!

Grafting is a way to make two different plants grow as one. Grafting is done by inserting a piece of one plant into a slit made in a second plant. Many types of fruit trees are grown by grafting. For example, navel orange trees are propagated only by grafting or by cuttings. In fact, with this method, several kinds of fruit can be grown on one trunk.

Many plants are produced by growing tissue cultures. This method involves growing an entire plant from individual cells or from small pieces of leaf, stem, or root. This technique was developed in 1958 by American plant physiologist F. C. Steward. Steward grew entire carrot plants

Observing Asexual Reproduction in Plants

You can grow a new plant from a runner when you . . .

Try This

1 Select a healthy runner from a spider plant. Make a sketch of the parts of the runner.
2 Cut the runner from the plant. Place the cut end in a container of water, and drape the rest of the runner over a container of lightly dampened potting soil. Carefully press it into the soil.
3 Water the soil and observe changes in the runner every two days for a period of two weeks. Record changes by making additional sketches.

Analyze Your Results

1 Describe the changes in the runner.
2 From what structure on the runner did a new plant originate?
3 What would happen to the new plant if it were separated from the runner before acquiring roots? After?

from tiny pieces of carrot roots. Today, plant breeders use tissue cultures to reproduce plants that possess rare or desirable traits. For example, orchids and African violets are propagated by growing tissue cultures.

CHECKPOINT 19.3

1. Explain how asexual reproduction benefits plants.
2. List three structures that plants use for vegetative reproduction.
3. Describe three ways in which plants can be artificially propagated.
4. **Critical Thinking** How are artificial propagation and vegetative reproduction similar? How are they different?

Build on What You Know

5. What events might cause a new trait to appear in a cattail plant produced through cloning? *(Need to jog your memory? Revisit relevant concepts in Chapter 8, Section 8.4.)*

19.4 Sexual Reproduction in Plants

What you'll learn

IDEAS

- To identify the plant forms and the stages of alternation of generations
- To explain the characteristics of seeds and the process of germination

WORDS

gametophyte, sporophyte, seed, cotyledons, monocots, dicots

Explosive seeds

If you take a walk in the woods in late autumn, you might hear sounds of tiny projectiles hitting objects. The seeds of the witch hazel shrub are forcefully expelled by the natural constriction of the seed pod. The seeds can be thrown as far as 14 meters (m). Seeds are the products of sexual reproduction in seed plants.

SEXUAL REPRODUCTION

Tossing the salad

Almost all plants have a phase of sexual reproduction at some time during their life cycle. Thus, the ability to make genetic hybrids must be advantageous to almost all plant species.

As you have learned, genetic variation is beneficial to a population. Genetic variation can enhance organisms' ability to resist disease, predation, or changes in the environment. Survival is enhanced because genetic recombination leads to new hybrids with somewhat different characteristics from the parent plants. *Figure 19.12* shows a hybrid rose.

Although flowers may be the most common and recognizable reproductive plant structures, not all plants have them. Mosses, ferns, and conifers, for example, reproduce without flowers. These plants have specialized structures to house the egg and the sperm—the gametes of plant cells. Botanists, scientists who study plants, use the details of plants' reproductive structures and cells as key characteristics to classify plants into divisions or families. You will study the full life cycles and classification of various plant types in Chapter 20.

The process of sexual reproduction in plants is more complex than in most animals. As you have learned, the plant life cycle involves two distinct stages. Because of the differences between these two stages, the life cycle of plants is defined as the alternation of generations.

ALTERNATION OF GENERATIONS

Spores and more

What does alternation of generations mean? Plants' life cycles alternate, or switch, from a diploid ($2n$) generation to a haploid (n) generation. You can see a diagram of the alternation of

FIGURE 19.12

This hybrid tea rose was produced by transferring pollen from one variety of rose to another. Growers often use this type of sexual reproduction to produce flowers with new scents, colors, and shapes.

generations in *Figure 19.13.* What events occur between the diploid phase and the haploid phase?

Alternation of generations includes two phases, the gametophyte phase and the sporophyte phase. The two phases are named for their products: gametes and spores. As you have learned, gametes are haploid cells that unite during fertilization to form a diploid zygote. The haploid (n), gamete-producing phase of a plant's life cycle is the **gametophyte.**

A **sporophyte** is the diploid ($2n$) phase of a plant life cycle that produces spores. Spores are haploid reproductive structures of plants that produce the gametophyte phase. The cells of the sporophyte each contain two sets of chromosomes ($2n$). Spores are produced when certain cells of the sporophyte phase undergo meiosis.

The cycle continues as spores undergo cell division to produce the haploid (n) gametophyte phase. Notice the position of the gametophyte phase in the life cycle of plants shown in *Figure 19.13.* The gametophytes may be independent plants, as in the mosses, or groups of cells dependent on the sporophyte cells, as in flowering plants.

The life cycle of plants differs from the typical life cycle of animals in two ways. First, the body cells of animals are diploid. In different kinds of plants, either the sporophyte (diploid) or the gametophyte (haploid) phase may be the more visible stage of the life cycle. In most plants, the sporophyte is the dominant phase. In mosses, the gametophyte is dominant.

Second, meiosis in animals leads directly to the formation of gametes. Meiosis in plants leads to the formation of spores. In some plants, spores can become independent gamete-producing plants. In other plants, spores develop into gamete-producing structures dependent of the sporophyte.

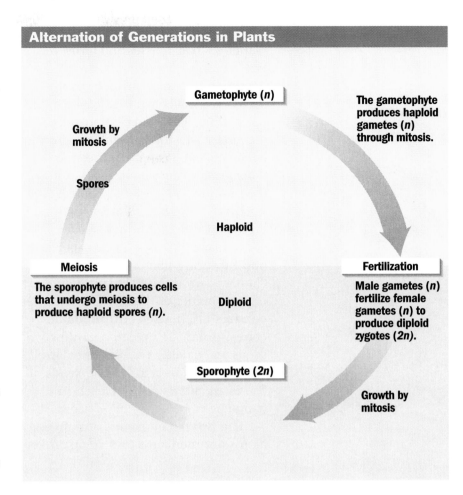

Alternation of Generations in Plants

Gametophyte (n)

Growth by mitosis

Spores

Haploid

Meiosis

The sporophyte produces cells that undergo meiosis to produce haploid spores (n).

Diploid

The gametophyte produces haploid gametes (n) through mitosis.

Fertilization

Male gametes (n) fertilize female gametes (n) to produce diploid zygotes ($2n$).

Sporophyte ($2n$)

Growth by mitosis

FIGURE 19.13
The figure above represents the alternation of generations in plants. How are gametes produced?

As in animals, fertilization in plants involves two gametes and yields a new diploid ($2n$) zygote. In some plants, such as mosses and ferns, fertilization takes place in water. In conifers and flowering plants, fertilization does not require water.

REPRODUCTION BY SEEDS

Packed and ready to travel

Many plants produce seeds during sexual reproduction. A **seed** is a protective structure that contains a diploid plant embryo and stored food, mainly in the form of starch. Most seeds have a tough, protective seed coat. Carried by wind, water, or animals, seeds can travel far away from the parent plants, just as spores can.

It takes a lot energy for a plant to produce seeds. What advantages could seeds provide for plants? In non-seed plants, such as mosses and ferns, the newly formed embryo must immediately develop into a sporophyte. In contrast, a seed can remain dormant for long periods of time. The seed coat provides protection for the embryo until the growing conditions are favorable. Once the embryo starts developing again, the seed's stored food provides nourishment.

Kinds of seed plants Two groups of plants produce seeds: cone-bearing plants (gymnosperms) and flowering plants (angiosperms). Conifers are the oldest surviving type of seed plants on Earth. The seeds of conifers are housed within female cones. Botanists describe conifer seeds as "naked" because they are not enclosed in a fruit. The seeds of flowering plants are enclosed in fruits.

The two major groups of flowering plants are monocots and dicots. A key difference between monocots and dicots is the number of seed leaves, or **cotyledons** (KOT-ih-LEE-dunz), in the plant's embryo. Although cotyledons look like leaves, they are different from the leaves you see on an adult plant. You may recall that "mono-" means "one," and "di-" means "two." **Monocots** are flowering plants with seeds that have one cotyledon. Monocots include bamboo, lilies, wheat, and corn. **Dicots** are flowering plants with seeds that have two cotyledons. Dicots include peas, tomatoes, grapes, and apples. You will learn about other distinguishing characteristics of monocots and dicots when you read Chapter 20.

Seed dispersal Seeds can be dispersed long distances or carried away from the parent plants. This adaptation has allowed seed plants to successfully colonize a wide variety of land habitats. Various adaptations

FIGURE 19.14

Germination

Root growth
The primary root responds to gravity. It grows downward by cell divisions in the apical meristem (the growing tissue at the tip of the root).

Primary shoot
The primary shoot grows upward toward the sun, shedding its seed casing.

Seed
The embryo inside its seed casing becomes metabolically active after water activates enzymes that convert starch to sugar.

Primary root
The first sprout, the primary root, forces its way out of the seed casing.

enable seeds to be dispersed. Some seeds are light enough to be carried on wind currents. Some seed coats have hooks that attach easily to a passing animal. A few seed packets have the ability to burst open and propel seeds through the air. Still other seeds remain inside a fruit. After the fruit is eaten by an animal, the undigestible seed is dispersed in animal wastes.

Differentiation
Axillary buds and apical meristems form cells which become specialized as the plant grows.

Germination When conditions are favorable for growth, seeds sprout and grow in a process called germination. You can follow this process in *Figure 19.14*. During germination, the embryo uses energy from the food stored in the seed. The embryo grows, splits the seed coat, and forms a root and a shoot. The root and shoot enlarge as the seedling develops.

Two environmental conditions affect germination: water availability and temperature. During the first stage of germination, water activates many enzymes, including the enzymes that convert starch into sugar. Sugar supplies energy for the growth of the embryo.

Temperature also affects germination. Many seeds need moderate to warm temperatures to germinate. Why do you think there is an abundance of plant growth in spring? When temperatures begin to get warmer, many dormant seeds sprout. Because seeds of different plants germinate at different temperatures and under different moisture conditions, plants are adapted to a wide range of niches.

CHECKPOINT 19.4

1. Describe the life cycle of alternation of generations in plants.

2. Compare the seeds of monocots and dicots. Explain the process of seed germination.

3. Critical Thinking At which stage of the plant's sexual reproduction cycle does genetic recombination occur? Which phase—gametophyte or sporophyte—is the first to inherit such variations?

Build on What You Know

4. Compare meiosis and mitosis with respect to plant and animal gametes. *(Need to jog your memory? Revisit relevant concepts in Chapter 5, Section 5.3.)*

Observing Seedlings

WHAT YOU WILL DO Design an experiment to test the effect of a variable on the growth of corn grains or bean seeds, observe their growth over a 14-day period, and graph the number of seeds that sprout

SKILLS YOU WILL USE Observing, measuring, collecting and recording data

WHAT YOU WILL NEED Two resealable plastic bags, paper towels, metric ruler, stapler, corn grains or bean seeds, marker

Propose a Hypothesis

Choose a variable that you think will affect the germination and growth of corn grains or bean seeds, such as temperature, amount of light, or water. Design an experiment to test if and how the variable affects seedling germination and growth. Propose a hypothesis about how the variable will affect the seedlings' growth.

Conduct Your Experiment

DAY 1

1 Line two plastic bags with paper towels. Place a line of staples through the bags 3 centimeters (cm) below the reclosable seal on each bag. Add enough water to soak the towels.

2 Place five corn grains or bean seeds in each bag so they rest on the staple line, as shown in the photo. Using the marker, number the seeds 1–5 and 6–10.

3 Close the bags and set them up to test the variable you chose. Record the date and time.

DAYS 2–14

4 Check the seeds at the same time each day. Draw the seeds and record the number that have germinated. Measure and record the length of each root and the height of each shoot.

5 Once the seeds germinate, leave the bags open.

6 Repeat step 4 for 12 days.

Analyze Your Data

1 Graph the number of seeds sprouted as compared to the number of days passed.

2 Calculate the average root length each day and graph the results.

3 Calculate the average shoot height each day and graph the results.

4 Add your data to a class data table. Compare the growth rates of the two bags of seeds.

Draw Conclusions

Was your hypothesis supported? Summarize the effects of the variable you chose on the seedlings' growth rates.

Design a Related Experiment

Design an experiment to compare the germination rates of two species of plants.

Lab: Observing Seedlings

Objective: To germinate corn or bean seeds, observe their growth over a 14-day period, and graph the number of seeds that sprout.

Day 1: February 8, 10:00 a.m.

Day 2: Number of seeds germinating = 0

19.5 Focus on Flowers

Flowers that set sail
Pollination of water celery plants occurs when the free-floating male flower encounters a slight trough, or depression, in the water caused by the female flower, which is anchored by an underwater stem. The male flower slides into the trough and collides with the female. In the process, the female is dusted with pollen. While flowers are pollinated in a variety of ways, they all contain the structures that enable reproduction to take place.

What you'll learn

IDEAS
• To identify the male, female, and sterile parts of a flower
• To explain the process of fertilization

WORDS
flower, ovary, ovule, pollen, pollination

CHARACTERISTICS OF FLOWERS

The gender of a flower

Roses, tulips, lilacs, orchids—how dull the world would be without flowers! However, the importance of a flower is not in the way it looks or smells to humans, but in what it does. A **flower** is the reproductive structure of a flowering plant, or angiosperm.

Flowers are modified stems with specialized leaves and other structures for reproduction. Most flowers have three kinds of parts: male, female, and sterile. Male and female parts produce gametes. A flower may contain both male and female parts (a "perfect" flower), or just one of the two (an "imperfect" flower). Sterile parts attract pollinators and protect developing flowers or embryos.

The male structures of flowers produce sperm. **Pollen** grains are structures that contain sperm cells. The male part of a flower is called the stamen. Stamens usually have two parts: anther and filament. The anther produces pollen. The filament supports the anther.

The female structures of flowers produce eggs. All of the female parts form the pistil. Pistils are often located at the center of a flower and usually have three parts: stigma, style,

and ovary. You can locate these parts in *Figure 19.15*.

Each part of a pistil has a different function. The stigma is the structure on which pollen lands and germinates. The stigma is often sticky so the pollen grains will cling to it. The style connects the stigma to the ovary. The **ovary** is the structure that develops into a fruit. Each ovary contains one or more ovules. An **ovule** is a structure in which an egg develops. Ovules eventually become seeds.

FIGURE 19.15

A Typical Flower

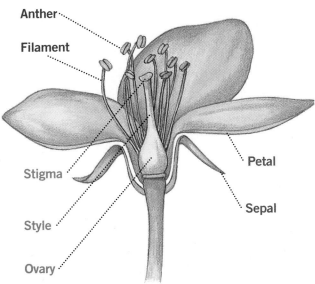

Anther
Filament
Stigma
Style
Ovary
Petal
Sepal

Male parts
These structures produce pollen that contain sperm.

Female parts
These structures produce ovules that contain eggs.

Sterile parts
These structures provide protection and attract pollinators to the flower.

FIGURE 19.16

Seed Development

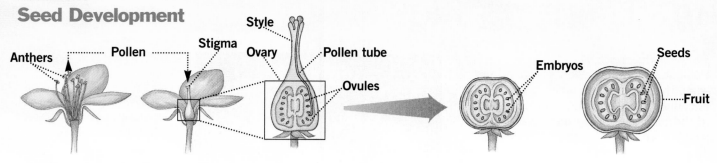

Pollination and fertilization
Pollen lands on a stigma; the pollen tube grows into the style. Two sperm are produced in the pollen by mitosis and travel to the ovary. One sperm fertilizes the egg in an ovule, forming a zygote. The other combines with two polar nuclei.

Seed development
The zygotes become embryos, the ovules develop into seeds, and a fruit forms around the seeds.

The sterile parts of a flower include the petals and sepals. Petals are the usually colorful, leaflike appendages on a flower. Petals often attract pollinators. The protective leaves at the base of a flower are sepals. Sepals, which are often green, cover the bud of a flower and protect the developing flower parts as they grow.

POLLINATION AND FERTILIZATION

Traveling gametes

During **pollination,** pollen is transferred from an anther to a stigma. When a pollen grain lands on a stigma, it sends out a pollen tube that grows through the style to the ovary. Sperm nuclei are carried along in the pollen tube as it grows. When the pollen tube reaches the ovary, it enters the ovule, which contains an egg.

Fertilization occurs when a sperm nucleus from a pollen tube fuses with the egg and forms a zygote. While one sperm fertilizes an egg, a second sperm nucleus from the pollen tube fertilizes two polar nuclei. The second

fertilization forms a food-storing tissue in the seed called endosperm tissue. Endosperm tissue is triploid ($3n$). The process in plants that involves two fertilizations is called double fertilization; it happens only in angiosperms.

After fertilization, several processes occur. The zygote develops into an embryo, and the ovule becomes a seed. At the same time, the other parts of the ovary and surrounding tissues form a fruit that encases the developing seeds.

CHECKPOINT 19.5

1. Identify the male, female, and sterile parts of a flower.
2. Briefly explain the process of fertilization, including the roles of the male and female parts of flowers.
3. **Critical Thinking** Would you expect pollen grains of wind-pollinated flowers to be sticky? Why or why not? How can you test the accuracy of your answer?

Build on What You Know

4. How are plant adaptations related to pollinator adaptations? *(Need to jog your memory? Revisit relevant concepts in Chapter 10, Section 10.4.)*

FIGURE 19.17
Some beetles become pollinators as they move from flower to flower in search of pollen.

What are some ways that plants reproduce asexually? Sexually?

Chapter 19 Review

THE BIG
IDEA!

19.1–19.2 Plants respond to and affect the environment.
19.3–19.5 Plants reproduce both asexually and sexually.

Sum It Up

Use the following summary to review the main concepts in this chapter.

19.1 Plants Respond to the Environment

- Plants respond to conditions in their internal and external environments. A plant may respond to light, gravity, or touch.
- Plants produce small quantities of chemicals that control growth and response.
- Seasonal changes determine the timing of bud and flower production.
- Plants usually become inactive during periods of extreme cold or in dry conditions, and many seeds and bulbs are inactive for a time before they sprout.

19.2 Plants Change the Environment

- Colonizer plants usually arrive first in open land.
- Over time, a succession of plant species inhabit a given area. Small nonwoody plants are often replaced by larger woody plants. As the plant species change, so do the animal species that live in the area.
- As plants die and decay, the soil is enriched with nutrients. Plants also protect soil from erosion.

19.3 Asexual Reproduction in Plants

- Asexual reproduction produces offspring that are well suited to an existing stable environment.
- Farmers use cutting and grafting techniques on seed-bearing plants to produce genetically identical offspring.
- Plant asexual reproduction can involve structures such as runners, tubors, corms, and bulbs.

19.4 Sexual Reproduction in Plants

- Sexual reproduction involves the alternation of diploid and haploid generations.
- Many plants produce seeds during sexual reproduction.
- Temperature and the availability of water affect seed germination.

19.5 Focus on Flowers

- Most flowers have male, female, and sterile structures.
- Fertilization in angiosperms requires pollination, growth of pollen tube, and fusion of the egg and sperm nuclei. In angiosperms, fertilization leads to the development of seeds and fruit.

Use Terms and Concepts

Use each of the following words or terms in a complete sentence. If you need to review a meaning, turn to the page indicated.

stimulus (p. 446)

tropism (p. 446)

hormone (p. 447)

auxin (p. 449)

photoperiodism (p. 449)

dormancy (p. 450)

colonizers (p. 452)

vegetative reproduction (p. 456)

artificial propagation (p. 456)

gametophyte (p. 459)

sporophyte (p. 459)

seed (p. 459)

cotyledons (p. 460)

monocots (p. 460)

dicots (p. 460)

flower (p. 463)

ovary (p. 463)

ovule (p. 463)

pollen (p. 463)

pollination (p. 464)

Use Your Word Power

COMPLETION **Write the word or phrase that best completes each statement.**

1. A plant produces _____ , which are released in one part of the plant and affect another part of the plant.

2. Many seeds and bulbs need a period of _____ before they sprout.

3. The hormone _____ promotes the growth of roots, buds, and stems.

4. In a process called _____ , people use vegetative reproduction and other methods to produce new plants.

5. The first species to invade an uninhabited tract of land are _____ .

6. The process of transferring pollen from an anther to a stigma is called _____ .

7. A plant response that is linked to the hours of light and darkness is called _____ .

8. The growth of a plant in a certain direction in response to a stimulus is a(n) _____ .

MULTIPLE CHOICE **Choose the letter of the word or phrase that best completes each statement.**

9. During the alternation of generations, plants form a diploid (a) sporophyte; (b) gametophyte; (c) spore; (d) gamete.

10. The growth of plants from stolons and tubers are examples of (a) artificial propagation; (b) pollination; (c) vegetative reproduction; (d) colonization.

11. The seed leaves of flowering plants are called (a) monocots; (b) cotyledons; (c) dicots; (d) flowers.

12. In flowering plants, the structures that contain sperm cells are (a) spores; (b) pollen grains; (c) ovaries; (d) cotyledons.

13. The structure of a plant that develops into a fruit is a(n) (a) cotyledon; (b) seed; (c) spore; (d) ovary.

Show What You Know

14. Use the example of gravity to explain how a tropism can be positive or negative.

15. Contrast the seeds of monocots and dicots.

16. What are two environmental conditions that affect seed germination?

17. What are some effects of hormones in plants?

18. How do the typical life cycles of plants and animals differ?

19. Are the terms "long-day" and "short-day" really accurate? Explain why or why not.

20. What benefits do legumes provide to soil?

21. **Make a Concept Map** Complete the concept map below by adding the following terms: eggs, gamete, ovary, ovule, pollen, pollination, seed, sperm.

Take It Further

22. **Applying Concepts** Arctic lupines are plants whose seeds have evolved the ability to remain dormant for thousands of years. Explain why that characteristic could be an advantage in an arctic environment.

23. **Identifying Cause and Effect** Explain why it is advantageous for seed germination to begin with the emergence of a root rather than a shoot.

24. **Organizing and Classifying** Consider the methods of artificial propagation described in this chapter. Which method(s) would you use to produce an apple tree that bears two different kinds of apples?

25. Designing an Experiment Design an experiment to show how different colors of light affect seed germination and plant growth.

26. Analyzing Data Suppose you are a gardener with a shady yard and moist soil. Use the table below to find a short flower that would bloom in your garden during the summer. What other flower(s) could grow in your garden?

Planning Your Garden

Plant	Flowering Period	Height	Light	Soil
Canada phlox	Late spring	30 cm	Light shade	Moist
Gentian	Mid- to late summer	20–30 cm	Light shade	Moist
Himalayan blue poppy	Early to mid-summer	0.6–1.8 m	Light shade	Well-drained
Mountain bluet	Early summer to early fall	60 cm	Full sun	Well-drained
Sea pink	Late spring to mid-summer	30–45 cm	Full sun	Well-drained

27. Interpreting a Graph The graph below shows how the mass of Texas bluebonnet seedlings, after one month's growth, compared to the mass of the seeds from which they sprouted. What is the relationship between the mass of the seedlings and the mass of the seeds? What hypothesis could you state that would explain these results?

Differences in Seed Size of Texas Bluebonnets

Consider the Issues

28. Going Wild In many states, laws prevent people from picking native species of wildflowers. What is your opinion about these laws? Should the laws apply only to certain plants? Should people be allowed to pick wildflowers on their own property? Should people be allowed to collect seeds from wildflowers to plant in their own gardens? Present a logical argument for or against picking wildflowers.

Make New Connections

29. Biology and Art Many artists are known for their paintings of plants. Use museums or art books to find examples. Compare the paintings with illustrations and photographs in field guides and other references.

Striped Camellias,
1927
by Beatrice Bland

30. Biology and the Community Investigate how dominant types of plants in your area reproduce. Report your findings with drawings or photographs.

FAST-FORWARD TO CHAPTER 20

In Chapter 20, what you have read about transport and reproduction in plants will help you understand how plants are classified.

Origin and Diversity of Plants

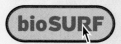

You can find out more about plant diversity by exploring the following Internet address: *http://plants.biosurf.com*

In this chapter . . .

FEATURES

Everyday Biology
- Absorbent Cells
- Weeds in the Mail
- Orchid Seeds in Your Ice Cream?

In the Community
Classifying Plants

 Environmental Awareness
What Bugs Bees

LAB ZONES

Discover It!
- Observing Plant Diversity

Do It!
- Examining Fern Leaves and Sori
- Examining the Structure of a Pine Cone

Think About It!
- Analyzing Changes in a Flower

Investigate It!
- Observing Plant Reproduction

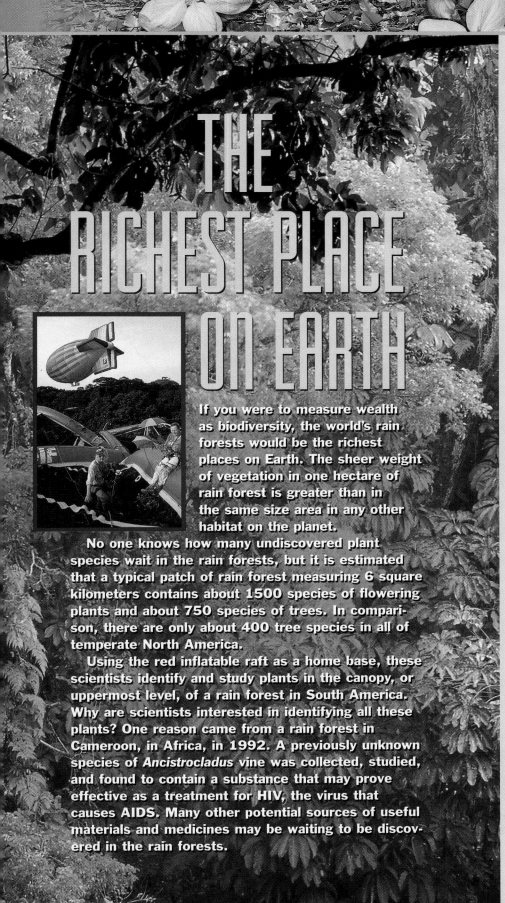

THE RICHEST PLACE ON EARTH

If you were to measure wealth as biodiversity, the world's rain forests would be the richest places on Earth. The sheer weight of vegetation in one hectare of rain forest is greater than in the same size area in any other habitat on the planet.

No one knows how many undiscovered plant species wait in the rain forests, but it is estimated that a typical patch of rain forest measuring 6 square kilometers contains about 1500 species of flowering plants and about 750 species of trees. In comparison, there are only about 400 tree species in all of temperate North America.

Using the red inflatable raft as a home base, these scientists identify and study plants in the canopy, or uppermost level, of a rain forest in South America. Why are scientists interested in identifying all these plants? One reason came from a rain forest in Cameroon, in Africa, in 1992. A previously unknown species of *Ancistrocladus* vine was collected, studied, and found to contain a substance that may prove effective as a treatment for HIV, the virus that causes AIDS. Many other potential sources of useful materials and medicines may be waiting to be discovered in the rain forests.

LAB ZONE Discover It!

Observing Plant Diversity

You need several types of plants and a hand lens

1. Work in a small group. Discuss with other students what types of plants you may be able to bring to class. Try to include mosses, ferns, conifers, and flowering plants. Have your teacher approve your choices.
2. Examine your group's plant specimens with a hand lens and compare them.

What structures are common to all the plants? What structures appear only on certain types of plants?

WRITE ABOUT IT!

Think of a habitat and the type of plant life it contains. It could be a place you have visited or one you have read about, such as a rain forest. Write a poem or a story that takes place in the habitat, and include descriptions of the local flora.

469

20.1 Natural History of Plants

What you'll learn

IDEAS

• To compare and contrast the characteristics of modern plants and algae
• To discuss the characteristics that are used in classifying plants

WORDS

division

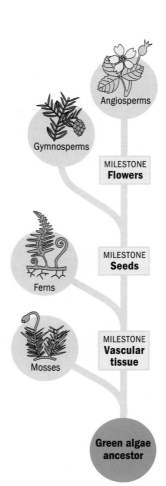

Pioneering plants

The plants that first took hold on land (in the late Silurian and early Devonian periods, 421 to 387 million years ago) were small photosynthetic herbs. By the time dinosaurs first appeared (at the end of the Triassic period, about 208 million years ago) there were pockets of lush vegetation and taller plants, which probably resembled this modern-day swamp, near coasts and waterways.

PLANTS AND GREEN ALGAE

A search for ancestors

Despite the significant differences between today's plants and green algae, biologists have established that plants evolved from ancient multicellular green algae. They base their conclusions on fossil evidence and the biochemical and structural similarities of plants and green algae. These similarities include

• similar chloroplasts
• the same photosynthetic pigments
• cell walls that contain cellulose
• a cell plate that develops during cell division

Although plants and green algae share the characteristics just described, the differences between

them are so numerous and significant that they are classified in different kingdoms. Many of the differences arise because plants are adapted to live on land, whereas green algae are adapted to live in water.

To survive on land, plants have to be able to transport materials, prevent water evaporation, support themselves, and reproduce. Based on the fossils that have been found in coal, scientists hypothesize that the earliest plants were probably similar to mosses—short structures without leaves, stems, or roots. Because the ancient plants were only a few cells thick, transporting materials was not a challenge.

The first land plants had to prevent the loss of water by evaporation in dry conditions. One adaptation that enabled plants to conserve water was the cuticle. As you have learned, the cuticle is a waxy, waterproof layer that coats plants and prevents water loss from evaporation.

Because they were small, the first land plants did not need much support. Early adaptations for support may have included specialized cells and compounds such as lignin. Lignin

FIGURE 20.1

Today's plants probably evolved from green algae. As they evolved, plant groups with new adaptations to life on land appeared. Each successive evolutionary step in the phylogenetic tree represents a new adaptation. What was the last group of plants to evolve?

is a hard substance that strengthens cell walls, enabling cells to support additional weight.

Evidence indicates that the first land plants had a life cycle that involved alternation of generations. Recall that the process of fertilization is part of the alternation of generations. Like their ancestors, the early plants were probably dependent on water for reproduction. Water was the medium through which sperm swam in order to fertilize an egg.

Because ancient plants needed water for fertilization, they probably grew only in moist areas, such as marshes and estuaries, where water was plentiful. Such environments also would have provided ancient land plants with a means of obtaining the minerals necessary for their survival.

TODAY'S PLANTS

Great variety from a lowly beginning

Most modern plants can now survive on land because they have specialized structures that green algae lack. These structures include leaves, stems, and roots. They perform the vital functions of transport and support.

Many different kinds of plants have evolved. The kingdom Plantae comprises 12 divisions of living plants. A **division** is a major taxonomic group used in classifying plants and fungi. For animals, the comparable taxonomic group is a phylum. With the exception of phyla, botanists use all the taxonomic levels you learned about in Chapter 13: class, order, family, genus, and species.

Nonvascular plants The first land plants were short nonvascular plants that lived in moist habitats. The modern descendants of these plants are classified in three divisions: mosses, liverworts, and hornworts.

Although the three divisions of nonvascular plants look different, they share many characteristics. For example, nonvascular plants lack true leaves and roots, and absorb most of their water through the plant body. Nonvascular plants reproduce without seeds and are therefore classified as seedless plants. Because their sperm must swim through water in order to reach the eggs, nonvascular plants need a readily available source of water for fertilization.

Mosses are members of the division Bryophyta (BRY-oh-FY-teh). In all mosses the gametophyte phase is the most prominent phase of the life cycle. The short, soft mats you see growing on rocks, trees, and other places are the moss gametophytes.

The liverworts comprise the division Hepatophyta. The name "liverwort" refers to the body of the plant, which resembles the lobes of a liver. Like the mosses, the most prominent phase of the liverwort life cycle is the gametophyte phase.

Hornwort gametophytes resemble liverwort gametophytes, but hornwort sporophytes can perform photosynthesis, unlike the sporophytes of other nonvascular plants. Botanists use this unique characteristic to classify the

FIGURE 20.2
These fossilized leaves came from a 360-million-year-old ancestor of today's cone-bearing plants. The fernlike leaves topped a large woody trunk.

hornworts in a separate plant division, the Anthocerophyta.

With the evolution of vascular systems, ancient plants no longer needed to live in very moist environments. Vascular plants have internal transport systems that allow them to move water and dissolved nutrients from their roots to other parts of the plant. As vascular systems became more specialized, vascular plants were able to populate drier regions of Earth.

Vascular plants Nine divisions of plants are vascular, either with or without seeds. As shown in *Figure 20.4,* there are four divisions of vascular seedless plants and five divisions of vascular seed plants.

All vascular plants have leaves, stems, and roots which all contain vascular tissue. Like all plants, vascular plants have both haploid (gametophyte) and diploid (sporophyte) generations.

FIGURE 20.3

The Plant Kingdom

Vascular plants without seeds

Vascular plants with seeds

Horsetails

Flowering plants

Gnetae

Cycads

Club mosses

Ferns

MILESTONE
Flowers

Conifers

Whisk ferns

MILESTONE
Seeds

Mosses

Ginkgoes

Hornworts

PLANTS

MILESTONE
Vascular tissue

Liverworts

Nonvascular plants

Green algae ancestor

In a seedless plant, the sporophyte releases spores. A spore grows into small, separate gametophyte which produces gametes. Fertilization and new sporophyte formation occurs on the gametophyte. Seeds are not made.

A seed plant does not release spores. A gametophyte structure develops in flowers or cones of the sporophyte, where gametes are produced, and fertilization occurs. After fertilization, the new embryo is in a seed. After release, the seed can grow into a new sporophyte.

The largest and most familiar of the seedless vascular plants are ferns, members of the division Pterophyta (TER-eh-FY-teh). Although ferns can survive without constant contact with water, they do need water for fertilization. Most ferns have feathery leaves that collect light efficiently in shaded areas. Their stems are structurally simple and generally reach a maximum height of about 2 meters.

The club mosses (division Lycophyta), the horsetails (division Sphenophyta), and the whisk ferns (division Psilophyta) are other groups of seedless vascular plants. Although the ancestors of these plants were abundant during the Carboniferous period (340–280 million years ago), their modern descendants are comparatively scarce. All of the plants in these three divisions have vascular tissue, but not all have leaves.

The evolution and specialization

Plant Classification

Botanical Name	Common Name	Living Species
NONVASCULAR PLANTS		
Division Bryophyta	Mosses	10,000
Division Hepatophyta	Liverworts	6500
Division Anthocerophyta	Hornworts	100
VASCULAR PLANTS		
Seedless Plants		
Division Pterophyta	Ferns	12,000
Division Lycophyta	Club mosses	1000
Division Sphenophyta	Horsetails	15
Division Psilophyta	Whisk ferns	13
Seed Plants		
Gymnosperms		
Division Coniferophyta	Conifers	550
Division Cycadophyta	Cycads	100
Division Gnetophyta	Gnetae	70
Division Ginkgophyta	Ginkgoes	1
Angiosperms		
Division Anthophyta	Flowering plants	235,000

FIGURE 20.4

The number of species in each of the major classifications of plants varies. Which division has the most species? The fewest?

of vascular systems allowed plants to colonize drier areas. However, embryos of seedless plants will dry out and die if they are not kept moist. The evolution of seeds was another factor that helped plants survive in dry areas.

The five divisions of seed plants are subdivided into two general categories according to the ways they produce seeds. The two categories are gymnosperms and angiosperms. Gymnosperms (JIM-noh-spermz) are vascular plants that produce seeds within cones. Angiosperms (AN-jee-oh–spermz) produce

FIGURE 20.5

Plants have adaptations that enable them to live in a wide variety of environmental conditions. The spatterdock (left) is a flowering plant that thrives in swamps. The bloodwood tree of Australia (right) survives where water is scarce.

seeds that are encased in fruits.

The largest and most familiar division of gymnosperms is Coniferophyta, the conifers. Conifers include cone-bearing evergreens such as pines, firs, spruces, redwoods, and cypresses. A cone is a specialized reproductive structure that produces seeds without fruit. Most conifers have needlelike leaves.

The cycads (division Cycadophyta), ginkgoes (division Ginkgophyta), and the gnetae (division Gnetophyta) are other gymnosperms. All of these plants have vascular tissues and produce seeds. Cycads look like small palm trees and typically grow in tropical climates. Unlike palms (which are angiosperms), cycads produce seeds in cones. Ginkgoes, trees that lose their leaves in winter, are the sole survivors of a small division of plants. The gnetae are a group of three orders of unusual plants.

Angiosperms are characterized by the evolution of two important features: flowers and fruits. Flowers, which produce sperm, egg cells, or both, are important to plant reproduction because they attract pollinating organisms. These pollinating organisms, in search of food or mates, help to disperse the pollen that produces

the sperm cells of the plant.

Fruits, the other key angiosperm characteristic, are important to plant reproduction in two ways. Fruits protect seeds and can help disperse them.

The majority of the trees, bushes, and houseplants you are familiar with belong to the angiosperms. In fact, there are about a quarter of a million different species of angiosperms—more than 300 times the number of species of gymnosperms.

CHECKPOINT 20.1

1. Compare and contrast the physical characteristics of modern plants and algae.
2. Identify and discuss the major evolutionary adaptations that biologists use to classify plants.
3. **Critical Thinking** Suppose a friend gives you a plant and challenges you to classify it. How would you do this? Explain your answer.

Build on What You Know

4. Using what you know about natural selection, explain how the first nonvascular land plants might have evolved into vascular plants. *(Need to jog your memory? Revisit relevant concepts in Chapter 10, Section 10.2.)*

20.2 Mosses

Mosses growing on Mount Kenya in Africa lead very unstable lives. During the hot, damp day, the mosses flourish. At night, however, temperatures drop, the soil freezes, and the mosses lose their grip on the mountain. Turning into dry balls, they are blown by the wind to new locations. How does this adaptation help the moss species survive?

What you'll learn

IDEAS
- To identify the common characteristics of mosses
- To compare and contrast the haploid and diploid phases of mosses

WORDS
archegonium, antheridium, capsule, peat bog

CHARACTERISTICS OF MOSSES

Masses of mosses gather on wet stones

Many kinds of plants are called mosses—reindeer moss, Spanish moss, and Irish moss are just a few. Are they really entitled to that name? Actually, no! None of these is a true moss. Reindeer moss is a lichen, Spanish moss is a flowering plant related to pineapple, and Irish moss is a red alga, a type of seaweed. What, then, is a moss?

A moss is the most common type of nonvascular plant—a plant that has no vascular system. As you just read, the nonvascular plants also include liverworts and hornworts. This section, however, discusses only the mosses.

If you look carefully, you will probably find mosses growing in many familiar places. Mosses grow on damp brick walls, in sidewalk cracks, as thick mats on forest floors, and on the shaded sides of trees. Some mosses are even adapted to life in deserts. Mosses need water for reproduction. All of these places—even deserts—have enough water for mosses to complete their life cycle.

Mosses have a relatively uncomplicated system for transporting water. Water can pass from moss cell to moss cell by osmosis because most mosses are only a few cells thick. As you may recall from Chapter 3, osmosis is the diffusion of water from an area of high concentration to an area of low concentration. Osmosis does not use a cell's energy.

Mosses do not have roots. Instead, they are anchored by slender projections called rhizoids. Mosses also lack true leaves, although they do have leaflike structures. These structures are often only one cell thick.

Mosses are small land plants, but they vary in appearance and habitat. Compare the three types of mosses shown in *Figure 20.6*.

FIGURE 20.6

Seen from a distance, mosses look like lush green carpets. Up close, their thin green leaflike structures become visible. How does water move through these structures?

Male gametes get wet

As you can see in *Figure 20.7,* mosses, like most other plants, alternate between a haploid (*n*) gametophyte phase and a diploid (*2n*) sporophyte phase. The gametophyte of a moss is familiar to most people because it is usually the larger, more obvious, and longer-lived generation of the moss life cycle.

The moss gametophyte produces eggs and sperm. These gametes are surrounded by a jacket of sterile cells. Sterile cells protect the gametes from drying out and dying. The eggs of mosses are large and immobile. The egg-producing organ of a moss is

called an **archegonium** (ar-kih-GOH-nee-um). Each flask-shaped archegonium (plural: *archegonia*) produces one egg.

Sperm are smaller than eggs and have flagella, enabling them to reach the eggs by swimming through dew or rainwater. The sperm find the moss eggs by following a trail of chemicals in the water. The sperm-producing organ of a moss is called an **antheridium** (an-thuh-RIH-dee-um). Each antheridium (plural: *antheridia*) produces many sperm. You can identify these structures in *Figure 20.7.*

As in all plants, fertilization produces a zygote, which undergoes mitosis and becomes a sporophyte. The sporophyte of a moss is usually

FIGURE 20.7

The Life Cycle of a Moss

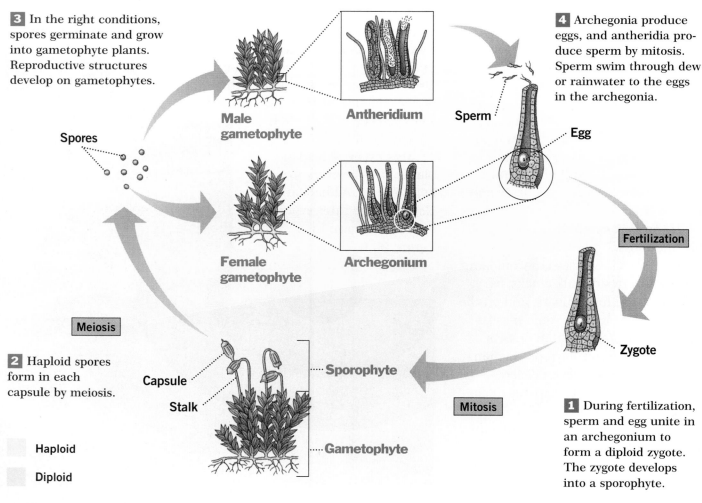

3 In the right conditions, spores germinate and grow into gametophyte plants. Reproductive structures develop on gametophytes.

Spores

Male gametophyte

Antheridium

Female gametophyte

Archegonium

Sperm

Egg

4 Archegonia produce eggs, and antheridia produce sperm by mitosis. Sperm swim through dew or rainwater to the eggs in the archegonia.

Fertilization

Zygote

Meiosis

2 Haploid spores form in each capsule by meiosis.

Capsule

Stalk

Sporophyte

Gametophyte

Haploid

Diploid

Mitosis

1 During fertilization, sperm and egg unite in an archegonium to form a diploid zygote. The zygote develops into a sporophyte.

smaller than the gametophyte to which it is attached. Because the sporophyte lacks chlorophyll, it depends on the gametophyte for food. You can see the diploid (2n) sporophyte in *Figure 20.7*.

The sporophyte consists of a stalk and a foot that anchors it to the gametophyte. Atop the long, slender stalk is the capsule. The **capsule** is the moss structure that forms haploid (n) spores by meiosis. When the spores are mature, the capsule opens and the spores are carried off by the wind. If a spore lands in a moist place, it sprouts and forms a new gametophyte. What are the advantages of producing spores on top of stalks rather than at ground level?

Most mosses can reproduce asexually by fragmentation and from gemmae (JEM-ee). Fragmentation occurs when small pieces break off a gametophyte and grow into a new plant. Gemmae (singular: *gemma*) are tiny pieces of tissue that grow in various structures on moss gametophytes. Raindrops splash gemmae from the parent plant and carry them to another area, where they can form new gametophytes.

MOSSES IN THE BIOSPHERE
Small but significant

There are about 14,000 living species of mosses. Most live in tropical environments and have various roles in ecosystems. Some mosses help decomposers break down dead wood. Other mosses are pioneer species on bare rock surfaces. Many mosses also help keep the soil moist and prevent soil erosion. They provide shelter for insects and other small animals, and they are used as nesting material by birds and mammals.

One of the best-known mosses is sphagnum (SFAG-num), which is also called peat moss and which forms peat bogs. A **peat bog** is a wet ecosystem that consists of large mats of sphagnum. As the sphagnum grows, it releases an antibacterial chemical and acids, both of which prevent the growth of most other organisms, including many decomposers. As a result, dead sphagnum decomposes slowly. Gradually, dead sphagnum builds up around the small ponds and other open wetland areas where it grows. Eventually, so much accumulates that it converts a pond into marshy soil. You can see how peat moss is cut for use as fuel in *Figure 20.8*.

FIGURE 20.8
When burned, sphagnum provides more heat than an equal mass of wood. For that reason it is used for fuel in some parts of the world.

CHECKPOINT 20.2

1. What are the common characteristics of mosses?
2. Compare and contrast the haploid and diploid phases of mosses.
3. How are peat bogs formed?
4. **Critical Thinking** During World War I, the British army used peat moss to bandage millions of wounds. What properties of peat moss make it suitable for use in bandages?

Build on What You Know

5. Explain the process by which moss cells obtain water from the environment. *(Need to jog your memory? Revisit relevant concepts in Chapter 3, Section 3.5.)*

EVERYDAY BIOLOGY

Absorbent Cells

Dry peat moss is extremely absorbent. This absorbency makes it a good additive to dry, sandy soil. It is also used as a protective cushion for shipping other plants. Peat moss has even been added to diapers.

What are some of the characteristics of plants that enable them to survive on land?

20.3 Ferns

What you'll learn

IDEAS
• To identify the common characteristics of ferns
• To compare the haploid and diploid phases of the fern life cycle

WORDS
rhizomes, sorus

When seedless plants ruled Earth
Long before dinosaurs roamed Earth, dense pockets of vegetation flourished. This vegetation was not the kind we are familiar with today. Seedless, fernlike plants, not grasses, covered the ground, and tall fernlike trees formed the canopy. These plants—now extinct—had leaves, and many had spores, just as modern ferns such as this tree fern (right) do.

FIGURE 20.9
Many ferns have lacy compound leaves, but the staghorn fern (lower left) has leaves that resemble antlers.

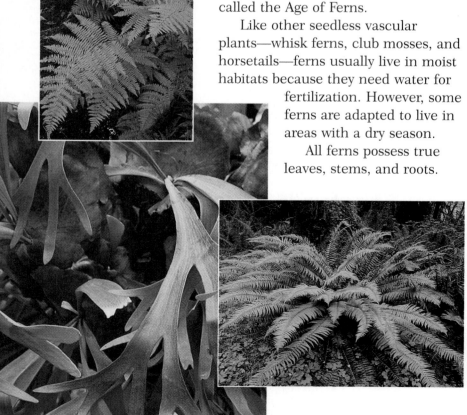

CHARACTERISTICS OF FERNS

The ferns' turn

Ferns, the largest group of seedless vascular plants alive today, have a long history. As you read in the introductory paragraph, ferns and other seedless vascular plants once dominated Earth's landscape. In fact, the late Carboniferous period (about 300 million years ago) is sometimes called the Age of Ferns.

Like other seedless vascular plants—whisk ferns, club mosses, and horsetails—ferns usually live in moist habitats because they need water for fertilization. However, some ferns are adapted to live in areas with a dry season.

All ferns possess true leaves, stems, and roots.

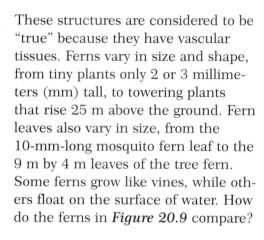

These structures are considered to be "true" because they have vascular tissues. Ferns vary in size and shape, from tiny plants only 2 or 3 millimeters (mm) tall, to towering plants that rise 25 m above the ground. Fern leaves also vary in size, from the 10-mm-long mosquito fern leaf to the 9 m by 4 m leaves of the tree fern. Some ferns grow like vines, while others float on the surface of water. How do the ferns in *Figure 20.9* compare?

FERN LIFE CYCLE

Spores in the wind

Figure 20.10 illustrates the life cycle of a typical fern. Like other plants, ferns alternate between a haploid (n) gametophyte phase and a diploid ($2n$) sporophyte phase. Can you find the green, heart-shaped fern gametophyte in *Figure 20.10*? This tiny plant is able to carry out photosynthesis. In most ferns, the gametophytes do not grow longer than 12 mm. As with other seedless vascular plants, the sporophyte generation is larger than the gametophyte. How does this pattern compare with that of mosses?

The sporophyte stage is probably the one that is more familiar to you.

In this stage, a typical fern has a stem with roots and leaves. Most ferns have leaves that are divided into smaller leaflets. Fern leaves are also called fronds. Each frond consists of two parts, a blade and a petiole. The blade is the broad, flat surface of the frond that contains the chloroplasts. The petiole is the stalk that attaches the blade to the stem. Most ferns have underground stems called **rhizomes.**

Fern sporophytes produce spores through meiosis. Some ferns form their spores on stalklike leaves. Others form their spores in structures that appear in groups on the underside of the leaves. A **sorus** (plural: *sori*) is a group of spore-containing structures clustered on the underside of a fern leaf. Notice the sori in the lower left of *Figure 20.10*. Some ferns have sori that can eject the spores a distance of several meters. If a spore lands in a suitable location, it develops into a gametophyte. What type of environment would be best for the development of a spore?

The fern life cycle is in some ways similar to the moss life cycle. Fern spores form gametophytes. Sperm swim in dew or rainwater from antheridia to the eggs in archegonia. (Notice that fertilization is dependent on water.) When fusion between the

FIGURE 20.10
The Life Cycle of a Fern

2 Haploid spores form in sori by meiosis. In the right conditions, spores germinate and grow into tiny gametophyte plants. Reproductive structures develop on gametophytes.

3 Archegonia produce eggs, and antheridia produce sperm by mitosis. Sperm swim in dew or rainwater to the eggs in the archegonia.

1 During fertilization, sperm and egg unite in an archegonium to form a diploid zygote. The zygote grows into a sporophyte plant by mitosis.

Sperm

Antheridium

Egg

Archegonium

Gametophyte

Mitosis

Spores

Meiosis

Fertilization

Zygote

Developing sporophyte

Mitosis

Mitosis

Sorus

Haploid

Diploid

Sporophyte

LAB ZONE Do It!

Examining Fern Leaves and Sori

You can observe the reproductive structures of a fern sporophyte when you . . .

Try This

1 Obtain a small piece of a fern frond that has sori on its underside. Sketch the leaf and sori as they appear without magnification.

2 Place the leaf on a slide. View the sori under a dissecting microscope using low and high power. Draw a magnified sorus.

3 Using a scalpel, make a thin cross section of the leaf, cutting through a sorus. **Caution:** Use care when handling the scalpel. Place the cross section on a slide. Examine and draw the interior of a sorus as it appears under low power.

4 View the cross section under high power and examine an individual spore. Draw and label the parts.

Analyze Your Results

1 Based on your examination of the structures inside a sorus, how do you think the fern distributes its spores? Explain.

2 Summarize the steps in the life cycle of the fern after the sporophyte releases spores.

The roles ferns play

Ferns often play a role in ecological succession. Some types of ferns can grow in the crevices of rocks. Others can grow in wetlands before the area is taken over by larger plants. Still others grow abundantly in fields that are no longer cultivated.

Several fern species, including the ostrich fern, are used for food. In the spring, the newly forming leaves of one species—called fiddleheads because of their shape—serve as a source of food.

The mosquito fern is important in Southeast Asia for the cultivation of rice. The leaves of this fern are home to nitrogen-fixing cyanobacteria. Cyanobacteria convert nitrogen gas into a form the plants can use, greatly enhancing the growth of plants and the productivity of rice paddies.

Ferns are also valuable economically because of their use in horticulture. Each year millions of ferns are bought for home decoration or for outdoor landscaping. What types of ferns have you seen used as indoor decoration?

CHECKPOINT 20.3

1. Describe the common characteristics of ferns.

2. Compare the haploid and diploid phases of the fern's life cycle.

3. Critical Thinking Why do ferns flourish in damp areas?

Build on What You Know

4. Identify the similarities and differences between ferns and algae. *(Need to jog your memory? Revisit relevant concepts in Chapter 15, Section 15.3.)*

two gametes occurs, a zygote is formed. For a time, the zygote remains inside the archegonium, relying on the gametophyte for nutrition. The zygote grows into a sporophyte, eventually growing larger than the gametophyte and becomes nutritionally independent. The gametophyte eventually dies. As the sporophyte grows, it produces leaves with sori, and the fern's life cycle is repeated.

 What are the main characteristics of ferns?

20.4 Conifers

Sitting pretty
This pine siskin nests in coniferous forests, finding shelter amid the thick, tough leaves, called needles. The needle shape is an adaptation that protects the tree from drought. Unlike the leaves of deciduous trees, needles are shed and regrown throughout the growing season. Conifers are vascular seed plants.

What you'll learn

IDEAS
• To identify common characteristics of conifers
• To describe the life cycle of a conifer

CHARACTERISTICS OF CONIFERS

Standing tall

Conifers include some of the largest and oldest organisms on Earth. The giant redwood tree, which can be taller than a 30-story building, is one of Earth's largest organisms. The bristlecone pine is among the oldest living individual organisms. Some bristlecone pines are more than 5000 years old.

Conifers are vascular plants that bear cones. Although some conifers lose their leaves in the winter, most conifers are trees that possess needle-like leaves throughout the year, which is why they are commonly called "evergreens." The needles are hard structures covered with a waterproof cuticle. Needles give off much less water during transpiration than do the flat leaves of deciduous trees. This adaptation enables many conifers to thrive in harsh conditions.

Conifers are a division of the gymnosperms. Like other gymnosperms, conifers produce their seeds in cones—specialized reproductive structures with many compartments. Like some other gymnosperms, conifers carry out fertilization without water by means of male and female cones.

Compare the male and female cones of the loblolly pine in *Figure 20.11*.

When the seeds of gymnosperms are released from their cones, the seeds are not encased in any protective covering. Botanists call the seeds of gymnosperms "naked seeds" because they are not enclosed in fruit. Remember that the seeds of angiosperms are typically encased in fruit.

Very recently, scientists in Australia found a grove of living conifers that were previously thought to be extinct. These trees, called Wollemi pines, are descendants of plants that lived during the time of the dinosaurs. This

FIGURE 20.11
Conifers bear male cones (above) and female cones (near right). The male cones produce cells that develop into pollen grains. Wind carries the pollen to female cones, where pollination occurs.

discovery has given scientists a chance to study a plant that thrived many millions of years ago.

As you read in section 20.1, conifers and three other divisions of gymnosperms still survive today. One of these divisions, the gnetae, are cone-bearing desert plants. Another division, the cycads, have palmlike leaves and produce seeds or seed cones. The third division, the ginkgoes, have fan-shaped leaves that turn yellow and fall from the trees in autumn. Unlike other gymnosperms, cycads and ginkgoes require water for fertilization.

Blowing in the wind

The pine tree is a typical conifer. Like other vascular plants, it undergoes alternation of generations in which the sporophyte stage is dominant. The gametophyte stage consists of only the pollen and part of the female pinecone.

Perhaps you have used pinecones as decorations or as part of an art project. You probably used the large, familiar cones that are actually the female cones of a pine tree. Pine trees also have male cones, which are smaller than the female cones.

FIGURE 20.12

The Life Cycle of a Conifer

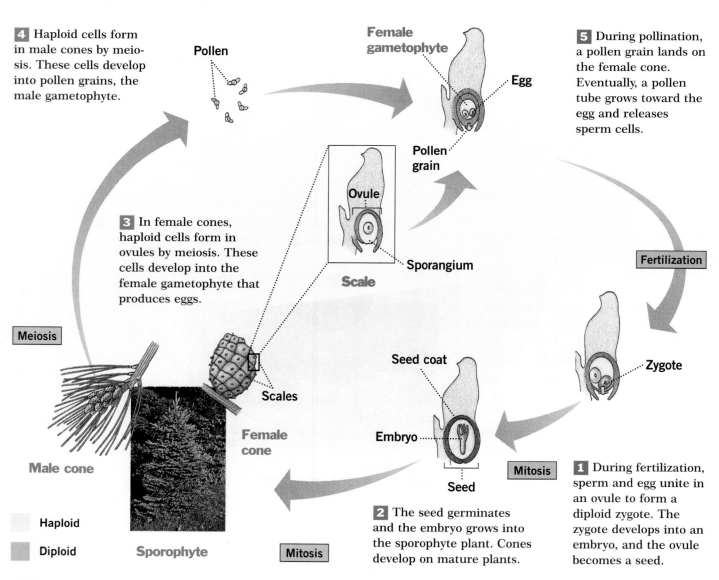

4 Haploid cells form in male cones by meiosis. These cells develop into pollen grains, the male gametophyte.

3 In female cones, haploid cells form in ovules by meiosis. These cells develop into the female gametophyte that produces eggs.

5 During pollination, a pollen grain lands on the female cone. Eventually, a pollen tube grows toward the egg and releases sperm cells.

1 During fertilization, sperm and egg unite in an ovule to form a diploid zygote. The zygote develops into an embryo, and the ovule becomes a seed.

2 The seed germinates and the embryo grows into the sporophyte plant. Cones develop on mature plants.

Female gametophyte

Pollen

Egg

Pollen grain

Ovule

Sporangium

Scale

Fertilization

Meiosis

Scales

Female cone

Seed coat

Zygote

Embryo

Mitosis

Seed

Male cone

Haploid

Diploid

Sporophyte

Mitosis

The female cones consist of spirally arranged scales that secrete a sticky resin. At the base of each scale are two ovules. As you have learned, an ovule is a structure that develops into a seed. An ovule consists of a female gametophyte with an egg.

Each male cone produces huge amounts of pollen grains that are released in the spring. The pollen grains have winglike structures that keep them aloft in the wind. Because of these structures, pollen grains can be carried long distances, which increases the opportunities for pollination. As you may recall, pollination is the transfer of pollen from the male to the female part of a plant.

When a pollen grain reaches a female cone, it sticks to the cone's resin. As the resin dries, the pollen grain begins to grow a structure called a pollen tube, which extends to an ovule near the base of a scale. Eventually a sperm cell is released from the pollen tube. The sperm fertilizes an egg in the ovule. A zygote forms and grows into an embryo surrounded by a seed coat.

As the embryo matures, the female cone grows larger and the scales separate. The seed is then released from the female cone. If the seed lands in an environment with the proper conditions for growth, it will germinate. The complete pine life cycle takes two to three years from the time the cones form until the seeds are released.

GYMNOSPERMS IN THE BIOSPHERE

Comfortable in the cold

Gymnosperms flourished and diversified about 250 million years ago, during the cold, dry Permian period. As a result, the plants that evolved in that environment were adapted to live

Do It!

Examining the Structure of a Pine Cone

Review the life cycle of the conifer as you . . .

Try This

1 Select two female pine cones, one with scales closed and one with scales open. Sketch the two cones.
2 Remove a single scale from each pine cone. Use a scalpel if necessary. **Caution:** Use care when handling the scalpel. Compare the appearance of the two scales and sketch.
3 Cross-section each scale by slicing it into thirds. Draw one of the cross sections from each pine cone. Identify and label the structures you see.

Analyze Your Results

1 Do you think your pine cone was pollinated? Why or why not?
2 Summarize the differences you observed between the two pine cones.

in cold climates, where many of their descendants thrive today. If you have the chance to climb a mountain, you will find conifers growing at altitudes that would be too cold for deciduous flowering trees.

Some gymnosperms, including conifers such as cypresses and giant redwoods, do thrive in mild climates. The bald cypress can even thrive in a swamp. Swampy conditions are inhospitable to most trees, because the waterlogged soil is low in oxygen. But the cypress has specialized roots called breathing roots that grow above the water surface and enable the tree to collect oxygen.

Conifers often grow together in stands and may shade the forest floor throughout the year. The needles and scales that they drop decompose more slowly than deciduous leaves, and produce an acidic humus. The shady,

FIGURE 20.13
Residing in coniferous forests are longhorn beetles that live on wood and owls that prey on small mammals. Red squirrels collect and store pinecones by the hundreds.

acidic environment is inhospitable to many other types of plants. However, some types of mosses and ferns thrive in the conifers' leaf litter, as do toadstools and other fungi.

In their communities, conifers are key producers and providers of shelter. Animals that live on or near conifers include adult and larval insects as well as mammals and birds. Some moths and fly larvae eat pine needles, while some wasps and flies eat the wood. Squirrels and birds such as nutcrackers and crossbills eat conifer seeds.

Other residents of conifer forests may include moose, reindeer, foxes, and wolves. Woodpeckers, warblers, hawks, owls, and various other birds use conifers for shelter. However, vertebrates that do not maintain a constant body temperature, such as frogs and snakes, are uncommon in the colder regions where many types of conifers thrive.

People have made use of conifers in many different ways. Many conifers are harvested for building lumber. Some humans eat the nuts of pines. For many years pine nuts were part

of a system of trade among Native Americans in the western United States.

Conifers and other gymnosperms are also used as ornamental plants in gardens, parks, and other landscaped areas. Conifers such as yews make excellent ground cover while especially tall evergreens are used as windbreaks. Ginkgoes are so hardy that they can be grown in cities where air pollution is high. Conifers are used for the art of bonsai, in which trees are grown in a dwarflike condition in containers, producing plants such as those shown on page 435.

CHECKPOINT 20.4

1. What are the main characteristics of conifers?
2. Describe the life cycle of a conifer.
3. **Critical Thinking** What adaptations do conifers have that enable certain species to live for thousands of years?

Build on What You Know

4. What advantage is gained by evergreens that retain green needles throughout the winter? *(Need to jog your memory? Revisit relevant concepts in Chapter 4, Section 4.2.)*

20.5 Flowering Plants

Why flowers?

Most of the plants that you are familiar with, including most trees, are flowering plants—about 235,000 species in all. How do plants benefit from flowers? Flowers contain the reproductive structures of plants. Because of their color and scent, flowers attract a variety of pollinators. These pollinators are vital to the process of reproduction, which ensures the continuation of the species.

What you'll learn

IDEAS
• To identify the common characteristics of flowering plants
• To describe the life cycle of a flowering plant

WORDS
double fertilization, pollinators

CHARACTERISTICS OF FLOWERING PLANTS

Flower power

In the previous chapter you read about the importance of flowers—they are the reproductive organs of flowering plants. Flowers may be large and conspicuous, or they may be tiny and hidden. Whatever their size, shape, or color, flowers are an essential part of life on this planet. Flowers not only enable certain plants to reproduce, but flowers also produce the pollen, nectar, fruit, and seeds that sustain many other types of organisms.

You now know that flowering plants are the most abundant types of plants. Flowering plants have certain characteristics that identify them as members of the division called angiosperms. These include the following:

- flowers
- leaves, stems, and roots that contain vascular tissue
- stems, branches, and roots that may be woody or nonwoody
- gametophytes that grow within the sporophyte plant
- sexual reproduction that depends on air currents or pollinating organisms, not water
- seeds
- double fertilization
- fruit

Angiosperms can be further classified according to differences in their seeds, flowers, stems, leaves, or roots. For example, all flowering plants are either monocots or dicots, depending on the characteristics of their seeds. As you have learned, monocot seeds have one cotyledon, or seed leaf, that nourishes the young seedling. Dicot seeds have two cotyledons. Monocots and dicots also differ in their leaf and flower structures, the arrangement of their vascular tissue, and their overall root shapes.

Monocots have parallel leaf veins. In their stems, the xylem and phloem bundles are scattered in a complex pattern. The flower parts of monocots come in multiples of three. And, monocots have fibrous root systems. Some examples of monocots are lilies, orchids, corn, and grasses.

FIGURE 20.14
A flower produces seeds, which can produce new plants. You can see seeds in many familiar foods, including apples and squash.

Comparison of Two Major Groups of Angiosperms

Group	Seed leaves	Leaf veins	Stems	Flowers	Roots
Monocot	One cotyledon	Veins usually parallel	Vascular bundles in complex arrangement	Floral parts usually in multiples of three	Fibrous root system
Dicot	Two cotyledons	Veins usually branched	Vascular bundles arranged in ring	Floral parts usually in multiples of four or five	Taproot usually present

FIGURE 20.15
This table shows the major structural differences between monocots and dicots. Based on their different root structures, which group do you think tends to have the larger plants?

In contrast, the leaf veins of dicots usually have a branching, netlike arrangement. In the stems, the xylem and phloem bundles are arranged in a circle. The flower parts of dicots come in multiples of four or five. And dicots usually have taproots. Roses, beans, clovers, and most trees are examples of dicots. *Figure 20.15* illustrates the major differences between monocots and dicots.

FLOWERING PLANT LIFE CYCLE

Nature's beautiful seed machines

In some ways, the life cycle of an angiosperm is similar to the life cycle of a gymnosperm or even a fern. As you can see in *Figure 20.16,* an angiosperm undergoes alternation of generations. Certain cells in the sporophyte undergo meiosis to form spores. The spores divide mitotically to form male and female gametophytes. The gametophytes form the gametes—the eggs and sperm.

For many years the next steps of the life cycle—the gametophyte stage and the processes of pollination and fertilization—were not well understood. Today botanists know that the gametophytes are quite tiny and always develop in the flower of the sporophyte plant.

Eggs form in ovules. Ovules are structures located inside the ovary. An ovary is an organ located where the petals connect to the plant. Inside the ovule, meiosis produces haploid (n) cells of which only one–the megaspore–survives. The megaspore undergoes three rounds of mitosis to form a haploid, multicellular female gametophyte. The female gametophyte contains a haploid egg and a large cell with two nuclei called polar nuclei.

Sperm form in pollen, which develop in anthers. Meiosis in anthers forms haploid cells called microspores. Each microspore undergoes mitosis to become a two-celled male gametophyte, the pollen grain.

In the next step—pollination—pollen is transferred from an anther to a stigma. A stigma is the sticky part at the top of the pistil. When a pollen grain lands on a stigma, the pollen grain produces a pollen tube that grows through the style to the ovary. Once in the ovary, the pollen tube enters an ovule. At this point, one cell in the pollen grain divides by mitosis to become two haploid sperm.

Fertilization occurs when a sperm nucleus from the pollen tube fuses with the egg in the ovule. The egg and sperm are both haploid, and the resulting zygote is diploid. The zygote develops into a diploid embryo within the ovule. The embryo soon stops developing and becomes dormant.

In angiosperms, a unique process occurs during fertilization, called double fertilization. In **double fertilization,** the second sperm nucleus from the pollen tube fuses with the two polar nuclei in the ovule. The result is a triploid (3*n*) cell, which divides to become triploid tissue called endosperm.

A tough seed coat forms from ovule tissue. The seed coat surrounds and protects the dormant embryo and endosperm. The endosperm will nourish the seed embryo when it sprouts. The seed coat, embryo, and endosperm form the seed. This structure is a fruit—the

FIGURE 20.16
The Life Cycle of an Angiosperm

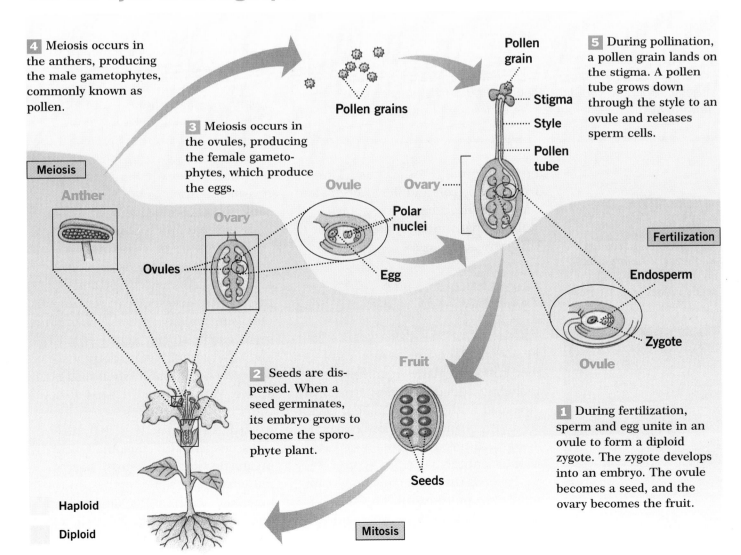

4 Meiosis occurs in the anthers, producing the male gametophytes, commonly known as pollen.

3 Meiosis occurs in the ovules, producing the female gametophytes, which produce the eggs.

5 During pollination, a pollen grain lands on the stigma. A pollen tube grows down through the style to an ovule and releases sperm cells.

Pollen grains

Pollen grain

Stigma

Style

Pollen tube

Meiosis

Anther

Ovary

Ovule

Ovary

Polar nuclei

Egg

Ovules

Fertilization

Endosperm

Zygote

Ovule

Fruit

2 Seeds are dispersed. When a seed germinates, its embryo grows to become the sporophyte plant.

1 During fertilization, sperm and egg unite in an ovule to form a diploid zygote. The zygote develops into an embryo. The ovule becomes a seed, and the ovary becomes the fruit.

Seeds

Haploid

Diploid

Mitosis

Analyzing Changes in a Flower

The graph below shows the changing temperature (left axis) in a *Sauromatum* flower as it begins to bloom. The graph also shows how much CO₂ is produced (right axis) during the same period. While the flower was blooming, the air temperature stayed at about 27°C.

Analyzing the Graph

1 How would you describe the change in the flower temperature?
2 What is the relationship between the flower temperature and the plant's production of CO₂?
3 What evidence suggests that metabolism is involved in the blooming process?
4 When it blooms, the flower releases an odor of rotting meat that attracts pollinating insects. What can you infer about the process of odor release? How might the release of odor be beneficial to the plant?

end result of this fertilization. The fruit may be soft and fleshy or dry and hard. The tomatoes, corn, apples, and walnuts that you enjoy are formed by this intricate process.

FLOWERING PLANTS IN THE BIOSPHERE

Fruitful strategies

Flowering plants are an important food supply to many organisms, including humans. Angiosperms provide food in the form of pollen, nectar, seeds, and fruit. Some flowers, such as nasturtiums, can actually be eaten in their entirety.

Pollen is usually carried from plant to plant by **pollinators.** The most common pollinators are wind and various animals. Animal pollinators and

flowering plants live in mutually beneficial relationships. For example, the bee in *Figure 20.18* obtains nectar and pollen from the plant. At the same time, the bee provides a means of pollen dispersal for the plant. This process of transferring pollen enables angiosperms to reproduce without water. Pollen grains are a nutrition source for insects, including honeybees. Some insects consume pollen as adults, and some insect larvae are raised on a diet consisting only of pollen.

Pollinators also include organisms that obtain nectar produced by flowers. Nectar is a sweet, sugary liquid that attracts pollinators. Nectar-consuming pollinators include bats, hummingbirds, moths, and butterflies. As they obtain nectar, these organisms transport pollen from flower to flower.

Flowers attract pollinators in a variety of ways. The pleasant fragrances of flowers attract pollinating organisms. Many flowers also attract pollinators visually as a result of their colorful patterns. Some of these colorful patterns are visible only under ultraviolet light, which makes them invisible to humans but visible to some insects and spiders.

The seeds and fruits of many flowering plants are also important sources of energy. Seeds are consumed by mammals, birds, and insects. Because they can remain dormant for extended periods of time, seeds can be stored. Squirrels, mice, and other animals store dormant seeds over the winter when food is scarce. What part of the seed do you think is most nutritious?

Fruits, the structures that enclose the seeds, are also consumed by many organisms, including birds, insects, mammals, and some reptiles. In the process of eating fruits, larger animals often ingest the seeds. You, too, ingest seeds when you eat fruits such as

FIGURE 20.17
This cardinal is feasting on wild grapes. Animals that eat fruits may deposit the seeds in locations far from the parent plant.

blueberries, strawberries, and blackberries. The protective coat of the seed keeps the seed intact as it passes through an animal's digestive tract. The seed may then be deposited some distance from the parent plant. In some cases, migrating birds enable plants to colonize previously inaccessible environments.

What bugs bees

What would happen if bees died out? Albert Einstein said the result would be the disappearance of plant life on Earth. That might seem like an exaggerated prediction, but consider that bees are the primary pollinators of many thousands of species of flowering plants. While bees are not yet endangered species, bee populations in the United States and several other countries have been decreasing as a result of two types of parasitic mites. In New York State alone, 60–70 percent of the bee population already has been destroyed.

One culprit is the voroa mite, which attaches itself to a bee's body and uses the bee's blood for nourishment. The other—the tracheal mite— invades a bee's windpipe, where it breeds and eventually cuts off the flow of oxygen. To complicate matters, both parasites can carry a virus. So bees may die directly from the effect of the mite or be so weakened that they cannot survive the winter.

Research into treatments to rid bees of mites is ongoing. To date, two synthetic chemical treatments have been found effective against one or both types of mites. Botanical preparations such as oil of peppermint have some curative effect, although more study is underway. One of the most promising solutions under investigation is the breeding of bees that are resistant to the mites.

These treatments pose no known health risks to the bees or to humans who eat honey from treated hives. But some beekeepers are using pesticides that have not been approved for use on bees. Of course, none of these treatments helps wild bee populations, which are also at risk.

In the United States, bees pollinate about 200 different types of agricultural crops. These crops—which include citrus and orchard fruits, almonds, cranberries, and cucumbers—are worth approximately 15 billion dollars a year! With fewer bees available, the price of honey and certain foods is likely to increase as harvests decrease.

FIGURE 20.18
Lured by the nectar and pollen in flowers, bees visit one flower after another, transferring pollen as they travel. How are bee populations being threatened?

CHECKPOINT 20.5

1. Describe the main characteristics of flowering plants.
2. Compare the two phases of an angiosperm's life cycle, and show how they fit the general pattern called alternation of generations.
3. Critical Thinking What are some adaptations that a flower pollinated by the wind might have? Explain.

Build on What You Know

4. Describe the coevolution of flowering plants and pollinators. *(**Need to jog your memory?** Revisit relevant concepts in Chapter 10, Section 10.4.)*

Why have seed plants been able to colonize large areas of land? **?**

Observing Plant Reproduction

WHAT YOU WILL DO Plant four *Brassica rapa* seeds, observe their growth over a period of 38 days, and graph the plants' daily height.

SKILLS YOU WILL USE Observing, measuring, collecting data, graphing

WHAT YOU WILL NEED *Brassica rapa* seeds, metric ruler, peat pots, soil, small wooden stakes, toothpicks, growth lights

Propose a Hypothesis

Flowering plants reproduce by means of flowers. Propose a hypothesis about the sequence of events in flowering.

Conduct Your Experiment

DAY 1

1 Measure four *B. rapa* seeds in millimeters. Record the size, shape, color, and texture of each seed on a sheet of paper. Draw a seed and label it *Day 1*.
2 Fill two peat pots with soil to within 1 centimeter (cm) of the top. Put two *B. rapa* seeds into each pot and cover with 0.5 cm of soil. Make two labels on wooden stakes. Write *#1* and *#2* on one, *#3* and *#4* on the other, and put them in the pots.
3 Water the soil and place the pots under the growth lights. Record the date and time, and any observations.

DAYS 2–38

4 Observe, record, and draw the changes that occur to the seeds each day. Keep the soil moist.

5 When flowering occurs, observe a *B. rapa* flower. Draw and label the structures of the *B. rapa* plant.
6 Cross-pollinate within three days of flowering. Use a toothpick to collect pollen from the anthers of plant #1, and transfer it to the stigma of plant #2.
7 Repeat step 6, transferring pollen from plant #2 to #3, from plant #3 to #4, and from plant #4 to #1. Be sure to use a new toothpick for each transfer. Record the transfer date.
8 Harvest mature seeds, and compare them to the seeds you planted on Day 1.

Analyze Your Data

1 When did the first plant emerge? When did true leaves appear? When did flowering occur?
2 What are the parts of the flower? Where are they located?
3 Graph the height of each plant as well as the average height of the four plants on each day.

4 What changes occurred when pollination was successful? How did the seeds you harvested compare to the seeds you planted?

Draw Conclusions

1 Did you hypothesize correctly? Support your answer with your observations.
2 Does the emergence of certain plant parts depend on the plants' height or on time? Use your observations and graphs to support your answer.

Design a Related Experiment

Design an experiment using the seeds you harvested from your *B. rapa* plants. You may want to determine the genetic variability of offspring for various characteristics.

Chapter 20 Review

 20.1–20.2 Plants are multicellular organisms with adaptations for life on land.

20.3 Ferns have vascular systems and reproduce by means of spores.

20.4–20.5 Seed plants do not require water for fertilization and have therefore colonized extensive areas of land.

Sum It Up

Use the following summary to review the main concepts in this chapter.

20.1 Natural History of Plants

- Plants are thought to have evolved from ancient multicellular, water-dwelling green algae.
- Land-dwelling plants have adaptations for transport, support, water conservation, and reproduction.
- Plant species can be classified by the presence or absence of a vascular system, seeds, cones, flowers, and fruits.

20.2 Mosses

- Mosses are the most common nonvascular plants.
- Mosses can reproduce sexually through a life cycle that involves alternation of generations, or asexually by specialized structures.
- Mosses help decompose wood, colonize bare rock surfaces, keep soil moist, and prevent erosion.

20.3 Ferns

- Ferns are seedless vascular plants that usually live in moist habitats. Ferns require water for fertilization.
- Ferns reproduce sexually by alternation of generations. Sporophytes are the dominant phase in ferns.

- Ferns, which play a role in ecological succession, occasionally serve as food and are frequently used for landscaping and as houseplants.

20.4 Conifers

- Conifers are cone-bearing vascular seed plants.
- Conifers, which reproduce sexually through alternation of generations, do not need water for fertilization; pollen from male cones is carried by wind to female cones.
- Conifer forests provide food and shelter for many animal species.

20.5 Flowering Plants

- Flowering plants are vascular plants that produce seeds enclosed in a fruit.
- Flowering plants can be divided into monocots and dicots, based on their number of cotyledons; monocots and dicots differ in their pattern of leaf veins, geometry of floral parts, type of root system, and arrangement of vascular tissues.
- Flowering plants have life cycles that involve alternation of generations where the sporophyte is dominant.
- Many organisms use the pollen, nectar, seeds, and fruit from flowering plants for nourishment.

Use Terms and Concepts

Use each of the following words or terms in a complete sentence. If you need to review a meaning, turn to the page indicated.

division (p. 471)

archegonium (p. 476)

antheridium (p. 476)

capsule (p. 477)

peat bog (p. 477)

rhizomes (p. 479)

sorus (p. 479)

double fertilization (p. 487)

pollinators (p. 488)

Use Your Word Power

COMPLETION **Write the word or phrase that best completes each statement.**

1. A(n) _____ is a moist ecosystem formed from mats of sphagnum.

2. The egg-producing organ of a moss or fern is called a(n) _____.

3. _____ is a unique reproductive process of flowering plants in which a sperm fertilizes two polar nuclei to form an endosperm.

4. Underground stems are called _____.

5. A(n) _____ is the sperm-producing structure of a moss or fern.

TRUE-FALSE **Write true if the statement is true. If the statement is false, replace the underlined word to make the statement true.**

6. A <u>division</u> is a major taxonomic group used in botany in place of a phylum.

7. A sorus is the structure in <u>mosses</u> that produces spores.

8. Pollinators carry <u>seeds</u> from one flower to another.

9. Wind carries away the mature spores produced in a moss <u>capsule</u>.

Show What You Know

10. What evidence have biologists used to identify the ancestors of plants?

11. Summarize the way plants are classified.

12. Explain the relationship between water diffusion and the size of typical mosses.

13. Are the gemmae of mosses haploid or diploid? Explain your answer.

14. What do biologists mean by "true" leaves, stems, and roots? Which plants have them? Which do not?

15. Compare the gametophyte stages of mosses and ferns.

16. What is the difference between an antheridium and an archegonium? Name two groups of plants that have these structures.

17. How is pollen transferred between male and female pine cones?

18. Why are many gymnosperms able to live in cold, harsh climates?

19. Describe the life cycle of an angiosperm.

20. How do seeds enclosed in fruit give angiosperms a reproductive advantage over gymnosperms?

21. **Make a Concept Map** Complete this concept map, which shows how biologists classify some main groups of plants. Add the following terms: angiosperm, cone, dicot, fern, fruit, gymnosperm, monocot, moss, seed, spore.

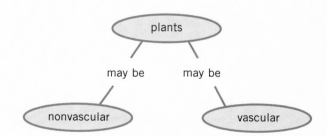

Take It Further

22. **Developing a Hypothesis** Based on what you know about mosses and certain climates in the tropics, explain why most species of moss live in tropical environments.

23. **Making an Analogy** Scientists envision sending astronauts on long journeys to distant planets. What characteristics would an astronaut traveling through space have in common with a dispersed seed?

24. **Designing an Experiment** Do you think a bee or a hummingbird would be attracted to nectar if it were not packaged in a flower? Describe an experiment to test your hypothesis.

25. Interpreting a Graph The pie graph below shows one way to categorize plant species. How does the number of nonvascular plant species compare with the number of ferns species? What percentage of all plant species are seed plants?

Species of Living Plants: 265,349

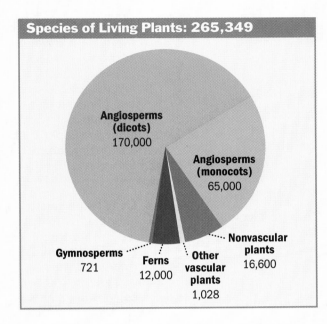

Angiosperms (dicots) 170,000

Angiosperms (monocots) 65,000

Gymnosperms 721

Ferns 12,000

Other vascular plants 1,028

Nonvascular plants 16,600

26. Analyzing Data The plant shown in the illustration below is called *Rhynia*. At one time, scientists thought it was the ancestor of all land plants. Based on the illustration, how are *Rhynia* and modern-day plants similar? How are they different?

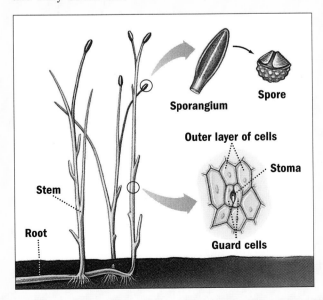

Sporangium

Spore

Outer layer of cells

Stoma

Stem

Guard cells

Root

Consider the Issues

27. Plant Imports As you may know, climates and native plants vary in different areas of the country. When people move, they sometimes transport plants from one location to another. Some desert-dwellers, for example, import grass to plant lawns. And some communities import plants for parks or public gardens. Nonnative plants often have different growing requirements than native plants. Many states have specific laws and regulations about transporting and importing plants. Why do you think this is so? Do you think plant imports should be regulated? Explain your answer.

Make New Connections

28. Biology and Art A landscape architect starts with what exists and imagines what might be. Select a small plot of land near your home or school. Make a scale drawing of the plot, using one or more sheets of graph paper. Draw and label the existing plants and structures. Tape tracing paper over the drawing. On the tracing paper, specify how you would change the plants in the plot. Remember to select plants that can survive your local climate conditions.

29. Biology and Community Find out whether your state has an official flower, tree, or other plant. If so, when and why were the plant(s) chosen? Were there any other competitors for the title? Create an illustrated poster to inform others about your state plant.

FAST-FORWARD TO CHAPTER 21

In the next chapter, you will learn how animals are adapted to carry out essential life processes, beginning with sponges and cnidarians.

Unit 5 Review

THE BIG IDEA! Answering the following questions will help you to link ideas and grasp the core concepts.

Connect the Chapters

1. What characteristics of mosses and ferns make them good colonizers in moist environments?

2. What is the function of vascular tissue in plants? Describe the types of vascular tissues, and identify which groups of plants contain vascular tissue.

3. Water conservation is a key issue for terrestrial plants. Describe at least four adaptations that enable plants to conserve water.

4. Which group, or groups, of plants would be most important for reducing the greenhouse effect? Explain your answer.

5. What types of tissues— dermal, vascular, or ground— are produced from meristems in plants? Explain your answer.

Connect the Units

6. What is the connection between plants and the basic discoveries in genetics?

7. Both plants and animals use energy. Why then is it customary to describe plants as producers and animals as consumers in food chains?

8. How are algae similar to ferns? How are they different?

Connect to Themes

9. **Patterns of Change/Cycles** Describe how plants respond to seasonal changes in the daily periods of light and darkness.

10. **Energy** How do cells in the epidermis, mesophyll, and vascular tissues contribute to photosynthesis?

11. **Unity and Diversity** Compare the process of gamete production in conifers and in flowering plants.

project plans

1 Conduct library research to determine the important plants of a country such as one of the following: Argentina, Brazil, Greece, Italy, China, Japan, Kenya, Mexico, England, France, Peru, Ireland, Nigeria, Spain. Create a visual display identifying at least five important plants of the country and several uses for each plant. In doing research, you may want to use plant geography maps, world statistical abstracts, and journals written by early explorers or plant collectors.

2 Many home gardeners grow plants from seeds planted in soil. But professional growers often use other methods, such as cloning, grafting, or hydroponics (growing plants without soil), to reproduce plants. Find out how these and other techniques work and why growers use them. In addition to using library resources, you may want to interview a commercial grower for more information. Prepare a class presentation with visual aids to explain your findings.

CRITIC'S CORNER

A CD-ROM REVIEW BY LILY FOSSNER SCHENECTADY, NY

SimLife, the experimental ecosystem game by Maxis, is a challenging and thought-provoking program. By manipulating environmental and genetic factors, several varied life-forms can be created and observed in their own habitats. *SimLife* provides an interesting application of biology curricula, as well as the opportunity to do experiments that range from the simple to the complex. This is not a game that can be mastered in an hour's time, but is definitely a new way to look at biology in action.

VERONICA WISNIEWSKI

Project coordinator, educator, and reforester at the Salmon Enhancement Association

EDUCATION: B.S. in biology, M.S. in forestry

❝ What we're doing is trying to restore streamside plant cover, in order to help the salmon. On the West Coast, salmon are a big part of our culture. They are threatened by overdevelopment and by dams on the waterways. There are a lot of things we can do to help them. Increasing the plant cover over the stream so water temperatures go down, is one. Having more plants hang over the stream also provides more nutrients for the fish—insects live in the plants and drop in the water. . . . I like what I do because I contribute to everyone's quality of life. I also love being outside.❞

bioSURF Search the Internet site *http://plants.biosurf.com* for more information about the efforts of the Washington State Department of Fish and Wildlife.

> "I like what I do, because I contribute to everyone's quality of life."
> —VERONICA WISNIEWSKI

JESSICA LIBORIO

Volunteer with the Food Project, which coordinates the efforts of urban and suburban teens to grow produce for charity

EDUCATION: College student

❝ My interest in the Food Project was political. I was interested in fighting hunger and learning about peoples' connection to the food supply and to the land. My nature is to care about the social part of things—but I am learning how important it is to understand the biology of things, too. I like just being out there working in the fields, weeding and harvesting. It's therapeutic. Farming is really about providing the best circumstances for plants. The most important thing is to take good care of the soil and to give it enough water. The soil is where plants get nutrients. Other than that, plants do a pretty good job growing all by themselves.❞

bioSURF Visit the Internet site *http://plants.biosurf.com* to find out more about research by the United States Department of Agriculture on better ways to grow crops.

Which of these amazing statements about invertebrate animals are fact, and which are fiction?

Hit *or* Myth?

An **octopus** can open a jar.

(Fact. In lab experiments, octopuses have unscrewed lids on jars containing shrimp and other favorite foods of theirs.)

Many **insects** make tasty, protein-rich treats.

(Fact. In many countries, certain insects, such as this grasshopper, are considered delicacies.)

Cicadas remain adolescents longer than any other insect.

(Fact. Cicadas take either 13 or 17 years to develop into adults.)

To humans, **maggots** serve no useful purpose.

(Fiction. Maggots can be used to remove dead skin from frostbitten and burned areas of the body.)

Some clams **go surfing.**

(Fact. The coquina clam comes to the surface of the sand and rides the waves to stay near the ocean edge, where it can find food.)

Worms are shorter than people.

(Fiction. The beef tapeworm can attain a length of 23 meters—one fourth the length of a football field.)

Jellyfish can do a disappearing act.

(Fact—well, almost. Because they are about 95 percent water, if beached, jellyfish evaporate, leaving just a damp spot on the sand.)

The **starfish** is a type of fish.

(Fiction. Now commonly called a sea star, the starfish is an invertebrate. Fishes are vertebrates.)

Tarantula bites are dangerous to humans.

(Fiction. The bite of a tarantula is like a sharp pinprick, but it is not harmful to humans.)

CHAPTER 21
Sponges and Cnidarians

You can find out more about sponges and cnidarians by exploring the following Internet address:
http://invertebrates.biosurf.com

In this chapter . . .

FEATURES

Everyday Biology
• Just a Skeleton Crew
• Coral Cautions

In the Community
The Business of Sponges

 Frontiers in Biology
Rx . . . Sponges and Jellyfish

LAB ZONES

Discover It!
• Take an Animal Quiz

Do It!
• Calculating the Pumping Capacity of a Natural Sponge

Think About It!
• Finding Examples of Symmetry

Investigate It!
• Observing Hydra

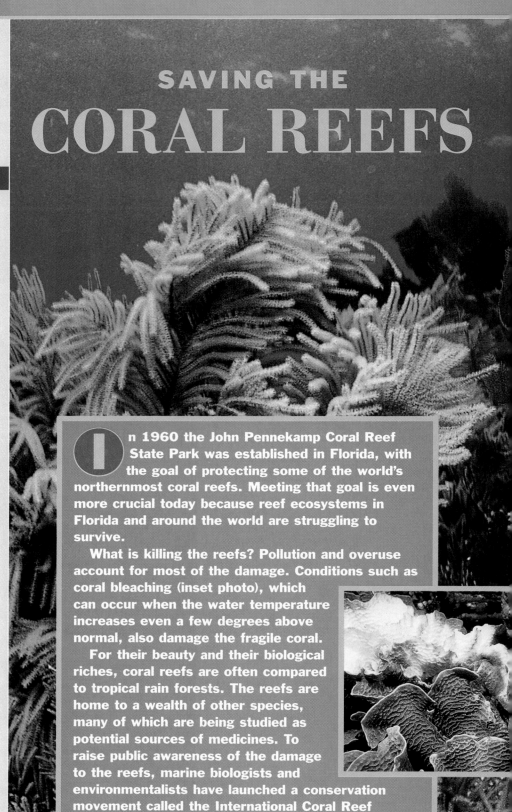

SAVING THE
CORAL REEFS

In 1960 the John Pennekamp Coral Reef State Park was established in Florida, with the goal of protecting some of the world's northernmost coral reefs. Meeting that goal is even more crucial today because reef ecosystems in Florida and around the world are struggling to survive.

What is killing the reefs? Pollution and overuse account for most of the damage. Conditions such as coral bleaching (inset photo), which can occur when the water temperature increases even a few degrees above normal, also damage the fragile coral.

For their beauty and their biological riches, coral reefs are often compared to tropical rain forests. The reefs are home to a wealth of other species, many of which are being studied as potential sources of medicines. To raise public awareness of the damage to the reefs, marine biologists and environmentalists have launched a conservation movement called the International Coral Reef Initiative, which combines the efforts of the United States and many other countries.

Discover It!

Take an Animal Quiz

1. Consider all of the animals you have seen and read about. List the characteristics that you think all animals share.
2. From the following list, identify the organisms that are animals: sponge, bacterium, spider, lion, jellyfish, coral, mushroom, diatom.

Animals are amazingly numerous and diverse. As you read this chapter, revisit your answers to the above quiz and revise them as needed.

WRITE ABOUT IT!

In your science journal, write about a favorite animal or any memorable experiences you have had with animals. You may describe the behavior of a pet or another animal.

21.1 Introduction to Animals

What you'll learn

IDEAS

• To distinguish animal characteristics from those of other organisms
• To describe the functions essential for animal survival
• To identify major milestones in the evolution of animals

WORDS

animals, sessile, motile, blastula, gastrula, blastopore, vertebrates, invertebrates

Real animals, artificial environment
Any structure that settles to the ocean floor, such as a whale carcass or a wrecked ship, becomes a habitat, or "artificial reef," for many animals. Over time, the number and variety of animals increase as they provide food and shelter for each other. Some artificial reefs, hot spots for fishing, are intentionally made from old tires, durable construction waste, and even discarded offshore oil platforms.

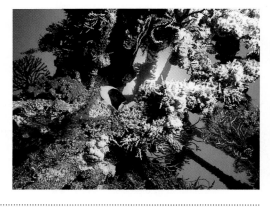

CHARACTERISTICS OF ANIMALS

Adaptability is all

Although animals look different and inhabit strikingly different environments, they share several common characteristics. **Animals** are eukaryotic, multicellular heterotrophs whose cells lack cell walls. These four characteristics differentiate animals from the organisms in the other kingdoms—Monera, Protista, Fungi, and Plantae. How exactly do these characteristics make animals different?

First, animals have eukaryotic cells. This characteristic distinguishes them from monerans, which have prokaryotic cells. Second, animals are multicellular, unlike monerans and unicellular protists. As heterotrophs, animals are different from the autotrophic plants and plantlike protists. Finally, animals have cells that lack cell walls, distinguishing them from plants, plantlike protists, and fungi.

Although animals differ from the members of the other kingdoms, recall that all organisms must perform a similar set of functions. Like all living things, animals reproduce, grow, use energy, and respond to their environment. Animals must perform these vital functions to survive. As you study the animal kingdom, you will discover some amazing adaptations that enable animals to perform these essential life functions.

Support and movement The structures that provide an animal with support must be strong enough to allow the animal to retain its basic shape, yet flexible enough to enable movement. Most animals have some type of skeletal system that provides support and serves as a framework for muscle attachment. The muscles that are attached to the skeletal system enable an animal to move.

Most animals are active and require energy for movement. Some animals are passive, however, and move only when carried by another force, such as wind or water currents. Still others are **sessile,** or permanently attached to one spot. However, most sessile animals have a **motile,** or

FIGURE 21.1

Is this sea squirt an animal? What characteristics would make it an animal?

FIGURE 21.3
These horses support a tremendous amount of weight as they run. What adaptations enable them to do so?

free-moving, stage in their life cycle. Motility enables the offspring of sessile animals to settle in a new place. Why would the ability to find new habitats enhance survival?

Energy and wastes Living requires a large amount of energy. In order to produce a constant energy supply, heterotrophic animals must find and ingest food, digest it, and absorb its nutrients. Then they must egest and excrete wastes. Egestion is the process of eliminating undigested food waste. In the process of excretion, nitrogen-containing waste products from cell metabolism are eliminated.

Respiration Animals need oxygen to release energy from the nutrients they have absorbed. Carbon dioxide is produced during this process and must be removed. The respiratory system enables an animal to absorb oxygen and release carbon dioxide. In land animals, the respiratory system often includes lungs; in aquatic animals, it often includes gills.

Sensing the environment Animals must obtain their own food, protect themselves from predators, find mates, and satisfy other needs.

Thus, they must be aware of their environment. In many animals, a nervous system gathers and processes information from the environment, enabling the animal to respond. The nervous systems of animals vary in structure from relatively simple to highly complex.

Reproduction Living things must reproduce to maintain their species. Almost all animals can reproduce sexually. Some animals are able to reproduce asexually.

Most animal species have two separate sexes. Their gametes—eggs and sperm—join in a process called fertilization. Animals that reproduce sexually may lay eggs and leave them unattended; they may lay eggs and care for them until they hatch; or their eggs may develop internally so that they give birth to live young.

By adapting to their environment animals can overcome obstacles to performing the essential life functions you just read about. As you explore the diversity of animals in the next two units, notice their varied environments. Think about how different animals are adapted to survive in different environments.

FIGURE 21.2
What unique characteristics do you see in this spider? How do these adaptations help spiders to survive?

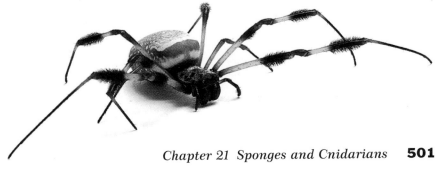

Chapter 21 Sponges and Cnidarians **501**

FIGURE 21.4
Embryo Development

A series of orderly, precise steps transform a
zygote into a multicellular embryo. The embryo
is organized into discrete layers of cells from
which tissues and organs will develop.

1 Fertilized egg
Fertilization of an
egg by a sperm
creates a zygote.

2 Cleavage
Cleavage is a series
of rapid cell divisions
that result in the for-
mation of many cells.

3 Blastula
As the ball of cells
forms, it develops a
fluid-filled center. This
hollow ball of cells is
called the blastula.

4 Gastrulation
Cells at one location
on the blastula's
surface begin to
move into the inte-
rior of the blastula.

5 Gastrula
During gastrula formation,
cell layers develop that will
later give rise to different
tissues and organs in the
organism. Both the number
of cell layers and the way they
form vary with the type of
animal that is developing.

Ectoderm

Blastopore

Endoderm

What a zoo!

The fossil record of the Cambrian
period, about 600 million years ago, has
a large number of fossils of the earliest
known animals. By then animals had
evolved hard body parts that could be
preserved or recorded as fossils. But
the fossil record is incomplete, and it
is difficult to understand relationships
based only on fossils. As you may
recall from Chapter 13, living things
are classified by evolutionary relationships. These relationships can be
determined by analyzing shared structural, developmental, and molecular
characteristics.

Development of animal embryos
provides some of the most critical
insight into evolutionary relationships.
Embryological development begins
when a zygote is formed at fertilization, as shown in *Figure 21.4*. After
many cell divisions, a zygote forms a
hollow ball of cells called a **blastula**.
Some cells begin to move inward from
the surface of the blastula, resulting in
a two-layered cuplike ball of cells
called a **gastrula**. The inner layer of
cells is called endoderm, and the
outer cell layer is called ectoderm.
The digestive tract and respiratory system develop from endoderm; the skin,
sense organs, and nerves develop
from ectoderm.

In most animal embryos, three cell
layers—not two—result from the formation of a gastrula. A middle layer of
cells, the mesoderm, forms between
the ectoderm and endoderm in all but
the most primitive animals. Mesoderm
gives rise to muscles and to the circulatory, reproductive, and excretory
systems.

Animals exibit similarities and
differences in their embryological
development. By studying these similarities and differences, taxonomists
have recognized four major milestones

in the evolution of animals—evolution of tissues, of body symmetry, of internal body cavities, and of a new pattern of embryo development. You can trace these milestones in *Figure 21.5.*

Early in animal evolution, the first of these milestones occurred when animals developed tissues from ectoderm and endoderm—and later from mesoderm. As a result of tissue development, parts of animals could become specialized for different functions.

A second milestone was reached when some animals with true tissues developed body symmetry. Body symmetry refers to the arrangement of body parts around a central point or plane.

A third milestone occurred when some animals evolved body cavities that were at least partially lined with tissue. These body cavities formed from embryonic mesoderm.

The fourth major milestone occurred relatively recently in the evolution of animals. This milestone involves differences in the embryonic development of the **blastopore**—an opening that develops at the point where cells of the blastula move inward to form the cell layers of the gastrula.

Biologists also tend to group animals by whether or not they have a backbone. Animals with a backbone are called **vertebrates;** those without a backbone are called **invertebrates**.

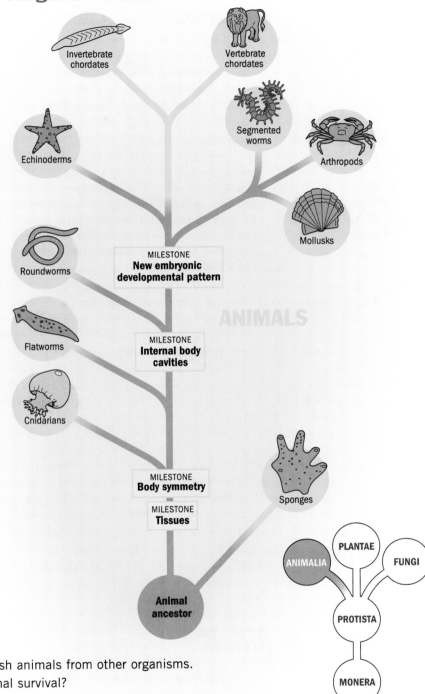

FIGURE 21.5
Kingdom Animalia

CHECKPOINT 21.1

1. Identify the characteristics that distinguish animals from other organisms.
2. What are the functions essential for animal survival?
3. List the four major milestones in the evolution of animals.
4. **Critical Thinking** How does the ability to move enhance survival?

Build on What You Know

5. How is the process of mitosis important in the development of a blastula? *(Need to jog your memory? Revisit relevant concepts in Chapter 5, Sections 5.1 and 5.2.)*

What adaptations have evolved in animals that enable them to perform essential functions of life?

21.2 Characteristics of Sponges

What you'll learn

IDEAS

- To describe the structure of typical sponges
- To compare and contrast the methods of reproduction in sponges

WORDS

osculum, amebocytes, spongin, spicules, gemmule, hermaphrodite

FIGURE 21.6

This vase sponge displays the typical porous structure of a sponge, which enables water to flow through it freely.

A multitude of sponges

A live natural sponge can be pressed through a fine sieve into a culture medium. When this is done, the individual cells will migrate and clump together. As they clump together, they form multicellular clusters. These clusters will then form new sponges, creating many where there once was one.

STRUCTURE OF SPONGES

Water in, water out

Organisms of the phylum Porifera (poh-RIF-eh-ruh) are commonly called sponges. The word *porifera* comes from the Latin *porus,* meaning "pore," and *fera,* meaning "bearers." Their porous structure enables sponges— sessile organisms that live in water— to perform essential life functions.

Sponges lack specialized tissues and organs, but they are well adapted to their stationary existence. Sponges have evolved with structures that allow water to be pumped through their bodies. The flowing water enables the sponge to digest, respire, circulate materials, and excrete wastes. The water-pumping ability of sponges is impressive. A 1-gram (g) sponge can pump as much as 1 liter (L) of water through its body per hour. How much water can this sponge pump in a day?

Many sponges have a body plan similar to the one shown in

Figure 21.7. The body forms a vaselike wall around a hollow cylinder, or sac. The sac is closed at the bottom and open at the top. The opening at the top of the sac is called the **osculum** (OS-kyoo-lum). The interior of a sponge is lined with flagellated cells called collar cells. The beating flagella of many collar cells create a current that moves water into the central cavity through pores in the sac, and out through the osculum. As water flows through a sponge, the collar cells trap particles of organic matter and microscopic organisms, which sponges use as food. This method of obtaining food is called filter-feeding or suspension-feeding.

Food may be digested in the collar cells or passed on to **amebocytes** (uh-MEE-boh-syts)—cells that move through the sponge's body, supplying nutrients to other cells and removing wastes. Wastes are later released into the water flowing through the sponge and carried out through the osculum.

In addition to cells that pump water and process food, sponges have structures that provide support. These structures are made of spongin, spicules, or both. **Spongin** is a network of

FIGURE 21.7
Structure of a Sponge

Sponges have very simple organization with no true tissues. They vary in shape, but all have the basic structure shown here. Can you explain how this structure would be well adapted to a sessile marine existence?

Spicules
Spicules are made of either calcium carbonate or silicon dioxide and come in a variety of shapes.

Outgoing water

Osculum

Pore cells

Central cavity

Spicule

Collar cells
These flagellated cells create a current flowing through the sponge and trap food particles.

protein fibers. What you see in a natural bath sponge, for example, is mostly spongin. **Spicules** are tiny needlelike structures made of silicon dioxide (glass) or calcium carbonate.

REPRODUCTION OF SPONGES

A fragmented relationship

The ability to find mates and reproduce can be a problem for sessile organisms. Sponges, however, have adapted—they are capable of both sexual and asexual reproduction.

Asexual reproduction Sponges reproduce asexually by budding, by regeneration, or by forming structures called gemmules. When sponges bud, the buds either detach and form new

LAB ZONE Do It!

Calculating the Pumping Capacity of a Natural Sponge

A typical natural sponge measuring **10 centimeters (cm)** high and **1 cm** in diameter can pump about **23 L** of water in a day. How long would it take for this sponge to empty all the water in an aquarium holding **38 L** of water? You can answer this problem when you . . .

Try This

1 Write an equation that includes the facts you know and the unknown factor, as follows: 24 hours ÷ 23 L = (x) hours ÷ 38 L.
2 Perform the mathematical calculations.

Analyze Your Results

How long would it take for the sponge to empty the aquarium?

FIGURE 21.8
A female tube sponge releases thousands of golden eggs held together by sticky strands of mucus. The eggs of this sponge, *Agelas,* are fertilized externally when spawning male sponges release sperm. How does this differ from fertilization in most other sponges?

sponges, or remain attached to the parent, forming a colony of sponges.

Sponges also have a remarkable ability to reproduce by regeneration. Fragments broken off a sponge can settle and grow into complete, new sponges. Regeneration is a useful adaptation, as sponges are frequently broken up by pounding surf or partially eaten by predators.

During extreme conditions such as droughts or periods of freezing temperatures, sponges form gemmules. A **gemmule** (JEM-yool) is a dormant mass of sponge amebocytes surrounded by protective layers of spicules. When favorable conditions return, the amebocytes emerge and grow into new sponges.

Sexual reproduction Sexual reproduction begins with the formation of gametes—eggs and sperm. Many species of sponges are hermaphrodites. A **hermaphrodite** is an individual organism capable of producing both eggs and sperm. A hermaphroditic sponge can mate with any other sponge of its species.

Fertilization in sponges can be external, as shown in *Figure 21.8,* or internal. Most sponges have internal fertilization, a process that begins when sperm are released into the water flowing out through the osculum. If the

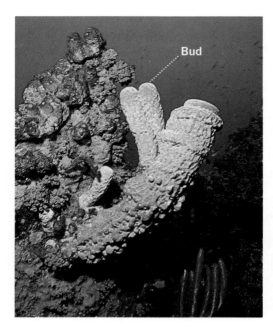

FIGURE 21.9
Notice the many buds forming on the parent colony. The members in a colony such as this can be genetically identical because they were formed by asexual reproduction.

sperm reach another sponge, they flow in through its pores. Amebocytes transport the sperm to an egg, enabling fertilization to occur. The resulting zygote develops into a flagellated larva that swims away from the parent sponge and settles on a new surface. The flagellated cells of the larva then reorganize and develop into a new sponge.

CHECKPOINT 21.2

1. Describe the structure of a typical sponge.
2. Compare and contrast the methods of reproduction in sponges.
3. Critical Thinking How would hermaphroditism be an advantage for sessile animals?

Build on What You Know

4. Which aspects of a sponge's structure and function are most like those of protists? *(Need to jog your memory? Revisit relevant concepts in Chapter 15, Section 15.2.)*

21.3 Origin and Diversity of Sponges

Could you fit inside a sponge?
You bet you could! If you were diving in the ocean and came across a huge basket sponge—possibly 100 years old—you might even be tempted to slip inside it. Divers should avoid doing so, however, because the sponge is much more delicate than it appears and could be damaged by human contact.

What you'll learn

IDEAS
• To explain one hypothesis about the origin of sponges
• To compare different habitats of sponges

ORIGIN OF SPONGES
Uncommonly old

Scientists think sponges evolved from protists very early in the Cambrian period. In fact, the flagellated collar cells in sponges bear a striking resemblance to the cells in a group of colonial protists. This similarity has led scientists to hypothesize that sponges evolved from such colonial protists. Sponges living today have not changed much from their fossilized ancestors.

Sponges have very little in common with other animals. They lack specialized tissues or organ systems and have only some specialized cells. Most sponges have no body symmetry. Scientists have concluded that sponges probably evolved separately from all other animals.

DIVERSITY OF SPONGES
Colorful creatures

Most of the approximately 8000 known species of sponges live in the oceans, although about 3 percent live in freshwater lakes and streams. Marine sponges are found at many depths and display a remarkable variety of sizes,

FIGURE 21.10
Phylum Porifera

shapes, and colors; they are often brilliant shades of red, orange, yellow, or blue. Freshwater sponges are more likely to be a dull brown or green. The smallest sponges can live on tiny mollusk shells, whereas the largest can exceed humans in size.

Sponges are organized into classes based on whether they have spongin, spicules, or both. As you have learned, spongin is a strong organic fiber, and spicules are calcareous or glasslike skeletal components that take on a variety of forms. The size, shape, and composition of spicules are used to classify sponges further. *Figure 21.11* illustrates sponge diversity.

Kingdom: Animalia
Phylum: Porifera
Four classes:
Calcarea
Hyalospongiae
Demospongiae
Sclerospongiae

Although many species of sponges have already been identified, scientists think that many have yet to be discovered. One recently discovered deep-sea sponge has no collar cells, and it does not filter water. This sponge obtains its food somewhat differently than most sponges. Its Velcro-like surface is covered with spicule-studded filaments that move. Tiny crustaceans get caught on the sharp spicules and, within the space of a day, can be covered by new filaments. By this process the sponge ingests and gradually digests its prey. Researchers hypothesize that, because of its environment, this deep-sea sponge has developed a different system for obtaining food.

CHECKPOINT 21.3

1. Explain one hypothesis about the origin of sponges.
2. Describe some of the diverse habitats occupied by sponges.
3. **Critical Thinking** What characteristics of sponges enable them to live in diverse habitats?

Build on What You Know

4. Compare and contrast the characteristics of sponges and plants. *(Need to jog your memory? Revisit relevant concepts in Chapter 17, Section 17.1.)*

FIGURE 21.11

The Diversity of Sponges

Some sponges assume the shape of the object on which they grow; others have their own distinctive shape. Colors may vary even among sponges of the same species.

1 Orange sponge
2 Azure vase sponge
3 Tube sponges
4 Vase sponge
5 Pacific coast sponge
6 Brittle stars on rope sponges

? How can sponges survive without specialized tissues and organs?

21.4 Characteristics of Cnidarians

So aptly named

Medusa, a character in Greek mythology, had hair made of serpents. In their adult medusa stage, jellyfish have waving, serpentlike tentacles trailing from their bell-shaped bodies. Although they can not turn humans to stone as Medusa did, jellyfish use stinging barbs on their tentacles to immobilize or kill their prey.

What you'll learn

IDEAS
- To describe the structure and symmetry of cnidarians
- To compare and contrast sexual and asexual reproduction in cnidarians

WORDS
radial symmetry, asymmetry, polyp, medusa, nematocyst, planula

STRUCTURE OF CNIDARIANS

Harpoon carriers

Have you ever seen a stinging jellyfish? Sometimes beaches are closed to swimmers when jellyfish are abundant. The sting of a jellyfish can be painful, or even fatal in some cases.

Jellyfish are a type of cnidarian (ny–DAYR–ee–uhn). Cnidarians have **radial symmetry,** which means their body parts radiate from a central point. This type of symmetry might remind you of the spokes of a wheel radiating from its center, or hub. Radially symmetrical objects do not have a front or a back side. Most sponges, as you just learned, exhibit **asymmetry;** that is, they lack body symmetry.

Along with corals, hydra, and sea anemones, jellyfish belong to the phylum Cnidaria. Cnidarians are named for their unique cells called cnidocytes (NY-doh-syts). Cnidocytes contain stinging, poisonous barbs that cnidarians use to capture their prey.

Cnidarians are soft-bodied animals with a hollow central cavity. This single opening is surrounded by tentacles. Cnidarians have two basic body types.

The cylinder-shaped or vase-shaped **polyp** (PAH-lip) has its opening on the dorsal surface and tentacles that point upward. The umbrella-shaped or bell-shaped **medusa** (meh-DOO-suh) has its mouth on the ventral surface and tentacles that point downward. Which body form does the sea anemone in *Figure 21.12* have? Some cnidarians, such as the freshwater

FIGURE 21.12
Animal Body Symmetry

Most sponges (below left) lack body symmetry. Like most animals, cnidarians, such as the sea anemone (below right), have body symmetry.

A sponge is asymmetrical.

A cnidarian has radial symmetry.

FIGURE 21.13

Structures of Cnidarians

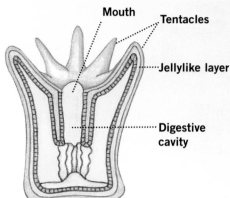

Polyp
A polyp is shaped like
a cylinder.

Mouth
Tentacles
Jellylike layer
Digestive cavity

Medusa
The medusa is a bell-
shaped, mouth-down
version of the polyp.

Jellylike layer
Digestive cavity
Mouth
Tentacles
Coiled filament

Cnidocytes
Coiled nematocysts in
cnidocyte cells are triggered
by touch. Poison discharged
from the barb kills or
paralyzes the prey.

Nematocyst
Prey
Barb

hydra and the sea anemone, exist only as polyps. Other cnidarians have both polyp and medusa life stages.

You may recall that sponges are filter-feeders, trapping food particles that flow into their bodies. Cnidarians, on the other hand, are carnivores that capture prey. Several types of specialized tissues and structures have evolved in cnidarians that enable them to capture food. You may remember that the development of such tissues represents the first major milestone in the evolution of animals.

In cnidarians, tissues lining the digestive cavity and on the outer surface are made up of musclelike contractile cells. These cells contain proteins that can contract, or shorten in length, causing the cnidarian to change its shape. This change of shape enables some cnidarians to swim.

Another specialized tissue in cnidarians is made of cells called cnidocytes. Cnidocytes are armed with stinging organelles called nematocysts, which you can see in *Figure 21.13*. A **nematocyst** (nuh-MAT-uh-sist) is a coiled filament with a tiny harpoonlike barb on the end. When a cnidocyte touches an object or animal, it launches its nematocyst barb like a tiny harpoon. The poison in the barb kills or paralyzes the prey, which becomes tangled in the filament. The cnidarian can then use its tentacles to draw the prey into its mouth.

For the cnidocytes and tentacles to function effectively, cnidarians must

Finding Examples of Symmetry

You can check your understanding of asymmetry and radial symmetry when you . . .

Try This

1 Look around your classroom to find living or nonliving examples of both asymmetry and radial symmetry.
2 List as many examples of each as you can find.
3 Sketch one item you have listed as asymmetrical and one you have listed as symmetrical. Explain why you think each item belongs in the category you selected.

have a nervous system. A diffuse, decentralized nerve net carries signals through the body of a cnidarian, coordinating the cnidocytes and tentacles.

REPRODUCTION OF CNIDARIANS

A bud off the old polyp

Like sponges, most cnidarians can reproduce either asexually or sexually. However, sexual reproduction in some cnidarians may require complex cycles that involve both the medusa and polyp forms.

For example, in the life cycle of the common jellyfish, the medusa is the dominant form. The medusa is also the form that produces gametes by meiosis. A medusa may produce either sperm or eggs and release them into the water, where fertilization takes place. The resulting zygote develops into a **planula,** or free-swimming larva. A planula uses cilia to move to a

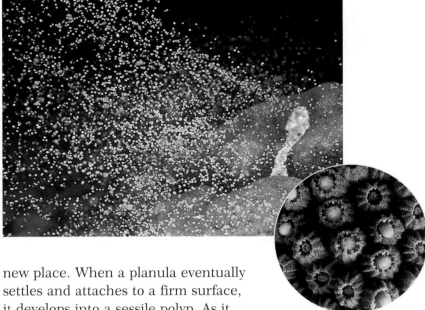

new place. When a planula eventually settles and attaches to a firm surface, it develops into a sessile polyp. As it grows, the polyp develops a stack of medusae that bud off asexually and become the free-swimming jellyfish.

Other cnidarians, such as the common freshwater hydra, often reproduce asexually by budding. However, low water temperatures can stimulate the hydra to reproduce sexually. Fertilization occurs by a process similar to that of the jellyfish. After an egg is fertilized, it grows into a ball of cells with a hardened coat. This structure can survive low temperatures, whereas the soft-bodied adult hydra cannot. When environmental conditions improve, a new polyp grows.

FIGURE 21.15
Coral polyps in coastal Florida waters release egg and sperm bundles (above) during sexual reproduction.

FIGURE 21.14
Reproduction in the *Aurelia* Jellyfish

Reproduction in the jellyfish involves both the medusa and polyp stages. The larva, called a planula, develops into a polyp. The polyp buds, asexually producing many new medusa.

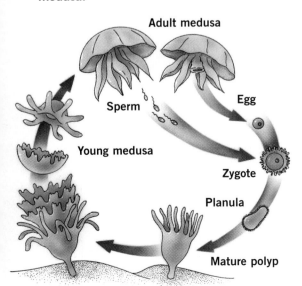

Adult medusa
Sperm
Egg
Young medusa
Zygote
Planula
Mature polyp

CHECKPOINT 21.4

1. Describe the structure and symmetry of cnidarians.
2. How do cnidarians reproduce?
3. Critical Thinking In the polyp and medusa stages of cnidarians, how is the position of the mouth adapted to its function?

Build on What You Know

4. How do the structures that cnidarians use for movement compare with the flagella and cilia of other organisms? *(Need to jog your memory? Revisit relevant concepts in Chapter 3, Section 3.3.)*

Observing Hydra

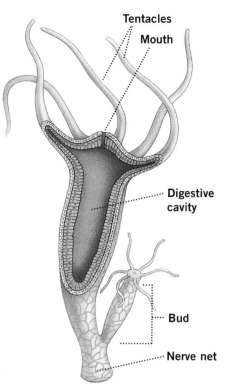

Tentacles
Mouth

Digestive cavity

Bud

Nerve net

WHAT YOU WILL DO Observe the structure and activity of hydra, including feeding behavior

SKILLS YOU WILL USE Observing, collecting and recording data, predicting, experimenting

WHAT YOU WILL NEED Dissection probe, two droppers, two depression slides, cultures of *Hydra* and *Daphnia,* dissecting microscope, toothpick

Propose a Hypothesis

Formulate a hypothesis about the process by which a hydra captures prey.

Conduct Your Experiment

1 Using the dissection probe, gently dislodge a *Hydra* from the culture container.
2 Draw the *Hydra* into the dropper and quickly transfer it to the depression slide. (The *Hydra* may attach itself to the inside of the dropper.)
3 Examine the slide of the *Hydra* for several minutes under low and high power. Note its shape, its size, and any movement of its tentacles. Record your observations, using words and diagrams.

4 Using the first dropper, transfer a drop of the *Hydra* culture to another depression slide. Using the second dropper, transfer a drop of the *Daphnia* culture to the same slide. If necessary, gently use a toothpick to connect the two drops.
5 Observe the slide under the microscope. Record your observations of the *Hydra's* feeding behavior, and make a drawing of a *Hydra* ingesting a *Daphnia*. (Note: If your *Hydra* does not exhibit feeding behavior, transfer another organism from the *Hydra* culture.)

Analyze Your Data

1 What were your observations of the *Hydra's* shape and the movement of its tentacles before you added the *Daphnia?*

2 Describe any changes in the *Hydra's* shape and the movement of its tentacles when in the presence of food.

Draw Conclusions

1 Do your results support your hypothesis?
2 Is a hydra a sessile organism? Is a daphnia a sessile organism? On what do you base these conclusions?
3 Based on your observations of the feeding behavior of a hydra, can you infer anything about the feeding behavior of other sessile organisms? Explain.

Design a Related Experiment

Suppose you wanted to find out if the hydra prefers one type of food over another. Propose a hypothesis and design an experiment to test your hypothesis.

Lab: Observing Hydra

Objective: to find out how the hydra moves and feeds
The tentacles of the hydra moved slowly around; after the nematocysts of the tentacles touched the daphnia, the tentacles started to bend inward.

21.5 Origin and Diversity of Cnidarians

Quite a sting

If you ever see this animal, watch out! This is a sea wasp, or box jellyfish. Although sea wasps are about 25 cm in length, their toxin is more lethal than any snake venom, and they can kill a human in minutes. In fact, in Australian waters sea wasps kill more people than sharks do.

What you'll learn

IDEAS
- To explain two important milestones in the evolution of cnidarians
- To compare the three classes of cnidarians

ORIGIN OF CNIDARIANS

Soft as jelly

Cnidarians are soft-bodied and do not preserve well as either impressions in sediments or actual fossils. So scientists have not been able to learn much about the origin of cnidarians from fossils.

Instead, scientists have relied on information obtained from studying cnidarians' embryological development. From this information, scientists have identified two important milestones in the evolution of cnidarians— the development of true tissues and of radial symmetry.

True tissues enable cnidarians to use different body parts for different functions. For example, when stimulated, the tentacles of cnidarians move to capture prey. Without nerve and muscle tissues, cnidarians would not be able to obtain food.

Because cnidarians have radial symmetry, their sense organs are located in a radial pattern around their bodies. This form of body symmetry enables an organism to sense its environment from all sides. How would this sensory adaptation benefit an organism?

Scientists study embryological development and compare anatomy to determine cnidarians' evolutionary origin. In their larval form, cnidarians resemble animal-like, ciliated protists such as paramecia. You learned about paramecia and other protists in Chapter 15. The structural similarities between cnidarian larvae and ciliated protists suggest that the organisms have a common ancestor.

Kingdom: Animalia

Phylum: Cnidaria

Three classes:
Hydrozoa
Scyphozoa
Anthozoa

FIGURE 21.16

Phylum Cnidaria

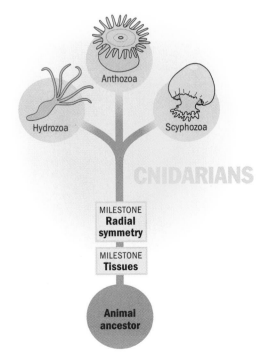

FIGURE 21.17
The hydra is a freshwater hydrozoan that spends most of its life in the polyp form. It usually reproduces by budding.

DIVERSITY OF CNIDARIANS

Very touchy creatures

Cnidarians are a highly diverse group of organisms. Most live the greater part of their lives in one of two distinct forms. While most cnidarians live as individual animals, others such as the corals live in colonies. To classify cnidarians more accurately, scientists have recently begun using molecular technology to sequence and compare DNA, RNA, and proteins. In the future, this technology should reveal more information about cnidarians' evolutionary relationships. Presently, cnidarians are grouped in three classes—Hydrozoa, Scyphozoa (sy-foh-ZOH-uh), and Anthozoa.

Hydrozoa Most hydrozoans alternate between the polyp and medusa forms, which are illustrated in *Figure 21.13* on page 510. For hydrozoans, the polyp stage is generally the more conspicuous form.

The Portuguese man-of-war is an example of a colonial hydrozoan. It consists of many highly specialized medusae and polyps living together. This colonial hydrozoan, which you can see in *Figure 21.18*, has a life cycle similar to that of a jellyfish. The tentacles, which hang from an inflated bladderlike structure, can be meters long and contain many toxin-injecting nematocysts.

Scyphozoa Like the hydrozoans, most scyphozoans alternate between polyp and medusa forms. However, the primary body form of scyphozoans is the medusa.

If you have ever been swimming in warm ocean water, you may have seen a scyphozoan. This class of cnidarians comprises the animals we call jellyfish. There are more than 200 species of jellyfish, and they all are marine organisms.

Like the Portuguese man-of-war, jellyfish float near the surface of the ocean. Their tentacles hang in the water and trap prey. The medusae of some scyphozoan species can attain great size—several meters in diameter—if they can avoid being broken apart by waves.

Anthozoa Anthozoans, meaning "flower animals," make up the largest class of cnidarians and occur only in the polyp form. All anthozoans have a plantlike body, which is topped with a tuft of hollow tentacles. There are more than 6000 species of anthozoans, and they are all marine animals. Members of this class include the sea anemones and corals.

FIGURE 21.18
The Portuguese man-of-war's tentacles may be as long as 9 meters. Although the poison discharged from this cnidarian's tentacles can kill its prey, its sting is rarely fatal to humans.

FIGURE 21.19
Jellyfish are prominent members of the class Scyphozoa. In which body form is this mangrove jellyfish?

Most sea anemones live independently, and they exhibit a wide variety of sizes and colors. The tentacles of sea anemones are particularly noticeable when they are feeding. A sea anemone "harpoons" a small fish or crustacean, then folds its tentacles over the prey until digestion is

FIGURE 21.20
Named for their resemblance to anemone flowers, sea anemones usually attach to a hard surface such as coral.

Polyp

The living polyps are connected by a thin sheet of tissue.

Exoskeleton

FIGURE 21.21
Live coral polyps are found only on the top surface of a reef. The carbonate skeletons that form the coral reef are below.

complete. Although sea anemones may actively hunt their prey, some species obtain nutrients from symbiosis with their photosynthetic partners.

Probably the best-known of the anthozoans are the corals. Corals are tiny, sessile, colonial polyps—many of which secrete an exoskeleton. Individual corals, or polyps, live on the surface of these exoskeletons, building on those of previous generations. As calcium carbonate is deposited in the exoskeletons of corals, old and new skeletons fuse to form a reef. Reef-building corals are found in clear, shallow, warm waters.

CHECKPOINT 21.5

1. Explain the significance of the development of true tissues and radial symmetry in cnidarians.
2. Compare and contrast the three classes of cnidarians.
3. **Critical Thinking** Why do jellyfish sting their prey before folding their tentacles around them?

Build on What You Know

4. Using diagrams, compare the structure and function of specialized cnidocytes with those of a typical cell. *(Need to jog your memory? Revisit relevant concepts in Chapter 3, Section 3.2.)*

Coral Cautions
To prevent killing fragile, living coral polyps, snorkelers and scuba divers need to avoid stepping on, grabbing, or breaking off any coral. Even touching coral polyps with oily hands can cause them to die.

What are the characteristics of cnidarians?

Chapter 21 Sponges and Cnidarians **515**

21.6 Sponges and Cnidarians in the Biosphere

What you'll learn

IDEAS

• To identify the varied roles of cnidarians and sponges in their natural environments

• To describe how these organisms can affect humans

A sponge hotel?

Would you guess that many different organisms actually make their homes inside sponges? For example, the snapping shrimp, *Synalpheus regalis,* inhabits sponges in the Caribbean Sea. How do these organisms benefit from their sponge homes? The sponge is used by its residents as a shelter and a place to hide from their predators.

ECOLOGICAL ROLES

Living together for profit

Because of their great diversity, sponges and cnidarians are a form of food, camouflage, and protected habitats for many organisms. Sponges and cnidarians often benefit from the organisms that use them. As you have learned, relationships in which one organism benefits from another is known as symbiosis.

Corals and sponges are the two most abundant kinds of animals on many reefs, and are at the base of many aquatic food chains. Sponges are not eaten by many animals because their sharp spicules discourage most predators. Cnidarians, however, are consumed by small fish, crustaceans, and other animals. For example, sea stars, certain fish, and other reef dwellers graze on living coral.

FIGURE 21.22

Corals of the Great Barrier Reef

1 Fan coral
2 Soft tree coral
3 Staghorn coral
4 Lilypad coral

Sponges and cnidarians have many colors and shapes that provide other animals with a highly camouflaged environment. Certain sponges attach themselves to the back of a crab. One species of crab actually places sponges on its back. This strategy camouflages the crab and provides a sponge with the crab's leftover food. Both the sponge and the crab benefit from this symbiotic relationship.

Some cnidarians also form symbiotic relationships with other organisms. Reef-building corals have dinoflagellates—plantlike protists—living inside their cells. Although corals can grow without these protists, they form reefs only when they live symbiotically with them. This phenomenon is not yet fully understood.

Several species of fishes use the poisonous tentacles of sea anemones for protection. When a fish coats itself with a sea anemone's mucus, the sea anemone does not sense the fish as prey and cannot discharge its nematocysts. The fish can then live among the sea anemone's tentacles. The tentacles protect the fish from predators, and the fish, in turn, may help the sea anemone by removing parasites and debris.

Sponges and cnidarians provide habitats for a great variety of creatures. Small invertebrates, such as shrimps, can live in the pores and central cavities of sponges. Even small fish can live in the cavities of some sponges. A single sponge can house an astonishing number and variety of organisms.

Coral reefs also provide shelter for many organisms, and nooks and crannies for hiding. Coral reefs are, in fact, second only to tropical rain forests in the diversity of life they support.

HUMAN USES

Environmental snitches

Sponges and cnidarians are important indicators of changes in their environments. Living things that provide information about environmental conditions are called bioindicators. When a sponge filters water through its body, it tends to concentrate pollutants from the water in its cells. Eventually, the concentration of pollutants poisons and kills the sponge. An area that contains dead and dying sponges is a sure indication of environmental pollution.

FIGURE 21.23
Part of the Great Barrier Reef, which extends along the northeast coast of Australia, is shown in the aerial view below. The largest group of coral reefs in the world, most of the Great Barrier Reef lies within a national park and is protected by the regulations of a government agency.

IN THE COMMUNITY

The Business of Sponges

Check at home and visit local stores to see how many different sponge products you can find. What is the composition of artificial sponges? Look in department stores and bath shops to find natural sponges too. Conduct library research into the business of harvesting sponges from the Caribbean Sea and the Mediterranean Sea. How large is the sponge industry? How many sponges are harvested in a year? Does the harvesting of sponges threaten their ecosystems? Write a brief report explaining your findings.

FIGURE 21.24
These are the skeletal remains of spongin-containing sponges. Such natural sponges are prized for washing cars.

Like sponges, corals are sensitive to water pollution, changes in water temperature or oxygen concentrations, and water clarity, or the amount of sediment. Some scientists are studying coral reefs as possible bioindicators of global warming. Offshore reefs help protect shorelines from erosion. By decreasing the force of incoming waves, the reefs create an area of calm, peaceful waters at the shore. Reefs also protect marine life that humans use for food.

In addition to protecting the shoreline and marine life, sponges are used as consumer products. It is only in the twentieth century that artificial sponges—made of rubber, nylon, or cellulose—have become commonplace. For centuries, humans have harvested natural sponges—dull colored and irregularly shaped—for bathing and cleaning. These natural sponges contain only spongin. Spicule-containing sponges would be too abrasive for household use.

Sponge spicules are not without their consumer uses, however. Members of a South American tribe that inhabits the Amazon region add sponge spicules to the clay they use for making pottery. The spicules greatly strengthen their ceramic pots.

FRONTIERS IN BIOLOGY

Rx . . . sponges and jellyfish

A more recent use for sponges and cnidarians, especially jellyfish, is in the biomedical and pharmaceutical industries. Researchers have found promising new antibiotic and anticancer compounds in the small percentage of sponge species they have studied. Researchers are also investigating possible medical uses for the paralyzing toxins that some jellyfish use to capture prey. This branch of biotechnology is quite new, but very exciting. Research will probably result in the development of new medicines.

CHECKPOINT 21.6

1. Describe the roles of sponges and cnidarians in marine environments.
2. Explain how sponges and corals can be used for environmental monitoring.
3. **Critical Thinking** How would the death of a coral reef affect the island it surrounds and the inhabitants of that island?

Build on What You Know

4. What benefits might the dinoflagellates living in reef-building corals derive from their symbiotic relationship? How would the coral benefit? *(Need to jog your memory? Revisit relevant concepts in Chapter 15, Section 15.3.)*

 How are sponges and cnidarians important in their ecosystems?

Chapter 21 Review

21.1 Animals have evolved a number of adaptations enabling them to perform essential functions of life.
21.2–21.3 Sponges are sessile animals without specialized tissues and organs.
21.4–21.5 Cnidarians are radially symmetrical animals with specialized tissues and stinging tentacles.
21.6 Sponges and cnidarians provide food and protection for a large number of organisms.

Sum It Up

Use the following summary to review the main concepts in this chapter.

21.1 Introduction to Animals

- Animals are eukaryotic and multicellular.
- Animals are heterotrophic organisms, and their cells lack cell walls.
- The evolution of animals is highlighted by four major developmental milestones.
- Animals perform certain functions for survival: movement, respiration, reproduction, digestion, excretion, and sensing their environment.

21.2 Characteristics of Sponges

- Sponges are sessile filter-feeders.
- Sponges have a simple, asymmetrical body organization supported by spongin and/or spicules.
- Sponges can reproduce sexually and often are hermaphrodites. They can also reproduce asexually by regeneration.

21.3 Origin and Diversity of Sponges

- Sponges most likely evolved from flagellated colonial protists.
- Sponges do not have specialized tissues and most are asymmetrical.
- Sponges are numerous and vary in size, shape, and color.

21.4 Characteristics of Cnidarians

- Cnidarians are soft-bodied and have radial symmetry. They have two basic body plans: polyp and medusa.
- Cnidarians have stinging cells armed with nematocysts.
- Some cnidarians have ciliated planula larvae.

21.5 Origin and Diversity of Cnidarians

- Cnidarians probably evolved from ciliated colonial protists.
- Most hydrozoans have both a polyp and medusa stage.
- Scyphozoans, the common jellyfish, have a prominent medusa stage.
- Anthozoans are colonial polyps that include corals and sea anemones.

21.6 Sponges and Cnidarians in the Biosphere

- Sponges and cnidarians form symbiotic relationships with other organisms. Some are the principle organisms of reefs.
- Sponges and cnidarians are indicators of pollution and have biopharmaceutical applications.

Use Terms and Concepts

Use each of the following words in a sentence. If you need to review a meaning, turn to the page indicated.

animals (p. 500)
sessile (p. 500)
motile (p. 500)
blastula (p. 502)
gastrula (p. 502)
blastopore (p. 503)

vertebrates (p. 503)
invertebrates (p. 503)
osculum (p. 504)
amebocytes (p. 504)
spongin (p. 504)

spicules (p. 505)
gemmule (p. 506)
hermaphrodite (p. 506)
radial symmetry (p. 509)

asymmetry (p. 509)
polyp (p. 509)
medusa (p. 509)
nematocyst (p. 510)
planula (p. 511)

Use Your Word Power

TRUE-FALSE **Write true if the statement is true. If the statement is false, change the underlined word to make it true.**

1. A(n) <u>gemmule</u> is a free-swimming ciliated larva.

2. A(n) <u>sessile</u> organism is attached to one location.

3. The network of protein fibers that makes up a sponge skeleton is made of <u>spicules</u>.

4. The opening at the top of a sponge through which water flows is the <u>polyp</u>.

5. Animals capable of producing both eggs and sperm in one body are called <u>nematocysts</u>.

6. <u>Radial symmetry</u> is exhibited by organisms that have a central body axis from which other body parts extend.

7. A(n) <u>planula</u> is the vase-shaped body plan of a cnidarian.

8. Free-moving animals are <u>motile</u>.

COMPLETION **Write the word or phrase that best completes each statement.**

9. _____ have no backbones.

10. Needlelike structures in sponges that are made of silicon dioxide or calcium carbonate are called _____ .

11. A(n) _____ is a dormant mass of sponge amebocytes surrounded by layers of spicules.

12. _____ are the stinging barbs of a cnidarian.

13. Animals with backbones are _____ .

14. _____ are migrating cells in a sponge that carry food and wastes.

15. The jellyfish _____ is umbrella shaped.

16. _____ are eukaryotic, multicellular heterotrophs whose cells lack cell walls.

Show What You Know

17. What criteria do scientists use to classify organisms and to identify evolutionary relationships?

18. List and describe the four major milestones in the evolution of animals.

19. What animal tissues are formed by the embryonic cell layers?

20. Explain how sponges obtain food.

21. What are cnidocytes? What is their function?

22. Describe the difference between fragmentation, budding, and regeneration as methods of reproduction.

23. Give some examples of symbiotic relationships formed between sponges, cnidarians, and other organisms.

24. **Make a Concept Map** Use the following terms to make a concept map that shows the classification and characteristics of sponges and cnidarians: cnidaria, animalia, radial symmetry, porifera, sessile, asymmetry, motile, cnidocytes, porous, polyp, medusa.

Take It Further

25. **Applying Concepts** Some of the animals you studied in this chapter are sessile their entire lives, and others are motile. Still others have both motile and sessile stages. What are the advantages and disadvantages of each lifestyle?

26. **Applying Concepts** Why is it important for a motile animal to be able to sense its environment?

27. **Making a Prediction** Predict what would happen to a coral reef ecosystem if all of the sponges were eliminated.

28. **Analyzing Data** Draw a diagram to illustrate the four main evolutionary branches of sponges that are recognized by scientists.

29. Interpreting a Graph Coral growth is affected by sea level. If the sea level rises too rapidly, reefs are "drowned" and die. Using the graph, explain how much the rate of coral growth must increase to reach its maximum annual growth. The projected rise in sea level over the next century is 15 millimeters per year. How will that increase affect coral reefs?

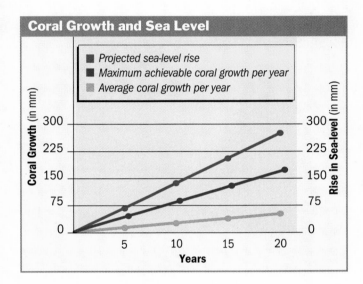

Coral Growth and Sea Level

- ■ Projected sea-level rise
- ■ Maximum achievable coral growth per year
- ▪ Average coral growth per year

Coral Growth (in mm) — 300, 225, 150, 75, 0
Rise in Sea-level (in mm) — 300, 225, 150, 75, 0
Years — 5, 10, 15, 20

Consider the Issues

30. Protecting the Reefs Many coral reefs are experiencing significant long-term damage. Collectors remove organisms and coral skeletons, and tourists walk on the fragile reefs. Simple warnings and prohibitions have not been effective. What else could be done to alleviate the problem? Should people be prohibited from collecting the coral?

31. Protecting the Animals Marine invertebrates have become prime targets of pharmaceutical research because of the medically important chemicals they produce. How might the discovery of new chemicals affect the populations of these marine invertebrates? What could be done to ensure that these chemicals could be manufactured, without threatening the species that produced the chemicals?

Make New Connections

32. Biology and Geology Corals produce calcium carbonate ($CaCO_3$). Limestone, a type of rock, is formed from compacted $CaCO_3$. Research the properties of limestone. How is limestone involved in cave formation? Report your findings.

33. Biology and Physics The movement of a hydra's nematocyst is one of the fastest known cell activities. A hydra nematocyst travels at two meters per second. The formula used to calculate speed is: Speed = Distance/Time. Calculate the time that it would take for a nematocyst to travel 0.02 mm (the typical distance between a hydra and its prey).

34. Biology and the Community The widespread use of plastic bags and balloons, which are released at parades, games, and other special events, has caused problems when these items make their way into the ocean. Floating plastic bags and balloons can look like jellyfish. Find out the jellyfish predators that are most affected by this problem. Find out what happens to plastic bags in your community. Are they recycled? Where?

FAST-FORWARD TO CHAPTER 22

Sponges are asymmetrical and cnidarians have radial symmetry. The four phyla you will learn about in the next chapter exhibit bilateral symmetry. They include flatworms, roundworms, mollusks, and segmented worms.

Worms and Mollusks

You can find out more about worms and mollusks by exploring the following Internet address:
http://invertebrates.biosurf.com

In this chapter . . .

FEATURES

Everyday Biology
• Protect Your Pet
• Planting Pearls

In the Community
Worms for Profit

 Environmental Awareness
Mussels on the Move

LAB ZONES

Discover It!
• Examining Mollusks

Do It!
• Observing Roundworms

Think About It!
• Solving a Reproduction Puzzle

Investigate It!
• Observing Earthworms

OCEAN CHIMNEYS SUPPORT LIFE

Many stretches of ocean floor are barren and bleak with few signs of marine life, but there are exceptions. One occurs where the gigantic plates that comprise Earth's crust are moving apart, allowing lava—hot, molten rock—to emerge. As the lava cools, it adds new ocean floor between the crustal plates. Cold seawater sinks deep into vents, or cracks, created in the ocean floor. When the seawater, heated to temperatures as high as 400°C (750°F), spews back out of the vents, it contains dissolved minerals. These minerals are deposited around the vents, forming hollow, cylindrical "chimneys," some of which reach heights of more than 10 meters (m).

The hot water exiting these chimneys encourages the growth of bacteria, which in turn feed and support an amazing array of animals. Picture, for example, the thriving life in a vent community in the eastern Pacific Ocean: tall, smoking chimneys surrounded by clusters of tube worms and clams and mussels, all feeding on the abundant clouds and mats of bacteria. These giant worms, a sensation when they were first discovered, live in tubes they build from seafloor debris cemented with mucus. Using submersible vehicles, scientists can observe the teeming life in these unusual ecosystems thousands of meters below the ocean's surface.

Examining Mollusks

You need *a hand lens and several fresh or canned clams or mussels*

1. If you can obtain fresh clams or mussels, do so.
   Caution: As you open them, be careful not to cut yourself on the shells.
   If you are using canned clams or mussels, open the can and lay the mollusks on a clean surface.
2. Examine the mollusks, and draw what you see.
   Caution: Wash your hands thoroughly after touching the clams or mussels.

Worms and mollusks share many features, including the soft, muscular body you just observed. Save your drawings, and use them to write labels or notes about common parts of these mollusks as you read this chapter.

WRITE ABOUT IT!

Suppose you were invited on an underwater research voyage to the depths of the vent communities. Describe what you might see, and write a journal entry for the activities of one day in your imaginary deep-sea adventure.

22.1 Flatworms and Roundworms

What you'll learn

IDEAS

- To explain the concept of bilateral symmetry
- To compare the characteristics of flatworms and roundworms

WORDS

bilateral symmetry, pharynx, hydrostatic skeleton

A time-honored relationship

Many flatworms and roundworms are parasites that have coevolved with their specific animal hosts, including humans. The eggs of parasitic flatworms have actually been found in mummified humans from ancient Egypt and other places.

STRUCTURE AND CHARACTERISTICS

A head for symmetry

Flatworms and roundworms are classified in separate phyla. However, the organisms that comprise both phyla share characteristics related to their body plans and nervous systems.

Flatworms and roundworms are bilaterally symmetrical. As you can see in the diagram in *Figure 22.1*, when animals with **bilateral symmetry** are cut longitudinally (lengthwise), the result is right and left mirror images. The word *bilateral* is formed from "bi-," meaning "two," and "lateral," meaning "sides." Animals with bilateral symmetry have an anterior (front) end, a posterior (rear, or tail) end, a ventral (lower, or front) side, and a dorsal (upper, or back) side.

Most organisms with bilateral symmetry, including flatworms and roundworms, have nervous systems that consist of sensory receptors and nerve cells. Ganglia are clusters of nerve tissues. Sensory receptors and ganglia are concentrated at the anterior end of the body. How would the location of these structures benefit an organism?

FIGURE 22.1

Structures of a Planarian

Name some ways that a flatworm's body shape affects its ability to survive.

Bilateral symmetry

Dorsal   Posterior

Anterior   Ventral

Mouth   Nerve chords
Pharynx
Digestive cavity
Eyespot
Ganglia

FIGURE 22.2

Structures of a Roundworm

A roundworm's tubelike digestive system is efficient because food moves in one direction, and foods at different stages of digestion do not mix.

Mouth

Ganglia

Anus

Dorsal nerve

Ventral nerve

Intestine

Flatworms Flatworms are unsegmented and appear flat. They are classified in the phylum Platyhelminthes (plat-ih-HEL-min-theez).

In *Figure* 22.1 you can see a typical flatworm—a planarian. Cilia on a planarian's ventral surface push the animal along on slimelike material that it secretes. A planarian moves to escape predators and to obtain food. Chemical receptors, light-sensitive eyespots, and touch receptors help a planarian navigate through its environment.

A planarian's digestive system includes a single ventral opening in the middle of its body—the mouth—through which food enters and undigested wastes leave. To feed, a planarian extends a muscular tube called the **pharynx** (FAR-inks) through the mouth. The pharynx sucks in food, which then passes into the digestive cavity, where it is broken down and absorbed.

Planarians have an excretory system that consists of small, bulblike structures called flame cells. Flame cells excrete water and chemical wastes. Planarians do not have a circulatory or respiratory system; their flat body structure enables gases to diffuse directly across the skin and to their internal tissues.

Planarians reproduce asexually by regeneration, but they can also reproduce sexually. Planarians are hermaphrodites. As you may recall, hermaphrodites are organisms capable

of producing both eggs and sperm. However, individual planarians cannot fertilize their own eggs. Instead, they exchange sperm with other planarians.

Roundworms Roundworms are members of the phylum Nematoda (NEE-muh-tohd-uh). As you can see in *Figure* 22.2, a very important difference between roundworms and

Observing Roundworms

Many roundworms live in soil. You can observe and examine roundworms when you . . .

Try This

1 Moisten a few teaspoons of soil that you have collected from underneath decaying leaves or near a compost pile. **Caution:** Wear gloves and use care when collecting soil, and wash your hands thoroughly when you are done.
2 Examine a small amount of the soil under a microscope, using low and then high power.
3 Examine the external anatomy of a roundworm. Draw and label what you see.

Analyze Your Results

1 How many roundworms did you observe?
2 Describe the surface of a roundworm.
3 How does the anterior end of the roundworm differ from the posterior end?

FIGURE 22.3

Flatworms and Roundworms

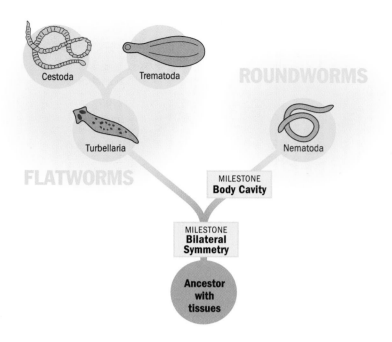

The good host

As embryos, flatworms and roundworms have three layers of tissue—ectoderm, endoderm, and mesoderm. Embryos of cnidarians have only ectoderm and endoderm. These layers develop into various body tissues and organs. For example, the lining of an animal's digestive tract comes from endoderm and an animal's outer body covering comes from ectoderm. The evolution of mesoderm resulted in muscles in flatworms and roundworms.

You may recall from Chapter 21 that a major milestone in animal evolution was the appearance of a body cavity. A body cavity is a fluid-filled space between the digestive tract and the outer body wall. As you can see in *Figure 22.4,* flatworms (and sponges and cnidarians) do not have a body cavity. Roundworms (and most other

flatworms is the presence of a tubelike digestive system with two openings. Food enters a roundworm through its mouth, and wastes leave its body through an anus. How does a digestive system with two openings function differently from a digestive system with one opening?

Another difference between roundworms and flatworms is that roundworms have a hydrostatic skeleton. A **hydrostatic skeleton** includes muscles that surround, and are supported by, a water-filled cavity. Water pressure in the cavity keeps the body firm, like air pressure in a tire. Muscles push against the water-filled cavity to cause movement. The cavity also serves as a circulatory system, carrying materials throughout a roundworm's body.

Unlike flatworms, roundworms only reproduce sexually. Most species of nematodes have separate sexes, and fertilization occurs inside a female's body. Many flatworms and roundworms are parasites with life cycles that require two or more different hosts.

FIGURE 22.4

Cross Sections of an Acoelomate and a Pseudocoelomate

Acoelomate (flatworm)
Why are flatworms classified as acoelomates?

Pseudocoelomate (roundworm)
Why is the body cavity of a roundworm described as false?

animals) have a body cavity.

A "true" body cavity is called a coelom and is completely lined with mesoderm. Organisms without a body cavity, such as flatworms, are called acoelomates. ("A-" means "no.") Organisms with a body cavity that is not completely lined with mesoderm tissue are called pseudo-coelomates. ("Pseudo-" means "false.") Roundworms are pseudocoelomates.

The many thousands of known flatworm species belong to three classes: Turbellaria, Trematoda, and Cestoda. All free-living flatworms belong to the class Turbellaria. Organisms that are free-living can feed and reproduce independently of living hosts. You may remember from Chapter 14 that parasites need living host cells to reproduce. Flatworms that belong to the classes Trematoda and Cestoda are parasitic.

Members of the class Turbellaria live in oceans, lakes, ponds, and moist places on land. A planarian is a typical turbellarian. Most turbellarians range in length from 0.5 to 50 centimeters. Turbellarians are either scavengers that eat dead organic matter or carnivores that prey on small organisms.

Parasitic flatworms called flukes belong to the class Trematoda. Several

structures enable flukes to survive in animal hosts. For example, some flukes have tough, protective body coverings that prevent hosts from digesting them. Other flukes have hooks that help them attach to their hosts. Still other flukes have suckers, which they use to attach to a host or to ingest a host's cells and body fluids.

Most flukes have life cycles that involve two to four different hosts. Blood flukes belong to the genus *Schistosoma*. In humans a blood fluke can cause a serious disease called schistosomiasis (shis-toh-soh-MY-uh-sis), which is characterized by allergic responses, swelling, ulcers, and liver damage.

Parasitic flatworms are widespread in human populations living with substandard or nonexistent sewage

Kingdom: Animalia
Phylum: Platyhelminthes
Three classes:
Turbellaria
Trematoda
Cestoda

FIGURE 22.5
This colorful marine flatworm (*Pseudoceros zebra*) is a free-living member of the class Turbellaria. How can you identify its anterior end?

LAB ZONE — Think About It!

Solving a Reproduction Puzzle

A common New Zealand freshwater snail is host to a parasitic flatworm belonging to the class Trematode. In lakes where this flatworm is rare, snails commonly reproduce asexually. In lakes with large populations of this trematode, however, snails most often reproduce sexually.

Analyzing the Data

1 Propose a hypothesis to explain these findings.
2 How would you go about testing your hypothesis?

Kingdom:	Animalia
Phylum:	Nematoda

Two classes:
Adenophorea
Secernentea

FIGURE 22.7
Notice the scolex of this tapeworm. The scolex is a specialized attachment structure equipped with hooks and suckers.

FIGURE 22.8
Hookworms are parasitic roundworms (phylum Nematoda) that infect humans and other animals. Notice the highly adapted mouth on the hookworm in this photograph. How do you suppose these parasites came to be called hookworms?

systems. Human feces contaminate water supplies, and poor sanitary practices may allow worm larvae on unwashed hands to contaminate food.

Tapeworms are members of the class Cestoda. Like many trematodes, tapeworms live in the digestive tracts of their hosts. They have neither a mouth nor a digestive system. To obtain food, they absorb nutrients through their body walls. Tapeworms do have an excretory and a nervous system, as well as a highly developed reproductive system.

The life cycles of tapeworms include at least two different hosts, such as cattle and humans. Tapeworm eggs are consumed by beef cattle if the eggs are on the grass the cattle eat. Inside the cattle's digestive system, the eggs hatch into larvae that bore into intestinal blood vessels. The larvae travel in the blood to the muscles of the cattle, where they form cysts. Thorough cooking of beef kills

tapeworm cysts. However, when a human eats undercooked, infected beef, the larvae are released in the person's intestine. There they develop and grow into tapeworms like the one shown in *Figure* 22.7. Tapeworms shed proglottids—body segments containing a complete reproductive system—full of eggs. The proglottids pass out of the human host with feces, continuing the life cycle.

Roundworms, or nematodes, live in all of Earth's climate regions. In a single shovelful of topsoil, you might find a million nematodes. The round-ended, unsegmented bodies of nematodes clearly distinguish them from other worms. They range in length from 1 millimeter to about 1 meter. Some scientists estimate that more than one million species of nematodes exist. Most are free-living and harmless, but some are parasitic.

A roundworm called *Ascaris* is a common human parasite. Humans become infected with *Ascaris* if they eat food or drink water that is contaminated with *Ascaris* eggs. The roundworms that develop from these eggs grow in the small intestine, where they may cause intestinal blockage.

IN THE BIOSPHERE

Just a fluke of nature

Flatworm and roundworm parasites significantly impact human populations. Blood and liver flukes, in particular, infect millions of people around the world. Although fluke infections in humans are rarely fatal, they can be debilitating. Flukes are often resistant to drugs, so instead of working on new drugs, scientists are trying to control these parasites by interrupting their life cycle in the alternate host or in the free-swimming larval stages. In some cases, the alternate host can be eliminated from certain bodies of water. In other cases, a body of water can be treated to kill the free-swimming larvae.

Mosquitoes can spread some parasitic roundworms called filariae. Filariae can invade the human lymphatic system, which is part of the circulatory system. Filariae may become so numerous that they block lymph vessels, causing swelling. *Figure 22.9* shows the swollen leg of a person with elephantiasis, a disease caused by filariae.

Some roundworms cause serious diseases in livestock, pets, and crops. Agricultural losses from parasitic nematodes can amount to billions of dollars each year.

Certain situations increase the chance of infection by parasitic flatworms and roundworms. For example, eating undercooked beef, pork, or fish that is infected with tapeworm cysts can cause infections in humans. Inadequate sanitation conditions and unhealthy drinking water allow many parasites to spread among human hosts. It is estimated that roundworm parasites alone infect more than one billion humans worldwide. In addition to *Ascaris*, roundworm parasites that commonly infect humans include hookworms and pinworms, which are both spread by fecal contamination.

In contrast to parasitic worms, free-living flatworms and roundworms tend to be beneficial. They decompose organic matter and help recycle nutrients. Some free-living nematodes prey on tiny organisms that cause plant diseases. Scientists are exploring one species of roundworm that may control mosquito populations.

Filaria

FIGURE 22.9
When filariae clog lymph vessels, severe swelling can occur, as in the patient pictured above. At left you can see a filaria found in a blood sample.

Medical and pharmaceutical researchers are interested in enzymes and other types of proteins secreted by some roundworms. For example, hookworms secrete a protein that prevents blood from clotting. After further testing, this protein may be used to treat dangerous blood clots.

CHECKPOINT 22.1

1. Explain the concept of bilateral symmetry, and give one example of an object or organism with bilateral symmetry.
2. Compare and contrast the characteristics of flatworms and roundworms.
3. **Critical Thinking** Why would it be a disadvantage for parasitic worms to kill their hosts?

Build on What You Know
4. List some fundamental differences between flatworms and cnidarians. *(Need to jog your memory? Revisit relevant concepts in Chapter 21, Section 21.4.)*

EVERYDAY BIOLOGY

Protect Your Pet

Did you know that pets can get worms from insect bites? Fleas carry tapeworm larvae and transmit them when they bite your dog or cat. To protect your pet from parasites, keep it free of fleas.

What characteristics do flatworms and roundworms share?

22.2 Mollusks

What you'll learn

IDEAS

- To describe the characteristics of mollusks
- To distinguish among the four classes of mollusks

WORDS

mantle, coelom, closed circulatory system

Have you ever seen a slug race? In Elma, Washington, where banana slugs are abundant, slug races are a highlight of the Elma Slug Festival. Training for the big race may include a special vegetarian diet and trial workouts. A "fast" winner takes about 43 seconds to go 0.003 furlongs at 0.055 kilometers per hour (0.034 miles per hour)—not too sluggish for a slug.

CHARACTERISTICS OF MOLLUSKS

Soft and squishy?

What do snails, slugs, scallops, and squids have in common? They are all mollusks. Although mollusks differ in appearance, they share important structural characteristics. Mollusks have a soft body that may be protected by a hard shell. Some mollusks, such as snails, have a single shell. Other mollusks, such as clams, have a two-piece shell. Squids and slugs have a light internal shell, and octopuses have no shell at all.

With or without a shell, all mollusks have a structure called a mantle—one of their three common characteristics. The **mantle** is the soft outer tissue layer on mollusks. In most mollusk species, the mantle produces a protective shell. An internal chamber—the mantle cavity—forms between the mantle and underlying

tissues. The mantle cavity houses a mollusk's respiratory structures.

A second characteristic common to all mollusks is a muscular foot that is used for locomotion or attachment. In *Figure 22.10,* you can see two types of muscular foot.

Between the mollusk's foot and mantle is the visceral mass—the third structural characteristic of all mollusks. The visceral mass contains most of the mollusk's internal organs, such as the heart, gonads, and stomach.

Most—but not all—mollusks share a fourth characteristic: an open circulatory system. In this type of system, blood is enclosed in vessels in some places, but flows freely over body tissues in other places. A heart pumps blood into vessels that are open-ended. The blood flows out of the vessels and bathes the body organs. It then drains into small vessels, which carry it to the respiratory structures. These structures include the gills in the mantle cavity of aquatic mollusks and the lunglike mantle cavity of terrestrial mollusks. Gas exchange occurs in the respiratory structures as water or air moves over them. From the respiratory structures, blood moves back into the heart.

Clam foot

Squid foot

FIGURE 22.10

A clam's spade-like foot digs the clam into mud. A squid's modified foot is in the form of tentacles used to capture prey.

Mollusks can move in a variety of ways. For example, clams burrow by using their foot as a shovel and a wedge. Snails "slide" on the mucus secreted by their foot. Squids and octopuses move by taking in water and then forcefully expelling it. A few mollusks, such as oysters and mussels, are sessile as adults.

Like roundworms, all mollusks have a digestive tract with two openings and specialized regions. In some mollusks, the digestive tract is a straight tube. In other mollusks, the digestive tract is coiled. A coiled intestine increases the length of the digestive tract and enables the animal to digest and absorb more nutrients.

Mollusks have evolved many methods of obtaining food. Most sessile and slow-moving mollusks are filter feeders. Filter feeders draw water into their mantle cavity, filtering bits of food from the water. Some mollusks, such as snails, are herbivores with special mouthparts adapted to gather vegetation or algae. Predatory mollusks, such as squids and octopuses, use their beaklike jaws to capture prey.

Some mollusks have simple nervous systems and lack true sense organs. Octopuses, however, have a complex nervous system, which includes a brain, eyes, and other sense organs.

Most mollusks have separate sexes, and all mollusks reproduce sexually. Reproduction in mollusks can involve external fertilization, as in clams, or internal fertilization, as in squids and some snails. External fertilization can

FIGURE 22.11

Structures of a Mollusk

No single organism is truly representative of mollusks because this phylum is so diverse. The snail pictured here illustrates some characteristics common to all mollusks.

Respiratory tissue

Shell

Visceral mass
The body organs—heart, gonads, and stomach—comprise the visceral mass.

Heart

Gonads

Stomach

Eyes

Mantle cavity

Mantle
The mantle is composed of soft tissue that drapes over the internal body organs, creating a space called the mantle cavity.

Foot
Mucus secreted from the broad, flat foot provides a layer of slime on which the snail can glide.

Kingdom: Animalia
Phylum: Mollusca
Four classes:
Polyplacophora
Gastropoda
Bivalvia
Cephalopoda

FIGURE 22.12

Phylum Mollusca

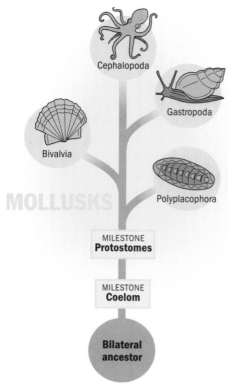

From sea to desert

Mollusks are an ancient group of organisms that have adapted to almost every environment on Earth. With more than 100,000 species, mollusks are the second largest animal phylum.

Mollusks are descendants of the first animals to evolve with a coelom. A **coelom** (SEE-lum) is a body cavity completely lined with mesoderm. Animals with a coelom are called coelomates. A cross section of a coelomate is illustrated in *Figure 22.13*.

Recall from Chapter 21 that a major milestone in animal evolution involves different embryonic development patterns. Different patterns produce protostomes and deuterostomes. You will learn about these development patterns in Chapter 24. Mollusks are protostomes.

Scientists classify mollusks by their shell type, foot structure, and internal body arrangement. Of the seven mollusk classes currently recognized, four contain the most familiar mollusks.

Polyplacophora Chitons, which belong to the class Polyplacophora (poly-plak-oh-FOR-uh), are the most primitive mollusks and probably most closely resemble ancient mollusks. All chiton shells consist of eight overlapping plates, which are used to protect the chiton from predators. Chitons have a broad suction foot. In shallow marine waters, the foot helps chitons cling tightly to rocky surfaces. Using the broad foot for a hold, chitons move slowly across rocks, scraping

FIGURE 22.13

Cross Section of a Coelomate

A true coelom is a body cavity that is completely lined with mesoderm.

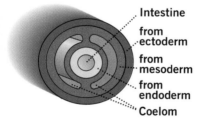

occur when two organisms simultaneously release sperm and eggs into the water, as clams do. In the water, the gametes fuse to form a zygote. Internal fertilization can occur when a male mollusk transfers sperm from his mantle cavity into the mantle cavity of a female mollusk. After fertilization, the female deposits the fertilized eggs in a protected place, where they continue their development.

FIGURE 22.14
These chitons cling tightly to the rock, using their suction-cup-like foot to move and their radula to feed.

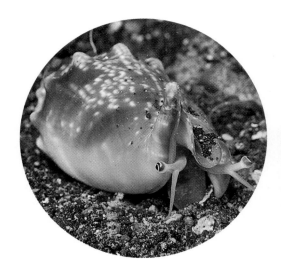

FIGURE 22.15
Some gastropods (left) have shells and others do not. Marine nudibranchs (below) have no shells, but their startling shapes and colors warn predators that they may be poisonous.

algae from the rocks with a tonguelike organ called a radula. A chiton's radula can have as many as 250,000 sharp, tiny, teethlike projections. You can see a close-up of radula in *Figure 22.14*.

Gastropoda This large class includes mollusks with shells, such as snails and conches. Gastropods also include slugs, which lack an external shell. Gastropods have a radula that either scrapes algae or shreds leaves. Their nervous system is more complex than that of chitons, as is their respiratory system. Aquatic gastropods have gills. Terrestrial gastropods have a mantle cavity lining that is modified for gas exchange.

Bivalvia Have you ever eaten a bivalve—a clam, mussel, scallop, or oyster? The word *bivalve* comes from "bi-," meaning "two," and "valvia," meaning "shells." A hinge attaches the two shells of a bivalve. Strong muscles control the opening and closing of the hinged shells, allowing a bivalve to control the flow of water over its body.

Most bivalves are filter feeders. As water containing plankton flows over their gills, mucus produced by the gills traps the plankton. Cilia on the gill cells move the plankton from the gills into the bivalve's mouth. In mollusks and other filter feeders, gills can function in both feeding and respiration.

Although some bivalves live in fresh water, most inhabit marine environments. Bivalves such as clams are slow-moving; others, such as mussels, are sessile.

Eyespots

FIGURE 22.16
Scallops can rapidly open and close their shells, allowing them to move through the water. Their eyespots enable them to see predators.

Nautilus

Squid

Cuttlefish

Octopus

FIGURE 22.17

Shell Evolution in Cephalopods

Beginning with the nautilus, the cephalopods' shells have gradually reduced over time. Squid and cuttlefish have only small, internal shells, and octopuses have entirely lost their shells.

Cephalopoda Cephalopods (SEF-uh-loh-pahdz) include nautiluses, cuttlefishes, squids, and octopuses. Scientists think this group is the most recently evolved class of mollusks. There are four cephalopods shown in *Figure 22.17*. Cephalopods first appeared in the fossil record of about 500 million years ago. The modern cephalopods, such as the octopus, differ little from its ancient ancestor.

Cephalopods have a highly developed nervous system. A large brain and an extensive network of nerves enable cephalopods to respond quickly and control their body motions efficiently. Octopuses are considered to be among the most intelligent invertebrates.

Unlike other mollusks, cephalopods have a **closed circulatory system.**

In a closed circulatory system, blood travels inside a continuous network of vessels. A closed circulatory system provides tissues with a more controlled supply of oxygen and nutrients than does an open circulatory system. The closed circulatory system has probably contributed to the success of cephalopods as fast-moving predators. In a closed circulatory system, the supply of blood to different body parts can be controlled. This system supports the active, predatory lifestyle of cephalopods by more rapidly supplying their muscles with oxygen and nutrient-rich blood.

Some species of squids and octopuses grow very large. The giant squid *Architeuthis* is the world's largest living invertebrate. The largest one measured was longer than 18 meters! Giant squids live in deep waters of the North Atlantic, where their only predators are thought to be sperm whales.

FIGURE 22.18

The cuttlefish (left) has remarkable color-changing abilities, blending with the background or contrasting with it when excited or threatened. The octopus (below) has a large brain and versatile tentacles that make it a fearsome predator.

MOLLUSKS IN THE BIOSPHERE

Put a foot in your mouth

Many mollusks—such as clams, oysters, mussels, scallops, snails, squids, and octopuses—are valued as food in many cultures. Humans even eat chitons and sea slugs. Mollusks also have a role in other food chains—either as predators or prey.

In addition to being a food source, mollusks are used to monitor environmental conditions. Filter-feeding mollusks concentrate pollutants in their tissues, which scientists can analyze to determine water purity. Some mollusks, including sea slugs, are also being investigated as potential sources of medicines.

Mollusks are not always beneficial, however. Snails and slugs consume crops, costing farmers millions of dollars annually. Marine mollusks called shipworms destroy boats and docks constructed of wood.

ENVIRONMENTAL AWARENESS

Mussels on the move

In 1988 a small freshwater species of zebra mussel was accidentally introduced into Lake Erie from Europe. Less than ten years later the mollusks had spread into all the Great Lakes and their tributaries. These rapidly reproducing mussels compete with other species for food. They also clog water-intake pipes, causing major problems for water-treatment and power plants. They have even clogged farm-irrigation pipes miles inland.

In order to stop the spread of zebra mussels into other lakes and streams, county extension services distribute information to people who use mussel-infested waters for industry or recreation. Boaters and anglers are reminded not to carry water from one lake or stream to another. The larval stage of the mussel is microscopic and can live undetected for days in bilges and bait buckets. Although natural predators of zebra mussels exist in Europe, none has been identified in North America. Most states east of the Mississippi River are gearing up for an "invasion" of these pests, and researchers are feverishly investigating ways to control them.

The spread of zebra mussels has had one benefit, however. Where zebra mussels have heavily colonized cloudy Great Lakes waters, their filter-feeding action has made the water clearer.

CHECKPOINT 22.2

1. Describe the main structures of mollusks. How can they vary?
2. Compare the four classes of mollusks.
3. **Critical Thinking** In addition to being transported by boaters and anglers, how might zebra mussels spread to new environments?

Build on What You Know

4. How is filter feeding in mollusks similar to the way sponges gather food? **(Need to jog your memory? Revisit relevant concepts in Chapter 21, Section 21.2.)**

FIGURE 22.19
Zebra mussels reproduce rapidly, settling on any available hard surface, including one another. Treatments to kill the mussels that have settled in pipes do not necessarily remove them. What are some ways engineers might deal with this problem?

What characteristics are common to all mollusks?

22.3 Segmented Worms

What you'll learn

IDEAS
• To identify the characteristics of segmented worms
• To compare and contrast the three classes of segmented worms

WORDS
annelids, setae, nephridia, parapodia

That's a lot of worms!
More than a century ago, Charles Darwin estimated that one acre of British farmland contained about 50,000 earthworms, which ingested up to 18 tons of soil in a year! More recently, when biologists compared the weight of worms and of cattle supported by an acre of pasture, the worms won out—they weighed more!

CHARACTERISTICS OF SEGMENTED WORMS

Not just for fishing

Earthworms, leeches, and other wormlike animals whose bodies are divided into segments are called **annelids** (phylum Annelida). Three common annelids are shown in *Figure* 22.20. You can see the structures of an earthworm, a familiar annelid, in *Figure* 22.21.

Annelids are true coelomates. As you may recall, coelomates have body cavities completely lined with mesoderm. Muscles and fluid in the coelom act as a hydrostatic skeleton. The muscles run both lengthwise and around the annelid's body. They contract against the firm wall of the coelom, moving the annelid.

Annelids also have external structures for movement. Earthworms move by using small bristles called

FIGURE 22.20

Typical Annelids

Annelids are wormlike animals with segmented bodies. A worm from each class of annelid is shown here. Notice that segmentation is clearly visible in each one.

setae (SEE-tay), which are located on the ventral side of each segment.

Another characteristic of annelids is a well-developed nervous system. The annelid nervous system typically consists of a small brain that extends into a solid nerve cord running along the ventral side of the worm.

Many annelids have specialized sense organs. Earthworms have receptors in their skin that are sensitive to light, temperature, moisture, vibrations, and chemicals. Light receptors are concentrated in the earthworm's anterior and posterior regions. How does the location of these receptors benefit the earthworm?

Annelids also have specialized structures for the removal of wastes. In earthworms, wastes from cellular metabolism are excreted through tubes called **nephridia** (nih-FRID-ee-uh). Earthworms have two nephridia (singular: *nephridium*) in each of their segments. One end of a nephridium opens into the coelom, and the other end opens to the outside. Water and wastes from the coelom enter the coiled tubules of the nephridia. There water is absorbed by the surrounding blood vessels, and wastes pass out of the body.

Annelids lack respiratory structures. Instead, gas exchange takes place by diffusion across a worm's skin. Gases must dissolve in water before diffusion can take place. The moisture that covers an annelid's skin provides the needed water. In earthworms, a cuticle that surrounds the skin slows down evaporation, while mucous secretions keep the skin moist.

You can locate these structures and the roles they play in annelids' systems, in *Figure* 22.21.

Although annelids can reproduce asexually by regeneration, they usually reproduce sexually. Some annelids have separate sexes, but most are hermaphroditic: They have both male and female reproductive systems. However,

annelids do not fertilize their own eggs. *Figure* 22.22 shows two earthworms joining to exchange sperm. Each worm stores the donated sperm inside a small internal pouch. After separating, the worm secretes a band of mucus that forms a cocoon around its body. When the worm slips out of the cocoon, it releases its own eggs and its mate's sperm into the cocoon, where fertilization occurs. Young worms hatch from the cocoon in two to three weeks.

FIGURE 22.21

Systems of an Annelid

All earthworm segments, except the first three head segments and the last tail segment, contain two nephridia and four pairs of setae. The digestive, circulatory, and nervous systems run the length of the body.

Digestion

The earthworm's digestive tract has two openings. Soil enters the pharynx through the mouth and passes into the crop for storage. The gizzard grinds the food into small pieces, which are digested as they pass through the intestine.

Circulation

An earthworm's closed circulatory system is a continuous network of vessels. Contractions of the dorsal blood vessels send blood to five muscular aortic arches and then to the ventral vessel, which carries blood to the posterior end of the body. Ring vessels in each segment connect the ventral vessel to the dorsal vessel.

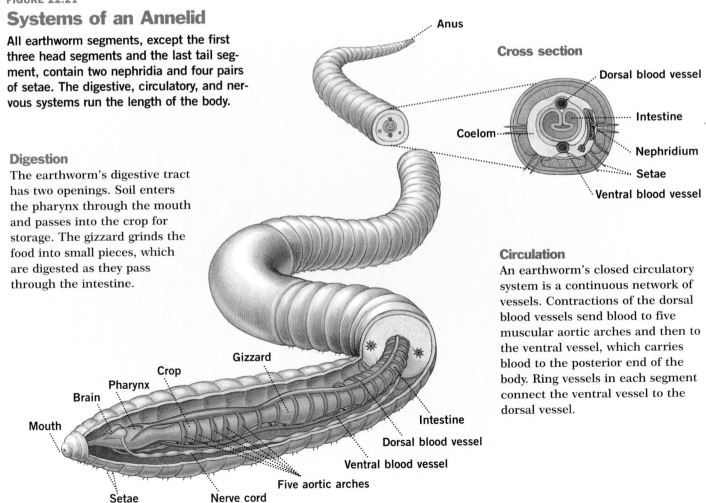

Anus

Cross section

Dorsal blood vessel

Intestine

Coelom

Nephridium

Setae

Ventral blood vessel

Gizzard

Crop

Pharynx

Brain

Mouth

Intestine

Dorsal blood vessel

Ventral blood vessel

Five aortic arches

Setae

Nerve cord

FIGURE 22.23

A leech loops its body as it moves across a solid surface. It makes a loop by holding on with one end and moving with the other end. How does this type of movement compare with an earthworm's movement?

ORIGIN AND DIVERSITY OF SEGMENTED WORMS

Wormy ways

Because annelids and mollusks have similar patterns of early tissue development, scientists think they share a common ancestor. Like mollusks, annelids are coelomates and protostomes, and most have a ciliated larval form called a trochophore (TROK-oh-for). Both annelids and mollusks have body plans with distinct regions, but in annelids these regions are separated by tissue to form true segments. Segmentation is common in many animal phyla—from insects to humans.

Polychaeta The largest class of annelids includes the polychaetes (POL-ih-keets), which are mostly free-living or tube-dwelling marine worms like the ones you see in the photograph on page 522-523. All polychaetes have a pair of paddlelike structures on most body segments. The structures are

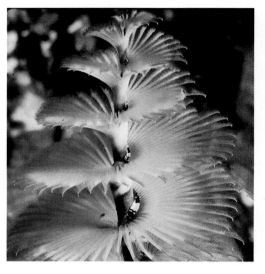

FIGURE 22.25

This tube-dwelling polychaete has feathery appendages on its head to trap food particles in the water.

called **parapodia**—from "para" meaning "almost," and "podia" meaning "feet." Parapodia are used for locomotion, for anchoring the worm's body, and for increasing the surface across which gases are exchanged. Bundles of setae usually extend from the parapodia.

Polychaetes have a distinct head that contains organs for sensing the environment and mouthparts for feeding. Some tube-dwelling polychaetes such as the one shown in *Figure 22.25* have feathery tentacles that trap food particles and provide additional surface area for respiration.

Oligochaeta This class includes earthworms and other terrestrial worms, as well as some marine and freshwater oligochaetes (OL-ih-goh-keets). These worms do not have parapodia or specialized sense organs. Some oligochaetes reach a remarkable size. For example, giant Australian earthworms can grow to more than three meters in length.

Kingdom: Animalia

Phylum: Annelida

Three classes:
Polychaeta
Oligochaeta
Hirudinea

FIGURE 22.24

Phylum Annelida

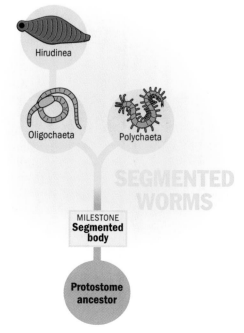

Hirudinea

Oligochaeta

Polychaeta

SEGMENTED WORMS

MILESTONE
Segmented body

Protostome ancestor

Hirudinea Hirudineates (hi-ROO-dih-neets) are the leeches. They are the only annelids without setae or parapodia. Most leeches live in fresh water or moist tropical areas. Some are scavengers or predators, but most are blood-sucking external parasites.

Groups of segments at both ends of a leech are modified to form suckers. A leech uses the suckers to move and to attach to its host as it feeds. The leech's anterior sucker is armed with teeth that clamp onto the surface of the host. After injecting an anesthetizing substance that numbs the site, the leech breaks through the host's skin and secretes an anticlotting chemical into the wound. The leech then sucks as much blood as it can—sometimes more than ten times its own weight. After feeding, it drops off its host.

SEGMENTED WORMS IN THE BIOSPHERE

Rx for crops and clots

Annelids are important components of the marine food chain. Many fish feed on annelids—in fact they are a favorite bait of anglers. Planktonic annelid larvae also provide food for filter-feeding animals. Earthworms and other terrestrial annelids are eaten by birds, frogs, snakes, and many other small animals.

Earthworms also play an essential role in plant growth. As they burrow in the soil, they allow air and water to penetrate and make it easier for plant roots to spread. By breaking down large pieces of organic matter, earthworms also increase the nutrients

available to plants. Earthworms are essential for high crop yields.

For centuries, leeches were used by physicians for "blood letting," which was thought to remove bad blood and spirits from the body. Although that medical practice fell into disfavor for many years, modern medical researchers continue to study the painkilling and anticlotting chemicals in leech saliva. In fact, "medicinal leeches" are now used to remove clotted blood from badly bruised areas and to keep blood circulating around serious wounds that do not heal easily.

CHECKPOINT 22.3

1. What characteristics are common to segmented worms?
2. Compare and contrast the three classes of annelids.
3. **Critical Thinking** Why do you often see more earthworms after it rains?

Build on What You Know

4. Diagram the proposed evolutionary relationship that exists among sponges, cnidarians, flatworms and roundworms, mollusks, and annelids. *(Need to jog your memory? Revisit relevant concepts in Chapter 21, Section 21.1.)*

IN THE COMMUNITY

Worms for Profit

Worm farms exist, believe it or not! Find out if there is a worm farm in your community. Worms are sold to anglers for bait, to gardeners for compost piles and gardens, and to pet shops and owners of exotic animals for pet food. Look in the yellow pages of your telephone directory under "bait shops" and contact your local fishing and pet stores to see if such a farm is located in your area. Find out how the worms are sold and priced. Log on to: http://invertebrates.biosurf.com to find out more about worms.

FIGURE 22.26
Leeches can be used to treat serious bruises and stimulate blood circulation in tiny blood vessels. After certain types of surgery, doctors sometimes use leeches to remove tiny blood clots and keep blood flowing in a traumatized area.

What characteristic do all annelids have in common?

Observing Earthworms

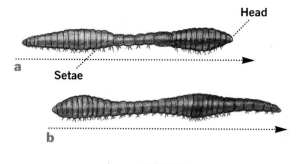

WHAT YOU WILL DO Observe earthworms, studying their movement and their response to light

SKILLS YOU WILL USE Observing, collecting and recording data, designing an experiment

WHAT YOU WILL NEED Live earthworms, moist soil, microscope, glass pan, flashlight

The forward movement of an earthworm is shown above (from a to c).

Make Some General Observations

Gently place one earthworm on a clean piece of paper and observe it. Notice its external structure and record what you see. Observe how the earthworm moves and describe this type of movement. As you write your description, explain how the internal structures allow the earthworm to move the way it does.
Caution: Handle all living organisms carefully and respectfully.

Propose a Hypothesis

Now that you have observed earthworms closely, you will find out if they react to an external stimulus such as light, sound, temperature, or vibration. Propose a hypothesis that states what will happen when earthworms are exposed to an external stimulus you have selected.

Conduct Your Experiment

1 Place the earthworms in the moist soil in the glass pan. Observe them and record the type and level of activity they exhibit.

2 Choose a stimulus. Expose the earthworms to the stimulus for several minutes and record the type and level of activity they exhibit.

Analyze Your Data

1 What changes in activity, if any, did the earthworms demonstrate after the stimulus?
2 Did all of the earthworms react the same way?

Draw Conclusions

1 Do you think you can apply your results to earthworms' activity in their natural environment? Why or why not?
2 Do you think there is a link between the earthworm behaviors you observed and their survival? Explain.

Design a Related Experiment

Suppose you want to find out how earthworms react to a new stimulus. Propose a hypothesis, and design an experiment to test it.

Lab: Observing Earthworms

Objective: To study the movement of earthworms and their response to light.
My earthworm was 12 centimeters long when it was resting or not moving. I made five measurements of it when it was actively moving and averaged them to find out...

Chapter 22 Review

22.1 Flatworms and roundworms have bilateral symmetry and specialized tissues.
22.2 Mollusks share a common body plan that includes a muscular foot, a visceral mass, and a mantle.
22.3 Annelids are wormlike animals with a segmented body.

Sum It Up

Use the following summary to review the main concepts in this chapter.

22.1 Flatworms and Roundworms

- Flatworms and roundworms have a body that is bilaterally symmetrical, with a nervous system concentrated at the anterior end.
- Flatworms are flat and unsegmented acoelomates. They have a single opening for feeding and excretion, and no circulatory or respiratory system. They reproduce both asexually and sexually.
- Of the three classes of flatworms, one includes free-living flatworms, and two include parasitic worms.
- Roundworms have a pseudocoelom and a tubelike digestive system with a mouth and an anus. They reproduce sexually.
- Some roundworms are free-living; others are parasitic.

22.2 Mollusks

- All mollusks have a mantle, a muscular foot, and a mass of internal organs in a mesoderm-lined body cavity or coelom. Some mollusks also have a hard protective shell.

- All mollusks have respiratory organs and a tubelike digestive tract with two openings. Most have an open circulatory system. All mollusks reproduce sexually.
- Mollusks are members of the second-largest animal phylum. They range from organisms that appear similar to their fossil ancestors to organisms with highly developed nervous systems and closed circulatory systems.

22.3 Segmented Worms

- These worms have a body with most segments identical; there are setae on each body segment.
- Segmented worms have true body cavities or coelom. They have internal and external structures for locomotion, but no specialized respiratory structures.
- Segmented worms have a well-developed nervous system, excretory organs, and a closed circulatory system. Their common form of reproduction is sexual.
- Segmented worms include marine and terrestrial worms, as well as parasitic leeches.

Use Terms and Concepts

Use each of the following words or terms in a complete sentence. If you need to review a meaning, turn to the page indicated.

bilateral symmetry (p. 524)
pharynx (p. 525)
hydrostatic skeleton (p. 526)

mantle (p. 530)
coelom (p. 532)
closed circulatory system (p. 534)

annelids (p. 536)
setae (p. 536)
nephridia (p. 536)
parapodia (p. 538)

Use Your Word Power

COMPLETION **Write the word or phrase that best completes each statement.**

1. The roundworm's _____ includes muscles and a water-filled cavity.

2. A(n) _____ is composed of a continuous network of blood vessels.

3. The soft outer tissue layer of mollusks is called the _____ .

4. Earthworms use external _____ for movement.

5. A(n) _____ is a body cavity completely lined with mesoderm tissue.

6. Wormlike _____ have bodies that are divided into segments.

TRUE-FALSE **Write true if the statement is true. If the statement is false, replace the underlined word(s) to make it true.**

7. Gastropods such as snails and slugs have a <u>closed</u> circulatory system.

8. In animals with <u>bilateral symmetry</u>, body parts are organized around a central plane.

9. When a planarian feeds, it extends its <u>mantle</u> through its ventral opening.

10. Marine worms use paddle-like structures called <u>parapodia</u> for locomotion.

11. The <u>setae</u> that earthworms use for waste removal are paired in each segment.

Show What You Know

12. Compare the planarian's structures for movement with those of a nematode.

13. Explain why the development of a coelom is an important evolutionary milestone.

14. How is the flatness of a planarian's body related to its lack of a circulatory or respiratory system?

15. What is the advantage of a closed circulatory system to certain mollusks such as the cephalopods?

16. **Make a Concept Map** Make a concept map to relate the structures and characteristics of worms and mollusks. Include the following terms: coelomate, annelid, acoelomate, flatworm, mollusks, pseudocoelom, roundworm, segmentation.

Take It Further

17. **Identifying Cause and Effect** From the piles of shells left behind, archaeologists can infer that mollusks (clams) were a primary food source for many Native Americans. There are far fewer edible mollusks available to modern consumers. Suggest two possible explanations for the decrease in mollusk populations.

18. **Analyzing Data** Quahogs can develop at temperatures from 15°C to 32°C, but the optimum growth occurs at 25°C to 29°C. The salinity range for development is 17 to 35 parts per thousand (ppt), with optimal growth in the range of 22 to 32 ppt. Make a graph that shows these temperature and salinity ranges, and then answer the following question: Which of the following groups of quahogs is likely to grow best—Group W, at 18°C and 18 ppt salinity; Group X, at 22°C and 22 ppt salinity; Group Y, at 26°C and 26 ppt salinity; or Group Z, at 32°C and 32 ppt salinity? Explain your answer.

19. **Designing an Experiment** Nematodes, which are by far the most numerous animals on Earth, can be found in a wide range of environments. Design an experiment to show relative numbers of nematodes present in a gram of soil, a gram of pond water, and a gram of sand. Propose a hypothesis about which habitat will contain the largest number of nematodes.

20. Developing a Hypothesis Even though all planarians and some annelids are hermaphroditic, they do not fertilize their own eggs. Suggest a possible explanation for this.

21. Interpreting a Graph In Georgia the minimum marketable size for clams is 44 millimeters (mm). According to the graph below, about how many years does it take newly seeded clams to reach marketable size? What generalizations can you make about clam growth from the graph? How much did clams grow per year, on average, in the first 5 years? How much in the second 5 years?

Clam Shell Growth Over Time in Georgia

23. Preventive Pipe Cleaning Zebra mussels that attach themselves to industrial and agricultural water-intake pipes tend to remain attached even after they die. Flooding the pipes periodically with pesticides is one way to prevent the zebra mussels from getting a foothold in the pipes. What drawbacks are there to the use of pesticides to control zebra mussels? Think of an alternate approach that has fewer harmful side effects.

Make New Connections

24. Biology and Physics Newton's Third Law of Motion states that for every action there is an equal and opposite reaction. Using this law of physics, compare the motion of a rocket with that of a squid.

25. Biology and Literature In the Howard Pyle classic *The Merry Adventures of Robin Hood*, there is a description of the death of Robin Hood. Explain how the circumstances of Robin Hood's death are related to the topics in Chapter 22.

26. Biology and Farming Some farmers raise mollusks such as clams, oysters, and mussels. Prepare a research report on the resources needed to raise and harvest mollusks. Share your report with the class.

Consider the Issues

22. Fighting Parasites Debilitating diseases caused by parasites are widespread in certain tropical countries. The problem can be addressed by (1) building modern sewage treatment systems; (2) providing drug therapy to those who contract the diseases; and (3) educating the population about ways to avoid infection. Which of these methods do you think would be most effective overall? Which might be most cost-efficient? How could you measure effectiveness and cost-efficiency?

FAST-FORWARD TO CHAPTER 23

Mollusks belong to the second-largest animal phylum. In Chapter 23 you will study the largest and most diverse animal phylum—the arthropods. You will discover what scorpions, spiders, bees, and fleas have in common.

CHAPTER 23
Arthropods

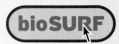

You can find out more about arthropods by exploring the following Internet address:
http://invertebrates.biosurf.com

In this chapter . . .

FEATURES

Everyday Biology
- Silk Stops Bullet
- No Stinger, Less Pain

In the Community
Insect Control?

 Frontiers in Biology
Pesticide Alternatives

LAB ZONES

Discover It!
- Looking Under a Rock

Do It!
- Look at Those Sensors!

Think About It!
- Identifying Insect Camouflage and Mimicry

Investigate It!
- Observing the Mealworm Life Cycle

MONARCHS
FLY MORE THAN 2000 MILES

One of the most spectacular animal migrations occurs each fall, when vast swarms of monarch butterflies leave the United States for the winter. For years no one knew where the monarchs actually went, but in the mid-1970s their winter hiding place was discovered in a stretch of highlands just west of Mexico City. There, in warmer temperatures, the butterflies roost—as many as 4 million per acre—covering the trees with brilliant blankets of color.

During this amazing odyssey, several generations of the monarchs are born, breed, and die before a generation reaches the Mexican mountains—as far as 2200 miles from the departure point. The same is true during the monarchs' return migration from Mexico in the spring, when some of the butterflies travel as far north as Canada.

How do monarch butterflies that have never been to the roosting sites in Mexico find their way there each year? This is one of many mysteries that scientists seek to unlock as they study arthropods.

Looking Under a Rock

You need some small boxes or jars in which to collect your specimens

1. Find at least three large flat rocks or decaying logs. Turn them over and collect a representative sample of the organisms living there. Identify as many as you can. Then return the specimens where you found them, and replace the logs or stones. Caution: Some organisms bite and may be poisonous.
2. Repeat step 1 in a different environment. Environments to sample may include a stream, the woods, a field or pasture, a stone wall, a woodpile, desert areas, or city parks.
3. Compare your results with those of your classmates. How many different environments did you and your classmates sample? How many different organisms did you all find?

Arthropods are present in just about every environment. If you chose two sufficiently different environments to investigate, you should have found a different group of organisms in each.

WRITE ABOUT IT!

In your journal, write a story from the perspective of one of the insects you collected.

23.1 Arthropods

What you'll learn

IDEAS
- To describe the characteristics of arthropods
- To compare the three arthropod subphyla

WORDS
exoskeleton, endoskeleton, compound eyes

World-class weight lifter
The rhinoceros beetle—able to carry up to 100 times its own weight—is a model of biomechanical efficiency. Because it can tote over 200 grams on its 2-gram frame, it is, gram for gram, the world's strongest animal. Researchers are studying the beetle's muscles and skeleton to try to explain its mighty strength.

CHARACTERISTICS OF ARTHROPODS

Bend a leg

The phylum Arthropoda is the largest and most diverse animal phylum. Arthropods inhabit every region of Earth—from ocean bottoms to mountain tops. Spiders, crabs, scorpions, and lobsters; bees, beetles, caterpillars, and fleas; ticks, mites, and lice are all arthropods. Why are such different organisms classified together?

All arthropods share certain structural characteristics. Like annelids, arthropods have segmented bodies. But in most arthropods, the segments are fused into larger body regions.

Unlike annelids, arthropods have jointed appendages. (In fact, the word *arthropoda* means "jointed feet.") The jointed appendages of arthropods are specialized for sensing, eating, reproducing, defending, or moving.

In addition to a segmented body with jointed appendages, arthropods have an exoskeleton made of chitin. An **exoskeleton** is a hard covering on the outside of the body, which provides both support and protection. The muscles that move the appendages of arthropods are attached to the inside of the exoskeleton. In contrast, humans and other vertebrates have an endoskeleton. An **endoskeleton** is a framework of bones and cartilage on the inside of the body. Exoskeletons provide greater protection for the body than do endoskeletons.

Although an exoskeleton provides protection, it limits the size of the organism. To grow, arthropods must shed their exoskeletons periodically in a process called molting. When an arthropod molts, it grows a new layer of chitin beneath its exoskeleton. Then it forces fluid between the new layer of chitin and its old exoskeleton. The pressure from the fluid splits the old exoskeleton, and the arthropod crawls

FIGURE 23.1
Arthropods have specialized jointed appendages. Notice the differences between the three pairs of legs on this praying mantis. How is the first pair of legs adapted to a predatory lifestyle?

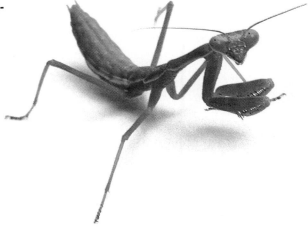

out. In *Figure 23.2,* you can see an arthropod that has just molted. At first, its new exoskeleton is tough, but soft and flexible. Eventually it hardens. The hardening process can take from minutes to days, depending on the species. During and immediately after molting, arthropods are highly vulnerable to injury and predation.

Along with specialized jointed appendages, arthropods have evolved a complex muscular system. This system is more extensive than the circular and longitudinal muscles that are common to the invertebrates discussed earlier. This extensive muscular system enables the arthropod to perform a great variety of movements.

The arthropod nervous system consists of a ventral nerve cord and brain. In each body segment, the nerve cord swells into additional ganglia (nerve cell clusters). Nerve impulses are transmitted to and from the body parts through these ganglia.

You may recall that most mollusks have an open circulatory system, in which blood flows through open-ended vessels and bathes the body tissues directly. Arthropods also have an open circulatory system.

Aquatic arthropods, such as crabs, have external gills for respiration. Terrestrial arthropods, such as insects, have tracheal tubes—chitin-lined channels—where the exchange of oxygen and carbon dioxide occurs.

Many arthropods have **compound eyes**—multifaceted eyes with many separate lenses that work together to form a single, mosaic image. In a compound eye, such as that of the horsefly shown in *Figure 23.3,* each lens sees a slightly different part of an object. It is possible that the image of the object is not in focus, but its motion and color are clearly sensed. Not all arthropods have compound eyes. Many, such as spiders, have single-lens eyes. Some arthropods, such as horseshoe crabs, have both types of eyes.

ORIGIN AND DIVERSITY

From trilobites to insect bites

Trilobites are an extinct group of arthropods that scientists think were the first arthropods to evolve. This group of organisms thrived on Earth about 600 million years ago. More than 4000 species of trilobites have been identified from the fossil record. Like all arthropods, trilobites had segmented bodies. Each trilobite body segment had an identical pair of jointed legs. But unlike modern arthropods, none of the trilobite species had legs modified for a special function.

Modern, more recently evolved arthropods tend to have fewer body

FIGURE 23.3
The compound eye—a structure that evolved only in arthropods—has many separate lenses. Do compound eyes detect images as we see them?

FIGURE 23.2
This cicada has just molted, leaving behind its old exoskeleton. A newly molted arthropod has difficulty moving until its new exoskeleton hardens.

Kingdom: Animalia
Phylum: Arthropoda

Four subphyla:
Crustacea
Chelicerata
Uniramia
Trilobita

segments than trilobites had. Many have highly specialized appendages adapted for very specific functions.

It is not clear whether arthropods and annelids both evolved from a common ancestor, or whether arthropods evolved from annelids. The wormlike *Peripatus,* shown in *Figure 23.5,* has some characteristics of annelids and others of arthropods. Some biologists think that ancestors of *Peripatus* may represent an evolutionary link between annelids and arthropods. For this reason, they classify *Peripatus* in a separate phylum.

One possible theory of arthropod evolution is shown in the phylogenetic tree in *Figure 23.4.* The three living subphyla of arthropods are distinguished by differences in their appendages. Crustaceans (krus-TAY-shunz) have legs with claws, chewing mouthparts, and two pairs of antennae. Chelicerates (kee-LIS-er-uhts)

FIGURE 23.4

Phylum Arthropoda

The evolutionary history of arthropods is not well established. This depiction is only one theory of arthropod evolution.

Chelicerata

Uniramia

Trilobita
(extinct)

Crustacea

ARTHROPODS

MILESTONE
**Jointed
appendages**

**Protostome
ancestor**

FIGURE 23.5

Peripatus **is segmented and has paired appendages, as well as antennae and claws typical of arthropods. However, its appendages are not jointed, and it lacks a hard exoskeleton. Is** *Peripatus* **more like an annelid or an arthropod?**

have pincerlike mouthparts and no antennae. Uniramians (yoo-nih-RAY-mee-unz) have chewing mouthparts, one pair of antennae, and no claws. You will learn about each of these groups as you continue reading this chapter.

CHECKPOINT 23.1

1. Describe the main characteristics of all arthropods.
2. What are the distinguishing features of the three living subphyla of arthropods?
3. **Critical Thinking** Why might arthropods that have just molted be more at risk from predators?

Build on What You Know

4. What characteristics do arthropods and mollusks share? *(Need to jog your memory? Revisit relevant concepts in Chapter 22, Section 22.2.)*

What characteristics are common to all arthropods?

23.2 Crustaceans

Spiny lobsters, single file
When fall arrives and the Atlantic waters off the Florida coast get cold, spiny lobsters migrate toward warmer waters. As many as 100,000 lobsters travel day and night in chains of 50 or 60. They move single file in a crustacean "conga line," using their antennae to keep in touch.

CHARACTERISTICS OF CRUSTACEANS

Moving swimmingly

Crustaceans, like all arthropods, are so diverse that no single species is truly representative of the entire group. However, the lobster shown in *Figure 23.6* and the crayfish in *Figure 23.7* show some typical crustacean characteristics.

Most crustaceans have two body regions: a cephalothorax and an abdomen. The **cephalothorax** (sef-uh-loh-THOR-aks) is the fused head and thorax, or chest region, to which legs and other appendages are attached. The cephalothorax is covered by a hard shield of chitin called the carapace, which protects the body organs. The abdomen in lobsters and crayfish is the long narrow tail region that ends with the central telson and paired uropods.

As you study *Figure 23.6,* observe the appendages on the anterior end. The first two pairs of appendages are antennae. The first pair of antennae is short, but the second pair is usually as long as the crustacean's body. All crustaceans also have one pair of jaw-like appendages called **mandibles** that chew and crush food. Behind the mandibles are two other pairs of

mouthparts, called maxillae, that hold food and pass it to the mouth. The lobster has three pairs of jaw feet, called maxillipeds, that touch, taste, and handle food. Large claws are used for catching food and for defense. The last four segments of the cephalothorax have one pair of walking legs each.

FIGURE 23.6

The Appendages of a Crustacean (lobster)

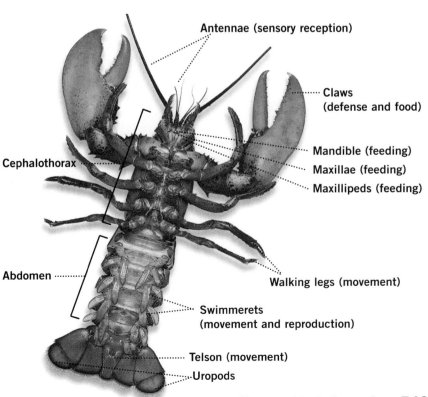

Antennae (sensory reception)

Claws (defense and food)

Cephalothorax

Mandible (feeding)
Maxillae (feeding)
Maxillipeds (feeding)

Abdomen

Walking legs (movement)

Swimmerets (movement and reproduction)

Telson (movement)
Uropods

Kingdom: Animalia

Phylum: Arthropoda

Subphylum: Crustacea

Classes:
Copepoda
Cirripedia

Orders:
Decapoda
Isopoda

The abdomen has pairs of appendages called swimmerets that are used for swimming. In female crabs, crayfish, and lobsters, developing eggs are attached to the swimmerets. At the end of the abdomen is the telson and uropods which are used for rapid backward locomotion.

Crustaceans, like all arthropods, have a ventral nerve cord. In each body segment, the nerve cord swells into a pair of ganglia. Nerve impulses are transmitted to and from other body parts through the ganglia. The brain, located at the front end of the nerve cord, consists of fused ganglia.

Like most crustaceans, the crayfish has a pair of compound eyes. The eyes are located above the sensory antennae,

at the ends of movable eyestalks. The eyestalks allow the animal to look in any direction, and even in two different directions at once.

The crayfish begins feeding by crushing and chewing food with its mandibles. In the stomach, teeth made of chitin located on the stomach wall grind the crushed food into smaller particles. The food particles are moved to a structure called the digestive gland, where food is mixed with digestive enzymes and nutrients are absorbed into the body. Undigested material is passed through the intestines and out the anus.

At the base of the antennae is an excretory organ called the green gland, which regulates the amount of salt

FIGURE 23.7

The Structures of a Crustacean (crayfish)

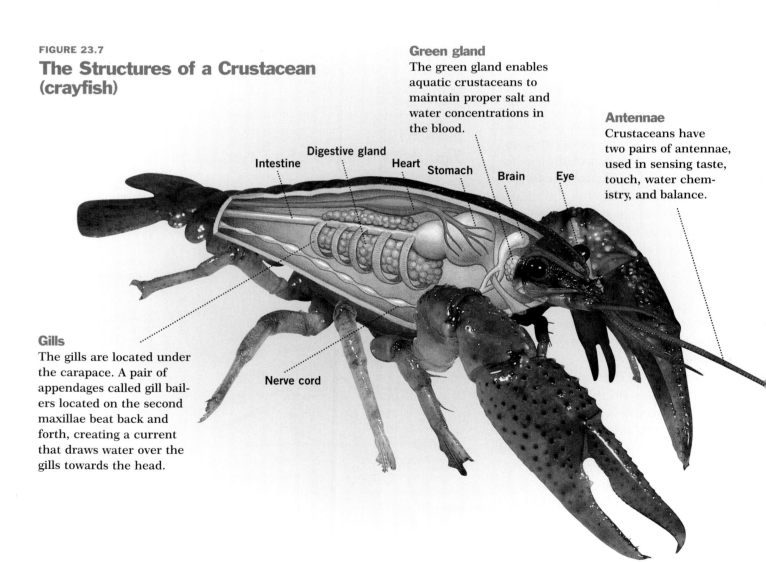

Green gland
The green gland enables aquatic crustaceans to maintain proper salt and water concentrations in the blood.

Antennae
Crustaceans have two pairs of antennae, used in sensing taste, touch, water chemistry, and balance.

Intestine   Digestive gland   Heart   Stomach   Brain   Eye

Nerve cord

Gills
The gills are located under the carapace. A pair of appendages called gill bailers located on the second maxillae beat back and forth, creating a current that draws water over the gills towards the head.

and liquid in the blood. In freshwater crustaceans, the green gland is especially important because it retains salt and removes excess water.

CRUSTACEAN DIVERSITY

A crabby bunch

Lift a rock or a log, and you will probably see small, gray bugs scurrying away. In the supermarket, you have probably seen tanks of live lobsters or crabs. These animals, along with shrimps, barnacles, and hermit crabs, are all crustaceans. Most of the tens of thousands of crustaceans are adapted to a marine environment. But some, like the crayfish, live in fresh water. Pill bugs and a few species of tropical crabs are some of the only crustaceans that live in terrestrial environments.

Crustaceans vary in size. Among the smallest crustaceans are copepods, which are less than 0.25 millimeter (mm) across. Copepods are a main component of plankton; they feed on microscopic algae. They have five pairs of appendages on the thorax, but do not have gills or abdominal appendages.

Crustaceans with 10 walking legs are decapods. ("Deca-" means "ten.") Crayfish, crabs, lobsters, and shrimp are all decapods. Decapods are the largest crustaceans; the king crab can grow as large as 5 meters (m) across. Most decapods are carnivores and scavengers that live on the ocean bottom.

Pill bugs, sow bugs, and wood lice are all isopods. These isopods are well adapted to moist, dark, terrestrial environments, feeding on decayed organic matter. Their swimmerets are modified to obtain oxygen from the air. When threatened, pill bugs roll up into a tight ball for protection, as shown in *Figure* 23.8. How might this behavior protect them from predators?

FIGURE 23.8
Commonly called pill bugs, these isopods can be found in almost any dark, terrestrial environment— even in houses. Have you ever seen them in or around your house?

Cerripeds, which include the barnacles shown in *Figure* 23.9, are shelled, sessile crustaceans. They are often found attached to coastal rocks, boat hulls, and even whales and sea turtles. Adult barnacles secrete a pyramid-shaped exoskeleton with an opening at the top. They extend specialized appendages— featherlike legs—through this opening to sweep food from the water into their mouths.

Unlike most crustaceans, adult barnacles have no eyes, gills, heart, or blood vessels. However, the free-swimming larvae of barnacles closely resemble the larvae of other crustaceans. Until scientists studied their motile larval stage, barnacles were not classified as crustaceans.

FIGURE 23.9
Large numbers of barnacle larvae attach themselves to an underwater object, where they remain for the rest of their lives. These adult barnacles have their feeding appendages extended.

CHECKPOINT 23.2

1. Describe the main characteristics of crustaceans.
2. What are the differences between the four groups of crustaceans discussed?
3. Critical Thinking Nearly all crustaceans are aquatic. What challenges do terrestrial crustaceans face, and what adaptations help them overcome these challenges?

Build on What You Know

4. How do marine crustaceans differ from cnidarians that live in the ocean? *(Need to jog your memory? Revisit relevant concepts in Chapter 21, Section 21.4.)*

23.3 Spiders and Their Relatives

What you'll learn

IDEAS

• To describe the characteristics of chelicerates
• To compare types of chelicerates
• To describe structures and adaptations of chelicerates

WORDS

chelicerae, Malpighian tubules, pedipalps

EVERYDAY BIOLOGY

Silk Stops Bullet

In 1881 a physician noted that the fatal bullet in a man's chest had not penetrated his silk pocket handkerchief, which protruded from the wound. Some spider silk is even stronger. In many ways it is superior to the material used in bulletproof vests.

A spider video-dating service?
Male wolf spiders have hairy legs; males of a related species do not. Researchers altered images of both species of males, adding hair to hairless legs and removing it from hairy legs. When female wolf spiders viewed videos of the males, they reacted positively to those with hairy legs, regardless of the species.

CHARACTERISTICS OF CHELICERATES

Good reception without antennae

Like the bodies of crustaceans, those of most chelicerates are divided into two segments: a cephalothorax and an abdomen. Chelicerates—spiders and their relatives—share three broad characteristics. First, unlike other arthropod groups, chelicerates do not have sensory antennae. Second, most chelicerates have simple eyes, not compound eyes. Third, all chelicerates have a pair of appendages called chelicerae. **Chelicerae** (kih-LIS-uh-ray) are the anterior-most appendages, modified into pincers or fangs for killing prey. The chelicerae of some species can inject poison. *Figure 23.10* shows the chelicerae of a tarantula.

Most chelicerates live in terrestrial environments. To live successfully on land, the organisms had to evolve with ways to retain water in their bodies. Terrestrial chelicerates, such as spiders, have three structures that aid in water retention: Malpighian tubules, an exoskeleton, and book lungs. **Malpighian** (mal-PIG-ee-uhn) **tubules** are excretory structures that remove metabolic wastes from blood and return water to the cells. The hard exoskeleton of chelicerates prevents excessive water evaporation. The book lungs provide efficient gas exchange without excessive water loss. These respiratory structures are called book lungs because they look like the inverted pages of a book. The location of the Malpighian tubules and book lungs is shown in *Figure 23.11*.

Chelicerae

FIGURE 23.10
Chelicerates have a pair of anterior appendages, called chelicerae, which are often modified into fangs.

ORIGIN AND DIVERSITY OF CHELICERATES

Legs, legs, legs…

There are two classes of chelicerates. Horseshoe crabs are marine animals that belong to the small class Meristomata. There are only four living species of horseshoe crabs. Three of these species live off the coast of Southeast Asia, and one species of horseshoe crab lives in the coastal regions of the western North Atlantic and the Gulf of Mexico.

Arachnids (uh-RAK-nidz) are terrestrial chelicerates that make up the much larger class Arachnida. There are three familiar orders of arachnids: spiders, scorpions, and mites and ticks. All arachnids have a cephalothorax with six pairs of appendages: one pair of chelicerae, one pair of specialized appendages called **pedipalps,** and four pairs of walking legs.

FIGURE 23.11

The Structures of a Spider

Like all chelicerates, spiders have pedipalps, chelicerae, and a two-part body. This spider also has Malpighian tubules, book lungs, and spinnerets.

Spinnerets
Paired spinnerets release silk strands that are used for web building, movement, and shelter. The silk is produced in silk glands located in a spider's abdomen.

Walking legs

Intestine
Heart
Stomach
Silk gland
Ovary
Brain
Poison gland

Pedipalps
A pair of appendages called pedipalps hold food and are used as sense organs.

Chelicerae
A pair of appendages called chelicerae are modified to seize food and inject poison.

Malpighian tubules
These structures secrete wastes into the intestine for excretion and return water back into the spider's circulatory system.

Book lungs
Chelicerates have folds of tissue called book lungs for gas exchange. The book lungs are enclosed in an abdominal pouch to stay moist.

Kingdom: Animalia

Phylum: Arthropoda

Subphylum: Chelicerata

Two classes:
Meristomata
Arachnida

Horseshoe crabs
How many pairs of walking legs can you find on this horseshoe crab (above)? What other chelicerate characteristics do you see?

Horseshoe crabs   Horseshoe crabs are not really crabs. They belong to an ancient class of marine arthropods that evolved about 400 million years ago. Scientists often refer to the four surviving species of horseshoe crabs as "living fossils" because they closely resemble their fossil ancestors.

Horseshoe crabs have both compound and simple eyes. They do not have Malpighian tubules. Horseshoe crabs exchange gases in five pairs of book gills. Book gills are similar to book lungs and may have evolved into the book lungs found in terrestrial arachnids. Horseshoe crabs are among the few chelicerates that eat solid food. They feed on clam worms, soft-shelled clams, and other animals.

Spiders   Most scientists divide spiders into two groups, based on how they gather food. One group includes spiders that actively hunt and capture prey. The other group includes spiders

FIGURE 23.12

Diversity of Chelicerates

The chelicerates include two classes: horseshoe crabs and arachnids. How do these classes compare?

Hunting spider
This hunting spider has caught a frog. Hunting spiders are strong, agile predators with keen eyesight. How can a spider subdue a frog?

that weave webs to catch prey. Hunting spiders usually have strong legs and excellent eyesight. In some species, two pairs of eyes swivel together or independently, while two other pairs provide peripheral vision. Web weavers generally have long, slender legs and relatively poor eyesight.

Although not all spiders weave webs, they all produce silk. Some spiders use silk for movement—as droplines or parachutes, for example. Other spiders use silk for protection—as a covering for their burrows or a canopy under which they sleep. Still other spiders use silk to wrap their food for storage.

Spiders paralyze or kill their prey with chelicerae modified into fangs. While holding their prey with their pedipalps, spiders secrete enzymes that digest and liquefy the prey. They then suck the liquefied food into their stomach.

Scorpions   The second order of arachnids includes scorpions. Unlike other arachnids, scorpions have a long segmented abdomen that ends in a poisonous stinger. A scorpion's pedipalps are modified into large claws for

Web-weaving spider
A web-weaving spider is born knowing how to weave the unique web of its ancestors. How would you explain this phenomenon?

capturing and holding prey. As it curls its abdomen over trapped prey, the scorpion stings and paralyzes it, then crushes it and sucks its internal liquids. Despite their reputation, only a few species of scorpions are harmful to humans.

Mites Mites are classified in a third order of arachnids. Unlike spiders, mites have only one body segment. Some mites use their piercing and sucking mouthparts to drain the contents of plant cells. Other mite species eat bacteria that live in animal hair follicles. Some mites even feed on the dead skin cells of humans. Millions of dust mites live in our houses. They are usually harmless but can cause problems for people with allergies. What do you think dust mites feed on?

Ticks The third order of arachnids also includes ticks. Most ticks are parasites that require meals of blood before they molt. Ticks attach to their hosts with specially adapted mouthparts. Their feeding process can take several days,

Stinger

during which they may grow to many times their original size. Ticks differ from spiders in that they have only a single fused body section.

You may have seen ticks feeding on dogs, cats, or humans. Ticks can be dangerous because they can act as hosts to parasites that cause diseases such as Rocky Mountain spotted fever. A common dog tick is easy to see because it is as large as a sesame seed. However, the deer tick, which carries the parasite that causes Lyme disease, is very small and difficult to see.

CHECKPOINT 23.3

1. Describe the main characteristics of chelicerates.
2. Discuss the variations among members of the chelicerate classes.
3. **Critical Thinking** Why are Malpighian tubules absent in aquatic arthropods?

Build on What You Know

4. Chitin is made of protein and polysaccharides. What are these two substances? *(Need to jog your memory? Revisit relevant concepts in Chapter 2, Section 2.1.)*

Tick
Ticks may tranmit disease-causing organisms when they feed. What can you conclude about the tick in this photograph?

Scorpion
A scorpion captures insects and spiders with its claws. This female scorpion carries her young on her back.

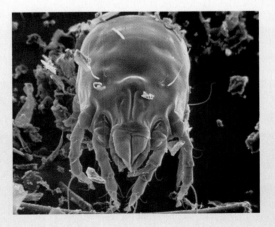

Dust mite
If you looked at a dust mite under a powerful microscope, this is what you would see. What are the similarities and differences between dust mites (above) and ticks (above right)?

23.4 Insects and Their Relatives

What you'll learn

IDEAS

• To describe the characteristics of uniramians
• To compare and contrast the diversity of uniramians
• To explain several adaptations of insects

WORDS

spiracles, metamorphosis, pheromone, social insects, mimicry

Gourmet insects

Have you ever had leaf-footed bugs on your pizza? Many people choose to eat those insects and others for their protein and their taste. For example, grasshoppers boiled in soy sauce are a popular snack in Japan, toasted stinkbugs flavor salsa in Mexico, and mopane caterpillars are tasty treats in Africa.

CHARACTERISTICS OF UNIRAMIANS

A buggy bunch

Although picnics vary in location, participants, and menu, most picnics have one thing in common—insects! Insects, along with centipedes and millipedes, are classified in the subphylum Uniramia. As you can see in *Figure 23.13,* mouthparts in uniramians are varied and specialized. Although their mouthparts may be different, most uniramians share two characteristics: a single pair of antennae and unbranched appendages. You can locate these structures in the grasshopper shown in *Figure 23.14.*

The uniramians, and particularly the insects, are the most numerous and diverse group of organisms on Earth. One reason for their successful survival is that uniramians have a wide range of senses. Uniramian antennae are very sensitive to odors. In addition, some insects have thin, flexible tympanic membranes that detect sound. Although the insects'

Mosquito

Housefly

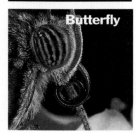

Butterfly

FIGURE 23.13

The close-up photos of these insects show mouthparts that are piercing (top), sponging (center), and sucking (bottom).

compound eyes might not form sharp images, they easily detect movement. If you have ever tried to swat a fly, you know how well its quick response to your slightest motion helps it escape danger.

Uniramians also have a complex digestive system with specialized organs. In a grasshopper, for example, food passes through an esophagus to a crop, where it is moistened. From the crop, food moves to a gizzard, which is lined with hard, toothlike structures that grind the food into small pieces. The small food pieces then move to the midgut, where digestive enzymes break them down. Nutrients are then absorbed and transported to cells. Undigested wastes move into the hindgut and leave the body through the anus. Like arachnids, uniramians have Malpighian tubules that remove nitrogen wastes from body fluids.

The uniramians' respiratory system enables them to obtain oxygen from the air without losing too much moisture. Their respiratory system is composed of a branched system of internal air tubules. Air enters a uniramian's respiratory system through **spiracles**— small openings in the exoskeleton. It then passes directly into tracheal tubes that wind through the body tissues and carry oxygen directly to body cells.

ORIGIN AND DIVERSITY OF UNIRAMIANS

Legs and segments bug taxonomists

With their exoskeletons and specialized appendages, the arthropods were among the first animals that could survive on land. Of the arthropods, it was the uniramians—especially the insects—that prospered during the Carboniferous and Permian periods (about 300–250 million years ago). A second evolutionary explosion in the number of uniramian species occurred at the end of the Cretaceous period (about 65 million years ago). This explosion coincided with the evolution of flowering plants. Today, insect populations continue to grow. Approximately one million insect species have already been described. Millions more are known to exist, and new ones are discovered every day.

Centipedes Uniramians are divided into three classes. The first class, Chilopoda, contains the centipedes. Centipedes are carnivores with one pair of fanglike claws. You can see a photograph of a centipede in

Phylum: Arthropoda

Subphylum: Uniramia

Three classes:
Chilopoda
Diplopoda
Insecta

FIGURE 23.14

Structures of a Grasshopper

Like all uniramians, grasshoppers have one pair of antennae and unbranched appendages. Grasshoppers also have compound eyes and specialized mouthparts.

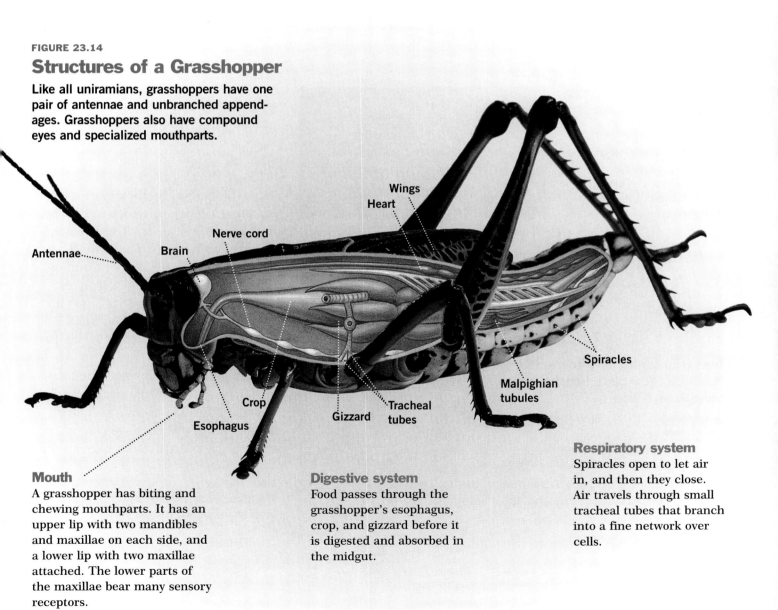

Mouth
A grasshopper has biting and chewing mouthparts. It has an upper lip with two mandibles and maxillae on each side, and a lower lip with two maxillae attached. The lower parts of the maxillae bear many sensory receptors.

Digestive system
Food passes through the grasshopper's esophagus, crop, and gizzard before it is digested and absorbed in the midgut.

Respiratory system
Spiracles open to let air in, and then they close. Air travels through small tracheal tubes that branch into a fine network over cells.

Chapter 23 Arthropods **557**

Figure 23.15. They have 15 or more pairs of walking legs, one pair per segment. Centipedes hide during the day and feed on earthworms, insects, and snails at night.

Millipedes The members of the class Diplopoda are the millipedes, which are often confused with centipedes. Although millipedes have two pairs of walking legs per segment, they move slowly. When alarmed, they roll up into a ball. Millipedes are herbivores and vary in size. Small millipedes are common in houses and gardens, but some tropical species can reach almost half a meter in length.

Insects Insects belong to the class Insecta. More than three

FIGURE 23.15
Many people confuse centipedes (right) and millipedes (above). What differences are there between these two uniramians?

LAB ZONE Do It!

Look at Those Sensors!

Insect antennae are incredibly varied in form and function. You can observe just a few of the possible variations if you . . .

Try This

1 Collect as many different intact, dead insects as you can.
Caution: Dead bees and wasps still have stingers.
2 Group them roughly by type (moths, beetles, and so on).
3 Using a microscope, examine their antennae carefully, and sketch the different types.

Analyze Your Results

1 What basic differences did you observe?
2 Based on what you know about the types of insects you collected, how does the form of the antennae match their function?

FIGURE 23.16

Insect Diversity

Uniramians vary enormously in size, form, and habitat. How many different insects can you name?

quarters of all known animal species are insects. Scientists classify insects by structural differences, such as the type of mouthparts they have or the number and structure of their wings.

The diversity of insects is truly amazing. There are aphids, bees, crickets, dragonflies, earwigs, fireflies, gnats, horseflies, inchworm moths, Japanese beetles, katydids, ladybugs, mosquitoes, nectar-sucking blister beetles, orb weavers, potato bugs, queen bees, roaches, scale, termites, unlined giant chafers, velvet mites, wasps, *Xylocopa*, yellow jackets, and zebra butterflies—and thousands more, covering every letter of the alphabet.

Unlike crustaceans and chelicerates, insects have three distinct body regions: a head, a thorax, and an abdomen. All insects have compound eyes, and some also have simple eyes.

FIGURE 23.17
The three body regions of insects are shown below.

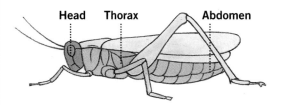
Head   Thorax   Abdomen

1. *Diptera*, mosquito
2. *Hymenoptera*, wasp
3. *Orthoptera*, katydid
4. *Lepidoptera*, butterfly
5. *Odonata*, dragonfly
6. *Coleoptera*, glorious beetle
7. *Hemiptera*, water beetle

Egg

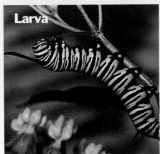

Larva

Pupa

Adult

Insects have three pairs of mouthparts and three pairs of walking legs—one for each segment of the thorax.

Some insects have two pairs of wings, some have one pair, and others have no wings at all. Insect wings are not appendages; they are folded extensions of the exoskeleton. With their ability to fly, insects could inhabit new environments and were better able to escape from predators, obtain food, and migrate.

Insects often display a developmental pattern called metamorphosis. **Metamorphosis** is a series of changes young organisms undergo as they develop into adults.

Insects such as grasshoppers, termites, cicadas, and aphids undergo incomplete metamorphosis. This type of metamorphosis includes three stages: egg, nymph, and adult. Nymphs are insects that resemble an adult but are very small and lack wings and reproductive organs. After hatching from the eggs laid by an adult female,

nymphs go through a series of molts. Each molt results in an insect that more closely resembles the adult.

Many other insects, such as butterflies, beetles, and flies, undergo complete metamorphosis. *Figure 23.18* shows the stages of complete metamorphosis. Larvae—often called caterpillars, grubs, or maggots—hatch from eggs laid by an adult. The larvae are greedy eaters. They munch their way through leaves, plants, and decaying organic matter, molting as they grow. Once the larvae reach a certain size, they find a sheltered place and surround themselves with a protective case, or cocoon. In this stage of metamorphosis, the organism is referred to as a pupa. While in the cocoon, the larval tissues break down. Adult tissues

FIGURE 23.18
During complete metamorphosis of a butterfly (shown top to bottom), the insect develops from an egg into an adult.

develop from a few specialized cells. After development is complete, an adult emerges from the cocoon.

Networking in the insect world

Insects have evolved many adaptations to the different environments they inhabit. Some of these adaptations are behavioral, and some are structural.

Behavioral adaptations Insects display many different kinds of behaviors, ranging from the simple to the complex. Have you ever watched fireflies signal each other at dusk? Have you seen ants carry food back to their nests? These behaviors are not learned. They are instincts—automatic behaviors coded for by genes.

Insects behave in predictable patterns based on the stimuli they sense. Some stimuli that insects sense come from other members of their species. Many species of insects communicate with one another. Male and female fireflies use flashes of light to find each other. Crickets and grasshoppers rub their wings together to produce sounds that attract mates or mark their territories.

A chemical signal used by insects for communication is called a **pheromone** (FAIR-uh-mohn). When pheromones are smelled or tasted, they affect the behavior of other insects. For example, ants leave a trail of pheromones for other ants to follow to a new food source. Some female moths secrete pheromones to attract mates. By sensing pheromones, a male moth can find a female several kilometers away.

Some insect species have a complex social system. These species are often called social insects. **Social insects** live in colonies where individual insects perform specific jobs in the colony and are usually adapted structurally to do so.

Many species of bees, ants, and termites are social insects. An individual social insect, such as a honeybee, cannot survive on its own. A beehive has

EVERYDAY BIOLOGY

No Stinger, Less Pain

When a honeybee stings you, the stinger and its poison gland remain in your body, and the gland continues to pump its toxin. The sooner you pull out the stinger, the less pain, swelling, and itching you will experience.

FIGURE 23.19
These photos illustrate several insect adaptations. Moths' feathery antennae (left) are highly sensitive to airborne pheromones. Crickets (top right) rub their forewings together to produce the familiar chirping noise and attract a mate. Leafcutter ants (bottom right) clasp each other's head to assure that they are from the same colony.

FIGURE 23.20

The patterns of the round and waggle dances of bees (far right) communicate information about the location of food. Why is the queen bee (near right) so much larger than the others?

Round dance

Waggle dance

three types of individuals: a queen, drones, and workers. Workers—female bees that cannot reproduce—are the most numerous members of a hive. Their job in the colony is to build and maintain the hive, collect food, feed the queen and larvae, and defend the hive.

One type of worker bee is a food scout. The scout uses complicated dances to communicate the location of a food source to other workers. If the food source is closer than 50 m from the hive, the scout performs a round dance. When the food source is more than 50 m away, the scout performs a waggle dance. Food-gathering workers follow the scout's dance and touch antennae to communicate the scout's information. Then they fly off to find and gather the food.

Another type of worker cares for larvae. The larvae, which will become the hive's new bees, will develop into various types of bees depending on the food they receive from workers. Workers feed an enriched diet—called "royal jelly"—only to larvae that are destined to become queens.

The sole function of the one queen bee and the many male drones in a hive is reproduction. The queen lays all the eggs from which new bees first hatch into larvae. She produces a pheromone that tells worker bees not to feed "royal jelly" to growing larvae. When

the queen dies or leaves the hive, the absence of her pheromone signals the workers to feed "royal jelly" to some of the larvae. The new queens that emerge fight to the death, and the survivor becomes the new queen of the hive.

A hive limits the number of its drones because their sole function is reproduction, and a queen mates only once in her life. The inhabitants of a hive behave as if drones are their most expendable members.

LAB ZONE Think About It!

Identifying Insect Camouflage and Mimicry

Insects use both form and color to protect themselves or hide in their environment. You can study how insects use camouflage and mimicry to avoid detection by predators and prey when you . . .

Try This

1 Look at the pictures in this chapter. How many examples of camouflage can you find? How many examples of mimicry?
2 Can you identify examples of camouflage or mimicry that you have seen among insects in the environment?

Analysis

1 Look at Figure 23.18. Why might the larval stage of an insect, such as a caterpillar, be more highly camouflaged than the adult stage?
2 How do camouflage and mimicry help an insect to increase its food supply?

Structural adaptations One of the most remarkable ways that insects have adapted to their environment is by evolving with structures that enable them to blend in with their surroundings. Some insects blend in with the textures, shapes, and colors of their environment. This adaptation is called camouflage. Other insects resemble plants or other animals. This adaptation is called **mimicry.** Using camouflage or mimicry, insects often avoid detection by predators and prey. Although other animals use camouflage and mimicry, these adaptations are most diverse and visible in insects.

The adaptations of camouflage and mimicry can occur at any stage of an insect's life. For example, insects that undergo complete metamorphosis are vulnerable during the pupal stage. So the pupae are often

disguised as something else—a dead leaf or a twig perhaps. This disguise decreases the chance that the pupae will be eaten. You can see some remarkable examples of insect camouflage and mimicry in *Figure* 23.21 and *Figure* 23.22.

CHECKPOINT 23.4

1. Describe the common characteristics of uniramians.

2. Compare and contrast insects, millipedes, and centipedes.

3. List two types of insect adaptations and give examples of each.

4. Critical Thinking What characteristics have helped insects to diversify so successfully?

Build on What You Know

5. Compare the individual members of an insect colony with the individual cells in an organism. *(Need to jog your memory? Revisit relevant concepts in Chapter 3, Section 3.1.)*

FIGURE 23.22
This caterpillar (left) flattens and twists its abdomen, which is patterned like the head of a snake, to scare away predators. The sphinx moth (right) closely resembles its wooden resting place.

? How are arthropods classified?

Observing the Mealworm Life Cycle

WHAT YOU WILL DO Observe the stages in the life cycle of a mealworm

SKILLS YOU WILL USE Observing, measuring, collecting and recording data, hypothesizing

WHAT YOU WILL NEED Spoon, specimen dish, container, marker, mealworm larvae, hand lens, metric ruler, cornmeal, cheesecloth

Propose a Hypothesis

Propose a hypothesis about the size of the mealworm at each stage in its life cycle and the amount of time it spends in each stage.

Conduct Your Experiment

1 Using a spoon, carefully place a mealworm larva into a specimen dish. Use a hand lens to observe the larva. Draw and label the parts of the larva, then measure and record its length.
Caution: Always handle living organisms carefully.
2 Label a container and place the larva in it. Add two spoonfuls of cornmeal and cover the container with cheesecloth. Set the container aside.
3 Observe and measure the mealworm daily until it reaches its adult stage. Be sure to record your observations and measurements.

Analyze Your Data

1 Make a line graph from your data on the length of the mealworm.
2 In which stage was the mealworm the longest? Was there a period of rapid growth, or was its growth gradual?
3 Make a bar graph to show the number of days the mealworm spent in each stage of its life cycle.
4 In which stage did the individual spend the most time? How long?
5 What body parts are common to all stages?

Draw Conclusions

Was your hypothesis supported by the results of the experiment? What conclusions can you draw from the results? Explain.

Design a Related Experiment

Suppose you wanted to study the effects of a variable, such as amount of food, light, or temperature, on the development of a mealworm. Propose a hypothesis and design an experiment to test it.

Lab: The Mealworm Life Cycle

Objective: To observe the stages in the life cycle of a mealworm

	Length	Appearance
Day 1		
Day 2		
Day 3		
Day 4		

23.5 Arthropods in the Biosphere

What you'll learn

IDEAS

• To identify several key roles arthropods play in the biosphere
• To describe the effects of arthropods on humans

FIGURE 23.23
This bumblebee is gathering pollen from apple blossoms. Notice the heavily laden pollen baskets on its hind legs.

Bugs become plant food

The sundew plant (near right) traps a bug in its sticky nectar, then the plant closes over the insect (far right) and digests it. Another predatory plant, the pitcher plant, entices insects to its opening. Spiky hairs point downward, trapping the insects, which the plant then digests in its pool of enzymes. Insects and other arthropods supply nutrients to many organisms.

ECOLOGICAL ROLES

Arthropods can really bug you

Arthropods—by far the largest phylum—play important roles in the biosphere. Many other animals and plants, including food crops, depend upon arthropods for their existence.

On land and in water, arthropods are an important food source for other animals. Many crustaceans and insects, for example, are near the base of the food chain in their respective environments. Krill—crustaceans in plankton—provide food for much of the Antarctic ecosystem. Fishes, seabirds, seals, and penguins all consume vast quantities of krill, and a single blue whale may eat up to four tons of krill a day! Insects are the main dietary component for a great many animals, including birds, reptiles, amphibians, and many small mammals.

Some arthropods also serve as food for other arthropods. One web-spinning spider, for example, is capable of catching about 100 insects a day. Some wasps sting caterpillars or spiders and carry the paralyzed prey to their nests. The wasps then lay eggs on the immobilized prey, and when the larvae hatch, the prey provides a ready supply of fresh food.

Insects eat many plants, but they help to increase the numbers of others through pollination. In fact, many plants have coevolved with the insects that pollinate them. Coevolution is a process in which species adapt to each other after closely interacting for millions of years. In many cases, only a single insect species can pollinate a particular plant species. How would an insect's extinction affect the plant species that depends on it?

Some insects can cause great damage to crops. For example, boll weevils devastate cotton plants, hornworms destroy tomatoes, and borers ruin corn crops. Termites can also be destructive, causing so much damage to wooden structures that the structures have to be torn down.

Arthropods are host to many dangerous parasites. They can transmit a number of serious, even fatal, diseases. For example, mosquitoes can carry parasites that cause malaria, yellow fever, and encephalitis. Malaria is one of the largest public-health problems in some parts of the world today. Some ticks transmit parasites that cause Lyme disease, and others carry the organisms that cause Rocky Mountain spotted fever. Rats, and the fleas that live on them, carry the bacteria that cause bubonic plague—a deadly disease that drastically reduced Europe's population during the Middle Ages. Today, because of improved living conditions and public-health measures, only isolated cases of bubonic plague occur.

Certain biting flies native to tropical regions also carry disease-causing organisms. For example, the tsetse fly of East Africa transmits a parasite that causes trypanosomiasis (tri–PAN-uh-soh–MY–uh–sis), or sleeping sickness, which afflicts cattle and humans. Another fly carries the agent of river blindness.

Blood-sucking arthropods transmit disease in many other animals, too. The flea is a host for the dog tapeworm. Mosquitoes transmit heartworm between dogs and other animals. In a few tropical regions, insect-borne diseases are so common and dangerous that neither humans nor their livestock inhabit those areas.

IN THE COMMUNITY

Insect Control?

What county do you live in? Did you know that each county in the United States has an agricultural extension service? Extension service agents ("county agents") will answer questions about crops, gardens, and arthropod pests. Call your county extension service to find out about the mosquito or tick diseases that are prevalent in your area. Find out if a control program is in place for your community, and determine the precautions you should take against arthropod pests. Log on to *http://invertebrates.biosurf.com* to find out more about insect-born diseases.

IMPORTANCE OF ARTHROPODS TO HUMAN USES

Feast and famine

In addition to transmitting diseases, arthropods can affect the human food supply. We depend on insects, such as honeybees, to pollinate a huge variety of flowering plants and crops. A bad year for honeybees is a bad year for farmers, because the decrease in pollination results in fewer successful crops. In addition to their role as pollinators, bees are valued for honey and beeswax, which are used in products ranging from candles to skin moisturizers.

Other arthropods of importance to humans include silkworms and crabs. Silkworms spin the threads to make silk fabric. Crab shells yield chitin, used to make surgical thread and dressings for wounds. Horseshoe crab blood is used for testing the purity of pharmaceuticals and lab equipment.

Finally, arthropods are an important source of food for humans. In

FIGURE 23.25
This tomato hornworm caterpillar, a member of the sphinx moth family, can quickly destroy tomato plants as it eats its way to maturity.

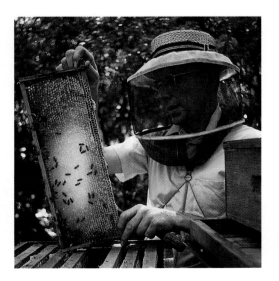

FIGURE 23.24
This beekeeper is inspecting a section of honeycomb that he has pulled out of a hive. The comb's cells are filled with honey and capped at the end with beeswax.

FIGURE 23.26
The success of an organic garden (right) depends, in part, on insects. In the photos below, a ladybug beetle (top) is making a meal of aphids, while a praying mantis (bottom) dispatches a tomato hornworm.

many cultures, people consume large amounts of shrimp, lobster, crabs, and crayfish. In some parts of the world, people consume many insects, including grasshoppers, termites, and caterpillars.

FRONTIERS IN BIOLOGY

Pesticide alternatives

Humans have used chemical pesticides for many years to control insect pests. Scientific evidence indicates that the long-term use of many pesticides has harmful effects on the environment and on humans. In addition, insects targeted by pesticides often develop a resistance to specific chemicals in the pesticides, making them useless. For these reasons, scientists and farmers are developing integrated pest management that uses biological methods to control insect pests, called integrated pest management. For example, certain plant species produce chemicals that are toxic to some pests. The pest-resistant species provide crop species some protection against pests when the two types of plants are grown together.

In other attempts to control insects, researchers are studying the reproductive cycles of insects and trying to develop sterile adults of certain species. The adults can mate but cannot reproduce, thereby reducing their populations. Another technique is to infect targeted insects with a parasite, bacteria, or viruses. A common control method is to expose pests to natural predators. For example, home gardeners often purchase ladybug beetles and praying mantises to help control other insects.

CHECKPOINT 23.5

1. Describe at least five roles arthropods have in the biosphere.
2. List three ways in which arthropods are important to humans. List three ways in which they can be harmful to humans.
3. **Critical Thinking** If all insects were suddenly eliminated, what would be some immediate consequences?

Build on What You Know

4. What other organisms make up plankton? What is plankton's role in the biosphere? *(Need to jog your memory? Revisit relevant concepts in Chapter 15, Section 15.5.)*

 What role do arthropods play in the biosphere?

Chapter 23 Review

 23.1 Arthropods are segmented invertebrates with jointed appendages and an exoskeleton.

23.2–23.4 In general, arthropods are classified by the number of body segments they have and the structure of their appendages.

23.5 Arthropods, as members of the largest phylum, have many important roles in the biosphere.

Sum It Up

Use the following summary to review the main concepts in this chapter.

23.1 Arthropods

- Arthropods comprise the largest and most diverse phylum. The segmented bodies of arthropods have jointed appendages.
- Arthropods have a chitinous exoskeleton which must be molted and shed for growth to continue.
- Many arthropod appendages have specialized functions.

23.2 Crustaceans

- Most crustaceans have two main body parts: a cephalothorax and an abdomen.
- Most crustaceans have two pairs of antennae, a pair of jawlike mandibles, and at least four pairs of walking legs. They have eyestalks with compound eyes.

23.3 Spiders and Their Relatives

- Chelicerates have a cephalothorax and an abdomen. They have no sensory antennae or mandibles, but they have chelicerae and pedipalps.
- Chelicerates are divided into two classes: Meristomata (horseshoe crabs) and Arachnida (arachnids).

- Arachnids have four pairs of walking legs, book lungs, Malpighian tubules, and simple eyes. They include spiders, scorpions, mites, and ticks.

23.4 Insects and Their Relatives

- Uniramians have one pair of antennae, compound eyes, varied mouthparts, spiracles, and tracheae. They have highly developed nervous systems and sensory organs, as well as complex digestive systems.
- Centipedes, millipedes, and insects are three groups of uniramians.
- Metamorphosis, ability to communicate, complex social systems, camouflage, and mimicry are adaptations of insects.

23.5 Arthropods in the Biosphere

- Arthropods play a key role in food chains and in plant pollination. They supply products such as honey and silk.
- Arthropods transmit diseases to humans and other animals. Some arthropods can cause great damage to crops; others can be used to control pests.

Use Terms and Concepts

Use each of the following words or terms in a complete sentence. If you need to review a meaning, turn to the page indicated.

exoskeleton (p. 546)

endoskeleton (p. 546)

compound eyes (p. 547)

cephalothorax (p. 549)

mandibles (p. 549)

chelicerae (p. 552)

Malpighian tubules (p. 552)

pedipalps (p. 553)

spiracles (p. 556)

metamorphosis (p. 559)

pheromone (p. 560)

social insects (p. 560)

mimicry (p. 562)

Use Your Word Power

COMPLETION Write the word or phrase that best completes each statement.

1. Arthropod jawlike appendages that crush food are called _____ .

2. During _____ caterpillars develop into butterflies.

3. The muscles in an arthropod are attached to the inside of its _____ .

4. Spiders have _____ that secrete poisons and digestive enzymes.

5. Insects that live in cooperative groups are called _____ .

6. In spiders' excretory systems, _____ filter wastes from water.

7. A chemical called _____ is secreted by some insects to communicate and to attract mates.

8. Terrestrial chelicerates have respiratory structures called _____ .

MULTIPLE CHOICE Choose the letter of the word or phrase that best completes each statement.

9. All uniramians have (a) compound eyes; (b) one pair of walking legs per segment; (c) wings; (d) fanglike claws.

10. Arthropods do NOT have (a) jointed appendages; (b) an endoskeleton; (c) a complex system of muscles; (d) an open circulatory system.

11. Chelicerae (a) digest food; (b) chew food; (c) crush food; (d) paralyze food.

12. Arthropods are the only organisms that have (a) segmented bodies; (b) compound eyes; (c) mimicry; (d) an open circulatory system.

13. Openings in an exoskeleton that let in air are (a) gills; (b) spiracles; (c) spicules; (d) book lungs.

Show What You Know

14. When are insects especially vulnerable to predators? How do insects minimize the danger?

15. Describe the sequence of events that take place during molting.

16. What alternatives are there to pesticides for controlling insect pests?

17. What role do pheromones play in the life cycles that occur in a beehive?

18. How do the extinct trilobites differ from modern arthropods?

19. Explain why scientists observing only adult barnacles would be unlikely to classify them as crustaceans.

20. How do web-building spiders differ from hunting spiders?

21. **Make a Concept Map** Use the following terms to create a concept map: adult, cocoon, exoskeleton, incomplete metamorphosis, larva, molt, nymph, pupa, and wings.

22. Is this arthropod a chelicerate or a uniramian? Give at least 3 reasons for your answer.

Take It Further

23. **Developing a Hypothesis** Many characteristics of organisms have drawbacks as well as benefits. Compound eyes in some insects are one example. What advantages could compound eyes provide that would compensate for the possibly blurry images they produce?

24. **Making an Analogy** Suppose you decided to attend a sports rally at a rival school. What could you do to blend in? Compare your behavior to adaptations in insects.

25. Interpreting a Graph The type of population increase shown in the graph below is called exponential growth because each population increases by an exponent of 10 with each generation. If insect B loses 90 percent of offspring in each generation, what will its actual growth be? How many individuals could theoretically be produced in generation 3 by insects A, B, and C? In generation 4? Could this happen in nature? Explain your answer.

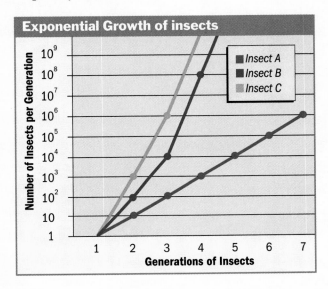

Exponential Growth of insects

Number of Insects per Generation

10^9, 10^8, 10^7, 10^6, 10^5, 10^4, 10^3, 10^2, 10, 1

■ Insect A
■ Insect B
■ Insect C

Generations of Insects

26. Analyzing Data The eastern cicada has a 17-year life cycle, most of it spent underground in the juvenile stage. These cicadas last emerged in great numbers in Connecticut in 1996. The southwestern cicada has a 13-year life cycle. Its last great emergence was in Arkansas in 1985. When will both groups emerge in the same year? How many generations will have passed for each type of cicada?

Consider the Issues

27. Collecting Specimens In the late nineteenth century, it was popular for amateur naturalists to have large collections of mounted insects or birds' eggs. Today collections are usually centralized at natural history museums. For example, the Smithsonian Institution in Washington, D.C., has over 31 million preserved specimens of chelicerates and insects. The public can visit the museum and qualified researchers can borrow specimens from the collection for two years or more. What are the benefits and drawbacks of private and public collections? What advances in technology have improved access to public collections?

28. Using Pesticides Make a list of pros and cons for the use of insecticides in a home garden. Using this list, make a recommendation for insect control in your area.

Make New Connections

29. Biology and Literature The title character in E. B. White's *Charlotte's Web* is a grey web-building spider whose species is *Araneus cavaticus*. Other than the fact that Charlotte can talk, how accurate is White's description of the spider's anatomy and behavior?

30. Biology and Mythology Arachnids share their name with the mythological Lydian princess Arachne, who was a skilled weaver. Find out what happened when the goddess Athena (also known as Minerva), another weaver, challenged Arachne to a contest.

FAST FORWARD TO CHAPTER 24

Most crustaceans are marine invertebrates. So are horseshoe crabs. In Chapter 24 you will study a phylum that contains many other species of marine invertebrates. You will also be introduced to some invertebrates that share a phylum with vertebrates.

Echinoderms and Invertebrate Chordates

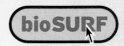

You can find out more about echinoderms and invertebrate chordates by exploring the following Internet address: *http://invertebrates.biosurf.com*

In this chapter . . .

FEATURES

Everyday Biology
- A Writing Urchin?
- Echinoderm Drillers

In the Community
Looking for Echinoderm Specimens

 Environmental Awareness
Coral Attack!

LAB ZONES

Discover It!
- Modeling Suction

Do It!
- Modeling Symmetry

Think About It!
- Comparing Structures and Systems of an Echinoderm and a Chordate

Investigate It!
- Exploring Echinoderm Diversity

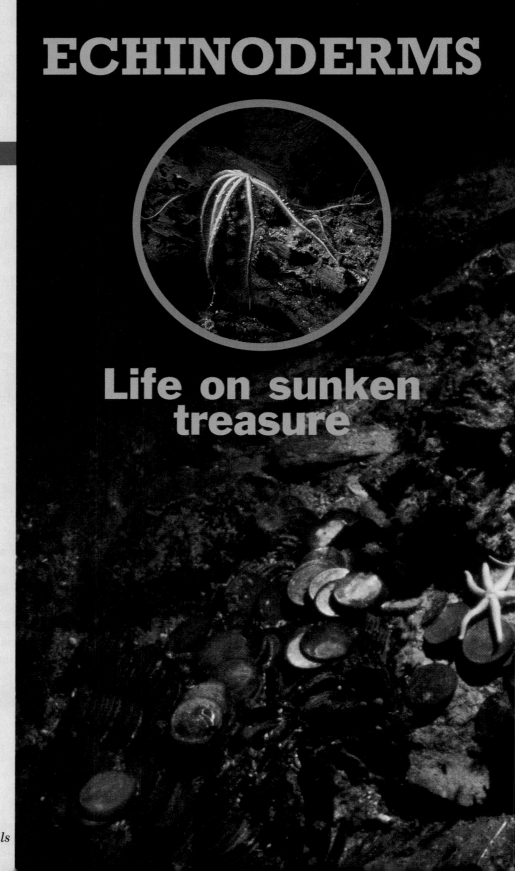

ECHINODERMS

Life on sunken treasure

In 1988, almost 130 years after it sank in a hurricane en route from Panama to New York, the steamer SS *Central America* was found about 270 kilometers (km) off the coast of Cape Fear, North Carolina. Of the more than 550 people aboard, 425 perished, and several tons of gold from the California gold fields were lost. Today the ship and its treasure rest under 2200 meters (m) of water, on a dark, silent deep-sea ridge.

In the environment that surrounds the shipwreck, almost no marine life exists, but a research submersible discovered that the wreck itself was teeming with life. Like an artificial reef, the wreck housed a diverse community of animals. A wide variety of echinoderms—including sea lilies, sea stars, feather stars, and brittle stars—were attached to or crawling on the ship and among stacks of gold coins and bullion.

How do the echinoderms and other animals survive? The shipwreck provides an ecosystem for the deep-sea animals. The organic materials at the site, including decaying food and wood, attract various species. The ship's framework provides shelter and a place for these species to reproduce. Over time, a large, self-sustaining community has been established. The site has provided an unusual opportunity for marine biologists to study echinoderms in an artificial-reef habitat.

Discover It!

Modeling Suction

You need a medicine dropper and a beaker.

1. Fill the medicine dropper with water. Empty it. How does this tool work?
2. With the dropper empty, squeeze the bulb, place the tip firmly against one of your fingers, and reduce the pressure on the bulb. Can you feel the "suction" on your finger? What causes this phenomenon?

Many echinoderms use a similar method to the one you just demonstrated to move themselves around and to pry open the shells of prey.

WRITE ABOUT IT!

Imagine that you are a writer invited to descend in a submarine to observe the shipwrecked SS *Central America.* Write a paragraph, short story, or poem that conveys your first impressions of the ship.

24.1 Echinoderms

What you'll learn

IDEAS
• To describe the common characteristics of echinoderms
• To explain the origin and diversity of echinoderms

WORDS
echinoderm, water vascular system, ampulla, tube foot, protostome, deuterostome

EVERYDAY BIOLOGY

A Writing Urchin?

One urchin got its common name, the slate-pencil urchin, because its spines were used to write on slate boards. Now its spines are often used as wind chimes.

Multiplication, not subtraction

In the past, when people who harvested shellfish for a living caught sea stars, they chopped them up and threw them back into the sea. Why? Because the sea stars ate large numbers of shellfish. What the harvesters didn't know was that the pieces of sea stars could grow into new sea stars! So, instead of being eliminated, the sea star population increased.

CHARACTERISTICS OF ECHINODERMS

Prickly packages

If you have ever visited the seashore, you have probably seen the remains of sand dollars and sea urchins washed onto the beach. Perhaps you have seen live sea stars in a saltwater aquarium. These animals are echinoderms. An **echinoderm** (eh-KY-noh-derm) is a marine animal characterized by spiny skin, an endoskeleton, radial symmetry, and a water vascular system.

The word *echinoderm* comes from "echin-," which means "spiny," and "-derma," which means "skin." Spines can be external, as in the sea urchin, or internal, as in the sea star. In addition to having spiny skin, echinoderms have an endoskeleton made of calcium that supports the echinoderm's body.

Echinoderms are radially symmetrical. The body parts of radial animals are arranged around a central point, or axis. The body of most echinoderms consists of five parts in an arrangement known as penta-radial symmetry. For example, the sea star in *Figure 24.2* has five arms that radiate from the center of its body.

Another characteristic of echinoderms is a water vascular system, which allows them to move, obtain food, and exchange gases. An echinoderm's

FIGURE 24.1
A sea star pries open its prey's shell. The sea star pushes part of its stomach through its mouth and into the opened shell. The sea star then digests its prey.

water vascular system is a network of fluid-filled tubes. This system consists of a number of important structures: the ring canal, radial canals, ampullae, and tube feet. These structures are shown in *Figure 24.3*.

The water vascular system has one opening through which water enters and leaves. This opening—located on the dorsal surface of the sea star—is called the sieve plate. Water flows through the sieve plate, into the ring canal, and down the radial canal in each arm of the sea star. Ampullae extend from both sides of the radial canal. An **ampulla** (AM-pyoo-luh) is a muscular sac that helps force water into a tube foot. A **tube foot** is a hollow tube with a suction-cup-like end. A tube foot is located beneath each ampulla.

An echinoderm moves by pumping water into its tube feet. By contracting the muscles in each ampulla, the sea star forces water into the tube feet, causing them to extend.

FIGURE 24.3
Water Vascular System
The water vascular system functions in movement, obtaining food, and respiration. Gases diffuse across the membranes of the tube feet.

Sieve plate   Ring canal

Tube foot   Radial canal   Ampulla

FIGURE 24.2
Structures and Systems of a Sea Star

In a sea star, the digestive, reproductive, and nervous systems are stacked within the central disk and radiate outward into each arm. How does the fact that each arm contains all of the systems benefit the sea star?

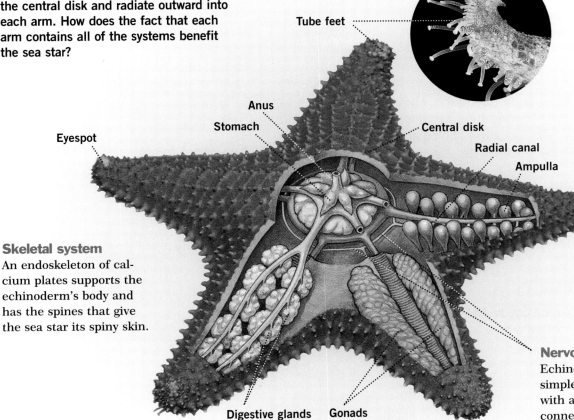

Tube feet

Anus

Stomach

Central disk

Eyespot

Radial canal

Ampulla

Skeletal system
An endoskeleton of calcium plates supports the echinoderm's body and has the spines that give the sea star its spiny skin.

Nervous system
Echinoderms have a simple nervous system with a central nerve ring connected to nerves in each arm.

Digestive glands   Gonads

Digestive system
Nutrients from food pass from the digestive organs to the coelom. Then the nutrients spread through the body. Digestive wastes leave the body through the anus.

Reproductive system
Each sea star has gonads—a pair of either testes or ovaries—in each arm.

The suction-cup-like ends of the extended tube feet then attach to a hard surface, such as a rock. When muscles in the tube feet contract, water flows out of the tube feet and back into the ampullae. The tube feet shorten, pulling the sea star forward.

Sea stars can also use their water vascular system to secure food. By attaching their tube feet to the two shells of a mollusk, for example, they can pry open its shell.

Like the water vascular system, the digestive, reproductive, and nervous systems in a sea star are stacked within the central disk and radiate into each arm. You can see the location of these systems in *Figure 24.2* on page 573.

Although many echinoderms can reproduce asexually by regeneration, all echinoderms reproduce sexually. Sea stars gather at certain times of the year to reproduce. They release sperm and eggs into the water, where fertilization occurs. The larvae produced swim freely for about two years, then settle to the ocean floor and mature into adults.

FIGURE 24.4
These starfish larvae have bilateral symmetry. They live as larvae for about two years. How does bilateral symmetry compare with radial symmetry?

Echinoderm larvae interest biologists because, unlike the adults, they have bilateral symmetry. Scientists speculate that the first adult echinoderms probably had bilateral symmetry, and that their radial symmetry evolved later.

ORIGIN AND DIVERSITY OF ECHINODERMS

It's all in the tissues

You learned in Chapter 21 that taxonomists can classify animals based on similarities in the development of their embryos. These similarities can be an indicator of evolutionary relationships between animals. Animal embryos develop from a fertilized egg into a blastula, as shown in *Figure 24.6*. The cells of the blastula then move inward to form the gastrula. The place where the cells move inward becomes an opening into a cavity of the gastrula. This opening is

FIGURE 24.5
Phylum Echinodermata

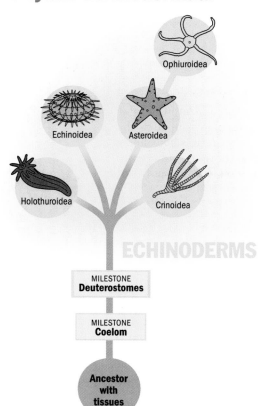

Ophiuroidea

Echinoidea

Asteroidea

Holothuroidea

Crinoidea

ECHINODERMS

MILESTONE
Deuterostomes

MILESTONE
Coelom

Ancestor with tissues

Do It!

Modeling Symmetry

You can model asymmetry, radial symmetry, and bilateral symmetry when you . . .

Try This

1 Experiment with pieces of paper to create models of each form.
2 Select three organisms that you have read about—each of which displays a different type of symmetry.
3 Trace the shape of each organism on tissue paper, cut them out, and fold them.

Analyze Your Results

Were your selections of organisms correctly matched to their type of symmetry?

called the blastopore. The blastopore will become either the mouth or the anus of the developing organism.

In many animals, such as mollusks, worms, and arthropods, the blastopore develops into a mouth. An animal in which a blastopore develops into a mouth is called a **protostome** (PRO-toh-stome), which means "first mouth." Later in the protostome's development, a second digestive tube opening forms at the opposite end of the digestive tract. This becomes the anus.

In echinoderms, the blastopore develops into an anus, and a mouth forms later at the opposite end of the digestive tube. An animal in which a blastopore develops into an anus is called a **deuterostome** (DOO-ter-oh-stome), which means "second mouth." The evolution of deuterostomes and protostomes represents a major milestone in the evolutionary development of animals.

In addition to echinoderms, animals called chordates are also deuterstomes. You will read about chordates in the next section. Taxonomists have concluded that echinoderms and chordates are closely related. The two groups may have shared a common ancestor.

Echinoderms are divided into five classes based on their structural differences. These classes are Asteroidea (ah-stur-OID-ee-uh), Ophiuroidea (ahf-ee-yur-OID-ee-uh), Echinoidea (eck-ih-NOID-ee-uh), Holothuroidea (hahl-oh-thur-OID-ee-uh), and Crinoidea (krih-NOID-ee-uh). Although these names may sound strange to you, you are probably familiar with some members of the classes.

Sea stars Sea stars, or starfish, make up the class Asteroidea. Although most sea stars have five arms, some species may have 20 or more! Look again at *Figure 24.2* to review the basic structure of sea stars.

FIGURE 24.6

Protostome and Deuterostome Development

1 Blastula
A blastula is the hollow ball of cells that forms after many cleavages—cell divisions—of the original zygote.

2 The blastopore opening forms when surface cells move inward. Inward movement of cells starts gastrula formation.

Blastopore

3 Gastrula
The gastrula has two cell layers—ectoderm and endoderm. The gastrula's cavity will become a digestive tube.

Ectoderm
Endoderm
Early digestive tube

4 A third cell layer, mesoderm, forms. The blastopore is the only opening in the gastrula.

Mesoderm
Ectoderm
Endoderm
Early digestive tube

Anus

Mouth

Mouth (blastopore)

Anus (blastopore)

Early digestive tube

Early digestive tube

5a Protostome
In a protostome, the blastopore becomes the mouth. Later in development, an anus forms where the digestive tube makes another opening.

5b Deuterostome
In a deuterostome, the blastopore becomes the anus. Later in development, a mouth forms where the digestive tube makes a second opening.

FIGURE 24.7
Some sea stars, like this one, have many arms. How many arms do most sea stars have?

Kingdom: Animalia

Phylum: Echinodermata

Five classes:
Asteroidea
Ophiuroidea
Echinoidea
Holothuroidea
Crinoidea

Most asteroids are scavengers and carnivores. They locate food sources by sensing them chemically. Asteroids feed primarily on gastropods, bivalves, crustaceans, polychaetes, and other echinoderms.

Brittle stars and basket stars

The brittle stars and basket stars comprise the class Ophiuroidea. Like most of the sea stars, these animals have five arms. Their arms, however, are longer, thinner, and more mobile than those of sea stars. Their tube feet lack suction-cup-like ends, and they do not have ampullae. Basket stars capture plankton with highly branched arms, which they then roll in toward the mouth.

The brittle stars and basket stars move more quickly than any other echinoderm. Brittle stars move by extending an arm in the direction they are headed. They trail two other arms behind and use the remaining two arms as oars. Like sea stars, ophiuroids tend to be scavengers and carnivores, although some obtain nutrition by filter feeding.

Sea urchins and sand dollars

The sea urchins and sand dollars are members of the class Echinoidea. The echinoids have bodies shaped like spheres or discs and have no arms. Their bodies are covered with movable spines. In some sea urchin species, the spines are very long and sharp and sometimes contain poisons. Methods of locomotion and feeding differ among echinoid species. Sea urchins use both their tube feet and their spines to move. Sand dollars burrow, using their spines to dig into the sand. Most sea urchins are grazers—although deep-sea species tend to be sediment feeders and scavengers.

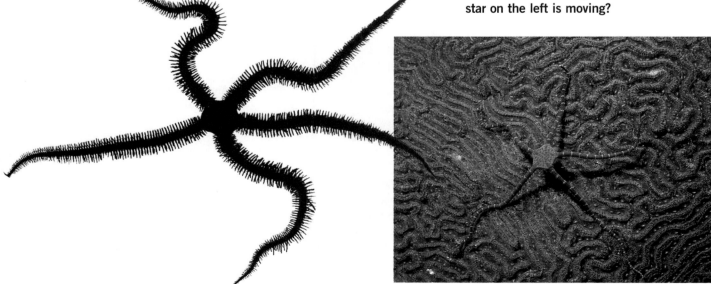

FIGURE 24.8
In what direction do you think the brittle star on the left is moving?

FIGURE 24.9
Protective, movable spines are characteristic of sea urchins. Note the radial symmetry in the view of the mouth (below).

Sand dollars are sediment feeders, selecting food particles from the sediments in which they burrow.

Sea cucumbers Sea cucumbers belong to the class Holothuroidea. Sea cucumbers lack the characteristics of many echinoderms, particularly the arms and a five-part body. The only obvious signs of a five-part body plan in sea cucumbers are the five rows of tube feet running the length of the body. Like sea stars and sea urchins, sea cucumbers use their tube feet for movement.

Some sea cucumbers have sticky tentacle-like tube feet surrounding the mouth, which collect plankton. When disturbed by a predator, a sea cucumber protects itself by shooting long thin tubules out of its anus. By doing so, a sea cucumber sometimes ejects its entire digestive system. However, because of its regenerative abilities, it can grow a new digestive tube in a matter of days.

Sea lilies and feather stars Sea lilies and feather stars comprise the class Crinoidea, the most ancient looking of echinoderms. Only a few species of this class remain today, but crinoids are quite common in the fossil record. Sea lilies have stalks and are sessile. Feather stars can creep and even swim. Unlike all other echinoderms, crinoids have their mouth on the dorsal surface. Five or more arms reach up, swaying around the mouth. Their tube feet, which are covered with sticky mucus, capture plankton and move it to their mouth.

Echinoderm Drillers

Sea urchins usually use their spines and teeth to burrow into sand and rocks. One sea urchin in California, however, drilled 10 millimeters (mm) into a solid steel girder—a feat that took 20 years!

FIGURE 24.10
Compare the sea cucumber (left) with the sea lily (right). Where are the mouths located in these two species?

ECHINODERMS IN THE BIOSPHERE

Food for thought

Sea cucumbers and sea urchin eggs are considered food delicacies in many cultures. Researchers also use sea urchin eggs for biological research. And like members of nearly all other marine invertebrate phyla, echinoderms are a potential source of new pharmaceuticals.

When sea urchins overpopulate, however, they prevent kelp and other seaweeds from attaching to the ocean floor. Their overpopulation can affect an entire ecosystem. In California, predation of abalone by sea otters led abalone harvesters to hunt sea otters. Sea otters are also a predator of sea urchins. What do you think happened to the marine ecosystem when otters were hunted to near extinction?

FIGURE 24.11
It might take several hundred years to grow the coral that this crown-of-thorns (*A. planci*) sea star can eat in one year.

ENVIRONMENTAL AWARENESS

Coral attack!

In 1969 the crown-of-thorns sea star, *Acanthaster planci*, destroyed 90 percent of the coral off the northwest coast of Guam. During the past 20 years, this sea star has also attacked more than 25 percent of the 2000-km-long Great Barrier Reef of Australia. In fact, just one sea star can consume the polyps from up to 13 square meters (m^2) of coral each year.

The effect of *A. planci* on the ecosystem is like that of a forest fire. In one reproductive season, one crown-of-thorns sea star can produce 65 million eggs. Normally, most of the freshly hatched larvae are eaten by fish and other animals. However, there are periodic population explosions, and a huge number of *A. planci* larvae mature into a hoard of hungry, coral-eating adults. Because the coral and the algae housed by coral are at the lowest level of the food chain, an outbreak of *A. planci* can destroy the ecosystem for many years.

CHECKPOINT 24.1

1. What are the common characteristics of echinoderms?
2. How does the embryonic development of echinoderms and chordates differentiate them from other animals?
3. **Critical Thinking** Compare tube feet—their structure and function—among the classes of echinoderms.

Build on What You Know

4. List ways in which echinoderms are structurally different from arthropods. *(Need to jog your memory? Revisit relevant concepts in Chapter 23, Section 23.1.)*

What characteristics do echinoderms share?

Exploring Echinoderm Diversity

WHAT YOU WILL DO Observe specimens or photographs of a variety of echinoderms and note differences and similarities

SKILLS YOU WILL USE Observing, hypothesizing, collecting and recording data, classifying

WHAT YOU WILL NEED Preserved echinoderm specimens or photographs of echinoderms

Propose a Hypothesis

Can you classify echinoderms by observing their external anatomy? Propose a hypothesis that suggests your opinion on this question.

Conduct Your Experiment

1 Briefly examine each of the echinoderm specimens or photographs of echinoderms.
2 Make a chart entitled "Echinoderm Features." Along the top of the chart, list the observable physical characteristics of echinoderms, including structures for feeding and movement. Along the side of the chart, list the names of the specimens or photographs.
3 Examine each of the echinoderms more closely. Fill in the relevant information about each echinoderm on your chart.
4 Draw each of the echinoderms and label its distinguishing features.

Analyze Your Data

1 Do any of the echinoderms on your chart share the same major features? If so, which animals share which features?
2 Which feature allows echinoderms to adapt to a slow-moving or sessile existence? Are any of the specimens you observed truly sessile?

Draw Conclusions

1 Are the echinoderms you examined more different than they are alike, or more alike than they are different? Explain.
2 Based on your observations, classify the echinoderms.

Design a Related Experiment

Suppose you were given an unidentified echinoderm and asked to classify it. What criteria would you use to determine the class to which it belongs? Design an experiment to test your procedure.

Lab: Exploring Echinoderm Diversity

Objective: To identify the differences and similarities among a variety of echinoderms.

Echinoderm Features

Specimen	Appendages	Shape	Feeding Structures	Movement Structures

24.2 Invertebrate Chordates

What you'll learn

IDEAS
- To describe the four characteristics of chordates
- To distinguish between the two subphyla of invertebrate chordates

WORDS
dorsal hollow nerve cord, notochord, gill slits, post-anal tail

A food chain surprise
Scientists have made a recent discovery about the food chain in the Antarctic Ocean. Krill, which are small, shrimplike crustaceans, have always been considered the main food supply there. But in some years, planktonic tunicates called salps (right) are so numerous that they replace krill as the base of the food chain.

CHARACTERISTICS OF CHORDATES

Missing links?

As you may recall from Chapter 21, scientists commonly divide animals into two main groups: vertebrates—animals with a backbone—and invertebrates—animals without a backbone. The phylum Chordata contains both types of animals and can therefore be subdivided into the invertebrate chordates and the vertebrate chordates.

The vertebrates—fishes, amphibians, reptiles, birds, and mammals—are the most familiar members of the phylum Chordata. The invertebrate chordates, which do not have a backbone, are less familiar. You will learn about the invertebrate chordates—tunicates and lancelets—in this section.

All chordates share four structural characteristics at some point in their life cycle: a dorsal hollow nerve cord, a notochord, gill slits, and a post-anal tail. In most chordates, including humans, these characteristics are present only during early stages of embryonic development. You can locate the four characteristic chordate structures in the lancelet shown in *Figure 24.12*.

Most invertebrates that are not chordates have a nerve cord that is solid and located on the ventral side

FIGURE 24.12
Structure of a Lancelet

The lancelet is a typical invertebrate chordate. Why might scientists think that an ancestor of today's lancelets may have given rise to the primitive fish?

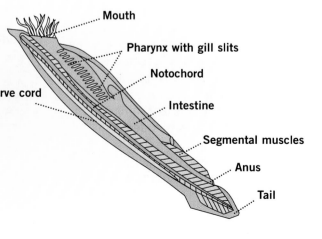

Mouth
Pharynx with gill slits
Notochord
Dorsal hollow nerve cord
Intestine
Segmental muscles
Anus
Tail

of the animal's body. Chordates, however, have a **dorsal hollow nerve cord**—a nerve cord that is located along the back of the animal. In most chordates, the anterior (front) end of the nerve cord develops into a brain.

A **notochord** is a firm but flexible supporting rod located just below the nerve cord. The notochord gives the phylum Chordata its name. Chordates are the only animals that have a notochord at some point in their lives. In nearly all vertebrate chordates, a backbone replaces the notochord during embryonic development. In invertebrate chordates, the notochord may or may not remain in the adults.

Gill slits are paired openings along the pharynx. Invertebrate chordates use the gill slits for filter-feeding. In most vertebrate chordates, the gill slits have become modified for gas exchange or other purposes.

At some point in development, all chordates, including humans, have a tail that extends beyond the anus. This tail is called a **post-anal tail**. In most invertebrates that are not chordates, both the body and digestive tract end at the anus.

ORIGIN AND DIVERSITY OF INVERTEBRATE CHORDATES

Relatively speaking

What might a starfish and a lancelet have in common? The question is not easily answered by looking at the adult organisms. But by comparing larval stages of echinoderms, invertebrate chordates, and vertebrate chordates, biologists have concluded that the three types of organisms may share a common ancestor. All three may have evolved from an organism that was a sessile, filter-feeding adult with a motile larval form.

There are two subphyla of invertebrate chordates: Urochordata and Cephalochordata. The urochordates

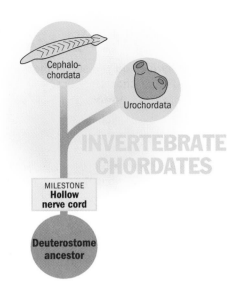

FIGURE 24.13

Phylum Chordata

There are two chordate subphyla that contain invertebrates: Urochordata (tunicates) and Cephalochordata (lancelets).

Kingdom: Animalia

Phylum: Chordata

Subphyla:
Urochordata
Cephalochordata

are the tunicates, and the cephalochordates are the lancelets.

Tunicates Tunicates, or sea squirts, are named for their leathery outer covering—a tunic—and for their tendency to squirt sea water when they are disturbed. Most adult tunicates are sessile, but the larvae are free-swimming. Larval tunicates have the four chordate characteristics. As *Figure 24.14* shows, adult tunicates retain only gill slits—they have lost all

---

LAB ZONE **Think About It!**

Comparing Structures and Systems of an Echinoderm and a Chordate

You have already read about the external structures and internal systems of several invertebrates. You can compare animals from two phyla when you . . .

Try This

1 The diagram on page 573 shows a sea star. Note the animal's structures and systems.
2 Review the lancelet diagram on page 580, noting its structures and systems.

Analyze Your Results

1 Do the the sea star and lancelet share any similar external structures? If so, which?
2 What characteristics does the lancelet have that the sea star, as an echinoderm, does not have?

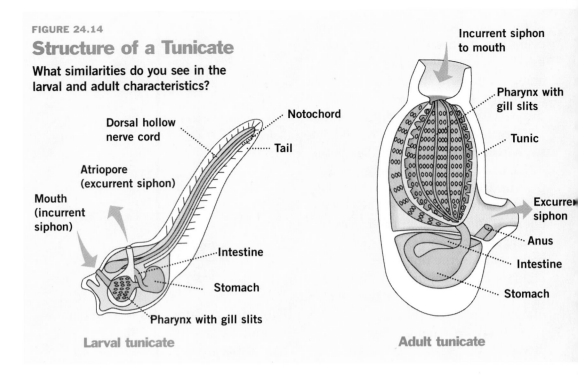

FIGURE 24.14

Structure of a Tunicate

What similarities do you see in the larval and adult characteristics?

Dorsal hollow nerve cord

Notochord

Tail

Atriopore (excurrent siphon)

Mouth (incurrent siphon)

Intestine

Stomach

Pharynx with gill slits

Larval tunicate

Incurrent siphon to mouth

Pharynx with gill slits

Tunic

Excurrent siphon

Anus

Intestine

Stomach

Adult tunicate

signs of a notochord, dorsal hollow nerve cord, and post-anal tail.

Lancelets The other invertebrate chordate subphylum includes the lancelets. Many biologists think that an ancestor of today's lancelets evolved into a primitive, fishlike vertebrate.

Lancelets retain the four chordate characteristics as adults. Although they can swim, they are usually buried in sand with just their heads exposed. Like tunicates, they feed by filtering particles from water through their mucus-lined gill slits.

FIGURE 24.15
What differences do you see between this tunicate and the sponges you saw in Chapter 21?

CHECKPOINT 24.2

1. What are the four characteristics of chordates?
2. How do urochordates and cephalochordates differ?
3. **Critical Thinking** Why would a free-swimming larval stage be an advantage for tunicates?

Build on What You Know

4. Compare how the following two sessile organisms obtain food: a sponge and a tunicate. *(Need to jog your memory? Revisit relevant concepts in Chapter 21, Section 21.2.)*

What is the evolutionary relationship between invertebrate chordates and vertebrates?

Chapter 24 Review

24.1 Echinoderms are marine animals with spiny skin, an endoskeleton, and a water vascular system.

24.2 Invertebrate chordates represent possible evolutionary links between invertebrates and vertebrates.

Sum It Up

Use the following summary to review the main concepts in this chapter.

24.1 Echinoderms

- Echinoderms are marine invertebrates. They have external or internal spines, an endoskeleton made of calcium, and radial symmetry.
- Echinoderms have a water vascular system—a network of fluid-filled tubes that allows them to move, obtain food, and exchange gases.
- A sea star's digestive, nervous, and reproductive systems extend from a central disk into each of the organism's arms.
- Although many echinoderms reproduce asexually by regeneration, all can reproduce sexually.
- Echinoderms are divided into five classes: Asteroidea, Ophiuroidea, Echinoidea, Holothuroidea, and Crinoidea.
- Echinoderms are a source of food and new pharmaceuticals for humans. Echinoderms can cause problems in the environment through overpopulation or predation.

24.2 Invertebrate Chordates

- Most members of the phylum Chordata are vertebrates. There are, however, two subphyla of invertebrate chordates: tunicates and lancelets.
- Invertebrate and vertebrate chordates share certain embryonic-stage characteristics: a dorsal hollow nerve cord, notochord, post-anal tail, and gill slits. Some adult chordates retain these features, but most lose them by the end of embryonic development.
- Tunicates have a leathery outer covering and are sessile as adults. Most chordate characteristics are seen in tunicate larvae only.
- Lancelets are filter-feeding, fishlike organisms.

Use Terms and Concepts

Use each of the following words or terms in a complete sentence. If you need to review a meaning, turn to the page indicated.

echinoderm (p. 572)

water vascular system (p. 573)

ampulla (p. 573)

tube foot (p. 573)

protostome (p. 575)

deuterostome (p. 575)

dorsal hollow nerve cord (p. 581)

notochord (p. 581)

gill slits (p. 581)

post-anal tail (p. 581)

Use Your Word Power

COMPLETION Write the word or phrase that best completes each statement.

1. _____ is an animal in which a blastopore develops into a mouth.

2. The _____ is a network of fluid-filled tubes.

3. Tunicates have _____ , paired openings along the pharynx that are used for filter feeding.

4. A muscular sac in echinoderms that helps pump water is called a(n) _____ .

5. A firm but flexible supporting rod present in lancelets is the _____ .

6. A(n) _____ is hollow, with an end that functions like a suction cup.

7. The _____ is an animal in which a blastopore develops into an anus.

TRUE-FALSE Write true if the statement is true. If the statement is false, replace the underlined word(s) to make the statement true.

8. A sea star's <u>water vascular system</u> stores wastes in the body.

9. An echinoderm larva has <u>bilateral</u> symmetry.

10. Adult <u>sea squirts</u> have a dorsal hollow nerve cord.

11. In vertebrate chordates, the <u>dorsal hollow nerve cord</u> is usually replaced by a backbone.

12. All chordates have a <u>post-anal tail.</u>

13. In a <u>protostome</u>, a mouth forms from a blastopore.

14. Invertebrate chordates use <u>gill slits</u> for filter feeding.

15. Sea stars and crinoids are examples of <u>vertebrates.</u>

16. When feeding, a sea star uses its <u>ampulla</u> to pry open the shells of clams.

Show What You Know

17. Compare the reactions of sea cucumbers and sea squirts to predators.

18. Explain how a decrease in abalone off the coast of California led to an increase in sea urchins.

19. How do sea stars use their vascular and digestive structures to feed on mollusks?

20. Briefly describe the process of sexual reproduction in sea stars.

21. Describe the process brittle stars use to move. How does this method of movement differ from that used by sea stars?

22. **Make a Concept Map** Make a concept map that shows how the relationships between invertebrate and vertebrate chordates are revealed through embryology. Use the following terms: gill slits, notochord, post-anal tail, lungs, backbone, dorsal hollow nerve cord, embryo, gills, protostome, deuterostome, anus, mouth, and blastopore.

Take It Further

23. **Developing a Hypothesis** Some scientists suggest that the common ancestor of chordates was sessile and looked something like a tunicate. They hypothesize that lancelets and vertebrates developed from the motile larvae of these sessile chordates. Evaluate this hypothesis and give reasons why you agree or disagree.

24. **Making a Generalization** What is the general pattern in the distribution of digestive, vascular, nervous, and reproductive systems in sea stars? Relate this pattern to a sea star's ability to reproduce by regeneration.

25. **Making an Analogy** *Urchin* comes from the Latin *ericius,* meaning "hedgehog." What do sea urchins and hedgehogs have in common?

26. Analyzing Data Organisms A and B have five arms. Organism C has internal spines. C and D have no arms, but D has movable spines. A and C feed on plankton and have sticky tentacles. B feeds on bivalves. Using these data, decide which class the organisms belong to: Asteroidea, Ophiuroidea, Echinoidea, Holothuroidea, and Crinoidea.

27. Interpreting a Graph An adult crown-of-thorns starfish can consume 13 square meters (m^2) of coral a year. This graph shows how many starfish were present on a hectare of reef at selected locations. (A hectare is equal to 10,000 m^2.) How much coral could be consumed in a year at location C? At location D? What is the maximum number of starfish that could theoretically be supported in one hectare? What do you think will happen at location E?

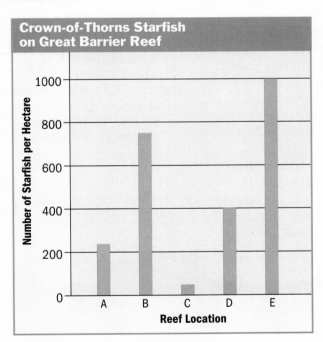

Crown-of-Thorns Starfish on Great Barrier Reef

Number of Starfish per Hectare (y-axis) vs. Reef Location (x-axis: A, B, C, D, E)

28. Designing an Experiment Sea stars have receptor cells that are sensitive to the concentration of chemicals in sea water. Predict how sea stars would respond to a sharp increase or decrease in the concentration of salt in the water. Design an experiment to test your prediction.

29. Coral Carnivores Suppose you were assigned to protect a coral reef that is under attack from sea stars. Local inhabitants have suggested the following solutions: (a) Chop up adult sea stars and return them to the ocean to provide food for other species. (b) Import predators to feed on the sea star larvae. (c) Disperse chemicals around the reef that are poisonous to sea star larvae. (d) Remove the sea star eggs before they can hatch. (e) Wait until there are no longer enough coral polyps to sustain the population of sea stars. Offer arguments for and against each proposed solution.

Make New Connections

30. Biology and Physics The ends of an echinoderm's tube feet act as suction cups. The ability of those structures to cling tightly to an object can be explained using principles of physics. Look up *fluid pressure* in a physical science book, and explain how these suction cups work.

31. Biology and Language Research the connection between common terms and biological terms. Find out what a Roman ampulla and a biological ampulla have in common. Compare a radial canal to the Erie Canal. What do a kitchen sieve and a sieve plate have in common? What traits do a basket and a basket star share? Compare a sea lily to a calla lily. What might a tunic and a tunicate have in common?

FAST-FORWARD TO CHAPTER 25

Biologists hypothesize that lancelets with their gill slits and fish with their gills share a common ancestor. In Chapter 25, you will learn about fish, which are vertebrate chordates.

Unit 6 Review

Connect the Chapters

1. What characteristics do the bodies of annelids and arthropods have in common? How do their body structures differ?
2. Both jellyfish and squid have tentacles surrounding their mouths. Compare how the tentacles function to capture their prey.
3. Describe the adaptations that sponges, mussels, and barnacles use to obtain food. What common obstacle do these adaptations address?
4. Compare the excretory structures of earthworms and spiders.
5. What characteristics do most ticks and leeches have in common?
6. Compare the habitats, locomotion, and food-gathering strategies of sea anemones and scorpions.
7. Using a sea star as an example, illustrate the four major milestones in the evolution of animals.

Connect the Units

8. Compare how sponges and some monerans respond to harsh conditions.
9. Zebra mussels eat green algae. How could removing zebra mussels from Lake Erie affect the amount of dissolved oxygen in the lake?
10. How does the absence of a complex transport system affect the structure of mosses and flatworms?

Connect to Themes

11. **Unity and Diversity** What features are common in the digestive systems of earthworms and grasshoppers? What features vary?
12. **Patterns of Change/Cycle** Compare the life cycle of jellyfish and butterflies.
13. **Evolution** What do trilobite fossils reveal about arthropod evolution?
14. **Systems and Interactions** How does the interaction of muscles with water influence the locomotion of roundworms and echinoderms?

project plans

1 Choose an insect that is a threat to either an agricultural crop or an ornamental plant that grows in your region of the country. Find out what farmers or gardeners have done in the past to limit damage from the insect. Are there any drawbacks to the traditional methods? Describe alternative control methods that have been, or are being, developed.

2 Amateur naturalists in North America take part in a butterfly census each July. Scientists who study butterflies can analyze the data collected over a number of years. Find out more about the annual butterfly count by writing to the North American Butterfly Association, 909 Birch Street, Baraboo, WI 53913. Ask what the requirements are to participate, and whether there are local groups in your area.

CRITIC'S CORNER

A BOOK REVIEW BY ABBY GREENBAUM GLOUCESTER, MA

The Sea of Cortez, by novelist John Steinbeck and marine biologist Ed Ricketts, chronicles the authors' six-week voyage in the Gulf of California. The book describes the marine wildlife of the Gulf and the people who participated in the expedition, and it includes several humorous anecdotes. The combination of scientific information and poetic description keeps the book moving and provides a rare insight into the wonders of the marine world.

SPOTLIGHT ON CAREERS

JUNE KANTZ

Lobster fisher off Peaks Island, Maine

EDUCATION: B.A. in sociology; Kantz's father is a lobster fisher, and she always wanted to work on the water.

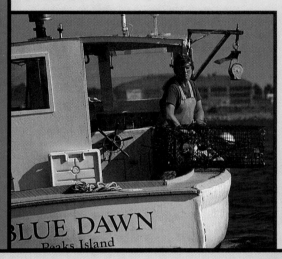

"I fish alone and I like it that way. It's peaceful. I've always liked being on the water. Once you pull the lobster traps in, you always end up throwing some back. If you have a female with eggs you have to notch its tail and throw it back, so that she can release her eggs. In Maine, there are minimum and maximum size limits for lobsters. They have to be at least $3\frac{1}{4}$ inches from the eyeball socket to the end of the carapace, where the tail starts. The reason for the limits is to allow them to spawn at least once before you trap them. . . . Lobsters need to shed their shells to grow. Just after they shed, they hide in the rocks because they are vulnerable to predators. Lobsters are cannibals; if a lobster finds a smaller one with a soft shell, it will eat it."

 Explore the Internet site http://invertebrates.biosurf.com to find out more about lobsters and lobster fishing.

DR. JOSHUA FEINGOLD

Visiting Professor of marine biology, Nova Southeastern University

EDUCATION: Ph.D. in marine biology, M.S. in biological oceanography, B.S. in biology and philosophy.

"What I like best about my work is the challenge of complex problem solving. I have new experiences every time I go back to the field. I'm discovering things about the natural world that nobody else knows, and I'm contributing to a better understanding of how coral ecosystems function. This work requires scuba diving, computer expertise, and the ability to maintain and repair scientific equipment. . . . In one project, I worked in the Galapagos Islands. . . . One of the great benefits of this job is the ability to work in the natural world and to see a lot of beautiful things. But when the water is cold and the equipment malfunctions, you still have to do the work! It is a glamorous-sounding job, but you need dedication and perseverance."

bioSURF Explore the Internet address http://invertebrates.biosurf.com to find out more about marine biology and coral reefs.

"My findings can make it easier for wildlife managers to protect and conserve natural resources."
— DR. JOSHUA FEINGOLD

Which of these amazing statements about vertebrates are fact, and which are fiction?

Hit *or* Myth?

There are **no penguins** at the North Pole.

(Fact. There are no penguins anywhere in the Northern Hemisphere. All 17 varieties of penguins are found below the equator, primarily in Antarctica.)

A rattlesnake **hears** its own rattle.

(Fiction—Snakes lack external ears, but a single earbone is attached to the jaw. Snakes can hear low-frequency sounds, but not sounds in the higher ranges, such as the rattle.)

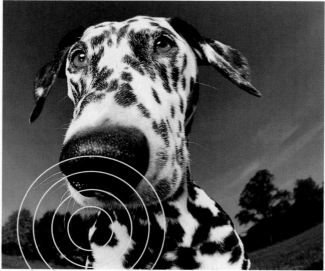

Woodpeckers get **headaches** from all their hammering.

(Fiction. Pockets of air in the woodpecker's head cushion its head bones as it bores or drills.)

Nose prints are used to identify dogs the way fingerprints are used to identify people.

(Fact. Breeders and trainers even keep nose prints on file, and insurance companies require them if a dog is being bonded.)

The chameleon's tongue is **longer than its body.**

(Fact. With a tongue several centimeters longer than its body, the chameleon can catch an insect some 25 centimeters away.)

The archerfish uses **spitballs** to catch prey.

(Fact. Adult archerfishes can shoot down insects by spitting water droplets up to 1.5 meters into the air.)

Birds keep their eggs **warm** by sitting on them.

(Fact and fiction. Although this is true in cool climates, in desert environments birds insulate their eggs from the heat by sitting on them.)

This amphibian is enjoying a tasty **meal.**

(Fiction. This frog has swallowed a poisonous insect and is eliminating the noxious food by ejecting its stomach.)

CHAPTER 25

Fishes and Amphibians

You can find out more about
fishes and amphibians at the
following Internet address:
http://vertebrates.biosurf.com

In this chapter . . .

FEATURES

Everyday Biology
• Greasing the Way to Health
• Frog Skin Cream

In the Community
Fish-Smart Markets

 Environmental Awareness
Amphibian Alarm

LAB ZONES

Discover It!
• Observing Vertebrate Jaws

Do It!
• How Does a Fish's Swim Bladder Work?
• How Is Tadpole Development Affected by Temperature?

Think About It!
• Comparing Amphibian and Fish Circulatory Systems

Investigate It!
• Analyzing the Respiration of a Fish

THE JAWS OF LIFE

More than 400 million years ago, long before any animal walked on land, the first sharks swam the seas. Compared with many other animals, sharks have changed relatively little since then. They have not had to change, because their basic structure has been so successful. Sharks share a feature with nearly all other vertebrates that later evolved: powerful, hinged jaws—an astounding collaboration of muscle, cartilage, and bone working together.

The tiger shark and the great white shark use their strong, flexible jaws, along with rows of razor-sharp teeth, to bite large chunks of meat from their prey. But the largest living shark, the whale shark, uses its immense jaws to swallow huge mouthfuls of sea water and then filter out the plankton and small crustaceans on which it feeds. Even the smallest sharks, which are only 10–15 centimeters (cm) long, have similar jaws that are capable of bearing down hard on prey.

Jaws that can snap shut are one of the adaptations that evolved in animals with backbones over millions of years, as they spread through the ocean, land, and air. What other adaptations do humans share with fishes and amphibians, the two oldest groups of vertebrates?

The tooth on the right came from a great white shark. On the left is a fossilized tooth from a shark that lived at least 5 million years ago. The megalodon shark could grow to 18 meters (m)—about the length of two school buses! The largest shark alive today is the whale shark, which grows to lengths of over 12m.

Observing Vertebrate Jaws

You need magazines and books that contain photographs of fishes, amphibians, and other vertebrates

1. Find at least three photographs of each type of vertebrate. Make a simple drawing of the jaw of each animal, including any specialized structures such as teeth.
2. Arrange your drawings in groups based on simi!arities and differences.

The structure of an animal's jaw can provide you with evidence about the type of food an animal eats and the way it obtains that food. Write one or more inferences about the feeding habits of the three vertebrate groups you examined. If your observations inspired any questions, write them down for later investigation.

WRITE ABOUT IT!

You have probably seen movies and read stories about sharks and other carnivores that attack their prey with powerful jaws. Outline your own story about such a predator, or write a summary of a story or scene that impressed you. Include a vivid description of the animal's appearance.

25.1 Vertebrates

The flexible ferret
The basic vertebrate skeleton includes a flexible but sturdy backbone. The ferret has a streamlined head, short legs, and an extraordinarily twistable spine. It is well adapted for slithering into the narrow holes of its prey—small rodents who live in underground burrows. Ferrets, which are sometimes also called polecats, are often kept as pets.

CHARACTERISTICS OF VERTEBRATES

No longer spineless

What do an elephant, a guppy, a turtle, and a parakeet have in common? Each has a backbone. Animals with a backbone are called **vertebrates.** Of all the animals, you are probably most familiar with vertebrates, for the simple reason that you are a vertebrate. Fishes, amphibians, reptiles, birds, and mammals are all vertebrates.

Recall from Chapter 24 that vertebrates belong to the phylum Chordata, which also includes the invertebrate chordates. At some stage in their development, all chordates share four main characteristics: a dorsal nerve cord, a notochord, gill slits or pouches, and a post-anal tail. As you may recall, these characteristics change as most vertebrates develop. For example, the dorsal nerve cord becomes a spinal cord and brain. The notochord is replaced by a backbone. In aquatic vertebrates, the gill slits or pouches become gills. In terrestrial vertebrates, the gill slits or pouches develop into other structures. The post-anal tail is the only characteristic of chordates that most vertebrates keep throughout their lives.

In addition to these four chordate characteristics, all vertebrates have an endoskeleton, which can support a larger body than an exoskeleton can. Also, an endoskeleton grows as the animal grows, so the animal does not have to molt.

As you can see in *Figure 25.1,* the vertebrate skeleton includes a backbone. The backbone is actually a series of bones called vertebrae (VER-tuh-bray; singular: *vertebra*). The vertebrae surround the spinal cord and provide a hard yet flexible structure that protects this vital organ while providing support.

Attached to the anterior end of the backbone is another vertebrate characteristic, a distinct skull. A well-developed brain and sensory organs are located in the skull, a characteristic known as cephalization.

In addition to a rigid endoskeleton and a distinct skull, all vertebrates have a closed circulatory system with a multichambered heart. A closed system means that all the blood that flows through the body is contained within blood vessels. The vertebrate circulatory system allows for the rapid circulation of blood and the efficient delivery of oxygen and nutrients to all the muscles and organs of the body.

FIGURE 25.1
Which parts of this lizard skeleton contain the greatest number of movable joints?

DIVERSITY OF VERTEBRATES

Vertebrate evolution runs cold and hot

Vertebrates first appeared in the fossil record about 500 million years ago. The earliest known vertebrates were fishlike animals called ostracoderms (as-TRAK-uh-durmz), which had neither jaws nor appendages. About 400 million years ago, some descendants of the ostracoderms evolved jaws and paired fins. Subsequent adaptations led to the evolution of other groups of vertebrates, such as amphibians, reptiles, birds, and mammals. You can see the groups of vertebrates in *Figure* 25.2. Notice that the appearance of each new group of vertebrates corresponds to an evolutionary milestone. You will learn about these milestones later in this unit.

One important difference among vertebrates is the ability to regulate body temperature. All animals produce some heat as a result of breaking down the food they eat. But some animals, such as fishes, amphibians, and reptiles, lose heat almost as fast as they produce it. Fishes, amphibians, and reptiles are **ectotherms,** which means their temperature is regulated mainly by their external environment ("ecto-" means "outside," and "-therm" means "heat").

Unlike the ectotherms, birds and mammals can maintain a constant body temperature. Animals that control their temperature with internal processes are **endotherms** ("endo-" means "inside"). Endotherms maintain their body temperature by converting food energy to heat and by controlling heat loss.

FIGURE 25.2

Phylum Chordata
Subphylum Vertebrata

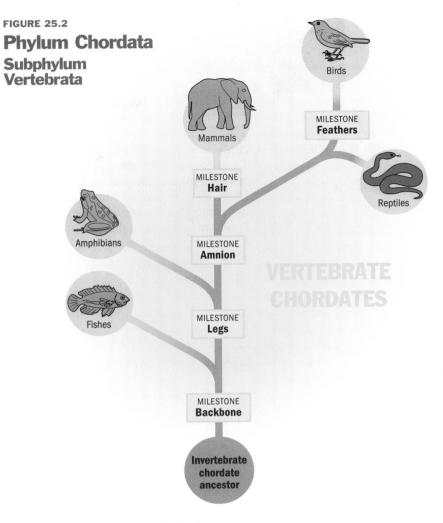

VERTEBRATE CHORDATES

CHECKPOINT 25.1

1. Why are vertebrates classified as members of the phylum Chordata?
2. What are the characteristics common to all vertebrates?
3. **Critical Thinking** Describe how the evolutionary milestone characteristics enabled some vertebrates to live on land.

Build on What You Know

4. By what process is food converted to energy within animal cells? How would endothermy affect an animal's need for food? *(Need to jog your memory? Revisit relevant concepts in Chapter 4, Section 4.3.)*

What is the main characteristic of a vertebrate?

25.2 Characteristics of Fishes

What you'll learn

IDEAS
• To explain the adaptations of fishes to their environment
• To describe the life cycle of fishes

WORDS
swim bladder,
lateral line system

Can you race that fish?
If you could match the speed of the fastest humans, you would run about 10 meters per second (m/s). The fastest you could swim would be only about 2 m/s. In contrast, a marlin can swim at a speed of over 20 m/s. The ability to move fast is just one way in which this fish is adapted for life in the water.

MOVEMENT AND RESPONSE

Sleek, slippery, and on the go

Fishes are well adapted for living in water. Look at *Figure* 25.3. Most fishes have overlapping scales that cover the skin. The scales are coated with slippery mucus, which helps insulate and protect their bodies from the cold. The smooth scales and narrow shape of a fish reduce friction as the fish swims through the water.

Most fishes have a **swim bladder** that helps them move up and down in the water or remain at a given depth. The swim bladder is a thin-walled sac that can inflate or deflate when gases from the blood pass into or out of it. You can see the swim bladder in *Figure* 25.3. As the swim bladder fills with gas, the fish becomes more buoyant and rises in the water. When the swim bladder deflates, the fish becomes less buoyant and sinks.

Sharks do not have a swim bladder, but they do have a large, oily liver. Because oil is less dense than water, the liver provides some buoyancy. To avoid sinking, some sharks never stop swimming, even when sleeping. The flow of the water over the lateral fins

provides lift, similar to the movement of air over an airplane wing. Fishes depend on their fins to steer and provide stability in the water.

Some fishes have well-developed sense organs that help them locate prey. A shark's keen sense of smell allows it to detect blood that is one-half a kilometer away. Salmon use their sense of

Fin
Notice the fins. Fins are adaptations for movement. Fishes use their fins to thrust, steer, brake, move up and down, and even swim backwards. Fins are attached to the fish's internal skeleton and are moved by muscle.

---

smell to identify and return to the stream in which they hatched. Some fishes also have specialized receptors on their head that enable them to sense weak electrical charges produced by the muscle contractions of predators and prey. These specialized receptors may also help fishes use Earth's magnetic field to navigate in the ocean.

Most fishes have a set of sensory organs called the **lateral line system** for detecting vibrations and changes in water pressure. The lateral line looks like a groove that runs from head to tail. This adaptation alerts fishes to the movement of other organisms in the water around them.

ENERGY AND WASTES

Fish gills are a gas

Most adult fishes are carnivores with sharp teeth and jaws. The bones and muscles of the jaw enable the mouth to open wide and clamp down on prey. Fishes do not chew their food. Each bite passes to the stomach whole, where it is stored and later digested in the intestine. The digested food is then carried in the blood to all cells of the body. The cells use the food to release energy and build tissues.

To release energy from food, a fish's body cells need oxygen. Fishes use their gills to obtain oxygen. Water

FIGURE 25.3

Structure of a Fish

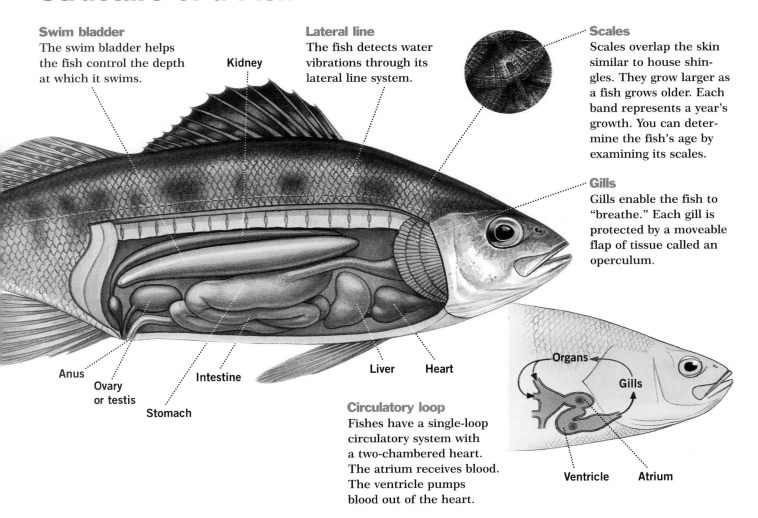

Swim bladder
The swim bladder helps the fish control the depth at which it swims.

Kidney

Lateral line
The fish detects water vibrations through its lateral line system.

Scales
Scales overlap the skin similar to house shingles. They grow larger as a fish grows older. Each band represents a year's growth. You can determine the fish's age by examining its scales.

Gills
Gills enable the fish to "breathe." Each gill is protected by a moveable flap of tissue called an operculum.

Anus

Ovary or testis

Stomach

Intestine

Liver   **Heart**

Circulatory loop
Fishes have a single-loop circulatory system with a two-chambered heart. The atrium receives blood. The ventricle pumps blood out of the heart.

Organs

Gills

Ventricle   **Atrium**

Blood vessels

Water flow

Detail of gill structure

FIGURE 25.4
The gills enable a fish to obtain oxygen and give off carbon dioxide. These projections contain blood vessels so thin that red blood cells pass through in a single file.

passes through the mouth of a fish into two cavities behind the mouth, where the gills are located. Blood vessels in the gills pick up oxygen and release carbon dioxide into the water. Water flows over the gills from front to back, but the blood flows through the

blood vessels of the gills in the opposite direction. The blood passing through the gills is constantly in contact with water that is high in oxygen and low in carbon dioxide. Gills are efficient organs for taking dissolved oxygen from water. Efficiency is important because there is less available oxygen in the water than in air. You can see the path that water takes through the gills in *Figure 25.4*.

The process of respiration is helped by the opening and closing of the movable flaps over the gills, called the opercula (singular: *operculum*). When the mouth opens, the opercula close. The mouth cavity expands and causes water to rush in. When the mouth closes, the opercula open, and water is forced over the gills to the outside. Sharks do not have opercula. Their constant movement keeps water flowing over the gills.

In fishes and other vertebrates, the kidney is an organ that excretes waste. It also plays a role in maintaining the proper amount of water and ions in body fluids. Also, glands in the gills regulate salt. Maintaining water balance is necessary because if there is too little or too much water in the body, the fish will die.

In freshwater fishes the concentration of ions is greater inside the body than in the surrounding water. So water tends to enter the body by osmosis. Freshwater fishes keep the proper water balance by excreting large amounts of water in their urine.

In fishes that live in salt water, the concentration of ions is lower inside the body than in the surrounding water. Without an organ to prevent water loss, saltwater fishes would dry up inside, even though they live in water! The kidneys of these fishes function to prevent water loss. Kidneys allow some fishes to live in both salt-water and freshwater environments.

Do It!

How Does a Fish's Swim Bladder Work?

The swim bladder of a bony fish enables the fish to remain at the same spot easily at any depth in the water. You can observe how the swim bladder works if you . . .

Try This

1 Fill a tank or a large basin with water and inflate a small balloon. Use a small clamp to tie off the balloon.
2 Try to submerge the balloon in the water. What happens?
3 Tie 8–10 keys together and drop them into the water. What happens?
4 Attach a paper clip to the clamp on the balloon. Hang the keys on the paper clip as close as possible to the balloon. Drop the objects into the water.
5 Using the clamp, add or release air until the balloon floats just under the surface of the water as shown in the diagram on the right.

Analyze Your Results

1 Think of the balloon-and-keys combination as a fish. What does the balloon represent?
2 How does this demonstration explain how a fish can remain at the same spot just below the surface of the water?

FIGURE 25.5
Life Cycle of the Salmon

Hatching
1 These salmon eggs hatch within four months of being fertilized. The hatchlings, called fry, will remain in the gravel for a few weeks, feeding from their yolk sac.

Juvenile
2 When they reach a length of about 15 cm, Pacific salmon will begin their journey to the sea, where they will live for months or years.

Adults
3 Adult salmon return to spawn in the river in which they were born. This trip can take several months, covering as much as 3200 kilometers.

Spawning
4 Upon reaching the spawning ground, the female scoops a nest out of gravel on the stream bed and lays her eggs. The male fertilizes the eggs, and the female covers them with more gravel.

LIFE CYCLE OF FISHES

Not a parent in sight

In most fishes, the individuals have a distinct sex. The reproductive habits of fishes are varied. Fertilization may be internal or external. In sharks, fertilization is internal. The eggs are fertilized inside the female's body, where they undergo development. The young sharks, called pups, are born alive.

The life cycle of salmon is an interesting example of external fertilization. You can follow the salmon life cycle in *Figure 25.5*. The female salmon, like all fishes who undergo external fertilization, releases her eggs into the environment. The male swims over the eggs and fertilizes them.

Female fishes typically lay hundreds, thousands, or even millions of eggs, many of which never become fertilized. With few exceptions, parents generally do not care for the eggs or the young, and most eggs are eaten or

die before they hatch. Only a very few individuals survive to become adults.

Reproduction in fishes is a good example of the process of natural selection. Fishes produce many more offspring than their environment can support. Only the fastest, strongest, best-adapted young survive to produce offspring and continue the species.

CHECKPOINT 25.2

1. List the key characteristics of fishes, and explain how each one is an adaptation.
2. Describe the stages in the life cycle of a typical fish.
3. **Critical Thinking** How do each of a fish's sense organs help it to locate prey or escape predators?

Build on What You Know

4. What does the life cycle of fishes illustrate about Darwin's evolutionary theories? *(Need to jog your memory? Revisit relevant concepts in Chapter 10, Section 10.2.)*

FIGURE 25.6
Playing an unusual reproductive role, this male *tilapia* protects the fertilized eggs by carrying them in his mouth. He does not eat until they hatch, about five days later.

Analyzing the Respiration of a Fish

WHAT YOU WILL DO Observe the respiration rate of a goldfish, and develop a hypothesis about the effect of a change in water temperature on fish respiration

SKILLS YOU WILL USE Observing, collecting and recording data, predicting

WHAT YOU WILL NEED Tap water exposed to room temperature air for 24 hours, 500-mL and 1000-mL beakers, fish net, one goldfish, thermometer, timer, ice, hot water (about 80°C)

Propose a Hypothesis

The amount of oxygen that can dissolve in water depends on the temperature of the water. The higher the temperature of the water, the lower the amount of oxygen that can be dissolved. Propose a hypothesis about the effect of water temperature on the rate of fish respiration.

Conduct Your Experiment

1 Pour 250 milliliters (mL) of the room-temperature water into the 500-mL beaker. Using the fish net, place the goldfish in this beaker. Place the thermometer in the beaker.

2 Allow the fish to adjust to its new surroundings for a few minutes. Observe its respiration rate by counting the number of times its opercula open during one minute. Record this rate, along with the temperature of the water.

3 Fill the 1000-mL beaker one-quarter full with crushed ice (as shown in the photo). Place the beaker containing the goldfish inside the large beaker. Allow time for the water temperature of the small beaker to drop to about 15°C.

4 Repeat step 2.

5 Remove the small beaker and empty the large beaker. Pour a small amount of 80°C water in the large beaker and replace the small beaker inside of it. **Caution:** Use care when handling the hot water. You may need an oven mitt.

6 Repeat step 2.

7 Add a small amount of hot water to the large beaker until the temperature of the water in the small beaker reaches 20°C. Record the temperature and the respiration rate of the fish.

8 Repeat Step 7 twice, increasing the temperature to 25°C and 30°C, taking measurements at each step. (**Caution:** Temperatures over 30°C may be harmful to the fish.) Return the fish to its aquarium after the water in the small beaker has reached room temperature.

Analyze Your Data

1 Make a graph to record the respiration rate versus temperature. Plot temperature on the x-axis.

2 What happens to the respiration rate as the temperature increases? Decreases?

Draw Conclusions

Did the results support your hypothesis? What can you conclude from this experiment?

Design a Related Experiment

Suppose you wanted to find out how fish movement is affected by water temperature. Propose a hypothesis and design an experiment to test it.

Temperature	Respiration Rate

25.3 Origin and Diversity of Fishes

How would you feel if you discovered a fish thought to be extinct for more than 70 million years? That is what museum curator Marjorie Courtenay-Latimer did when she recognized a coelacanth (SEE-luh-kanth). South Africans had been catching coelacanths regularly, unaware that they knew something that scientists did not. Today's coelacanths descended from ancestors that lived 400 million years ago.

What you'll learn

IDEAS
- To explain the evolutionary steps that led to modern fishes
- To contrast the different classes of fish

WORDS
lungfish

ORIGIN OF FISHES

Something's fishy in vertebrate evolution

Fishes may have evolved from invertebrate chordates similar to the lancelet shown in *Figure* 25.7. The lancelet shares many characteristics of the first fishes. It has a closed circulatory system similar to that of the early fishes, but it does not have a heart. Its blood is pumped by contractions of the blood vessels. The lancelet also has segmented muscles, which are characteristic of vertebrates, but its brain is as small as a blister at the anterior end of its nerve cord.

Although lancelets resemble fishes, they are invertebrates. The earliest known vertebrate fossils are of fishlike animals called ostracoderms. They were covered with body plates, inspiring their name which comes from *ostrakon,* meaning "shell," and "-derm," meaning "skin." These animals had no jaws or teeth, so their food was limited to small particles that could be strained from the water. Ostracoderms, such as the *Drepanaspis* in *Figure* 25.7, are the ancestors of the modern fishes.

Modern fishes have several adaptations that ostracoderms did not share. One important adaptation was the

FIGURE 25.7
The lancelet (left) closely resembles fossil organisms that are thought to be the ancestors of fishes. The heavily armored, jawless *Drepanaspis* (right) is an extinct ancestor of modern fishes.

FIGURE 25.8
Classes of Fishes

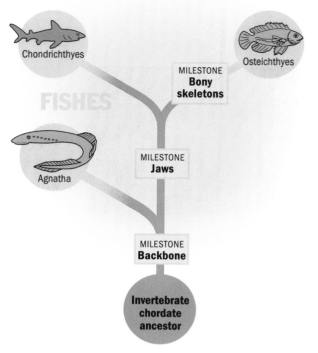

FISHES

Chondrichthyes

Osteichthyes

MILESTONE
Bony skeletons

Agnatha

MILESTONE
Jaws

MILESTONE
Backbone

Invertebrate chordate ancestor

Kingdom: Animalia

Phylum: Chordata

Subphylum: Vertebrata

Classes:
Agnatha
Chondrichthyes
Osteichthyes

FIGURE 25.9
Notice the lamprey's sharp teeth (right). It also has a strong rasplike tongue. Lampreys attach themselves to other fishes (left), living on their body fluids.

Agnathans These jawless fishes most closely resemble the earliest fishes from which all other vertebrates may have evolved. The agnathans are the only vertebrates that retain a notochord throughout life. The agnathans that survive today belong to two groups: the lampreys and the hagfishes.

Both groups have snakelike bodies without paired fins. Lacking paired fins, which help in balance and steering, agnathans are not good swimmers. Lampreys attach themselves to other fishes by means of a round mouth with rasping parts. As parasites, they feed on their host's body fluids. Hagfishes are scavengers. They move slowly through cold water, using sensory tentacles to locate dead and dying fishes.

Chondrichthyes The members of this class—sharks, rays, and skates—all have skeletons made almost entirely of flexible cartilage rather than rigid bone. You may think that these fishes are primitive because of the cartilage skeleton. Actually, it has been shown that the cartilage skeleton of these fishes may have evolved from an earlier bony skeleton. The cartilage skeleton may be an adaptation to deep-sea life.

formation of jaws. Another adaptation was paired fins, which gave the fishes more control over their movements in water. Later, fishes developed strong internal skeletons that could withstand the pulling force of powerful muscles.

FISH DIVERSITY

"And the survivors are. . ."

About 70 percent of Earth's surface is covered with water. Since most of this water is in the ocean, that is where most of the world's fishes live. Today's fishes are classified into three groups. These groups are represented in *Figure* 25.8.

FIGURE 25.10
Many sharks have streamlined bodies with fins and a powerful tail. These features allow the shark to move gracefully through the water.

Sharks have torpedo-shaped bodies, which are propelled through the water by the thrashing motion of their forceful tails. In *Figure 25.10,* you can see the pectoral, pelvic, and dorsal fins of the shark. While the tail provides downward thrust, the stiff pectoral fins counteract by producing upward lift. Pelvic and dorsal fins balance the swimming shark.

Osteichthyes While early cartilaginous fishes are thought to have evolved in deep oceans, evidence indicates that the bony fishes, or Osteichthyes, evolved in fresh water. The bony fishes are a more diverse group, compared with the sharks and their relatives. This is to be expected because bodies of fresh water are smaller than oceans. Changes in climate affect a lake more than an ocean and tend to divide it into smaller ponds during droughts. When this happens, freshwater animals can become isolated from the rest of their species. Changes in the environment and the isolation of populations are important factors in evolution. Many types of bony fishes are also adapted to live in the ocean.

The three surviving groups of bony fishes are lobe-finned fishes, lung-fishes, and ray-finned fishes. The fins of lobe-finned fishes are similar to the legs of early terrestrial vertebrates. This similarity is considered evidence that amphibians may have evolved from ancestral lobe-finned fishes. These fishes were thought to be extinct for at least 60 million years. But in 1938 a group of South African fishers caught an unusual fish. As you read at the beginning of this section, it was identified as a coelacanth, a type of lobe-finned fish. Modern coelacanths

FIGURE 25.11
The lungfish is able to breathe air due to its unique swim bladder, which also functions as a lung.

FIGURE 25.12

Ray-finned Fishes

Bluefin tuna
Most of the muscle tissue in a tuna is "red"—very vascular and well oxygenated. This tissue helps the tuna retain heat better than most fishes.

Clown trigger fish
When threatened, the triggerfish will wedge itself in a crevice and erect a long spine on its back, which is locked in place by a second spine, or "trigger."

Frog fish
The frog fish, a close relative of the angler fish, uses a modified fin as a lure to capture smaller fish.

Seahorse
The upright-swimming seahorse shows a great amount of parental care. The male of the species carries the eggs in a pouch until they hatch.

live in deep ocean water and do not have lungs. Fossil evidence shows that ancient coelacanths did have lungs. Scientists think that the lobe-finned fishes were the first vertebrates to live on land.

The **lungfish,** a close relative of the coelacanth, has lungs as well as gills. There are only a few living species of lungfishes. They live in shallow, tropical rivers. South American and African lungfishes regularly use their lungs to supplement the oxygen taken in by their gills. The Australian lungfishes use their lungs only during part of the year, when rivers dry up or have low levels of oxygen. These lungfishes also have lobed fins.

The ray-finned fishes are the largest group of bony fishes. They have fanlike fins made of thin membranes supported by bony rays. Salmon, guppies, and tuna are familiar examples. Ray-finned fishes vary greatly in shape, behavior, and habitat. They are successful because they have adapted to every kind of aquatic environment and have evolved into thousands of species. Compare the different species of ray-finned fishes shown in *Figure 25.12.*

CHECKPOINT 25.3

1. Name and describe the ancient groups of fishes. Compare them to modern fishes.
2. What are the key differences between the three classes of fishes living today?
3. **Critical Thinking** Besides breathing and movement, what other challenges would be faced by a fish trying to live on land?

Build on What You Know

4. What fish structure is similar to the mandible of an arthropod? How are the two kinds of structures different? *(Need to jog your memory? Revisit relevant concepts in Chapter 23, Section 23.2.)*

25.4 Fishes in the Biosphere

Floating fish food factories

Many fishes depend on algae for survival. Algae capture the energy of sunlight and store it in food molecules. These tiny photosynthesizers are at the base of aquatic food chains. Propelled by currents, they drift along near the surface of the ocean. Traveling with and living on the algae are protozoans and tiny animals. This floating mass of life supports many organisms in the food chain.

What you'll learn

IDEAS
• To compare the roles of different fishes in aquatic food webs
• To explain the importance of fish as a food source

ECOLOGICAL ROLES

A "fish eat fish" world

As you know, life on land involves food chains and food webs. The same relationships exist in water. In both freshwater and saltwater bodies, fishes play an important role in aquatic food chains.

Some fishes eat plants and plankton, which are the first links in an aquatic food chain. Others are bottom dwellers that live on dead and decaying organisms. A few other types of fishes are parasites. Most fishes, though, are carnivores, or meat eaters. The carnivorous fishes help maintain balanced ecosystems by limiting the number of organisms that survive long enough to reproduce.

All these fishes, in turn, are preyed on by other animals, including larger fishes, birds, aquatic mammals such as seals, and humans. They are also affected by disease-causing organisms such as bacteria and fungi.

HUMAN USES

And on his farm he had some . . . fishes?

You probably know that fish is eaten by people all over the world. Fish is nourishing because it contains about as much protein as red meat but much less fat and cholesterol. In fact, in some places around the world, fish is the primary protein source. As more people in the United States become health conscious, fish is becoming a staple in the Amerian diet.

Fishing is one of the world's major industries. Most of the fishes are taken from naturally occurring ecosystems. However, so much fishing is being done that the numbers of available fishes are dwindling. Still, as the human population increases, so does the demand for fish. To help meet these needs, fish farmers cultivate fishes in a controlled environment and harvest them when they reach the desired size. Currently, fish farms provide about 10 percent of the world's annual commercial fish supply.

Fish ranching is another way to increase fish numbers. It involves raising species in captivity for the first few years of their lives and then releasing them into the wild. In this way, greater numbers of fishes return to spawn and can be harvested at that time.

In addition to providing an important food source, fishes give people a lot of enjoyment. You may raise fishes in an aquarium because of the satisfaction you get from caring for these interesting animals and learning about their habits. Scuba divers also enjoy watching fishes in their natural environments.

FIGURE 25.13
Fish caught from lakes and streams are an important part of the bald eagle's diet. The eagle also scavenges dead or dying fish, such as salmon that have spawned.

FIGURE 25.14
Asthma sufferers can be helped by medicine made from the puffer fish. These fish are named for their ability to inflate their bodies with air or water.

Some people like to fish. They may view it as an opportunity to enjoy the outdoors, or they may enjoy the challenge of catching a game fish that puts up a powerful fight. Many people who enjoy fishing release the fishes they catch to avoid depleting natural populations.

Fishes are also at the cutting edge of medical research. For example, a recent study of native people in Greenland shed new light on the role that fish plays in reducing heart disease. On average, the adult Eskimos in the study ate about 1453.6 grams of fish per day. They also ate huge strips of fat from whales. You might think all this fat consumption would lead to heart disease. But researchers found that the oil in the fish seemed to counteract the effects of animal fat in the subjects' blood vessels. They rarely had heart dis-ease. This finding led to a study of Japanese people, who also eat large amounts of fish. The Japanese studied also had a lower incidence of heart disease than people who ate less fish.

Fishes are also used in other ways. Other products that are made from fishes include medicine, glue, livestock feed, and pet food.

CHECKPOINT 25.4

1. How do carnivorous fishes help to maintain a balanced ecosystem?
2. Why are fishes so important as a food source?
3. **Critical Thinking** Why is eating fish considered to be healthful? Explain your answer.

Build on What You Know

4. What effects do you think the extinction of a plantlike protist would have on fishes? *(Need to jog your memory? Revisit relevant concepts in Chapter 15, Section 15.5.)*

What characteristics make fishes adapted to life in the water?

25.5 Characteristics of Amphibians

Frog "love songs"
Frogs usually live alone. When the time comes to mate, males and females need a way to find one another. In many species of frogs, the male makes sounds to attract mates. Females hear the male's call and move toward the sound. Each species has a distinctive sound. Some people can more easily tell frog species apart by their songs than by their looks.

What you'll learn

IDEAS
• To explain the adaptations of amphibians to their environment
• To summarize the life cycle of a typical amphibian

WORDS
amphibian, cloaca

MOVEMENT AND RESPONSE

Legs give amphibians a lift

An **amphibian** is a vertebrate that is well adapted to life both in water and on land. Most amphibians start life as aquatic larvae but live their adult lives on land. One of the challenges of life on land for amphibians is being able to support their own bodies, because air provides less support than water. An additional challenge is the response of the organisms to their environment. Light and sound waves travel differently through air, requiring different sense organs.

With strong limb bones and muscles to lift their bodies off the ground, amphibians are well adapted to life on land. Amphibians have four strong limbs—two forelimbs and two hind limbs—the basic structure of a tetrapod. The strong bones, girdles, and muscles of amphibian limbs help them to support their bodies. Some fully aquatic amphibians have lost their legs and returned to fishlike locomotion. Others, like frogs, leap by rapidly straightening their long,

powerful hind limbs. Toads have shorter hind limbs than frogs and move by small hops rather than leaps.

Like all vertebrates, amphibians have a nervous system made up of a brain, spinal cord, and nerves. Many also have sensory organs that function well in both aquatic and terrestrial environments. For example, a frog's eyes see well in both water and air. They are covered by a transparent eyelid called a nictitating (NIK-tih-tay-ting) membrane. This membrane keeps the eye moist in air and protects it in water.

FIGURE 25.15
Tympanic membranes enable the frog to detect sound waves.

Frogs hear through two circular structures behind the eyes called tympanic (tim-PAN-ik) membranes. Find the tympanic membrane in *Figure 25.15* on page 605. These structures detect sound waves in air or water.

ENERGY AND WASTES

The skin that breathes

One key to the success of amphibians on land is their skin. Many amphibians have skin that enables the exchange of gases with the environment. Because oxygen and carbon dioxide must first dissolve in water before they can diffuse into or out of living tissues, an amphibian's skin must stay moist enough to allow the diffusion of gases and to prevent the animal from drying out. Many amphibians have mucous glands that keep the skin moist.

Although most amphibian larvae breathe through gills, the majority of adult amphibians breathe with lungs. The lungs of these amphibians contain internal air sacs that stay moist even if the outside environment is dry, allowing a constant exchange of gases.

The adult frog's digestive tract is similar to a human's. It consists of a mouth, esophagus, stomach, small intestine, and large intestine. Undigested food passes into a structure common to most vertebrates called the cloaca. The **cloaca** is a common chamber into which products of the digestive, reproductive, and excretory systems empty. Mammals, including humans, do not have a cloaca.

You will recall that fishes have a single-loop circulatory system and a two-chambered heart. Amphibians have a double-loop circulatory system and a three-chambered heart. This adaptation distributes oxygen efficiently to all the cells and removes carbon dioxide and other wastes.

FIGURE 25.16

Structure of a Frog

Powerful legs
The hind legs of a frog are so strong that it can jump a distance of more than ten times its own body length.

A three-chambered heart partially separates oxygen-rich from oxygen-poor blood.

Like fishes, amphibians have kidneys that excrete wastes from the bloodstream and regulate the amount of water in the body. In an aquatic environment, the kidneys form large amounts of dilute urine to rid the body of excess water. On land, the kidneys function to conserve water by forming small amounts of concentrated urine. Wastes from the kidneys remain in the bladder until they are released from the body.

Respiration

The frog has lungs that enable it to breathe air on land, but not enough air to keep the frog alive. It must also take in oxygen through its skin.

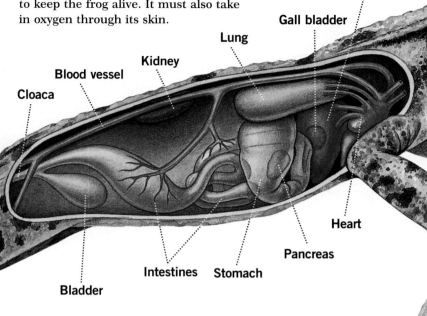

Cloaca
Blood vessel
Kidney
Lung
Gall bladder
Liver
Heart
Pancreas
Stomach
Intestines
Bladder

Circulation

The frog's blood carries oxygen and digested food to the body's cells. It carries carbon dioxide and other wastes away from the body cells.

Digestion

The frog's digestive system resembles that of a fish. Enzymes break down food into tiny particles that enter the bloodstream.

LIFE CYCLE

Going through stages

Some amphibian eggs look like a mass of clear tapioca pudding floating in the water. An amphibian's eggs are covered with a jellylike coating that protects them from injury, disease, and changes in temperature. The coating also provides nourishment for the developing embryos. Amphibians lay their eggs in water or in moist places on land so that the eggs will not dry out. Even though amphibians were the first land animals, water still plays an important role in their reproduction.

Frogs fertilize their eggs outside the body. In temperate climates, they migrate in large numbers to ponds or streams during the early, warm days of

LAB ZONE Think About It!

Comparing Amphibian and Fish Circulatory Systems

These diagrams show the circulatory systems of fishes and amphibians. As you have learned, fishes possess a single-loop circulatory system. Most amphibians, on the other hand, possess a double-loop circulatory system.

Analyzing the Diagram

1 Look at the diagrams. What is the most prominent difference between the two systems? Describe that difference.
2 What new adaptation is present in the amphibian's heart?
3 How did this adaptation help the amphibian function on land?

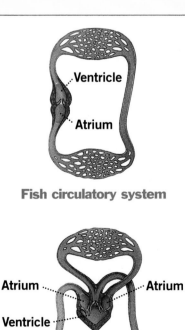

Fish circulatory system

Ventricle
Atrium

Atrium
Atrium
Ventricle

Amphibian circulatory system

FIGURE 25.17
Frog Life Cycle

Mating frogs
1 Mating occurs with the male frog clasping the female tightly. The male fertilizes the eggs as they are laid.

Eggs
2 As many as 20,000 eggs may be laid at once. Tadpoles hatch about six days after fertilization.

Young tadpole
3 After exhausting the food supply that it was born with, each young tadpole begins to feed on algae.

Developing tadpole
4 As the tadpole matures, internal gills develop, legs emerge, and the tail is absorbed.

Adult frog
5 Upon reaching adulthood, the frog can leave the water and breathe air, and pursue terrestrial prey.

spring. Males of some species call out loudly to attract females of their species. When a female approaches a calling male, the male climbs onto her back, grasps her tightly under the forelimbs, and the life cycle shown in *Figure 25.17* begins.

As is true for fishes, a great many eggs and tadpoles are eaten by aquatic predators. In most species, few of the fertilized eggs survive to grow and reproduce. However, some species of frogs have developed ways of providing parental care, including carrying young on their backs.

Amphibians are the only vertebrates that have a life cycle that includes metamorphosis. Metamorphosis in frogs is accompanied by many external and internal changes. It is triggered by a hormone called thyroxine, which circulates in the bloodstream. The major stages of metamorphosis are shown in *Figure 25.17*. What are some of the external changes that occur as the tadpole develops into an adult?

At the same time that external changes are taking place, internal changes are also occurring. The frog develops adult teeth and a jaw, as well as the shorter digestive tract typical of a carnivore. A double-loop circulatory system with a three-chambered heart replaces the single-loop, two-chambered heart system. The gills disappear, and lungs develop from saclike structures in the throat. Metamorphosis can be completed in as few as eight days in desert-dwelling toads, or it can take as long as two to three years in bullfrogs.

CHECKPOINT 25.5

1. How do the characteristics of amphibians differ from those of fishes?
2. What changes occur during the life cycle of a typical amphibian?
3. Critical Thinking Would you expect to find a nictitating membrane on animals other than amphibians? Why or why not?

Build on What You Know

4. Compare metamorphosis in amphibians and insects. *(Need to jog your memory? Revisit relevant concepts in Chapter 23, Section 23.4.)*

25.6 Origin and Diversity of Amphibians

Frogs from the sky?
There is an old myth that it sometimes rains frogs. Why would people believe that? Well, in places where conditions get too dry or too cold, frogs may find a patch of mud or leaf litter and bury themselves. When a warm rain signals the return of more favorable conditions, the frogs suddenly reappear.

What you'll learn

IDEAS
• To explain the evolutionary steps that led to modern amphibians
• To compare and contrast the different orders of amphibians

ORIGIN OF AMPHIBIANS

Legs and lungs invade land

If you could travel back in time to about 400 million years ago, you would probably find vascular plants growing abundantly in warm, swampy places. You would see only a few types of animals, however, most of which would be insects and arachnids.

Fast-forward to about 370 million years ago. There are still swampy areas, but some places are drier now. A few million years later, you might witness periodic droughts that shrink the size of lakes and streams. Among the vertebrates living at that time are lobe-finned fishes with primitive lungs. They also have a pair of muscular fins that function like legs. Some

of these fishes may have evolved into the first amphibians. *Figure 25.18* shows the structural features of the muscular fins of lobe-finned fishes and early amphibians. What similarities and differences can you see?

For the first vertebrates that left the water, land offered escape from both predation by other fishes and competition for food. Evidence indicates that there were no predators on land, and food in the form of insects and arthropods was plentiful. From about 345 million to 285 million years ago, the early amphibians thrived. Early amphibians thrived so abundantly that this period is often called the Age of Amphibians.

Fossils show that the early amphibians were similar to fishes. They lived mostly in water and fed on fishes and

FIGURE 25.18
Compare the muscular fin structure of the lobe-finned fish (left) with the leg of an early amphibian (right).

Lobe-finned fish

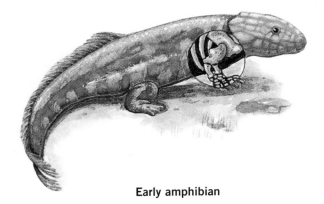

Early amphibian

FIGURE 25.19

Class Amphibia

AMPHIBIANS

Urodela

Anura

Apoda

MILESTONE
Legs

Fish ancestor

Kingdom: Animalia

Phylum: Chordata

Subphylum: Vertebrata

Class: Amphibia

Orders:
Anura
Urodela
Apoda

aquatic invertebrates. These early amphibians were covered with scales, had fishlike teeth, and had a lateral line system. Except for some rare caecilians (sih-SIH-lee-uhnz), present-day amphibians do not have scales and have only modified teeth. They may have a lateral line system in the larval stage, but most amphibians lose this feature as they mature.

DIVERSITY OF AMPHIBIANS

Variations on a theme

By about 245 million years ago, most amphibians had become extinct. A few, however, survived to become the ancestors of modern amphibians. The evolution of modern amphibians is summarized in the phylogenetic tree in *Figure 25.19*. Modern amphibians belong to three orders: Anura (frogs and toads), Urodela (salamanders), and Apoda (caecilians).

Anura Frogs and toads are similar in many ways, but there are noticeable differences. Compare the frog and toad shown in *Figure 25.20*. One important difference is their skin. Frogs have smooth, moist skin, while toads have dry, bumpy skin. Frogs also tend to have longer legs and more

tapered bodies than toads. Adult frogs live in or near water. Adult toads can live in drier environments than frogs can because their thicker skin is more resistant to drying. Toads typically return to water only to reproduce.

Anurans have adapted to a greater variety of environments than have other amphibians. They live in deserts, savannas, mountains, and tropical rain forests, as well as in temperate regions. Many anurans have adaptations that enable them to survive in a specific environment. The spadefoot toad, for example, has hind feet adapted for digging. It survives in hot, dry climates by burrowing into the ground and absorbing water from the soil.

Urodela Salamanders belong to the order Urodela. As you can see in *Figure 25.21*, salamanders typically have a long tail, a long body, and two pairs of legs. Like most amphibians, salamanders are covered by a smooth, moist skin. They retain their tail throughout life.

Salamanders vary in size and color. Most are from 5 to 15 cm long. However, the giant salamander *Andrias japonicus* grows to about 1.5 m long. Some salamanders are dull in color, which helps them blend with their

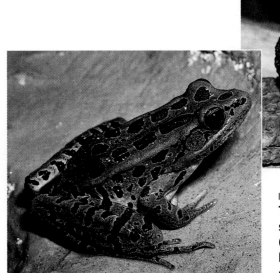

FIGURE 25.20
The pickerel frog (left) lives in streams, swamps, and meadows. The American toad (above) can be found in grassy areas and heavily forested mountains. How is the skin of each amphibian suited to its habitat?

FIGURE 25.21
The axolotl (left) becomes sexually mature while in a larval state and remains in water its entire life. The Kentucky salamander (right) has no lungs and must breathe through its moist skin.

environments. Many, however, are brightly colored, with stripes or spots that often secrete poisons. The bright colors are a warning to potential predators.

The larvae of most salamanders live in rivers, lakes, streams, or ponds. Aquatic larvae have gills for respiration. In most adult salamanders, the gills are replaced with lungs. Some species do not have gills or lungs. Instead, they respire by exchanging gases directly through their skin, just as earthworms and many other invertebrates do. Some urodelans, such as sirens, axolotls, and hellbenders, live in water most or all of their lives. They retain gills and other larval structures as adults.

Apoda Do you think the animal in *Figure 25.22* is an earthworm? Many people have been fooled by this organism. The long, wormlike caecilians have scales that make them look like segmented worms. However, unlike earthworms, caecilians have the skeleton of a vertebrate.

Caecilians are adapted to a life of burrowing through soil. Although they have tiny eyes, caecilians are blind or nearly blind. They feed on worms and insects as they burrow through the moist soil of tropical forests in South America, Africa, and Southeast Asia. A few species live in water. They average about 30 cm in length. Caecilians are rarely seen by humans, because they remain hidden in their burrows.

Caecilians reproduce by internal fertilization and have a larval stage. Some females guard their eggs until they hatch. Others produce live young and the embryos of some obtain nourishment from the tissues of the mother's reproductive system.

FIGURE 25.22
Caecilians may look like earthworms, but these burrowing carnivores have jaws and vertebrae. One species of caecilian can grow up to 1.5 m long!

CHECKPOINT 25.6

1. Explain the environmental conditions that led to the evolution of modern amphibians.
2. Contrast the three orders of amphibians.
3. **Critical Thinking** Caecilians do not have the varied color patterns found in the other two groups of amphibians. Why might this be so?

Build on What You Know

4. What vestigial structures would you expect to find in a caecilian? *(Need to jog your memory? Revisit relevant concepts in Chapter 10, Section 10.3.)*

25.7 Amphibians in the Biosphere

What you'll learn

IDEAS

• To explain the ecological roles of amphibians
• To summarize the importance of amphibians to humans

The shy ones versus the show-offs
If you visit a typical frog habitat in your area, you are not likely to see many frogs. Most frogs blend in with their surroundings. This camouflage helps them capture prey and escape predators. In contrast, the brilliant colors of other frogs advertise their presence. Many of these colorful frogs are poisonous, and predators have learned to leave them alone.

ECOLOGICAL ROLES

Keeping bugs in check

You might think amphibians are not very important to humans. After all, they are a major food source in only a few human societies. Although they may become medically useful in the future, applications to date are few.

Ecologically there is a different story. You now know that amphibians spend a portion of their lives in water and a portion on land. They are part of different but related food chains.

On land, amphibians of all types frequently prey on insects, both larvae and adults. They help to control the size of insect populations that could otherwise destroy important food crops and transmit diseases. Adult amphibians also eat worms and other animals such as birds, snakes, and small mammals, as you can see in *Figure 25.23*.

The food of young amphibians varies according to their species. In the water, most tadpoles feed on algae,

FIGURE 25.23
Yes, that is a half-grown rat being eaten by this large African bullfrog. Notice the frog's bleeding foot, bitten by the rat as it was caught.

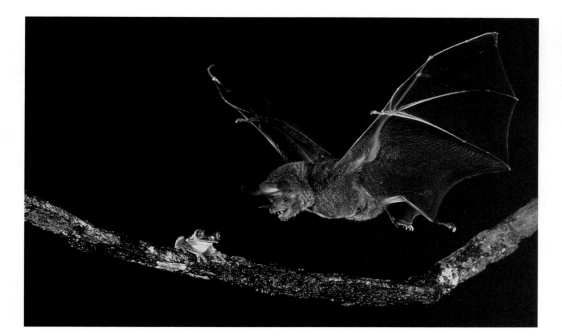

FIGURE 25.24
Some species of bats found in tropical environments have developed the ability to pinpoint frogs' mating calls.

small plants, and decaying animal matter. Newly hatched salamanders and caecilians are carnivores, with diets similar to those of their parents.

Amphibians, in turn, are eaten by other animals. Some animals that consume adult amphibians include fishes, snakes, turtles, birds, and some mammals. Recall, however, that poisons in their skins help protect many species from predators.

HUMAN USES

Pass the frog legs, please!

In section 25.3, you read that fishes are a major human food source. Amphibians are not. Some frog species are edible, and the flesh has a high protein content, but most frogs contain little meat. One large South American species is roasted whole, but most people tend to limit their frog meals to the legs.

Perhaps the most economically important role of amphibians is their ability to control insect pests that might otherwise threaten crops or spread disease. Home gardeners sometimes place toad shelters in their

 Do It!

How Is Tadpole Development Affected by Temperature?

Tadpole eggs hatch more quickly in warm water than in cool. You can find out if tadpoles develop more quickly into frogs in warm water when you . . .

Try This

1 Put several tadpoles in a water-filled glass aquarium or a large glass bowl and place it in a shaded area in your classroom. Leave it at room temperature. (Be sure to use water from the tadpoles' natural habitat and add some of the algae they feed on.)

2 Put several more tadpoles in a similar water-filled glass aquarium or bowl and place it in a spot that is warmer than the first one. The water can be warmed by the sun or artificial light, or heated by an aquarium heater if you have one.

3 For a minute or two each day, observe, compare, and record physical development of each group of tadpoles.

Analyze Your Results

1 Did the development of the tadpoles in the two tanks differ? If so, how did it differ?

2 Would there be a difference in tadpole development during a cold, rainy, spring season as opposed to a sunny one? Explain.

FIGURE 25.25
A hunter from the Embará Chocó people of Colombia holds down a poisonous frog as he rubs a dart against the frog's skin. The dart will remain poisonous for more than a year.

EVERYDAY BIOLOGY

Frog Skin Cream

Researchers have discovered a compound in the skin of an African frog that may be useful as an antibiotic in curing human skin infections.

yards to encourage amphibians to take up residence. Toads help control pests naturally.

Traditionally, frogs have assisted humans in other ways. They help to increase human knowledge about vertebrates. You probably already know that frogs are widely used in biology classes.

Even amphibian poisons have proved useful to humans. In certain cultures, poisoned arrows have been used for generations to hunt game. The arrows are carefully coated with poisons that are secreted by amphibians such as the poison arrow frog, shown in *Figure* 25.25. Usually, a leaf or some other object is used to avoid touching the amphibian.

ENVIRONMENTAL AWARENESS

Amphibian alarm

The life processes of amphibians are closely tied to their environments throughout their lives. As you have learned, amphibians live both on land and in the water and depend on the quality of these natural resources for

their survival. Their small ectothermic bodies, porous skins, and unshelled eggs make them very vulnerable to changes in the environment. For this reason, some scientists consider amphibians to be useful as bioindicators. A bioindicator is an organism or species whose health serves as an indicator of the health of the environment or ecosystem.

In recent years, researchers have noticed a worldwide drop in both the number and diversity of amphibians. Some people find this alarming, but no one has been able to determine the exact cause of the decline. Because the jellylike eggs of amphibians are not well protected, some scientists have hypothesized that the decline may be due to an increase in solar radiation— a result of the thinning of the ozone layer. Others have suggested air or water pollution as possible explanations. Still others have suggested global warming. Researchers are struggling to find the cause of the problem before it is too late for the populations to recover, or before other populations begin to decline as well.

CHECKPOINT 25.7

1. What is one important ecological role of amphibians?
2. List three ways that amphibians are important to humans.
3. **Critical Thinking** What might be the consequences of a global extinction of amphibians?

Build on What You Know

4. How would the pH of water affect amphibians? *(Need to jog your memory? Revisit relevant concepts in Chapter 2, Section 2.5.)*

What characteristics make amphibians well adapted to life both in water and on land?

Chapter 25 Review

25.1 Vertebrates are animals with backbones.

25.2—25.4 Fishes are a diverse group of vertebrates that are adapted for life in the water.

25.5—25.7 Although amphibians share some fish traits, they are adapted to life on land.

Sum It Up

Use the following summary to review the main concepts in this chapter.

25.1 Vertebrates

- The vertebrate skeleton contains a skull and a protective backbone that surrounds the spinal cord.
- Vertebrates have a closed circulatory system.
- The temperature of fishes, amphibians, and reptiles varies with the external environment. Birds and mammals have internal temperature controls.

25.2 Characteristics of Fishes

- A typical fish has scales for protection and insulation, fins for directional movement, a swim bladder to control buoyancy, a two-chambered heart, sense organs for locating prey and for navigation, kidneys to maintain water balance, and gills for respiration.
- Fertilization in fishes is usually external.

25.3 Origin and Diversity of Fishes

- The earliest fishes were filter feeders that resembled lancelets. With the evolution of paired fins and jaws, fishes could pursue prey.
- Agnathans are jawless parasites or scavengers. They lack scales and paired fins. Chondrichthyes have skeletons made of cartilage. Osteichthyes have bony skeletons.

25.4 Fishes in the Biosphere

- Most fishes are carnivores.
- Fishes provide food, a source of income, recreation, and medicine for humans.

25.5 Characteristics of Amphibians

- Amphibians live both on land and in water.
- The typical amphibian has moist skin and lungs for gas exchange, powerful limbs, and a three-chambered heart.
- Amphibians reproduce through external fertilization, and they undergo metamorphosis.

25.6 Origin and Diversity of Amphibians

- Amphibians evolved from lobe-finned fishes with primitive lungs.
- Frogs and toads have no tail; salamanders have visible tails; caecilians have no legs.

25.7 Amphibians in the Biosphere

- Amphibians help to control insect populations.
- Amphibians are useful as bioindicators.
- Amphibian populations are declining.
- In certain cultures, amphibians are a source of food.

Use Terms and Concepts

Use each of the following words or terms in a complete sentence. If you need to review a meaning, turn to the page indicated.

vertebrates (p. 592)

ectotherms (p. 593)

endotherms (p. 593)

swim bladder (p. 594)

lateral line system (p. 595)

lungfish (p. 602)

amphibian (p. 605)

cloaca (p. 606)

Use Your Word Power

COMPLETION **Write the word or phrase that best completes each statement.**

1. The _____ is a group of sense organs that many fishes use to detect vibrations.

2. A(n) _____ is a vertebrate that is adapted to both aquatic and terrestrial habitats.

3. The _____ is an internal organ that helps some fishes adjust their depth in the water.

4. A structure in amphibians that excretes undigested food is called a(n) _____ .

5. Organisms that can maintain constant body temperature are _____ .

TRUE-FALSE **Write true if the statement is true. If the statement is false, replace the underlined word(s) to make the statement true.**

6. Both fossil coelacanths and modern coelacanths have lungs as well as gills.

7. As invertebrate chordates develop, the notochord is replaced by a backbone.

8. An ectotherm is an organism in which body temperature is regulated by its surroundings.

9. Fishes in the class Chondrichthyes do not have swim bladders or opercula.

10. Mammals have a cloaca, which releases products of the digestive, reproductive, and excretory systems.

Show What You Know

11. How do the changes that accompany the metamorphosis from tadpole to adult frog enable the frog to adapt to a terrestrial environment?

12. How are jaws an important adaptation for fishes? How does their function in feeding compare to the feeding habits of jawless fishes?

13. What adaptations do most adult amphibians have that make the exchange of gases such as oxygen and carbon dioxide possible?

14. How do sharks adjust to the lack of a swim bladder or operculum?

15. How do the kidneys of amphibians adjust to life on land and in the water? In which of these environments are their kidneys acting like the kidneys of saltwater fishes? Explain.

16. How are the typical characteristics of members of the phylum Chordata displayed in adult bony fishes?

17. What adaptation does a double-loop circulatory system with a three-chambered heart provide that a single-loop system with a two-chambered heart does not?

18. **Make a Concept Map** Create a concept map that relates the following terms: Agnatha, amphibians, Anura, Apoda, caecilians, Chondrichthyes, fishes, frogs, lampreys, Osteichthyes, ray-finned fishes, salamanders, sharks, toads, Urodela, and vertebrates.

Take It Further

19. **Applying Concepts** Why is it important to control the temperature of an aquarium within narrow limits?

20. **Making a Generalization** How would the number of offspring produced by a species that uses internal fertilization compare with the number produced by a species that uses external fertilization? Explain your answer.

21. **Organizing and Classifying** Suppose you were visiting South America and you discovered an organism that reproduces by laying eggs. The organism has a backbone, lungs, kidneys, and a two-chambered heart. Is the organism a fish or an amphibian? Explain your reasoning.

22. **Making an Analogy** How is the use of a lateral line system to detect prey similar to the use of a seismograph to detect earthquakes?

23. Designing an Experiment Design an experiment to determine the effect of diet on tadpole development. What information would you need before you could begin? What variables would you need to control? How could you compare the development of individual tadpoles?

24. Interpreting Graphs The graph below shows the total number of fishes caught worldwide between 1970 and 1993. What conclusions can you draw from the graph? Can you draw any conclusions about future catches from the data shown? Explain your answer.

Fish Caught Worldwide

25. Analyzing Data Use the chart below to answer the following questions: In which country do people eat the least amount of fish? In which country the greatest amount? In which country is twice as much fish consumed as in the United States? Does that country have a population twice that of the United States? Explain your responses.

Human Consumption of Fish

Country	Total Fish Consumed Yearly (millions of metric tons)	Fish Eaten per Person (kg per year)
China	18	12.2
Japan	13	66.6
Russia	5	25.2
United States	7	20.4

Consider the Issues

26. Fish Supplies Sink Modern fishing technology includes remote sensing devices for locating schools of fishes; huge nets; and factory ships that can process fishes as they are caught. Because of overfishing, populations of fishes have been dramatically reduced. In many areas, fishing has been banned entirely or restricted to a few weeks a year. Should there be restrictions on the types of technology that can be used? How can fishing be regulated in international waters?

27. Absent Amphibians Some people argue that amphibians should be allowed to survive or disappear without any human interference. What is your opinion?

Make New Connections

28. Biology and Physics Some biologists study deep-sea fishes. When they bring these fishes to the surface rapidly, they often find that the fishes look distorted, as though they have exploded. Look up *fluid pressure* in a physics textbook, and use this information and your knowledge of fish anatomy to propose an explanation for the distortion of these fishes.

29. Biology, Photography, and Writing Create a field guide about the amphibians that are native to your community. Use a page for each species that you can observe. Include photographs or drawings. Describe the habitat for each species.

FAST-FORWARD TO CHAPTER 26

The amphibian life cycle involves periods on land and in the water. In Chapter 26, you will study reptiles—vertebrates that spend their entire life on land. You will also study the evolution of birds.

CHAPTER 26
Reptiles and Birds

You can find out more about reptiles and birds by exploring the following Internet address: *http://vertebrates.biosurf.com*

In this chapter . . .

FEATURES

Everyday Biology
• Heat-sensing Snakes
• Birds Re-tern

In the Community
Look! Up in the Sky!

 Frontiers in Biology
Poisons or Promises?

LAB ZONES

Discover It!
• Examining an Egg

Do It!
• How Does Egg-burying Behavior in Reptiles Benefit Reproduction?
• How Do Contour Feathers Compare with Down Feathers?

Think About It!
• Analyzing Bird Migratory Routes

Investigate It!
• Comparing Reptiles and Amphibians

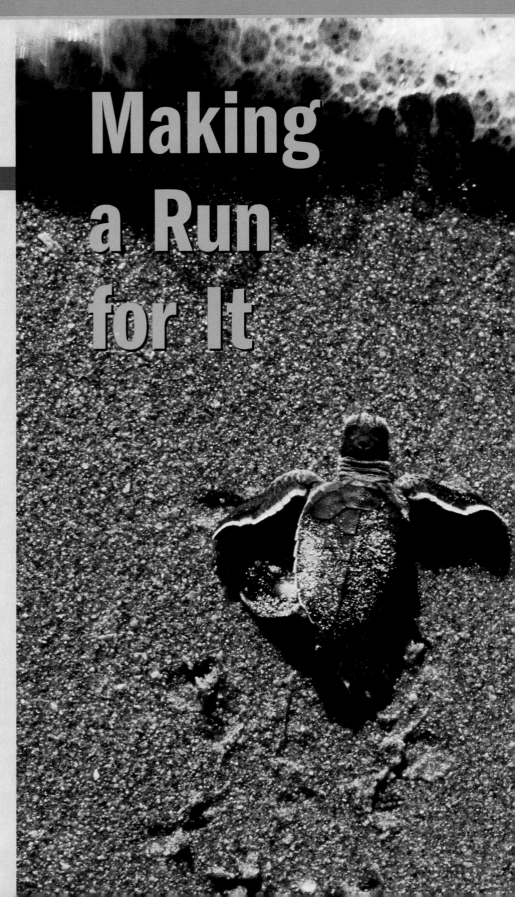

Making a Run for It

Examining an Egg

You need one raw egg, a container, tweezers

1. Crack the raw egg into a container. Examine the shell. How thick is it? What do the inside and outside surfaces look like? What do they feel like?
2. Examine the egg's contents. Use the tweezers to probe the egg. Can you recognize distinct parts of the egg? Can you identify the part of the egg that would develop into a chicken?
   Caution: Wash your hands with soap and warm water after this activity.

Birds and reptiles have amniotic eggs that protect a developing embryo. How do the structures of the amniotic egg serve this function?

WRITE ABOUT IT!

In your journal, write a description of what it might be like to be a bird or reptile developing inside an egg. What sounds or movement might you feel? What would it be like getting out of the shell when hatching?

Sea turtles live their lives coursing through the open ocean. But every two or three years, the females return—on a journey that may be thousands of kilometers—to the beach where they were born. There they lay their eggs, bury them in the sand to keep them warm and moist, and then return to the ocean. From 60 to 90 days pass before hatchlings break through the shells. On their own, baby turtles must make a perilous journey across open sand to the relative safety of the ocean. The dangers are many.

Sea turtles, compared to other turtles, have small shells that leave their head and limbs exposed. They are slow and awkward on land. Crabs threaten them on the beach and they are easily visible prey from the air, where gulls and terns fly in wait. If hatchlings make it to the ocean's edge, they will swim for 24 hours straight, into safer open water. The odds are against them. From a nest of 200 eggs, only one or two turtles may live to adulthood.

Turtles are reptiles, land animals, that thrive in the water. According to some scientists, birds may have descended from reptile-like ancestors that took to the air. What can we learn about evolution by studying these animals?

THE BIG IDEA! Reptiles represent the first vertebrates with adaptations that enable them to live their entire lives out of water. 26.1–26.3

26.1 Characteristics of Reptiles

What you'll learn

IDEAS

• To explain key reptile adaptations
• To describe the structures and functions of the amniotic egg

WORDS

amniotic egg, yolk, chorion

Egg-eating snakes

Although only as wide as your thumb, an African egg-eating snake eats nothing but eggs. It can even eat hard-shelled bird eggs that are twice as wide as its body. The snake's jaws unhinge as it swallows the egg. Sharp bones in the snake's throat cut the egg open. The contents of the egg slide down the snake's throat into its digestive system. The compacted shell is forced up the throat and back out the snake's mouth.

MOVEMENT AND RESPONSE

Life in a dry world

If you ever held a snake or lizard in your hand you may have been surprised to find that the animal's skin was smooth and dry, not wet and slimy. Did you notice the tight-fitting scales that covered the animal's body? A reptile's dry, scaly skin helps prevent the evaporation of water from its body. Conserving water is just one of many challenges reptiles face living on land.

Reptiles were the first vertebrates with adaptations that enabled them to survive completely independent of a water environment. A reptile's skin is one of its most important characteristics for surviving on land. The skin is covered with hard, dry scales made of a water-resistant protein called keratin. Human hair and fingernails, and bird feathers, are also made of keratin. Because keratin is water resistant, it helps prevent the escape of water from skin cells.

Another important structural adaptation that enables many types of reptiles to move on land is the position of their legs. You can see in *Figure 26.1* that reptilian legs are close to the body, compared to the legs of frogs and other amphibians you read about in Chapter 25. This leg position enables reptiles to run more quickly on land. As you read this chapter, you will see that modern reptiles have many adaptations—including the absence of legs—that result in efficient movement.

Many groups of reptiles have unique structures that enable them to sense and respond to their environments. Study the snake structures shown in *Figure 26.2*. How does the snake smell?

ENERGY AND WASTES

Awesome jaws

Structural adaptations in reptiles reflect their need to find and capture prey, exchange gases with the environment, transport nutrients and wastes, and maintain water balance—all in the absence of water. Some of these adaptations have also been

FIGURE 26.1

For reptiles, claws are an adaptation that enable them to live on land. Reptiles, such as these Komodo dragons, use their claws to dig burrows and nests. Reptiles also use their claws for traction when running and climbing.

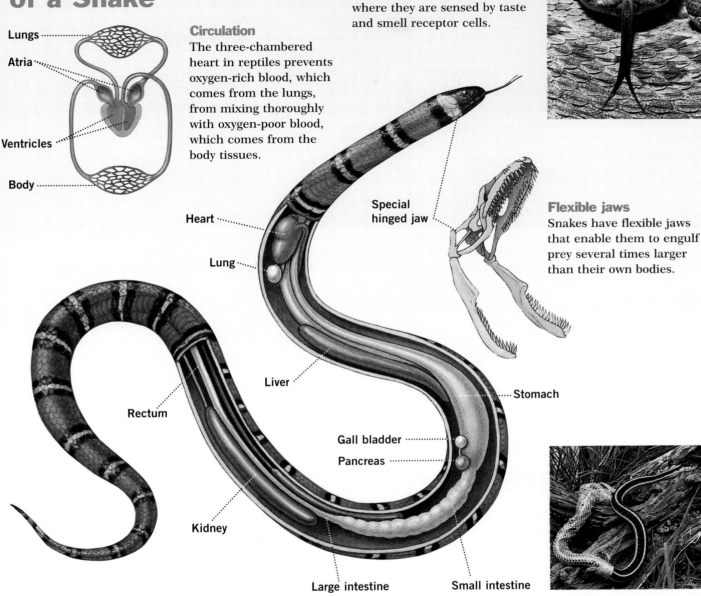

FIGURE 26.2

The Structure of a Snake

Circulation
The three-chambered heart in reptiles prevents oxygen-rich blood, which comes from the lungs, from mixing thoroughly with oxygen-poor blood, which comes from the body tissues.

Sense and response
As a snake darts its tongue in and out of its mouth, chemicals are carried into the mouth where they are sensed by taste and smell receptor cells.

Flexible jaws
Snakes have flexible jaws that enable them to engulf prey several times larger than their own bodies.

Lungs
Atria
Ventricles
Body

Heart
Lung
Liver
Rectum
Kidney
Large intestine
Special hinged jaw
Stomach
Gall bladder
Pancreas
Small intestine

Shedding skin
A snake's scaly skin protects it from drying out, but it does not increase in size as the animal grows. Instead, most snakes and other reptiles periodically shed their skin when it becomes worn out or too small.

inherited by birds and mammals. Other structural adaptations remain unique to reptiles.

Most reptiles are carnivores. They eat insects when they are young and other animals as they mature. Most reptiles do not chew food into small pieces. They simply bite or tear the food into pieces they can swallow. The food is digested mainly by enzymes in the stomach. In reptiles, digestion is a long, slow process.

Reptiles have a circulatory system that is more efficient for an animal that breathes only air. All reptiles, except crocodilians, have a partially divided, three-chambered heart. A reptile's heart is more distinctly divided than that of an amphibian. A reptile therefore achieves a greater separation of oxygen-rich and oxygen-poor blood. *Figure* 26.2 shows a diagram of a three-chambered heart. In crocodilians, the partition between the ventricles is complete, forming a four-chambered heart.

In addition to a more efficient circulatory system, reptiles have well-developed lungs with large internal surface areas. Unlike amphibians, reptiles do not depend on gas exchange through the skin, so they do not need to stay moist. Furthermore, reptiles inhale and exhale more frequently than amphibians, while filling their lungs with a larger volume of air.

The excretory system of most reptiles is adapted to conserve water from body wastes. Notice the snake's kidneys in *Figure 26.2*. Most of the water that the kidneys remove from the blood is returned to the tissues. Reptiles living in dry climates excrete thick, pasty urine containing very little water. Like fishes, aquatic reptiles excrete waste as a liquid.

Although reptiles require large amounts of energy to move quickly and easily on land, they do not require energy to maintain their body temperature. Reptiles are ectotherms. Recall from Chapter 25 that ectotherms control their body temperature by their

behavior. If its body temperature is too low, for example, the lizard lies in the sun's rays. If its body temperature is too high, the lizard usually seeks shade. How does this behavior affect the internal temperature of the lizard?

The "eggciting" new development

Another adaptation necessary for reproduction on land is internal fertilization. How is this different from fertilization in amphibians? Male reptiles have specialized organs to introduce sperm directly into the female's reproductive tract. This adaptation makes water unnecessary for sperm and egg to unite.

Another advantage of internal fertilization is that the fragile sperm are protected from the environment, ensuring a higher rate of fertilization. As a result, reptiles do not need to lay as many eggs as aquatic animals do to produce enough offspring to maintain the species. On average, reptiles lay between 8 and 100 eggs at a time, instead of the thousands laid by amphibians.

You have probably heard the question "Which came first, the chicken or the egg?" In terms of the theory of evolution, there is no doubt. The amniotic egg probably developed long before birds evolved. An **amniotic egg** is one that provides nourishment to the embryo and protects the embryo while it develops in a terrestrial environment.

Look at the illustration of the egg in *Figure 26.4*. The embryo is connected to the yolk by a stalk. The **yolk** is the food source for the developing embryo. The embryo is completely surrounded by a membrane called the amnion. The amnion is a fluid-filled envelope that cushions the embryo. The allantois (uh-LAN-toh-is) is a membrane-bound sac that stores wastes and is the site for

FIGURE 26.3
The lizard below is raising its body temperature by lying in the sun's rays. What would the lizard do if it was too hot?

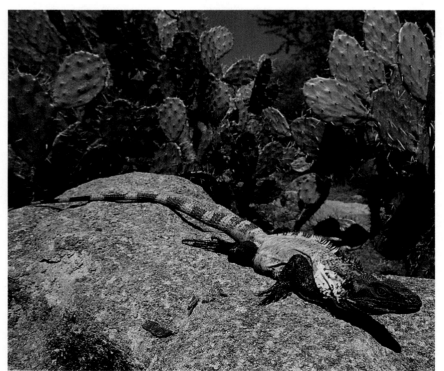

FIGURE 26.4

The Structure of the Amniotic Egg

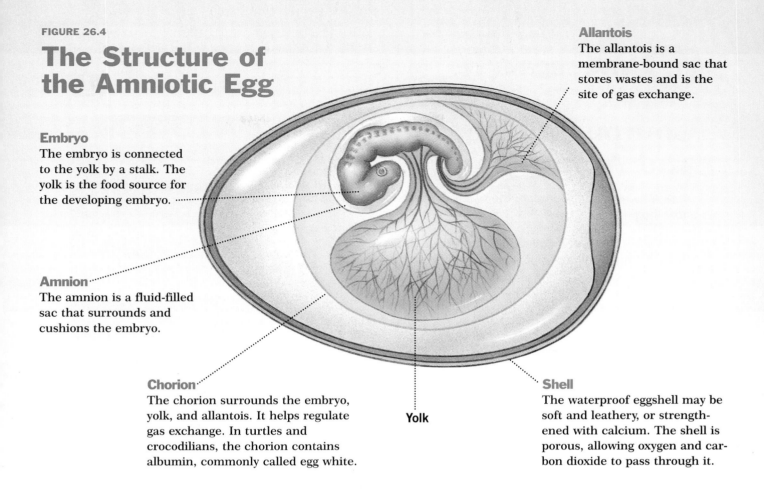

Embryo
The embryo is connected to the yolk by a stalk. The yolk is the food source for the developing embryo.

Amnion
The amnion is a fluid-filled sac that surrounds and cushions the embryo.

Allantois
The allantois is a membrane-bound sac that stores wastes and is the site of gas exchange.

Chorion
The chorion surrounds the embryo, yolk, and allantois. It helps regulate gas exchange. In turtles and crocodilians, the chorion contains albumin, commonly called egg white.

Yolk

Shell
The waterproof eggshell may be soft and leathery, or strengthened with calcium. The shell is porous, allowing oxygen and carbon dioxide to pass through it.

gas exchange. The allantois becomes larger as the embryo grows, while the yolk shrinks. The outermost membrane, called the **chorion** (KOR-ee-ahn), envelopes the embryo, yolk, and allantois. The chorion provides another layer of protection and helps regulate gas exchange.

The developing egg represents the most defenseless stage in a reptile's life. Environmental conditions, such as temperature and humidity, affect the developing embryo. Many eggs are lost to predators. Reptilian young, like the one shown in *Figure 26.5*, look like miniature adults when hatching from the eggs. Although the young are at risk from predators, they are much better equipped than fish or amphibian larvae to survive their first few months of life.

Not all reptiles lay eggs. Some lizards and snakes give birth to live young. Reptiles that produce live young carry the eggs inside their bodies until the young hatch. Other reptiles have a specialized sac that connects the developing embryo to the mother. These embryos still have a yolk for nourishment.

CHECKPOINT 26.1

1. Name three adaptations that enable reptiles to live in their environments.
2. What are the functions of the yolk, amnion, allantois, and chorion in the amniotic egg?
3. **Critical Thinking** Most reptiles produce fewer, larger eggs than amphibians and fishes. How is this adaptation an advantage?

Build on What You Know

4. How do the life cycles of reptiles differ from those of amphibians? *(Need to jog your memory? Revisit relevant concepts in Chapter 25, Section 25.5.)*

FIGURE 26.5
This Northern Diamond-back terrapin is freeing itself from its egg. The young terrapin will search out food—marine snails and worms—without the help of a parent.

LAB ZONE Investigate It!

Comparing Reptiles and Amphibians

WHAT YOU WILL DO Compare the external anatomies of a lizard and a frog

SKILLS YOU WILL USE Collecting and recording data, observing, analyzing, classifying

WHAT YOU WILL NEED Aquarium with live lizard, aquarium with live frog

Propose a Hypothesis
Scientists classify organisms in part by comparing their structures. Lizards and frogs are classified into different groups. Hypothesize which structures could be used for distinguishing between lizards and frogs.
Caution: Always handle live animals carefully and respectfully.

Conduct Your Experiment
1 Observe the lizard in the aquarium. Draw and describe what you see.

2 Have your teacher or a classmate pick up the lizard. Feel the texture of the lizard's skin. Record your observations.
3 Observe the frog in the aquarium. Record your observations.
4 Repeat step 2 with the frog.

Analyze Your Data
1 What is the most obvious difference between the external anatomies of the lizard and the frog? What are some other differences?
2 How does the skin of the two animals compare?
3 What behavioral characteristics did you observe in the two organisms. How did these characteristics compare?

Draw Conclusions
Did your observations support your hypothesis? What external structures can be used to distinguish reptiles from amphibians?

Design a Related Experiment
Design an experiment to observe one aspect of a snake's behavior. Behaviors to consider include reactions to light, temperature, and food preference.

Lab: Comparing Reptiles and Amphibians

Objectives: Comparing a lizard and a frog

Lizard
Observations:

Frog
Observations:

26.2 Origin and Diversity of Reptiles

No other reptile like it
The tuatara (TOO-uh-TAR-uh) is different from all other kinds of reptiles. A tuatara is active only at night. Even then, the tuatara moves and functions slowly. It also grows slowly, taking more than 20 years to reach its adult length of 60 centimeters (cm). Some tuataras live more than 100 years.

What you'll learn

IDEAS
• To explain two hypotheses about the origin and evolution of reptiles
• To compare the different orders of reptiles

ORIGIN OF REPTILES

A dry new world

About 300 million years ago, during the Carboniferous period, the land was probably covered by swamps and forests. Insects, arachnids, and amphibians were abundant. According to the fossil record, the first reptiles evolved during this time. These reptiles, called stem reptiles, looked very similar to the amphibians of the time.

Because the stem reptiles resembled amphibians, most scientists think they evolved from amphibians. Another hypothesis, however, states that stem reptiles evolved directly from lobe-finned fishes, not from amphibians. You will recall that ancient lobe-finned fishes had lungs and large, fleshy fins that enabled them to crawl. Because the fossil record does not clearly indicate the order in which legs, lungs, and shelled eggs evolved, we may never know which hypothesis is correct. What other types of evidence could scientists study to help resolve this issue?

At the end of the Permian period, about 245 million years ago, a mass extinction occurred. Some scientists hypothesize that the mountain ranges that formed during this time gradually caused the climate to change. The mountains may have prevented

rain from reaching many regions. Great swamps may have dried up and become deserts. The dry climate may have caused most amphibians to become extinct. Most of the stem

FIGURE 26.6

Class Reptilia

FIGURE 26.7
Land dinosaurs flourished during the Jurassic period. The largest animals ever to walk on Earth, the brachiosaurs, existed at this time.

reptiles also died out. Only a handful of species survived.

After the decline of the amphibians, the remaining species of reptiles probably flourished and soon became the most abundant animals on Earth. Through adaptive radiation, the ancestral species could have rapidly evolved. You may recall from Chapter 10 that adaptive radiation is the evolution of many different species from one common ancestor. The resulting reptiles are adapted to many different niches.

EXTINCT REPTILES

Terrible lizards that roamed Earth

Dinosaurs were the most abundant reptiles during the Mesozoic era, which lasted from about 245 million to 65 million years ago. Although the word *dinosaur* means "terrible lizard," the first dinosaur species were two-legged animals no larger than a chicken. Over time, dinosaur populations increased in size. One of the largest dinosaur species was an herbivore called *Apatosaurus*. This

reptile was 24 meters (m) long and may have weighed as much as 50,000 kilograms (kg). Some species, such as *Tyrannosaurus rex* stood 6 m tall. *Figure 26.7* illustrates what some of these dinosaurs may have looked like. Some scientists think the larger body was an adaptation that enabled dinosaurs to maintain a constant body temperature. As the body mass increased, the relative amount of body surface decreased, reducing the amount of heat lost through the skin.

Dinosaurs and other reptile populations began to decline toward the end of the Cretaceous period, the last period of the Mesozoic era. Many scientists think the period between the end of the Cretaceous and the beginning of the Tertiary, called the K-T boundary, lasted 5 to 10 million years. These scientists think the mass extinction occurred gradually, due to climatic changes caused by the land masses drifting north. *Figure 26.8* shows what the environment may have looked like during the Cretaceous period.

Some recent evidence indicates that a catastrophic event, such as a huge meteor crashing into Earth, or

FIGURE 26.8
During the Cretaceous period, dinosaurs continued to diversify until the extinctions began. Some of the reptile species that survived the extinctions are still alive today.

FIGURE 26.9

Horny shield layer

Bony layer

Skull

Neck vertebrae

FIGURE 26.9
The ribs and vertebrae of the tortoise are fused to the shell, but the neck and limbs are not fused and are retractable. The shell of a tortoise is composed of two layers. How do these layers compare?

the release of large amounts of carbon dioxide gas from volcanoes, may have caused a more abrupt extinction of dinosaurs. Such a catastrophic event might have shortened the K-T boundary to as few as 100,000 years. (Yes, in terms of Earth's history, 100,000 years are considered a few!)

There is still much debate over the length of the K-T boundary and the cause of the mass extinction at the end of the Mesozoic era. The only reptilian survivors were turtles, crocodilians, and the ancestors of other modern reptiles.

MODERN DIVERSITY OF REPTILES

Scales, tails, and shells

Today only three major orders of reptiles exist: Squamata, including snakes and lizards, Chelonia (keh-LOH-nee-uh), including turtles and tortoises, and Crocodilia. A fourth order, Rhynchocephalia (ring-koh-seh-FAY-lee-uh) has only one remaining species: the tuatara. Tuataras, the reptiles you read about at the beginning of this section, look much the same as they did more than 200 million years ago.

Tuataras Today, tuataras are found only on two small groups of islands off the coast of New Zealand. A few hundred years ago, they also

lived on mainland New Zealand. The introduction of sheep and goats to the mainland destroyed the tuatara habitat. Tuataras survive today in part because the New Zealand government has passed strict laws to protect them in their isolated island homes. On some islands, however, the number of tuataras has recently declined because of the introduction of Polynesian rats, which prey on young tuataras.

Turtles and tortoises Another one of the oldest living orders of reptiles is Chelonia. Chelonians are divided into three groups: tortoises, sea turtles, and freshwater turtles. Tortoises live entirely on land; sea turtles live in oceans. Male sea turtles rarely come to shore, and female sea turtles do so only to lay eggs. Freshwater turtles have webbed feet and live an amphibious life, sunning themselves on shore but feeding in the water.

A unique characteristic of chelonians is their shells. Turtles generally have flatter shells than tortoises. *Figure 26.9* shows the structure of a tortoise's shell. A streamlined body enables the turtle to move efficiently through water. Freshwater turtles and tortoises have shells that consist of a series of bony plates covered with hornlike scales. Sea turtles, by comparison, have lightweight, leathery shells.

FIGURE 26.10
Microscopic, hairlike structures on the pads of the gecko's toes enable it to climb on almost any surface. Geckos can scale walls and even walk on ceilings!

Although the shell reduces a turtle's mobility, it protects the turtle from predators. Most turtles can pull their head into their shell. Some can also pull their legs inside the shell. Because they are so well protected, individual turtles and tortoises can live a very long time. Some giant tortoises of the Galapagos Islands, for example, live as long as 150 years.

Snakes and lizards Although most lizards have four legs and snakes have none, both groups are classified in the order Squamata. Snakes and lizards live in most habitats on land and in water, with the exception of cold polar regions.

Although the absence of legs may seem like an evolutionary step backward, it actually increases a snake's mobility. By pushing its body against the ground, a snake can move quickly and fit into small spaces.

Lizards have many specialized adaptations that enable them to live in different habitats. The gecko shown in *Figure 26.10* has pads on its toes that help it to cling to trees. In what other ways are the gecko's toes an advantage?

Some lizards have unique adaptations to help them escape from predators. Chameleons and anoles can blend into their environment by changing the color of their skin. Skinks and geckos can cast off their tails when grabbed by predators. In skinks, the discarded tail will continue to wiggle after it has broken off, confusing the would-be predator. The lizard's tail will regenerate quickly.

Crocodilians Reptiles in the order Crocodilia include crocodiles, alligators, caimans, and gavials. Crocodilians have changed little in the past 150 million years. They differ from other reptiles by having a four chambered heart and by the care they give their young. These characteristics make crocodilians more similar to dinosaurs and birds than to other modern reptiles.

Compare the crocodile and alligator shown in *Figure 26.11*. Notice that the crocodile has a narrower head and a longer snout. Crocodiles live in the tropical regions of Africa, Asia, Australia, and North and South America. Both alligators and caimans have short, broad snouts. Alligators are found in tropical regions of China and in the southern United States. Caimans are native to Central and South America. Gavials have long, slender snouts that broaden slightly at the end. Gavials spend most of their lives in the water and are found only in India and Burma.

CHECKPOINT 26.2

1. Explain two hypotheses about the origin and evolution of reptiles.

2. Compare the different orders of reptiles.

3. Critical Thinking How might a huge meteor crashing into Earth have caused the extinction of dinosaurs?

Build on What You Know

4. How does reptilian evolution compare to amphibian evolution? *(Need to jog your memory? Revisit relevant con-*

FIGURE 26.11
Alligators and crocodiles are the largest reptiles. Both species can grow to lengths of over 6 m. What similarities and differences can you see in the head structure of the alligator (right) and the crocodile (far right)?

26.3 Reptiles in the Biosphere

The deadly look is in

The poisonous eastern coral snake (top right) and the nonpoisonous scarlet king snake (bottom right) both have brightly colored bands of red, yellow, and black along their bodies. Predators such as birds avoid these brightly colored snakes—poisonous or not. How is this pattern of coloration beneficial to both snakes?

What you'll learn

IDEAS

- To explain the ecological roles of reptiles
- To compare reptile behaviors

ECOLOGICAL ROLES

The hunter and the hunted

Although the section opener describes snakes as prey to birds, reptiles are not always prey. Many snakes and lizards are predators. Snakes and other reptiles are important predators in grasslands, prairies, and rain forests. On farms, snakes play a major role in controlling rat and mice populations that feed on crops. In many tropical countries, it is not uncommon to see small lizards crawling along sidewalks or even climbing on walls inside a house. Lizards are welcome guests because they consume large numbers of unwanted insects.

Reptiles have roles in all levels of a food chain. Some lizards, such as large iguanas and skinks, eat a variety of leafy green plants. Most reptiles, however, will eat whatever animal prey is available: insects, worms, snails, and mammals.

Some reptiles are preyed upon by birds such as eagles and owls, mammals such as pigs and cats, and even other larger, more aggressive reptiles. The unprotected young of many reptiles, including sea turtles and alligators, are easy prey after they hatch from their eggs.

REPTILE BEHAVIOR

Staying alive

Most reptiles spend their time quietly searching for food, adjusting their body temperature, and avoiding danger. When threatened, they run away or hide. Other reptiles, however, exhibit a wide variety of behaviors to keep their predators away.

The Australian frilled lizard, shown in *Figure 26.12*, employs one of the most spectacular methods of scaring

FIGURE 26.12
The South American armadillo lizard (far left) rolls itself into a tight ball when it spots a predator. The Australian frilled lizard (near left), on the other hand, takes a different approach. How might these behaviors help the lizards survive?

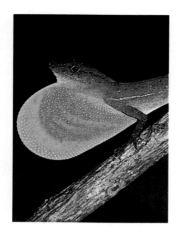

FIGURE 26.13
The male anole lizard inflates its fanlike throat sac to display aggression towards another anole. Though these displays can last for hours, violence is usually avoided when the weaker of the two lizards flees.

off predators. Most of the time the lizard avoids predators by lying very still, camouflaged against its environment. But when a predator comes too close, the lizard raises a frilled, colorful collar of skin around its neck, hisses loudly, puffs up its body with air, rises up on its clawed feet, and waves its tail back and forth. If all this fails, it turns around and runs.

Like other vertebrates, reptiles need to find and mate with a member of the opposite sex in order to reproduce. Many male lizards display colorful frills or flaps of skin to attract females. The male anole lizard, shown in *Figure 26.13,* inflates a brightly colored fanlike throat sac to attract its mate. Male anole lizards also display this throat sac to defend their territories and chase away other males.

After mating, many reptiles lay their eggs in sand, soil, or rotting logs.

Some reptiles bury their eggs in nests dug deep in the soil. Other reptiles lay their eggs in small depressions in the ground. The eggs are usually laid where they will stay warm, to ensure proper development. After they lay their eggs, most reptiles leave them. The young hatch on their own and receive no parental care.

The behavior of the American alligator does not follow the typical pattern. Female alligators provide care for their eggs and young. They lay their eggs in a hole, then cover the eggs with rotting plants and soil. After the eggs are laid, the female maintains the nest and protects it from predators. After the eggs hatch, the mother will often carry the young in her mouth, three or four at a time, and take them to water. The young follow their mother around for several weeks before going off on their own.

Some reptiles migrate during different stages of their life cycles. Giant sea turtles have roamed the world's oceans for millions of years. Using radio and satellite equipment, scientists have recently learned about the behavior of these mysterious animals. Sea turtles travel along regular migration routes, sometimes for thousands of kilometers (km). Every two or three years the turtles return to the same beaches where they hatched from eggs. Green turtles, for example, travel 3,340 km from the coast of Brazil to a small island in the middle of the Atlantic Ocean. Once there, females go ashore and lay their eggs.

LAB ZONE Do It!

How Does Egg-burying Behavior in Reptiles Benefit Reproduction?

Some reptiles bury their eggs under heaps of plant material and dirt. The eggs remain under this mixture until they hatch. You can find out how this behavior benefits the eggs if you . . .

Try This

1 Construct a compost heap outside of your school by alternating layers of dirt and dead plant material. Build up the heap until it is 0.5 m high.
2 Using a long thermometer, determine and record the air temperature and the temperature at the center of the compost heap. Take these measurements twice weekly for four weeks.

Analyze Your Results

1 Graph the changes in air temperature over the four weeks. Do the same for the temperature inside the compost heap. How do they differ?
2 How do you think the temperature in the heap would benefit developing eggs? What other advantages would burying eggs in this way provide?

HUMAN USES

Products are skin-deep

Humans use reptiles in many different ways. Sea turtles are eaten as food, as are turtle eggs. Some turtles, such as the hawksbill turtle, are hunted for their beautiful black and yellow shells. The shells are made into tortoiseshell hair combs and barrettes, jewelry, and decorations for the home. At one time, these turtles were hunted to near extinction because of the popularity of tortoiseshell ornaments.

Reptiles are raised or hunted for their colorful and strong skins, which are made into boots, belts, purses, and luggage. Some reptiles, including snakes, lizards, and turtles, are also raised as pets.

Today, many reptiles are endangered. Their numbers are decreasing rapidly due to hunting and loss of habitat. Fortunately, many endangered reptiles are now protected by international law. These laws prevent the sale and purchase of products made from the skins, bones, hides, or shells of endangered reptiles.

FRONTIERS IN BIOLOGY

Poisons or promises?

Zap! The snake's poison glands compress. Deadly venom enters the body of the bitten animal through razor-sharp fangs. Blood pressure drops, lungs burst, and the animal soon dies. The snake *Bothrops jararaca* of southern Brazil has claimed another victim.

Something in the snake's venom causes the blood pressure to drop in the bitten animal. Scientists hypothesized that the same substance could reduce blood pressure in humans. High blood pressure, or hypertension, is a leading cause of death in humans. To study the effects of the venom of the *Bothrops*, Brazilian scientist Dr. J. Ferreira collected snakes from the grasslands of Brazil. He then "milked" the snakes of their venom and tested it on lab

FIGURE 26.14
By studying the venom of the deadly *Bothrops jararaca* snake, scientists have been able to synthesize a lifesaving medicine.

animals. His work produced some very valuable results. The venom reduced the blood pressure in the lab animals.

Researchers have identified more than 25 active substances in the venom of reptiles. Most of these substances are large proteins that act as enzymes. The effect of the *Bothrops* venom is to widen the victim's blood vessels, causing the blood pressure to drop fatally.

Using Ferreira's information about the poison, researchers began to develop an artificial venom. The result of the research was a blood pressure drug called captopril, which has saved many lives since the 1970s.

CHECKPOINT 26.3

1. Name two reptiles and the role each plays in the environment.
2. List three behaviors of reptiles and explain their evolutionary significance.
3. **Critical Thinking** Why do you think it is important to protect reptiles from unnecessary hunting and collecting?

Build on What You Know

4. Compare one example of reptile behavior to one example of insect behavior. *(Need to jog your memory? Revisit relevant concepts in Chapter 23, Section 23.4.)*

EVERYDAY BIOLOGY

Heat-sensing Snakes

The rattlesnake belongs to a group of snakes known as pit vipers. These snakes have a shallow, heat-sensing pit located between their nostrils and eyes that allows them to sense changes in temperature, to a fraction of a degree. This organ helps the snake locate and strike the warm bodies of prey, even in total darkness!

What characteristics enable reptiles to live their entire lives out of water?

26.4 Characteristics of Birds

What you'll learn

IDEAS
• To explain the structural adaptations that allow birds to fly
• To summarize the life cycle of a typical bird

WORDS
crop, gizzard, chalaza

Which bird flies the fastest?
The fastest bird in the world is the peregrine falcon, which hunts other birds in the air. When chasing its prey, the falcon dives at speeds of up to 280 km/h. As it dives, the falcon slashes at its victim with sharp claws, interrupting its flight. The falcon, extremely agile, then wheels back to catch its victim as it falls.

MOVEMENT AND SUPPORT

Fly, fly away

Have you ever wondered how birds fly? A bird's entire body is adapted to enable flight. In fact, many differences between a bird's body and a reptile's body are the result of structural adaptations for flight. These adaptations do one of two things: reduce a bird's body weight, or make the body more compact. Some of the structural adaptations for flight are in a bird's feathers, skeleton, muscles, and skin.

The shape of a bird's wings is similar to the shape of an airplane wing. Its wings are slightly curved from front to back and are thicker in the front, as shown in *Figure 26.15*. The curved surface of the top of the wing causes air above the wing to travel faster than air beneath the wing. This difference in air speed decreases the relative air pressure above the wing, providing the lift needed for flight.

Birds have thin skin covered with feathers. The only gland that birds have in their skin is the oil gland at the base of the tail. The oil from this gland is used for smoothing and waterproofing feathers. The one reptilian characteristic of a bird's skin is the presence of scales covering the legs and feet. Feathers are modified from reptilian scales; they are larger and fringed along the edges. Like reptilian scales, feathers are made of keratin. Feathers insulate a bird's body, protect the bird against weather, and form a smooth, low-friction surface. But feathers wear out and must be shed, or molted, once or twice a year. The two main types of bird feathers are described in *Figure 26.16*.

A bird, or avian, skeleton is also an important adaptation that enables flight. Compared with a reptile's skeleton, a bird's skeleton is light in weight. As you can see in *Figure 26.16*, avian bones are hollow. The air inside the bone reduces the bone's density, greatly reducing the weight of the body. Hollow bones are not brittle and

FIGURE 26.15
A gliding bird uses the reduced air pressure above its wings to stay aloft, much like an airplane.

Reduced air pressure

Air flow

Constant air pressure

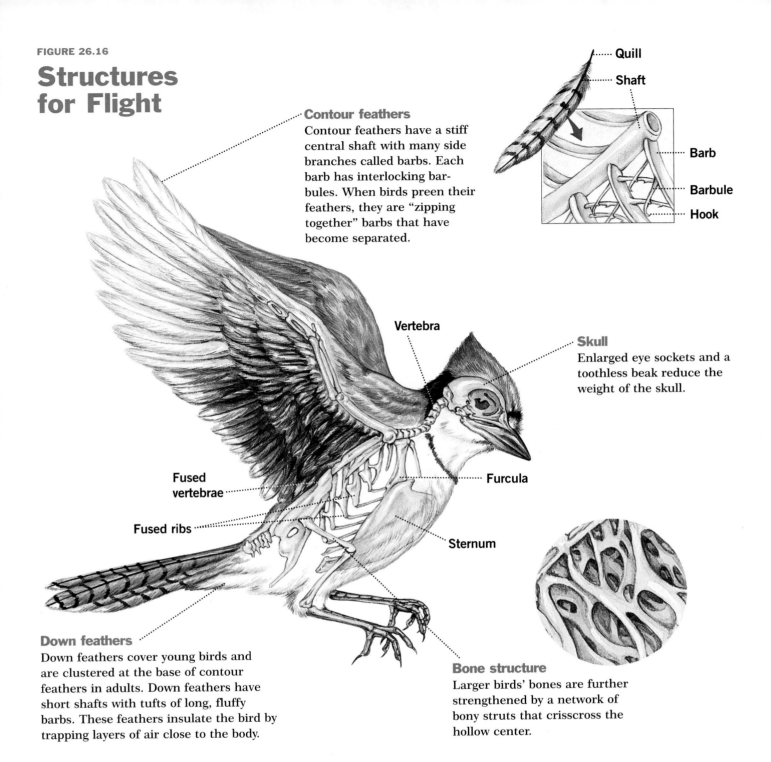

FIGURE 26.16

Structures for Flight

Contour feathers
Contour feathers have a stiff central shaft with many side branches called barbs. Each barb has interlocking barbules. When birds preen their feathers, they are "zipping together" barbs that have become separated.

Quill
Shaft
Barb
Barbule
Hook

Skull
Enlarged eye sockets and a toothless beak reduce the weight of the skull.

Vertebra

Fused vertebrae

Fused ribs

Furcula

Sternum

Down feathers
Down feathers cover young birds and are clustered at the base of contour feathers in adults. Down feathers have short shafts with tufts of long, fluffy barbs. These feathers insulate the bird by trapping layers of air close to the body.

Bone structure
Larger birds' bones are further strengthened by a network of bony struts that crisscross the hollow center.

weak; they are very strong, due to the network of cross braces, or struts within the bone.

Some of the bones that make up joints in reptiles and mammals are fused in birds. Fused bones make the skeleton more rigid and provide extra stability for flight. Fused bones also reduce the need for heavy ligaments.

As you can see in *Figure 26.16*, the ribs are attached to one another, and some of the vertebrae and the collarbone, or furcula, are also fused. The furcula is the bone commonly called the wishbone in poultry.

Although a bird's skeletal system is adapted to reduce body weight, its muscles are large and relatively heavy.

How Do Contour Feathers Compare with Down Feathers?

You can examine the structural differences between two types of feathers if you . . .

Try This

1 Obtain a contour feather, a downy feather, and a microscope.
2 Study the contour feather. Record your observations on paper. Is the feather curved or straight? Is it symmetrical? Now examine the feather under the low-power setting of the microscope. Note the individual barbs that are attached to one another. Draw what you see.
3 Repeat step 2 using the down feather.

Analyze Your Results

1 How are the barbs of a contour feather attached to one another? How do these attachments make the feather strong?
2 Explain why the barbs of a down feather do not fit together like the barbs of a contour feather.
3 How are the structures of the feathers related to their functions?

The chest, or pectoral, muscles make up almost 25 percent of a bird's body weight. The pectoral muscles are located on the sternum and are used to move the bird's wings.

ENERGY AND WASTES

Eating like a bird

Birds generate and maintain a constant internal body temperature. As you may recall from Chapter 25, animals that maintain a constant internal body temperature are called endotherms. Because birds are endothermic, they can live in very cold climates where reptiles cannot survive. Birds' overlapping feathers trap layers of air and minimize the loss of body heat. Birds prevent water from soaking into their feathers by preening with oil secreted by the oil gland at the base of the tail.

FIGURE 26.17
Because the snowy owl is an endotherm, it can exist in very cold climates. This owl lives in the Arctic.

Generating heat to maintain a constant body temperature requires a lot of energy. As is true for all aerobic organisms, energy is released in cells when food combines with oxygen. Cellular wastes, such as carbon dioxide and nitrogenous wastes, must be removed efficiently, too. Birds have more efficient respiratory, circulatory, and digestive systems than reptiles.

Birds have a rapid heartbeat and high blood pressure, making circulation fast and efficient. Birds also have a four-chambered heart that completely separates oxygen-rich blood from oxygen-poor blood. Because the blood is completely separated, the body tissues receive a high concentration of oxygen. As you may recall from section 26.2, crocodilians also have a four-chambered heart, which suggests that crocodiles and birds are closely related.

A bird's respiratory system can obtain large amounts of oxygen. Avian lungs are attached to a system of air sacs that extend into all parts of the body. Some air sacs even open into the hollow spaces inside bones. The respiratory system is unique in that air flows through the lungs in only one direction. Use *Figure 26.18* to trace the path of air during respiration.

Birds must eat and digest large amounts of food to provide enough energy for flight and for generating body heat. When birds eat, the unchewed food passes from the mouth to the esophagus. Notice in *Figure 26.18* that the lower end of the esophagus enlarges to form the **crop.** The crop is a storage area of the digestive tract where food is softened. Many birds store food in the crop to eat later or to feed their young in the nest.

From the crop, the food mixes with enzymes and is ground to a pulp in the gizzard. The **gizzard** is a digestive organ with muscular walls that often contains small stones swallowed by

FIGURE 26.18

Respiratory and Digestive Structures

Trachea

Anterior air sacs

Lungs

Posterior air sacs

1 When the bird inhales, fresh, oxygen-rich air is drawn down the windpipe, and fills the posterior air sacs. Simultaneously, stale carbon dioxide-rich air is drawn out of the lung and into the anterior air sacs.

2 When the bird exhales, all of the air sacs collapse forcing fresh air from the posterior air sacs into the lung for more gas exchange, and stale air out of the anterior air sacs and up the windpipe. Thus, the flow of air through the lungs is continuous, even when the bird is exhaling.

Beak
A bird's beak has no teeth for chewing food. So when a bird eats, the unchewed food mixes with saliva in the mouth, which helps the food pass smoothly down the esophagus.

Crop
The crop is a storage area where food is softened. Many birds store food in the crop to digest later or to feed their young.

Gizzard
The gizzard is a digestive organ that breaks food into very small pieces.

Posterior air sac

Anterior air sac

Lung

Intestine

the bird. The gizzard breaks the food into very small pieces, which travel to the intestines, where nutrients are absorbed.

The excretory system of birds is adapted to conserve water from body wastes. Urine is excreted in a pasty form, similar to the urine excreted by reptiles. Unlike reptiles and most other types of land vertebrates, however, birds do not have a urinary bladder in which to store liquid wastes. This modification lowers body weight by reducing the amounts of water and waste in the body.

Shore birds have a special adaptation to eliminate excess salt obtained from drinking sea water and eating marine animals. Small salt-excreting glands above the eyes remove excess salt, which leaves the body through the nostrils. The sparkling crystals that can be seen on the bill of a sea gull are actually dried salt excretions from the bird's nostrils.

As you have learned, birds are endothermic animals that fly and, therefore, require a great deal of energy. To meet their energy needs, birds must spend a lot of their time getting food. Birds eat almost every-thing, from seeds and insects to fishes and small land animals.

Because their forelimbs are adapted for flight, birds must use their feet to grasp food. Many birds use their beaks to break or tear food into pieces small enough to swallow. Special adaptations enable bird species to obtain food from a variety of sources. How do you think the adaptations shown in *Figure 26.18* enable a bird to live successfully in its environment and to get food?

FIGURE 26.19
This raven is using its strong beak and sharp claws to tear apart food, which may be fed to its young later.

LIFE CYCLE
Bird families are egg-cellent

Birds spend a lot of time and energy attracting mates, building nests, and caring for their young. Like reptiles, birds reproduce by internal fertiliza-tion. They also produce amniotic eggs. However, similar to birds' respiratory and digestive systems, their reproduc-tive system is adapted to enable flight.

During most of the year, the repro-ductive organs in both male and female birds are greatly reduced in size. As nesting season approaches, hormones stimulate the reproductive organs to enlarge and begin functioning. Unlike reptiles and mammals, most male birds do not have external reproductive struc-tures. Sperm are produced in internal testes, which are surrounded by air sacs that decrease the body temperature around the testes. The females of most bird species have only one ovary and oviduct, rather than two, as reptiles and mammals do.

Internal fertilization occurs through the cloaca, an opening near the base of a bird's tail. The cloaca also serves as the opening through which body wastes are excreted. After an egg is fertilized, it travels through a passage called the oviduct, where it is coated with albumin and a hard shell of calcium carbonate. The shelled egg leaves the female through the cloaca.

The amniotic egg of birds is similar in structure to that of reptiles. The yolk in the bird egg, however, is much larger. All bird eggs contain albumin, or egg white, which provides additional nutrients to the embryo. In birds, the yolk is supported by a ropelike strand of albumin, called the **chalaza** (kuh-LAH-zuh), which connects to the chorion. You can examine the structure of the avian egg in *Figure 26.20.*

Bird eggs vary greatly in size. The smallest eggs are laid by hummingbirds. The tiniest hummingbird egg is smaller than a pea and weighs only 0.35 gram (g), about one fifth the weight of an adult. The largest egg, from an ostrich, is about the same size as a grapefruit. Weighing in at about 1.5 kg, an ostrich egg weighs about one hundredth of what an adult bird weighs. An ostrich egg is almost 4500 times heavier than a hummingbird egg.

Because birds are endothermic, their eggs must be incubated—kept at a constant, warm temperature—while an embryo develops. Birds incubate their eggs in a variety of ways. Some birds sit on nests to keep eggs warm. A male emperor penguin holds an egg on its feet and tucks it under a fold of skin on its belly. The male and female penguins take turns incubating the egg in this way for about 52 days.

Many baby birds are helpless and depend entirely on their parents for food. Some parents feed their nestlings every few minutes, making 500 trips a day in search of food. The young birds gain weight rapidly and begin to grow feathers in three or four days.

Some birds, such as robins, hatch poorly developed young. They have a well-developed digestive system, but everything else is less well developed. Their eyes are still closed, and they have no feathers. In about two weeks, baby robins are fully developed and ready to leave the nest. Other birds, such as chickens, hatch well developed and covered with feathers. They can soon feed themselves and survive on their own.

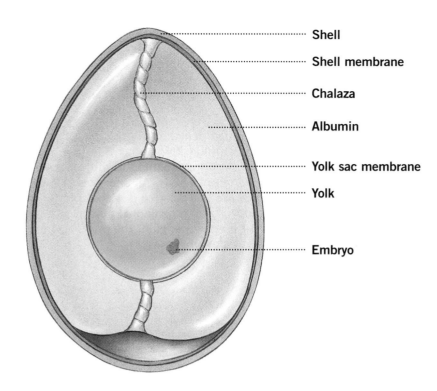

Shell
Shell membrane
Chalaza
Albumin
Yolk sac membrane
Yolk
Embryo

FIGURE 26.20
As you can see, the structure of the avian egg is very similar to that of the reptilian egg. However, the chalaza, which anchors the yolk, is a structure not found in the reptilian egg.

CHECKPOINT 26.4

1. What are two main ways in which structural adaptations assist birds in flight?

2. Summarize the life cycle of a typical bird.

3. Critical Thinking Air sacs remove the excess body heat that is produced during flight. Propose a hypothesis to explain how this function is accomplished.

Build on What You Know

4. What information do bird characteristics reveal about the evolutionary relationship of crocodilians and birds? *(Need to jog your memory? Revisit relevant concepts in Chapter 26, Section 26.2.)*

26.5 Origin and Diversity of Birds

What you'll learn

IDEAS

• To summarize the differences between birds and other vertebrates
• To analyze evidence for the evolutionary origin of birds

Penguins are not the only ones
Although penguins are the polar birds most familiar to humans, they are not the only birds adapted to the intense cold of polar seas. Another seabird able to brave the polar cold is the colorful puffin. Unlike penguins, puffins can fly. But like the penguin, the puffin swims and fishes in icy water.

ORIGIN OF BIRDS

Taking to the sky

Birds probably evolved from reptiles about 225 million years ago during the Triassic period. Fossils show evolutionary links between reptiles and birds. However, the fossil record of birds is fragmented and incomplete because their feathers and fragile bones do not fossilize well.

Several species of flying reptiles known as pterosaurs lived during the Mesozoic era. Although these reptiles resembled birds in their flight and environmental niche, they were distinctly different from birds.

In 1986 a fossil of a birdlike vertebrate was found in west Texas. The chicken-sized animal was named *Protoavis,* and it lived about 225 million years ago. It had some reptilian features but also had some characteristics of birds.

The earliest fossil known to have feathers is *Archaeopteryx,* which dates back 150 million years to the Jurassic period. Because feathers are a distinguishing feature of birds, scientists usually consider *Archaeopteryx* to be the first known bird.

However, recently discovered fossils of a small bird called *Liaoningornis,* which lived at about the same time, suggest that *Archaeopteryx* probably represents a smaller branch on the bird family tree and was not a direct ancestor of modern birds. In *Figure 26.21,* you can see that *Archaeopteryx* had reptilian as well as avian features. What reptilian features can you identify in the illustration of *Archaeopteryx?*

In addition to *Archaeopteryx,* the fossil record contains several birdlike animals with various combinations of reptilian and avian features. These animals were abundant 100 million years ago during the Cretaceous period.

After the extinction of dinosaurs, birds probably evolved rapidly. They filled many habitats on land and in water and air that once were occupied by dinosaurs and flying reptiles. Some scientists hypothesize that birds evolved from reptiles that ran very fast and fed upon flying insects. Those that could leap the highest and longest had an advantage in catching the insects. Feathers probably served as an adaptation for retaining body heat. Eventually, the feathered forelimbs enabled the animals to glide and, ultimately, to fly.

FIGURE 26.21
Scientists think that *Archaeopteryx* used its wings to pursue large, slow-flying insects.

FIGURE 26.22
Diversity of Birds

Falconiformes
This order includes harpy eagles (above), hawks, and vultures.

Passeriformes
This large order contains the perching birds, including cardinals (left), sparrows, swallows, and ravens.

Casuariiformes
This order includes emus (above) and cassowaries.

Podicipediformes
This order contains only grebes. A horned grebe is shown above.

Piciformes
This order includes keel-billed toucans (left), woodpeckers, barbets, and jacamars.

DIVERSITY OF BIRDS

A bird in every bush

Birds share so many characteristics with reptiles that some scientists think birds should be classified as an order of reptiles. Birds, however, are distinctly different from reptiles and other vertebrates in many ways. Birds are the only animals that have feathers. They are also the only vertebrates, except for bats, that can fly.

Birds make up a very diverse class of vertebrates called Aves. They range in size from the 6-cm Cuban bee hummingbird weighing 2 g to the 2.5-m ostrich weighing 136 kg. Among the largest flying birds are the Andean and California condors. They weigh about 11 kg and have a wingspan of 3 m.

At least 9000 different species of birds are alive today. They live high in trees, on the ground, and even on buildings. Birds eat seeds, insects, fruit, and small animals. Because of their number and diversity, it is difficult for taxonomists to classify birds. By using differences in body structure, beak structure, foot structure, behavior, and song, taxonomists have divided birds into 27 different orders. Some taxonomists divide birds into even more orders.

Some representative bird orders are listed and shown in *Figure 26.22*. Perching songbirds have the greatest range of adaptations and live in nearly every environment. Perching songbirds account for 60 percent of all avian species. Grebes are classified in their own order. These highly specialized diving birds use their streamlined bodies and lobed toes to swim underwater in search of prey.

CHECKPOINT 26.5

1. Name two characteristics that distinguish birds from other kinds of vertebrates.
2. Explain one hypothesis for the evolutionary origin of birds.
3. **Critical Thinking** Use Figure 26.22 to compare the orders Passeriformes and Ciconiiformes.

Build on What You Know

4. Why do feathers and fragile bones not fossilize well? *(Need to jog your memory? Revisit relevant concepts in Chapter 10, Section 10.1.)*

Ciconiiformes
This order includes great blue herons (above), storks, ibis, flamingos, and spoonbills.

26.6 Birds in the Biosphere

What you'll learn

IDEAS

- To explain the roles that birds play in ecosystems
- To compare courtship behavior in birds

What do vultures eat?
Vultures feed only on dead animals. They sometimes spend a great amount of time searching for a meal. They circle at heights up to 3500 m and locate food with their incredibly sharp eyesight. Some vultures can spot a dead animal from more than 1.6 km away. Vultures play an important role in many different food chains.

ECOLOGICAL ROLES

The appetite of a bird

Birds play many important roles in the environment. Some birds, such as hummingbirds, are important pollinators of plants. Birds are also important in the dispersal of seeds. Many birds eat ripe fruits from trees and bushes. The seeds from the fruit pass undamaged through the birds' digestive systems. As the birds fly, they disperse the seeds from place to place.

Birds also have roles in all levels of a food chain. Many live entirely off the seeds and fruits of plants. Birds also eat large numbers of insects—sometimes thousands in a single night! This helps to control the populations of insect pests, such as mosquitoes and grasshoppers. As you have read, birds such as vultures feed on dead animals.

Eagles, owls, and hawks are predators, birds of prey, feeding on fishes, reptiles, amphibians, small mammals, and even other birds. Birds in turn are preyed upon by many different animals, including snakes, lizards, and mammals.

BIRD BEHAVIOR

Public displays of attraction

Compared with reptiles, birds have large brains in relation to their body size. Areas of the brain that control flight and flight-related activities are highly developed. Also well developed are the areas of the brain that control complex reproductive behaviors, such as nest building, mating, singing, and caring for young. These complex behaviors are not learned. They are instinctive, or inborn, behaviors. Some of these instincts, however, may be modified by experience.

Have you ever been awakened in the morning by singing birds? Bird songs play a very important role in mating. When mating season begins, males establish a territory and defend it from other males. Perching birds, such as robins and red-winged blackbirds, use song to establish and defend their territories. When females arrive

FIGURE 26.23
The cactus wren builds its nest on the side of cacti or thorny bushes. How might this location help protect the young shown here?

in the area, they are attracted to the males of their species by song.

Most courtship behaviors have evolved to help a female find and select mature males of her own species. To attract a female, male peacocks and turkeys spread their brightly colored tail feathers and parade around the females. Male bower birds build elaborate nests of many different sizes and shapes, then decorate them with flowers and fruit or even coins, ribbons, and jewelry that they find. The male frigate bird attracts a female by inflating a large, red throat pouch to the size of a soccer ball. It then throws back its head, lets out a piercing cry, and shakes its wings.

In most species of birds, once a male and female are attracted to each other and mate, they stay together as a pair for the rest of the breeding season. Some species remain a pair for a much longer period of time. The eagle, for example, mates for life.

Birds build nests in which they lay their eggs and protect their young. They build their nests from just about anything they can find, including mud, leaves, animal hair, moss, string, and paper. Some birds even decorate their nests with brightly colored buttons and bits of aluminum foil. Others make their nests in almost any available shelter, even an empty tin can or abandoned flowerpot.

Nesting behavior differs from species to species. Eagles return to the same nests year after year. The twig nests they build can grow to an enormous size, sometimes measuring 3 m wide and 7 m high, and weighing 275 kg. Baltimore orioles have distinctive baglike nests that hang from branches. Weaverbirds are able to tie knots using their beaks and feet. They use this skill to build elaborate tunnel-like or bell-shaped nests.

Many birds remain in the same location year-round. Other birds make

FIGURE 26.24

Courtship, nest building, and migration are examples of complex, instinctive behavior. These photographs all show birds displaying inborn behavior (clockwise from right): the masked weaverbird building a nest, geese migrating in formation, and the courtship display of the male frigate bird.

yearly migrations in the spring and fall. In the Northern Hemisphere, birds generally fly north in the spring to their breeding grounds. In the winter, they fly south to warmer weather and their winter feeding grounds. The rufous hummingbird, for example, travels nearly 4000 km (2500 miles) from Alaska to Central America every fall and returns in the spring by the same route.

Scientists are still studying the perplexing question of how birds find their way over such long distances. Research shows that birds navigate in a number of ways. Some birds use landmarks such as rivers, mountains, and coastlines, or monitor Earth's magnetic field. Others navigate by the position of stars, while those that migrate in flocks follow their neighbors.

HUMAN USES

Pass the poultry

Humans use birds in many different ways. Birds have been an important food source for humans for thousands of years. Their meat is high in protein and low in fat. Around the world, people hunt or raise chickens, turkeys, ducks, geese, pheasants, and guinea

Birds Re-tern

Arctic terns migrate farther than any other bird. A few weeks after it hatches in June, a tern chick leaves its nest in Greenland on its yearly migration. It flies 18,000 km to the South Pole where it spends the summer. It returns to Greenland the following spring—a round trip of 36,000 km!

Analyzing Bird Migratory Routes

Many species of migratory birds use the same routes, or flyways, to travel to new habitats in the winter and the spring. The map below shows migration flyways used by some North American raptors, such as sharp-shinned hawks and Cooper's hawks.

Analyzing the Map

1 Judging from the flyways represented on the map, do all raptors in North America migrate the same distance each year?
2 What are some of the environmental factors that might determine the paths of such flyways?
3 What are some of the geographical features that may assist a young raptor in recognizing its migration route?
4 Choose one of the routes shown below. Using an atlas, estimate the number of miles in that route.

small, rocky islands, the Icelanders remove the down with which the birds line their nests. The female geese simply replace the down lining and raise their young without further interference.

Humans also wear jewelry and clothing decorated with colorful bird feathers. Many people enjoy birds as pets. They are attracted by the birds' brightly colored feathers, by their songs, and in some cases by their ability to imitate the sound of a human voice. Many tropical birds, such as parrots, are illegally trapped and sold as pets. The collection, export, and sale of these birds are regulated by law, but these laws are often difficult to enforce. When purchasing a parrot or other tropical bird for a pet, make sure it was bred in captivity for that purpose.

Over many years humans have come to appreciate birds for their beauty, flight, and song. Many bird-watchers use bird feeders to attract birds so they can watch them up close.

CHECKPOINT 26.6

1. What roles do birds play in ecosystems around the world?
2. Compare the courtship behaviors of two bird species.
3. Critical Thinking In bird species in which the males and females look exactly alike, each sex usually has very distinct and unique courtship rituals. How are these rituals advantageous to each sex?

Build on What You Know

4. How do the behaviors of birds compare with the corresponding behaviors of insects? *(Need to jog your memory? Revisit relevant concepts in Chapter 23, Section 23.4.)*

fowl for meat. They also raise ducks, chickens, and geese for their eggs.

Humans also use other products of some birds that live in the wild. Certain families in Iceland, for example, have tended flocks of wild geese called eiders for thousands of years. The families collect the birds' down feathers for use in pillows, comforters, and clothing. These soft feathers provide excellent insulation. When the eiders come to nest on a group of

How was the evolution of feathers a favorable adaptation for birds?

Chapter 26 Review

26.1–26.3 Reptiles represent the first vertebrates with adaptations that enable them to live their entire lives out of water.

26.4–26.6 With the development of feathers, birds were the first vertebrates able to maintain a constant body temperature.

Sum It Up

Use the following summary to review the main concepts in this chapter.

26.1 Characteristics of Reptiles

- Water-resistant skin helps reptiles conserve water. Reptile body structure allows quick movement on land.
- Reptiles have efficient lungs and water-conserving urinary bladders, and most have hearts with three chambers.
- Amniotic eggs, which are fertilized internally, provide nourishment and protection for embryos.

26.2 Origin and Diversity of Reptiles

- Reptiles may have evolved from amphibians or from lobe-finned fishes. Extinct reptiles include the dinosaurs, which were dominant during the Mesozoic era.
- Chelonians—turtles and tortoises—have protective shells.
- Snakes and lizards live in most land and water habitats.
- Crocodilians are more like dinosaurs or birds than they are like modern reptiles.

26.3 Reptiles in the Biosphere

- Reptiles are both predators and prey.
- Reptiles have a range of adaptations for combating predators and finding mates.
- Many reptiles are endangered because their flesh, shells, and skins are considered valuable.

26.4 Characteristics of Birds

- Adaptations for flight either reduce body weight or make the body more aerodynamic.
- Birds have four-chambered hearts, and lungs through which air flows in one direction.
- Birds eat large amounts of food to fuel flight and maintain a constant body temperature.
- Birds expend energy on mating, building nests, incubating eggs, and caring for young.

26.5 Origin and Diversity of Birds

- Birds evolved from a reptilian ancestor.
- Feathers and flight distinguish the diverse avian species from other vertebrates.

26.6 Birds in the Biosphere

- Birds pollinate flowers, disperse seeds, control insect pests, and serve as predators and prey.
- Many male birds attract mates with songs, displays, or by building physical structures.
- Many birds make seasonal migrations.
- Humans use birds as food and for their feathers.

Use Terms and Concepts

Use each of the following words or terms in a complete sentence. If you need to review a meaning, turn to the page indicated.

amniotic egg (p. 622)

yolk (p. 622)

chorion (p. 623)

crop (p. 634)

gizzard (p. 634)

chalaza (p. 637)

Use Your Word Power

COMPLETION **Write the word or phrase that best completes each statement.**

1. A(n) _____ has muscular walls for grinding food.

2. The food source for the developing reptile embryo is the _____ .

3. In the digestive system of birds, food is stored in the _____ .

4. The membrane that surrounds the embryo, yolk, and allantois is called the _____ .

5. The _____ is a strand of tissue that supports the egg yolk in a bird's egg.

6. The two functions of the _____ are nourishment and protection of the embryo.

TRUE-FALSE **Write true if the statement is true. If the statement is false, replace the underlined word(s) to make the statement true.**

7. Some birds can regurgitate food stored in the <u>gizzard</u> to feed their young.

8. The <u>yolks</u> of bird eggs are, on average, larger than those of reptile eggs.

9. Food is mixed with digestive enzymes and ground to a pulp in the <u>gizzard</u>.

10. The evolution of an amniotic egg occurred first in <u>birds</u>.

11. In bird eggs, the chalaza is a ropelike strand of tissue that supports the <u>yolk</u>.

12. The <u>chorion</u> is the outermost membrane in an amniotic egg.

Show What You Know

13. How was the evolution of reptiles affected by a decrease in precipitation?

14. What do snake skins and bird feathers have in common?

15. What characteristics of a bird's skeleton are adaptation for flight?

16. Why must an eggshell be porous?

17. What do the eggs of turtles, crocodiles, and birds have in common?

18. What is the advantage of a one-way flow of air through a bird's respiratory system?

19. Which adaptations of snakes make them efficient carnivores? Explain the contribution made by each adaptation.

20. Describe two situations in which anole lizards use coloration to their advantage.

21. What use have humans made of contour feathers? What use have they made of down feathers?

22. **Make a Concept Map** Construct a concept map that compares reptiles and birds using the following terms: amnion, bird, chorion, ectotherm, egg, endotherm, feathers, reptile, scales, yolk.

Take It Further

23. **Developing a Hypothesis** A hummingbird flaps its wings about 80 times per minute, on average. Why is it advantageous for a hummingbird to eat foods such as nectar and fruit, which contain simple sugars?

24. **Applying Concepts** Some birds rarely fly. But most birds spend a lot of time in the air. List at least four situations in which a bird might take to the air.

25. **Making an Analogy** Migrating birds often fly in a formation that saves energy. Explain how this strategy works by comparing it to similar strategies used by long-distance runners or bicycle racers.

26. **Designing an Experiment** In New Zealand, black-billed gulls raise their young in crowded, often noisy colonies on dry stream beds. Design an experiment to find out whether young gulls can recognize the calls of their parents when the parents return to the colony with food.

27. Interpreting Graphs The graph below compares the body temperature of a lizard to the air and burrow temperatures during the daytime. Describe what happens to the temperature of the burrow, the air temperature, and the lizard's body temperature between sunrise and sunset. When is the lizard likely to be in its burrow? In the sun? In the shade?

28. Analyzing Data The table below shows Nile crocodiles and the animals that were found in their stomachs. The crocodiles are grouped by size. What is the most common food source for each group? What is the relationship between size of crocodile and size of prey?

Percentage of Crocodiles Eating Food Sources			
Animals	Group A 0.3–0.5 m	Group B 2.5–3.0 m	Group C 4.5–5.0 m
Mammals	0%	18%	65%
Reptiles	0%	17%	48%
Fish	0%	62%	38%
Birds	0%	17%	0%
Snails	0%	25%	0%
Shellfish	0%	5%	0%
Spiders	20%	0%	0%
Frogs	35%	0%	0%
Insects	100%	2%	0%

Consider the Issues

29. No Admittance Sometimes human activities are restricted to protect other species. For example, some beaches where plovers nest are closed to the public during breeding season. Off-road vehicles are a common target of regulation. Do you support restrictions on the use of dune buggies, motorbikes, or skimobiles? What other alternatives exist? Explain your position.

Make New Connections

30. Biology and Art Many governments have issued postage or commemorative stamps that feature birds. Design a stamp that highlights a native bird from your region.

31. Biology and History A bird's ability to fly has often stirred the human imagination. Starting about 500 years ago with Leonardo da Vinci, inventors have made detailed observations of birds in order to understand the mechanics of flight. Report on one of the following people: Leonardo da Vinci, Sir George Cayley, Otto Lilienthal, Louis-Pierre Mouillard, or Etienne-Jules Marey. How did observations of birds contribute to each inventor's undestanding of flight?

32. Biology and Social Studies Reptiles or reptile-like figures have played a prominent role in the traditions of many cultures for many years. Investigate one example and decide which physical or behavioral traits of reptiles might have inspired the tradition.

FAST-FORWARD TO CHAPTER 27

Birds are not the only endotherms. In the next chapter, you will find out how mammals are similar to and different from other kinds of vertebrates.

CHAPTER 27
Mammals

You can find out more about mammals by exploring the following Internet address:
http://vertebrates.biosurf.com

In this chapter . . .

FEATURES

Everyday Biology
• Whole or Skim
• Monkey Help

In the Community
Cataloging Mammals

 Frontiers in Biology
Living in a Mammalian World

LAB ZONES

Discover It!
• Mammalian Preschool

Do It!
• How Does Mammal Hair Vary?
• Is Whale Blubber an Effective Insulator?

Think About It!
• Comparing the Gestation Periods of Various Mammals

Investigate It!
• Comparing Skeletons

Fast Food

A streak of furred lightning crosses the African savanna at more than 100 kilometers (km) per hour. A clawed limb slashes at a gazelle's hindquarters and the unlucky animal is grabbed by the throat. A cheetah, the fastest land animal in the world, has just caught a family meal.

Although cheetahs have a number of unique adaptations, they share mammalian characteristics such as the prolonged nurturing behavior that accompanies the development of mammary glands and milk. A cheetah mother lives with her cubs and helps feed them for nearly two years, teaching them hunting skills and licking their faces clean after meals. Cheetah mothers are extremely protective, moving their cubs frequently to keep them safe.

Mammals thrive in many different environments and may have many diverse adaptations, such as the cheetah's speedy hunting. What other characteristics unite—and separate—different types of mammals?

LAB ZONE Discover It!

Mammalian Preschool

You need to observe an active litter of kittens, puppies, or other mammals (a videotape will do).

1. Observe and list the interactions taking place among these youngsters. How would you distinguish between play and interactions that are not play? Are some clearly play and others not?
2. See if you can determine whether one youngster is clearly dominant and another clearly at the bottom of the "pecking order."

The play of young animals such as kittens and puppies often reflects behaviors that they would need to survive in the wild. Kittens will stalk toys or other kittens before pouncing on them as they would on prey. Puppies spend a lot of time mock fighting, an activity that would prepare them for their place in the pack hierarchy. And all young animals learn appeasement gestures—cringing, lowered posture—to ward off attack by other members of their species.

WRITE ABOUT IT!

Write a story or poem from the perspective of one of the young animals you observed.

27.1 Characteristics of Mammals

What you'll learn

IDEAS
- To identify characteristics of mammals
- To compare monotremes, marsupials, and placental mammals

WORDS

mammal, mammary glands, diaphragm, monotreme, marsupials, placental mammals, gestation period

FIGURE 27.1

Shrews such as the pygmy shrew (below) must eat continually throughout the day to satisfy their high energy requirements. Without food, a shrew can starve to death in as little as three hours.

The better to hear you

Many mammals, such as the kit fox (right), have large, well-developed outer ears that help direct sound to the inner ear. You have probably seen dogs perk up their ears when they hear something. Dogs and many other mammals can also move their ears in the direction of the sound. The ability to move the outer ear helps mammals locate the source of a sound with greater accuracy.

WHAT IS A MAMMAL?

Hairy animals drink milk

Mammals belong to the class Mammalia. A **mammal** is an endothermic vertebrate with hair. Female mammals have specialized glands called mammary glands, from which mammals get their name. The **mammary glands** secrete milk that nourishes the young.

Scientists have identified and described approximately 4500 species of mammals living on Earth. Familiar mammals include cats, dogs, horses, cows, and humans. The smallest mammal is the pygmy shrew, shown in *Figure 27.1.* It is about 8 centimeters (cm) long and weighs less than a dime. The largest mammal is the blue whale. It can reach 30 meters (m) in length and weigh 100,000 kilograms (kg)—as much as 32 adult elephants!

Mammals live in almost every environment on Earth, from cold arctic regions to hot, dry deserts. Many mammalian adaptations are associated with maintaining body temperature. Hair and body size, for example, affect heat loss. Mammals that live in warm climates are generally smaller than their cold-climate relatives. Their smaller size enables them to lose heat quickly. Also, mammals that live in warm climates usually have thinner coats of hair and layers of fat than mammals that live in cold climates.

MOVEMENT AND RESPONSE

Run, swim, and fly

Land mammals move at different speeds, from very slow to very fast. The slowest mammal is the South American two-toed sloth. Active for only about four hours each day, the sloth moves through trees at the speed of about 1 m every 15 seconds. In contrast, the cheetah, shown on pages 646 and 647, and in *Figure 27.2,* can cover 400 m in the same amount of time. The cheetah is the fastest land animal. The fastest humans run about 150 m in about 15 seconds.

The basic structure of the mammalian skeleton enables high-speed running. The long legs and flexible hip and shoulder joints of most mammals have a wider range of motion than

FIGURE 27.2
The cheetah's long, streamlined body structure allows it to achieve speeds of more than 100 km per hour. But the cheetah can maintain this level of exertion for only a few hundred meters. How are the cheetah's limbs adapted for running?

those of other vertebrates. This enables mammals to take long, rapid strides. Similarly, other modifications allow many types of mammals to move quickly in different environments. For example, the skeleton of a whale is modified for swimming, and the skeleton of a bat is modified for flying.

As a group, mammals have the largest and most well-developed brains in the animal kingdom. The largest part of the brain, called the cerebrum, processes information that makes thinking and learning possible. You will learn more about the brain's functions in Chapter 34.

In many mammals the organs of taste, smell, sight, and hearing are structurally similar to those of humans. The sensitivity of these organs, however, varies between mammalian orders. The sense of smell is more

developed in meat eaters such as cheetahs and dogs. The sense of hearing also varies. Many mammals, including dogs and bats, can detect higher-frequency sound waves than humans can.

Most mammals have good eyesight but do not see colors well. Underground mammals, such as moles, have poor vision. They sense their environment through smell and touch.

ENERGY AND WASTES

What big teeth you have

As you may recall from Chapter 26, endotherms require large amounts of food to generate the energy they need to maintain a constant body temperature. Specialized teeth, such as those shown in *Figure 27.3*, are an adaptation that helps mammals meet their

FIGURE 27.3
The size, shape, and type of teeth are modified according to a mammal's diet. What adaptations can be seen in the herbivore's skull that reflect its diet?

Carnivore

Herbivore

Canines are long, pointed teeth used for piercing and tearing.

Incisors are conelike teeth specialized for stripping and cutting.

Premolars and molars are the broad, flattened teeth adapted for grinding and crushing.

FIGURE 27.4

Internal Structure of an Elephant

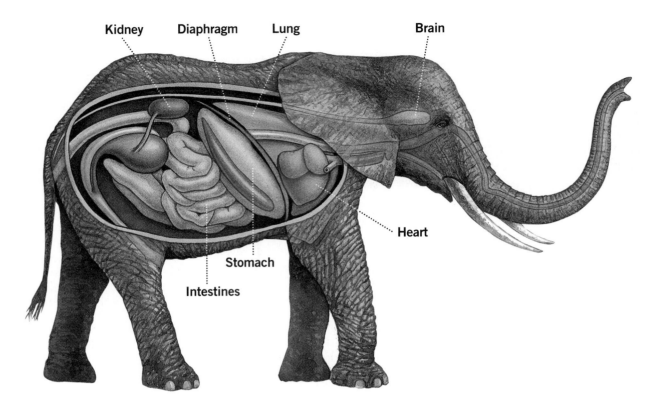

Kidney Diaphragm Lung Brain

Heart

Stomach

Intestines

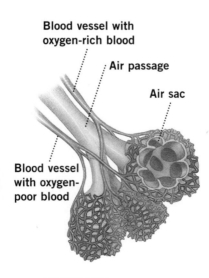

Blood vessel with
oxygen-rich blood

Air passage

Air sac

Blood vessel
with oxygen-
poor blood

FIGURE 27.5

**How do air sacs enable
animals to exchange
oxygen efficiently?**

energy needs. Compare the structures of these teeth with their functions.

Varied teeth enable various mammals to eat a wide range of food. Which types of teeth do humans have? How are they adapted to the human diet?

Figure 27.4 shows an elephant's digestive tract. The length and structure of the elephant's and other mammals' digestive tracts also reflects their diets. In general, mammals that eat only plants have longer digestive tracts than mammals that eat only meat. The trip through the digestive tract of an herbivore must be long and slow because plants contain tough fibers that take time to break down.

In addition to large amounts of food, endotherms require a rich supply of oxygen for cellular respiration. Mammals have two adaptations that increase the efficiency of the lungs: the diaphragm and air sacs. The **diaphragm,** shown in

Figure 27.4, is a dome-shaped sheet of muscle that separates the chest cavity and the abdomen. When the diaphragm contracts, the pressure in the chest cavity decreases, causing air to be forced into the lungs. When the diaphragm relaxes, the opposite happens; pressure in the chest cavity increases, and air is forced out of the lungs.

Oxygen enters the blood through vessels in the air sacs, which are shown in *Figure* 27.5. These tiny air sacs are located at the ends of breathing passages in mammalian lungs. The exchange of gases between the air and the blood occurs in the air sacs. The air sacs increase the surface area across which gas exchange takes place.

The circulatory system of mammals efficiently supplies oxygen to the cells of the body and collects wastes. Like birds, which are also endothermic, mammals have a double-loop circulatory system with a four-chambered heart. The four-chambered heart separates oxygen-rich blood coming from the lungs and oxygen-poor blood that has circulated through the body.

You can see in *Figure 27.4* that elephants, like other vertebrates, have kidneys. Mammalian kidneys remove cellular wastes and regulate the water balance in the body by producing urine. Mammalian urine is a dilute fluid composed of wastes and excess water.

LIFE CYCLE
Taking care of baby

All mammals have internal fertilization. All female mammals have mammary glands that secrete milk to nourish their young. These two characteristics are the only reproductive similarities shared by the three groups of mammals discussed below: monotremes (MON-oh-treemz), marsupials (mar-SOO-pee-ulz), and placental (pluh-SEN-tul) mammals.

Monotremes A **monotreme** is a mammal that reproduces by laying eggs. Shortly after fertilization, the female monotreme lays two or three eggs, which are incubated by the heat from her body. Like birds and reptiles, the developing monotreme embryos are nourished by nutrients inside the egg. After the eggs hatch, young monotremes feed on milk that flows from pores on the mother's belly. Newly hatched monotremes are very immature and must develop further under parental care before they can survive on their own.

Marsupials Mammals that give birth to small, immature young that further develop inside the mother's external pouch are called **marsupials.** After fertilization, a marsupial embryo is nourished inside its mother by a yolk sac similar to that in an amniotic egg. The yolk sac is not large enough to nourish the embryo through its complete development, however. About 30 days after fertilization, a female red kangaroo gives birth to a tiny, underdeveloped baby. The blind, hairless baby weighs about 28 grams (g) and is only about 2.5 cm long. It could fit easily inside a teaspoon!

After it is born, the baby kangaroo, like most marsupials, crawls into its mother's pouch. It remains in the pouch, as in *Figure 27.6,* until it is large enough and strong enough to survive on its own.

Marsupial reproduction has several differences from monotreme reproduction. Newborn marsupials are protected and kept warm in the mother's pouch. Also, marsupial mothers can move around to look for food or escape from predators even while their young are nursing. Monotreme mothers, on the other hand, must stay in one place while incubating their eggs or nursing their young.

EVERYDAY BIOLOGY

Whole or Skim

When baby kangaroos (called joeys) are born, they drink low-fat, high-protein milk. After they leave the pouch, joeys drink high-fat, low-protein milk from a different nipple. But, do not confuse this with the whole and skim milk you may drink. To create the low-percent milk or skim milk you find in stores, fat is removed from cow's milk.

FIGURE 27.6
The female duck-billed platypus (above) lays her eggs in a nesting burrow. Inside the pouch, the baby kangaroo (left) attaches to the nipple of a mammary gland and remains there, drinking its mother's milk, until it is fully developed. Which animal is a monotreme? A marsupial?

Do It!

How Does Mammal Hair Vary?

All mammals have hair, but not all mammal hair is the same. You can examine different kinds of hair when you . . .

Try This

1 Observe mammals with hair (pets, humans, livestock, and so on). Collect single hairs from a variety of mammals.
2 Observe the length, thickness, color, and shape of each type of hair. Record your observations.

Analyze Your Results

1 Which animal had the longest hair? The thickest? Considering the habits of these animals, how would these traits help the animals survive in their environment?
2 How might the color and shape of hair affect the survival of an animal?

FIGURE 27.7
Many placental mammals are born well developed. This calf will be able to walk within hours of its birth.

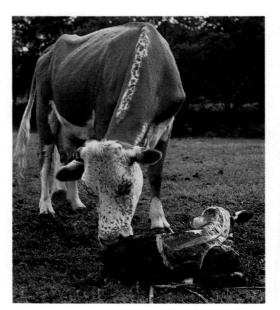

Placental mammals Mammals whose young develop inside the mother's body and are nourished by the mother's body until birth are called **placental mammals.** Compared with the young of marsupials, the embryo of a placental mammal develops more fully before birth. Almost 95 percent of all mammals are placental mammals.

Placental mammals get their name from the placenta, an organ through which nutrients, oxygen, carbon dioxide, and wastes are exchanged between the mother and the embryo. The placenta is a spongy tissue that completely surrounds the embryo. Blood vessels of the mother and the embryo intertwine in the placenta, enabling the exchange of materials to take place.

The time that the embryo stays inside the mother's body is called the **gestation period.** This period varies greatly among placental mammals. In general, the gestation period increases with the size of the adult and the degree to which the newborns are developed. Mice, for example, have a gestation period of 21 days, while elephants have a gestation period of 22 months. The gestation period of humans is approximately nine months.

Although some animals, such as birds and alligators, care for their young, mammals provide more care and protection for their young than most animals do. Nursing alone keeps mother and offspring together for a long time. The length of time that adults spend with their young, combined with the advantage of a well-developed cerebrum, enables the young to learn a great deal about survival. Many scientists think that the long period of parental care has contributed to the evolutionary success of mammals.

CHECKPOINT 27.1

1. Identify the key characteristics of mammals.
2. Compare the reproductive processes of monotremes, marsupials, and placental mammals.
3. Critical Thinking Many humans have their wisdom teeth extracted because their jaws are too small to accommodate them. What might this suggest about the evolution of the human jaw?

Build on What You Know

4. Compared with many fishes, mammals produce few offspring. How is the amount of time spent caring for offspring related to the number of offspring produced? Propose an explanation for this. **(Need to jog your memory? Revisit relevant concepts in Chapter 25, Section 25.2.)**

Comparing Skeletons

WHAT YOU WILL DO Compare the skeletons of different animals

WHAT SKILLS YOU WILL USE Collecting and recording data, observing, analyzing, classifying

WHAT YOU WILL NEED Three skeletons, or diagrams of skeletons, labeled *A*, *B*, and *C*

Propose a Hypothesis

The structure of an animal's skeleton can be used for classification. Hypothesize which skeletal structures are most useful in determining an animal's identity.

Conduct Your Experiment

1 Examine each skeleton.

2 Set up a chart using *Skeleton A, B, and C* as headings for three columns.

3 Count the number of vertebrae in each skeleton, and record the data in the chart.

4 The vertebrae that make up a tail are called caudal vertebrae. Do any of the skeletons have caudal vertebrae? Record these data in the chart.

5 Which skeleton or skeletons have limbs? Do the limbs point outward from the vertebrae or downward, underneath the vertebrae? Record these data.

6 For the skeletons with limbs, count the number of digits on each limb and record this number.

7 In the chart, describe the shape of each skeleton's skull.

8 Do any of the skulls have teeth in their jaws? What kind of teeth are they? Record this information in the chart.

Analyze Your Data

1 Do any of the skeletons lack limbs? If so, which one(s)? What kinds of vertebrate animals lack limbs? Based on this information, can you infer the identity of the limbless skeleton(s)? What other clues might help in your identification?

2 Of the skeletons that have limbs, which limbs have an outward orientation? Based on this information and the relative sizes of the limbs, can you infer what type of animal this skeleton belongs to?

3 Of the skeletons that have limbs, which limbs are oriented under the body? Can you infer what type of animal this skeleton belongs to?

Draw Conclusions

1 Write a paragraph discussing how you inferred the identity of each skeleton.

2 What features of the skeleton can be used to distinguish one type of organism from another?

Design a Related Experiment

Design a related experiment in which you infer the skeletal structure of an animal, based on a photograph of the animal.

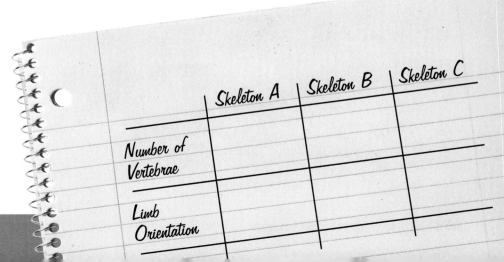

	Skeleton A	Skeleton B	Skeleton C
Number of Vertebrae			
Limb Orientation			

27.2 Origin and Diversity of Mammals

What you'll learn

IDEAS

• To describe the evolution of mammals

• To compare the three orders of mammals

A daring young lemur

Flying lemurs live in the rain forests of Southeast Asia. They do not really fly, but with large, thin folds of skin that connect the neck, legs, and tail, they certainly can glide. With these "wings" of skin outspread, a flying lemur—roughly the size of a cat—looks like a kite with legs. It can glide up to 91 m from tree to tree in search of the tropical flowers, fruits, and leaves to eat.

ORIGIN OF MAMMALS

Creatures of the night

As you learned in Chapter 12, the first mammals probably evolved about 245 to 195 million years ago, during the Triassic period, from a group of small mammal-like reptiles called therapsids. Fossil evidence indicates that the first mammals were small insect-eating animals similar to the one shown in *Figure* 27.8. These animals resembled modern shrews or mice and lived among the dinosaurs and other reptiles during the Mesozoic era.

Recall from Chapter 26 that Earth's climate was relatively warm during the Mesozoic era. The ectothermic reptiles of the time easily warmed their bodies by basking in the sun during the day. But at night their body temperatures dropped as the air cooled, and they became inactive. Unlike reptiles, ancient mammals were endothermic. They generated their own body heat and could remain active during the cold prehistoric nights.

Being endothermic had its disadvantages, however. To generate and maintain a warm body temperature, an endothermic mammal required about ten times more food than did an ectothermic reptile of the same size. Approximately 90 percent of a mammal's food is used to generate body heat. Therefore, mammals require more time, energy, and space than other animals seeking food. This huge demand for food and space limited the size of mammal populations for millions of years.

Fossil evidence indicates that many changes occurred at the end of the Mesozoic era (about 65 million years ago). The climate cooled, and angiosperms began replacing the gymnosperms that had previously dominated the land.

As dinosaurs died out at the end of the Mesozoic era, many habitats and resources became available to mammals. The mammals had little competition for food and space. As a result, a period of enormous adaptive

FIGURE 27.8

The first mammals, such as the *Eozostrodon* shown here, may have evolved from mammal-like reptiles. The early mammals probably occupied small niches not filled by dinosaurs.

radiation probably occurred during this time span. Many new species of mammals may have evolved as different mammal populations spread out and adapted to new habitats.

Mammals became the dominant class of vertebrates during the Cenozoic era, which is known as the Age of Mammals. During this time, Earth's climate became cooler, and endothermy became a distinct advantage. An animal with a constant body temperature could remain active in cold temperatures. Because its muscles were kept warm, an endothermic mammal could escape from a predator or pursue prey quickly at all times. Hair was also an advantage. The layer of hair common to all mammals provided insulation against the loss of body heat.

MONOTREMES AND MARSUPIALS

Eggs and pouches

Scientists theorize that, by the early Cenozoic era, mammals had split into the three groups that survive today: monotremes, marsupials, and placental mammals. As you have just learned, scientists classify these mammals according to the development of their embryo. In the descriptions that follow, consider how each group's adaptations enable the species to survive.

The monotremes were the first mammals to evolve from the therapsids. These primitive mammals retain some of the characteristics of their reptilian ancestors, such as laying eggs. Monotremes cannot control their body temperature as well as other mammals can and usually have a lower body temperature.

There are only three species of monotremes, and all are are native to Australia. The duck-billed platypus lives in a burrow. Its flat, beaverlike tail and webbed feet are adaptations to an aquatic lifestyle. The rubbery,

FIGURE 27.9
Class Mammalia

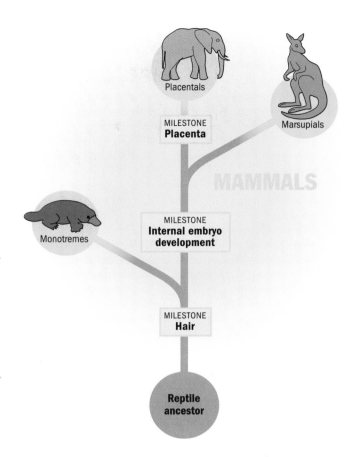

duck-bill-like muzzle probes for shellfish, insects, and worms in the muddy bottoms of lakes and streams.

The other two species of monotremes are echidnas, or spiny anteaters. They live in the forests, mountains, and plains of Australia and New Guinea. As you can see in *Figure 27.10,* the echidna has a long snout and is covered with a thick coat of hair and spines. The echidna's long snout searches for insects and earthworms in logs or soil. When an echidna is threatened, it burrows into the ground so that only its spiny back shows.

Most of the nearly 250 living species of marsupials live in Australia or on nearby islands. One exception is the opossum, which is abundant in parts of North and South America. At one time, marsupials lived throughout

FIGURE 27.10
Echidnas are toothless monotremes. They use their long, rough tongue to crush insects against the roof of their mouth.

FIGURE 27.11
The koala is a marsupial. How would this koala care for its offspring?

FIGURE 27.12
Though they look very different from each other, both chipmunks and porcupines are rodents. How are all rodents similar?

FIGURE 27.13
This black-tailed jackrabbit is a desert- and prairie-dwelling lagomorph. How does it differ from rodents?

the world. But they could not compete with placental mammals and eventually disappeared from most places.

Marsupials lived successfully in Australia because for many years Australia had no placental mammals. Scientists theorize that Australia broke away from other land masses before the Cretaceous period and before placental mammals had evolved. In this isolation, marsupials underwent adaptive radiation, filling niches that placental mammals occupied elsewhere. There are placental mammals in Australia today, however—many brought there by humans.

Two of the most familiar marsupials are the kangaroo and the koala. Most kangaroos are herbivores, and they can travel about 8 m in one hop. Koalas, like the one shown in *Figure 27.11,* live in the forests of Australia and eat only the leaves and shoots of the eucalyptus tree.

PLACENTAL MAMMALS

Lions, and tigers, and bears—oh my!

Ninety-five percent of all mammals are placental mammals. They are a very diverse group that make their homes in water, on land, and in the air. These mammals have specialized adaptations for movement and obtaining food that fit the environments in which they live.

Rodents The largest order of mammals is Rodentia, which includes more than 1700 species. Beavers, chipmunks, guinea pigs, mice, porcupines, rats, and squirrels are all rodents. Rodents are herbivores, with a pair of very long, sharp teeth in each jaw. Unlike the teeth of most mammals, these long teeth continue to grow. They enable rodents to gnaw on tough stems and roots, in addition to leaves and seeds.

Lagomorphs Hares, pikas, and rabbits are members of the order Lagomorpha (lay-go-MOR-fuh), which consists of about 65 species. Rabbits and hares have long ears, long and powerful hind legs, clawed toes, and a stubby tail. Pikas have rounded ears and legs of equal length. Although similar in appearance to rodents, lagomorphs differ from rodents in the structure of their teeth. A lagomorph's diet is also somewhat different from that of a rodent, consisting mostly of leaves, grasses, and bark.

Bats The order Chiroptera (key-ROP-ter-uh) is the second-largest order of mammals. All of the 925 species of chiropterans are commonly known as bats. Bats are small nocturnal (active at night) animals, the only mammals that can fly. Powerful muscles move the bat's wings, resulting in flight at speeds of up to 65 km per hour. Bats live wherever the climate is warm enough to support trees. In colder climates, bats migrate to warmer areas in the winter. The smallest bats weigh only about 4 g, and the largest bats weigh as much as 1.5 kg.

The diversity of bat diets is reflected in the variations in bats' teeth. Insect-eating bats have curved teeth that mash insects into a paste. Bats that eat fruit and other plant materials have flattened teeth that

FIGURE 27.14
Like most bats, the greater horseshoe bat uses ultrasonic echolocation to find prey. However, unlike most bats, it emits sounds through its nostrils, not its mouth.

grind the plants. Perhaps the most notorious adaptation of bats is the razor-sharp teeth of vampire bats. These bats feed on large mammals by cutting the skin and lapping up the blood. Vampire bats do not, however, suck the blood out of the prey's body.

Carnivores Most of the 240 species of the order Carnivora are strictly meat-eating mammals. But there are many exceptions, such as the panda which feeds primarily on bamboo shoots, and bears which eat roots, nuts, and berries in addition to meat. All carnivores evolved from ancestors adapted to a diet of meat. Carnivores have a pair of long, sharp teeth, strong jaws, and clawed toes, and are considered one of the strongest and most intelligent groups of animals. Lions, tigers, wolves, coyotes, weasels, skunks, and raccoons are all carnivores.

The order Carnivora includes a suborder of animals adapted to a somewhat aquatic lifestyle. These carnivores, called pinnipeds, include walruses, sea lions, otters, and seals. Pinnipeds have limbs modified for swimming, a streamlined body, and a thick layer of fat that insulates them in icy waters. These carnivores return to land to reproduce.

Cetaceans Dolphins, porpoises, and whales are members of the order Cetacea (seh-TAY-shuh). Cetaceans have a torpedo-shaped body with a long, pointed head and no neck. Cetaceans do not have hind limbs but they have a broad, flat, horizontal tail and flipperlike forelimbs for swimming. The cetacean body closely resembles that of a fish. As mammals, however, cetaceans have no gills and must come to the surface for air. Unlike sea lions, cetaceans are completely aquatic. They cannot move on land, and they reproduce entirely in the water.

Sirenians The order Sirenia (sy-REEN-ee-uh) is a small group of aquatic mammals that includes manatees and dugongs. Sirenians have a large, slow-moving, barrel-shaped body with flipperlike forelimbs, no hind limbs, and a flat, horizontal tail. Like all mammals, sirenians must come to the surface for air. Manatees are common off the coast of Florida. In fact, manatees seen from distant ships inspired legends about mermaids.

FIGURE 27.15
The black panther, a carnivore, is actually a species of leopard with dark fur, which makes its spots either hard to see or completely invisible. How does this carnivore differ from the carnivores shown below?

FIGURE 27.16
Though both are aquatic, carnivorous mammals, sea lions (above) and killer whales (left) are members of different orders. What are some of their physical similarities and differences?

Is Whale Blubber an Effective Insulator?

Unlike the skin of most land mammals, a whale's skin is smooth and almost hairless. Under its skin, the whale has a thick layer of fat, or blubber, which serves to insulate the whale from cold ocean water. You can test the effectiveness of blubber as an insulator when you . . .

Try This

Design your own experiment in which you demonstrate the insulating qualities of fat, using the following materials: test tubes, thermometers, warm water, vegetable shortening or animal lard, small plastic bags, large beaker filled with ice water, timer.

Analyze Your Results

1 What type of data are you collecting? How often do you plan to collect data?
2 What is your control?
3 How does your experiment model a whale's blubber?
4 What did your results show? Is blubber an effective insulator?
5 Given what you know about endotherms, how does blubber affect the whale's ability to live in a variety of environments?

FIGURE 27.19
All species of rhinoceroses are now threatened with extinction due to poaching. Perhaps the biggest reason they are hunted is for their horns, which are actually formed of compacted hair fibers.

uh). Members of the order Artiodactyla have an even number of toes. Pigs, hippopotamuses, camels, deer, antelopes, cows, goats, sheep, giraffes, elk, and bison are artiodactyls. Members of the order Perissodactyla have an odd number of toes. Horses, zebras, rhinoceroses, and tapirs are perissodactyls. Both groups of ungulates are herbivorous grazing mammals. They have flat teeth for grinding plant material, and in some species the digestive tract has a specialized chamber in which cellulose is broken down.

FIGURE 27.17
The manatee spends much of its time sleeping and consuming aquatic plants. It can grow up to 4.5 m in length and weigh 500 kg.

Insectivores As their name suggests, members of the order Insectivora are insect-eating mammals. Moles, shrews, and hedgehogs are insectivores. They have a high metabolic rate and sharp claws for digging insects from the ground.

Ungulates Ungulates, or hoofed mammals, are divided into two orders: Artiodactyla (ART-ee-oh-DAK-til-uh) and Perissodactyla (peh-riss-oh-DAK-til-

FIGURE 27.18
Though its vision is poor, the hedgehog's sense of smell is excellent. It uses this skill to sniff out insects, as well as worms, snails, and even small vertebrates.

FIGURE 27.20
Warthogs are herbivores, dining mainly on grasses and herbs, while avoiding humans and their crops. The warthog's even number of toes puts it in a different order than the rhinoceroses.

FIGURE 27.21
Elephants are the largest living terrestrial mammals; the African elephant (left) can grow to be larger than the Indian elephant (right). They are social animals and travel in groups of relatives that are most often led by an elderly female.

Elephants The order Proboscidea (pro-BOSS-id-ee-uh) has only two species: African elephants and Indian elephants. Elephants have a massive body, a large head, broad flat ears, a short neck, and thick skin with little hair. Their muscular, boneless trunk transfers food and water to the mouth and makes loud, trumpetlike noises. Elephants also have long, modified teeth called tusks that dig up plant roots or pry bark from trees. Elephants are herbivores, and it is not uncommon for them to eat plants for as many as 18 hours a day to obtain enough food to survive. What are some of the differences between the two species of elephants shown in *Figure 27.21*?

Primates The 175 species of the order Primates include humans, apes, monkeys, and prosimians. Primates have an opposable thumb on each hand and usually each foot as well. The position of the thumb enables primates to grasp branches and other objects. Primates also have large eyes that face forward. Primates are omnivores and will eat whatever food is available. They have large brains and live in organized social groups. With the exception of humans, most primates live in tropical and subtropical parts of the world.

Other placental mammals
The remaining orders of placental mammals are small groups, many containing only one species. Aardvarks are the only species in the order Tubulidentata. Hyraxes, small shrewlike animals, are the only members of the order Hyracoidea. The order Pholidota contains one genus of animals, called scaly anteaters. The classification of some placental mammals may change in coming years as more is learned about their evolutionary history.

CHECKPOINT 27.2

1. Explain the role of adaptive radiation in the evolution of animals.
2. Compare the many orders of mammals. What are some general characteristics that differentiate species?
3. **Critical Thinking** Which is more fully adapted to an aquatic lifestyle—cetaceans or pinnipeds? Explain your answer.

Build on What You Know

4. Both birds and mammals are thought to have evolved independently from reptilian ancestors. Compare the adaptations of birds to those of mammals. Discuss how birds and mammals are adapted to their different niches.
   (Need to jog your memory? Revisit relevant concepts in Chapter 26, Section 26.4.)

FIGURE 27.22
Though extremely different physically, the tarsier (top) and the gorilla (bottom) are members of the same order. The tarsier is a small nocturnal primate that spends its days in the trees. The gorilla, which weighs about 2000 times more than the tarsier, lives mainly on the ground.

What are the characteristics of all mammals?

27.3 Mammals in the Biosphere

What you'll learn

IDEAS

• To identify the roles of mammals in the biosphere
• To explain the interactions of humans and other mammals

The jaws that catch

The wolverine is not a very large animal. It measures, at most, 1 meter from head to tail. But its strength is awesome. The wolverine's jaws can crush the thick bones of large mammals like caribou and elk. Running on wide paws that help them go fast on deep snow, wolverines overtake their much larger prey. They then leap onto the back of the fleeing animal and bite its neck to bring it down.

ECOLOGICAL ROLES

What's for dinner?

Mammals live almost everywhere on Earth. They burrow underground, fly through the air, swing from tree to tree, and swim in the world's oceans. Everywhere they live, mammals are an important part of the ecosystem.

Mammals feed at various levels of the food chain. As you have read, some mammals are herbivores, feeding only on plants. Others, such as most members of the order Carnivora, are predators, often hunting other mammals. Some mammals, such as humans, are omnivores. They eat both plants and animals.

Although they may feed on plants, many mammals also play an important role in plant reproduction. Some mammals are important pollinators for many types of plants. Others are helpful in transporting seeds which allow plants to populate new areas.

Seeds may become stuck in a mammal's fur, or they may be deposited with its wastes. In either case, the seeds can end up far from the parent plant.

Some mammals alter the environment in which they live. The resulting changes can be either beneficial or harmful. Beavers chew down trees and make dams across rivers and streams. The lakes and ponds that form behind the dams are home to many species of animals, including fishes, amphibians, and insects. However, what is beneficial to one species may not be beneficial to another. Species living on the other side of the beaver's dam, for example, may be harmed by the reduction in the amount of available water.

Humans also have the ability to alter the environment physically. And like other mammals, our actions can affect other organisms in either positive or negative ways. You will learn more about the interactions of organisms and their environment in Unit 9.

Some mammals carry diseases that are spread to humans and other animals. Dogs and squirrels can carry

FIGURE 27.23

Beavers can build very effective dams out of trees and mud. How do you think a dam might change a stream?

and transmit the virus that causes rabies. Squirrels, rats, and prairie dogs can carry fleas that sometimes spread disease-causing organisms.

MAMMALIAN BEHAVIOR

Just for the fun of it

Mammals exhibit many different kinds of behaviors. Some behaviors, such as finding food, are common to many other animals. Other behaviors, such as playing and using tools, are most often observed in mammals.

Mammals have many different ways to locate and capture food. For example, bats are nighttime hunters that use echolocation to find food and avoid objects in the dark. While flying, a bat sends out a series of short, high-pitched squeaks or beeps through its nose or mouth. When the sound waves hit an object, echoes bounce back and are captured by the bat's large, sensitive ears. The bat can determine the location of the object, such as a moth, and tell whether the object is moving. Whales and dolphins also locate their prey by echolocation.

Mammals also have the ability to make and use tools. Chimpanzees, for example, strip the leaves off twigs, and insert them into termite mounds. They then pull out the termite-covered sticks and eat the insects. Sea otters use rocks as tools. As you can see in *Figure 27.24*, otters will sometimes crack a clam shell against a rock they hold on their chest. Of course, humans use a variety of tools every day, both for survival and to make life easier.

Many mammals play. Scientists are still not sure why mammals play, but they think that play enables them to learn skills used in hunting and fighting. Play may also help mammals gain physical strength and endurance. Why might a dog like to play fetch or a kitten be challenged with a ball of yarn?

LAB ZONE **Think About It!**

Comparing the Gestation Periods of Various Mammals

The gestation period of a placental mammal is the amount of time that an offspring spends developing in the mother's uterus before birth. Although gestation is affected by many factors and can vary greatly between mammal species, there are some general trends.

Analyzing the Diagram

1 Look at the graph of mammal gestation periods. For each mammal, estimate the length in weeks of each gestation period.
2 Estimate the mass of each of the mammals. What is the trend linking the mass of the animal with its gestation period?
3 Not all mammals follow the trend shown here. The elephant shrew, for example, has a gestation period of 76 days and weighs only 45 g. What other factors may affect the gestation rates in mammals?

1 year
9 months
3 months
6 months

Elephant   Lion
Whale   Dog
Chimp   Rat

Different mammals play in a variety of ways, sometimes alone and sometimes with others. In Churchill, Canada, people have observed polar bears wrestling and tumbling with sled dogs. Baby elephants have been known to wrestle using their trunks, and to roll around. Young wolves will chase each other for hours, seemingly for the fun of it. Young gorillas and chimpanzees often play with their mothers; so do lion and leopard cubs. Dolphins seem to be playing as they leap in the wakes of boats and ships.

FIGURE 27.24
After using this rock as a tool, the otter may store it in a pouch of skin under its foreleg and use it again later.

Monkey Help

Most mammals that humans train for work are large, strong, and four-footed. Horses, donkeys, oxen, and even elephants have been used for work and transport for thousands of years. But other mammals can also be trained. In Malaysia, the pig-tailed macaque monkey is taught to pick and carry coconuts from trees.

FRONTIERS IN BIOLOGY

Living in a mammalian world

Almost since the beginning of human history, people have used mammals for food. Today cows, sheep, pigs, goats, and other mammals are raised for food—either for their meat or for dairy products such as milk and cheese. Mammals provide leather for shoes, clothing, furniture, and other uses. The wool of sheep and other mammals is collected and woven into fabrics.

Many mammals help humans do their work. For example, people have used horses and donkeys for at least 5000 years to carry loads and passengers, and to pull wagons, carts, and plows. In India and Asia, people have used elephants for transportation and work for thousands of years. Llamas and camels carry heavy loads across high mountains and deserts.

Mammals also do a variety of other jobs for humans. Because of their intelligence and loyalty, dogs can be trained to perform many tasks. Hunting dogs retrieve ducks and geese. Some dogs assist people with disabilities. For example, seeing-eye dogs help guide their blind owners, and hearing dogs help people who are hearing impaired.

People around the world enjoy mammals as pets. Dogs, cats, hamsters, rabbits, and horses are popular pets. Some physicians think that having a pet reduces a person's stress level and improves health and well-being.

Mammals are also used in behavioral and medical research. Dolphins and chimpanzees have been studied extensively to learn more about the development of the brain and how mammals learn. Dolphins, thought to be one of the most intelligent mammal species, are also used in human therapy. People with some diseases and disabilities have experienced physical and emotional relief after swimming with captive dolphins.

Continued research in veterinary medicine has led to increased knowledge concerning animal health and maintenance. These advances in technology have improved the health of domestic pets and livestock.

CHECKPOINT 27.3

1. Describe three mammalian behaviors.
2. Describe four important interactions between humans and other mammals.
3. **Critical Thinking** Many mammals—such as whales, rhinoceroses, and elephants—have been hunted to near extinction. How would the extinction of one of these mammals affect other living things?

Build on What You Know

4. How do the roles of mammals in food chains compare with those of birds? *(Need to jog your memory? Revisit relevant concepts in Chapter 26, Section 26.6.)*

 What roles do mammals play in their ecosystems?

Chapter 27 Review

 27.1–27.2 Although different species have unique adaptations, all mammals are endothermic vertebrates with hair and mammary glands.

27.3 Mammals live almost everywhere on Earth and play important roles in ecosystems.

Sum It Up

Use the following summary to review the main concepts in this chapter.

27.1 Characteristics of Mammals

- A mammal's size and the thickness of its coat and fat layer usually reflect the climate of its habitat.
- The basic mammalian skeleton is an adaptation that enables running at high speeds.
- Mammals are endotherms. They obtain the energy they need by processing a wide range of food, using varied teeth.
- A diaphragm, air sacs, and a four-chambered heart are mammalian adaptations that help provide a continuous supply of oxygen.
- All mammals use internal fertilization. All female mammals secrete milk for their young.
- The three groups of mammals are: the egg-laying monotremes; the externally pouched marsupials; and the placental mammals, whose young develop within the mother's body.

27.2 Origin and Diversity of Mammals

- The first mammals, probably small insect-eaters, evolved from reptiles during the Triassic period.
- The endothermy of mammals, and the availability of resources following the dinosaurs' extinction,

led to a period of enormous adaptive radiation in mammals during the Cenozoic era.
- Monotremes retain some of the characteristics of their reptilian ancestors.
- Marsupials flourished in Australia because until recently they did not have to compete with placental mammals for resources.
- Most mammals are placental mammals. They are a diverse group and exhibit a range of adaptations to the environments they inhabit.
- A placental mammal's teeth can reveal its diet; for example, sharp-toothed rodents gnaw tough roots or stems, while flat-toothed ungulates eat grass.

27.3 Mammals in the Biosphere

- Mammals occupy various levels of the food chain. Many mammals have important roles in the reproduction of plants.
- Some mammals can alter their environments. The changes may be beneficial or harmful.
- Mammals exhibit many types of behaviors, including finding food, playing, and using tools.
- People use mammals to do work. They also use them as a source of food and clothing, as pets, and in valuable behavioral and medical research.

Use Terms and Concepts

Use each of the following words or terms in a complete sentence. If you need to review a meaning, turn to the page indicated.

mammal (p. 648)

mammary glands (p. 648)

diaphragm (p. 650)

monotreme (p. 651)

marsupials (p. 651)

placental mammals (p. 652)

gestation period (p. 652)

Use Your Word Power

COMPLETION **Write the word or phrase that best completes each statement.**

1. A _____ reproduces by laying eggs.

2. A hairy endothermic vertebrate is called a(n) _____ .

3. The immature young of _____ develop in an external pouch.

4. The _____ separates the abdomen from the chest cavity.

5. The time between conception and birth is called the _____ .

6. Female hares, hedgehogs, and humans have _____ , which produce milk.

7. The young of _____ develop in the mother's body until birth.

TRUE-FALSE **Write true if the statement is true. If the statement is false, replace the underlined word(s) to make the statement true.**

8. In general, the gestation period <u>increases</u> with the size of the adult mammal.

9. Competition with <u>monotremes</u> limited the number of niches available to marsupials.

10. In general, placental mammals have <u>higher</u> body temperatures than do monotremes.

11. When a diaphragm <u>relaxes</u>, air is forced into the lungs.

12. <u>Monotremes</u> were the first mammals to evolve from reptiles.

Show What You Know

13. In a cold climate, what advantage do endothermic predators have over ectothermic predators?

14. What physical characteristic distinguishes rodents from lagomorphs? How is this difference expressed behaviorally?

15. What evolutionary advantage does lengthy nurturing of young provide mammals?

16. What evidence suggests that monotremes may have been the first mammals to evolve from reptiles?

17. Describe the role of the diaphragm in increasing the efficiency of mammalian respiration.

18. Why is a panda classified as a carnivore if it does not eat meat?

19. How is the function of air sacs in the lungs similar to the function of a placenta?

20. What advantage did reptiles have over the first mammals when competing for niches?

21. **Make a Concept Map** Create a concept map that includes the following terms: ants and termites, carnivores, echidna, eggs, external pouch, herbivores, kangaroos, mammals, marsupials, meat, monotremes, placenta, placental mammals, rodents, roots and seeds.

Take It Further

22. **Applying Concepts** Describe two advantages of a sloth's inactivity and slow movement.

23. **Making an Analogy** Develop an analogy that compares a bat with a submarine.

24. **Developing a Hypothesis** In general, mammals that live in warm climates are smaller than related animals that live in cold climates. Why might larger mammals have an advantage in a cold climate? Hint: Surface area does not increase at the same rate as body mass.

25. **Designing an Experiment** A species' diet is influenced by evolution and by the food available in its niche. When the same types of food are presented to two individuals of a species, will they eat the same foods? Design an experiment to determine whether two members of the same mammal species—other than *Homo sapiens*—have different food preferences. What variables do you need to control?

26. Interpreting Graphs The graph below shows the gray whale's two-year breeding cycle. The dark arrows identify (1) the peak period of fertilization; (2) the peak birth period; and (3) the weaning period, when calves stop drinking milk. How long is the gestation period? At about what age are whales weaned? About how old are calves when they migrate north? How old when they reach Arctic waters?

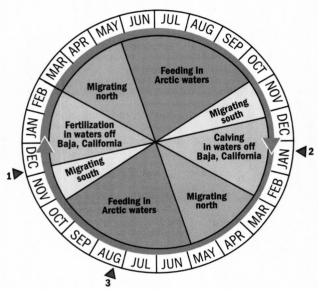

27. Analyzing Data Adélie penguins normally lay two eggs. However, not all successfully rear two chicks. The table below lists data collected from a population of Adélie penguins. What is the relationship between parents' age and their breeding success? Why is the weight of a fledgling (chick ready to leave the nest) listed for three-year-old parents with a breeding success of 0 percent?

Parental Age and Breeding Success		
Age of Parent (years)	Breeding Success (nest with two chicks)	Weight of Fledgling (kg)
3	0%	2.0
4	7.5%	2.4
5	19%	2.6
6	17%	2.9
7	25%	2.8
8	35%	2.8

Consider the Issues

28. Wolves Rebounding Predators such as wolves help limit the populations of ungulates, including deer. In the past, wolves in the United States were hunted because of their reputation as predators of livestock. Was this reputation deserved? Should wolves be reintroduced in places like Yellowstone National Park?

29. Nourishing Babies Unlike other female mammals, human birth mothers can decide whether or not to breast-feed their young. The popularity of breast-feeding in the United States has fluctuated since 1800. Why? What issues might a birth mother consider when deciding between breast-feeding and bottle-feeding her child?

Make New Connections

30. Biology and Geography Australian marsupials are adapted to types of niches that are filled by placental mammals on other continents. Research an Australian marsupial. How is it adapted to its niche? How has the introduction of placental mammals affected the survival of the marsupial species?

31. Biology and Literature The wolves and dogs in *Call of the Wild,* the horse in *Black Beauty*, and the lions in *Born Free* are examples of mammals that have had leading roles in fiction or nonfiction books. Read and report on a book in which a mammal is a main character. How scientifically accurate are the details about the mammal in the book you chose? Report your findings.

FAST-FORWARD TO CHAPTER 28

Do sowbugs move toward or away from the light? Do birds learn to fly by practicing? In Chapter 28, you will see how heredity and environment contribute to animal behavior.

Animal Behavior

You can find out more about animal behavior by exploring the following Internet address:
http://vertebrates.biosurf.com

In this chapter . . .

FEATURES

Everyday Biology
• Born to Run
• The Nose Knows

In the Community
Learning to Help

 Frontiers in Biology
Insect Robots

LAB ZONES

Discover It!
• Observing the Pupil Reflex

Do It!
• How Quickly Do Birds Become Habituated to Disturbances?
• How Do People's Sleep Needs Differ?

Think About It!
• Analyzing Firefly Behavior

Investigate It!
• Observing Sow Bugs' Behavior

INTERIOR DECORATION . . . for the Birds

The bowerbirds of New Guinea are no ordinary nest builders. Male bowerbirds build stagelike structures called bowers, in which they dance and display themselves to attract mates.

Each of the nearly 20 species of bowerbird has its own particular building style. When a male orange-crested gardener bowerbird wants to attract a mate, he pads a tree trunk with moss and builds a soft-roofed cabin one meter (m) in diameter around it. The male decorates his bower with berries, feathers, and bits of shell. This resourceful bird also uses pieces of cloth, colored glass, or tinsel taken from human communities. Each bower is usually decorated in a single color, often matching the coloration of the male or female of the species.

If a female visits the bower, the male will bow, dance, sing, and pick up the decorative berries or bits of glass in his beak to display them. If the female approves of the decorations, the birds mate inside the bower. The female then flies off to build her nest, and the male redecorates his bower to attract another female.

Each species of bowerbird displays a similar complex pattern of mating behavior, generation after generation. What patterns of behavior do other animals have?

Observing the Pupil Reflex

You need a flashlight

1. Have your lab partner shield his or her eyes from the light while keeping the eyes open. Look at your partner's eyes and note the size of the pupil (the dark opening in the center of the eye).
2. Shine the flashlight on just one of your partner's eyes. What happens to the pupil? Caution: You may experience temporary loss of vision from the bright flashlight. Wait a few moments before walking.

The automatic response of the eye's pupil to light and dark is a simple reflex action—you cannot control the opening (dilating) or contracting of your pupil. The pupil regulates the amount of light entering your eye in an effort to provide you, the viewer, with the optimum conditions for sight.

WRITE ABOUT IT!

Write a scene for a film in which the quantity or quality of light is very important. Describe for the director exactly the effect you want to achieve with lighting.

28.1 Animal Behaviors

What you'll learn

IDEAS
• To explain the relationship between a stimulus and a response
• To distinguish between innate and learned behavior

WORDS
behavior, response, stimulus, innate behavior, learned behavior

Marching to a tune of their own
Blue-footed boobies, named for their brightly colored feet, display complex courtship behavior. First the male parades before the female, showing off his colorful feet. If she is interested, she joins the parade. Both birds then throw their heads into the air and cry out. Before mating, the male and female gently touch bills. This courtship behavior is the same for all blue-footed boobies.

FIGURE 28.1
A single meerkat stands guard for the rest of the colony, exposing itself to predators. Is this kindness, or is it innate behavior?

WHAT IS BEHAVIOR?

The way you do the things you do

What do you think of when you hear the word behavior? To many people, behavior refers to the way a person acts in a particular situation. Scientists define **behavior** as the way an organism reacts to changes in its environment. A single, specific reaction to a change is called a **response.** A behavior may consist of more than one response. All organisms respond to their environment in one way or another. In this chapter, you will learn about animal behavior. The study of animal behavior is called ethology (ee-THOL-uh-jee). Ethologists want to know why an animal has a particular behavior and how the animal demonstrates it.

When an organism reacts to a change in its environment, it is responding to a stimulus. A **stimulus** (plural: *stimuli*) is something in the environment to which an animal reacts. Light, sound, gravity, chemicals, heat, and pressure are examples of stimuli. The presence or actions of another animal can also be a stimulus. By responding to stimuli, organisms interact with the environment and with one another.

When observing animal behavior, people often assume that animals are motivated by the same needs humans are. Many basic motivations, such as hunger and thirst, are similar in humans and other animals. But humans are also motivated by some factors that other animals do not have, such as ambition and generosity. Describing animal behaviors in human terms usually prevents a person from really understanding the behaviors. For example, you might assume that a bird caring for its eggs is motivated by parental love and concern. Experiments show, however, that many birds will give the same care to a substituted object placed in its nest, such as a battery or a bottle.

EVOLUTION OF BEHAVIOR

Is behavior in the genes?

Most behaviors appear to be focused on survival in an environment. Behaviors that enable organisms to avoid predators and find food, water, shelter, and mates help those individuals and their species survive. Behaviors are adaptations of an organism to its environment.

Behavioral adaptations may evolve in much the same way as physical adaptations. Behaviors that aid in survival and reproduction are favored by natural selection. For example, a mouse with a nervous system that produces a quick response to the presence of a cat is more likely to survive and reproduce than a mouse with a nervous system that produces a slow response. The offspring of the quick mouse may inherit the parent's quick-response genes. The offspring may then pass the quick-response genes to their offspring.

Behaviors fall into two general categories. A behavior that is present and complete without the need for experience is called inborn, or **innate behavior.** Innate behaviors are present at birth and are found among all members of a species. For example, newly hatched chicks walk, peck, eat, and drink. As you can see in *Figure 28.2,* newly hatched sea turtles run to the water, swim, and dive.

Behavior that is acquired as a result of experience is called **learned behavior.** A dog learns to sit on

FIGURE 28.2
Innate behavior is responsible for this newly-hatched sea turtle's mad dash for the ocean. The young turtle also inherently knows how to swim. How might these behaviors be adaptive?

command. Human babies learn to crawl and walk. Can you give some other examples of learned behavior? You will read more about innate and learned behavior later in this chapter.

The difference between innate and learned behaviors is not always clear. The extent to which behaviors are innate or learned is the subject of a very old controversy among behavioral scientists. The controversy is called the nature (innate) versus nurture (learned) debate. How much of human behavior is the result of heredity? How much is the result of life experience? What do you think?

Today scientists generally agree that most animal behaviors have both innate and learned components. Many learned behaviors are built on innate

IN THE COMMUNITY

Learning to Help

Guide dogs were originally trained to assist visually impaired people move about safely in their homes and public places. Dogs have now been trained to help other disabled humans—such as people in wheelchairs and people whose hearing is impaired—to live more independently. Learn about trained dog companions in your area. Find out from dog owners what tasks the animals perform, how owners communicate with their dogs, and how the owner and dog learned to work together as a team. If guide dogs are trained in your community, see if you can observe the process. You can find out more about these animals at the following web site: *http://vertebrates.biosurf.com.*

Analyzing Firefly Behavior

Fireflies, which can make their abdomens glow, use light to communicate during the mating season. A male princess firefly advertises for a female by blinking as he flies. A female at rest near the ground blinks back. The male then closes in on her. The male's rate of blinking starts slowly about 10 P.M., then speeds up about midnight, as shown in the top graph below. The bottom graph shows a female's response to a blinking artificial light.

Analyzing the Graphs

1. What is the relationship between the female's blinking and the male's blinking?
2. What is the relationship between the female's blinking and the blinking artificial light?
3. Is the female's response to a blinking light innate or learned? Explain.

Male — In flight

Female — At rest

Artificial light

Female

FIGURE 28.3
This chimpanzee has learned a basic form of sign language that it can use to communicate with humans.

behaviors. And some innate behaviors can be modified by learning. An animal's genes determine the limits of behavior. Learning determines what the behavior will be like within those limits. A chimpanzee, for example, can learn how to communicate through sign language. But a chimpanzee will never be able to communicate by talking because it does not have the physical structures needed for human speech.

FRONTIERS IN BIOLOGY
Insect robots

When robots are depicted in science fiction books, movies, and television programs, they usually resemble humans in their intelligence and behavior. But in real life, a group of scientists at Massachusetts Institute of Technology are working on a different type of robot. These machines are tiny robots that act more like insects than like humans.

Insects are very limited in their ability to learn or reason, but they can display complex behaviors. The "insect robots" have reflexlike behavior and respond to simple commands such as "move forward" or "avoid stuff." These responses enable the robots to "behave innately" in new situations. The developers foresee many uses for the insect robots in doing chores that may be too dangerous for humans, including space exploration and toxic-waste cleanup.

CHECKPOINT 28.1

1. List two examples of a stimulus and its corresponding response.
2. Contrast innate behavior and learned behavior.
3. Critical Thinking Very athletic people often have very athletic children. Could the children's interest and skills in athletics result from something other than inheritance? Give some examples.

Build on What You Know

4. You have learned how the Australian frilled lizard behaves to avoid predators. Do you think this behavior is innate or learned? Explain your answer. **(Need to jog your memory? Revisit relevant concepts in Chapter 26, Section 26.3.)**

28.2 Innate Behavior

Whose baby is this?
A European cuckoo lays its eggs in the nests of other birds, where they are cared for by "foster" parents. Even before it opens its eyes, a cuckoo chick responds to stimuli in the form of round objects in the nest. It rolls the eggs of the foster parents out of the nest. In spite of the loss of their own eggs, the foster parents are driven by automatic parenting behavior, and they continue to care for the young cuckoo.

What you'll learn

IDEAS
• To explain innate behavior
• To distinguish between a reflex and an instinct

WORDS
reflex, instinct, fixed-action pattern

WHAT IS INNATE BEHAVIOR?
Kids will be kids

As you learned in section 28.1, the capacity for innate behavior is present when an animal is born. Thus, innate behavior enables an animal to respond in a certain way the first time it encounters a specific stimulus. A young garter snake, for example, will flick out its tongue the first time it smells a slug, an important source of food. The young snake will even flick its tongue when presented with a cotton swab that smells like a slug. The young snake is responding to a stimulus—the scent of a slug—in a fixed, automatic, and predictable way.

Some animals rely entirely on innate behavior and are capable of learning very little. Protists, some mollusks, and insects, for example, behave almost entirely by innate behavior. In all members of a species, the response to a specific stimulus is always the same. A planarian always swims away from light. When threatened, a squid always propels itself backward with a quick burst of energy. When a female firefly sees a male firefly's flash, her behavior is always the same—she flashes back to the male at consistent intervals. In contrast, most human behavior is learned; relatively little is innate.

Most other vertebrates fall somewhere between the two extremes; they exhibit innate behaviors and also have some ability to learn.

Innate behavior can help an animal survive. For example, the behavior of nursing is innate in infant mammals. Newborn mammals are capable of nursing almost immediately after they are born. There is no time for this behavior to be learned if the baby is to survive.

TYPES OF INNATE BEHAVIOR
Don't think, just act!

Many different kinds of innate behavior exist in the animal world. Some innate behaviors, such as planarians moving away from light, are relatively simple.

FIGURE 28.4
If threatened, a squid will reflexively retreat with a powerful backward thrust. Some squids will also release a cloud of black ink to confuse predators.

FIGURE 28.5
A cat that has fallen from a significant height will reflexively turn itself over so that it lands on its feet. Because of this reflex, a cat can survive a 90-meter fall.

Other innate behaviors are much more complex. For many animals, the behaviors involved in mating, caring for the young, migrating, communicating, and finding food are partly or entirely innate.

Reflexes A **reflex** is a simple, innate, involuntary (not consciously controlled) response by a part of the body to a particular stimulus. A reflex is the simplest behavior of a well-developed nervous system. A particular stimulus always produces a particular response. Many reflexes are responses to avoid or withdraw from a harmful stimulus. What happens if you touch a sharp or hot object? Your response is a reflex.

A reflex enables an animal's body to adjust to changes in the environment quickly and smoothly. The presence of food triggers reflexes, including the production of saliva, that prepare the digestive tract to process food. Balance and posture in humans and other animals are also maintained by a set of reflexes. The ability of a cat to land on its feet after a fall is a reflex unique to cats. What might be the adaptive value of this reflex, shown in *Figure 28.5*?

What happens to you when you feel fear? The physical state of fear is composed of several reflexes, including an increased heart rate and an increase in blood supply to the muscles. These reflexes prepare an animal to fight or run away in a dangerous situation.

Complex innate behaviors A complex innate behavior is called an **instinct.** An example of an instinct is a mother hen protecting her chicks. In some cases, the hen will risk her own life to protect her offspring from danger. Instinctive behavior can be triggered by internal or external stimuli. Indeed, both types of stimuli are often involved. A silk worm caterpillar, for example, begins to build a cocoon

in response to an internal hormonal stimulus. Once the cocoon is started, however, the cocoon itself acts as the stimulus to continue building.

The mechanism for instinctive behavior is called a **fixed-action pattern,** or FAP. An FAP is triggered by an object or event called a sign stimulus. Chemicals and colors are common sign stimuli. When an organism detects a sign stimulus, an FAP begins automatically and without delay. Once an FAP begins, it will continue until complete, even if conditions change so that the behavior is no longer appropriate.

Geese demonstrate an FAP in their nesting behavior. Using a characteristic series of movements of the head and body, a female goose will retrieve an egg that has rolled out of its nest. If the goose begins these movements, it will complete the set of motions even if the egg is replaced with a different object. The goose responds with the same behavior to any object it sees near the nest, even if the object is not an egg.

Like different kinds of innate behavior, FAPs can be either simple or complex. A simple FAP usually involves only a single activity. Some animals exhibit complex innate behaviors that involve several steps. Innate behavior that involves a complex series of steps is called a complex programmed behavior.

FIGURE 28.6
This penguin is demonstrating a complex innate behavior by defending its nest. It will continue to exhibit this behavior until the stimulus, the intruder, is gone.

FIGURE 28.7

Complex Innate Behavior of a Digger Wasp

1 The female wasp carries a dead caterpillar to the nest that was dug earlier.

2 She removes the pebbles and opens the nest.

3 She pulls the caterpillar down into the nest.

6 The wasp places the pebbles over the opening to the nest and leaves. The caterpillar will serve as food for the hungry larva that emerges from the egg.

5 The wasp climbs out of the nest.

4 An egg is deposited on the caterpillar.

Such a behavior is similar to a computer program with many subprograms.

The nesting behavior of the female digger wasp is an example of a complex programmed behavior. The behavior begins when the female wasp digs an underground nest and seals the opening with small pebbles. She then flies off to find a caterpillar, stings it, and brings it back to the nest. The wasp finds the nest by recognizing the arrangement of objects, such as rocks or pine cones, surrounding the nest. *Figure* 28.7 shows the steps of the complex programmed behavior that follows.

Although complex programmed behaviors are common in insects, other animals display this type of behavior, too. Birds building nests and beavers building dams are behaviors that fall into this category.

CHECKPOINT 28.2

1. Explain innate behavior, giving one example of this behavior in humans.
2. Compare and contrast reflexes and instincts.
3. **Critical Thinking** Why is it important for the chicks of cliff-dwelling birds to be able to fly instinctively? What behavior might be of greater value for ground-nesting birds?

Build on What You Know

4. Describe one example of innate insect behavior and explain its survival advantage. *(Need to jog your memory? Revisit relevant concepts in Chapter 23, Section 23.4.)*

EVERYDAY BIOLOGY

Born to Run

You may scold your dog when it chases a car or a bicyclist. But this behavior, possibly dangerous in a pet, makes sense in the wild. Chasing large moving objects is a useful behavior for wild dogs hunting in packs.

Investigate It!

Observing Sow Bugs' Behavior

WHAT YOU WILL DO Determine what type of environment sow bugs prefer

WHAT SKILLS YOU WILL USE Collecting and recording data, controlling variables, making models, observing

WHAT YOU WILL NEED Shoe box with lid, 10 live sow bugs, posterboard, scissors, sandpaper, sponges, leaves, soil, sand, small rocks, lamp

Propose a Hypothesis

Organisms will tend to move into environments that best suit their needs. Propose a hypothesis about the type of environment that sow bugs prefer.

Conduct Your Experiment

1 Using materials available, prepare two different sets of environmental conditions at opposite ends of the shoebox. Leave a neutral strip about 4 centimeters (cm) wide running across the center width of the box.

2 Place the sow bugs on the center strip and leave them undisturbed for 10 minutes. **Caution:** Handle organisms carefully.

3 Count the number of sow bugs at each end of the shoebox, and record this data, along with the conditions at each end.

4 Remove the bugs gently and create another set of conditions in the box. Repeat the experiment with several variables. Hint: Test only one environmental variable for each trial run.

Analyze Your Data

1 What types of variables did you test? At each trial, what were your controls?
2 Did each trial result in a majority of sow bugs preferring one variable over another?
3 Which of the environmental conditions seemed most important? How could you tell?

Draw Conclusions

1 What conditions do sow bugs prefer?
2 Where might you find sow bugs in the environment?

Design a Related Experiment

Suppose you wanted to find out when sow bugs are most active. Propose a hypothesis and design an experiment to test it.

Sow Bug Behavior

Trial #	Condition 1		Condition 2	
	Type of Environment	Number of Bugs	Type of Environment	Number of Bugs

28.3 Learned Behavior

Sitting up for a reward

Dogs and other animals can learn to perform certain tricks by trial-and-error learning. If a dog is given a reward when it happens to sit up, roll over, or catch a frisbee, it may repeat the behavior. If the behavior is rewarded consistently, the dog may eventually learn to perform the action in response to a command stimulus.

What you'll learn

IDEAS

• To explain how and why behaviors can be learned

• To compare and contrast the types of learned behavior

WORDS

habituation, imprinting, classical conditioning, operant conditioning

---

WHAT IS LEARNED BEHAVIOR?

Learning about learning

Learning is any change in behavior that results from experience. Learned behavior is also called acquired behavior. The ability to learn is itself inherited because animals inherit brain structures that may be capable of learning. Also, many animals inherit a sense of curiosity that stimulates learning. Although we usually connect the ability to learn with humans, it also occurs in many other animals. However, no other animals are capable of the kind and amount of learning that human beings can accomplish.

Animals of species in which the ability to learn has evolved are capable of flexible behavior. They learn to adjust to new situations. However, learning occurs only in animals that have the time and opportunity to learn. You may recall from Chapter 27 that young mammals spend a relatively long time with their parents, from whom they learn social and survival behaviors.

Many animals, especially mammals, can learn new behaviors throughout life. Humans, like other animals, learn more quickly when they are young. Learning tends to become less flexible with age. Many skills, such as speaking a second language or learning a sport like skiing, may be more difficult to learn as an adult.

It is not always easy to define which part of a behavior is learned and which part is innate. Sometimes innate behaviors appear to be learned. For example, when a baby bird flaps its wings, people often say the bird is "learning to fly." But flying is an innate behavior. Even if they are prevented from "practicing," young birds begin to fly when they reach the proper stage of maturity. In contrast, other behaviors that seem innate are actually learned. For example, the domestic behaviors of dogs are almost entirely learned. However, the responses that are a part of these situations, such as the interest in food treats, may be innate.

FIGURE 28.8

Lion cubs, like many young mammals, often engage in play. How might the cubs benefit from this play later in life?

FIGURE 28.9
These nesting osprey have become habituated to the distractions of human activity. Can you think of other animals with this adaptation?

FIGURE 28.10
Austrian ethologist Konrad Lorenz, shown here with his goslings, received the Nobel Prize for his work on imprinting.

Some songbirds learn the song of their species through a combination of learned and innate behaviors. Young white-crowned sparrows, for example, have the innate ability to recognize their own species' song. To sing the complete song, however, they must hear it sung by adults of their species. Once they hear it, they can sing the song when they are mature. If they do not hear the song when they are young, they will never be able to sing the full song.

TYPES OF LEARNED BEHAVIOR

You move, I'll follow

Although many animals are capable of learning, different animals learn things in different ways and at different times during their lives.

Habituation An animal's environment is the source of thousands of stimuli. Some stimuli are important to the animal's survival. Other stimuli have little or no effect; if such a stimulus is present long enough, an animal may learn to ignore it. **Habituation** is the process by which an animal learns to ignore a particular stimulus.

Habituation prevents animals from wasting time and energy responding to nonthreatening stimuli. A newly hatched chick, for example, instinctively crouches when an object moves overhead. The chick remains crouched until the object moves away. If a specific object moves overhead several times and no harm comes to the chick, the chick becomes "used to" the object and ignores it. The chick no longer crouches when the same object passes overhead. If, however, a different, unfamiliar object passes over the chick's head, it will again crouch.

Imprinting Another simple type of learning was first studied during the 1930s by Austrian ethologist Konrad Lorenz. While studying the behavior of geese, Lorenz noticed that newly hatched goslings quickly learned to recognize and follow the first moving thing they saw. If they saw their mother first, they followed her and only her. If Lorenz was the first thing the hatchlings saw, they followed him and only him! You can see Lorenz and his goslings in *Figure 28.10.* Young geese continue this "following" behavior until they mature. The quick, early learning of a behavior that later becomes a permanent response to a stimulus is called **imprinting.**

Imprinted behaviors can be learned only once, during a specific time in the animal's life called the critical period. For goslings, the critical period is the first day and a half after hatching. If imprinting does not occur during this time, it will never occur. Furthermore, once imprinting has taken place, it is permanent. This one-time-only type of learning is a very efficient way for offspring to establish a bond with their parents.

Imprinting also accounts for other animal behaviors. Salmon imprint on the odor of the stream in which they hatched. Imprinting the smell enables the fish to return to the same stream years later to reproduce.

Classical conditioning Another pioneer in the study of learned behavior was Russian physiologist Ivan Pavlov. Pavlov's observations of learning began in the early 1900s, during an experiment designed to study digestion. Pavlov was investigating a reflex—the flow of saliva in response to the presence of food. He observed that a dog salivated when powdered meat was placed in its mouth. But, Pavlov observed, a dog often begins to salivate before the food is actually in its mouth. Is this behavior learned? To answer this question, Pavlov rang a bell on each occasion when he was about to put the meat powder in the dog's mouth. After several repetitions, the dog had learned to produce saliva in response to the sound of the bell. In fact, the dog produced saliva at the sound of the bell even when it was not given the meat powder.

Pavlov's experiment is an example of classical conditioning. During **classical conditioning,** an animal's reflexes are trained to respond to a stimulus. In addition to producing saliva in response to receiving the meat powder, the dog also produced saliva at the sound of the bell. Like other types of behavior, classical conditioning is helpful for an animal's survival. Because reflexes can be conditioned to respond to new stimuli, an animal's reactions can adjust to changes in the environment.

Operant conditioning As you just read, classical conditioning involves changes in simple reflexes. More complex behaviors are usually modified by a type of learning called trial-and-error learning, or operant (AH-per-int) conditioning. **Operant conditioning** takes place when the environment rewards or punishes behaviors that an animal performs randomly. The mouse shown in *Figure 28.11* is learning by operant conditioning and will be rewarded by reaching the end of the maze. American psychologist B. F. Skinner developed the theory of operant conditioning during the 1940s and 1950s.

Operant conditioning is called trial-and-error learning because it begins with a random behavior—the trial. Most trials result in errors, but occasionally a trial leads to a reward. For example, a hungry mouse

FIGURE 28.11
A mouse that finds its way to a reward at the end of a maze will learn how to reach the end of the maze more effectively in later trials. This is an example of operant conditioning.

shuffling about in the grass happens to kick over a leaf and finds a berry underneath. The berry is a reward that reinforces the behavior. Repetitions of similar accidental behavior are reinforced by finding food under other leaves. Eventually, the mouse may learn to turn leaves over in search of food.

Many young animals, especially primates, attempt to copy the behaviors of their parents. The first attempts may not be successful. But when they finally imitate their parents successfully, the behavior is usually reinforced. Chimpanzees strip leaves and bark from twigs and use them to collect termites, a favorite food, from rotten logs. Young chimpanzees learn this behavior by observing and copying older chimpanzees, and they are rewarded for their trials by getting the food they want.

Reasoning Humans can often solve problems without trial and error. Thinking of a solution to a problem reduces the time spent on trials and the risks involved in errors. This kind of learning is called reasoning, or insight. Reasoning is using one or more past experiences and perhaps new information to solve a problem. When you reason, you take what you have learned and apply it to a new situation.

Humans use insight to interpret new situations by relating them to memories of past experiences. The person recalls circumstances of similar problems he or she encountered in the past. By considering all

How Quickly Do Birds Become Habituated to Disturbances?

Animals that are repeatedly exposed to a source of disturbance will often become habituated to that stimulus if it proves to pose no real danger. After habituation, the animal will no longer react to that particular stimulus. You can observe the habituation of birds to a disturbance if you . . .

Try This

1 Set up a bird feeder near your school, close to a window in your classroom. For ten minutes each day, record the approximate number and species of birds that visit the feeder.

2 After you have witnessed regular visits to the feeder, choose a stimulus that produces a reaction in the birds. (For example, place a model of an owl or other predator near the feeder.)

3 For ten minutes each day, observe the actions of birds near your feeder. Keep a record of how many birds approach the feeder each day.

Analyze Your Results

1 What was the average amount of time that it took the birds to resume normal feeding behavior after the introduction of the stimulus? Did some aspects of their feeding behavior change?

2 Did some species of birds become habituated to the stimulus quicker than others? Which ones?

becomes a memory. The concept can then be applied to two chairs, two people, and so on, and can be used to reason a solution to new problems.

Animals other than humans, particularly other primates, are also capable of reasoning. In one famous experiment, a chimpanzee was placed in a room with several boxes on the floor and a bunch of bananas hanging from the ceiling. The bananas were hung too high for the chimpanzee to reach. After a period of inactivity during which the chimpanzee appeared to be thinking about the problem, the chimpanzee piled the boxes on top of each other, climbed up, and reached the bananas!

Very few examples of reasoning have been observed in invertebrates. Octopuses are an exception. One octopus living in an aquarium would climb out of its tank each night, raid neighboring tanks, and return undetected before people arrived in the morning! These intelligent mollusks have also been observed using reasoning to unscrew jars containing food.

CHECKPOINT 28.3

1. What is the difference between learned behavior and innate behavior?

2. Compare and contrast the types of learned behavior.

3. Critical Thinking Give an example of imprinting. What do you think the survival value of imprinting is?

Build on What You Know

4. How might the ability to learn be an adaptation? Choose one example to illustrate your answer. *(Need to jog your memory? Revisit relevant concepts in Chapter 10, Section 10.1.)*

the memories, the person can better understand a new problem or find the appropriate response to the new situation.

A small child may learn that when the teacher says "one plus one," a reward will follow for saying "two." At first, the child may attach no meaning to the response. The response is learned by simple operant conditioning. But when the student's mathematical skill improves, an abstract mental picture of "two"

How are animal behaviors adaptive?

28.4 Behavior in the Life of Animals

Attention all gorillas!
Many behaviors involve interactions with other animals, for example, claiming and defending territories, protecting offspring, and attracting mates. Social animals generally use several senses for communication. To issue a threat, a male gorilla makes loud hooting noises, beats his chest, and runs along shaking and tearing at trees. Finally, he thumps the ground with one or both palms.

What you'll learn

IDEAS
• To explain what functions are served by communication between animals
• To compare different means and forms of communication

WORDS
circadian rhythm

COMMUNICATION

If you could talk to the animals

The ways in which animals communicate are as varied as the animals themselves. Human speech is an obvious example of communication. However, humans are not the only animals to communicate with sounds. Other animals use sounds to identify members of their own species, to call for mates, to signal a threat or alarm, to show surrender, and to summon their young.

Like humans, other animals can also communicate without using sound. Body posture and facial expression in humans communicate as much as words do, sometimes even more. The chimpanzee in *Figure 28.12* is also using facial expressions. What does its facial expression communicate to you?

Many animals detect visual signals from the size, shape, and color of another animal's body. Some animals even communicate with flashes of light. In this way, visual displays are used to distinguish males from females and familiar animals from strangers.

A visual display is an action or posture meant to be seen by another animal. In a threat display, for example, an animal may use a posture that makes it look larger and more dangerous. This display may drive away an enemy. Postures that make an animal appear smaller are often used to communicate surrender. These include crouching and lowering the ears and tail.

In Chapter 23 you learned that many animals communicate with scent chemicals called pheromones (FAYR-oh-mohnz). Many animals use pheromones to mark their territories. In some animals, marker pheromones are released in the urine or feces. Domestic cats have scent glands along their jawlines with which they mark objects and people in their territories. Ants use pheromones to mark the trail to a food source; other ants follow this trail even if a much shorter path is available. Bees use a pheromone to signal a threat to the hive, which results in an attack against the perceived threat by other members of the hive.

FIGURE 28.12
Although it is usually a mistake to assume human motivations for animal behavior, apes, such as this chimpanzee, do use facial expressions to convey emotions.

INTERACTIONS BETWEEN INDIVIDUALS

When animals court

Animals attract and select mates using behaviors that involve sounds, visual displays, and pheromones. A specific behavior or series of behaviors that takes place prior to mating is called courtship behavior. Courtship behavior enables animals to identify healthy, reproductively fit mates of the same species. Mating with a member of a different species would be a waste of energy. Mating with an unhealthy individual could result in unfit offspring.

Courtship usually involves complex sequences of behaviors called rituals. A ritual is a series of communication behaviors performed the same way by all members of a population. In a ritual, a behavior performed by one animal may act as a sign stimulus that triggers an FAP in the other animal. In certain animals, courtship rituals last for days.

Courtship behaviors are highly specific and selective. If a potential mate does not perform the behavior correctly, it will be rejected. If a population is separated from the rest of its species, the courtship behavior of that group may change slightly over time. If so, the population will no longer be able to mate with members of the original group, causing reproductive isolation. The two populations may eventually evolve into separate species as a result of the isolation.

GROUP INTERACTIONS

A place to call their own

Animals also use rituals, visual displays, and pheromones to claim and defend their territories. Territories are areas that animals claim for their own uses, such as hunting and raising young. By claiming a territory, the animal keeps others a specific distance away and reduces competition for food and nesting sites.

In populations that share one territory, some species form social groups in which an individual occupies a position in a dominance hierarchy, or ranking system. An animal with a higher rank than another is said to be more dominant. The most dominant individual gets the best food and has the greatest opportunity to mate. Another individual is ranked as number two, and so on down the ranks. A hierarchy of this type is often called a pecking order, named after this behavioral characteristic in chickens.

Occasionally, animals will sacrifice their own lives or the opportunity to reproduce to help another member in their social group. Such behavior seems to be innate. But if a gene directs

FIGURE 28.13
Sage grouse (left) occupy distinct territories while displaying to potential mates. Arctic hares (right) perform a courtship ritual that resembles a boxing match. How do these behaviors help members of each species to identify fit mates?

FIGURE 28.14
These two male elk are struggling for control over a herd of females. The stronger of the two will receive exclusive mating rights.

behavior that results in death, there will be no offspring, and that gene will not be passed on. How, then, have such behaviors evolved?

Often the members of a group are closely related and carry many of the same genes. If an individual gives up an opportunity to reproduce in order to help a relative, it is helping to pass on its own genes through its relatives. Self-sacrifice for the protection of relatives is called kin selection, or altruism (AL-troo-ih-zum). Remember that the animal is not aware that it is helping relatives. The behavior is encoded in its genes—the same genes that are being passed on as a result of the behavior.

INTERACTIONS WITH THE ENVIRONMENT

Moving with rhythm

In addition to interacting with members of their own species, and members of other species, animals also interact with their environment. Many things in the environment repeat in never-ending cycles: day changes into night, the tides rise and fall, seasons change. All organisms are affected by these periodic cycles and rhythms.

The most obvious cycle is the day-night cycle. Some animals, such as bats, raccoons, and earthworms, are active primarily at night. Many animals, including robins, dogs, and most humans, are active during the day. Some snakes and lizards are active only at dawn and dusk. Animal responses to environmental cycles are adaptations to limit competition and make food gathering easier. Being active at different times also enables different species to live in the same habitat and use its resources at different times.

Many animals appear to have an internal timer, or biological clock, that maintains the body's natural cycles and rhythms. For example, fiddler crabs change color during a 24-hour period. They have a darker color during the day than at night. In one scientific study, the crabs were kept in round-the-clock darkness. Their color became darker and lighter just as it did in the natural environment. The crabs seemed to be following an internal rhythm and not merely responding to the external environment.

A rhythm that repeats approximately every 24 hours is called a **circadian** (sur-KAY-de-un) **rhythm.**

LAB ZONE Do It!

How Do People's Sleep Needs Differ?

The timing and amount of sleep that each person requires is dependent on the individual's circadian rhythm. No two circadian rhythms are the same, and the amount of sleep that people need varies greatly. You can witness the variance in people's sleep requirements when you . . .

Try This

1 In your notebook, set up three columns. Label the first column *Age*, the second column *Time of Sleep*, and the third column *Total Hours Slept*.
2 Conduct a survey among people that you know. Find out how many hours of sleep they get per night and when, on average, they go to sleep. Collect data from people of various ages—your friends, adults, older adults, and children. Try to obtain information from parents of infants about their children's sleep habits.
3 Collect and analyze your data. Plot a graph in your notebook, with *Age* on the x-axis and *Total Hours Slept* on the y-axis.

Analyze Your Results

1 What trends did you notice in your graph? What generalizations can you make?
2 What factors other than age might influence a person's sleep patterns?

FIGURE 28.15
Each fall, young monarchs migrate south for the winter. Along the way, large numbers of them will congregate to rest in the same trees every year.

The pattern of human sleep is an example of a circadian rhythm. In one experiment, one group of people were kept in constant daylight for several days. A second group were kept in constant darkness for the same period. Other environmental conditions, such as temperature, did not change. The people slept, ate, and worked when they wanted. Under these controlled conditions, each person maintained a daily activity cycle of approximately 24 hours.

Rhythmic behaviors of many animals are influenced by changes in the external environment. For example, large herds of wildebeests travel over the African plains from season to season in search of food. The monarch butterflies shown in *Figure 28.15* travel back and forth between the mountains of Mexico and parts of Canada.

Many birds fly south in the winter and return north in the spring. In fact, many species of ducks and geese spend summers on the arctic tundra, when temperatures there are warm. Insects and other sources of food are abundant, and space is available to raise young. As winter approaches, the hours of daylight decrease, temperatures begin to fall, and the position of the sun changes. The birds begin a long journey south to where the weather is warmer and food is available. These journeys are examples of migration, the seasonal movement from one region to another and back again.

CHECKPOINT 28.4

1. How do animals communicate? What are the basic functions of animal communication?
2. Compare the different means and forms of communication.
3. Critical Thinking How does kin selection benefit the survival of a species?

Build on What You Know

4. You have learned about several responses in plants. Describe how some of these responses are related to rhythmic cycles in the environment. *(Need to jog your memory? Revisit relevant concepts in Chapter 19, Section 19.1.)*

What types of interactions are involved in animal behavior?

Chapter 28 Review

 THE BIG IDEA! 28.1–28.3 Animal behaviors are adaptations that maximize survival and reproductive fitness.

28.4 Animal behavior involves interactions between individuals, between groups, and with the environment.

Sum It Up

Use the following summary to review the main concepts in this chapter.

28.1 Animal Behaviors

- Behavior is the way an organism reacts to changes in its environment. An organism's reactions are responses to stimuli.
- Natural selection favors behavioral adaptations that help a species survive and reproduce.
- Most types of behavior have components of both innate and learned behavior.

28.2 Innate Behavior

- An involuntary physical reflex allows an organism to respond quickly to danger, without conscious thought.
- An instinctive behavior is a complex innate response to a stimulus. The mechanism for instinctive behavior is a fixed-action pattern.
- Behaviors that require a specific series of steps, such as nest building, are examples of complex programmed behaviors.

28.3 Learned Behavior

- Learned, or acquired, behaviors are gained through experience. Most learning occurs when organisms are young.

- Organisms may have an inborn capacity to learn a specific behavior but never learn it because appropriate adult examples are lacking.
- Through habituation, an organism can learn to conserve time and energy by ignoring familiar stimuli.
- Imprinted behaviors can be learned only during a critical period, usually early in life.
- Classical conditioning can alter simple reflexes. More complex behaviors are modified through operant conditioning.
- When reasoning, humans apply memories of past experiences to new situations.

28.4 Behavior in the Life of Animals

- Animals communicate using behaviors that involve sounds, visual displays, or the production of scents.
- Communication is used in courtship and territory identification.
- Individuals in social groups may occupy assigned positions in a dominance hierarchy.
- Organisms respond to environmental cycles such as the day-night cycle and seasonal changes.

Use Terms and Concepts

Use each of the following words or terms in a complete sentence. If you need to review a meaning, turn to the page indicated.

behavior (p. 668)
response (p. 668)
stimulus (p. 668)
innate behavior (p. 669)
learned behavior (p. 669)

reflex (p. 672)
instinct (p. 672)
fixed-action pattern (p. 672)
habituation (p. 676)
imprinting (p. 676)

classical conditioning (p. 677)
operant conditioning (p. 677)
circadian rhythm (p. 681)

Use Your Word Power

COMPLETION **Write the word or term that best completes each statement.**

1. _____ behavior is present at birth and does not require experience to be expressed.

2. A pattern that repeats approximately every 24 hours is called a(n) _____ .

3. The mechanism for instinctive behavior is called a _____ .

4. A(n) _____ is any activity of an organism in response to changes in the environment.

5. An involuntary physical reaction to internal or external signals is called a(n) _____ .

6. _____ is training in which an animal learns to perform preprogrammed behavior in response to a new stimulus.

7. A complex innate behavior is called a(n) _____ .

MULTIPLE CHOICE **Choose the letter of the word or phrase that best completes each statement.**

8. Human parents often try to modify the behavior of their offspring through (a) imprinting; (b) operant conditioning; (c) fixed-action patterns; (d) complex programmed behavior.

9. Marking a territory with a pheromone is an example of (a) habituation; (b) a reflex; (c) innate behavior; (d) operant conditioning.

10. The object or event that triggers a fixed-action pattern is a (a) learned behavior; (b) response; (c) reflex; (d) sign stimulus.

11. Individuals learn to ignore unimportant stimuli through (a) imprinting; (b) a fixed-action pattern; (c) habituation; (d) innate behavior.

12. The type of learning for which timing is critical is called (a) imprinting; (b) operant conditioning; (c) habituation; (d) classical conditioning.

Show What You Know

13. Compare the adaptive advantages of innate and learned behaviors.

14. How do courtship rituals contribute to the survival of a species?

15. What types of visual communication do humans use?

16. Explain how imprinting differs from other types of learning.

17. In what way can altruistic behavior directed toward a relative benefit an individual?

18. How can operant conditioning modify behavior?

19. What causes the symptoms of jet lag—the fatigue and disorientation travelers feel after flying to a distant time zone?

20. In what ways does the claiming of territories benefit the individuals in a population?

21. **Make a Concept Map** Create a concept map that relates the following terms: conditioning, experience, fixed-action pattern, habituation, imprinting, innate behavior, instinct, learned behavior, reflex, stimulus.

Take It Further

22. **Applying Concepts** Fishes in an aquarium often swim to the surface when a person nears the tank. Is this behavior a type of classical conditioning or operant conditioning? Explain.

23. **Making an Analogy** What political, business, or similar organizations use hierarchies? What distinguishes each rank in the hierarchy? How do such hierarchies compare to the dominance hierarchies seen in animal populations?

24. **Designing an Experiment** Select a good habit that you would like to develop—studying at a set time, for example. Design a strategy for modifying your behavior. Apply the strategy. Keep track of how often you display the new behavior and measure the success of your strategy.

25. Developing a Hypothesis Linguists say that the ability to acquire a language is both an innate and a learned behavior. What evidence can you suggest to support this hypothesis?

26. Interpreting Graphs When temperatures are low and food is scarce, some mammals enter a state of torpor, an energy-saving adaptation in which metabolism decreases and body temperature declines. The graph below tracks a ground squirrel's body temperature from September to May. What happens to its body temperature during different times of the year? What can you infer about the squirrel's behavior at these different times?

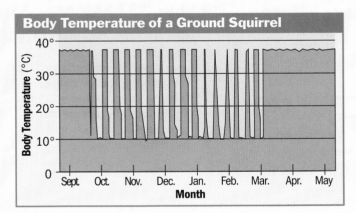

Body Temperature of a Ground Squirrel

27. Analyzing Data The table below lists some characteristics of three types of communication. What advantages does chemical communication have that visual communication lacks? Do visual signals have any advantages over audial signals? What is the relationship between usefulness as a locator, or rate, and risk level?

Comparing Three Types of Communication

Characteristic	Type of Communication		
	Chemical	Audial	Visual
Halted by barrier	No	No	Yes
Usefulness as a locator (rate)	Varies (slow)	Somewhat useful (fast)	Very useful (fast)
Usefulness at night	Varies	Very useful	Not very useful
Energy cost	Low	High	Low
Risk level when used	Low to medium	Medium	High

Consider the Issues

28. Animals as Entertainers Animals have performed in circus acts for centuries. Today, animals also are taught to perform at some theme parks and zoos. Should the behaviors of animals such as dolphins, birds, and elephants be modified for entertainment? How is an animal affected by training and performances? Should wild animals be captured for training? What about injured or orphaned animals? Explain your answers.

Make New Connections

29. Biology and Community You can learn about animals from tracks left in soil or snow, which can identify the type of animal, how fast it was moving, or what it was doing. Droppings, food remains, disturbed vegetation, and nests or burrows also provide valuable information. Look for evidence left by animals in your area. Use the clues to infer the animals' behaviors.

30. Biology and Music Some composers have been inspired by bird songs and images. Find compositions that have a bird-related theme, or passages that resemble birdcalls. What instruments imitate bird songs?

31. Biology and History Human behaviors, such as styles of dancing that are considered to be "acceptable" in public, change over time. Have you noticed any behavioral changes in the last ten years? Interview older members of your community. Ask them how social behaviors have changed during their lifetime.

FAST-FORWARD TO CHAPTER 29

The next chapter describes skin, bones, and muscles, which function together to help many organisms receive and respond to stimuli.

Unit 7 Review

Connect the Chapters

1. Compare the prey-locating methods used by many types of fishes with the methods used by bats.

2. Discuss how the jaws and teeth of carnivorous reptiles and of mammals reflect their different ways of food gathering.

3. Explain why a frog's skin must be moist but a lizard's skin can be dry.

4. How does a bird respond to hormones as nesting season approaches? What type of behavior does this response represent?

5. Describe some survival features that differ between placental mammal offspring and amphibian offspring.

6. What aspects of nest-building behavior are probably innate? What aspects are probably not?

Connect the Units

7. Compare the opercula of a fish with the guard cells in a plant.

8. How are seeds and amniotic eggs similar? How are they different?

9. Which type of insect metamorphosis is most similar to amphibian metamorphosis? Explain your answer.

Connect to Themes

10. Patterns of Change/ Cycles What are three different ways in which an animal might respond to the onset of winter?

11. Evolution Describe two pieces of evidence suggesting an evolutionary relationship between amphibians and reptiles.

12. Systems and Interactions How does the environment affect the excretory systems of fishes and amphibians?

project plans

1 The middle of the night may seem to be a relatively quiet time in most neighborhoods, but this observation can be misleading. Find out about the activities of nocturnal animal species in your neighborhood. Prepare an illustrated booklet or set of posters to show what you discover.

2 As a class, research the locations of some animal migration routes in North and South America. Create a large outline map that includes boundaries for countries, states, and provinces. Agree on a system for marking routes between feeding or spawning grounds. Try to include representative bird, reptile, insect, and mammal species.

CRITIC'S CORNER

A FILM REVIEW BY MICHAEL LEE FLORENCE, KENTUCKY

The film *Survival Island,* by David Attenborough, looks at wildlife coming back to the same island year after year. They return especially to reproduce. The film raises questions about where the wildlife go when they leave the island, what they do, and how they know to come back to the island every year. I enjoyed the video. It made me think about why specific animals inhabit a particular place.

SPOTLIGHT ON CAREERS

NEAL TUTTRUP
Environmental activist
EDUCATION: Three years of college, majoring in biology

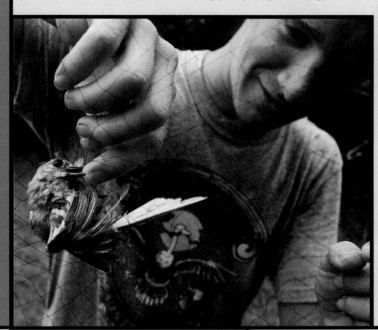

"I worked on a field study in college, studying the painted bunting, a central Texas native bird. We worked in an open field, mapping the territories of different birds. We looked at how birds defend territory, and when and why they stay in their own territories or fly to other areas. It's important to understand how animals behave if we want to help them survive. Most people don't really understand the dynamics of the natural world. If people had more knowledge of biology, I think there would be a real change in society."

bioSURF Explore the Internet site *http://vertebrates.biosurf.com* to find out more about bird watching and conservation.

DR. GREGG TAKASHIMA
Veterinarian; Owner, Parkway Veterinary Hospital
EDUCATION: Doctor of Veterinary Medicine

"Being a veterinarian has been very rewarding because I get to work with animals and people, and hopefully make them both feel good. We work with house pets like dogs, cats, hamsters, guinea pigs, turtles, frogs, and snakes. In order to give animals the best care, the pet owner has to understand what's wrong. Knowledge about biology allows people to understand that we are all animals, and we all have similar diseases and health needs. Sometimes I describe the animal's illness in terms of human illnesses. This helps people get the connection."

bioSURF You can learn more about veterinary medicine by visiting the Internet site *http://vertebrates.biosurf.com.*

"You can't do this job just because you like animals. You have to like people, too."
— DR. GREGG TAKASHIMA

Which of these amazing statements about human biology are fact, and which are fiction?

Hit *or* Myth?

You "see" the world **upside down.**

(Fact. Light entering the lens of the eye is bent so that images appear upside down on the retina. The brain interprets these images right side up.)

There is **fat** on the bottom of your feet.

(Fact. There is fat there. It helps protect the skin on the bottom of your feet when you walk.)

Your **jaws** move.

(Fiction. Only one jaw— your lower jaw—moves. Your upper jaw is fused into position and does not move at all.)

If all the **blood vessels** in your body were laid end to end, they would wrap around Earth's equator four times.

(Fact—or they would reach halfway to the moon!)

Newborns are protected from disease.

(Fact. Before birth, the fetus receives the mother's antibodies, and newborns have natural immunity to most infections—at least for the first few months. Breast-fed babies have longer-lasting resistance to specific infections.)

A bird can **swallow upside down,** but a human cannot.

(Fiction. The reverse is true. A human can swallow in that position, but a bird cannot.)

Goosebumps help keep you warm.

(Fiction. Goosebumps help furry and downy animals stay warm by trapping an insulating layer of air next to the skin—a technique that does not work on our furless, featherless bodies.)

CHAPTER 29
Skin, Skeletal, and Muscular Systems

You can find out more about the skin, skeletal, and muscular systems by exploring the following Internet address:
http://body_systems.biosurf.com

In this chapter . . .

FEATURES

Everyday Biology
- A Bony Slowdown
- Muscle Menu

In the Community
Training Bones and Muscles

 Frontiers in Biology
Test-Tube Skin

LAB ZONES

Discover It!
- Examining Bones and Muscles

Do It!
- Why Do Bones Have Minerals?

Think About It!
- Comparing Muscle Mass
- Analyzing the Incidence of Skin Cancer

Investigate It!
- Dissecting a Chicken Wing

Lost in space: muscle and bone

Astronauts in space and patients confined to bed rest on Earth share a common problem. Because they do not use their muscles and bones for weight-bearing activity, both astronauts and bed-rest patients tend to lose bone density and muscle mass in their lower extremities. This is a problem that the National Aeronautics and Space Administration (NASA) takes very seriously, especially for astronauts who spend many months in weightless conditions. In 1996 Dr. Shannon Lucid returned to Earth after completing six months in orbit aboard the space station *Mir*—the longest spaceflight by a woman and an American. Like all astronauts, she spent a portion of each day exercising to try to minimize bone and muscle deterioration.

"High-load," weight-bearing exercises, which are most effective against bone and muscle loss, cannot be done in the weightless environment of space. However, once secured to treadmills and exercise bicycles, astronauts can perform aerobic exercises, which have been shown to be somewhat successful in maintaining bone and muscle mass. NASA continues to research ways to more effectively counteract the negative effects of spaceflight and to apply what it learns to uses on Earth.

Dr. Shannon Lucid takes her turn on exercise equipment aboard *Mir*.

LAB ZONE **Discover It!**

Examining Bones and Muscles

1. Using the fingers of one hand, feel the bones in the other hand and try to count the number of individual bones. Then feel the bones in your wrist and arm. How many bones do you think there are in your arm?
2. Move your fingers and arm slowly and feel the action of your muscles. Bend your arm at the elbow and tighten your fist. What happens to your muscles when you do this?

You are able to move your bones because of the contraction and relaxation of the muscles attached to them. As you read this chapter, you will discover just how extensive the skeletal and muscular systems are.

WRITE ABOUT IT!

Write a poem or fictional story about what it would be like to be weightless. Include how you would move from place to place.

29.1 Body Systems

What you'll learn

IDEAS

• To categorize the organizational levels in human bodies
• To distinguish between human organ systems

WORDS

cephalization

We all need a little structure

Sponges, as you may recall, are animals. You, too, are an animal. There are thousands of characteristics that differentiate humans and sponges. One of the basic differences is the organization of cells. Cells in sponges are not organized into tissues. Your body not only has tissues, but tissues are further organized into organs, which are even further organized into organ systems.

LEVELS OF ORGANIZATION

You're organized!

You are one person, one organism. But the body you have is made of billions of individual cells. Although each cell performs basic life functions, such as using energy and excreting wastes, it is only a small part of the highly organized structure that is your body.

Groups of cells with similar structure and function are called tissues. The cells in a tissue are held together by a nonliving matrix or a sticky coating on the outside of the cells. Most animals have four main types of tissues: connective, muscle, epithelial, and nervous tissue. Each type of tissue has a specialized function.

Connective tissue joins together body structures, providing protection and support. Connective tissue can store or transport materials. It can be hard, soft, or liquid. Bones, tendons, cartilage, fat, and blood are examples of connective tissue.

Muscle tissue is made of cells that contract in response to signals from the spinal cord and brain. All body movement, including that of internal organs, is carried out by muscle tissue. Muscle tissue makes it possible for you to breathe, talk, and move your arms and legs. Many internal organs, such as the heart and stomach, contain muscle tissue.

Epithelial (ep-uh-THEE-lee-uhl) tissue covers the body and its organs. The skin is an organ that contains epithelial tissue. Inside the body, epithelial tissue lines organs and blood vessels. Some types of epithelial tissue form glands—structures that release chemicals. Human glands include sweat glands, mucous glands, and digestive glands.

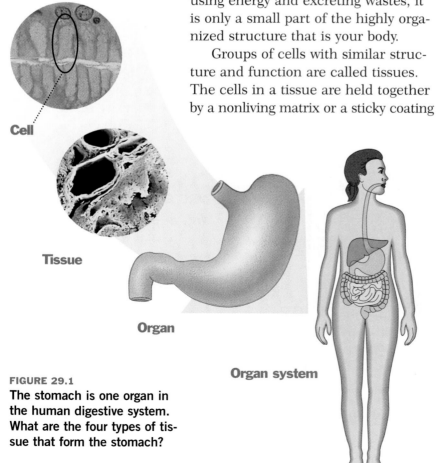

Cell

Tissue

Organ

Organ system

FIGURE 29.1

The stomach is one organ in the human digestive system. What are the four types of tissue that form the stomach?

Nervous tissue, composed of two types of cells, carries information throughout the body. One type of cell, called a neuron, conducts signals in the form of electrical impulses throughout the body. The other type of cell—a glial cell—supports, protects, and coordinates the neurons.

In most animals, tissues are organized into functional units called organs. The stomach is a saclike organ. It is made of epithelial, muscle, nervous, and connective tissue.

Groups of organs that work together to perform specific functions for the organism comprise organ systems. The stomach, large intestine, and small intestine together form a major part of the digestive system.

BASIC BODY PLAN

Left, right, front, back

The left and right sides of your body are almost mirror images. You may recall that other vertebrates and some invertebrates show this pattern called bilateral symmetry. Although the sides of your body are almost mirror images, they are not identical. You can find a few differences by studying the sides of your face in a mirror. Inside the body, many organs and organ systems do not show complete bilateral symmetry. For example, the two sides of the stomach and digestive system are quite different.

In Chapter 22 you learned that locations on the bodies of animals with bilateral symmetry can be described by four terms—anterior (top), posterior (bottom), ventral (front), and dorsal (back). Consider these four parts of your body. What structures do you have on your ventral side?

Like other animals with bilateral symmetry, humans have a high degree of cephalization (sef-uh-luh-ZAY-shun). **Cephalization** means that the

FIGURE 29.2

Human Body Cavities

The ventral body cavity is divided into a thoracic cavity and an abdominal cavity. The dorsal cavity is divided into a cranial cavity and a spinal cavity.

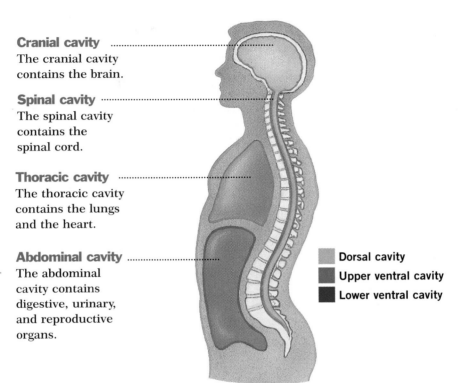

Cranial cavity
The cranial cavity contains the brain.

Spinal cavity
The spinal cavity contains the spinal cord.

Thoracic cavity
The thoracic cavity contains the lungs and the heart.

Abdominal cavity
The abdominal cavity contains digestive, urinary, and reproductive organs.

Dorsal cavity
Upper ventral cavity
Lower ventral cavity

sense organs and the structures that control the body are located in its anterior part. For example, your eyes, ears, nose, and mouth are all sense organs located in your head.

The internal organs are located within two large spaces called the ventral and dorsal body cavities. The body cavities develop from the coelom. You may recall from Chapter 22 that the coelom is a body cavity formed completely lined with mesoderm. When the body grows or moves, internal organs are stably contained within the body cavities. This explains why your heart does not move around when you exercise! *Figure* 29.2 shows the locations of the body cavities that comprise the larger ventral and dorsal cavities.

Organized systems

The tissues and organs that make up the human body are organized into twelve different organ systems, each serving a specific function in the body. A general overview of the twelve systems is presented in *Figure 29.3*. You will learn more details of each system and its component organs and tissues in the following chapters.

FIGURE 29.3

Human Body Systems

Compare the sizes and locations of the different systems.

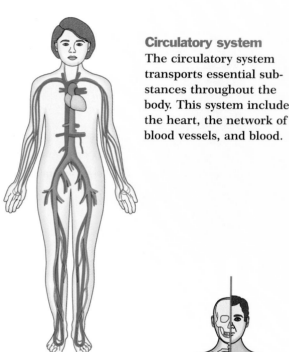

Circulatory system

The circulatory system transports essential substances throughout the body. This system includes the heart, the network of blood vessels, and blood.

Respiratory system

The respiratory system is made of a network of breathing passages and the lungs. These organs take in oxygen from the air and release carbon dioxide.

Excretory system

The excretory system removes wastes from the body. It includes the kidneys and the bladder. The skin and the lungs are sometimes considered part of the excretory system.

Integumentary system

The integumentary system includes the skin, hair, nails, and the glands in the skin. This system forms a waterproof protective barrier between a body and its environment.

Skeletal system

The skeletal system—the body's framework—is made of bones, joints, and cartilage. It helps with movement, stores minerals, makes blood cells, and protects internal organs.

Nervous system

The nervous system detects changes in the environment and signals responses. It includes the brain, the spinal cord, and the nerves that transmit information throughout the body.

Digestive system
The digestive system takes in and breaks down food and absorbs nutrients. It includes the mouth, esophagus, stomach, intestines, liver, gallbladder, and pancreas.

Immune system
The immune system defends the body against infectious agents. This system includes bone marrow and white blood cells, and organs such as lymph nodes and thymus.

Lymphatic system
The lymphatic system returns fluid from spaces between cells to the circulatory system. It also filters bacteria and particles out of the fluid. This system is made of a network of vessels and lymph nodes, as well as organs such as the spleen, tonsils, and appendix.

Endocrine system
The endocrine system secretes chemicals called hormones. This system includes the thyroid, the pituitary, and the adrenal glands.

Reproductive system
The reproductive system enables the body to produce offspring. This system includes some endocrine glands as well as the reproductive organs.

Muscular system
When muscles work with bones, they move parts of the body—including hands, fingers, legs, neck, and head. Muscles in internal organs move substances in the organs.

CHECKPOINT 29.1

1. Describe three levels of organization in the human body.
2. Name and describe the functions of each organ system.
3. **Critical Thinking** What body systems do you use when you participate in sports?

Build on What You Know

4. In addition to humans, what other animals have coeloms? *(Need to jog your memory? Revisit relevant concepts in Chapter 22, Section 22.2.)*

What are the twelve systems of the human body? **?**

29.2 Support

Necks can be deceiving
Nearly all mammals, whether they are tall or short, have seven vertebrae in their necks. Because of different patterns of alignment of bones and cartilage, mammal's necks vary in length, shape, and flexibility. These variations enable a giraffe to nibble treetops and you to look out the window.

What you'll learn

IDEAS
• To explain the functions of a skeletal system
• To compare three types of skeletal systems

WORDS
skeleton, hydrostatic skeleton, exoskeleton, endoskeleton

FUNCTIONS OF SKELETONS

Keeping the shape

Every living organism needs support to keep its shape. Unicellular organisms get all the support they need from their cell membranes and cytoskeletons. Humans and other large, multicellular animals need a rigid structure called a skeleton for support. The **skeleton** is a framework for the body. Like the steel girders that form the framework of a tall building, the skeleton determines an organism's overall shape.

In addition to supporting the body, a skeleton performs other functions, such as protecting the internal organs and allowing movement. For example, a mammal's hard, bony skull protects the animal's soft, fragile brain. A mammal can walk because muscles attached to long leg bones contract and cause the bones to move like a

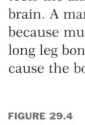

FIGURE 29.4

A skeleton forms a supporting framework for animals. What organism might have the skeleton shown at left?

lever. Mammal bones also contain a store of minerals, such as calcium and phosphorus, that can be used by the body when needed. Soft tissue on the inside of the bones manufactures blood cells.

SKELETONS IN ANIMALS

Three types of skeletons

An animal's skeleton should provide body support, protect the internal organs, and allow for movement. Over time, different groups of animals have evolved with three distinct types of skeletons.

Animals such as cnidarians, flatworms, nematodes, and annelids have a hydrostatic (hy-druh-STAT-ik) skeleton. A **hydrostatic skeleton** is a support system consisting of a body compartment filled with fluid under pressure. Unlike human skeletons, hydrostatic skeletons do not contain any hard structures such as bones. Either contractile cells or muscles surround the fluid-filled compartment. When contraction occurs, the compartment elongates and the animal moves forward. This type of skeleton provides adequate support for some

FIGURE 29.5
Kinds of Skeletons

How do these three types of skeletons differ?

Hydrostatic skeleton

1 An earthworm has no hardened supporting structure. Fluid that is held under pressure in a body cavity allows the earthworm to maintain a definite shape and to move.

Exoskeleton

2 An arthropod's nonliving exoskeleton provides excellent protection. To grow larger, the arthropod must shed its exoskeleton and then replace it with a larger one.

Endoskeleton

3 Vertebrates have living endoskeletons made of bone and/or cartilage. This hard, internal skeleton facilitates movement and provides support.

animals that live in water and some animals that live in soil, and cushions the animals' internal organs.

From Chapter 23 you may remember that arthropods, such as crabs and insects, have an exoskeleton. An **exoskeleton** is a hard covering on the outside of a body that provides both support and protection. The exoskeletons of arthropods are composed of a layer of nonliving material called chitin. The chitin layer covers the entire body, forming a jointed encasement somewhat like a suit of armor. Because exoskeletons cannot grow, animals with exoskeletons must molt, or shed their protective covering, to grow.

An exoskeleton provides excellent body support and protection for some animals living in water or on land. Muscles attached to the inside of the exoskeleton can contract to move an animal's appendages. Animals with this type of skeleton can move around freely. They may swim, crawl, walk, or fly.

Vertebrates, such as humans and other mammals, fishes, and birds, have skeletons made of bone and

cartilage located inside the body. An internal hard skeleton is called an **endoskeleton.**

An endoskeleton does not protect all soft body tissues as well as an exoskeleton does, but an endoskeleton does allow for freer movement and greater growth. In contrast to a nonliving exoskeleton, an endoskeleton is a living framework that can grow along with the animal.

CHECKPOINT 29.2

1. What are the functions of a skeletal system?

2. Compare and contrast the three kinds of skeletal systems.

3. Critical Thinking If you could design a new and improved skeletal system for humans, what features would you include? Why?

Build on What You Know

4. Explain how an earthworm's hydrostatic skeleton functions as a skeletal system even though it has no hard, mineralized parts. *(Need to jog your memory? Revisit relevant concepts in Chapter 22, Section 22.3.)*

Chapter 29 Skin, Skeletal, and Muscular Systems **697**

29.3 Human Skeleton

What you'll learn

IDEAS
- To identify the parts of the human skeletal system
- To analyze bone structure

WORDS

axial skeleton, appendicular skeleton, marrow, osteoblasts, joints, ligaments, tendons, arthritis, osteoporosis

Rubber skulls?

A human embryo's skeleton is made of cartilage. Before birth, calcium and phosphorus are added to most of the cartilage, producing bone. The soft spot in the skull of an infant is soft, connective tissue that allows the skull and brain to grow. In adults, the soft, connective tissue is replaced by bony skull plates.

THE SKELETON

More than 200 bones

The human skeleton is made of bones, the joints where bones meet, and the connective tissues that hold the bones together. There are 206 bones in the human skeleton. Some of these are identified in *Figure 29.6*. Each bone has a size and shape that suits its particular function.

Like the skeletons of other vertebrates, the human skeleton can be divided into two parts: the axial and the appendicular skeletons. The skull, vertebral column, and rib cage make up the **axial skeleton.** The bones of the axial skeleton protect vital organs such as the brain, heart, and lungs. The vertebral column, made of a stack of vertebrae, holds the body upright and allows it to bend and twist into many positions. Soft tissues inside the vertebrae, ribs, and sternum make red and white blood cells.

The arm and leg bones, with the bones of the pelvis and shoulder areas, form the **appendicular skeleton.** The arm bones and leg bones move like levers, allowing you to walk, run, obtain food, and perform all the activities of a mobile land animal. Soft tissues in the pelvis make red and white blood cells. Calcium is stored in the thick knobs at the ends of long bones. Calcium hardens bone and is an essential element needed by the body for muscle contraction and nerve impulse transmission.

FIGURE 29.6

The major bones of the human body are identified below. Which bones make up the axial skeleton? The appendicular skeleton?

- Metacarpels
- Carpels
- Radius
- Ulna
- Humerus
- Skull
- Ribs
- Sternum
- Vertebra
- Ilium
- Femur
- Patella
- Fibula
- Tibia
- Tarsels
- Metatarsel
- Clavicle

- ▪ Axial skeleton
- ▪ Appendicular skeleton

FIGURE 29.7

Bone Structure

The structure of this bone is typical of long bones such as the femur and humerus. What differences do you see between spongy bone and compact bone?

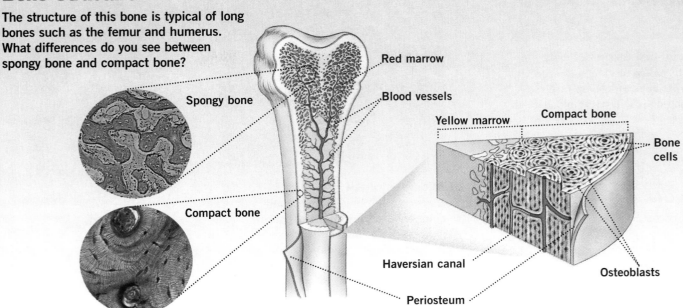

Spongy bone

Compact bone

Red marrow

Blood vessels

Yellow marrow

Compact bone

Bone cells

Haversian canal

Periosteum

Osteoblasts

FROM BONES TO BONE CELLS

Bones are alive

If you have ever struck a piece of bone while cutting into a steak, lambchop, or shortrib, you know that bones are hard and fairly rigid. Bones get their hard consistency from minerals, especially calcium and phosphorus. Because bone is so hard, you may think it is not alive. However, bone is living tissue made of cells and minerals.

Bones are covered by a membrane called the periosteum (payr-ee-OS-tee-um). Branching through the periosteum are small blood vessels. Blood moving through these vessels carries nutrients to the bone and takes wastes away. There is no periosteum at the ends of bones.

Bone tissue may be either spongy or compact. Spongy bone, tissue with many spaces, is found in the ends of long bones and in the middle part of short, flat bones. Compact bone is very dense. Its density provides support. Compact bone is found in the shafts of long bones such as the upper arm (humerus) and upper leg (femur).

A soft tissue that fills some spaces in bone is called **marrow.** In the micrograph of spongy bone, in *Figure 29.7,* you can see the large spaces that contain red bone marrow. Red bone marrow is a material that produces blood cells. Another type of bone marrow, yellow bone marrow, is mostly made up of fat cells. Yellow bone marrow is most often found in the cavities within the shafts of the long bones.

Look again at *Figure 29.7* and notice the circular channels in the compact bone. These channels are called Haversian canals and are spaces through which nerves and blood vessels pass. Because of the Haversian canals, compact bones are lighter in mass than they would be if they were solid.

Scattered throughout the bone are cells called osteoblasts (OS-tee-oh-blasts). **Osteoblasts** make the new bone cells needed for growth and repair. Found in both compact and spongy bone, osteoblasts are concentrated on the inner surface of the periosteum.

EVERYDAY BIOLOGY

A Bony Slowdown

A baby's bones are 50 percent longer one year after birth than they were when the infant was born. Why aren't six-year-olds as tall as adults? Protein signals may slow superfast growth, so that the annual rate of bone lengthening is only 7 percent a year by age 3.

FIGURE 29.8

Bone Functions

Blood-cell manufacturing
Cells called stem cells in red bone marrow develop into red blood cells and white blood cells.

Mineral storage
Bones store minerals, especially calcium and phosphorus, that are necessary for many of the body's biochemical reactions.

Protection
Bones protect internal organs. The skull protects the brain, and the ribs protect the heart, lungs, and other organs.

Movement
The anchoring of bones to muscles is necessary for body movement.

The structure of a bone is related to its function. The bones of the skeletal system support the body and give it shape. In addition to support, bones also serve the functions described in *Figure 29.8*.

Bone is continuously replaced throughout life. A fetal skeleton is mostly made of cartilage, a tough but flexible connective tissue. By the time a baby is born, much of the cartilage in its arms and legs has been replaced by bone. As the baby grows and develops, most of the remaining cartilage, is gradually replaced with heavier, harder bone. The skeletal system continues to replace cartilage with bone until a person is about 25 years old.

Some cartilage is always present in the skeletal system. For example, your outer ears, the tip of your nose, and the cushions between the vertebrae of your spine are all made of cartilage. Gently bend your nose and ears. As you can see, cartilage makes these parts flexible.

 Do It!

Why Do Bones Have Minerals?

Vinegar removes minerals from bones. Discover the function of bone minerals when you . . .

Try This

1 Weigh a chicken bone that is at least 7 centimeters (cm) long.
2 Determine the flexibility of the bone by gently bending it. Do not break the bone.
3 Submerge the bone in a jar of vinegar.
4 Weigh the bone and assess its flexibility each day for three consecutive days. Record your results.

Analyze Your Results

1 What happened to the bone's weight? Explain your results.
2 How did the bone's flexibility change after three days?
3 What is the function of bone minerals?

JOINTS

Where bones meet

The places where bones meet in the body are **joints.** Most of the body's joints allow movement between two bones; however, the structure of some joints prevents movement. Joints are classified as immovable, slightly movable, or freely movable.

No movement takes place in immovable joints, such as those between the bones in an adult human's skull. Slightly movable joints, such as those between the vertebrae of the spine, allow only a small amount of movement. Freely movable joints, such as the joints shown in *Figure 29.9,* allow the widest range of motion.

Cushions of cartilage in joints keep the ends of the bones from rubbing against each other. Some freely movable joints are also lubricated and protected by fluid-filled sacs called bursae (singular: *bursa*). You can find a bursa in the shoulder joint pictured in *Figure 29.10.* Bursae absorb the impact of sudden pressure on a joint. Some bursae are present at birth, but others develop later in life in joints that are frequently used.

The bones and muscles of freely movable joints are bound together by bands of tough connective tissues. **Ligaments** are connective tissues that join one bone to another. **Tendons** are connective tissues that attach muscles to bones.

FIGURE 29.10

The joints at the ends of long bones are protected by cartilage and bursae. How do cartilage and bursae help reduce friction and absorb shocks?

Fluid
Cartilage
Bursa
Tendon
Bone
Muscle

FIGURE 29.9

Freely Movable Joints

Movable joints are classified by the type of movement they allow.

Ball-and-socket joint
A ball-shaped end of one bone fits into a cup-shaped end of another, forming a ball-and-socket joint. This kind of joint allows for a wide range of motion.

Hinge joint
Bones connected by hinge joints move back and forth like a hinged door. The elbow is a hinge joint.

Pivot joint
In a pivot joint, bones rotate around each other. A pivot joint attaches your skull to your vertebral column.

Gliding joint
In gliding joints, bones slide over one another. Your wrist is a gliding joint.

Bones for a lifetime

Although most of your skeletal system is tough and durable, it can still be injured. A sprain is an injury to the ligaments and tendons. Overuse of a shoulder or other freely movable joint can cause the fluid-filled bursa to swell, a painful condition called bursitis.

An accident or fall may cause you to break, or fracture, a bone. A broken bone must have its ends aligned. Generally it must then be immobilized with a cast or splint. Healing takes place over time and involves the process shown in *Figure 29.11.*

Your skeletal system can also be affected by diseases. These include many forms of **arthritis,** a disease that causes joints to become inflamed and painful. Arthritis can result in a loss of joint function. Another disease, **osteoporosis,** causes brittle bones that break easily. In people who suffer from osteoporosis, the spine may degenerate, resulting in a noticeable hump in the back at the shoulder level or a shortening in height.

Proper diet and a program of weight-bearing exercise begun early in life can help prevent the development of osteoporosis. Calcium and vitamin D are needed to grow strong bones. To maintain the health of your skeletal system, it is important to eat foods high in these two nutrients. Calcium-rich foods include dairy products, shellfish, leafy green vegetables, and tofu. Dairy products are fortified with vitamin D, and the body can also make some of its own vitamin D, using sunlight. Weight-bearing exercise, such as walking or running, also helps strengthen bones.

FIGURE 29.11

Healing Bone

1 Bleeding occurs at a fracture site, but clots form quickly and the blood vessels begin to heal.

Fracture
Blood clot
Marrow
Periosteum

2 Some cells of the periosteum form a callus of fibrous connective tissue at the fracture site.

Callus

3 Bone cells produce cartilage to fill in the gaps between the broken ends of the bone.

New cartilage

4 As bone replaces the cartilage, the callus shrinks. The bone will eventually return to its original shape.

CHECKPOINT 29.3

1. Name the components of the skeletal system.

2. Describe the structure of a bone.

3. Critical Thinking If a friend suggests that a skeleton made entirely of cartilage would be better than one of bone, would you agree or disagree? Explain your answer.

Build on What You Know

4. Compare the skeletons of a bird and a human. *(Need to jog your memory? Revisit relevant concepts in Chapter 26, Section 26.4.)*

? **What does the body's skeleton do?**

29.4 Movement

You do not have to fly
Ostriches cannot fly, but they certainly can run. The giant birds can go as fast as 72 kilometers per hour (45 miles per hour), exceeding the speed limit on many highways. And they can maintain such speeds for a distance of 32 kilometers. Ostriches can outrun most mammals!

What you'll learn

IDEAS
• To analyze the functions of muscles
• To compare the muscular systems of different groups of animals

FUNCTIONS OF MUSCLES

Movement and more

Most types of animals are motile—they move from place to place. Bones help support an organism and work with muscles to enable movement. How do muscles work? All muscles can contract and shorten. They are located where a contraction causes movement. For example, some muscles move body parts. This movement takes place because the muscles are attached to part of the skeleton. As the attached muscles shorten, they move the corresponding body part.

In addition to making animals motile, muscles also move substances through the animals' bodies. The heart, an organ made of muscle, contracts repeatedly to pump blood. Muscle tissue in the walls of blood vessels contracts to affect blood flow

throughout the body. Muscle tissue in the walls of an animal's digestive system contracts to move food through the body and wastes out of the body.

Some muscles in a land animal's body may be slightly contracted at all times. The partially contracted muscles help the animal maintain an upright posture and keep internal organs in place.

As muscles contract, they use energy and generate heat. You may feel warm when you run or do hard physical work. Or you may shiver, stamp your feet, or wave your arms to stay warm while outside in cold weather. In these situations, your muscles produce heat as they work, warming your body.

Muscle Menu

Muscle tissue is usually a person's favorite type of animal food. We generally tend not to eat other types of animal tissue such as skin, hair, bones, and internal organs.

FIGURE 29.12
What part of a frog's body needs to have well-developed muscles?

Chapter 29 Skin, Skeletal, and Muscular Systems **703**

MUSCULAR SYSTEMS IN ANIMALS

Got to keep on moving

Some animals, such as sponges, do not have muscles. You may remember from Chapter 21 that sponges are sessile—they do not move. However, sponges use flagella to move large quantities of water through their saclike bodies as they filter out food particles.

Most animals have specialized cells, tissues, and organs to make movement possible. Cnidarians, such as jellyfish, move using fibers that contract. Cells with bundles of microfilaments are arranged into these fibers. The contracting fibers push against fluid in the central body cavity, elongating the cnidarian and allowing it to move through the water. How do you think this level of organization compares with that of a human?

Most animal phyla have true muscle tissue that consists of bundles of muscle cells. Some free-living flatworms have muscles in their body walls that allow them to swim through water with a wavelike motion. Roundworms have muscles that run the length of the body. When these muscles contract, the roundworm makes thrashing movements.

The muscle system of an animal enables it to move about in one or more ways, such as crawling, burrowing, walking, jumping, running, swimming, or flying. Do you recall observing earthworms while studying Chapter 21? Annelids such as earthworms have two sets of muscles. One set circles the body. Contracting circular muscles squeeze against the hydrostatic skeleton, extending the body. A second set of muscles runs the length of the body. When these muscles contract, the body shortens and is pulled forward.

FIGURE 29.13
Cells in the muscular foot of a snail secrete mucus to help the snail move.

FIGURE 29.14
How do the strong muscles in the rear legs of a grasshopper meet the insect's survival needs?

When the dorsal leg muscle contracts, the insect's leg straightens.

When the ventral leg muscle contracts, the leg bends.

Mollusks such as slugs and snails have a thick muscular foot used for gripping and creeping over surfaces. They also have muscles that allow them to withdraw into their shells. For example, a clam uses an elongated foot to move through wet sand. The tip of the foot extends, then widens to form an anchor. The rest of the foot then contracts, pulling the clam along. Clams also have muscles that allow them to tightly close their two shells.

If you have ever eaten clams, oysters, or mussels, you are familiar with these shell-closing muscles.

Arthropods such as lobsters and grasshoppers have muscles attached to a jointed exoskeleton. Muscle pairs operate each arthropod appendage. For example, you can see in *Figure 29.14* that a grasshopper's leg has one muscle that flexes the hind leg to get the grasshopper in position to jump. A second muscle forcefully extends the leg, sending the grasshopper into the air.

Vertebrates, such as fishes, birds, reptiles, amphibians, and mammals, have a system of muscles attached to the parts of an endoskeleton. Fishes have powerful swimming muscles that run along the sides of the body. Waves of muscular contraction move backward along the streamlined body, causing a wavelike motion that moves fishes forward.

Reptiles, amphibians, and mammals can walk and run because pairs of opposing muscles move each limb. Snakes, which are limbless reptiles, use muscles in the body wall to push themselves along the ground. Birds use powerful chest muscles attached to a bladelike breastbone to raise and lower their wings for flight. In all vertebrates, muscles generate heat and help maintain posture.

CHECKPOINT 29.4

1. What are four functions of muscles?

2. Compare the muscular systems of three groups of organisms that you have studied. How are they alike? How are they different?

3. Critical Thinking Muscle tissue simply contracts. How can it perform so many different functions in the body?

Build on What You Know

4. Compare movement in animals with movement in animal-like protists. How do the levels of organization in these two groups compare? *(Need to jog your memory? Revisit relevant concepts in Chapter 15, Section 15.2.)*

FIGURE 29.16
Explain how the muscular system of a hummingbird must accommodate the bird's feeding style.

FIGURE 29.15
How do this mammal's well-developed muscles support its lifestyle?

LAB ZONE Think About It!

Comparing Muscle Mass

In many animals, muscle is the most plentiful tissue. The table below indicates the percentage of muscle mass compared to the total body mass for three animals. Study the table and answer the questions that follow.

Comparing Muscle Mass	
Fishes	50–60 %
Antelopes	40–50 %
Squids	35 %

Analyzing the Table

1 Why do you think that the percentage of muscle mass to total body mass is greatest for fishes?

2 For what reason(s) might squids have a lower percentage of muscle mass to total body mass than fishes do?

3 Explain why antelopes have a lower percentage of muscle mass to total body mass than fishes.

4 Estimate the percentage of muscle mass to total body mass for the mountain lion shown on the left. Give reasons for your estimate.

29.5 Human Muscles

What you'll learn

IDEAS

• To compare the three types of human muscles

• To explain how human muscle contracts

WORDS

skeletal muscle, smooth muscle, cardiac muscle

Just one good yank

If the maximum strength of all the muscles in the body were exerted in one direction, they would produce a force of 25 tons—enough to pull a chain of 13 cars. But muscle contractions use a lot of energy. In one day, we each expend enough energy to lift nearly 11,000 kilograms (kg) of bricks.

MUSCLE STRUCTURE AND FUNCTION

Work that body

Human muscles do many different jobs in the body. When you walk, chew, or dance, muscles move your skeleton. Other types of muscle keep your heart beating, move food through your digestive tract, and help your other internal organs function.

FIGURE 29.17

The human body contains more than 600 skeletal muscles. Name any unlabeled muscles that you know.

Deltoid

Pectoralis major

Quadriceps

Biceps

Triceps

Gluteus maximus

Trapezius

Deltoid

Types of muscles The human body contains three types of muscles. Each type is specialized to perform a different function. The type of muscle that enables you to move your arms, your legs, and other parts of your body is called **skeletal muscle.** You can see the locations of some major skeletal muscles in *Figure 29.17*. Skeletal muscles are sometimes called voluntary muscles because they are under your conscious control.

Skeletal muscle tissue is striated (STRY-ayt-uhd), which means it has narrow bands that can be seen with a microscope. Unlike most cells in the human body, skeletal muscle cells do not divide into two new cells during mitosis. The nuclei of skeletal muscle cells divide, but the cells do not. As a result, skeletal muscle cells grow into cells with many nuclei called muscle fibers. These cells also contain more mitochondria than most other types of cells. Remember the function of mitochondria. Why would the presence of more mitochondria be an advantage?

Skeletal muscle fibers are arranged into bundles. The muscle bundles contract in response to nerve impulses. When a skeletal muscle contracts, it moves the part of the skeleton to which it is attached.

Many of your internal organs contain smooth muscles. A **smooth muscle** is sometimes called an involuntary muscle because it is not under your conscious control. Smooth muscles are controlled partly by the nervous system and partly by the hormones of the endocrine system. Smooth muscles regulate the width of blood vessels and the contractions of the digestive system. They make your pupils contract when you are in bright sunlight.

Compare the skeletal muscle tissue with the smooth muscle tissue in *Figure 29.18*. Smooth muscle tissue is not striated like skeletal muscle tissue. Another difference between these two types of muscles is that each smooth muscle cell contains only one nucleus.

A third type of muscle tissue, **cardiac muscle,** is found only in the heart and nowhere else in the body. This type of muscle is striated and involuntary. Cardiac muscle tissue contracts and relaxes continuously throughout life. Unlike skeletal muscles, which can run low on oxygen and fatigue if worked repeatedly, cardiac muscle is adapted to work slowly and constantly. In fact, a piece of heart muscle will continue beating for a time outside the body if it is placed in a warm saltwater solution similar to blood. Although cardiac muscle contracts without stimulation from the nervous system, the nervous system does affect the rate of the heartbeat.

Muscles and movement A skeletal muscle moves a bone by contracting, or shortening in length. The bone returns to its starting position when the muscle relaxes and returns to its former shape and length. Because a muscle exerts force only when it contracts, it can move a bone in only one direction.

To provide motion in two directions, many skeletal muscles work in pairs. For example, for a joint such as an elbow or a knee to function, two muscles alternate contracting and relaxing. The muscle that bends a

FIGURE 29.18
What difference do you see between the three types of muscle tissues?

Skeletal   **Smooth**   **Cardiac**

joint is called the flexor. The muscle that straightens a joint is called the extensor. In *Figure 29.19* you can see how the large muscles in the upper arm work together to bend and straighten the elbow.

Even when you are not consciously contracting your skeletal muscles, they are not completely relaxed. The skeletal muscles are always partially contracted. This slight contraction is called muscle tone. Muscle tone helps you maintain posture, keeps your skeleton aligned, and holds your internal organs in place.

Muscle contraction You can try a simple experiment to observe how skeletal muscles function in movement.

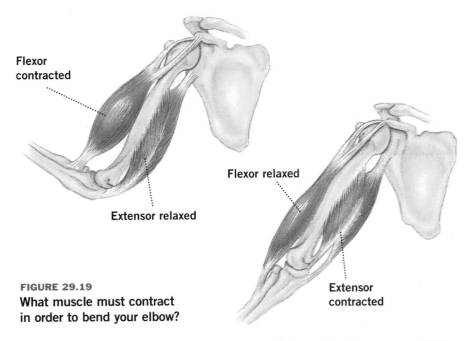

Flexor contracted

Extensor relaxed

Flexor relaxed

Extensor contracted

FIGURE 29.19
What muscle must contract in order to bend your elbow?

Hold your hands in front of you, palms up, fingertips touching. Move your hands together and apart, allowing your fingers to slide past each other. These movements are a simple model of a theory that explains how skeletal muscles move. This theory is called the sliding filament theory.

Skeletal muscle bundles are made of muscle fibers, which in turn are composed of myofibrils—tiny cylinder-shaped structures. Each myofibril contains tiny filaments. Some filaments are thin, others are thick. When a muscle is stimulated by a nerve impulse, the thin filaments slide past the thick filaments and the muscle shortens. The lower part of *Figure 29.20* shows what happens when a muscle contracts.

FIGURE 29.20

Muscle Contraction

Skeletal muscles are bundles of muscle cell fibers. Each bundle is covered by connective tissue.

Bundle
A bundle is composed of many muscle fibers. A muscle fiber can be as long as 40 cm.

Muscle fiber
Each muscle fiber is a single cell with many nuclei and is striated with a light and dark banding.

Myofibril
Muscle fibers are made of tiny cylindrical structures called myofibrils. Each myofibril is made of protein filaments.

Filaments
Each myofibril has thick and thin filaments. Thick filaments are made of the protein myosin, and thin filaments are made of the protein actin. A unit of alternating thick and thin filaments is called a sarcomere. Sarcomeres are separated by areas of dense matter called Z lines.

Contracted muscle Thick and thin filaments slide past each other until their ends almost touch. Z lines end up closer to each other as each sarcomere shortens.

Relaxed muscle The ends of the thick and thin filaments overlap slightly but do not touch. The Z lines are far apart.

Sarcomere

Z line

Thin filament (actin)

Thick filament (myosin)

Sarcomere

Exercise helps maintain healthy bones and muscles. There are many different forms of exercise. Does your community have playgrounds, pools, or gyms?

IN THE COMMUNITY

Training Bones and Muscles

Identify your community's exercise facilities. What kinds of activities can you perform at these facilities? What muscle groups are exercised by the different activities? For more information on how to keep physically fit, you may want to refer to *http://body_systems.biosurf.com*.

CARING FOR YOUR MUSCLES

No pains, no strains

If you have ever been stiff and sore after playing sports or doing other physical activity, you can appreciate how important it is to keep your muscular system healthy. Muscles need lots of exercise, but overworking a muscle may result in painful muscle cramps. There are several causes of muscle cramping. A cramp can occur when lactic acid—an end-product of anaerobic cellular respiration—is formed faster than it is removed.

An injury or a nerve problem can also cause muscle cramps, so muscle soreness should always be treated in some way. Untreated problems can lead to greater injury. Overstretching a muscle can cause an injury called muscle strain. In a severe strain the muscles actually tear and bleed.

Disorders resulting from improper nerve signals to the muscles can interfere with the normal functioning of muscles. For example, muscle spasms can occur when muscles involuntarily contract. Muscle spasms can cause discomfort or severe pain. When the nerve signals are lacking or interrupted, muscles can atrophy (waste away) or weaken. A disease called myasthenia gravis occurs when nerve signals fail to make muscles contract. A person with myasthenia gravis experiences a progressive weakening and tiring of the muscles.

To maintain healthy muscles, exercise regularly. To avoid injury, warm up and stretch before exercising. To avoid overstressing particular muscles, vary your exercise. Aerobic exercises improve overall conditioning, and isometric exercises strengthen specific muscles. To build muscle, you must also eat well. Your body's muscles need adequate amounts of protein and minerals such as potassium and calcium.

CHECKPOINT 29.5

1. Compare the three types of human muscles and their functions.
2. Explain how a muscle contracts.
3. **Critical Thinking** A muscle fiber can only be contracted or relaxed. Explain the difference between strong and weak muscle contractions.

Build on What You Know

4. Explain how lactic acid is formed. How does it affect muscles? *(Need to jog your memory? Revisit relevant concepts in Chapter 4, Section 4.3.)*

Explain how muscles move the body.

29.6 Covering

What you'll learn

IDEAS
• To explain the functions of animal coverings
• To distinguish the parts of the human integumentary system
• To summarize how to care for the skin

WORDS
integumentary system, epidermis, dermis, melanin

Getting in your licks
Cats and dogs do more than ease pain when they lick their wounds. The saliva of most mammals contains a chemical growth factor. This chemical signals skin cells to divide and replicate more quickly, which speeds up the healing process. Indeed, parents who try to kiss away a child's hurt may have more than emotional support on their side.

FUNCTIONS OF COVERINGS

Under wraps

Your body is covered with a waterproof wrapper called skin. Skin protects and insulates your body. Amphibians, reptiles, birds, and mammals also have skin. Amphibians have skin that stays moist and enables gas diffusion. A reptile's skin is composed of hard, dry scales. Birds have thin skin covered with feathers that insulate the body. For mammals that live in cold environments, such as white fox, fur is an important insulator. In addition to their heavy coats, polar bears have a thick layer of fat that keeps their bodies from losing heat.

All of these coverings are suitable for specific niches. Though it differs, skin in all animals is made of the same protein—keratin. Keratin is insoluble in water so it forms a barrier that prevents the evaporation of water.

FIGURE 29.21
Scales, fur, and feathers are animal coverings. All are made of keratin—a waterproof, insulating substance. What additional uses do birds have for feathers?

The skin of an animal, whether it has fur, feathers, or scales, performs many of the same functions performed by human skin.

HUMAN INTEGUMENTARY SYSTEM

It's got you covered

The **integumentary system** (in-TEG-yoo-MEN-tuh-ree) covers your body and consists of the skin and its glands, hair, and nails. The skin has a surface area of 1.4 to 1.9 square meters and is the body's largest organ. An average person's skin weighs about 3 kg, more than twice as much as the brain.

The integumentary system has several important functions. It protects the body by holding fluids in, and by keeping disease-causing microorganisms out. Pigments produced by your skin also protect you from the sun's harmful ultraviolet (UV) rays. Your skin makes vitamin D from sunlight and a lipid called cholesterol (koh-LES-tuh-rol), which is found in the membranes of all animal cells. Millions of tiny nerve endings enable the skin to serve as a sense organ. The nerve endings sense heat, cold, and pressure.

FIGURE 29.22
Skin Structure

Skin structure is complex. What types of tissues can you see in skin?

Hair

Dead cells

Living cells

Sebaceous gland

Sweat pore

Muscle

Hair follicle

Epidermis

Dermis

Artery

Vein

Nerve

Subcutaneous (fat) layer

Duct of sweat gland

Sweat gland

FIGURE 29.23
What do you think is the purpose of these flaky, dead cells of the skin's upper epidermal layer?

The skin has two main layers—the epidermis and the dermis. If you have ever had a blister, you have seen the two layers separate. You can see both layers and the structures within them in *Figure 29.22.* You can also see the layer of fat called the subcutaneous (suhb-kyoo-TAY-nee-uhs) layer. This layer insulates the body and stores energy.

Epidermis The **epidermis** (ep-ih-DER-mis) is the skin's outer layer. This skin layer is 10 to 30 cells thick—about as thick as this page. The epidermis is covered with tiny openings called pores. Sweat and oils secreted by the skin leave the body through the pores.

If you were to look at the epidermis under a microscope lens, you would see a scaly surface, such as the one shown in *Figure 29.23.* The top layer of the epidermis is made of flat, dead cells. These cells are full of keratin, the waterproof protein that helps keep bacteria from entering your body through your skin. Sebum, an oily substance produced by glands in the dermis, keeps the epidermis soft and flexible. The dead cells of the epidermis are constantly being shed. They are replaced by new cells from deeper within the epidermis. The entire layer of dead cells is replaced by the body about every 28 days.

Dermis The thick inner layer of the skin is the **dermis.** The cells of the dermis make collagen, a protein that makes skin supple and strong. Collagen forms the ridges on your fingertips that make your fingerprints. It also forms ridges on the palms of your hands, your toes, and the soles of your feet. The ridges act as nonskid treads for your hands and feet.

Specialized cells in the dermis produce **melanin,** the pigment that gives skin its color. Melanin protects the skin from the ultraviolet rays of the sun. Exposure to the sun increases the amount of melanin and darkens, or "tans," the skin.

The dermis contains nerve endings, blood vessels, and hair follicles. The sebaceous (seh-BAY-shus) glands, which produce sebum, are also located in the dermis. Sebaceous glands are usually attached to hair follicles. Sebum contains oil, which keeps hair from drying out. When sebaceous glands become blocked by sebum, a whitehead appears on the skin surface. When the sebum dries and darkens, it becomes a blackhead. If sebaceous glands become infected with bacteria, pimples and acne result.

Sweat glands are also located in the dermis. If your body is too hot, sweat glands produce sweat—a fluid containing water, salt, and wastes. When sweat evaporates, it takes heat away from your body. Tiny blood vessels in the skin also help regulate your body temperature and store blood that can be used elsewhere in the body when needed. Notice in *Figure 29.22* that hair follicles and sweat glands pass through the epidermis all the way to the surface of the skin.

FIGURE 29.24
Hair texture depends on a hair follicle's shape. Round, cylindrical follicles produce straight hair. Flat, ribbonlike follicles produce curly hair.

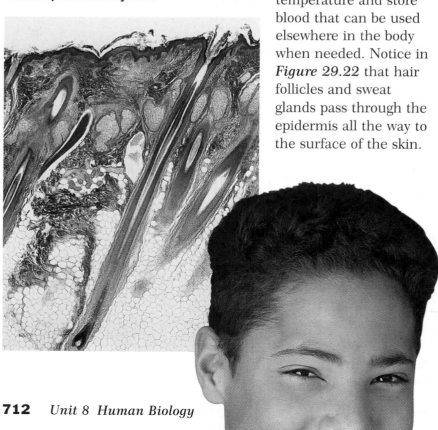

Hair and nails Hair and nails are made of dead epidermal cells. Each hair shaft grows from a root inside a hair follicle. *Figure 29.24* shows a cross section of a hair follicle. The whole shaft of the hair, except for the living root, is made of dead cells similar to those in the top layer of the epidermis. Hair grows when cells in the root divide and push the rest of the shaft up and out of the follicle.

Fingernails and toenails are solid plates of epidermal cells. Each type of nail grows from a root that lies in a groove hidden by a fold of skin called the cuticle. The small white crescent that you see at the base of each nail is part of this growing area.

CARING FOR YOUR SKIN
Tanning isn't healthy

Your skin is highly susceptible to injury. Have you watched small cuts on your skin heal, forming scabs that disappear from the edges inward as new skin forms?

A bruise occurs when some of the skin's small blood vessels break. Blood from the broken vessels forms pools that look blue under the skin.

Burns are a painful form of skin injury. A burn from a hot object may redden, blister, or even char the skin. Exposure to the sun can cause a burn, regardless of your skin composition. Blistering and intense itching can result from contact with plants such as poison ivy or poison oak.

Infectious organisms can cause diseases of the skin. A bacterial infection of the sebaceous glands causes acne. Bacteria can cause other skin infections, such as impetigo. Herpes viruses can cause sores to erupt in human skin. A fungus can cause the disease called athlete's foot.

Skin cancer is a disease that results from the abnormal growth of skin cells. It is often associated with exposure to the sun and may appear as lumps, sores that do not heal, or unusual moles.

Frequent baths or showers help to keep skin healthy. You should also eat a healthful diet with adequate B vitamins. Most importantly, you should protect your skin from overexposure to the sun by avoiding strong sunlight and wearing protective clothing and a sunscreen with a sun protection factor (SPF) of at least 15. Inspect your skin on a regular basis and report any changes to your doctor.

FRONTIERS IN BIOLOGY

Test-tube skin

For people whose skin has been severely burned, a new technique has been developed in which burned areas can be healed with new skin that is nearly identical to the patient's original skin.

The technique uses a product referred to as test-tube skin. Test-tube skin begins with protein fibers from cowhide and polysaccharides from shark cartilage. The material is made into a thin membrane that looks like wet tissue paper. Medical technicians seed the artificial membrane with cells from healthy areas of the patient's epidermis. Then the seeded membrane is laid over the burned area and covered with a silicone bandage to prevent it from drying out.

In time, cells under the burned tissue divide and grow into new cells, forming the inner skin layer. Through repeated mitotic divisions, the cells seeded onto the surface of the membrane grow into a new outer skin. The new skin is just like the original skin,

LAB ZONE — Think About It!

Analyzing the Incidence of Skin Cancer

About 90 percent of all skin cancers are caused by exposure to sunlight because the sun is a strong source of damaging UV rays. The table below shows the risk of melanoma in the United States over several decades. Study the table and answer the related questions.

Risk of Melanoma in the United States	
Year	Occurrence
1935	one in 1,500
1996	one in 100
2000	one in 75

Analyzing the Table

1 Create a graph using the statistics in the table.
2 What is the trend in the occurrence of melanoma since 1935?
3 What are some preventive measures you have learned about that can help you avoid skin cancers?

except that it has no sweat glands or hair follicles.

CHECKPOINT 29.6

1. What are the functions of animal coverings?
2. Compare the structures and functions of the epidermis and the dermis.
3. Critical Thinking Why does cutting your skin hurt, while cutting your hair or nails does not?

Build on What You Know

4. Compare the structures and functions of a human's skin and an arthropod's exoskeleton. *(Need to jog your memory? Revisit relevant concepts in Chapter 23, Section 23.1.)*

What is the function of the skin?

Dissecting a Chicken Wing

WHAT YOU WILL DO Observe a chicken wing's skin, muscles, bones, and joints, relating structure to function

SKILLS YOU WILL USE Observing, classifying, comparing and contrasting, recording data

WHAT YOU WILL NEED Raw chicken wing, dissecting tray and pins, scalpel, scissors, forceps, disposable gloves, hand lens

Propose a Hypothesis

How does the structure and function of a chicken wing correspond with joints in your body? Propose a hypothesis.

Conduct Your Experiment

1 Put on the disposable gloves and examine the chicken wing. **Caution:** Handle the chicken wing and dissection tools only when wearing the disposable gloves. Raw chicken often carries *Salmonella* bacteria, which can make you very ill. Do not touch your mouth with your hands or the tools during this lab. Remember that scalpels and scissors are sharp.

2 Using the hand lens, observe the skin. Record your observations. Keeping the chicken in the dissecting tray and using the tools provided, remove as much skin from the wing as you can. Try not to damage any underlying structures.

3 Draw a diagram of the wing, labeling as many joints and parts as you can.

4 Locate the muscles in the wing and tug each one gently. Observe and record what happens to the rest of the wing when you tug. Add the muscles to your diagram.

5 Locate and diagram the tendons, the white ribbonlike

structures that attach the muscles to the bones.

6 Remove the muscles to expose the bones and joints. Find the ligaments, the tough, shiny structures connecting the bones. Draw another diagram of the wing, labeling the bones, joints, and ligaments.

Analyze Your Data

What part of your body corresponds to the wing of a chicken? How many parts of the chicken wing correspond to parts of your body? Make a table showing this comparison.

Draw Conclusions

Compare the movement of the chicken wing with that of the relevant part of your body. What are the similarities? What are the differences?

Design a Related Experiment

Design a model of a joint. Include the bones, muscles, ligaments, tendons, and covering in your model.

Lab: Dissecting a Chicken Wing

Objective: To observe the skin, muscles, bones, and joints of a chicken wing. Relate structure to function.

	Chicken wing	Human arm
joints		
muscles		
tendons		

Chapter 29 Review

THE BIG IDEA!

29.1 **The human body consists of twelve systems.**

29.2–29.3 **The body's skeleton provides support and protection.**

29.4–29.5 **Muscles contract to move the body.**

29.6 **The skin covers and protects the body's internal organs.**

Sum It Up

Use the following summary to review the main concepts in this chapter.

29.1 Body Systems

- Groups of cells with similar structures and functions are called tissues. Different types of tissues combine to form organs; groups of organs that work together to perform specific functions make up systems. The human body is organized into twelve organ systems.
- In humans, internal organs are located in the ventral and dorsal body cavities.

29.2 Support

- Skeletons provide body support, protect internal organs, and enable movement.
- Animals have evolved with three types of skeletons: hydrostatic skeletons, exoskeletons, and endoskeletons.

29.3 Human Skeleton

- Vertebrate skeletons are divided into two parts: axial and appendicular skeletons.
- Bone tissue may be either spongy or compact. Bone marrow fills the spaces in spongy bone. Compact bone contains Haversian canals, through which nerves and blood vessels pass.
- Connective tissue holds bones together at joints and attaches muscles to bones. Joints are classified by the degree of movement they allow.

29.4 Movement

- Muscles move body parts; they move substances through a body; they maintain posture and placement of organs; and they generate heat.
- All muscles work by contracting. Muscles that attach to skeletons work in pairs.

29.5 Human Muscles

- Human muscles can be striated or smooth. Skeletal and cardiac muscles are striated.
- Muscles can be voluntary or involuntary. Smooth and cardiac muscles are involuntary. Skeletal muscle is voluntary.

29.6 Covering

- Skin keeps body fluids and body temperature in balance; it provides a barrier to pathogens; and it acts as a sense organ.
- The outermost layer of skin, hair, and nails consists of dead epidermal cells. Living epidermal cells produce melanin and vitamin D.
- The dermis contains nerve endings, blood vessels, hair follicles, and sweat glands.

Use Terms and Concepts

Use each of the following words or terms in a complete sentence. If you need to review a meaning, turn to the page indicated.

cephalization (p. 693)

skeleton (p. 696)

hydrostatic skeleton (p. 696)

exoskeleton (p. 697)

endoskeleton (p. 697)

axial skeleton (p. 698)

appendicular skeleton (p. 698)

marrow (p. 699)

osteoblasts (p. 699)

joints (p. 701)

ligaments (p. 701)

tendons (p. 701)

arthritis (p. 702)

osteoporosis (p.702)

skeletal muscle (p. 706)

smooth muscle (p. 706)

cardiac muscle (p. 707)

integumentary system (p. 710)

epidermis (p. 711)

dermis (p. 711)

melanin (p. 712)

Use Your Word Power

MATCHING Write the term from the list of key terms that best matches each of the phrases below.

1. A tissue located in spongy bone that produces blood cells.

2. A pigment that protects skin from ultraviolet radiation.

3. The tendency for sense organs to be located in the anterior portion of a body.

4. The system that provides a protective barrier between the body and its environment.

5. A disease that involves inflammation of the joints.

6. A striated, involuntary type of muscle that is found only in the heart.

7. Tissue that attaches muscles to bones.

8. Cells that produce new bone cells.

9. The set of bones that are formed by the arms, legs, pelvis, and shoulders.

10. An involuntary muscle found in blood vessels and internal organs.

MULTIPLE CHOICE Choose the letter of the word or phrase that best completes each statement.

11. Your vital organs are protected by your (a) appendicular skeleton; (b) axial skeleton; (c) endoskeleton; (d) epidermis.

12. An internal hard skeleton is (a) an exoskeleton; (b) a hydrostatic skeleton; (c) a cardiac muscle; (d) an endoskeleton.

13. The type of skeleton that must be shed as an organism grows is an (a) endoskeleton; (b) exoskeleton; (c) axial skeleton; (d) appendicular skeleton.

14. Sweat glands are located in the (a) epidermis; (b) mesoderm; (c) endoderm; (d) dermis.

15. Which of the following are part of a human skeleton? (a) skeletal muscles; (b) joints; (c) ligaments; (d) tendons.

16. A diet rich in calcium and vitamin D can help prevent (a) periostitis; (b) osteoporosis; (c) bursitis; (d) arthritis.

17. Cnidarians have (a) skeletal muscles; (b) smooth muscles; (c) a hydrostatic skeleton; (d) an endoskeleton.

Show What You Know

18. How do sweat glands help regulate body temperature?

19. What do hair and nails have in common?

20. Which parts of the integumentary system perform functions in other body systems? Explain your answer.

21. Explain what causes muscle cramps.

22. What is the function of Haversian canals in compact bone?

23. How is the healing of a broken bone similar to the development of the skeleton in a fetus?

24. Are striated muscles thicker when relaxed or when contracted? Explain your answer.

25. Make a Concept Map Make a concept map that relates the human skeletal system and muscular system.

Take It Further

26. Developing a Hypothesis Suppose you heard that someone had a bone marrow transplant. For what type of problem would such an operation be needed?

27. Applying Concepts One symptom of the childhood disease called rickets is bowed legs. The bones are not strong enough to support the body's weight. What treatment would you recommend for rickets? Explain your answer.

28. Analyzing Data In a boxing match there are rules against "hitting below the belt." Based on what you know about the human skeleton, explain why this rule makes sense.

29. Interpreting a Graph A sphinx moth has powerful flight muscles located in its thorax region. Pairs of muscles alternate contractions to produce wing beats. As a preflight warmup, the moth contracts both sets of muscles at the same time. According to the graph, how long does it take the moth to warm up its flight muscles? What temperature must those muscles be before the moth can fly?

Flight Muscle Temperature in a Moth

Preflight   Warm-up   Flight

Temperature (°C): 40, 35, 30, 25, 0

Time from Onset of Warm-up (minutes): -1, 0, 1, 2, 3, 4

30. Analyzing Data There are two types of skeletal muscle fibers—slow-twitch and fast-twitch. People are born with different amounts of each type. Type X is best for short bursts of activity that require maximum strength. Type Y is better for aerobic activities that require a lot of endurance. Based on the following table, are slow-twitch fibers Type X or Type Y?

Physical Activity and Slow-twitch Muscle Fibers

Activity	Proportion of Slow-twitch Muscle Fibers
Cross-country skier	80%
Long-distance runner	65%
Swimmer	58%
Weight lifter	55%
Sprinter	50%

31. Designing an Experiment Flexibility is the ability to bend joints and stretch muscles. Design an experiment to measure the effects of exercise on flexibility. How could you measure flexibility? What exercises could you do to increase flexibility? Caution: Do not perform any tests or exercises without the help of a trained adult supervisor.

Consider the Issues

32. The Steroid Quick Fix Some athletes take a synthetic version of the male hormone testosterone to increase muscle fibers. The potential side effects of steroid use include increased blood pressure, higher cholesterol levels, infertility, severe depression, and violent behavior. Should athletes who take steroids be allowed to compete with those who do not?

Make New Connections

33. Biology and Literature Locate the Achilles tendon in the body. How did it get its name? What is the relationship between the Achilles tendon and the phrase "Achilles' heel"?

34. Biology and Physical Education People with varying physical abilities participate in a variety of strenuous activities. For example, some wheelchair athletes compete in marathons. Research other examples. Find out the different methods athletes use to meet their goals.

FAST-FORWARD TO CHAPTER 30

Muscles get the energy they need from cellular respiration. In Chapter 30 you will study the digestive system, which supplies the fuel for cellular respiration, and the excretory system, which removes waste products from the body.

CHAPTER 30
Digestive and Excretory Systems

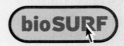

bioSURF

You can find out more about digestive and excretory systems at the following Internet address:
http://body_systems.biosurf.com

In this chapter . . .

FEATURES

Everyday Biology
- Thin Fat
- Outside Help, Inside
- Why Does Urine Change Color?

In the Community
A Helping Hand with the Groceries

 Frontiers in Biology
Kidney Help

LAB ZONES

Discover It!
- Modeling the Function of Bile

Do It!
- How Do You Read a Food Label?
- How Does Peristalsis Work?

Think About It!
- Determining How Many of Your Calories Come from Fat

Investigate It!
- Digesting Lactose

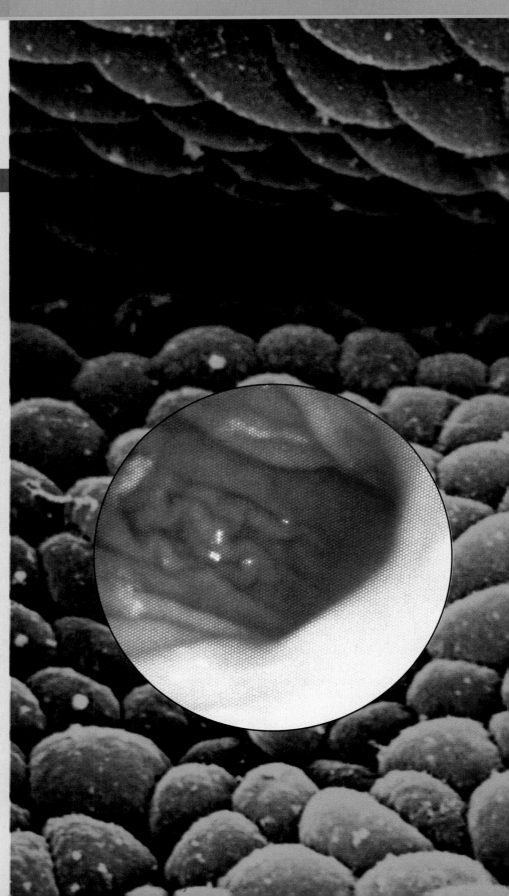

The man with a hole in his stomach

In 1822 Dr. William Beaumont, a young army surgeon at Fort Mackinac on the northwestern frontier, met the most important patient of his career. A 19-year-old French Canadian, Alexis St. Martin, received a shotgun blast to his chest and stomach at close range. It left a hole larger than the palm of his hand. No one, least of all the surgeon, expected him to live. But Beaumont treated St. Martin, who gradually improved over the next two years. At first St. Martin could not eat and had to be fed with a tube. Eventually, Beaumont was able to patch the hole with daily compresses.

Although the opening was partially healed, it would not close, despite Beaumont's best efforts. Fascinated by his "window" on St. Martin's digestive system, Beaumont began to experiment on his patient (with St. Martin's permission). Beaumont was able to look directly into St. Martin's stomach and observe the process of digestion. For example, food such as oysters or meat could be tied to string, inserted, and reexamined at specific intervals. In 1833 Beaumont published the results of more than 200 experiments on St. Martin.

St. Martin eventually recovered and lived to the age of 86. Beaumont and St. Martin's unusual doctor-patient relationship greatly contributed to our knowledge of the human digestive system. Today, sophisticated medical devices provide us with internal views of the stomach, like those shown on these pages.

LAB ZONE ▶ Discover It!

Modeling the Function of Bile

You need a bowl, water, vegetable oil, dishwashing liquid, a medicine dropper

1. Using the dropper, add about ten drops of vegetable oil to a bowl of water. Observe and record what happens.
2. Add five or six drops of dishwashing liquid to the middle of the bowl. Observe and record what happens.

The detergent breaks up the large drops of oil into smaller droplets. In a similar manner, bile in your digestive system breaks fat globules into smaller droplets of fat.

WRITE ABOUT IT!

Imagine that you are the young surgeon. Write a letter to a friend describing your experience treating St. Martin.

719

30.1 Digestion

Big (and small) appetites
During the four months each year that blue whales eat, they consume about 4000 kilograms (kg) of plankton a day. To eat that amount, a whale takes 79 immense gulps of ocean water daily. A rat eats only 12 to 15 grams (g) of food a day. Both animals replace 4 to 5 percent of their body weight each day, regardless of the food quantity they eat.

THE DIGESTIVE PROCESS

Chew, chew, chew...

How much food do you eat in a day? What foods do you eat every day to stay healthy? Humans and other animals have a **digestive system** to process food. The processing begins when an animal ingests food by taking it into the body. The animal moves the food through its digestive system, breaking down the food to extract nutrients. A **nutrient** is a substance needed by the body for growth, repair, and maintenance. Finally, the animal eliminates the remaining material as solid waste.

During this process, three activities take place to extract nutrients from foods: mechanical digestion, chemical digestion, and absorption. Mechanical digestion breaks food into tiny pieces without changing its chemical structure. Chemical digestion breaks food down into smaller, simpler molecules—nutrients. Absorption

occurs when these nutrients are taken into the body's cells.

Heterotrophic organisms have various ways of digesting food. *Figure 30.1* shows a unicellular protist called *Paramecium*. Paramecia ingest food particles and digest them in specialized food vacuoles. This type of digestion, called intracellular digestion ("intra-" means "inside"), is relatively slow and can process only small amounts of food at a time. You may remember from Chapter 16 that fungi secrete chemicals into their foods and then absorb the food's nutrients. This process is called extracellular digestion, ("extra-" means "outside"). Simple multicellular organisms, such as sponges, also depend on intracellular digestion to obtain their nutrients.

Most types of animals need a faster way to digest food. They have specialized digestive systems for ingesting and processing larger amounts of food. Nutrients from the processed food are transported to body cells. In complex multicellular animals, nutrients are transported to body cells by another specialized organ system, the circulatory system. The digestive system eliminates any undigested material from the body.

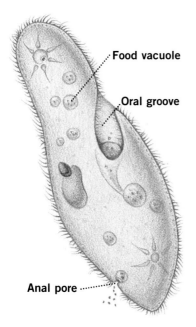

Food vacuole

Oral groove

Anal pore

FIGURE 30.1

Why is the digestive process of this paramecium described as intracellular?

Some animals, such as cnidarians and certain flatworms, have a saclike digestive system with one opening to the outside of the body. This opening serves both to ingest food and expel wastes. For example, the sea anemone in *Figure 30.2* uses a ring of tentacles to capture prey. The tentacles push food into the body opening of the sea anemone. The food is partly digested in the animal's digestive cavity. Fragments of partly digested food are ingested by cells lining the digestive cavity, and digestion is completed intracellularly. After the food is digested, any wastes exit out of the same opening through which they entered.

Other animals, such as worms, mollusks, echinoderms, arthropods, and vertebrates, have a tubelike digestive system with two openings to the outside of the body. You can see two examples of this type of digestive system in *Figure 30.3*. Food enters through a mouth opening and moves in one direction through the body as it is processed. Undigested material moves out of the body through an opening called an anus.

Along the way through the body, different parts of the digestive system perform different jobs. There may be areas for cutting and grinding, storing, and mixing food, and for its chemical breakdown. There are also areas for the absorption of nutrients and storage of waste.

For example, mechanical digestion begins in the mouth of a mammal, as teeth cut and chew the food. Glands in the mouth produce saliva to mix with the food and start the process of chemical digestion. After being swallowed, the food travels to the stomach, where muscular action softens it to a pulpy mass and digestive fluids break it down chemically. Glands in the liver and pancreas secrete fluids into the digestive system that break the food down further as it travels through the small intestine. There, nutrients from food are absorbed into the bloodstream to be transported all over the body.

FIGURE 30.2

What type of digestion occurs in this sea anemone?

Mouth/anus

Digestive cavity

FIGURE 30.3

What must happen to food as it moves between the mouth and anus of a grasshopper or a bird?

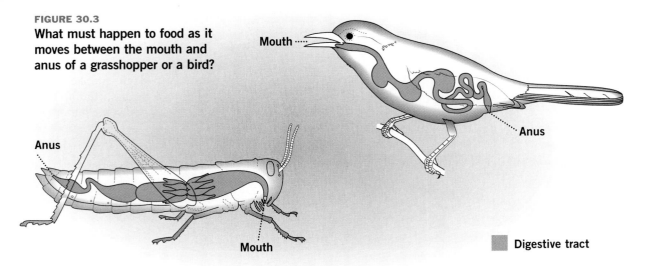

Mouth

Anus

Anus

Mouth

Digestive tract

Chapter 30 Digestive and Excretory Systems **721**

Undigested material moves into the large intestine and leaves the body through the anus.

CHEMISTRY OF FOODS

Little things count

Foods contain five types of chemical nutrients: carbohydrates, fats, proteins, vitamins, and minerals. Each nutrient has a role in keeping a body healthy. Although it is not a nutrient, water is another substance that is vital to life.

The food pyramid in *Figure 30.4* represents the relative amounts of each type of food a person should eat daily to obtain all the necessary nutrients. How does your own daily diet compare to the food pyramid recommendations?

Carbohydrates Human body cells obtain most of their energy from carbohydrates. Carbohydrates (KAR-boh-HY-drayts) are compounds made of carbon, hydrogen, and oxygen in a 1:2:1 ratio. Sugars and starches are examples of carbohydrates.

There are three types of carbohydrates. Single sugars, such as glucose, are monosaccharides (MON-oh-SAK-uh-rydz). Disaccharides (DY-sak-uh-rydz), such as sucrose or table sugar, consist of two single sugars linked together. Starches, like those in potatoes and bread, are polysaccharides (POL-ee-SAK-uh-rydz). Polysaccharides are carbohydrates made of long chains of simple sugars.

Fats Fats and oils belong to a group of compounds called lipids. As you may recall from Chapter 2, lipids are important for energy storage, and for the formation of cell membranes, hormones, and the oils on skin and hair. Most of the lipids your body needs come from the fats you eat. If your diet is very low in fat, your body will make lipids from other nutrients.

EVERYDAY BIOLOGY

Thin Fat

Food chemists have invented olestra, a fat that passes through the digestive system without being absorbed. To some people, olestra is a guilt-free fat. Others dislike olestra's taste and question whether it is healthful.

FIGURE 30.4

Food Pyramid

According to this food pyramid, what food group should form the largest part of your diet?

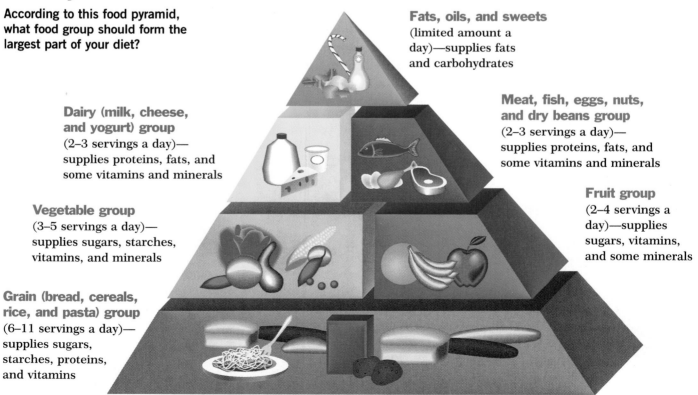

Fats, oils, and sweets (limited amount a day)—supplies fats and carbohydrates

Dairy (milk, cheese, and yogurt) group (2–3 servings a day)—supplies proteins, fats, and some vitamins and minerals

Meat, fish, eggs, nuts, and dry beans group (2–3 servings a day)—supplies proteins, fats, and some vitamins and minerals

Vegetable group (3–5 servings a day)—supplies sugars, starches, vitamins, and minerals

Fruit group (2–4 servings a day)—supplies sugars, vitamins, and some minerals

Grain (bread, cereals, rice, and pasta) group (6–11 servings a day)—supplies sugars, starches, proteins, and vitamins

A fat is made of three fatty acids joined to a glycerol molecule. Fatty acids are chains of carbon and hydrogen atoms with a weak acid attached to one end. When you eat foods containing fats, your body breaks the fats down into glycerol and fatty acids. Your body can use these raw materials to make the lipids it needs.

Fats are classified as either saturated or unsaturated, depending on the type of chemical bonds between the carbons in the fat molecule. Fats with one or more double bonds are unsaturated fats. A fat with one double bond is a monounsaturated fat, while a fat with many double bonds is a polyunsaturated fat. Most unsaturated fats, such as vegetable oil and olive oil, are liquids at room temperature. Saturated fats have no double bonds and are usually solid at room temperature. Butter and lard are common examples of saturated fats.

Proteins Your body contains hundreds of different proteins. Proteins are materials used to construct body parts such as muscle, skin, and blood. All these proteins are formed from 20 different amino acids. Twelve of these amino acids can be made by your body. Amino acids that cannot be made by the body are called essential amino acids. Humans must obtain the eight essential amino acids from proteins in food.

In order for your body to use the proteins in foods, the proteins must be broken down into their component amino acids. Cells then use the amino acids to make new proteins. These proteins are used for growth, repair, and as enzymes in cellular metabolism. During severe dieting or starvation, the body will break down the protein in its own muscles to obtain the energy it needs.

Vitamins Vitamins are complex organic molecules that are needed by the body in very small amounts. Unlike other nutrients, vitamins do

Some Important Vitamins

	Vitamin	Major Sources	RDA
Water Soluble	Thiamin (B1)	Beans, peanuts, meat (especially pork), whole grains, eggs	1.1–1.5 mg
	Riboflavin (B2)	Dairy products, eggs, green leafy vegetables, yeast	1.3–1.7 mg
	Niacin	Meat, poultry, fish, peanuts	20 mg
	B6	Meat, poultry, fish, potatoes, sweet potatoes	2.0–2.2 mg
	B12	Meat, poultry, fish, eggs, dairy products	3–6 mg
	C	Fruits and vegetables, especially citrus fruits, cantaloupe, strawberries, tomatoes, green leafy vegetables	60 mg
Fat Soluble	A	Dark yellow vegetables (such as carrots), green leafy vegetables, liver, eggs	4000–5000 IU*
	D	Sunlight, fish liver oil, fortified milk	400 IU
	E	Vegetable oils, seeds, whole grains	30 IU
	K	Green leafy vegetables, cabbage, pork liver, intestinal bacteria	55–70 mg

*IU = international unit

FIGURE 30.5
What vitamins did you ingest with your breakfast this morning?

not contain energy. Most vitamins play a role in cellular reactions by acting in conjunction with enzymes. With the exception of vitamin D, vitamins are not made by the body and must be obtained from food.

Water-soluble vitamins cannot be stored in the body and must be obtained from the daily diet. Fat-soluble vitamins, on the other hand, can be stored in the liver or body fat for future use.

The United States government has established guidelines for the recommended daily allowance (RDA) of each vitamin. These numbers are updated periodically to reflect current research. *Figure 30.5* lists some important vitamins and their sources. What foods are major sources of vitamin B6? Vitamin C?

Minerals Minerals are inorganic molecules that perform vital functions in the body. For example, calcium is a major component of bones and teeth. Iron is essential for transporting oxygen in the blood. Nerves and muscles need potassium, sodium, calcium, and

FIGURE 30.6
A balanced diet usually provides all the minerals the body needs each day.

Some Important Minerals

Mineral	Major Sources	RDA
Calcium	Dairy products, shellfish, green leafy vegetables	800–1200 mg
Phosphorus	Milk, eggs, meat, poultry, fish, beans, whole grains	800 mg
Magnesium	Dairy products, whole grains, beans	300–350 mg
Iron	Meat, liver, shellfish, dried fruit, molasses	10–15 mg
Iodine	Shellfish, fish liver oil, iodized salt	0.15 mg

magnesium to function properly. Some important minerals are listed in *Figure 30.6*.

Your body cannot store most minerals. Therefore, minerals must be included regularly in your diet. Some minerals come from plants, which absorb the minerals from the soil. Other minerals can be obtained by eating animal products.

Water Although it is not a nutrient, water is necessary for life. Water in body tissues accounts for at least half of your total body mass. About 90 percent of plasma, the liquid part of the blood, is water. Every day your body loses 3–5 liters (L) of water through sweat, urine, and exhaled air. The water is replaced when you drink and eat. Water is also produced in the body as a by-product of cellular respiration.

Water serves many functions in the body. It transports nutrients and wastes and is necessary for many chemical reactions. Water also helps cool the body through perspiration.

CHECKPOINT 30.1

1. What are the three activities of the digestive system?
2. Compare and contrast the digestive systems of a paramecium and an arthropod.
3. **Critical Thinking** Imagine you have a friend who is trying to lose weight by eating only eggs and grapefruit. Explain to this friend what nutrients are missing from the diet, and suggest foods that might balance the diet.

Build on What You Know

4. How are enzymes involved in an animal's digestive process? *(Need to jog your memory? Review relevant concepts in Chapter 2, Section 2.3.)*

LAB ZONE Do It!

How Do You Read a Food Label?

A food label contains important information about the nutritional value of a food. You can determine a food's nutritional value if you . . .

Try This

1 Locate the nutrition label on a packaged food product. Find the serving size on the label.
2 Locate the total amount of calories, fat, cholesterol, sodium, carbohydrates, and protein in a serving.
3 Record the percentages of the total daily requirements for all nutrients, minerals, and vitamins in a serving of the product.

Analyze Your Results

1 How are the percentages of nutrients, minerals, and vitamins calculated?
2 Is the listed serving size the amount of that food that you would normally eat? If necessary, recalculate all data to reflect your usual serving size.
3 What nutrients, vitamins, and minerals might we have too little of in our diet? Why? Too much? Why?

2% REDUCED FAT MILK

Nutrition Facts
Serving Size: 1 cup (240 mL)
Servings Per Container: 8

Amount per serving

Calories 130 Calories from fat 45

	%Daily Value*
Total Fat 5g	8%
Saturated Fat 3g	15%
Cholesterol 20g	7%
Sodium 130g	5%
Total Carbohydrate 12g	4%
Dietary Fiber 0g	0%
Sugars 12g	
Protein 8g	

Vitamin A	15%	Vitamin C	4%
Calcium	30%	Iron	0%
Vitamin D	4%		

*Percent Daily Values are based on a 2000 calorie diet. Your daily values may be higher or lower depending on your calorie needs.

30.2 Human Digestive System

A round and skinny diet?

What if you decided to eat only spaghetti? In order to get enough calories, a 56-kg teenage girl would need to eat nearly 3.8 kg of pasta a day, about 36 large servings. A 61-kg boy would need to eat nearly 5 kg, about 44 servings each day. And that is without the sauce.

What you'll learn

IDEAS
• To describe the organs and structures of the human digestive tract
• To explain the processes of digestion and absorption in humans

WORDS
salivary glands, esophagus, peristalsis, stomach, small intestine, villi, large intestine, liver, gallbladder, pancreas

FROM DIGESTIVE TRACT TO BODY CELLS

Digestion is absorbing

Could you create a list of foods that contain all the nutrients your body needs in a day? Your body cannot use the nutrients in foods you eat until the food is chemically broken down into small molecules. As you learned in the previous section, digestion is the process by which foods are broken down into usable nutrients. Digestion in humans occurs in the organs of the digestive tract. The process is assisted by other organs of the human digestive system. Is digestion in humans intracellular or extracellular?

The human digestive tract (shown on page 726) consists of the mouth, pharynx, esophagus, stomach, small intestine, and large intestine. All three activities of the digestive process—mechanical digestion, chemical digestion, and absorption—occur in the human digestive tract. As you read about these organs, try to identify which activities occur at each step in the digestive process.

Mouth The first step in the human digestive process is to begin chewing food. Chewing starts the process of mechanical digestion. You may remember from Chapter 27 that different types of chewing are performed by different teeth: incisors, canines, molars, and so on. At the same time, the **salivary glands** produce saliva to begin the process of chemical digestion. Study *Figure 30.7*. Where are the salivary glands located in your mouth? The watery saliva mixes with the chewed food. Enzymes in saliva kill bacteria and begin the breakdown of starches into sugars. The food is pushed to the back of the mouth by the tongue and then swallowed.

FIGURE 30.7

What is the digestive function of each structure in the mouth?

Incisor
Bicuspid
Canine
Premolars
Molars
Uvula
Tongue
"Wisdom tooth"
Salivary glands
Opening of a salivary gland duct

FIGURE 30.8

The Human Digestive System

What structures shown in this diagram produce chemicals that aid in digestion?

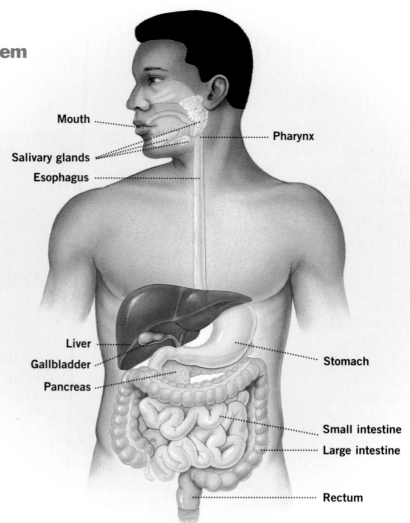

Mouth
Pharynx
Salivary glands
Esophagus
Liver
Stomach
Gallbladder
Pancreas
Small intestine
Large intestine
Rectum

Pharynx and esophagus As you swallow food, it moves through the region in the back of the throat called the pharynx (FAIR-inks). When you swallow, a small flap of tissue called the epiglottis closes the trachea at the entrance to your respiratory tract. This ensures that food enters a long muscular tube called the **esophagus** (eh-SOF-uh-gus). Food moves toward the stomach by **peristalsis,** a successive wave of smooth muscle contractions in the esophagus wall. A circular muscle at the bottom of the esophagus acts as a valve. When the muscle relaxes, the valve opens, and food enters the stomach.

Stomach Your **stomach** is a muscular sac with thick, expandable walls. Mechanical digestion occurs as the stomach walls contract strongly,

mixing and churning the food you have swallowed. Chemical digestion continues as hydrochloric acid and an enzyme called pepsin are secreted by glands in your stomach. Pepsin breaks down protein. Glands in the stomach also produce mucus. Mucus lubricates the digestive tract and coats the stomach lining to protect it from digestive fluids.

After about three hours in the stomach, food is reduced to a soft pulp called chyme (kym). Chyme is made of acids, partially digested proteins and carbohydrates, and undigested fats. A valve at the bottom of the stomach opens, allowing small amounts of chyme to pass into the small intestine.

Small intestine In the **small intestine,** digestion of carbohydrates and proteins is completed, fats are digested, and nutrients are absorbed. Your small intestine is about 2.5 centimeters (cm) wide and 7 meters (m) long. You can see fingerlike projections called villi in *Figure 30.9*. **Villi** line the internal surface of the small intestine, increasing its surface area and making absorption more efficient.

Nutrients are absorbed in the cells of the villi and passed into blood vessels and lymph vessels called lacteals. Blood vessels absorb carbohydrates and proteins. Lacteals absorb fats and fatty acids. Absorbed nutrients are carried to your body's cells by your circulatory system. Undigested material passes through a valve at the end of the small intestine to enter the large intestine.

Large intestine Your colon, or **large intestine,** is about 6 cm wide and 1.5 m long. In the large intestine, water and water-soluble vitamins are absorbed from undigested material. The water is redistributed to the rest of your body.

When most of the water has been removed, a solid waste matter, called feces (FEE-seez), remains. The feces move through the large intestine and into the rectum. Feces move out of the body through the anus.

The complete journey through the digestive tract is a long one. From mouth to anus, a bite of food must travel a distance of about 9 m. Typically 8 to 48 hours pass from the time food first enters your mouth until what remains of that food leaves your body.

LAB ZONE Do It!

How Does Peristalsis Work?

You can duplicate the way muscles move pieces of food through the esophagus to the stomach if you . . .

Try This

1 Place a marble inside one end of a 25- to 30-cm length of flexible plastic or rubber tubing.
2 With a squeezing motion of your hands, try to move the marble down and out the other end of the tube.
3 Repeat the process with two or three marbles in the tube.
4 Try it with one hand held tightly around the bottom end of the tube.

Analyze Your Results

1 What pattern of squeezing did you use to move the marble in the right direction?
2 Did including more marbles make a difference?
3 Which part of the esophagus did your closed hand at the bottom of the tube act like?

FIGURE 30.9

Villi are fingerlike projections that line the small intestine. What nutrients are absorbed by lacteals in the villi?

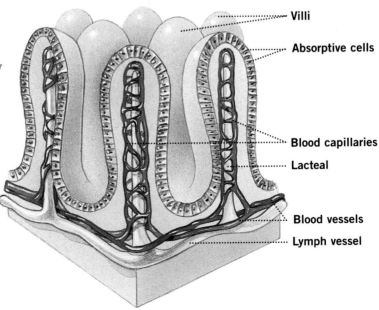

Villi
Absorptive cells
Blood capillaries
Lacteal
Blood vessels
Lymph vessel

Villi

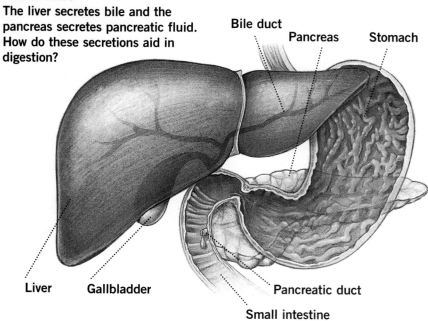

FIGURE 30.10

The liver secretes bile and the pancreas secretes pancreatic fluid. How do these secretions aid in digestion?

Bile duct
Pancreas
Stomach
Liver
Gallbladder
Pancreatic duct
Small intestine

ACCESSORY DIGESTIVE ORGANS

Digestive fluids and more

Although food does not pass through the liver, gallbladder, and pancreas, these organs play a key role in digestion. Each of these organs produces digestive fluids that are delivered to the digestive tract through ducts. In addition to aiding the digestive process, these organs perform many other vital body functions.

The **liver** is one of the largest organs of your body. In *Figures 30.8* and *30.10,* you can see the liver's size relative to other organs. This vital organ produces bile, which is a digestive fluid, and carries out more than 500 other functions. The liver is the body's main chemical factory. It processes nutrients, such as carbohydrates, fats, and proteins, into substances needed by the body.

Nutrients are also stored in the liver. For example, the liver converts glucose to glycogen for storage. The liver also stores iron and fat-soluble vitamins. Detoxification is another

important function of the liver. The liver breaks down alcohol, drugs, or toxic chemicals that enter the body.

As you can see in *Figure 30.10,* the **gallbladder** is a small saclike organ connected to the liver. The gallbladder's main function is to concentrate and store the bile produced by the liver. Bile is a yellow-green liquid containing cholesterol, pigments, bile salts, and other compounds. Bile emulsifies fats, breaking up large fat globules into many tiny droplets to make them easier to digest. The bile is released as needed through a duct to the small intestine.

The pancreas is located near the gallbladder. The **pancreas** is a gland that secretes pancreatic fluid into the small intestine. Pancreatic fluid is a mixture of digestive enzymes and sodium bicarbonate. Some cells of the pancreas also secrete hormones, chemical messengers of the endocrine system, into the blood. The pancreatic hormone called insulin controls the uptake of glucose by the cells of the body. You will learn more about the endocrine function of the pancreas in Chapter 33.

CHECKPOINT 30.2

1. Name the parts of the human digestive system, and explain what each part does.

2. Compare and contrast digestion and absorption.

3. Critical Thinking How would standing on your head while you ate a meal affect your digestive process?

Build on What You Know

4. Indigestion can occur when the stomach's contents become too acidic. Baking soda, also known as sodium bicarbonate, can be dissolved in water and taken as a remedy for indigestion. Why? (*Need to jog your memory? Revisit relevant concepts in Chapter 2, Section 2.5.*)

30.3 Health of the Digestive System

Lying down on the job

When you exercise, your metabolism speeds up. Running burns up more than ten times as much fuel as resting. Those who exercise regularly also increase their resting metabolism. In general, people who exercise often need to consume more calories than those who do not exercise regularly.

What you'll learn

IDEAS

• To analyze the overall balance between eating food and using energy
• To identify injuries and disorders of the digestive system
• To evaluate ways to maintain a healthy digestive system

WORDS

metabolism, calorie, anorexia, bulimia

ENERGY BALANCE

A balancing act

Have you ever heard someone being told that they have a high metabolism? This usually means that their bodies use the energy in food almost as fast as they eat it. Recall from Chapter 2 that **metabolism** is the combination of all the chemical processes that take place within an organism. Metabolic processes control and manage the organism's energy resources.

Metabolism is a two-way street. Some metabolic pathways store energy, and others release energy. Pathways that release energy by breaking down complex compounds into simpler ones are called catabolic pathways. Pathways that use energy to build complex molecules from simpler ones are called anabolic pathways. Together, catabolic pathways and anabolic pathways make up metabolism.

Measuring energy One unit used to measure energy is the calorie. A **calorie** is the amount of heat energy needed to raise the temperature of 1g of water by 1°C. A calorie represents a very small amount of energy, so nutritionists use a unit called the kilocalorie (kcal) to measure energy. A kilocalorie is 1000 calories and is usually written as

Calorie with a capital C. The calories you see listed on food labels are actually Calories, or kilocalories.

To measure the energy value of a food, a small sample of the food is burned, and the amount of heat it gives off is measured with an instrument called a calorimeter. Using a calorimeter, scientists have determined the approximate energy value of fats, proteins, and carbohydrates. As you can see in the table in *Figure 30.11,* fats have more than twice the energy per unit of mass than do carbohydrates or proteins.

Many doctors and nutritionists recommend that people obtain no more than 30 percent of their energy from fats. To determine the percentage of kilocalories derived from fat in a commercial food product, check the nutritional information label. If the percentage is not shown, multiply the number of fat grams by 9. Then divide this number by the total number of

Outside Help, Inside

Bacteria—nearly enough to fill a soup can—live inside the human intestines. These bacteria aid in the process of digestion and secrete useful vitamins, including thiamine and vitamin K. The antibiotics taken to kill disease-causing germs can also kill these helpful organisms and upset the digestive system.

Approximate Energy Values	
Compound	**Energy Value (kcal/g)**
Fats	9
Carbohydrates	4
Proteins	4

FIGURE 30.11

Scientists measure the approximate energy value of compounds in food in kilocalories per gram (kcal/g).

1000
900
800
700
600
500
400
300
200
100
0

kilocalories in the food product, and multiply by 100.

Metabolic rate If a laboratory technician measured your metabolism while you were at rest, the result would be a number called the basal metabolic rate (BMR). Your BMR is equal to the number of kilocalories you use in a set amount of time just to stay alive. The BMR of a human female is about 1300 to 1500 kcal per day. A human male has a BMR of about 1600 to 1800 kcal per day. Your actual BMR depends on factors such as your age and level of fitness. Your overall metabolic rate is your BMR plus the number of kilocalories you use during your activities. If you participate in more strenuous activities, your overall metabolic rate rises.

Storing energy Your body is constantly balancing the calories you consume with the calories you use. This balance can be upset, however, by changing either the number of calories you eat or the number of calories you use for activities. The body stores extra calories first as glycogen in the liver and muscles, and then as fat. A healthy body stores enough glycogen to last approximately one day, and enough fat to last several days.

If you regularly take in more calories than you use, you will gain weight. On the other hand, if you take in fewer calories than your body uses every day, you will gradually lose weight. Deprived of food, the body starts using stored glycogen. Then the body uses stored fat. Finally, the body uses protein stored in muscles and other organs. Burning calories as you exercise can also help you lose weight. Which activities in *Figure 30.12* use the most calories? The fewest calories?

DIGESTIVE SYSTEM DISORDERS

It must be something you ate

Your digestive system constantly processes food from the environment. As a result, it is susceptible to attack by infectious organisms. Bacteria such as *Salmonella*, which grow in contaminated food, produce a poison or toxin that irritates the digestive tract. The body tries to eliminate the toxin by means of vomiting and diarrhea. Many ulcers, once thought to be caused by stress, are actually caused by a type of bacteria. Meats and fish that are eaten rare or raw may transmit parasites, such as worms or flukes. Undercooked pork can sometimes transmit a parasitic disease called trichinosis.

Hepatitis is a viral infection of the liver that can result in scarring of the liver—a condition called cirrhosis. The scar tissue prevents the liver from functioning properly. Excessive alcohol consumption can also cause cirrhosis. Severe cirrhosis can result in death.

Eating disorders are a serious health problem in the United States. A person with **anorexia** refuses to eat and may overexercise. Without treatment, a person with anorexia can literally starve to death. A person with **bulimia** eats huge amounts of food, and then vomits or takes laxatives to get rid of the food. Bulimia can result in many health problems including swollen salivary glands; kidney, liver, and pancreas problems; stomach and esophagus irritations; and tooth decay from stomach acids. Both psychological and physical treatments are needed for these disorders. If left untreated they can be life-threatening.

CARE OF YOUR DIGESTIVE SYSTEM

Watch what you put in your mouth!

You can keep your digestive system healthy by paying attention to what you put into it. There are several ways to avoid infecting your digestive tract with viruses, bacteria, and parasites. Always wash your hands before eating or preparing food. Make sure that the water you drink is from an uncontaminated source. Avoid eating spoiled or improperly cooked food. "When in doubt, throw it out."

Avoid ingesting foods or beverages that damage or irritate your digestive

system. For example, people who lack the enzyme to digest lactose (milk sugar) can prevent painful cramps by avoiding milk and other dairy products. By avoiding alcohol you can prevent digestive irritation and serious liver damage.

CHECKPOINT 30.3

1. Why does a person who is physically active need to take in more Calories than a person who is inactive?
2. What are some digestive problems? What can you do to avoid them?
3. **Critical Thinking** A meal of a large hamburger, french fries, and a milkshake can provide about 900 Calories. How many hours would you have to swim to burn the energy?

Build on What You Know

4. How is energy obtained from food? *(Need to jog your memory? Revisit relevant concepts in Chapter 4, Section 4.3.)*

LAB ZONE Think About It!

Determining How Many of Your Calories Come from Fat

Nutritionists recommend that you get no more than 30 percent of your energy from the fat you eat. Look at the milk nutrition label on page 724.

Analyzing the Diagram

1 How many Calories does one serving of milk contain? How many Calories come from fat?
2 Determine the percentage of energy obtained from fat in a serving of milk—dividing the Calories from fat by the total Calories.
3 How does the percentage of Calories obtained from fat compare with recommendations of nutritionists? How would you determine if your overall daily diet met nutritionists' standards?

FIGURE 30.13
Your body functions better when you eat healthful foods. What is the meaning of the saying "You are what you eat"?

What is the function of the digestive system?

LAB ZONE Investigate It!

Digesting Lactose

WHAT YOU WILL DO Test a product that is used to treat milk

SKILLS YOU WILL USE Analyzing, hypothesizing, observing, recording data

WHAT YOU WILL NEED Liquid milk treatment product, slides, eyedropper, whole and skim milk, water, glucose solution, glucose test strips

Background Information

All infant mammals drink milk, but adult mammals, except for humans, do not. The ability to digest lactose, or milk sugar, depends on the ability to secrete lactase, the enzyme that digests lactose. Many adults experience cramps after drinking milk. This condition is known as lactose intolerance.

Propose a Hypothesis

Propose a hypothesis to explain why adults tend to become less tolerant of lactose as they become older, and how lactose intolerance might be alleviated.

Conduct Your Experiment

1 Place several drops of the glucose solution on a microscope slide. Follow the instructions on the glucose test strip container to test the glucose content of the solution. Record your observations.

2 Design an experiment to test the other liquid—whole milk, skim milk, and water—both before and after treating them with the milk-treatment product. Do not forget to include an experimental control. In your notebook, write your predictions for the outcome of each test.

Analyze Your Data

1 What happened when you tested the untreated liquids for glucose? What happened when you tested the treated liquids?

2 What are the ingredients of the milk-treatment product? How did it change the milk? How would it help a person who is lactose intolerant?

Draw Conclusions

1 In some countries and cultures, nearly all adults are lactose intolerant. In others, such as Sweden, for instance, nearly all adults can digest lactose. Identify possible reasons for this difference and explain your reasoning.

2 Why might lactose intolerance increase with age?

3 How can lactose intolerance be alleviated?

Design a Related Experiment

Does the use of a milk treatment product change the taste of milk? Propose a hypothesis and carry out an experiment to test it, using materials from this lab.

Lab: Digesting Lactose

Objective: To investigate lactose intolerance and to test a milk treatment product

My hypothesis:

30.4 Excretion

Who drinks like a fish?
Freshwater fishes never drink water. They need to maintain an osmotic balance of salt and water roughly like that of the ocean—while living in a nearly salt-free home. Unlike the kidneys of most other vertebrates, the kidneys of freshwater fishes do not excrete salt. The fishes do not drink water but actively transport salt into their bodies through their gills.

What you'll learn

IDEAS
• To explain the functions of the excretory system
• To contrast the excretory systems of various organisms

FUNCTIONS OF EXCRETORY SYSTEMS

Get rid of it

Animals produce waste materials that must be removed. The skin and digestive system help to remove some wastes. Most animals have a specialized system to deal with nitrogen-containing wastes, which form when animals break down proteins and nucleic acids. These wastes are removed by the excretory system.

During metabolism, proteins and nucleic acids break down to form ammonia—a toxic nitrogen-containing waste. Ammonia must be quickly eliminated from the body. The process of removing nitrogen-containing wastes is called excretion.

In addition to removing wastes, the excretory system helps control homeostasis. It maintains osmotic balance and pH by either excreting or conserving salts and water.

EXCRETION IN ANIMALS

Gotta have a plan!

Excretory systems in animals have a variety of designs. Many animals that live in water, such as cnidarians, echinoderms, and some fishes and planarians, have a simple strategy for getting rid of nitrogen-containing wastes. Since ammonia dissolves easily in water, most aquatic animals simply excrete ammonia by diffusion through gills or other body surfaces into the environment. For these aquatic animals, the main function of the excretory system is aiding homeostasis.

As shown in *Figure 30.14*, flatworms have a system made of closed tubules with bulblike ends called

FIGURE 30.14
The main function of this planarian's excretory system is to maintain osmotic balance. How does this aquatic organism excrete ammonia?

Flame cell

Pore in body wall

Tubule

Tubules

FIGURE 30.15
Earthworms have long, twisted nephridia for excretion.

Opening in body cavity

Nephridium

External pore

flame cells. Flame cells filter body fluids, which enter the system of tubules and are excreted through pores in the body.

Animals that live on land cannot simply excrete ammonia by diffusion into the environment. Instead, they must convert ammonia to a less toxic substance that can be stored safely in the body until the waste can be excreted with minimal water loss. Why is this strategy important in land animals?

Birds, reptiles, land snails, and many types of insects convert ammonia to uric acid, which they excrete in semisolid or liquid form. Mammals, amphibians, and some fishes convert ammonia to urea which, along with other wastes, passes out of the body dissolved in water.

Annelids such as earthworms have excretory tubules called nephridia (singular: *nephridium*). Body fluids in

a segment enter the open end of the nephridium. As fluids move through the nephridium, salts and nutrients are reabsorbed, while wastes and excess water leave through a pore in the body wall.

Arthropods that live on land, such as the grasshopper shown in *Figure 30.16,* have an excretory system composed of Malpighian tubules. Uric acid collects in the tubules and is excreted into the stomach. It leaves the body through the anus.

Vertebrates such as humans have kidneys—excretory organs that filter urea and other wastes from the blood. In the next section, you will learn more about the function of the kidneys.

CHECKPOINT 30.4

1. What are the functions of an excretory system?

2. Compare the excretory systems of three types of organisms. How are they alike? How are they different?

3. Critical Thinking Why do different groups of animals excrete different forms of nitrogen-containing wastes?

Build on What You Know

4. What is osmosis? How does it affect excretory systems? *(Need to jog your memory? Revisit relevant concepts in Chapter 3, Section 3.5.)*

FIGURE 30.16
The excretory system of this grasshopper handles both osmotic balance and excretion of nitrogenous waste. What type of nitrogenous waste does it excrete?

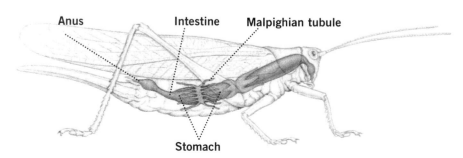

Anus   Intestine   Malpighian tubule

Stomach

30.5 Human Excretory System

A giant thirst

Would you be able to drink 170 L (about 45 gallons) of water a day? You would need that much water if your kidneys excreted all the water that they filter in a day. Fortunately, the kidneys retain 99 percent of the water that they filter. So, humans need to replace only the 1–2 L of water excreted daily as urine.

What you'll learn

IDEAS
• To describe the structure and function of the human excretory system
• To judge the importance of the kidneys to blood chemistry and human health

WORDS
kidneys, nephrons

EXCRETION IN HUMANS

Parts make a whole

Like all organisms, you must eliminate a variety of different waste materials in order to function properly. Different organ systems help in this process. Part of the digestive system moves undigested matter out of the body as solid waste. Wastes are also excreted through the skin in sweat. The human excretory system is specialized for removing most of the body's nitrogen-containing waste. The nitrogen-containing waste produced by the human body is urea. The excretory system also plays a crucial role in maintaining the homeostasis of body fluids. As you may recall from Chapter 2, homeostasis is the maintenance of a stable set of internal conditions within an organism.

The main organs of the excretory system are the **kidneys**, located at the bottom of the rib cage near the back, or dorsal, side of the body. Blood enters the kidneys from vessels that branch from the aorta, the body's largest artery. The kidneys remove wastes from the blood and process them into a yellow-colored liquid called urine. The kidneys also help control the amount of salts, water,

minerals, and vitamins in the blood, and they regulate the pH and volume of the blood. At any given time, up to 25 percent of the body's blood may be in the kidneys.

Urine produced by each kidney flows into a long thin tube called a ureter. There are two ureters, one for each kidney. Each ureter carries the urine a distance of 25 to 30 cm to a muscular bag called the urinary bladder. You can see how the ureters connect to the bladder in *Figure 30.17*.

The bladder, located in the lower pelvis, has a tube that opens to the outside of the body. This tube is called the urethra (yoo-REE-thruh). Rings of

FIGURE 30.17
The human excretory system removes the body's nitrogen-containing waste and helps maintain osmotic balance.

Aorta

Kidney
Renal artery
Renal vein

Ureter

Urinary bladder

Urethra

muscle around the junction of the bladder and urethra keep the urine in the bladder. When the bladder is full, its smooth muscles send signals to the brain. The brain then signals muscle contractions which expel urine from the bladder and out of the body through the urethra.

Three for the price of one

Each kidney is a bean-shaped organ about 10 cm long. Notice the two regions of the kidney shown in *Figure 30.18*: the cortex and the medulla. A complex network of veins, arteries, and capillaries runs through the medulla and cortex. The blood vessels transport blood to the kidneys for filtration and back to the body after filtration.

Each kidney has approximately one million functional units called nephrons (NEF-rahnz). **Nephrons** are the kidney's filters; they remove wastes from the blood. Find the parts of the nephron shown in *Figure 30.18*. Each nephron consists of a long renal tubule surrounded by capillaries. The cup-shaped end of the renal tubule, called Bowman's capsule, surrounds a clump of capillaries called the glomerulus

(glom-AYR-yoo-lus) (plural: *glomeruli*). Blood pressure forces fluids and wastes out of the blood in the glomerulus. The fluids and wastes move into Bowman's capsule and accumulate in the renal tubule, where urine forms. Urine consists mostly of water, but it also contains urea, uric acid, and salts.

The renal tubules of a kidney's nephrons empty into a system of collecting tubules. As urine passes through the collecting tubules, water is removed, making urine more concentrated. Eventually, the system of collecting tubules empties into the ureter. From the ureter, the urine can move into the bladder and out of the body through the urethra.

Each day about 180 L of fluid from your blood passes through your kidneys. This amount is enough to fill a bathtub! Not all this fluid becomes urine. Most of it is returned to the bloodstream, along with glucose, salts, vitamins, and other substances needed by your body. Your kidneys form urine and control the homeostasis of your blood by three different processes: filtration, reabsorption, and secretion.

Figure 30.19 shows a model of these three processes and where they occur in the nephron. In each nephron, the glomerulus acts as a filter. The resulting filtered solution (filtrate) passes out of the capillary membranes through Bowman's capsule and into the renal tubules. During reabsorption in the renal tubules, water and other useful substances in the filtrate are returned to the blood in the capillaries.

Some wastes move from the blood directly to the renal tubules in a process called secretion. What are some of the substances that are secreted? Secretion is an important kidney function because it maintains the pH of your blood.

FIGURE 30.18
In the kidneys, the nephrons filter the blood.

Cortex

Medulla

Capillaries

Renal artery

Kidney

Nephron

Bowman's capsule

Glomerulus

Renal tubule

Collecting tubule

Ureter

Renal vein

FIGURE 30.19

Nephron Function

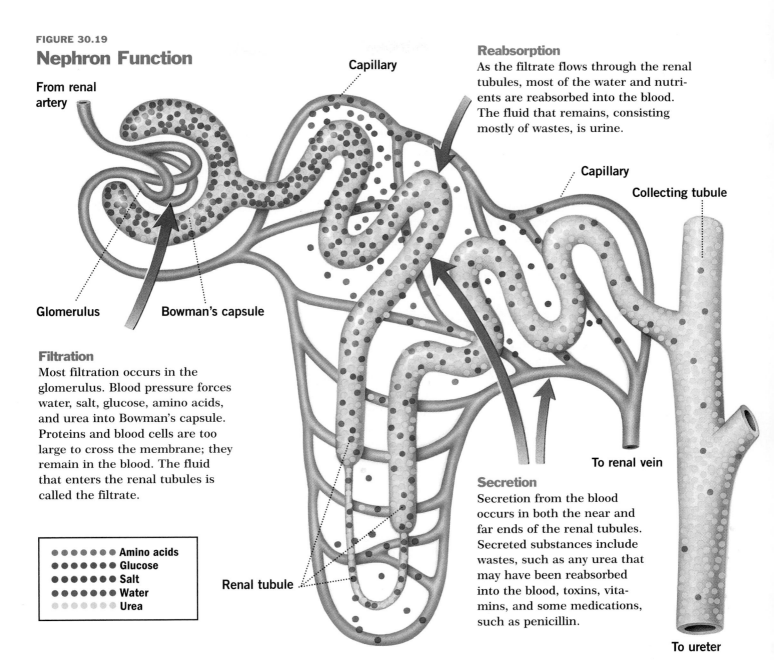

From renal artery

Capillary

Reabsorption
As the filtrate flows through the renal tubules, most of the water and nutrients are reabsorbed into the blood. The fluid that remains, consisting mostly of wastes, is urine.

Capillary

Collecting tubule

Glomerulus

Bowman's capsule

Filtration
Most filtration occurs in the glomerulus. Blood pressure forces water, salt, glucose, amino acids, and urea into Bowman's capsule. Proteins and blood cells are too large to cross the membrane; they remain in the blood. The fluid that enters the renal tubules is called the filtrate.

- Amino acids
- Glucose
- Salt
- Water
- Urea

Renal tubule

Secretion
Secretion from the blood occurs in both the near and far ends of the renal tubules. Secreted substances include wastes, such as any urea that may have been reabsorbed into the blood, toxins, vitamins, and some medications, such as penicillin.

To renal vein

To ureter

HEALTH OF THE EXCRETORY SYSTEM

Water, water, water

Like all body systems that are connected to the outside of the body, your excretory system is susceptible to infection. The urethra is located in the genital area. The anus is a source of *E. coli* bacteria, a normal component of the feces. These bacteria can enter the urethra and infect the urinary bladder. From the bladder, the bacteria can move up the ureter and infect the kidneys. If a kidney infection is not treated promptly, the kidneys can be seriously damaged. Symptoms of problems of the excretory system include loss of bladder control, blood in the urine, excessive urination, and pain near the kidneys, conditions that require prompt medical attention.

The most important thing you can do to take care of your excretory system is to drink enough water. The whole system depends on water to carry wastes out of the body. Try to drink eight to ten glasses of water every day in addition to other

Drinking large amounts of water lightens the color of urine. After exercising or after some time without drinking water, urine will have a heavier, amber color.

FIGURE 30.20

For people with damaged kidneys, dialysis machines perform the functions of the kidneys. What are those functions?

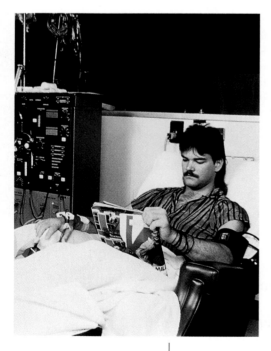

beverages. Urinate frequently, as often as needed. It is also important to avoid drugs and toxic substances, as these substances can damage the kidneys.

Personal hygiene plays an important role in preventing bladder and kidney infections. Keep the area around the urethra clean with regular baths or showers. Be aware of the symptoms of a bladder infection so that you can seek prompt treatment if needed. These symptoms include pain or itching of the urethra, fever, and a frequent, intense need to urinate.

FRONTIERS IN BIOLOGY

Kidney help

Advances in medical technology have been a great benefit to people with kidney problems—for example, those who develop kidney stones. Kidney stones form from the crystallization of mineral salts and uric acid salts in the urine. These stones can block the passage of urine, causing extreme pain in the kidneys and urinary tract. Until recently, the only treatment was surgery. Today ultrasound waves are used to crush kidney stones while they are in the kidneys. The fragments then flush out in the urine.

A more serious condition exists when the kidneys fail to function. The most common causes of kidney failure are long-term diabetes, infections, physical injuries, and chemical poisoning. Kidney failure causes toxic materials in the body to build up to lethal levels.

One solution for kidney failure is dialysis. During dialysis, the patient is connected to a dialysis machine, which removes wastes from the patient's blood in a manner similar to the way that the kidneys remove wastes from the blood. The development of the dialysis machine was possible only after extensive research showed how the kidneys function.

People with kidney failure must undergo dialysis every week for the rest of their lives unless they receive a kidney transplant. Because a human can live a normal life with one kidney, it is possible for a person to donate a kidney to someone with kidney failure. Kidneys were the first organs to be successfully transplanted, in 1954 by Nobel Prize winner Dr. Joseph Murray.

CHECKPOINT 30.5

1. Compare the structures and functions of each part of the excretory system.
2. Describe how the kidneys form urine and control the blood's volume.
3. **Critical Thinking** Thousands of people need kidney transplants, but there are never enough donor kidneys available. What criteria should be used to decide who gets a kidney transplant? Explain your reasoning.

Build on What You Know

4. What kind of transport must be involved between a nephron tubule and its environment? Explain your answer. **(Need to jog your memory? Revisit relevant concepts in Chapter 3, Section 3.5.)**

What does the excretory system do?

Chapter 30 Review

 THE BIG IDEA! 30.1–30.3 The digestive system breaks down food into usable compounds.
30.4–30.5 The excretory system eliminates nitrogen-containing wastes and helps maintain homeostasis.

Sum It Up

Use the following summary to review the main concepts in this chapter.

30.1 Digestion

- During digestion, nutrients are extracted from food and absorbed by cells. Complex multicellular animals have a tubelike digestive tract with two openings—one for food and one for waste.
- A healthy diet includes appropriate amounts of different nutrients.

30.2 Human Digestive System

- In humans, mechanical digestion occurs in the mouth and stomach. Chemical digestion occurs in the mouth, stomach, and small intestine. Nutrients are absorbed into the circulatory system from the small intestine.
- In the large intestine, water and water-soluble vitamins are reabsorbed; solid undigested waste matter is expelled through the anus.

30.3 Health of the Digestive System

- The energy available in food is measured in calories. Per gram, fats contain twice the calories of proteins or carbohydrates.
- Exercise increases the body's metabolic rate and helps burn excess calories.

- The digestive tract is subject to attack by infectious organisms.
- Eating disorders can be life-threatening.

30.4 Excretion

- Excretion removes nitrogen-containing wastes and maintains osmotic balance.
- Many aquatic animals excrete water-soluble ammonia through gills or pores in the body wall. Terrestrial animals convert toxic ammonia into uric acid or urea before excretion.
- Annelids, arthropods, and vertebrates have tubular structures for filtering body fluids.

30.5 Human Excretory System

- The kidneys filter wastes from blood and produce urine, which flows through ureters to the urinary bladder. Contractions of the bladder expel urine through the urethra.
- Nephrons perform three functions—filtration of wastes from blood, reabsorption of water and nutrients back into the blood, and secretion of wastes from blood into the urine.

Use Terms and Concepts

Use each of the following words or terms in a complete sentence. If you need to review a meaning, turn to the page indicated.

digestive system (p. 720)
nutrient (p. 720)
salivary glands (p. 725)
esophagus (p. 726)
peristalsis (p. 726)
stomach (p. 726)

small intestine (p. 726)
villi (p. 727)
large intestine (p. 727)
liver (p. 728)
gallbladder (p. 728)
pancreas (p. 728)

metabolism (p. 729)
calorie (p.729)
anorexia (p. 731)
bulimia (p. 731)
kidneys (p. 735)
nephrons (p. 736)

Use Your Word Power

MATCHING **Write the term from the list of key terms that best matches each of the phrases below.**

1. Fingerlike projections in the small intestine that increase the surface area for absorption.

2. All the chemical reactions that take place in an organism.

3. Substances released from food during digestion, which are needed by the body for growth, repair, and maintenance.

4. The organ that produces bile, converts glucose into glycogen, and breaks down toxic chemicals.

5. A wave of smooth muscle contractions in the esophagus.

6. The organ that secretes digestive enzymes and hormones such as insulin.

7. The structures in kidneys that remove wastes from blood.

8. A unit of measurement of heat energy.

9. A type of eating disorder that is characterized by a refusal to eat and a tendency to over-exercise.

Multiple Choice Choose the letter of the word or phrase that best completes each statement.

10. Bulimia can cause (a) kidney stones; (b) incontinence; (c) ulcers; (d) tooth decay.

11. Fats are digested in the (a) stomach; (b) small intestine; (c) large intestine; (d) gallbladder.

12. Nitrogen-containing wastes are excreted in the (a) urinary bladder; (b) gallbladder; (c) kidneys; (d) large intestine.

13. Bile is stored in the (a) gallbladder; (b) liver; (c) pancreas; (d) small intestine.

14. Salivary glands produce enzymes that digest (a) sugar; (b) protein; (c) fat; (d) starch.

Show What You Know

15. How do organs in the digestive and excretory systems maintain a balance of water?

16. What role do vitamins and minerals play in metabolism?

17. How do scientists know that low-fat milk contains 130 Calories per cup?

18. What happens over time if a person consumes fewer Calories than he or she expends on a daily basis?

19. What is the advantage of extracellular digestion for a multicellular organism?

20. Your digestive tract is about 9 m long. Why is it advantageous that most of that length, 8.5 m, is occupied by intestines?

21. What is the source of the nitrogenous wastes that the kidneys excrete?

22. How do the glomerulus and Bowman's capsule in a nephron work together?

23. **Make a Concept Map** Create a concept map that shows the role digestive enzymes play in the digestive system.

Take It Further

24. Developing a Hypothesis How would prolonged chewing affect the digestion of carbohydrates and proteins?

25. Applying Concepts Some people consume quantities of vitamins that far exceed the recommended daily allowances. Explain why consuming large amounts of vitamin A on a daily basis would be riskier than consuming large quantities of vitamin C.

26. Developing a Hypothesis Explain why cirrhosis of the liver can be life-threatening.

27. Applying Concepts Are stomach muscles smooth or striated? Explain your answer.

28. Analyzing Data Over-the-counter products for indigestion often contain carbonate salts. What function does sodium bicarbonate perform in pancreatic fluid, which is emptied into the small intestine just below the stomach?

29. Making an Analogy In what ways is an automatic car wash similar to a digestive tract?

30. Designing an Experiment During carbohydrate digestion, water breaks some bonds between the glucose units in starch. Design an experiment to determine if digestive enzymes are necessary for the reaction between water and starch. What materials would you need?

31. Interpreting a Graph A vampire bat feeds at night on the blood of large mammals as they sleep. The graph below shows how the bat's excretory system adjusts to the sudden intake of a protein-rich liquid. What happens to the concentration and flow of urine when the bat begins to eat? Describe the concentration and flow of urine three hours after eating.

32. Analyzing Data The following table shows the number of Calories in certain foods and the amount of time it would take to burn off those Calories while resting, walking, or jogging. How does walking compare to resting in terms of burning Calories? How does walking compare to jogging?

Time Needed to Burn Calories			
Food (kcal)	Resting	Walking	Jogging
Glass of orange juice (110)	85 min	22 min	11 min
Pizza slice (185)	142 min	37 min	18.5 min
Small steak (330)	254 min	66 min	33 min
Cup of shelled peanuts (840)	646 min	168 min	84 min

Consider the Issues

33. Organic Foods Because all foods contain carbon-based compounds, all foods are organic, strictly speaking. However, in the marketplace the label "organic" is often used for foods grown without pesticides and processed without preservatives. Have you purchased foods that were labeled organic? Did they taste or look different from other fruits and vegetables? Did you have to pay more?

Make New Connections

34. Biology and Art Design your own version of the USDA food pyramid, shown on page 722. Use the nutrients that your body needs—carbohydrates, proteins, fats, vitamins, minerals—as categories for your illustration.

35. Biology and Mathematics Design a menu for a family of four for three days that provides a balanced diet. Make a list of all the menu items and estimate their costs. Compare your estimates against supermarket prices.

FAST-FORWARD TO CHAPTER 31

The circulatory system transports the nutrients extracted from the digestive system to all the cells in the body. The respiratory system supplies the oxygen needed for metabolism. You will learn more about these systems in Chapter 31.

Respiratory and Circulatory Systems

bioSURF

You can find out more about the respiratory and circulatory systems by exploring the following Internet address:

http://body_systems.biosurf.com

In this chapter . . .

FEATURES

Everyday Biology
• Something He Swallowed?
• Ah-choo!

In the Community
Breaths of Life

 Issues in Biology
Effects of Smoking

LAB ZONES

Discover It!
• Measuring Your Breathing

Do It!
• What Happens When You Exhale?
• Examining the Effect of Exercise on Heart Rate

Think About It!
• Relating Blood Pressure to Health

Investigate It!
• Measuring Lung Capacity

a breath

taking feat

@t the **1996 Summer Olympics in Atlanta, Georgia, swimmer Amy Van Dyken of the United States won four gold medals—an accomplishment that no other female athlete has ever achieved at a single Olympics. Amy's accomplishments are particularly remarkable because she has suffered from a severe case of asthma since childhood.**

The strenuous training that athletes endure usually requires optimal respiratory and circulatory capacity. For Amy, however, maximum respiratory capacity is far less than average. As she says, "On a good day, my large airways are only 65 percent of normal. On a bad day, I'm at about 30 percent."

Amy Van Dyken's determination and hard work have helped her to excel in spite of all the obstacles. In high school, for example, her teammates did not want to include her on their relay swim team because they thought she was not capable. But Amy persevered. As she phrases it, "For all the kids out there who are struggling, . . . I hope I am an inspiration. If they love it and just keep plugging away at it, something good will come out of it." It certainly did for Amy. She left everyone breathless.

Discover It!

Measuring Your Breathing

You need a watch or clock with a second hand

1. On three separate occasions, hold your breath for as long as you comfortably can and measure your time.
2. Calculate your average time and record it on a chart with the average times of your classmates. Organize and graph your data. Find the class average.

Most people can hold their breath for just under a minute. How long could you hold your breath? Your time gives you an idea of how long you could stay underwater without breathing equipment.

WRITE ABOUT IT!

Write a fictional story about the experiences of a character who can stay underwater indefinitely.

31.1 Respiratory Systems

What you'll learn

IDEAS
- To compare respiratory systems in animals
- To identify the parts of the human respiratory system

WORDS
respiration, alveoli

Amphibians do it all!
Some animals exchange gases through skin, and others through gills or lungs. Some adult amphibians exchange gases using all three organs—skin, gills, and lungs. Others, like this red-eyed tree frog, breathe through gills as young aquatic animals, through lungs as adults, and through skin during both youth and adulthood.

GAS EXCHANGE IN ANIMALS

As they live and breathe

All living organisms depend on cellular respiration for the energy to survive. You may recall from Chapter 4 that during cellular respiration food molecules are broken down to make ATP. The most efficient form of cellular respiration uses oxygen (O_2). Animals must obtain O_2 from the environment. Cellular respiration produces carbon dioxide (CO_2), which is expelled into the environment. The gas exchange of O_2 and CO_2 between animals and their environment is vital for cellular respiration.

Gas exchange takes place in the respiratory system of an animal. The respiratory system provides surfaces where O_2 and CO_2 diffuse across cell membranes. Respiratory system tissues are moist, because O_2 and CO_2 must be dissolved in water before they can efficiently diffuse across cell membranes.

Different types of respiratory systems are adaptations that allow animals to live in different habitats. Terrestrial animals must obtain O_2 from air. Aquatic animals must use the O_2 dissolved in water. The size of an animal can influence the size of its respiratory sytem. In general, larger organisms require more gas exchange to support a greater amount of cellular respiration. Therefore, the respiratory systems of larger animals have greater surface areas.

Some animals that are relatively small obtain O_2 by direct diffusion through the skin. This method provides enough O_2 for all life processes. For example, O_2 can dissolve directly into the moist secretions on an earthworm's skin. In order for its skin to stay moist, an earthworm must live in a damp habitat.

Fishes and some amphibians have gills to absorb O_2 from water. Gills are specialized extensions of folded skin.

FIGURE 31.1
How does the recycling of oxygen and carbon dioxide in the environment relate to cellular respiration?

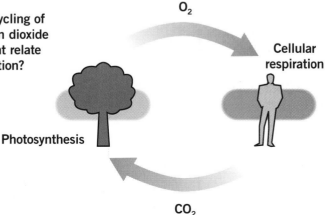

O₂

Cellular respiration

Photosynthesis

CO₂

The greater surface area of gills can provide enough O_2 for larger animals. Maintaining a moist surface is not a problem for aquatic animals.

Animals that live in dry environments do not absorb O_2 directly through their skin. These animals have internal respiratory systems. Insects have a system of tubes called tracheae through which air passes. The O_2 dissolves in the moist lining of these respiratory tubes and then diffuses into the insect's cells.

Most terrestrial vertebrates have respiratory systems that include lungs. Lungs are spongelike organs where gas exchange takes place. Mammals have millions of moist air sacs in lungs. In an adult male human, the surface area for gas exchange is about 70 to 80 square meters (m^2)—about one third the area of a tennis court! How do you think this increased surface area affects O_2 diffusion?

THE HUMAN RESPIRATORY SYSTEM

Full of hot air

Take a deep breath and let it out. When you breathe, you exchange gases with the environment. When you breathe in, or inhale, you absorb oxygen-rich air. When you breathe out, or exhale, the air you release into the environment contains CO_2. Your respiratory system brings O_2 from the air to the blood and releases CO_2 from the blood to the air.

Take another breath and let it out. Sometimes you can control your breathing. However, you probably cannot hold a breath for very long. In a short time, CO_2 begins to build up in your blood, and your body's control mechanisms cause you to start breathing again.

Respiration is the process by which a body obtains and uses O_2 and eliminates CO_2. Breathing is the

FIGURE 31.2

Gas Exchange Between Animals and the Environment

Earthworm
In earthworms, gases diffuse through moist skin.

- Cross section of respiratory surface (skin)
- Capillaries

CO_2
O_2

Insect
Insects have a network of tiny tubes, called tracheae, that weave throughout body cells.

- Body surface
- Respiratory surface (tracheal tubes)
- Body cells

O_2
CO_2

Fish
Most aquatic animals, such as fishes, exchange gases through respiratory organs called gills.

- Body surface
- Respiratory surface (gill)
- Capillaries

CO_2
O_2

Mammal
The internal lungs of mammals contain millions of air sacs where gases are exchanged.

- Body surface
- Respiratory surface (lung)
- Capillary

CO_2
O_2

FIGURE 31.3
The left lung is slightly smaller and has fewer sections, or lobes, than the right lung.

Right   Left

Something He Swallowed?

Exhaled air rushes through the voice box to produce sound. The voice box is supported by cartilage that meets in a ridge in the throat. This ridge, called the Adam's apple, is usually larger in men than in women.

mechanical part of respiration. Respiration is both a chemical and a mechanical process.

The complete process of respiration occurs on three levels: cellular, internal, and external. Cellular respiration is the process by which cells get energy from the oxidation of glucose. Internal respiration is the exchange of O_2 and CO_2 between the blood in your

capillaries and your body cells. The circulatory system carries out internal respiration. External respiration exchanges O_2 and CO_2 between the blood in the capillaries and the air. External respiration is made possible by the respiratory system. The human respiratory system consists of the lungs and the passageways that enable air to reach the lungs.

Your nose is the primary passageway by which air enters your body. Air can also enter and exit through your mouth. The air you breathe is filtered, cleaned, warmed, and moistened as it moves through the air passages that lead to your lungs. If air entering your body was not processed in these ways, the air could damage or carry diseases to lung tissue.

Air then passes through a series of tubes. The tubes of the respiratory system have similar structures and linings. Most respiratory tubes are surrounded by C-shaped cartilage structures that keep the tubes firm and open. Cilia and a moist tissue called the mucous membrane line the nasal cavity and other respiratory tubes. Mucus traps small particles of dust and bacteria. Cilia move the mucus and its trapped particles to the throat to be swallowed. Mucus-coated particles are destroyed by digestive juices in the stomach.

The first tube that air enters is the pharynx (FAH-rinks). The pharynx branches into the esophagus, a tube that leads to the stomach, and the larynx (LAYR–inks). A flap of tissue called the epiglottis covers and protects the larynx when you swallow. This prevents food from entering your respiratory system.

The larynx leads to the trachea (TRAY-kee-uh), the main passageway to the lungs. The trachea divides into two branches, the bronchi. Bronchi (singular: *bronchus*) are respiratory tubes that lead to the lungs. As you

LAB ZONE Do It!

What Happens When You Exhale?

You can observe what happens when you exhale if you . . .

Try This

1 Pour some limewater into a clear glass container.
2 Exhale through a straw into the limewater.
3 Observe and record what happens.

Analyze Your Results

1 What happened to the limewater?
2 What gas is causing this change in the limewater?
3 Why do you think this is happening?
4 Compare what is happening to the limewater with what happens when you exhale into the surrounding air.

FIGURE 31.4

The Human Respiratory System

Nasal cavity
Air passing over the mucous membrane of the nasal cavity is moistened, warmed, and filtered.

Pharynx
The pharynx, or throat, is located where passages from the nose and mouth come together.

Epiglottis
The epiglottis is a flap of elastic tissue that forms a lid over the opening to the trachea.

Larynx
The larynx, or voice box, is located between the pharynx and the trachea. It contains two ligaments—the vocal cords—that produce sound when air moves through them.

Lungs
If one lobe is injured or diseased, the other lobes may be able to function normally.

Bronchiole
Inside the lungs, the bronchi branch into smaller tubes called the bronchioles.

Alveoli
At the ends of the bronchioles are bunches of alveoli, air sacs, arranged like grapes on a stem.

Trachea
From the larynx, air enters the trachea, or windpipe, which leads toward the lungs.

Bronchi
The trachea divides into two tubes called bronchi.

---

can see in *Figure 31.3,* the lungs surround the heart and fill most of the chest cavity within the rib cage. The lungs are divided into sections called lobes.

In the lungs, bronchi branch into smaller and smaller tubes called bronchioles. The bronchioles end in tiny air sacs called **alveoli** (al-VEE-oh-lie) (singular: *alveolus*). Most of the gas exchange occurring between the circulatory and respiratory systems takes place in the alveoli.

CHECKPOINT 31.1

1. What gases are exchanged in animal respiratory and circulatory systems?

2. What are the structures of the human respiratory system?

3. Critical Thinking Compare three systems for gas exchange in animals.

Build on What You Know

4. Compare gas exchange in animals and in plants. *(Need to jog your memory? Revisit relevant concepts in Chapter 18, Section 18.1.)*

31.2 Every Breath You Take

Blowing up a storm

Like a person inflating a balloon, a musician who plays a wind instrument that makes a sustained sound needs to exhale a large steady flow of air into the instrument. To do this, people playing instruments such as clarinets, saxophones, tubas, or trumpets often use circular breathing. This technique involves inhaling air through the nose while blowing it out through the mouth.

PROCESS OF BREATHING

Good air in, bad air out

Place your hands on your ribs and take a deep breath. Can you feel your rib cage expand? Your lungs do not have muscles. The work of breathing is done by the diaphragm (DY-uh-fram) and the intercostal muscles, the muscles between the ribs. The **diaphragm** is a sheet of muscle below the lungs that separates the chest cavity from the abdomen. *Figure 31.5* illustrates how the position of the diaphragm changes as you breathe.

An adult's lungs can hold up to 6 L of air. During normal, quiet breathing, only about 0.5 L of air is exchanged with each breath. However, up to 5 L of air can be exchanged with one breath during strenuous exercise. At least 1 L of air always remains in the lungs. This reserve of air keeps the lungs partially inflated at all times. The amount of air you normally inhale and exhale is called tidal volume. The largest volume of air that can be inhaled and exhaled is called the vital capacity of the lungs. Trained athletes, such as long-distance runners, have a large vital capacity.

FIGURE 31.5

You breathe by changing the air pressure in your lungs in relation to the atmospheric pressure. With inhalation, your diaphragm and intercostal muscles contract, expanding the chest cavity. The larger chest cavity decreases the air pressure in your lungs so that it is lower than the atmospheric pressure. Air then rushes into the lungs. What must happen with exhalation?

Ribs

Diaphragm

Inhalation
The diaphragm contracts and moves down.

Exhalation
The diaphragm relaxes and moves up.

Most people take 12 to 15 breaths per minute when they are at rest. You can consciously accelerate or slow your breathing for a short period. Most of the time, however, breathing is controlled automatically. The depth and rate of breathing are affected by several factors including exercise and stress. The nervous system basically adjusts breathing rate according to CO_2 levels. Only when O_2 levels are severely depressed do a few specialized sensors pick up O_2 deficiency.

Normally your breathing rate is regulated by the amount of CO_2 in your blood. The CO_2 dissolves in the blood, forming carbonic acid (H_2CO_3). Carbonic acid then breaks down into bicarbonate (HCO_3^-) and hydrogen ions (H^+). As you learned in Chapter 2, when the concentration of hydrogen ions in a solution increases, the pH drops. Blood that is high in CO_2 has a lower pH than blood that is low in CO_2.

Body sensors monitor blood pH. If the sensors detect a drop in the blood pH, they send nerve signals to the breathing center in the brain. The breathing center sends signals to the diaphragm and intercostal muscles, triggering deeper breathing. As more CO_2 is exhaled, CO_2 in the blood decreases, and the pH returns to normal.

GAS EXCHANGE IN THE LUNGS

A little give and take

As occurs in all other animals, gases are exchanged within the human body by diffusion. In Chapter 3 you learned that, when diffusing, substances move down a concentration gradient from an area of high concentration to an area of low concentration.

In the alveoli, O_2 is more concentrated than in the surrounding capillaries. The O_2 diffuses from the air across the cell membranes of the

 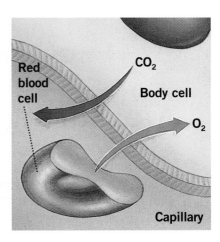

alveoli to the blood in the capillaries, as shown in *Figure 31.6*. In contrast, CO_2 is more concentrated in the capillaries of the lungs than it is in the alveoli. Therefore, CO_2 diffuses out of the capillaries into the alveoli, where it can be exhaled by the lungs. Body cells use O_2 and produce CO_2 during respiration. O_2 diffuses from the capillaries into body cells, and CO_2 diffuses out of body cells into the capillaries.

Most of the O_2 needed by the body is bound to a protein in red blood cells called hemoglobin. Hemoglobin is found in most animals and in some protists. You will learn more about hemoglobin later in this chapter.

FIGURE 31.6
In the lungs (left), gas exchange occurs by diffusion across the membrane of an alveolus and a capillary. What is happening to the oxygen and carbon dioxide in the body cell (right)?

CHECKPOINT 31.2

1. Describe the mechanisms that control breathing.
2. Compare the diffusion of oxygen and carbon dioxide in alveoli and in body cells.
3. **Critical Thinking** A person who takes many deep, rapid breaths may feel dizzy. What has happened to the balance of oxygen and carbon dioxide in this person's blood?

Build on What You Know

4. What is a concentration gradient? How do concentration gradients affect diffusion? *(Need to jog your memory? Revisit relevant concepts in Chapter 3, Section 3.5.)*

Measuring Lung Capacity

WHAT YOU WILL DO Measure your tidal volume, vital capacity, and total lung capacity

SKILLS YOU WILL USE Observing, recording data, measuring, calculating, designing an experiment

WHAT YOU WILL NEED Round balloon, metric tape measure

Propose a Hypothesis
Can lung capacity be measured using simple tools? Propose a hypothesis stating your position on this question.

Conduct Your Experiment
Caution: Do not share balloons. You should have your own balloon for this activity.
1 Stretch the balloon by blowing it up several times.
2 Inhale normally through your nose, then exhale normally through your mouth into the deflated balloon. The air you just exhaled is called your tidal volume. Hold the balloon closed with your index finger and thumb.

3 Have a partner fit the tape measure around the widest part of the balloon, as shown in the photograph above. Record the circumference of the balloon in centimeters (cm).
4 Repeat steps 2 and 3 four times. Calculate the average circumference of the balloon. Calculate the average volume of the balloon using the following formula: Volume = $\frac{1}{6}$ x $\frac{1}{\pi^2}$ x C^3 (C = average circumference). The volume is in cubic centimeters, or cm³. (One cm³ is equal to one mL.) Record the volume. This is your tidal volume.
5 Repeat steps 2–4, this time inhaling as deeply as you can through your nose and exhaling the air into the balloon. Record the volume. This is your vital capacity.

Analyze Your Data
1 What percentage of your vital capacity is your tidal volume?
2 Even after you exhale deeply, some air remains in your lungs. This air is called the residual volume. The average residual volume for females is 1000 mL and for males is 1200 mL. Calculate your total lung capacity by adding the residual volume to your vital capacity. What is your total lung capacity?

Draw Conclusions
1 Why is your vital capacity much larger than your tidal volume?
2 Would an animal that had no residual volume have an evolutionary advantage?

Design a Related Experiment
Propose a hypothesis about a smoker's vital capacity compared with that of a non-smoker. Design an experiment to test your hypothesis.

Lab: Measuring Lung Capacity

Objective: To measure and calculate tidal volume, vital capacity, and total lung capacity

31.3 Health of the Respiratory System

Morgan's lifesaving mask
In 1914, African American inventor Garrett Morgan patented a gas mask. In 1916, this safety mask became a life-saver. Morgan and his brother, wearing the new devices, rescued more than 20 workers trapped by an explosion inside a tunnel filled with poisonous gases near Cleveland, Ohio.

What you'll learn

IDEAS
• To explain how viruses, bacteria, and fungi can affect the respiratory system
• To show ways to protect the respiratory system

RESPIRATORY DISORDERS

Trouble in the airways

Your respiratory system is constantly exposed to substances and organisms in air. Four disorders that affect the respiratory system are the cold, pneumonia, bronchitis, and asthma.

Colds Chances are you have had at least one cold. A cold is a disease caused by a virus. There are many different viruses that can cause a cold.

Viruses that cause colds can affect any part of your respiratory system, but most often they first attack nasal mucous membranes. When this happens, white blood cells respond by producing a chemical called histamine. Histamine causes blood vessels to expand, resulting in swollen respiratory tissues that make breathing difficult. Histamine also causes eyes to tear and nasal passages to secrete more mucus. Medications can relieve cold symptoms, but they cannot destroy cold-causing viruses.

Pneumonia Pneumonia is a disease that causes inflammation of the alveoli. Like a cold, pneumonia can be caused by viruses, but it can also be caused by bacteria, fungi, and chemical agents. The body responds to these agents and organisms by accumulating fluid and debris in the alveoli. The fluid interferes with gas exchange, resulting in less oxygen entering the blood. As a result, a person with pneumonia feels weak and tired. To help reduce symptoms, people with pneumonia are often given oxygen. If the pneumonia is caused by bacteria or fungi, the patient may be treated with antibiotics.

Bronchitis Bronchitis is an inflammation of the membranes of the bronchial tubes. People may develop bronchitis from bacteria or from the viruses that cause colds or flu. Like a cold, bronchitis results in an increased production of mucus that blocks the airways, making breathing difficult. As a result, a person with bronchitis feels very tired and weak. In addition, a

EVERYDAY BIOLOGY

Ah-choo!
A single sneeze shoots out a million droplets of particle-laden fluid at more than 161 kilometers per hour. In less than a second, most of the water evaporates; the tiny packets of viruses and bacteria can float in the air for weeks.

FIGURE 31.7
By sneezing, a person with a cold clears excess mucus from the nasal passages.

FIGURE 31.8
To quickly open the bronchial tubes of a person with an asthma attack, medication can be delivered directly to the bronchi by inhalation.

person with bronchitis coughs frequently to clear the bronchial tubes of mucus. The symptoms of bronchitis can be treated with cough syrup and cold medications. Antibiotics may be used to treat bacterial bronchitis.

Asthma A person with an asthma attack has difficulty breathing because their bronchial tubes are narrowed. Asthma results from a sudden spasm of the bronchial tubes or from swelling of their mucous membranes. People with asthma may wheeze, trying to move air through the narrowed bronchial tubes. Treatment for an asthma attack involves using drugs that relax the bronchial tubes, increasing their openings.

Doctors do not know what causes asthma. However, many doctors think asthma is a type of allergic reaction. Attacks often seem associated with emotional and physical stress, with fatigue, and with hormonal factors.

Many harmful substances and organisms are present in the air.

Measures that can help to keep your respiratory system healthy are illustrated in *Figure 31.9.*

ISSUES IN BIOLOGY
Effects of smoking

Health researchers estimate that as many as 30 percent of Americans smoke. These people place themselves and others at risk for diseases associated with smoking.

Tobacco smoke contains harmful substances, such as cyanide, cancer-causing tar, and carbon monoxide (CO). When CO is inhaled, it binds with hemoglobin, preventing the hemoglobin from carrying oxygen. Tobacco also contains nicotine, an addictive drug that stimulates the nervous system, resulting in such effects as increased heart rate and narrowed blood vessels.

Several types of cancer are associated with tobacco use. Among the most common is lung cancer. People who smoke, as well as people who use smokeless tobaccos, such as snuff and chewing tobacco, increase the likelihood of developing cancers of the mouth and throat. These cancers have

Cardiopulmonary resuscitation (CPR) is a procedure that might restore the natural functioning of a person's lungs and heart. It requires no equipment and is relatively simple to learn. Explore how CPR is taught in your community, then sign up to learn the procedure. A local hospital, American Red Cross office, fire department, or rescue squad is a good place to start. You can learn which professionals use CPR regularly and who teaches the procedure to the public. Find out if there are special methods of CPR for infants and for pets. You can learn more about CPR and the American Red Cross on the Internet at *http://body_systems.biosurf.com.*

IN THE COMMUNITY
Breaths of Life

even been detected in new tobacco users and people who have not used tobacco products for a while.

Smoking is associated with a number of respiratory problems. Chronic "smoker's cough" can develop because smoking paralyzes the cilia that line the respiratory system, making them unable to move mucus. A person must cough to clear mucus from the respiratory system. Eventually, smoking destroys the cilia, increasing the smoker's risk of respiratory infections.

Another respiratory ailment associated with smoking is emphysema. Emphysema is a lung disease that is often linked to smoking, although long-term exposure to specific air pollutants can also cause emphysema. In this disease, the walls of the alveoli lose their elasticity and stay filled with air when the person exhales. A person with emphysema must work very hard to exhale. Eventually, damaged alveoli are replaced by connective tissue, and the area for gas exchange is reduced.

Breathing smoke from another person's cigarette can result in many of the health problems described above. For this reason, smoking has been banned in many public areas.

CHECKPOINT 31.3

1. How can viruses, bacteria, and fungi affect your respiratory system?
2. How can you protect your respiratory system from harmful substances?
3. **Critical Thinking** Do smoking bans limit smokers' rights? Explain.

Build on What You Know

4. Compare and contrast carbon monoxide and carbon dioxide. *(Need to jog your memory? Revisit relevant concepts in Chapter 2, Section 2.2.)*

FIGURE 31.9
Caring for Your Breath

You can help to keep your respiratory system healthy by doing the following:

Limit your exposure to air particulates by using air purifiers. Wear a face mask when working on projects that release dust or other irritating particulates.

Do not smoke and, when possible, avoid environments in which people are smoking.

Avoid direct or close contact with people who have a cold, the flu, pneumonia, or some other infectious disease of the respiratory system.

Exercise regularly. This will increase your lung capacity, allowing your lungs to work more efficiently.

What vital processes occur in the respiratory system?

31.4 Circulatory Systems

What you'll learn

IDEAS
• To compare open and closed circulatory systems
• To describe the structure and function of the human circulatory system

WORDS
heart, blood, blood vessels

Can you trust your heart?
In one day, your heart can pump as much as 43,000 L of blood. That much blood has a total weight of 21,844 kg—nearly seven times the weight of a bull elephant. Quite a feat for an organ the size of a fist! When diseased, the heart may not be able to handle this workload—and, in serious cases, open-heart surgery (right) may be the only answer.

INTERNAL TRANSPORT IN ANIMALS

System on the move

You now know that an animal obtains nutrients through the digestive system, and oxygen (O_2) through the respiratory system. Most animals have a circulatory system for transporting O_2, nutrients, and other essential compounds to all cells. At the same time, a circulatory system transports carbon dioxide (CO_2) and other wastes away from cells for elimination from the body. The circulatory system also helps to maintain homeostasis of body cells.

The circulatory system has three main parts. The **heart** is the main

pump of the circulatory system. **Blood** is a liquid tissue containing blood cells in suspension. **Blood vessels** are the tubes through which blood flows to and from different parts of an animal.

In some animals such as cnidarians, a specialized circulatory system is not necessary. The exchange of essential materials and wastes occurs by diffusion between the main body cavity and the other cells of the animal. In many animals, diffusion would not be an efficient method for exchange of essential materials and wastes. These animals have open or closed circulatory systems.

In an open circulatory system, the heart pumps blood into open-ended blood vessels. The heart pumps blood out of the vessels to the body tissues.

FIGURE 31.10
What are the differences between the open circulatory system of a grasshopper and the closed system of a fish?

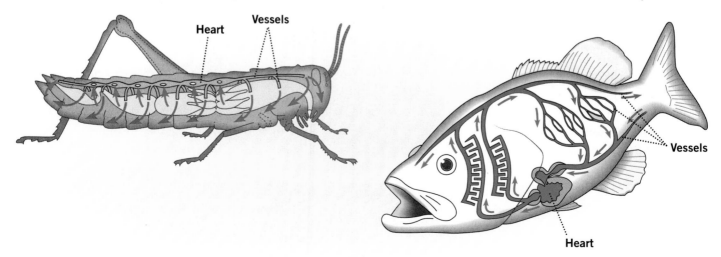

Heart · Vessels

Vessels

Heart

The motion of skeletal muscles moves blood through the body. When the heart relaxes, blood returns through pores in the heart. Most arthropods and mollusks have an open circulatory system.

In a closed circulatory system, the heart pumps blood only through blood vessels, which have extensive branches that carry blood to all body tissues and return blood to the heart. Earthworms, squids, and vertebrates have a closed circulatory system. You can compare the open and closed circulatory systems shown in *Figure 31.10*.

What kind of circulatory system do you have? Humans, like all vertebrates, have a closed circulatory system. Within the human body, blood travels in two paths or circuits: the pulmonary circuit and the systemic circuit.

The pulmonary circuit is a short loop that carries blood between your heart and lungs. In the lungs, the blood absorbs O_2 and releases CO_2. The oxygenated blood returns to the heart and is pumped to the systemic circuit, which carries the oxygenated blood to all other body cells. The blood releases O_2 to the cells and picks up CO_2 and other wastes. The deoxygenated blood is returned to the heart, where it again enters the pulmonary circuit to be oxygenated. The path of blood in each pulmonary circuit is shown in *Figure 31.11*.

In addition to the circulatory system, you have a transport sytem called the lymphatic system. The lymphatic system consists of vessels and nodes and some associated organs that collect and clean the fluid around your cells. Chapter 32 provides information about this system.

FIGURE 31.11
The arrows show the path of blood through the pulmonary and systemic circuits.

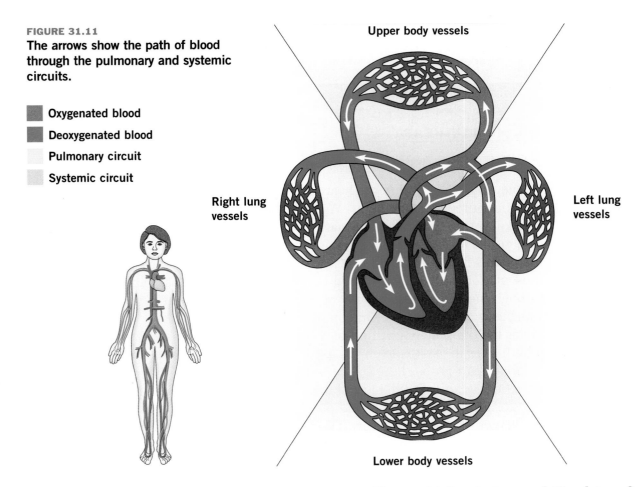

- Oxygenated blood
- Deoxygenated blood
- Pulmonary circuit
- Systemic circuit

Right lung vessels

Upper body vessels

Left lung vessels

Lower body vessels

FIGURE 31.12
Blood Flow Through the Heart

The heart is a pump that moves blood through a circulatory system. What differences do you see between the left and right sides of the heart? Trace the flow of blood through the heart.

Valves
Valves, such as the one in the photo (left), channel blood into, through, and out of the heart. Closed valves keep blood from moving backward.

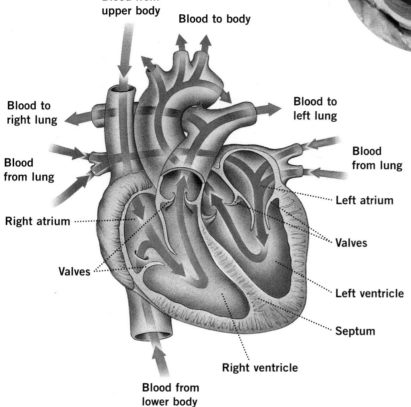

Blood from upper body

Blood to body

Blood to right lung

Blood to left lung

Blood from lung

Blood from lung

Left atrium

Right atrium

Valves

Valves

Left ventricle

Septum

Right ventricle

Blood from lower body

THE HUMAN HEART
Pumping chambers

People once thought that the heart was the source of all emotions. We now know that the brain is primarily responsible for feelings. Then what is the heart's function? The heart is a muscular organ that forces blood through the body. You can think of your heart as two pumps. One pump drives the pulmonary circuit; the other drives the systemic circuit.

Your heart is about the size of your clenched fist. It is located just beneath the sternum, or breastbone, and near the center of your chest cavity. The heart is a hollow organ with thick walls made of cardiac muscle. It is surrounded by a loose-fitting, double-walled sac called the pericardium. In addition to covering and protecting the heart, the pericardium anchors the heart by connecting it to structures such as the diaphragm and the breastbone.

The heart has two sides, separated by a thick wall of muscle called the septum. The heart has a total of four chambers, two on each side. The upper chambers of the heart are called atria (singular: *atrium*). Atria receive blood coming into the heart from the lungs or the body. They pump blood into the two lower chambers called ventricles. Ventricles pump blood out of the heart to the lungs or the body. You can follow the flow of blood through the heart in *Figure 31.12*.

Atria are small and have relatively thin walls. Ventricles are larger than the atria and have thicker, more muscular walls. The muscular walls are important because ventricles work harder than atria, pumping blood to the entire body.

The heart has valves that keep blood moving in one direction. Valves located between the atria and the ventricles prevent blood from flowing back into the atria. Other valves are located between each ventricle and the major blood vessels leading to the lungs and the rest of the body.

756   *Unit 8 Human Biology*

Life's plumbing

The human body has three types of blood vessels: arteries, veins, and capillaries. Each type of vessel has a different job in the circulatory system. The size and structure of each type vary according to the vessel's function. The inner layer of all three vessels, composed of epithelial tissue, is a barrier between blood and the rest of the body. Capillaries consist of only epithelial tissue. Arteries and veins also have smooth muscle and connective tissue layers. Smooth muscle allows vessels to contract. Connective tissue gives vessels elasticity.

Arteries Vessels that carry blood away from the heart are called arteries. You can feel the pulsing pressure of blood in an artery at several places on your body where arteries are near the skin. These places are called pulse points.

Arteries branch throughout the body into smaller arteries. The smallest arteries are called arterioles. The arterioles eventually become capillaries. By the time blood enters capillaries, its pressure has dropped significantly.

Capillaries Thin-walled blood vessels are called capillaries. Many capillaries are so small that blood cells flow through them in single file. Most of the exchange of gases, nutrients, and wastes takes place by diffusion through the thin capillary walls.

Some capillaries directly connect arteries and veins. Others form branching networks. These networks provide a greater surface area for diffusion, enabling large amounts of material to be exchanged rapidly.

Veins Capillaries merge to form vessels called venules, which in turn merge to become veins. Blood returns to the heart in veins. Blood in veins is under very low pressure and often

FIGURE 31.13

The Structure of Blood Vessels

The photo (right) shows a vein next to a thicker walled artery. What are the differences between the structure and function of an artery, a vein, and a capillary?

Vein

Artery

Capillary

Epithelial tissue

Epithelial tissue

Smooth muscle

Connective tissue

Valve

Epithelial tissue

Smooth muscle

Connective tissue

Arteriole

Venule

Artery

Vein

Examining the Effect of Exercise on Heart Rate

You can demonstrate the relationship between heart rate and exercise when you . . .

Try This

1 Sit quietly and press your middle and ring fingers firmly, but not hard, on the carotid artery in your neck, as shown in the photo.
2 Count the pulses for 15 seconds and multiply this number by 4 to calculate beats per minute. Record this number as *Heart Rate at Rest.*
3 Run in place for 2 minutes. Repeat step 2—but this time record the number as *Heart Rate after Exercise.*

Analyze Your Results

1 What is the difference between your heart rate at rest and your heart rate after exercise?
2 Create a graph that shows the heart rates of each student at rest (in blue) and after exercise (in red).
3 What are the highest and lowest rates at rest? After exercise?

Open valve

Skeletal muscles

Closed valve

Vein

FIGURE 31.14
The squeezing of skeletal muscles surrounding a vein helps move the blood against gravity, toward the heart.

flows against gravity. To keep the blood flowing in one direction, veins have valves that prevent backflow. The squeezing action of skeletal muscles around the veins also helps move blood toward the heart.

HEART RATE

You've got rhythm!

The number of times your heart beats each minute is your heart rate. Each heartbeat has two parts, the diastole and the systole. During diastole (dy-AS-tuh-lee) the heart muscle relaxes, enabling blood to flow into the atria and ventricles. During systole (SIS-tuh-lee) the ventricles contract, pumping the blood out to the body.

If you use a stethoscope to listen to a heart, you can hear a "lub-dup" sound caused by the closing of heart valves. The "lub" sound is made as valves between the atria and ventricles close. The shorter "dup" sound is made when the valves close between the ventricles and the blood vessels.

Two masses of nerve and muscle cells called nodes send out electrical signals that control your heart beat. The sinoatrial (SY-noh-AT-re-uhl) node, or SA node, located in the wall of the right atrium, signals the atria to contract. The SA node's signal also travels to the atrioventricular (AT-ree-oh-ven-TRIK-yoo-ler) node, or AV node, which is located in the septum between the atria. The AV node signals the ventricles to contract. The SA node controls the rate of the heartbeat and is called the pacemaker. Electrical signals through the heart can be detected by a machine called an electrocardiograph (ee-LEK-troh-KAR-dee-oh-graf). This device draws the heart's electrical activity, which is called an electrocardiogram (EKG or ECG).

Your heart beats faster when you are angry or afraid, or after you exercise. In times of stress, body cells send messages to the brain, demanding more O_2 and nutrients. The brain relays the messages to the SA node, which speeds up the rate at which the heart pumps the needed O_2 and nutrients to body cells.

CHECKPOINT 31.4

1. Compare the circulatory systems of a grasshopper and a fish.
2. Diagram the flow of blood through the human circulatory system.
3. Critical Thinking How does the structure of capillaries compare to that of arteries and veins?

Build on What You Know

4. Compare the heart structures of humans, amphibians, and fish. *(Need to jog your memory? Revisit relevant concepts in Chapter 25, Section 25.2 and Section 25.5.)*

31.5 Blood

An ocean of cells

One drop of blood from a finger prick contains 250,000–500,000 white cells and 15–20 million platelets. Most blood cells, however, are red cells. There are approximately 200 million red blood cells in a drop of a woman's blood and over 250 million in a man's blood. But don't worry about pricking your finger. In one second, the body produces 2 million new red blood cells to replace those that are lost.

What you'll learn

IDEAS
• To compare the components of blood
• To explain the role of antigens in blood typing

WORDS
plasma, red blood cells, white blood cells, platelets

PLASMA AND BLOOD CELLS

Red, white, and . . .

Your body contains about 5 L of blood. Blood is a type of connective tissue in which specialized cells are suspended in a liquid. The yellowish liquid in which blood cells are suspended is called **plasma.** Plasma is 90 percent water, but it also contains dissolved salts, proteins, nutrients, wastes, and other chemicals.

Almost half of the blood's volume consists of blood cells. Blood cells begin as unspecialized cells called stem cells, which are formed in the red marrow of bones. Stem cells differentiate and mature into blood cells as your body needs more blood cells. When stem cells mature, they enter the bloodstream as red blood cells, white blood cells, or platelets.

Red blood cells Red blood cells are the most numerous cells in your blood—you have about 25 trillion of them in your body! **Red blood cells,** or erythrocytes (eh-RITH-roh-syts), carry oxygen (O_2) to all cells of the body.

As you read in section 31.2, red blood cells contain a large, complex protein called hemoglobin. Each red blood cell contains about 250 million hemoglobin molecules. Each hemoglobin molecule can bind four molecules of O_2. Thus, a single red blood cell can contain about one billion O_2 molecules. Red blood cells that contain O_2 bound to hemoglobin molecules cause blood to be red.

Hemoglobin binds or releases O_2 depending on the O_2 concentration in the environment. In the alveoli of the lungs, the concentration of O_2 is high. The O_2 diffuses into the blood of the lungs' capillaries and is bound by hemoglobin in the red blood cells. In muscle and other organ cells, the O_2 concentration is low. In these body areas, O_2 is released by the hemoglobin in red blood cells passing through nearby capillaries. The released O_2 diffuses into the body cells.

Hemoglobin can also bind carbon dioxide (CO_2). It releases or binds CO_2 depending upon the concentration of the gas in the area surrounding the hemoglobin. However, most of the CO_2 in blood is carried in the blood plasma, not in the red blood cells.

Red blood cells are disk-shaped, giving them

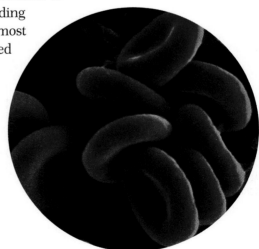

FIGURE 31.15
Normal red blood cells are disk-shaped. How does this shape aid in gas diffusion?

FIGURE 31.16
White blood cells are larger than red blood cells. What other differences can you see between white blood cells and red blood cells in the photo above?

a large surface area for efficient gas diffusion. Red blood cells lack a nucleus as well as any organelles. Therefore, red blood cells cannot reproduce or repair themselves. A red blood cell lives for three to four months before being broken down in the spleen. New red blood cells form continuously in red bone marrow. Iron, a component of hemoglobin, is recycled into newly-produced hemoglobin molecules.

White blood cells Leukocytes (LOO-koh-syts), or **white blood cells,** help the body fight disease. There are fewer leukocytes than red blood cells in blood, as you can see in *Figure 31.16.* In contrast to red blood cells, white blood cells have nuclei and organelles, and they can move out of blood vessels and into tissue where they may be needed. White blood cells are larger than red blood cells. Lymphoid tissues, such as the spleen, tonsils, and thymus, store white blood cells.

White blood cells can fight disease in different ways. One way is to engulf and digest dead or harmful cells such as bacteria. This method is called phagocytosis, and these white blood cells are phagocytes. In *Figure 31.17*

FIGURE 31.18
Strands of insoluble fibrin trap blood cells, forming a mesh that prevents blood from leaving a damaged blood vessel.

you can see five types of white blood cells and the role each plays in fighting disease. You will learn more about how some types of white blood cells function when you study the immune system in Chapter 32.

Platelets Platelets are involved in the formation of blood clots. **Platelets** are formed from pieces of cytoplasm that break off of large cells in the bone marrow. A cell membrane forms around the cytoplasmic pieces. However, no nuclei form, even as platelets mature.

When you cut or injure yourself, platelets move to the damaged blood vessel in large numbers. The resulting plug of platelets prevents excessive loss of blood during the time it takes for a blood clot to form. The platelets secrete chemicals called clotting factors into the blood. Clotting factors react with fibrinogen, a protein in blood. The fibrinogen is converted into an insoluble threadlike substance

Types of White Blood Cells		
Cell Type	**Appearance**	**Function**
Neutrophils		Kill bacteria by phagocytosis
Eosinophils		Kill parasitic worms Inactivate allergic reactions
Basophils		Release histamines that cause inflammation and allergies
Lymphocytes		Produce antibodies that fight disease and destroy cancerous and virus-infected body cells
Monocytes		Destroy bacteria, infected cells, and old red blood cells by phagocytosis

FIGURE 31.17
Compare the appearance and function of white blood cells.

Blood Donor Table		
Blood Type	Can Donate To	Can Receive From
A	A, AB	A, O
B	B, AB	B, O
AB	AB	A, B, O
O	A, B, AB, O	O

FIGURE 31.19
Using information in the table, what blood types might have been mixed together in the sample shown in the photo?

Clumped blood cells

called fibrin. Strands of fibrin entwine, making a mesh that traps blood cells and prevents them from passing through the damaged blood vessel. You can see these strands in *Figure 31.18*. The resulting clot of fibrin, platelets, and blood cells forms a scab that seals the wound until it can be replaced with new tissue.

BLOOD TYPES

All in the family

You have just learned about the components of blood—plasma, red blood cells, white blood cells, and platelets. These components are present in everyone's blood. Yet everyone's blood is different. Why? Because human blood types differ.

As you learned in Chapter 6, your blood type is determined by your genes. Humans have four different, familiar blood types: type A, type B, type AB, and type O. The type of blood you have is determined by the presence or absence of molecules called antigens on the surfaces of your red blood cells. For example, people with type B blood have a molecule called the B antigen on their red blood cells. The red blood cells of people with type A blood have the A antigen. People with type AB blood have both A and B antigens. Those with type O blood have neither A nor B antigens.

Everyone's blood type is identified not only by letter, but also as being positive or negative. The identification of a blood type as positive or negative refers to the presence or absence of an anti-gen called the Rh group or Rh factor. When the Rh group antigen is present, a person is identified as being Rh positive, or Rh^+. A person who does not carry the Rh factor on their red blood cells is described as being Rh negative, or Rh^-.

As long as you remain healthy, the types of antigens present on your red blood cells is of little concern. However, should you require a blood transfusion, this information is vital. For a blood transfusion to be successful, the blood from a donor must have the same antigens as the patient's blood. When the antigens are different, the patient's lymphocytes will usually produce antibodies that bind the antigens on red blood cells of the transfused blood. This will cause the red blood cells to clump together, which can be fatal to the recipient. Study the table in *Figure 31.19*. What type of blood can be given to all patients?

CHECKPOINT 31.5

1. Name and describe the components of blood.
2. Explain the role of antigens in blood typing.
3. **Critical Thinking** If you had an infection, would the number of leukocytes in your blood be higher or lower than normal? Why?

Build on What You Know

4. Describe the patterns of inheritance of blood types. *(Need to jog your memory? Revisit relevant concepts in Chapter 6, Section 6.5.)*

31.6 Health of the Circulatory System

What you'll learn

IDEAS
- To describe illnesses of the cardiovascular system
- To explain ways to care for the cardiovascular system

The heart of an athlete
Athletic training can increase the size and power of heart muscle. A swimmer's heart pumps one-third more blood than does the heart of an unfit person. Also, an athlete's resting pulse is slower, because the heart pumps more blood per beat. It is literally true that athletes put a lot of heart into their sport.

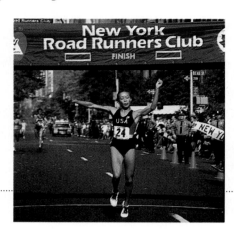

CARDIOVASCULAR DISEASES

A "broken heart"

Cardiovascular diseases—diseases of the heart and blood vessels—are the number-one cause of death among people in the United States today. About 63 million people, or about one out of four people in the United States, have a cardiovascular disease. Two common cardiovascular diseases are atherosclerosis and hypertension.

Atherosclerosis The disease atherosclerosis (ATH-er-oh-skler-OH-sis) is a cardiovascular condition in which arteries have narrowed. A narrowed artery is shown in *Figure 31.20*.

The arteries of a person suffering from atherosclerosis narrow because fatty deposits called plaques form inside blood vessel

FIGURE 31.20
Blood flows freely through a healthy artery (right). In atherosclerosis, plaques reduce the flow of blood (left).

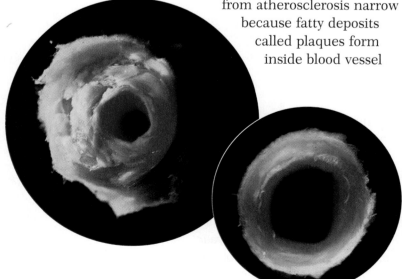

walls. If the disease progresses, the plaques may become hardened by deposits of calcium. The result is a related condition called arteriosclerosis, commonly known as hardening of the arteries.

Atherosclerosis creates two problems. First, a narrowed blood vessel reduces the flow of blood through the vessel. Second, the plaques roughen the smooth endothelial lining. The rough surface seems to stimulate platelets to form clots. If the clot breaks free, it can get stuck in a narrow artery and block the flow of blood. As a result, any organ or tissue served by the artery is deprived of its oxygen supply. If a clot blocks the blood flow in a coronary artery—an artery that carries blood to the heart—a heart attack can result. If a clot blocks the blood flow in an artery of the brain, a stroke can result.

Although many unanswered questions about the cause of atherosclerosis remain, scientists have gathered a lot of data about the disease. A person's tendency to develop atherosclerosis is related to the ratio of two kinds of cholesterol in the blood. One kind of cholesterol, called low-density lipoprotein (LDL), increases the tendency of plaques to form in arteries. The other form of cholesterol, high-density lipoprotein (HDL), reduces the tendency of plaques to form. The higher the ratio of LDL to HDL in the blood, the greater the risk of atherosclerosis.

Hypertension High blood pressure, or hypertension, occurs when the force of blood pumping through blood vessels is too great. Your blood pressure normally increases temporarily from exercise, fever, or stress, but usually returns to normal relatively quickly. When blood pressure remains high for a longer period, however, it eventually overworks the heart and damages the arteries. Hypertension often increases the risk of heart attack and stroke. Atherosclerosis often causes high blood pressure, but heredity also plays a role.

Have you ever had your blood pressure measured? Blood pressure is recorded in millimeters of mercury (mm Hg). The device used to measure blood pressure is shown in *Figure 31.21.* A person's blood pressure is recorded in two parts. The first number is systolic pressure, the force of the blood in the arteries when the ventricles contract. The second number is diastolic pressure, the force of the blood in the arteries when the ventricles relax. An average adult's blood pressure is 120/80, or "120 over 80." A high diastolic pressure is usually more indicative of hypertension than a high systolic pressure.

BLOOD DISEASES

Blood can be sick and tired, too

When a person has a condition called anemia, the blood transports too little oxygen. A person with anemia feels tired and weak. Anemia can result from too little iron in the diet, bleeding due to injury or menstruation, or other causes.

Sickle-cell disease, characterized by the misshapened red blood cells you see in *Figure 31.22,* can cause anemia. The sickle shape of the blood cells also causes them to clog blood vessels. Unlike most other types of anemia, sickle-cell disease is hereditary. The hereditary factors of the disease were discussed in Chapter 6.

Blood can also be affected by a form of cancer called leukemia. In a person with leukemia, the bone marrow produces immature stem cells in great numbers and releases them into the bloodstream. Because these stem cells are not fully mature, they cannot fight infection as normal white blood cells do. At the same time, fewer red blood cells and platelets may be formed, making the body prone to anemia and abnormal bleeding.

Although doctors are uncertain what causes a person to develop leukemia, they have found ways to treat some forms of the disease. One of the most recent developments in this area involves the use of bone marrow transplants. In this procedure, healthy bone marrow from a matched donor is used to replace cancerous marrow from a leukemia sufferer. Stem cells from umbilical cords have also been used to treat leukemia.

FIGURE 31.21
Because there are usually no symptoms of hypertension, people should have their blood pressure checked regularly.

FIGURE 31.22
The sickled red blood cells (top) are caused by a mutation in the hemoglobin gene. Normal blood cells (bottom) have normal hemoglobin.

LAB ZONE Think About It!

Relating Blood Pressure to Health

High blood pressure, or hypertension, generally causes no symptoms but is dangerous to your health. It is one of the three major risk factors for cardiovascular disease. Smoking and high LDL/HDL blood cholesterol ratios are the other two risk factors. Study the graph below and then answer the questions that follow.

Analyzing the Graph

1 What is the relationship indicated in the graph between blood pressure and the risk of dying from heart attack or stroke?
2 When does the risk of dying from heart attack or stroke start to increase noticeably?
3 Write a paragraph describing what your ideal blood pressure would be based on the graph's data. Include a plan for reaching that blood pressure.

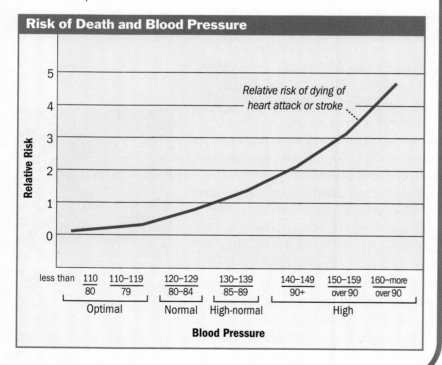

Risk of Death and Blood Pressure

Relative risk of dying of heart attack or stroke

Relative Risk (y-axis: 0, 1, 2, 3, 4, 5)

Blood Pressure (x-axis):

less than 110/80	110–119/79	120–129/80–84	130–139/85–89	140–149/90+	150–159/over 90	160–more/over 90
Optimal		Normal	High-normal	High		

CARE OF YOUR CIRCULATORY SYSTEM

The heart of health

Can a person reduce the risk of developing cardiovascular disease? The tendency to develop atherosclerosis and hypertension is inherited. However, a healthy lifestyle is the most important preventive factor.

Smoking increases the risk of cardiovascular disease. Nicotine in tobacco raises the heart rate and narrows arteries. Smoking also lowers the efficiency of respiratory organs. Consequently, the heart must pump faster to deliver oxygen to the body's cells.

Diet and exercise also affect the cardiovascular system. Exercise increases the lungs' vital capacity, influences the body's weight, and reduces stress. It also strengthens muscles, including heart muscle.

A high dietary intake of cholesterol and saturated fats can lead to high levels of LDL cholesterol. A diet low in saturated fats can help reduce your risk of cardiovascular disease.

CHECKPOINT 31.6

1. Name and describe two cardiovascular disorders.
2. List three factors that can increase a person's risk of cardiovascular disease.
3. Critical Thinking HDL is sometimes referred to as good cholesterol, and LDL has been called bad cholesterol. Explain.

Build on What You Know

4. What are the dietary recommendations regarding foods high in fats? *(Need to jog your memory? Revisit relevant concepts in Chapter 30, Section 30.1.)*

? How are materials transported throughout the body?

Chapter 31 Review

31.1–31.3 The vital exchange of oxygen and carbon dioxide occurs in the respiratory systems of animals.

31.4–31.6 Circulatory systems transport materials necessary for life.

Sum It Up

Use the following summary to review the main concepts in this chapter.

31.1 Respiratory Systems

- Oxygen and carbon dioxide are exchanged in respiratory systems.
- Gases may be exchanged through skin, gills, tracheal tubes, or lungs.
- In humans, dissolved gases are carried to and from the lungs by the blood.
- As air travels to air sacs in the lungs, it is cleaned, moistened, and warmed.

31.2 Every Breath You Take

- The diaphragm and intercostal muscles control breathing. The carbon dioxide concentration in blood regulates the breathing rate.
- Carbon dioxide and oxygen are exchanged by diffusion during respiration.

31.3 Health of the Respiratory System

- The symptoms of respiratory ailments are excess mucus, inflamed membranes, and narrowed passages—which make breathing difficult.
- In addition to causing lung cancer, smoking increases the risk of respiratory infections and of emphysema.

31.4 Circulatory Systems

- Circulatory systems can be open, as in arthropods, or closed, as in vertebrates.
- The heart pumps oxygen-poor blood through the pulmonary circuit and oxygen-rich blood through the systemic circuit. Valves keep blood flowing in one direction.
- Thick-walled arteries carry blood away from the heart; diffusion occurs in thin-walled capillaries; blood returns to the heart in veins.

31.5 Blood

- The blood cells are suspended in a liquid called plasma. Red blood cells carry oxygen, white blood cells fight infection, and platelets secrete clotting factors.
- Antigens on the surface of red blood cells determine blood type.

31.6 Health of the Circulatory System

- In atherosclerosis, the arteries are narrowed by plaque deposits, which can lead to heart attacks or strokes. Hypertension can also increase the risk of heart attack and stroke.
- Anemia limits oxygen transport by the blood; leukemia limits the normal functioning of white blood cells.

Use Terms and Concepts

Use each of the following words or terms in a complete sentence. If you need to review a meaning, turn to the page indicated.

respiration (p. 745)
alveoli (p. 747)
diaphragm (p. 748)
heart (p. 754)
blood (p. 754)
blood vessels (p. 754)

plasma (p. 759)
red blood cells (p. 759)
white blood cells (p. 760)
platelets (p. 760)

Use Your Word Power

COMPLETION Write the word or phrase that best completes each statement.

1. Blood cells are suspended in a watery liquid called _____ .

2. The muscle that separates the chest cavity from the abdomen is the _____ .

3. The blood cells that secrete clotting factors are called _____ .

4. In the lungs, gases diffuse between air in the _____ and blood in capillaries.

5. Leukocytes is another name for the _____ that fight disease.

6. The _____ is the organ that is the main pump of the circulatory system.

7. In arthropods and mollusks _____ are open-ended.

TRUE-FALSE Write true if the statement is true. If the statement is false, replace the underlined word(s) to make the statement true.

8. Most of the carbon dioxide transported in blood is carried by red blood cells.

9. White blood cells have nuclei and organelles.

10. The exchange of gases between blood and body cells is called internal respiration.

11. The blood that travels from the heart to the lungs is oxygen-poor.

12. The antigens on the surface of white blood cells determine blood type.

13. When the diaphragm relaxes, air rushes into the lungs.

Show What You Know

14. Explain why people with Type O blood are called universal donors.

15. Relate the structure of atria and ventricles to their functions.

16. What is the role of stem cells in the circulatory system?

17. What is the importance of surface area to respiration? How do the structures of the respiratory and circulatory systems provide the maximum surface area possible?

18. Explain why valves are needed in veins but not in arteries.

19. What roles do cilia and mucous membranes play in respiration?

20. Name at least three conditions that can cause heart rate to increase.

21. **Make a Concept Map** Make a concept map that relates the respiratory and circulatory systems.

Take It Further

22. **Developing a Hypothesis** Before birth, a fetus produces a form of hemoglobin that can bind more oxygen at lower concentrations than can the hemoglobin produced after birth. Why would fetal hemoglobin need to be different from adult hemoglobin? (Hint: A fetus gets oxygen from its mother's blood, not from the air.)

23. **Applying Concepts** One possible cause for shock—a sudden lowering of blood pressure—is massive internal or external bleeding. Replacing blood volume quickly is critical. If there is no time to find a matching blood type, doctors use blood plasma to restore blood volume. Why is blood plasma an effective alternative to whole blood in an emergency?

24. **Making an Analogy** Compare the role of a piston in an automobile engine to that of the diaphragm in the respiratory system.

25. **Developing a Hypothesis** What symptoms might lead a doctor to consider installing an artificial pacemaker in a patient?

26. Designing an Experiment Suppose you had four vials of blood, one each of Type A, Type B, Type AB, and Type O. You want to confirm that the labels are accurate. Design an experiment to verify the contents of the vials. Would you be able to tell all the types apart without any additional blood samples?

27. Interpreting a Graph The graph shows how the concentration of inhaled gases affects the breathing rate. How does the breathing rate change as the percent of carbon dioxide (CO_2) in inhaled air increases? What is the effect on the breathing rate of a decrease in the oxygen (O_2) content of inhaled air? Based on the graph, is the breathing rate more sensitive to the O_2 content or the CO_2 content of inhaled air?

Effect of Inhaled CO_2 and O_2 on Breathing Rate

Percent CO_2 in Inhaled Air ——

Breathing Rate (per min)

Percent O_2 in Inhaled Air ——

28. Analyzing Data The following table shows the relative blood flow through various organs in the human body—that is, the fraction of blood that flows through a given human organ. Through which organ(s) does all of the blood flow? Describe and explain the change in blood flow to skeletal muscles during exercise. The kidneys consume only 6 percent of the oxygen used in the body. Why would 22 percent of blood flow through the kidneys?

Blood Flow Through Human Organs	
Organ	**Percentage of Total Flow**
Brain	14%
Heart muscle	5%
Kidneys	22%
Liver	13%
Lungs	100%
Skeletal muscles	18%
Skeletal muscles during exercise	75%
Skin*	4%

*Maximum dilation of blood vessels

Consider the Issues

29. Air Quality When the level of pollutants in the air is high, communities warn their citizens, especially those with respiratory problems, to stay indoors. What are the major sources of air pollution? What local or federal regulations have been enacted to alleviate the problem? Describe their effectiveness.

Make New Connections

30. Biology and Mathematics Large animals usually live longer and have a slower heart rate than do smaller animals. Collect data on the average lifespans and heart rates for different mammals. Compute and compare the number of heartbeats per lifetime.

31. Biology and History Learning about human anatomy by dissecting human remains, or cadavers, was initially very controversial. Research the history of anatomical studies beginning in Great Britain during the 1600s.

FAST-FORWARD TO CHAPTER 32

The lymphatic system, which you will study in Chapter 32, also circulates materials through the body. The lymphatic system helps to defend the body against foreign substances.

You can find out more about the immune system by exploring the following Internet address: *http://body_systems.biosurf.com*

In this chapter . . .

FEATURES

Everyday Biology
- End Run Around the Defense
- Coming Back to Haunt Us
- Hope for a One-Two Punch

In the Community
Shots for Everyone

 Frontiers in Biology
Shutting Down Immunity

LAB ZONES

Discover It!
- Graphing Vaccinations

Do It!
- How Does Skin Protect Humans?
- Creating a Personal Health Journal

Think About It!
- Calculating Bacterial Growth

Investigate It!
- Modeling Disease Transmission

A CHILLING AMERICAN QUILT

In October 1996, when the AIDS Quilt was unfurled in Washington, D.C., it stretched eleven blocks along the Mall, from the Washington Monument to the Capitol. The names of the deceased were read aloud, and parents and other family members, friends, and observers moved reverently and silently around the panels. Begun in 1987, the AIDS Quilt now contains about 45,000 individual panels—each one lovingly crafted by family members and friends to commemorate a life lost to AIDS. Each panel bears the name of a victim and attached memorabilia that relate to the person's life, ranging from baseball caps and other favorite clothing items to stuffed animals and car keys.

As yet, no cure has been found for AIDS—a viral disease that attacks the human immune system and leaves the body unable to fight infection. Although education about the causes of this disease is helping to slow its spread, AIDS has killed more than 300,000 Americans—people of all ethnic groups and ages, including teenagers and children. The worldwide death toll is estimated at 4 million to 6 million. In this chapter you will learn how your immune system works and how to keep it healthy and strong.

Graphing Vaccinations

1. Survey the class to find out which diseases your classmates have been vaccinated against.
2. Record the total number of classmates that were vaccinated for each disease.
3. Make a graph to show your findings.

Each vaccination you have received has helped to stimulate your immune system in a way that creates resistance to a specific disease. What vaccinations are the most common among your classmates?

WRITE ABOUT IT!

Talk to several persons of different generations and ask them whether they think a cure will be found for AIDS. Record their ideas and responses in your journal.

32.1 Protecting the Organism

Shark attacks germs
Sharks—like humans but unlike some other chordates—have complex immune systems. Like us, they produce antibodies and other chemical protectors to fight bacteria and viruses. Because sharks are extraordinarily resistant to cancer, scientists are eager to learn more about how the immune system evolved.

PATHOGENS AND DISEASE

The enemy within

Your body is constantly exposed to harmful organisms and substances in the environment. The immune system is the body's defense system against attack. A main function of the immune system is to fight infectious diseases. An infectious disease is any illness caused by organisms or viruses that enter and reproduce inside a host. The common cold, pneumonia, and influenza (the flu) are a few of the many infectious diseases that affect humans.

Not all illnesses are infectious diseases. For example, an illness caused by the bite of a poisonous snake is not an infectious disease. Illness from a snake bite is caused by snake poisons, not organisms or viruses that enter the body.

FIGURE 32.1
Entamoeba histolytica (top) is a protist that causes a type of dysentery. A tapeworm (bottom) attaches itself to the digestive wall of a host, sustaining itself on the host's nutrients.

Pathogens A virus or organism that causes an infectious disease is a **pathogen** (PATH-oh-jen). Viruses, bacteria, protists, fungi, and some invertebrate animals such as roundworms and flatworms can be pathogenic to humans.

Pathogens cause disease in different ways. Some pathogens produce poisons called toxins that disrupt the normal functioning of cells. For example, the bacterium that causes tetanus produces a toxin that affects nerve cells involved in muscle contraction.

As you learned in Chapter 14, viruses use the body's cells to replicate. In the process, the viruses destroy healthy cells. Chicken pox and the common cold are caused by viruses.

Protists and roundworms that cause disease destroy body tissues by feeding on and burrowing into the tissue. For example, one type of dysentery is caused by an ameba that eats colon cells, causing the host to suffer from internal sores and diarrhea. The roundworm that causes trichinosis burrows into muscle cells, forming cysts within the tissue.

Germ theory Before the 1800s it was not known that microscopic pathogens caused disease. Three nineteenth-century scientists—Louis Pasteur, Joseph Lister, and Robert Koch—pioneered the study of infectious disease. Their discoveries formed the basis of the germ theory of disease. The germ theory proposes that there is a relationship between a microorganism and a specific disease.

In 1876 Robert Koch used four experimental steps to demonstrate that anthrax, a deadly disease of cattle and sheep, is caused by a specific bacterium. Called Koch's postulates, these steps are still used to study and identify the causes of infectious diseases. Koch's postulates are shown in *Figure 32.2.*

THE TRANSMISSION OF DISEASE

Germ warfare

Although they are caused by different pathogens, most infectious diseases are spread in one of four ways: through direct contact with an infected person, through indirect contact with an infected person, through the ingestion of contaminated food or water, or through the bite of an infected animal.

Direct contact Infectious diseases that spread from one person to another are called contagious diseases. Contagious diseases are often spread through direct contact. A healthy person contracts the disease by touching an infected person. For example, the viruses that cause colds can be transmitted by direct contact, especially by shaking hands.

Certain pathogens are transmitted through sexual contact with an infected person. Syphilis, gonorrhea, and AIDS are transmitted this way and are called sexually transmitted diseases.

Indirect contact Most contagious diseases are spread by indirect contact with an infected person.

FIGURE 32.2
Koch's Postulates

Koch's postulates are used to identify the pathogens that cause certain diseases. How do the four steps relate to the scientific method?

1 The suspected pathogen must be found in the bodies of sick organisms but not in the bodies of healthy organisms.

No disease organisms

Suspected disease organisms

Healthy rat

Dead rat

Suspected disease organisms

Organisms grown in pure culture

Dead rat

2 The pathogen must be removed from the infected host and grown in a pure culture in the laboratory.

3 When the laboratory-grown pathogen is placed in a healthy organism, the pathogen must cause the same disease in the new host that was observed in the original host.

Organisms from pure culture injected into healthy rat

Rat dies

Suspected disease organisms

Dead rat

4 Once the new host has developed the disease, the pathogen must be recovered from the newly infected host.

FIGURE 32.3
Contagious diseases can be spread in many ways. What three ways of transmitting disease are depicted in the photos above?

Indirect contact requires a carrier, or vector, for the pathogen. Air can be a vector for pathogens. When you sneeze, your respiratory system releases droplets into the air. Cold viruses in droplets can be transmitted to a person as far away as 5 meters. Cold viruses can also contaminate objects on which they settle. If you touch a contaminated object and then touch your nose, eyes, or mouth, you can become infected.

Water and food Some diseases are spread by contaminated water or food. Disease transmission through water is a serious problem in parts of the world with poorly designed sanitation systems and untreated sewage. Amebic dysentery is a disease spread by contaminated water.

Food poisoning can be caused by eating food that contains pathogens.

The bacteria *Salmonella* grow in foods such as eggs, chicken, turkey, sausage, and ground meat. Eating raw or undercooked foods containing *Salmonella* can cause vomiting, stomach cramps, and fever.

Botulism is a form of food poisoning caused by a bacterium that cannot live in the presence of oxygen. The bacterium can grow and produce a toxin in improperly canned foods. When ingested, the toxin attacks the nervous system. Serious cases of botulism can cause death from heart or respiratory failure.

Animal bites Animals, often insects, are vectors for many infectious diseases. For example, the bubonic plague, which killed 40 percent of Europe's population during the Middle Ages, is caused by a pathogen spread by fleas. The pathogen that causes malaria is transmitted through the bite of infected mosquitoes. Lyme disease is spread through the bite of an infected tick.

Rabies is a disease caused by a virus. The saliva of infected mammals, such as dogs or squirrels, contains the rabies virus. If an infected animal bites a human, the virus can be transmitted to the human.

FUNCTIONS OF THE IMMUNE SYSTEM

Recognizing the enemy

In many ways, your body is like a fort under constant attack. Pathogens try to enter your body so they can loot its nutrients. Fortunately, your defense system, the immune system, is usually successful in fighting off the attackers.

Like other body systems, the immune system is made of many specialized cells and tissues. Some prevent pathogens from entering the body. If pathogens do enter the body, other cells and tissues identify, seek out, and destroy the pathogens.

The immune system recognizes harmful organisms and substances that can cause disease. To do this, the body distinguishes "self" cells, which belong to the body, from "nonself" cells, which do not. The cellular components of the immune system recognize specific molecules on the surface of the body's self cells and do not attack those cells.

Little is known about the immune mechanisms of invertebrates. These animals do not seem to have a complex response to invading pathogens or substances. However, many invertebrates seem to be able to distinguish self cells from nonself cells.

Most vertebrates have three lines of defense against pathogens and foreign substances. Each line of defense has a different responsibility. The first and second lines of defense are effective against many different kinds of pathogens. These mechanisms are called **nonspecific defenses.** In contrast, the third line of defense protects an organism from specific pathogens. Defenses to specific pathogens are called **specific defenses.** These defenses are collectively known as the immune response.

LAB ZONE — Think About It!

Calculating Bacterial Growth

A single bacterium that manages to enter the body can multiply exponentially for a long time if not attacked by the body's defense system. Bacteria undergo binary fission. Many bacteria can reproduce every 20 minutes. In one hour a single bacterium can become eight bacteria. Answer the following questions, assuming that there is one bacterium at time zero and the body's immune system is nonfunctional (unless instructed otherwise).

Analyzing the Graph

1 How many bacteria would be present after four hours? After five hours? After six hours?
2 Plot the values you calculate on a semi-log graph. Describe the line that appears when you connect the points.
3 Suppose a single bacterium has entered a body with a healthy immune system. How would the graph line be different?

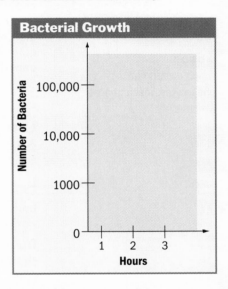

CHECKPOINT 32.1

1. What is a pathogen? Give four examples of pathogens.
2. Explain the difference between specific defenses and nonspecific defenses.
3. Critical Thinking Hereditary diseases are not classified as contagious diseases. Why?

Build on What You Know

4. An important step in investigating an outbreak of food poisoning is to identify the bacteria present. How might scientists make this determination? *(Need to jog your memory? Revisit relevant concepts in Chapter 14, Section 14.5.)*

What does the immune system do?

32.2 Overview of the Immune System

The amazing blobs
Phagocytes are white blood cells that surround and digest unwanted body visitors. They squeeze out of gaps in the walls of capillaries, then plump up and move toward an invader, oozing around the foreign matter. Dead phagocytes are the major components of the white material called pus.

LYMPHATIC SYSTEM AND ORGANS

Defense department

The immune system of the human body comprises a variety of cells, organs, and organ systems, ranging from individual white blood cells to the lymphatic system. White blood cells are specialized cells that help fight disease. Both the circulatory system and the lymphatic system transport white blood cells through the body.

The lymphatic system plays a critical role in the immune system by producing, storing, and circulating white blood cells. As you can see in *Figure 32.4,* the lymphatic system is a network of vessels and associated organs. Lymph capillaries intertwine with blood capillaries, absorb the intercellular fluid that leaks from blood capillaries, and move the fluid into larger lymph vessels. The fluid in the lymph vessels is called **lymph.**

As lymph travels through lymph vessels, it is filtered through densely packed areas of tissue called **lymph nodes.** White blood cells are stored in lymph nodes and can attack pathogens in the lymph. When the body is fighting an infection, white blood cells are produced in great numbers, and the lymph nodes can become swollen and sore. You may notice the swollen lymph nodes in your neck when you are sick.

The tonsils, thymus, and spleen are all composed of lymphoid tissues. Located in the back of the mouth, the tonsils filter and destroy bacteria. The thymus gland produces hormones that play a role in the maturation of white blood cells. The spleen removes worn-out red blood cells, platelets, bacteria, and other particles from the blood. The spleen stores lymphocytes which attack pathogens.

In addition to its role as part of the immune system, the lymphatic system returns fluid to the circulatory system. Intercellular fluid keeps the body's cells moist. The main component of intercellular fluid is plasma, which leaks from blood capillaries into surrounding tissues. Up to 3 liters of plasma a day may leak from the capillaries and must be replaced to maintain the blood's fluid volume.

The lymphatic system collects the intercellular fluid, cleans it, and returns it to the circulatory system. As lymph travels through the body, it moves into increasingly larger lymph vessels. In the neck region, lymph is returned to the circulatory system through two ducts that connect the lymphatic vessels with large veins underneath the collarbone. Unlike the circulatory system, the lymphatic system has no pump. Lymph is moved by the contraction of surrounding skeletal muscles. Lymph vessels have one-way valves, which direct fluid flow. Exercise also helps fluids move through the lymphatic system.

CELLS OF THE IMMUNE SYSTEM

The troops

White blood cells, the specialized cells of the immune system, are also called leukocytes (LOO-koh-syts). They are the main cellular components of the immune system. All leukocytes originate in the red bone marrow. Some leukocytes develop in the red bone marrow, while others migrate and develop in the thymus. Leukocytes reside in the lymph nodes, organs of the lymphatic system, and bloodstream. When an invasion of the body is detected, leukocytes gather at the infection site in great numbers.

Different kinds of white blood cells are involved in the nonspecific and specific defense systems. **Phagocytes** are leucocytes that engulf and digest unwanted cells and pathogens in a nonspecific manner. For example, phagocytes in the spleen engulf old red blood cells. **Macrophages** are the largest phagocytes. Each macrophage can engulf hundreds of bacterial cells.

Lymphocytes are leukocytes involved in the body's specific defense system. Some lymphocytes secrete antibodies specific to different invading pathogens. Other lymphocytes

FIGURE 32.4

The Human Lymphatic System

Fighting infection and returning fluid to the circulatory system are the two functions of the lymph vessels and organs.

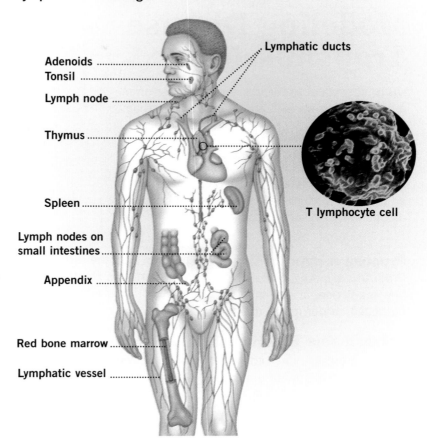

Adenoids

Tonsil

Lymph node

Thymus

Spleen

Lymph nodes on small intestines

Appendix

Red bone marrow

Lymphatic vessel

Lymphatic ducts

T lymphocyte cell

recognize and destroy body cells that have been infected by specific pathogens. You will learn more about lymphocytes in the next section.

CHECKPOINT 32.2

1. What are the components of the immune system?

2. Describe the path of lymph through the lymphatic and circulatory systems.

3. Critical Thinking Compare the roles of phagocytes and lymphocytes in combating pathogens.

Build on What You Know

4. Compare the structure and function of the lymphatic system with those of the circulatory system. *(Need to jog your memory? Revisit relevant concepts in Chapter 31, Section 31.4.)*

Modeling Disease Transmission

WHAT YOU WILL DO Model the transmission of a disease as it spreads through your classroom

SKILLS YOU WILL USE Modeling, observing, recording and analyzing data

WHAT YOU WILL NEED grease pencil; clean, empty baby-food jar; safety goggles; rubber gloves; dropper; stock solution; phenol red indicator

Propose a Hypothesis
Propose a hypothesis stating how many people a single pathogen carrier might infect.

Conduct Your Experiment
1 Use a grease pencil to write your name on an empty baby-food jar.
2 Using a dropper, transfer three dropperfuls of the stock solution provided by your teacher into your jar.
Caution: Wear goggles and gloves while handling solutions. Do not allow solutions to come in contact with skin or clothing.
3 Choose a classmate as a partner. Exchange one dropperful of solution with your partner. Add the dropperful of your partner's solution to your jar. Gently swirl the solution in the jar.
4 Record the name of your partner on a piece of paper.
5 Find two different partners and repeat steps 3 and 4 with each of them.
6 Add one dropperful of phenol red indicator to the solution in your jar. Record the color of the solution.
7 If the solution turned red, you were infected; if it turned yellow, you were not infected. Your teacher will write the names of the infected persons and their partners on the board.
8 As a class, try to deduce the original source of the infection—there was only one—and the route of transmission.

Analyze Your Data
1 Diagram the route of transmission of the infection.
2 If you were infected, who infected you? Did you in turn infect anyone else?
3 How many of you were infected after each round of transfers?
4 What represented the infectious agent? (Phenol red is yellow in acidic solutions and red in basic solutions.)

Draw Conclusions
Write a paragraph about the way diseases are spread and how difficult it might be to track their sources.

Design a Related Experiment
Design an experiment to model the transmission of disease by using talcum powder on the hands.

Lab: Modeling Disease Transmission

Objective: To show how disease can be transmitted

Partner 1	Partner 2	Partner 3

32.3 Activities of the Immune System

It helps to cry

Tears do more than express emotion. Tears also defend the body against some pathogens. Your eyes tear all the time. Tears contain enzymes that kill bacteria. An eye produces an overload of tears if a particularly irritating piece of dust or dirt enters it. The extra tears help wash foreign substances from the eye.

What you'll learn

IDEAS
• To explain the functions of nonspecific defenses
• To identify the components and functions of specific defenses

WORDS
inflammatory response, histamine, antigen, humoral immunity, antibody, B lymphocytes, cell-mediated immunity, T lymphocytes

NONSPECIFIC DEFENSES

The front lines

Each day you come in contact with many potential pathogens. Despite constant exposure to pathogens, you probably have only a few minor illnesses each year. With so many pathogens in the world, how does your body manage to stay healthy?

As mentioned in section 32.1, your body has three lines of defense against pathogens. *Figure 32.5* summarizes the role of each line of defense. First your immune system works to prevent disease-causing agents from entering your body. However, if pathogens do enter your body, your immune system has ways to fight them. Some of the weapons your immune system uses to fight disease are nonspecific—they are effective against many pathogens. Both the first and second lines of defense are nonspecific components of the immune system.

First line of defense Pathogens must enter the body in order to cause disease. The job of the body's first line of defense is to keep pathogens out. This role is carried out by the skin, mucus, tears, and sweat.

As you may recall from Chapter 29, skin covers all the external parts of your body, as well as your internal organs. Unbroken skin acts as a wall that blocks out most pathogens. Glands in the skin secrete sweat. The salinity and acidity of sweat helps prevent the growth of harmful bacteria. Sweat also contains an enzyme that destroys some bacteria. In addition, the many types of harmless bacteria that normally live on the skin help prevent pathogens from growing there.

Some parts of the body, such as your mouth and nose, provide openings through which pathogens can enter. These openings are lined with cells that secrete a sticky substance called mucus. Mucus coats the openings

Defenses of the Human Immune System		
Type of Defense	**Line**	**Characteristic**
Nonspecific	First line	Principle barriers such as skin
	Second line	Inflammatory response
Specific	Third line	Immune responses—humoral and cell-mediated

FIGURE 32.5
The defenses of a human immune system include both specific and nonspecific defenses. What are the differences between the two?

and traps pathogens so they can be eliminated or destroyed. For example, bacteria entering your nose can become trapped by mucus. The beating of the cilia that line your nasal passages moves the mucus toward your throat, where it is swallowed. Bacteria that are trapped in the mucus are destroyed by strong acid in the stomach.

Second line of defense Pathogens sometimes evade the first-line defenses and invade body tissues. This activates the inflammatory response. The **inflammatory response** is a nonspecific defense reaction to tissue damage caused by injury or infection.

Imagine that you have cut your finger. The cut injures some cells and provides an opening for pathogens to enter your body. The injured cells release a chemical called **histamine,** which triggers the inflammatory response. You can follow the activities of the inflammatory response in *Figure* 32.6.

During the inflammatory response, capillaries in an injured or infected area expand. This increases blood flow to the injured site and increases the amount of plasma leaking into the intercellular fluid. The increase of intercellular fluid causes the area to

FIGURE 32.6

Steps of the Inflammatory Response

The inflammatory response is a body's second line of defense against invasion by pathogens. Why is it important that clotting factors from the circulatory system have access to the injured area?

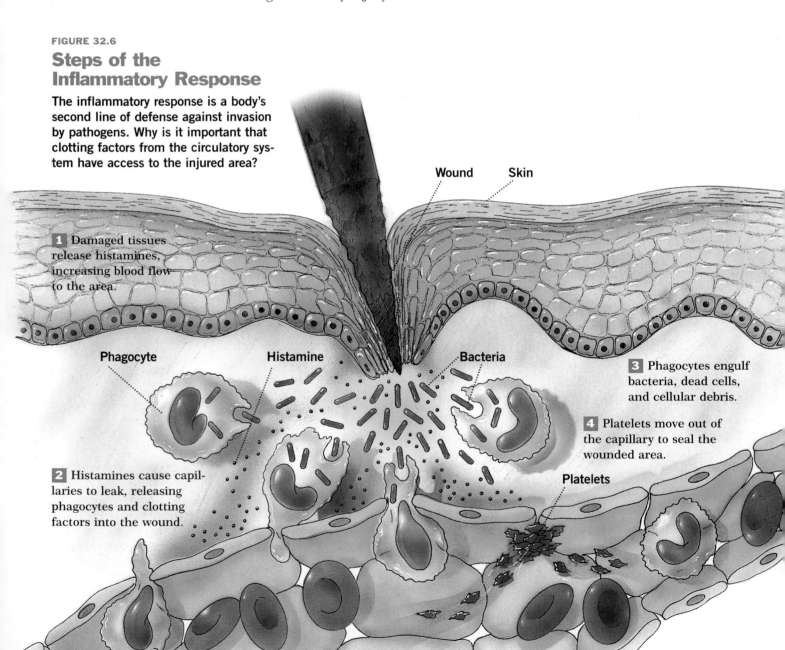

Wound   Skin

1 Damaged tissues release histamines, increasing blood flow to the area.

Phagocyte   Histamine   Bacteria

3 Phagocytes engulf bacteria, dead cells, and cellular debris.

4 Platelets move out of the capillary to seal the wounded area.

Platelets

2 Histamines cause capillaries to leak, releasing phagocytes and clotting factors into the wound.

become red and swollen. The plasma that leaks into the injured tissue contains platelets, the clotting factors in blood, which help seal the wounded area. Plasma also contains phagocytes—the white blood cells that engulf pathogens and other unwanted materials. These phagocytes engulf and kill bacterial cells that enter the body.

Sometimes a person with an infection develops a fever. Fever results when macrophages release chemical substances called pyrogens. Pyrogens stimulate the brain to raise body temperature. Fever causes phagocytes to be more active and makes it more difficult for pathogens to grow and reproduce.

Two other components of the second line of defense are interferon and natural killer cells. Interferon and natural killer cells attack many types of viruses, as well as cancer cells. Interferon (in-ter-FEER-ahn) is a protein that interferes with the replication of viruses. It is released by cells that have been invaded by viruses. Interferon cannot save an infected cell, but it can help protect nearby healthy cells.

Blood and lymph both contain natural killer cells. Unlike phagocytes, which attack invading cells, natural killer cells attack body cells that have been infected by viruses. Natural killer cells attack the cell membranes of virus-infected body cells and cause them to burst. Viruses can replicate only inside a host cell, so destroying the host cell also destroys the virus.

SPECIFIC DEFENSES

Knowing the enemy

In addition to nonspecific protection, the immune system has defenses against specific toxins and pathogens. Each specific defense affects only one kind of pathogen. The specific defenses

of the body are collectively known as the immune response. The immune response is the body's third line of defense against disease.

Bacteriologists E. A. von Behring and Shibasaburo Kitasato began to unravel the mystery of the immune response in the 1890s, using parts of blood serum. Serum is the liquid part of the blood that does not contain red blood cells or clotting proteins. Von Behring and Kitasato discovered that part of the blood serum from an animal that had survived tetanus could protect the animal from getting tetanus again. They also discovered that injecting the blood serum from an animal that had survived tetanus into a healthy animal protected the healthy animal from getting the disease.

In their research, von Behring and Kitasato discovered three characteristics of the immune response. First, the immune response is specific. Each defense of the immune response targets a specific pathogen. Second, the

---

LAB ZONE Do It!

How Does Skin Protect Humans?

You can model how the skin helps protect the human body from disease-causing pathogens when you . . .

Try This

1 Cut an apple in half.
2 Cover one half of the apple with plastic food wrap and leave the other half uncovered.
3 Using a dropper, release several drops of food coloring on each half of the apple.

Analyze Your Results

1 What happened to the uncovered half of the apple? To the covered half?
2 How does the plastic wrap provide a model of the human skin?
3 What are a few traits of human skin that are not represented by the plastic wrap?

immune response is most effective against a pathogen that an organism has previously encountered. Third, the immune response works throughout the entire body of an organism.

Other scientists later discovered that lymphocytes are the key players in the immune response. How do lymphocytes know when to act? Lymphocytes respond to antigens. An **antigen** is a molecule that elicits the immune response. Most antigens are molecules on the surfaces of pathogens. Certain toxins are also antigens. The immune response recognizes that an antigen is foreign to the body.

Macrophages play an important role in the immune response by bringing antigens to the lymphocytes. When a macrophage engulfs an invading cell, proteins on the outer surface of the macrophage interact with proteins on the outer surface of the invading cells to form a hybrid protein. The hybrid proteins on the surface of macrophages are recognized by lymphocytes as antigens, and the immune response is generated. The body can mount two different immune responses to antigens: humoral immunity and cell-mediated immunity.

Humoral immunity Blood and lymph were once known as humors. For this reason, immunity against pathogens in the body fluids is called **humoral** (HYOO-muh-rul) **immunity** Antibodies in body fluids are the agents of humoral immunity. An **antibody** is a disease-fighting protein produced in response to a specific antigen.

Antibodies are produced by white blood cells called **B lymphocytes,** or B cells. B cells originate and then mature in the red marrow of bones. After they mature, B cells move to the lymph nodes where they secrete antibodies into the lymph and blood.

The antibodies made by each B cell are produced in response to a specific antigen. Antibodies are Y-shaped proteins with binding sites at the tips of the Y, as shown in *Figure* 32.7. The antibodies bind to an antigen like a key fits into a lock. Each antibody can bind to only one site on one antigen molecule. Antibodies do not destroy antigens— they mark them for destruction. For example, antibodies bound to antigens on the surface of bacteria clump the bacteria together. Clumped bacteria are engulfed by macrophages.

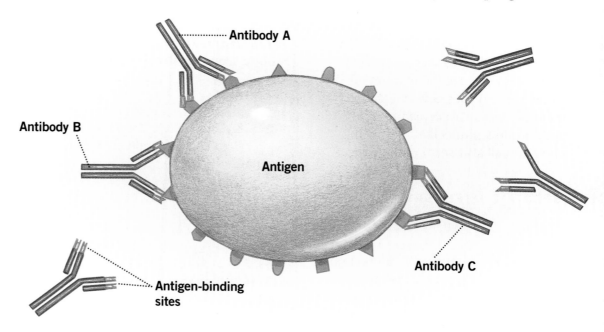

FIGURE 32.7
Antibodies attach to specific regions on antigens. Several types of antibodies may attach to one antigen. Each antibody is made of four proteins.

Pathogen

Macrophage

Macrophage after engulfing pathogen

Helper T cell

Receptors

Hybrid proteins

Stimulates killer T cells to divide

Killer T cell

Infected body cell

Antigen

Killer T cell

Ruptured body cell

Scientists estimate that your body has millions of different B cells, each ready to respond to a different antigen. When your body is exposed to a pathogen, B cells that recognize the antigens on the pathogen's surface respond by dividing many times. The result is a large army of B cells secreting antibodies against the pathogen.

Cell-mediated immunity A second immune response relies on lymphocytes themselves instead of antibodies produced by lymphocytes. In **cell-mediated immunity,** special lymphocytes directly attack cells that are harmful to the body. These harmful cells include cancerous cells, infected body cells, or cells of another person that enter the body during a transfusion or transplant. Because of cell-mediated immunity, organ transplants and skin grafts may be rejected. You can follow the process of cell-mediated immunity in *Figure 32.8.*

The specialized lymphocytes of cell-mediated immunity are T lymphocytes. **T lymphocytes,** or T cells, are white blood cells that recognize and destroy cells dangerous to a body. The T cells originate in the bone marrow, but they mature in the thymus gland. Unlike B cells, T cells do not produce antibodies. Each T cell has molecules on its surface that recognize a specific antigen on one type of dangerous cell.

There are several kinds of T cells. A cytotoxic T cell, or killer T cell, attacks a dangerous cell by producing a protein that ruptures the cell membrane. Killer T cells function in a manner similar to that of natural killer cells. However, unlike natural killer cells, killer T cells are specific — each killer T cell attacks only one specific type of dangerous cell.

Two other kinds of T cells, helper T cells and suppressor T cells, control the activity of killer T cells. Helper T cells stimulate killer T cells to divide, forming a large army of active killer T cells. Suppressor T cells inhibit the activity of other T cells when they are no longer needed. Helper T cells also play a role in humoral immunity and antibody production by stimulating B cells.

Because of specific proteins on their surface, helper T cells are also called T4 cells. T4 cells have recently received much attention because of their role in AIDS. You will learn about the role of T4 cells in AIDS later in this chapter.

Acquired immunity You probably know that if you have had certain diseases such as chicken pox or mumps you are immune to these diseases. Acquired immunity is the body's resistance to previously encountered pathogens. What happens when you acquire immunity?

FIGURE 32.8
During the cell-mediated immune response, macrophages with surface hybrid proteins bind and activate helper T cells with matching receptors. The helper T cells then stimulate killer T cells which also have matching receptors. The killer T cells divide, forming an army that recognizes and attacks infected body cells.

FIGURE 32.9
A killer T cell (right) recognizes an antigen on a cancer cell (left). The killer T cell will secrete a protein that destroys the cancer cell.

Coming Back to Haunt Us

The virus that causes chicken pox does not leave the body after the pox markings fade. In rare cases, the virus hides in the nerve cells of its host. It can emerge again in its host's adult body as a disease called shingles.

The first step toward acquired immunity is called the primary immune response which was just described. This response begins when the immune system encounters a new pathogen. Time is required for the antigen-specific B cells and T cells to be found, and for them to multiply. The primary response can take five to ten days to reach its maximum production of B and T cells. During this time, an infection can become widespread and cause serious illness.

The second time the body is infected by the same pathogen, the immune response is faster. The rapid response of the immune system to a pathogen it has previously encountered is called the secondary immune response. The secondary response is so fast that the pathogen is often destroyed before an illness occurs.

Specialized cells called memory cells are responsible for the secondary immune response. These cells store information about the antigens they have encountered in the past. Your body has both memory B cells and memory T cells. Both types of cells are made during the primary immune response. Whereas other B cells and T cells live only a few days, memory cells can live for decades or even for your entire life. During a second encounter with a pathogen, the memory cells respond at once to a particular antigen and begin to divide rapidly. The actions of memory cells result in the production of many antibodies and active T cells in a day or two.

CHECKPOINT 32.3

1. How do humoral immunity and cell-mediated immunity differ?
2. Describe the roles of three types of T lymphocytes.
3. **Critical Thinking** Develop a flowchart that traces the series of events involved in cell-mediated immunity.

Build on What You Know

4. Describe the structure of a virus. Why can killer T cells not destroy viruses directly? *(Need to jog your memory? Revisit relevant concepts in Chapter 14, Section 14.1.)*

 How do the different parts of the immune system respond to pathogens?

32.4 Health of the Immune System

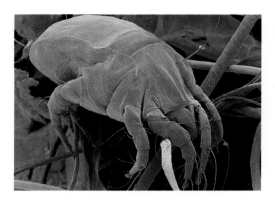

Dragons in your mattress
It may be too late to keep this creature out of your home. This is a dust mite that eats skin flakes and lives in mattresses, pillows, and carpets. In an average double bed there may be as many as 2 million dust mites. Each mite produces about 20 fecal pellets which, along with the bodies of dead mites, float up and provoke allergic sneezes in many people.

What you'll learn

IDEAS
• To identify causes of allergies
• To explain the effect of HIV on the immune system
• To analyze the effects of different lifestyles on the immune system

WORDS
allergy, autoimmune disease, HIV, vaccine

IMMUNE SYSTEM DISORDERS

A weakened army

The function of the immune system is to keep the body free of disease. But the activities of the immune system itself can sometimes cause unpleasant or even life-threatening problems. For example, fever is one way your immune system fights disease, but a very high fever can cause brain damage and other serious problems. Certain disorders can occur when the immune system overreacts or underreacts. If the immune system itself is attacked by pathogens, as in the case of AIDS, its normal functioning can be disrupted.

Allergies The immune system can usually distinguish pathogens from harmless chemicals and particles in the environment. However, the immune system occasionally reacts to a harmless substance as if it were an antigen, producing antibodies. This kind of response is called an **allergy.** For example, the symptoms of hay fever result from an allergy.

Earlier in this chapter you learned about the role of histamine in the inflammatory response. During an allergy attack, antibodies stimulate macrophages to release histamine. Histamine causes the blood vessels to expand, the eyes to produce tears, and the nasal passages to secrete mucus. Drugs called antihistamines decrease these actions of histamine.

Common causes of allergies include flower pollen, dust, mold spores, and some foods. You can see these kinds of particles in *Figure 32.10.* Chemical

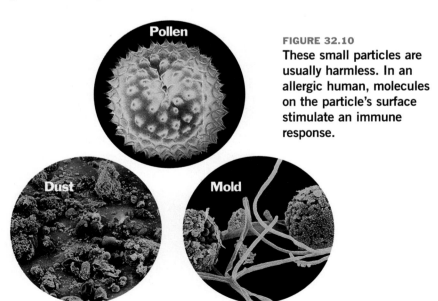

FIGURE 32.10
These small particles are usually harmless. In an allergic human, molecules on the particle's surface stimulate an immune response.

FIGURE 32.11

Humans have allergic reactions to the chemicals of plants like these. What characteristics of these plants would help you identify them?

Poison ivy

Poison oak

Poison sumac

substances in some plants—such as poison ivy, poison oak, and poison sumac—can also cause allergic reactions, including skin rashes and itching.

In a severe allergy attack, the blood vessels expand so much that blood pressure drops dangerously low and breathing may become difficult. Such an attack is called anaphylactic (a-nuh-fuh-LAK-tik) shock, and it can be life-threatening. Treatment with epinephrine, a chemical of the nervous system, reverses the effects of anaphylactic shock.

Autoimmune disorders
Sometimes the immune system mistakes its own cells for pathogens. When this happens, the immune system attacks the tissues of the body, causing an **autoimmune disease.** Multiple sclerosis is an autoimmune

disease. In multiple sclerosis, T cells destroy the myelin sheath that surrounds the nerve cells in the central nervous system. As the myelin sheath is destroyed, nerve cell function is disrupted. Some scientists think that Type I diabetes may result from an immune system attack on the insulin-producing cells of the pancreas. Scientists do not fully understand how and why the immune system sometimes turns against the body.

FRONTIERS IN BIOLOGY

Shutting down immunity

The immune system is the body's best natural defense against infectious diseases. However, some medical procedures are more successful when a person's immune system is inactive. Organ or tissue transplants are examples. After an organ transplant, the recipient's immune system identifies the new tissue as "nonself." Killer T cells rapidly multiply and attack the new tissue. A physician can stop a patient's body from rejecting a transplanted organ by administering drugs that suppress the patient's immune system.

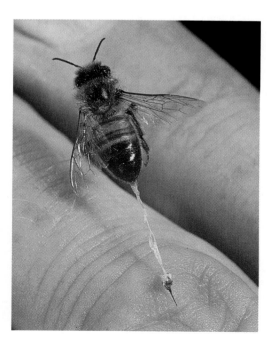

FIGURE 32.12

A sting from a bee stimulates an allergic reaction in some humans. What occurs during an allergy attack?

Drugs that suppress the immune system act by interrupting mitosis. With mitosis interrupted, immune cells cannot multiply in response to the presence of foreign tissue. Some cancer medications are also designed to interrupt mitosis, but in this case the goal is to stop the cancer cells from reproducing. Unfortunately, a side effect is to suppress the immune system, as well. As a result, cancer patients sometimes have weakened immune systems as a complication of their treatment.

AIDS

Living without defenses

AIDS stands for Acquired Immune Deficiency Syndrome. AIDS is not a specific disease; it is a condition in which the body's immune system cannot protect itself against pathogens. This condition is caused by the human immunodeficiency virus, or HIV. **HIV** is a virus that attacks the human immune system, destroying the body's ability to fight infection.

HIV replicates inside helper T cells, or T4 cells, eventually destroying them. As you have learned, T4 cells stimulate the production and activity of B cells and killer T cells. By attacking T4 cells, HIV interferes with both humoral and cell-mediated immunity and destroys the body's ability to defend itself.

HIV can be spread from one person to another only through direct contact of certain body fluids, such as blood, semen, or breast milk. HIV is not spread by casual contact, such as shaking hands or using dishes previously used by a person with HIV. It is also not transmitted by insects. Most often, HIV is transmitted through sexual intercourse, through the sharing of needles among intravenous (IV) drug users, or by the transfusion of contaminated blood products. HIV can

FIGURE 32.13
In this series of micrographs, you can see an HIV invading a T cell.

cross the placenta from mother to the fetus. It can also be transmitted to newborns through breast-feeding.

HIV infection is the fastest-growing epidemic in the world. Education about HIV is essential to reduce the incidence of the disease, as well as to improve people's attitudes toward those who have HIV.

At present, there is no known cure for HIV infection. Researchers worldwide are looking for effective treatments and cures, and trying to develop vaccines to prevent the disease. Even after years of research, there is much to be discovered about HIV. For now, the best way to prevent HIV infection is to learn as much as you can about HIV transmission and to avoid behaviors that place you at risk of contracting the virus.

Facts About HIV Transmission

Condoms reduce the risk of transmitting HIV from one person to another during sexual intercourse.

Using IV drugs and sharing needles with others who use IV drugs is one of the main ways HIV is transmitted from person to person. Having sexual intercourse with a person using IV drugs increases the risk of contracting HIV.

There is no risk of getting HIV while donating blood. HIV testing has almost eliminated the risk of getting HIV from receiving a blood transfusion.

FIGURE 32.14
HIV cannot be transmitted through casual contact. What other facts do you know about HIV transmission?

FIGURE 32.15

During the course of an HIV infection, the immune system becomes progressively weaker.

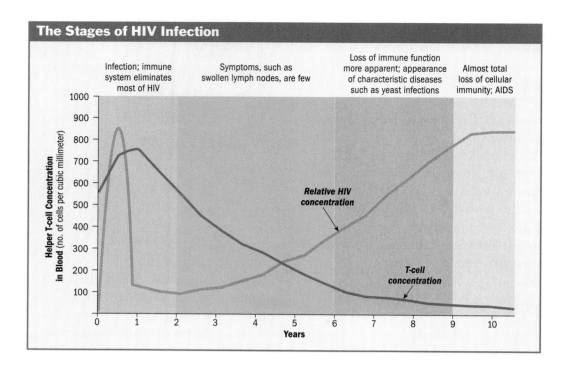

The Stages of HIV Infection

Infection; immune system eliminates most of HIV

Symptoms, such as swollen lymph nodes, are few

Loss of immune function more apparent; appearance of characteristic diseases such as yeast infections

Almost total loss of cellular immunity; AIDS

Helper T-cell Concentration in Blood (no. of cells per cubic millimeter)

Relative HIV concentration

T-cell concentration

Years

An HIV infection progresses along a fairly predictable course. Each stage of the infection is associated with certain symptoms, but the timing of the stages varies widely with different people.

When first infected by the virus, a person may have flulike symptoms or no symptoms at all. Within a few weeks to several months, antibodies to HIV begin to appear in the blood. The presence of antibodies in the blood is used to diagnose the disease and to screen donated blood. A person is said to be HIV-positive when HIV antibodies are present in the blood. However, even when a person is diagnosed as HIV-positive, other symptoms of the syndrome may not appear for months or years.

At first, an HIV-positive person may experience a phase of mild symptoms, including fever, weight loss, and swollen lymph nodes. As the HIV concentration increases, the T4 cell concentration decreases, and the immune response becomes less effective against disease. When the number of T4 cells in the body becomes so low that the immune system cannot fight disease,

an HIV infection has developed into AIDS. The length of time it takes for an HIV infection to become AIDS varies from person to person, but it may take an average of 10 years. *Figure 32.15* shows the change over time of T4 cell concentrations in blood.

People with AIDS may have a variety of diseases, including a kind of cancer called Kaposi's sarcoma. It was the outbreak of this rare cancer that led to the discovery of AIDS in 1981. Typically people with AIDS become sick when they are infected by pathogens that do not normally cause disease in people with healthy immune systems. These are called "opportunistic" infections because the pathogens have the opportunity to infect only people with unhealthy immune systems. For example, a kind of pneumonia caused by the protozoan *Pneumocystis carinii* is common among AIDS patients but rare among healthy people.

An HIV infection is generally considered fatal. However, not everyone who has been diagnosed as HIV-positive has developed AIDS. People with AIDS die when their body's weakened immune system cannot fight off an infection caused by a pathogen.

CARE OF YOUR IMMUNE SYSTEM

An ounce of prevention

Throughout this chapter, you have learned about how your immune system works to keep your body healthy. For your immune system to work at its best, however, it is essential that you practice behaviors that reduce your exposure to pathogens and help keep your body in good health. These behaviors are summarized in *Figure 32.16*.

Diet, exercise, and rest You know that food provides your body with the nutrients and energy your cells need to function properly. These functions include producing white blood cells and repairing cells that are damaged through injury or disease. To help all your other body systems work at their best, it is important that you eat a balanced diet that provides your body with the nutrients it needs.

In section 32.2, you learned that the squeezing action of skeletal muscles helps move lymph throughout the body. Exercise provides much of this action and therefore aids in this movement. Adequate rest is also important for keeping your body functioning at its best. For most people, adequate rest means getting about eight hours of sleep each night.

Personal hygiene Keeping your body clean is an important way to reduce your exposure to pathogens. Bathing or showering removes dirt and pathogens that may be present on the skin. Brushing your teeth several times each day reduces the number of bacteria that can enter your body through the mouth. Brushing your teeth also keeps your teeth healthy so you can digest your food properly.

Taking Care of Your Immune System
Eat a well-balanced and healthful diet.
Get plenty of exercise and rest.
Brush your teeth and bathe or shower regularly.
Keep your home clean.
Avoid tobacco, drugs, and alcohol.
Abstain from sexual activities.
Get vaccinations that prevent diseases.

FIGURE 32.16
There are many things a person can do to maintain the health of the immune system. In which ways do you maintain your immune system?

A clean environment You can help reduce the number of pathogens you come in contact with by keeping your home—particularly the kitchen and bathroom—clean. For example, you have learned that food contaminated with bacteria can cause food poisoning. By regularly cleaning surfaces where food is prepared, you can reduce your risk of picking up pathogens.

Avoiding drugs Drugs, alcohol, and tobacco products can have harmful effects on the body. Many types of drugs, including alcohol, can slow or suppress the immune system. And as you just learned, sharing needles

LAB ZONE Do It!

Creating a Personal Health Journal

You can check on the status of your health habits by creating a personal health journal for your own use.

Try This

1 Look at the list of behaviors in Figure 32.16.
2 Write each of the behaviors at the top of a separate piece of paper.
3 Jot down your habits related to each behavior during a typical week.

Analyze Your Results

1 Do you think that your weekly habits are healthy?
2 Clip the pages together and place them in your journal. Continue to record your health behaviors in your journal.

IN THE COMMUNITY

Shots for Everyone

among IV drug users is one of the main ways HIV is transmitted. This practice also provides a means by which other pathogens, including the viruses that cause the various types of hepatitis, can be transmitted.

Sexual responsibility In this chapter, you learned that HIV, syphilis, gonorrhea, and some other diseases can be spread through sexual contact with an infected person. The only way to absolutely prevent exposure to sexually transmitted diseases is to abstain from all sexual activity. For sexually active people, the use of condoms can reduce the risk of exposure. You will learn more about sexually transmitted diseases in Chapter 33.

Vaccinations Many serious diseases can be prevented through the use of vaccines. A **vaccine** is a preparation containing dead or weakened pathogens that is designed to increase the body's immunity. The pathogens in a vaccine are too weak to cause illness, but their presence stimulates the immune system to make antibodies

that resist the disease. Vacinations have almost eliminated diseases, such as polio, that were once widespread.

CHECKPOINT 32.4

1. What is an allergy? Identify three common causes of allergies.
2. Explain the roles of diet, exercise, good hygiene, and vaccination in keeping the immune system healthy.
3. **Critical Thinking** Bone marrow transplants are a method of treatment being considered for some AIDS patients. How might a bone marrow transplant benefit some AIDS patients? What might be some problems with this treatment?

Build on What You Know

4. In this chapter, you learned about the lock-and-key binding of antibodies to an antigen. What other biological example with a similar type of system have you learned about? *(Need to jog your memory? Revisit relevant concepts in Chapter 14, Section 14.1.)*

How do you care for your immune system?

Chapter 32 Review

THE BIG IDEA!

32.1 The immune system protects the body from harmful organisms and substances.

32.2–32.3 The immune system consists of specialized cells, organs, and organ systems that respond to the presence of a pathogen.

32.4 A healthy immune system requires a healthy lifestyle.

Sum It Up

Use the following summary to review the main concepts in this chapter.

32.1 Protecting the Organism

- The immune system fights infections.
- Koch's postulates provide a method for identifying the cause of an infectious disease.
- Diseases can be spread by direct contact with an infected person, by indirect contact through the air, through contaminated food or water, and by animal bites.
- Most vertebrates have both nonspecific and specific defenses against disease. Nonspecific defenses are effective against many different types of pathogens. Specific defenses, or the immune response, protect an organism against specific pathogens.

32.2 Overview of the Immune System

- The lymphatic system is a network of organs and vessels. The lymphatic and circulatory systems are intertwined.
- White blood cells stored in lymph nodes attack pathogens in lymph fluid.
- The lymphatic system collects, filters, and returns plasma that leaks from the bloodstream.
- Some leukocytes engulf unwanted cells and pathogens in a nonspecific manner. Others recognize and attack specific pathogens.

32.3 Activities of the Immune System

- The body's first line of defense—skin, mucus, tears, and sweat—acts as a barrier to pathogens.
- Histamine, released by injured cells, increases blood flow—bringing phagocytes and platelets to the injured area.
- Interferon and natural killer cells are nonspecific defenses against viruses.
- B cells attack specific pathogens by producing antibodies that bind to antigens on the pathogens' surface. T cells can directly attack cells recognized as dangerous to the body. The body can acquire immunity to pathogens.

32.4 Health of the Immune System

- Sometimes the immune system responds to harmless substances, or even to the body's own cells, as though they were pathogens. Organ transplants require suppression of the body's immune system.
- By attacking helper T cells, or T4 cells, HIV interferes with humoral and cell-mediated immunity.
- A well-balanced diet, exercise, rest, and vaccinations contribute to a healthy immune system. Maintaining personal hygiene and avoiding drugs and unsafe sexual activities limit exposure to pathogens.

Use Terms and Concepts

Use each of the following words or terms in a complete sentence. If you need to review a meaning, turn to the page indicated.

pathogen (p. 770)
nonspecific defenses (p. 773)
specific defenses (p. 773)
lymph (p. 774)
lymph nodes (p. 774)

phagocytes (p. 775)
macrophages (p. 775)
lymphocytes (p. 775)
inflammatory response (p. 778)
histamine (p. 778)
antigen (p. 780)

humoral immunity (p. 780)
antibody (p. 780)
B lymphocytes (p.780)
cell-mediated immunity (p. 781)
T lymphocytes (p. 781)

allergy (p. 783)
autoimmune disease (p. 784)
HIV (p. 785)
vaccine (p. 788)

Use Your Word Power

MATCHING **Write the term from the list of key terms that best matches each of the phrases below.**

1. A response designed to protect against a specific toxin or pathogen.

2. Molecules that trigger an immune response.

3. A virus that destroys helper T cells.

4. Densely-packed areas of tissue in which white cells are stored.

5. The response of the immune system to a normally harmless chemical such as a food protein.

6. An organism or virus that causes an infectious disease.

7. The white blood cells that produce antibodies.

MULTIPLE CHOICE **Choose the letter of the word or phrase that best completes each statement.**

8. An inflammatory response is triggered by (a) an antigen; (b) an antibody; (c) histamine; (d) pyrogens.

9. An example of a nonspecific defense is a(n) (a) antibody; (b) macrophage; (c) T lymphocyte; (d) vaccine.

10. The attack of cancer cells by lymphocytes is an example of (a) cell-mediated immunity; (b) an autoimmune response; (c) humoral immunity; (d) an inflammatory response.

11. The major component of pus is (a) lymph; (b) mucus; (c) phagocytes; (d) lymphocytes.

12. Vaccines stimulate the production of (a) antigens; (b) antibodies; (c) T lymphocytes; (d) histamine.

Show What You Know

13. Compare the roles of phagocytes and natural killer cells.

14. Is the transmission of HIV an example of direct or indirect contact? Explain.

15. Describe two ways that a person can acquire immunity to a specific disease.

16. What information could doctors obtain by examining lymph nodes?

17. What is the role of B cells in the immune system?

18. Why is bone marrow considered part of the immune system?

19. What can a T4 cell count indicate?

20. How do expanded blood vessels help heal injured tissues?

21. **Make a Concept Map** Some people are allergic to sulfur-containing compounds called sulfites, which are used as food preservatives. Create a concept map that describes the immune system's response to sulfites.

Take It Further

22. **Developing a Hypothesis** Cardiovascular diseases are the major cause of death in the United States. Infectious diseases are the primary cause of death worldwide. Suggest possible reasons for the difference.

23. **Applying Concepts** If a doctor wants to know whether a patient has an infection, the doctor may draw blood and ask for a test called a white blood cell count. Explain the reasons for the doctor's action.

24. **Applying Concepts** What does it mean to describe a pathogen as waterborne or airborne?

25. **Applying Concepts** Why is a second bee sting more dangerous than the first for a person who is allergic to bee stings?

26. **Designing an Experiment** Suppose a student needs to provide proof of immunity to certain diseases before entering college, but the student is unable to locate any record of his or her vaccinations. Design an experiment that would show which vaccines the student had received.

27. Interpreting a Graph The graph below shows the fatality rates for reported cases of AIDS in adults and adolescents in the United States for specific years. Which year had the highest percentage of deaths among reported cases of AIDS? Which year had the highest number of deaths? Explain how the year with the lowest percentage of fatalities could have the highest number of deaths.

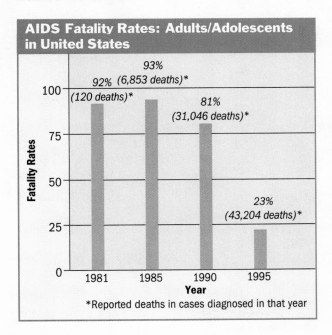

AIDS Fatality Rates: Adults/Adolescents in United States

93%
92% (6,853 deaths)*
(120 deaths)*
81%
(31,046 deaths)*
23%
(43,204 deaths)*

Fatality Rates

1981   1985   1990   1995
Year
*Reported deaths in cases diagnosed in that year

28. Analyzing Data A person with red, itchy, swollen skin might have contact dermatitis. The culprit might be clothing, metal jewelry, or a cosmetic product. The following statistics show how different categories of cosmetic products contribute to the overall incidence of dermatitis caused by cosmetics. Skin products, 28% of cases; hair products, 24%; facial makeup, 11%; nail products, 8%; fragrances, 7%; personal hygiene products, 6%; shaving products, 4%; eye makeup, 4%; sunscreens and suntan lotions, 3%; other cosmetic products, 5%. What percent of cases result from makeup? The fragrance category includes items such as colognes. In what other cosmetics might colognes be used? What do you think it means when a product is labeled "hypoallergenic"?

Consider the Issues

29. Allergies on the menu Food allergies are common in humans. Examples include allergies to peanuts, garlic, or citrus fruits. While some food allergy reactions are minor, others can be severe, or even lethal. Do you think school or office cafeterias should avoid foods commonly associated with allergies in the dishes they prepare? Should they post ingredients to all dishes? What other solutions can you think of to help people with food allergies?

Make New Connections

30. Biology and First Aid Call your local Poison Control Center. Find out what to do if a person ingests a poison. Prepare a poster to educate others.

31. Biology and Consumer Education Make a survey of over-the-counter (OTC) medications. Ask a local pharmacist what OTC products are best-sellers. Which of these products contain antihistamines? How would antihistamines help an allergy victim's runny nose?

32. Biology and Medicine Non-Hodgkin lymphoma, a cancer of the immune system, is the sixth most common cancer in the United States. Research the theories that have been proposed to explain this cancer's rapid increase in recent decades. Evaluate the evidence for each theory.

FAST-FORWARD TO CHAPTER 33

The thymus gland is one of the glands in the endocrine system. The hormones produced in the endocrine system help regulate body functions. You will learn about the endocrine and reproductive systems in Chapter 33.

bioSURF

You can find out more about the endocrine and reproductive systems at the following Internet address: *http://body_systems.biosurf.com*

In this chapter . . .

FEATURES

Everyday Biology
• Instant Sleep?
• Funny, You Don't Look Like Twins

In the Community
Making the Most of Long Life

 Issues in Biology
Dangers of Steroids

Frontiers in Biology
Health of the Fetus

LAB ZONES

Discover It!
• Observing Newborns

Do It!
• Can You Raise Your Pulse Rate?
• What Is the Average Human Growth Rate?

Think About It!
• Comparing STD Occurrence

Investigate It!
• Identifying a Negative Feedback System

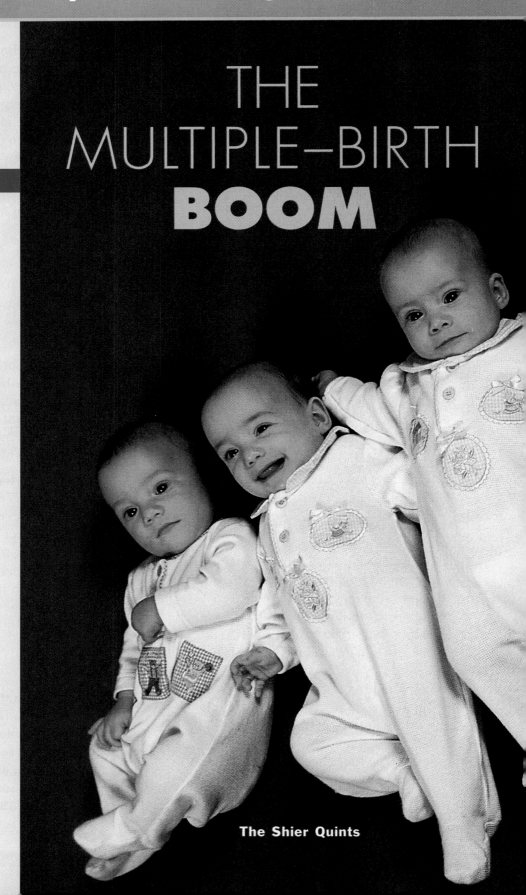

THE MULTIPLE–BIRTH BOOM

The Shier Quints

Observing Newborns

You need *photographs of newborn humans*

1. Examine photographs of newborn humans.
2. Record your observations of several newborns. Do they all seem to share certain characteristics? If so, what are they?

The development of a newborn human from a fertilized egg is truly dramatic. In this chapter, you will learn about reproduction, including the growth and development of the fetus prior to birth.

WRITE ABOUT IT!

Write a paragraph or a poem from the point of view of a human newborn. In your writing, express the sensory changes you think a baby may be experiencing as it is born.

When the Shiers or the Aymondses go out on a family excursion, they are the object of intense interest. Maybe it is the sight of five children—all the same age! The Shier and Aymonds quintuplets are part of a growing trend toward multiple births. In 1992, there were 23 sets of quints in the United States; in 1996, there were at least 40.

How do multiple-birth families cope? Faced with lack of sleep, mounds of daily diapers, and countless other challenges, many families like these two manage their situation with a lot of help from family and friends.

The Aymond Quints

Whether it leads to a single birth or to multiple births, reproduction is a complex process that relies on hormones. How are hormones involved? How are eggs fertilized, and how do they develop? What other body systems are affected by hormones? You will find the answers to these questions as you learn more about the endocrine and reproductive systems.

33.1 Endocrine Control

The caregiving hormone
A chemical may not be warm and cuddly, but a chemical messenger called prolactin induces protective, nurturing behavior in many animals. In mammalian mothers, prolactin stimulates milk production. In birds, this hormone can make even nonparents care for eggs and bring food to baby birds.

FUNCTIONS OF ENDOCRINE SYSTEMS

Controlling slow changes

An animal's cells, tissues, and organs need control systems to coordinate and regulate their many activities. In most animals two control systems work to regulate these activities—the nervous system and the endocrine system. These two systems monitor all other body systems in order to respond to changes and maintain homeostasis.

Although both the nervous system and the endocrine system act to control the body, they do so in different ways. The nervous system controls the body through high-speed nerve impulses. It can quickly respond to immediate changes either inside or outside the body. In contrast, the endocrine system controls the body by means of chemical messengers. The endocrine system brings about slower, longer-lasting responses and changes that may occur over hours or years. For example, an animal's changes as it develops into an adult are controlled by the endocrine system.

Hormones are the chemical messengers of the endocrine system.

Specialized endocrine cells secrete hormones. In vertebrates, including humans, endocrine cells are located in organs called **endocrine glands.** Hormones are produced in one part of an animal's body, but usually affect another part of the body. Hormones control a wide range of activities that include growth, development, metabolism, behavior, and reproduction.

ENDOCRINE SYSTEMS IN ANIMALS

Hormones in control

The best understood feature of invertebrate endocrine systems is hormonal control of reproduction. For example, the cnidarian *Hydra* uses one hormone to stimulate growth and asexual reproduction by budding. The same hormone suppresses sexual reproduction. The mollusk *Aplysia*, also known as the sea hare, produces a hormone that stimulates egg laying. This hormone also suppresses feeding and movement, behaviors that could prevent the animal from laying eggs.

Arthropods have diverse and complex endocrine systems. Crustaceans, such as crabs and lobsters, produce a variety of hormones. These hormones

FIGURE 33.1
Hormones control whether this hydra will reproduce sexually or asexually.

control processes such as growth, reproduction, homeostasis, metabolism, and coloration. The hormonal control of insect molting is the most well understood. During molting, an insect sheds its old exoskeleton and secretes a new one. Molting also involves changes and growth in the insect's body. All of these processes are controlled by three different hormones secreted by the insect.

The endocrine systems of vertebrates, such as amphibians, reptiles, birds, and mammals, produce more than 20 different hormones. These hormones control a range of activities including growth, development, and reproduction. For example, hormones in amphibians trigger the metamorphosis that changes a tadpole into a frog. In mammals, specific hormones support pregnancy, trigger the birth of young, and make the mother's mammary glands produce milk.

Hormones are not exclusive to the animal kingdom. As you may recall from Chapter 19, plant hormones trigger growth and reproduction. Stem growth and the production of flowers and fruits are two examples of hormone action. What is the name given to plant hormones?

CHECKPOINT 33.1

1. What are the functions of the endocrine system?

2. Give examples of endocrine control in three groups of animals.

3. Critical Thinking Why is it advantageous for an animal to have both a nervous and an endocrine system?

Build on What You Know

4. How does the circulatory system carry hormones to body parts? *(**Need to jog your memory?** Revisit relevant concepts in Chapter 31, Section 31.4.)*

FIGURE 33.3
Three hormones that interact with the nervous system and each other monitor molting in arthropods. Why does an arthropod have to molt?

FIGURE 33.4
Hormones control many activities in mammals, including reproduction, birth, and milk production.

33.2 Human Endocrine System

What you'll learn

IDEAS
- To identify and describe the human endocrine glands
- To analyze how hormones function

WORDS
hypothalamus, pituitary gland, feedback control, insulin, glucagon

Do, re, mi . . .
Why do a female's vocal cords produce sounds with a higher pitch than the sounds produced by a male's vocal cords? This occurs because the surge of hormones produced in the body of an adolescent male causes the vocal cords—a pair of muscles inside the larynx—to thicken. Thinner vocal cords vibrate more rapidly than thicker ones, which is why females can reach those high soprano notes.

EVERYDAY BIOLOGY

Instant Sleep?

As we age, the pineal gland makes less melatonin, a hormone that helps regulate our sleep cycle. Scientists are investigating whether taking melatonin capsules might be a safe way to promote sleep.

THE ENDOCRINE GLANDS

Ductless control

As you now know, the organs of the human endocrine system are the endocrine glands. Located throughout the body, these ductless glands secrete hormones directly into the bloodstream. You can see some of the human endocrine glands and read about the hormones they produce in *Figure* 33.5. What types of activities are controlled by hormones?

Humans produce over 20 different hormones, each with a different function. Because the blood carries the hormones to all parts of the body, each hormone reaches many organs. Some hormones affect many organs, while others affect only one or a few organs. In the organs, the cells that are affected by hormones are called target cells.

Some endocrine glands are also a part of other body systems. For example, the pancreas is part of both the endocrine system and the digestive system. As an endocrine gland, the pancreatic endocrine cells called islets of Langerhans release hormones directly into the blood.

The pancreas also releases sodium bicarbonate and enzymes directly into the digestive tract, as you may

remember from Chapter 30. As a digestive organ, the pancreas acts as an exocrine gland. Unlike a ductless endocrine gland, an exocrine gland has tubelike ducts that carry secretions directly to a specific location.

There are also exocrine glands in your stomach that secrete digestive acids. Other exocrine glands in the human body are sweat glands and salivary glands. What substances are produced by sweat glands and salivary glands?

The endocrine system and the nervous system are both functionally and structurally connected. As you have learned, both of these systems regulate the activities of the body.

One important link between the endocrine system and the nervous system is the hypothalamus. A part of the nervous system, the **hypothalamus** is the region of the brain that controls blood pressure, body temperature, and emotions. The hypothalamus is also an endocrine gland that makes and secretes hormones. The hypothalamus is physically connected to the pituitary gland and controls the release of pituitary hormones. You will learn more about the functions of the pituitary gland and the hypothalamus and their interactions later in this chapter.

FIGURE 33.5

Human Endocrine System

Endocrine glands produce hormones
that control many body functions.

Hypothalamus
The hypothalamus makes hormones that control the pituitary gland. It also makes the hormones ADH and oxytocin, which are stored in the pituitary gland.

Pituitary gland
Responding to signals from the hypothalamus, the pituitary gland releases hormones some of which control other endocrine glands.

Pineal gland
The pineal gland secretes melatonin, which controls body functions in response to daylight and seasonal changes.

Parathyroid gland
These four patches of tissue on the thyroid gland release the parathyroid hormone, which regulates the blood calcium level.

Thyroid gland
The hormone thyroxine, which speeds up metabolism and helps manage growth and development, is secreted by the thyroid gland.

Thymus
Thymosin, which stimulates the development of T cells for the immune system, is secreted by the thymus.

Pancreas
The pancreas has patches of tissue called the islets of Langerhans, which have cells that make the hormones insulin and glucagon. Insulin and glucagon control the blood sugar level.

Adrenal glands
The adrenal glands make epinephrine and norepinephrine, two hormones which cause the "fight or flight" response. They also secrete aldosterone, which affects the body's osmotic balance, and cortisol, which promotes glucose synthesis.

Ovaries
The hormones estrogen and progesterone are made in the ovaries. They maintain the female reproductive system and secondary sex characteristics. Progesterone maintains the uterus during pregnancy.

Testes
The testes make testosterone, a hormone that maintains the male reproductive system and secondary sex characteristics.

FIGURE 33.6
Both lobes of the pituitary gland are controlled by the hypothalamus but release different hormones.

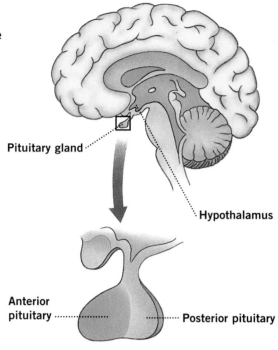

Pituitary gland

Hypothalamus

Anterior pituitary

Posterior pituitary

FIGURE 33.7
What other endocrine glands are controlled by the pituitary gland?

CONTROL BY HORMONES
The message is chemical

When a hormone reaches its target organ, the hormone binds with specific molecules in target cells. Just as a specific key opens a specific lock, a hormone binds only to specific target cells.

The effect of a hormone on a cell depends on the type of hormone it is. Protein hormones are peptides—chains of amino acids. Protein hormones bind to receptor molecules on the outside of a target cell membrane and cause a substance protein inside the

cell to be activated. This protein then activates enzymes that change the cell's activity.

Steroid hormones are made of lipids. A steroid hormone can enter a cell easily because lipids pass easily through cell membranes. Once inside a target cell, steroid hormones cause changes in a cell by gene regulation. As you have learned, gene regulation can alter a cell's activity. A steroid hormone causes a specific section of DNA to "turn on" or "turn off." This affects the production of proteins coded by the genes near that section of DNA.

Different hormones can control the activities of a target organ through opposing effects. Usually, one hormone will stimulate an organ while another will inhibit it. The balance of the two opposing hormones affects the organ's functions.

Many organs, including endocrine glands, are controlled by hormones. The **pituitary gland** releases hormones that control several other endocrine glands. As you can see in *Figure 33.6,* the hypothalamus is located directly above the pituitary gland. The pituitary and hypothalamus are connected by blood vessels and nerves. Nerve impulses allow the hypothalamus to control the pituitary directly. The pituitary gland has two lobes—an anterior lobe and a posterior lobe. These lobes secrete different

Pituitary Hormones	
Anterior Lobe Hormones	**Functions**
Growth hormone (GH)	Stimulates the division and growth of bone, muscle, and other body cells
Thyroid-stimulating hormone (TSH)	Stimulates the development and activity of the thyroid gland
Adrenocorticotropic hormone (ACTH)	Stimulates the adrenal glands to secrete other hormones
Follicle-stimulating hormone (FSH)	Stimulates the gonads to produce eggs and sperm
Luteinizing hormone (LH)	Stimulates the gonads to produce sex hormones
Posterior Lobe Hormones	**Functions**
Antidiuretic hormone (ADH)	Controls water absorption by the kidney
Oxytocin	Stimulates uterine contractions during childbirth and the flow of milk while nursing

hormones with different functions. The table in *Figure 33.7* summarizes these functions.

One function of the hypothalamus and the pituitary gland is to regulate the reproductive system by stimulating the sex organs to secrete sex hormones. The main sex hormone produced in males is testosterone. In females, the main sex hormones produced are estrogen and progesterone.

At puberty, usually between the ages of 10 and 16 for human males and females, the hypothalamus stimulates the pituitary gland to release two hormones—luteinizing (LOO-tuh-ny-zing) hormone (LH) and follicle-stimulating hormone (FSH). LH stimulates the gonads—testes or ovaries—to produce sex hormones. LH also stimulates the release of an egg from an ovary. FSH stimulates the testes to produce sperm and the ovaries to produce eggs.

Large amounts of sex hormones released by the testes or ovaries cause the development of secondary sex characteristics. In males, these characteristics include the growth of facial and body hair and a deepening of the voice. In females, secondary sex characteristics include the growth of the breasts and the widening of the hips.

One way in which pituitary and other hormones regulate the body is through feedback control. In **feedback control,** the rate of a process is controlled by a substance made in the process. There are two types of feedback control—negative and positive. In negative feedback control, the product of the process inhibits, or stops, the process. In positive feedback control, the product of the process accelerates the process.

Figure 33.8 shows how the pancreas regulates the blood sugar level with negative feedback control. When blood sugar is high, cells called beta (β) cells in the pancreas produce insulin. **Insulin** is a hormone that stimulates

FIGURE 33.8

Negative feedback control manages the relationship between insulin and glucagon. What factor affects the release of both hormones from the pancreas?

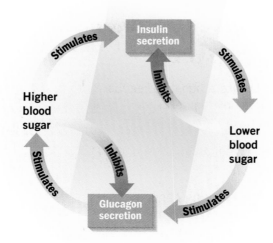

cells to absorb sugar from the blood and causes the liver to convert blood sugar, or glucose, to glycogen. The end result of insulin secretion—lower blood sugar—inhibits insulin secretion.

When blood sugar is low, alpha (α) cells in the pancreas produce glucagon. **Glucagon** is a hormone that stimulates the liver and muscles to convert stored glycogen into glucose, raising the amount of glucose in the blood. High blood sugar, in turn, inhibits glucagon secretion.

CHECKPOINT 33.2

1. Name four major endocrine glands and list their functions.

2. What are insulin and glucagon, and how are their functions related?

3. Critical Thinking Make an analogy between a thermostat and the control of the blood sugar level by hormones.

Build on What You Know

4. How do the functions of human hormones compare with the functions of plant hormones? *(Need to jog your memory? Revisit relevant concepts in Chapter 19, Section 19.1.)*

Investigate It!

Identifying a Negative Feedback System

WHAT YOU WILL DO Locate a negative feedback system in your everyday environment. Identify and analyze the elements of the system.

SKILLS YOU WILL USE Predicting, observing and recording data, organizing

WHAT YOU WILL NEED Sketching paper

Background Information

A home heating system is an example of a system controlled by negative feedback. The flow of heat through a house is controlled to keep room temperatures at a steady level. The mechanism of control is a thermostat—a thin coil made of two different metals fastened together. Because the different metals expand and contract at different rates, the coil bends and unbends with changes in air temperature. The moving coil pushes on an electric switch that turns the heat source on or off.

The four elements of a negative feedback system are 1) the process that is controlled (in this case the flow of heat); 2) the feedback signal (here the measured air temperature); 3) the feedback mechanism (in this case the thermostat and switch); and 4) the outcome (here a steady level of desired heat measured as a constant room temperature).

Propose a Hypothesis

Find a system in your everyday life that you think is controlled by negative feedback. Propose a hypothesis about how accurately this model represents a negative feedback system in your body.

Conduct Your Experiment

1 List and diagram the parts of your proposed negative feedback system.
2 Identify the process that is controlled.
3 Identify the feedback signal.
4 Identify the feedback mechanism.
5 Identify the outcome of the system.

Analyze Your Data

How do the parts of your negative feedback system interact?

Draw Conclusions

Analyze a human body system that involves negative feedback. Are the same elements present in the body mechanism that were present in the heating system example? Diagram them in the same way.

Design a Related Experiment

Design a model of a negative feedback system that you could build yourself.

Lab: Identifying a Negative Feedback System

Objective: To select a negative feedback system in everyday life and analyze how it works

My hypothesis:

33.3 Health of the Endocrine System

Mom's milk, Mom's touch

Mother's milk protects a baby against disease. Immune factors made by a mother's body are passed to her child with each drop of milk. Besides the content of her milk, the touch of a mother or any other caring human also helps to keep a baby healthy. Stroking a baby starts a chain of hormonal messages that help the baby's cells absorb more food.

What you'll learn

IDEAS
• To distinguish between disorders of the endocrine system
• To assess the dangers of steroid use

WORDS
diabetes mellitus

ENDOCRINE SYSTEM DISORDERS

Out of control

When the messages carried by the endocrine system are not sent or received, the body cannot function properly. One of the most serious endocrine disorders is diabetes mellitus (dy-uh-BEE-teez ME-luh-tus). **Diabetes mellitus** is a disorder in which the body is unable to control blood sugar levels. Diabetes may lead to a dangerously high level of glucose in the blood, which can result in a coma or even death. The kidneys of a person who suffers from diabetes release large amounts of glucose in the urine. Sugar in the urine is one of the main warning signs of diabetes mellitus.

There are two main types of diabetes mellitus. The more serious type, Type I diabetes, is also called juvenile diabetes because it usually develops during childhood. In Type I diabetes, the beta cells of the islets of Langerhans do not produce insulin. The treatment for Type I diabetes requires regular injections of insulin and a carefully controlled diet. In the past, insulin was obtained from animal sources. Today, human insulin can be made in bacteria through genetic engineering.

Type II diabetes usually develops in people over the age of 40. In Type II diabetes, the beta cells may produce insulin, but body cells do not respond to the hormone properly. As a result, not enough glucose is removed from the blood. Type II diabetes is treated with exercise, medication, and a carefully controlled diet. People with either type of diabetes are advised to control the intake of sugary foods in their diets.

Disorders of other endocrine glands can cause problems in development or metabolism. For example, when the thyroid gland does not produce enough thyroid hormone—a condition called hypothyroidism—the body's metabolism slows down. A person feels sluggish and cold and may gain weight easily. In hyperthyroidism, the opposite condition, a person feels irritable and has high body temperature, sweating, weight loss, and high blood pressure.

Long-term stress can be harmful to your body because of the effects on the endocrine system. Short-term stress causes the adrenal glands to secrete epinephrine and norepinephrine. These two protein hormones are involved in what is called the "fight or flight" response. This response helps the body in an emergency by increasing alertness and providing a

FIGURE 33.9
Human insulin made by genetically engineered bacteria, is being packaged. What is the advantage of using human insulin to treat diabetes, as opposed to using insulin from other animals?

Do It!

Can You Raise Your Pulse Rate?

Stress can affect your circulatory system. Your pulse can give you an indication of how your heart is doing. You can monitor your heart rate if you . . .

Try This

1 Follow your teacher's directions to find, measure and record your pulse rate.
2 To check your results, take your neighbor's pulse rate.
3 Visualize an upsetting situation such as a surprise quiz. Take your pulse again.

Analyze Your Results

1 How did your pulse rate change?
2 How can you explain the change in your pulse rate?

burst of energy. Epinephrine and nor-epinephrine do this by raising the blood pressure and the blood glucose levels. When stress occurs over a long period of time, the adrenal glands secrete steroid hormones instead of the two protein hormones. Long-term exposure to steroid hormones can cause increased blood pressure and a suppressed immune system.

To maintain the health of your endocrine system, your body needs proper diet, exercise, and rest. Your diet needs to contain adequate protein and lipids to make all the various protein and steroid hormones. Exercise and rest help you manage stress and prevent overproduction of the adrenal hormones. You can also help your endocrine system by being aware of the symptoms of a disorder, such as diabetes or hypothyroidism, and seeking prompt treatment if necessary.

ISSUES IN BIOLOGY
Dangers of steroids

The growth and maturation of your body depends on the endocrine system. Growth hormone will increase your height up to the time of your teens or early twenties. Sex hormones maintain the secondary sex characteristics in both males and females for a lifetime.

Sometimes young people are tempted to "boost" their development by abusing drugs that affect the endocrine system. Anabolic steroids are hormones that athletes and body-builders sometimes use illegally to stimulate the growth of muscles and increase strength and performance.

Steroid use can disrupt many body systems and eventually cause liver and heart disease. In males it can cause testes to shrink and female sex characteristics to develop. Females who take steroids may stop menstruating and develop male sex characteristics, such as increased body hair and a deep voice. Young people who take steroids can develop serious health problems that can lead to an early death.

CHECKPOINT 33.3

1. Name and describe two disorders of the endocrine system.
2. How can steroids affect human health?
3. Critical Thinking A friend of yours is thinking about using steroids to build bigger muscles. What could you say to discourage this person?

Build on What You Know

4. How is genetic engineering used to produce insulin? *(Need to jog your memory? Revisit relevant concepts in Chapter 9, Section 9.2.)*

 What are the functions of the endocrine system?

33.4 Reproduction

Many are called—one is chosen
A drop of human semen may contain five million sperm cells. Most of the sperm cells die as they race toward an egg. Many sperm cells live to lock onto the egg's surface, as shown in this photomicrograph. As soon as one sperm breaks through the egg's coating, the egg secretes a substance that prevents other sperm cells from entering.

What you'll learn

IDEAS
• To distinguish between the human male and female reproductive systems
• To describe the human female reproductive cycle

WORDS
eggs, sperm, testes, penis, ovary, uterus, ovarian cycle, menstrual cycle, ovum, ovulation, menstruation

REPRODUCTION IN ANIMALS

And so on . . .

If a species is to survive, individual members of the species must reproduce, or make offspring. In humans and other multicellular animals, the body system that accomplishes this task is the reproductive system. The reproductive system uses hormones to trigger sexual maturity so that an organism is physically able to reproduce. The reproductive system also produces the cells that develop into the new individual. In some organisms, the reproductive system provides a place for the new individual to grow and develop.

Some animals, such as sponges and cnidarians, can reproduce asexually. Each individual can grow a new individual from body cells. Only one parent is required. The result is an offspring that is genetically identical to the parent.

In animals that reproduce sexually, the reproductive system produces sex cells called gametes (GAM-eets). Recall from Chapter 5 that gametes are haploid sex cells that contain only half of the normal number of chromosomes. Females produce large gametes called **eggs.** Males produce much smaller gametes called **sperm.**

Sexual reproductive systems can vary widely from one type of animal to another. For example, some annelids have separate sexes but do not have specialized organs to produce gametes. The gametes are made by cells in the body cavity and leave the body through excretory pores. In insects, males have organs that produce sperm, and a system of ducts and storage vesicles that release the sperm during mating. Female insects have organs that produce eggs, and ducts that carry the eggs to a body opening where fertilization can occur.

Vertebrates, such as birds and mammals, also have complex reproductive systems. Males have sex organs that produce sperm and a system of ducts

FIGURE 33.10
How does this sea anemone, a cnidarian, reproduce?

FIGURE 33.11

Why might the fishes shown above release large numbers of eggs at one time when they reproduce?

FIGURE 33.12

A penguin's egg is fertilized internally but develops externally. What do you think the male penguin in the photo above is doing with the developing egg?

FIGURE 33.13

In some mammals, such as the kangaroo, development of the young takes place both internally and externally. Where are the kangaroo's eggs fertilized?

that carry the sperm out of the body when needed. Females have sex organs that produce and transport eggs. Both male and female sex organs produce hormones to control sexual function. As you can see above in *Figure 33.11,* some vertebrates, such as fishes, reproduce externally. The female lays eggs to be fertilized outside of her body. Other vertebrates, such as those in *Figures 33.12* and *33.13,* fertilize eggs internally. The female either lays the fertilized eggs, or the young develop inside her body.

REPRODUCTION IN HUMANS

Dynamic duos

Humans, like other mammals, reproduce sexually. Each individual has a reproductive system made up of either male or female reproductive organs. Production of eggs, fertilization, and development all take place inside structures of the female reproductive

system. The function of the male reproductive system is to produce sperm cells and deliver them to the female reproductive system.

Male reproductive organs *Figure 33.14* shows the human male reproductive system. The **testes** (singular: *testis*) are the male organs that produce sperm cells and the hormone testosterone. Each male has two testes. At puberty the testes begin to produce large amounts of testosterone, starting sperm cell production and the development of secondary sex characteristics.

The testes are inside a sac called the scrotum. Before birth, a male's testes are inside the pelvic cavity. The testes move down into the scrotum just before birth. Located outside the body cavity, the scrotum protects the testes and keeps them slightly cooler than body temperature. The cooler temperature is important for sperm cell development and survival.

FIGURE 33.14

Seminal vesicle

Rectum

Prostate gland

Urinary bladder

Vas deferens

Urethra

Testis

Scrotum

Penis

Epididymis

Urinary bladder

Prostate gland

Vas deferens

Testis

Urethra

Scrotum

Each testis is made of tightly coiled structures called seminiferous tubules. Among the tubules are cells that produce testosterone. In the tubules, specialized diploid cells undergo meiosis to produce haploid sperm cells. As a result of meiosis, each specialized diploid cell forms four equal-sized sperm cells.

After meiosis, a developing sperm cell undergoes many changes. It first forms a long flagellum, or tail. Soon after the flagellum forms, the haploid nucleus condenses and becomes longer, forming the head. A tightly packed area of mitochondria forms between the head and tail. During its development, the sperm cell loses most of its cytoplasm. In *Figure 33.15* you can see the mature sperm cells that result from all of these changes.

Mature sperm are stored for a time in a coiled tube called the epididymis. The epididymis lies alongside each testis inside the scrotum.

For an egg to be fertilized, a sperm cell must leave the male and enter the reproductive system of the female. This occurs during sexual intercourse. The **penis** is the male organ that delivers sperm cells during intercourse.

Sperm cells from a male's testes travel from the epididymis through the vas deferens to the urethra in the penis. Strong contractions of the smooth muscles lining the vas deferens force semen through the urethra and out of the penis. Semen consists of sperm cells, fluids made by several glands such as the prostate gland, and fructose, which is an energy source for sperm cells.

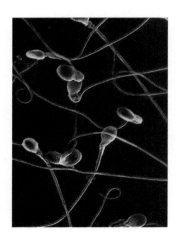

FIGURE 33.15

What parts of these mature sperm can you identify?

FIGURE 33.16

Female Reproductive Structures

What are the major organs of the female reproductive system?

Rectum

Cervix

Vagina

Vaginal opening

Fallopian tube

Ovary

Uterus

Urinary bladder

Urethra

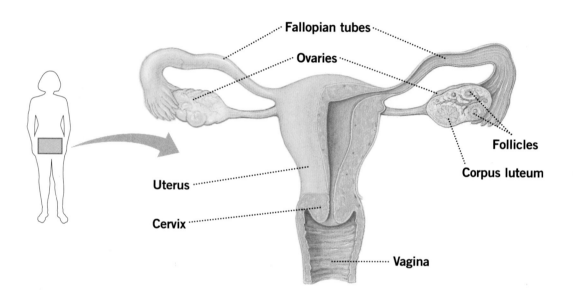

Fallopian tubes

Ovaries

Follicles

Corpus luteum

Uterus

Cervix

Vagina

Female reproductive organs
Two diagrams of the female reproductive system are shown in *Figure 33.16.* The **ovary** is the female organ that releases eggs and produces the hormones estrogen and progesterone. A female has two ovaries. The hormones produced by the ovaries control the female reproductive cycle and the development of secondary sex characteristics. Located close to each ovary is a structure called the fallopian tube, or oviduct. The fallopian tube is an organ that acts as a pathway through which an egg, released from an ovary, travels to the uterus.

The **uterus** is an organ with strong, muscular walls in which a fetus develops into an individual capable of surviving outside the mother's body. A structure called the cervix, located at the base of the uterus, connects the uterus with the vagina. The vagina is a muscular, tube-shaped organ that opens to the outside of the body. The vagina is sometimes called the birth canal because this is the opening in a female's body through which a baby is born. The vagina also provides the opening through which sperm can enter a female's body.

An egg a month?

A major function of the female reproductive system is to develop and release eggs. These events occur during the female reproductive cycle. The cycle is regulated by hormones secreted by the hypothalamus, the pituitary gland, and the ovaries.

Two sets of changes occur at the same time during the female reproductive cycle. The changes that take place in the ovary, including the development and release of an egg, are called the **ovarian cycle.** The ovarian cycle has two phases: the follicle phase and the luteal phase.

The changes that prepare the lining of the uterus to receive a fertilized egg are called the **menstrual cycle.** The lining of the uterus is called the endometrium. The menstrual cycle begins with the discharge of the uterine lining and an unfertilized egg.

The female reproductive cycle takes about 28 days, although the length of time can vary from 20 to 40 days. As you read about the cycle, you can use *Figure 33.18* on page 808 to follow the changes that occur in hormonal levels of the blood, in the ovaries, and in the endometrium.

The follicle phase of the ovarian cycle usually occurs during days 1 through 14 of a 28-day cycle. This phase begins when the hypothalamus stimulates the pituitary gland to release two hormones, FSH and LH. FSH stimulates a follicle to develop. Located in ovaries, follicles are structures where individual eggs develop.

Every female is born with a set number of potential eggs. In contrast, males produce sperm continuously. The ovaries contain 10,000 to 400,000 immature eggs at puberty. Immature eggs are diploid cells called oocytes. As an oocyte develops, it completes the

first division of meiosis to form a mature egg, called an **ovum,** and a nonfunctional cell, called a polar body. The polar body later disintegrates. The ovum has a large amount of cytoplasm that contains stored food.

An oocyte matures into an ovum in a follicle. As the ovum matures, other cells of the follicle release estrogen, stimulating the endometrium to grow new tissue and blood vessels. This process prepares the uterus for receiving a fertilized egg.

As the follicle develops, it releases increasing amounts of estrogen. When the estrogen in the body reaches a critical level, the hypothalamus triggers the pituitary gland to release an increased amount of LH and FSH. This event usually occurs around days 12 to 14 of a 28-day cycle.

The high amount of LH stimulates the follicle to release an ovum. You can see an ovum being released from a follicle in *Figure 33.17*. This process is called **ovulation.** After ovulation, the ruptured follicle develops into a structure called the corpus luteum.

The formation of the corpus luteum begins the luteal phase of the ovarian cycle, which usually lasts from about day 15 until the end of the cycle. The corpus luteum releases large amounts of progesterone and estrogen. High levels of progesterone and estrogen have a negative feedback effect. The high levels stop the hypothalamus from signaling the pituitary gland to release LH and FSH. The increasing levels of progesterone and estrogen also cause the endometrium to grow even thicker.

The ovum released at ovulation moves through a fallopian tube to the uterus. The ovum is in the fallopian tube for approximately three days. During this time, fertilization may occur. If the ovum is fertilized, it completes a second meiotic division. The fertilized ovum becomes embedded in the

FIGURE 33.17
As shown in these photos, an ovum is released from an ovary during ovulation. What hormonal changes take place during these events?

FIGURE 33.18

The hormones LH, FSH, progesterone, and estrogen control the female reproductive cycle. On what day does each hormone peak?

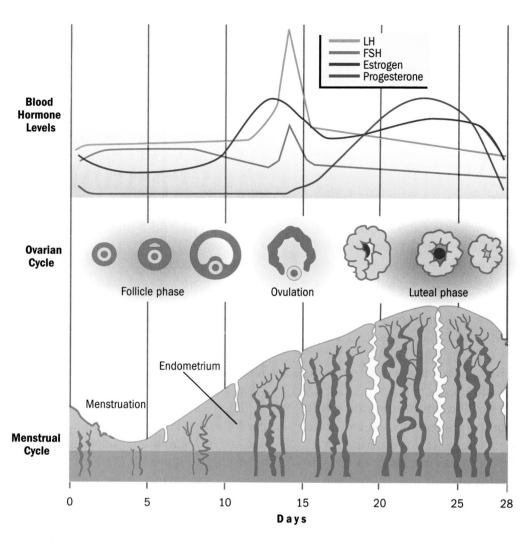

Blood Hormone Levels

LH
FSH
Estrogen
Progesterone

Ovarian Cycle

Follicle phase   Ovulation   Luteal phase

Endometrium

Menstruation

Menstrual Cycle

0   5   10   15   20   25   28

Days

endometrium, resulting in pregnancy. The female reproductive cycle is interrupted.

If the ovum is not fertilized, the corpus luteum disintegrates, which results in decreasing levels of estrogen and progesterone. The drop in these two hormonal levels decreases the blood supply to the endometrium. This results in the breakdown of excess endometrial tissue.

The disintegrating endometrial tissue and the unfertilized ovum leave the body in a process called **menstruation** (men-stroo-AY-shun). Menstruation generally lasts from three to seven days. The first day of menstruation is the first day of the female reproductive cycle.

The cycle begins when a female reaches puberty, usually between ages 10 and 16. It continues until menopause—the hormonal changes that lead gradually to the cessation of the female reproductive cycle.

CHECKPOINT 33.4

1. Contrast the structures of the human male and female reproductive systems.
2. Describe the physical and hormonal changes that take place during the female reproductive cycle.
3. **Critical Thinking** What are some of the evolutionary advantages and disadvantages of internal fertilization and development?

Build on What You Know

4. Why do sperm cells contain many mitochondria? *(Need to jog your memory? Revisit relevant concepts in Chapter 4, Section 4.3.)*

33.5 Human Development

Talking baby talk
Goo-gooing to a baby may make you feel a little foolish. But go ahead; babies pay attention to the slowed-down pace, big gestures, facial expressions, and simple words of baby talk. Even hearing-impaired infants are more responsive to the exaggerated motion of baby talk in sign language.

What you'll learn

IDEAS
• To describe the steps in the development of a human embryo
• To explain the birth process
• To describe the life stages of a human

WORDS
implantation, placenta, fetus, puberty

FERTILIZATION, DEVELOPMENT, BIRTH

1 + 1 = 1

The development of a human begins with fertilization, or the joining of an egg and a sperm. Fertilization occurs in the fallopian tubes, and it requires ovulation and sexual intercourse to have taken place. During ovulation, an egg is released from an ovary. The egg then moves into one of the two fallopian tubes. The egg stays in the tube for up to three days after ovulation.

During sexual intercourse, sperm-laden semen is deposited in the vagina. Millions of sperm swim rapidly from the vagina through the cervix, into the uterus, and on into the fallopian tubes. Although many sperm die along the way, some sperm live for up to three days in the fallopian tubes.

When a single sperm breaks through the outer membrane of an ovum, fertilization occurs. The sperm's nucleus enters the egg's cytoplasm and fuses with the egg's nucleus. The new cell formed as a result of fertilization is called a zygote.

As the zygote moves through the fallopian tube and undergoes a series of mitotic divisions called cleavage. During cleavage, the zygote divides again and again. By the fourth day, the zygote has become a solid ball of cells called a morula (MOR-yoo-luh). The morula continues to divide, forming a hollow ball of cells called a blastocyst (BLAS-toh-sist).

Within a week after fertilization, the blastocyst embeds itself in the uterine wall in a process called **implantation.** You can see the stages of fertilization, leading up to implantation, in *Figure 33.20* on page 810. If implantation is unsuccessful, the blastocyst will be discharged during the next menstrual flow. A pregnancy will not occur.

If implantation is successful, the blastocyst continues to develop into a structure called the gastrula. Three layers of cells form in the gastrula—the ectoderm, the mesoderm, and the endoderm. These layers are called germ layers because they later develop into all of the body's tissues and organs. The ectoderm, the outer germ layer, develops into the nervous system, skin, and sweat

FIGURE 33.19
During the gastrula stage of embryo development (shown here in cross section), three distinct cell layers are formed.

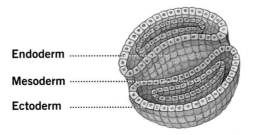

Endoderm ....
Mesoderm ....
Ectoderm ....

EVERYDAY BIOLOGY

Funny, You Don't Look Like Twins

There are two types of human twins. Identical twins grow from one fertilized egg and share identical genes. Fraternal twins grow from two different fertilized eggs that develop at the same time, each with a unique set of genetic characteristics.

FIGURE 33.20
Embryonic Implantation

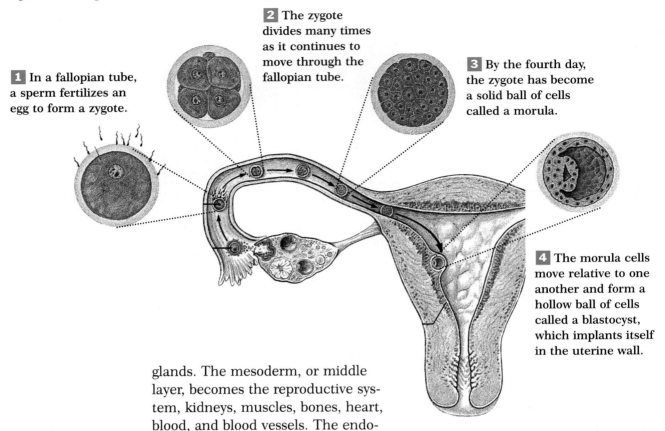

1 In a fallopian tube, a sperm fertilizes an egg to form a zygote.

2 The zygote divides many times as it continues to move through the fallopian tube.

3 By the fourth day, the zygote has become a solid ball of cells called a morula.

4 The morula cells move relative to one another and form a hollow ball of cells called a blastocyst, which implants itself in the uterine wall.

glands. The mesoderm, or middle layer, becomes the reproductive system, kidneys, muscles, bones, heart, blood, and blood vessels. The endoderm, or inner layer, forms the lungs, liver, linings of the digestive organs, and some endocrine glands.

After the development of the germ layers, the embryo is formed. The embryo has two outer supporting membranes, the amnion and the chorion. Along with some of the mother's endometrial cells, the chorion forms the placenta. The **placenta** (pluh-SEN-tuh) is an organ through which nutrients, oxygen, and wastes are exchanged between the mother and the developing embryo. The embryo is connected to the placenta by the umbilical cord, a tube containing blood vessels from the embryo. The amnion eventually fills with a fluid that forms a protective cushion around the embryo.

From the ninth week until birth, the developing embryo is called a **fetus.** Some stages of fetal development are shown in *Figure 33.21.* By

about three months, the fetus has started to develop most of the features of a human. What are the major developments at 5 weeks? At 22 weeks? Rapid growth of the fetus continues from the fourth month until birth.

After nine months of development, a surge in the amount of the pituitary hormone oxytocin in the mother starts the birth process, or labor. During labor, the uterus contracts strongly and rhythmically. The amniotic sac breaks, releasing its fluid. The cervix widens, allowing the fetus to pass through. The contractions become stronger and more frequent until the baby is delivered through the vagina. The baby begins to breathe on its own, and the umbilical cord is cut. After the baby is born, the uterus continues to contract for about 15 minutes to expel the placenta, now called the afterbirth.

FIGURE 33.21

Human Development

It takes 40 weeks for a fertilized egg to develop into a human infant. This amazing process involves millions of events that occur in a precisely timed and orderly sequence.

2 After 8 weeks, all body systems are present, and the embryo is called a fetus. Muscles move, the nervous system develops, and blood cell formation starts. This fetus is about 10 weeks old and weighs as much as an ordinary letter.

1 Most organs have begun to form in this embryo, which is about 5 weeks old and 1 centimeter (cm) long. The embryo's heart—the dark, rounded structure in the photo—is beating. Notice that both the arms and legs are developing.

3 By 14 weeks, a fetus's hands, arms, legs, and feet have reached their birth proportions. Notice the well-developed eyes, nose, and ears. This fetus is about 6 cm long.

4 By 22 weeks, a fine downy hair—including eyebrows—and a waxy substance covers the body. The fetus is about 30 cm long and has regular sleep patterns. When awake, the fetus is active, and the mother can feel the movement.

5 By 32 weeks, the fetus is fully developed. The bones have hardened, and the lungs and heart are ready for breathing air. As the fetus grows and runs out of space, it becomes less active. At birth, after 40 weeks, the average baby weighs 3.4 kilograms (kg).

Health of the fetus

Recent scientific and technological advances have enabled doctors to use a variety of diagnostic tools to monitor developing fetuses. For example, ultrasound waves directed at a pregnant woman's uterus can be used to make an image of a fetus. This technique allows doctors to check the growth and development of the fetus.

A method of checking for serious genetic diseases is called amniocentesis. In amniocentesis, a long needle is inserted into the amnion, and a sample of amniotic fluid is withdrawn. Fetal cells in the fluid are grown in a lab for two to four weeks. These cells can then be analyzed to determine if

the fetus has any chromosomal abnormalities or genetic disorders. This test is usually performed around the sixteenth week of pregnancy.

Chorionic villi sampling is a technique that has been developed more recently for the same purpose. In this test, a small sample of chorionic tissue is removed from the placenta. The tissue is analyzed for genetic abnormalities. Chorionic villi sampling can be performed earlier in the pregnancy than amniocentesis, and the results can be obtained in a few hours. Both amniocentesis and chorionic villi sampling pose some risk to the fetus. With the help of genetic counselors, parents must weigh these risks against the chance of severe genetic abnormalities in the fetus.

FIGURE 33.22

Human Birth

During a normal birth, a baby is delivered headfirst through the vagina. The muscles of the uterus contract to push the baby out.

Placenta

Umbilical cord

Uterus

Placenta (detaching)

Uterus

Umbilical cord

STAGES OF LIFE

Not ageless

Birth is the end of fetal development, but humans continue to grow and change throughout life. Having developed from an infant into a child, and from a child into a young adult, you have experienced many of these changes already.

For the first two years after birth, an infant develops rapidly. During this time, the infant learns to sit up, stand, walk, eat solid foods, babble, perform simple reasoning, speak a few words, and imitate the actions of others. Height increases by about 20 cm per year. The brain grows to 75 percent of adult size by the age of 30 months.

From age 2 to age 5, a child learns to use the toilet and to master motor skills including the fine use of the hands as well as larger body movements. Language skills develop, and the child learns problem-solving and social skills. Do you remember how much you grew between the ages of 5 and 12? During this stage, a child grows to about 70 percent of his or her eventual adult height and weight. Vocabulary and reasoning skills increase, as do physical coordination and higher-level thinking skills.

Sometime between the ages of 10 and 16, puberty begins. **Puberty** is the human life stage during which the sexual organs mature and secondary sexual characteristics develop. You may recall that the hypothalamus secretes a hormone that triggers the release of two other hormones, LH and FSH. These hormones "tell" the testes to release testosterone or the ovaries to release estrogen and progesterone. Both sexes experience hair growth in the pubic area and under the arms. Females begin menstruating, and the breasts grow and the hips broaden. In males, facial hair develops, the voice deepens, and the muscles and genitals grow

FIGURE 33.23
What are some of the developmental changes occurring in each of the life stages shown here?

What Is the Average Human Growth Rate?

Humans grow and develop throughout life—but at different rates. You can compare the growth rates of human males and females when you . . .

Try This

1 Use the data in the table below to plot two graphs: *Mass by Age* and *Height by Age*. Use different colors for males and females.

Analyze Your Results

1 When is the increase in female mass the greatest? In male mass? When is the increase in female height the greatest? In male height?
2 Calculate the average growth rate in mass for males and for females between ages 8 and 18. Using the same age group, calculate the average growth rate in height for males and for females.
3 Explain the difference between the average male and female growth rates.

Average Human Mass and Height				
Age	Mass (kg)		Height (cm)	
	Female	Male	Female	Male
8	25	25	123	124
10	31	31	135	135
12	40	38	147	145
14	50	50	159	161
16	57	62	163	172
18	58	68	163	178

larger. After puberty is complete, the body reaches its adult stage. In early adulthood, the body works at its peak efficiency. After about the age of 30, the body's functioning begins to decline slowly and gradually. Over time, the skin becomes less elastic, and the muscular, circulatory, and respiratory systems become less efficient. Reproductive functions also decline. Bodily changes leading to menopause in females usually begin between the ages of 45 and 50. After the age of 60, the decline in body functioning becomes more rapid. Eventually, important organs, such as the kidneys and the heart, begin to wear out. When the body can no longer function, natural death occurs.

FIGURE 33.24
Maintaining a healthy lifestyle can pay dividends in later life.

CHECKPOINT 33.5

1. Describe the events that occur from fertilization to development of an embryo.
2. Describe the human birth process.
3. List the developmental changes that occur during three life stages.
4. **Critical Thinking** Occasionally a zygote does not move into the uterus but instead attaches to the wall of a fallopian tube. Why might this be a dangerous situation for the mother?

Build on What You Know

5. Compare the development of a human fetus to that of a marsupial fetus. *(Need to jog your memory? Revisit relevant concepts in Chapter 27, Section 27.1.)*

33.6 Health of the Reproductive System

An answer to infertility
With in vitro fertilization, healthy eggs and sperm cells are removed from infertile couples and united in a laboratory. Four-celled embryos that result from the laboratory fertilization are implanted in the woman's uterus. The process succeeds in about one of five attempts.

What you'll learn

IDEAS
- To describe disorders of the reproductive system
- To distinguish between sexually transmitted diseases

REPRODUCTIVE SYSTEM DISORDERS

Much can go wrong

In order to function correctly, a human reproductive system must be healthy. Unfortunately, a variety of disorders are possible. Some disorders result in infertility, or the inability to produce offspring. Other disorders result in pregnancy problems, illness, or even death.

In men, infertility can result from the production of too few sperm cells or the production of defective sperm cells that are unable to travel the distance to the fallopian tubes. Infertility in women can have many causes. Hormonal imbalances may prevent ovulation. Scarring of the fallopian tubes can physically block an egg from entering the uterus. This scarring can be caused by a pelvic infection or by a disease called endometriosis.

In endometriosis, parts of the uterine lining, the endometrium, migrate outside the uterus. This tissue thickens and bleeds each month as does the uterine lining, but it has no way to leave the body. Blood-filled cysts may appear in the abdomen. The cysts expand and contract each month, causing intense abdominal pain.

If a fertilized egg implants in a fallopian tube instead of in the uterus, an ectopic pregnancy occurs. A woman with an ectopic pregnancy will experience the physical changes of a normal pregnancy accompanied by severe abdominal pain. As the egg grows, the tube will rupture and massive internal bleeding will occur. Ectopic pregnancy is a medical emergency requiring immediate surgery.

The prostate gland is a gland near the base of the penis. The prostate often becomes enlarged as a man ages. An enlarged prostate may constrict the urethra so that a man is not able to pass urine. Prostate cancer is also a serious problem that can be deadly if not diagnosed and treated promptly. Regular prostate examinations can detect any problems.

Cancer may affect women's reproductive organs as well. Women should undergo a test called a Pap smear every year to check for cervical cancer. They should also perform a monthly breast self-examination to help spot any lumps that may be cancerous tumors. Any bleeding between periods, unusual abdominal pain, or masses in the abdomen should be reported to a physician, particularly if there is a family history of ovarian cancer.

FIGURE 33.25
What differences can you see between the healthy sperm cell (top) and the defective sperm cell (bottom)?

Comparing STD Occurrence

The table below shows a summary of reported cases of STDs in the United States. Use the data in the table as you answer the following questions.

Analyzing the Table

1 Create a bar graph that shows the data in the table.
2 Which STD has a steady decline in reported cases in the time period shown?
3 How would you describe the trend in reported AIDS cases for the years shown?

Reported Cases of Selected STDs in the United States

Disease	1985	1990	1993	1994
AIDS	8,249	41,595	103,533	78,279
Syphilis	27,131	50,223	26,498	20,627
Gonorrhea	911,419	690,169	439,673	418,068

FIGURE 33.26

A red ribbon has become a symbol of support for people living with AIDS.

SEXUALLY TRANSMITTED DISEASES

S-T-O-P STDs

Many diseases that affect the reproductive system are infections acquired through sexual contact. The infections are known as sexually transmitted diseases (STDs). Bacteria and viruses cause the most common STDs.

The STDs gonorrhea, chlamydia, and syphilis are caused by bacteria. They all can cause severe damage to the reproductive system and may lead to infertility. Women with untreated chlamydia or gonorrhea may develop an infection called pelvic inflammatory disease (PID). Prompt treatment with antibiotics is important to stop the spread of any of these STDs.

The most deadly STD is acquired immune deficiency syndrome (AIDS). Recall from Chapter 32 that AIDS is caused by HIV (human immunodeficiency virus), which can be transmitted through human body fluids. A variety of drugs can slow the course of AIDS, but a cure has not yet been found.

Viruses other than HIV can infect the reproductive system. The herpes virus causes painful genital sores that can last a week or two. The herpes virus remains in the body, leading to repeated outbreaks. Flat or cauliflower-shaped growths called genital warts are caused by the human papilloma virus. Removal of the warts by a physician is the only treatment.

The risk of contracting an STD can be greatly reduced by avoiding direct contact with the genitals and body fluids of an infected person. The use of condoms and spermicides during intercourse can reduce, but not eliminate, the risk. Abstinence, choosing not to have sexual intercourse, is the most effective way to avoid sexually transmitted diseases.

CHECKPOINT 33.6

1. Describe three disorders that affect the human reproductive system.
2. Which sexually transmitted diseases are caused by bacteria? By viruses?
3. Critical Thinking Why is it important to maintain the health of your reproductive system?

Build on What You Know

4. How does a virus reproduce in the human body? *(Need to jog your memory? Revisit relevant concepts in Chapter 14, Section 14.1.)*

What do reproductive systems do?

Chapter 33 Review

Sum It Up

Use the following summary to review the main concepts in this chapter.

33.1 Endocrine Control

- Fast-acting nerve impulses and slower-acting hormones control an animal's activities.
- Hormones control activities such as molting, metamorphosis, and milk production.

33.2 Human Endocrine System

- Hormones released from endocrine glands into the bloodstream are carried to target cells.
- The hormones produced by the pituitary gland control other endocrine glands.
- The hypothalamus and the pituitary gland trigger the release of sex hormones at puberty.
- Processes can be controlled by feedback from the products they produce. Insulin and glucagon control the level of glucose in the blood through negative feedback.

33.3 Health of the Endocrine System

- Diabetes is a disorder in which body cells do not produce or use insulin properly.
- Thyroid disorders affect metabolic rates.
- Adrenal glands produce hormones in response to short-term or long-term stress.

33.4 Reproduction

- Testes produce sperm, which are stored in the epididymis and released through the urethra.
- Ovaries produce estrogen and progesterone.
- During the ovarian cycle, an oocyte forms a mature egg, the lining of the uterus thickens, and an egg passes into the fallopian tubes.
- An unfertilized egg and extra uterine tissue are shed during menstruation.

33.5 Human Development

- A fertilized egg implanted in the uterus develops into three germ layers, plus an amnion and a chorion. The germ layers develop into the embryo; the amnion fills with fluid; the placenta exchanges materials between the embryo and the mother.
- The health of the developing fetus can be tested with ultrasound and amniocentesis.

33.5 Health of the Reproductive System

- Reproductive disorders can cause infertility.
- Sexually transmitted diseases (STDs) can damage the reproductive system and may lead to infertility. AIDS is an STD caused by the human immunodeficiency virus (HIV).

Use Terms and Concepts

**Use each of the following words or terms in a complete sentence.
If you need to review a meaning, turn to the page indicated.**

hormones (p. 794)

endocrine glands (p. 794)

hypothalamus (p. 796)

pituitary gland (p. 798)

feedback control (p. 799)

insulin (p. 799)

glucagon (p. 799)

diabetes mellitus (p. 801)

eggs (p. 803)

sperm (p. 803)

testes (p. 804)

penis (p. 805)

ovary (p. 806)

uterus (p. 806)

ovarian cycle (p. 807)

menstrual cycle (p. 807)

ovum (p. 807)

ovulation (p. 807)

menstruation (p. 808)

implantation (p. 809)

placenta (p. 810)

fetus (p. 810)

puberty (p. 813)

Use Your Word Power

COMPLETION Write the word or phrase that best completes each statement.

1. The epididymis stores _____ until they are expelled by muscle contractions of the _____ .

2. The development of secondary sex characteristics begins at _____ .

3. The fallopian tube carries gametes that are released by the _____ and move into the _____ .

4. At birth, the _____ move from the pelvic cavity to the scrotum.

5. The mature _____ that develops from an oocyte is called a(n) _____ .

6. The thymus is the ductless _____ that secretes the _____ thymosin.

7. The umbilical cord attaches the _____ to the embryo.

TRUE-FALSE Write true if the statement is true. If the statement is false, replace the underlined word(s) to make the statement true.

8. A zygote embeds itself in the uterine wall during <u>ovulation</u>.

9. <u>Type II diabetes mellitus</u> is usually controlled with diet, medication, and exercise.

10. There are two phases of the <u>menstrual cycle</u>—the follicle phase and the luteal phase.

11. The control of progesterone and estrogen production by the corpus luteum is an example of <u>negative feedback control</u>.

12. <u>Menstruation</u> occurs if an egg is not fertilized.

13. The <u>pituitary gland</u> controls the release of pituitary hormones.

14. <u>Glucagon</u> lowers the amount of blood sugar.

15. From the ninth week until birth, the developing embryo is called a <u>fetus</u>.

Show What You Know

16. What is the difference between endocrine and exocrine glands?

17. Compare the ways that protein hormones and steroid hormones control the activity of target organs.

18. Describe what happens to an egg during the luteal phase of the ovarian cycle.

19. What is the role of the amnion and chorion in the young embryo?

20. Explain how negative feedback controls the production of pancreatic hormones in the islet of Langerhans.

21. How does the structure of mature sperm cells support their function?

22. How do the adrenal glands respond differently to short-term and long-term stress?

23. How can doctors check for genetic disorders of a fetus?

24. **Make a Concept Map** Make a concept map that relates the endocrine system to the male and female reproductive systems.

Take It Further

25. **Applying Concepts** Diabetics avoid foods that are high in sugar. Why might a Type 1 diabetic keep a candy bar or orange juice nearby?

26. **Making an Analogy** In urban areas during rush hour, radio stations broadcast traffic reports. How are traffic reports similar to hormones? How do the reports act as a feedback control mechanism for the flow of traffic?

27. **Designing an Experiment** Women who live or work closely together may experience menstrual synchrony—menstruating at the same time. Suggest two experimental designs that could test the existence of menstrual synchrony.

28. Interpreting a Graph The dietary needs of women change when they are pregnant. The graph shows the increases in recommended dietary allowances for women who are pregnant. For which mineral is the increase most dramatic? How much extra calcium does a pregnant woman need? How much extra vitamin B-6 is recommended?

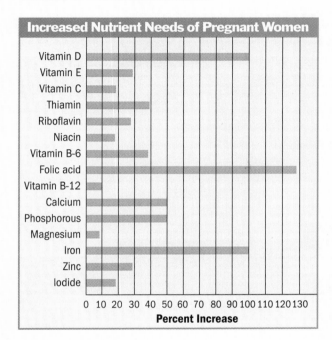

29. Analyzing Data The table shows what factors are involved in the regulation of some human endocrine glands. Which glands are regulated by external factors? internal factors? Using Figure 33.4, relate the functions of the glands to their source of regulation.

Endocrine Gland Regulation	
Gland	**Regulated by**
Pineal gland	Light/dark cycles
Ovaries	FSH and LH
Testes	FSH and LH
Pancreas	Glucose in blood
Parathyroid	Calcium in blood
Posterior Pituitary (ADH)	Osmotic balance
Posterior Pituitary (Oxytocin)	Nervous system

Consider the Issues

30. Infertility Every year, people who are having trouble conceiving a child visit fertility clinics. The procedures they undergo can be time-consuming, expensive, and stressful. Despite the effort, some women do not conceive. Those who do conceive have an increased rate of multiple births. Are fertility clinics an effective use of health-care dollars? Should more effort be given to the prevention of infertility or to alternatives such as adoption?

Make New Connections

31. Biology and Art Draw two different human characters. A viewer should be able to tell which character has hypothyroidism and which has hyperthyroidism from observing your drawing.

32. Biology and Mathematics Young infants sleep almost continually. By late childhood, children need only about eight or nine hours of sleep each night. After puberty, the need for sleep temporarily increases. Are you getting enough sleep? Keep track of your sleep patterns for two weeks. On average, how many hours of sleep do you get each night? Compare your sleep patterns to those of other family members.

FAST-FORWARD TO CHAPTER 34

In Chapter 34, you will learn about the endocrine system's partner in controlling cellular activities—the nervous system. The nervous system allows you to respond quickly to signals from your external and internal environments.

Nervous Systems

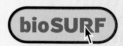

You can find out more about nervous systems by exploring the following Internet address:
http://body_systems.biosurf.com

In this chapter . . .

FEATURES

Everyday Biology
- Bigger Is Not Wiser
- Protective Pain
- Wrong!

In the Community
Drug Abuse Prevention

 Frontiers in Biology
Watching a Movie?

Issues in Biology
Fetal Alcohol Syndrome

LAB ZONES

Discover It!
- Testing Your Memory

Do It!
- Can One of Your Reflex Arcs Be Stimulated?
- Where Are Your Temperature Receptors?

Think About It!
- Analyzing Pain Pills and Their Cost

Investigate It!
- Analyzing Response Time

One morning, a successful 65-year-old artist sustained a concussion in a traffic accident. Within days, the color drained from his vision. Traffic lights and color television became meaningless. Apples appeared black; oranges, bananas, and grapes a dull gray. He looked at a rainbow and saw only a colorless semicircle in the sky. How could an artist whose entire life had been based on seeing and creating color deal with a world in black and white?

In his book *An Anthropologist on Mars,* Dr. Oliver Sacks tells his patient's story. The concussion gave the artist a rare condition called achromatopsia—total color blindness caused by damage to one small part of the brain that processes color. Slowly the artist began to adjust to his new world. He came to prefer the nighttime—when his vision sharpened so that he could read license plates four blocks away—to the confusing grays of the day. He even ate in black and white, favoring foods like black olives and white rice. He continued painting, but only in black and white. His art flowered again, but without color.

We perceive our surroundings through an amazing—and sometimes fragile—chain of sensory organs, nerves, and brain cells. What can biology tell us about how our senses make sense of the world?

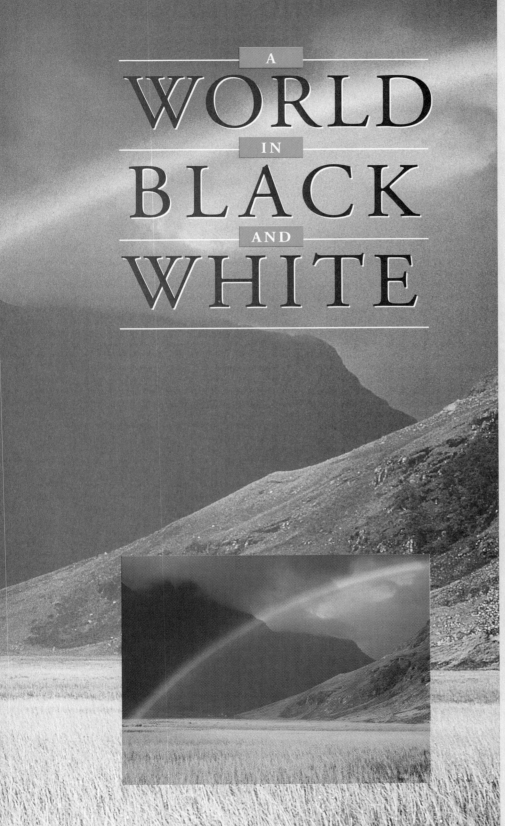

A WORLD IN BLACK AND WHITE

Testing Your Memory

You need a watch or clock with a second hand

1. Look at the two-column list below for one minute, and attempt to memorize it.

734	sst
LJX	9248
OOG	bDJk
116	lz62

2. After one minute, cover the list and try to re-create it on a piece of paper.
3. Check your list against the original. Were you able to remember it all?

Memorizing and re-creating this list involves many signals that are transmitted by your nervous system. In this chapter, you will learn how those signals work.

WRITE ABOUT IT!

Have you noticed how certain sensations can trigger vivid memories? In your science journal, make a list of sensations—a song you hear, a scent you smell, a picture you see. List the memories you recall when you experience each sensation.

34.1 Sensing and Control

What you'll learn

IDEAS

- To identify the functions of the nervous system
- To compare the nervous systems of different animals
- To describe the parts of the human nervous system

WORDS

ganglia, central nervous system, peripheral nervous system, neurons, glial cells

A numbing cold
It is cold and you left your gloves at home. Nerve messages cause the blood vessels in your hands to narrow, preventing warm blood from reaching them. Instead, more blood flows to your internal organs. Nervous systems help regulate temperature and many other body functions. Animals have different methods of controlling their responses to environmental stimuli.

FIGURE 34.1
The nervous system of a hydra consists of a nerve net. Why might the hydra's nervous system be described as simple?

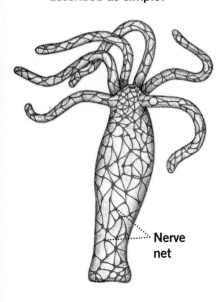

Nerve net

SENSING AND CONTROL IN ANIMALS

Information networks

To survive, all organisms need to be able to sense changes in the environment and control their responses. Single-celled organisms, such as bacteria and protists, can react directly to chemical or tactile clues and light. Most animals have two systems that control and coordinate their body systems. The endocrine system, as you may recall from Chapter 33, produces slower, longer-lasting responses. The nervous system enables the body to gather information and respond quickly to changes inside or outside the body.

A nervous system performs four functions that enable an animal to respond quickly. First, the nervous system uses sensors to gather information from inside and outside the body. Then the nervous system transmits the information over a network of specialized nerve cells to processing areas, such as the brain. Frequently animals have a nerve cord that transmits information between the network of nerve cells and the brain. The information is processed into possible responses.

Finally information to direct the best response is sent back through the network of nerve cells to the muscles, glands, and other parts of the animal.

All animals except sponges have nerve cells, but the organization of the nervous system varies depending on the animal. Cnidarians, such as the hydra in *Figure 34.1,* have nerve cells organized into a simple nerve net. The nerve net surrounds the body with simple sense receptors that the animal can use to detect and respond to changes all around it. Unlike most animals, the hydra does not have a central processing area such as a brain.

Figure 34.2 shows that annelids such as a leech have a small brain made of two ganglia (GANG-lee-uh). **Ganglia** are clusters of nerve cells. A ventral nerve cord that runs along the length of the animal is connected to the ganglia in each body segment.

In *Figure 34.2* you can see that insects such as grasshoppers have a brain made of several ganglia fused together. Insects have highly developed eyes, antennae, and other sense organs. A ventral nerve cord connects the brain with the rest of the body. Branched ganglia connect each body segment to the nerve cord.

FIGURE 34.2
How are the nervous systems of the leech (left) and the grasshopper (right) similar?

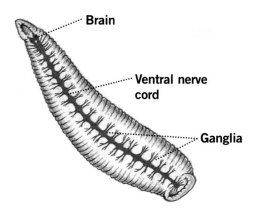

Brain

Ventral nerve cord

Ganglia

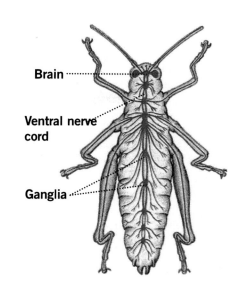

Brain

Ventral nerve cord

Ganglia

HUMAN NERVOUS SYSTEM

Central command

The human nervous system is typical of the vertebrates. It includes a large, well-developed brain. A thick spinal cord connects the brain with a system of nerves that reaches all parts of the body. Specialized sense receptors in the eyes, ears, nose, and skin pick up sensory input from the environment and send it to the brain. The brain processes this input and sends messages back through the system of nerves to control all body parts.

The human nervous system has two main parts, as shown in *Figure 34.3.* The **central nervous system** (CNS) is the body's main control center and consists of the brain and the spinal cord. This part of the nervous system processes information and sends instructions to other parts of the body. The **peripheral nervous system** (PNS) is made of a network of nerves that extend throughout the body. The PNS gathers information and delivers it to and from the CNS. The CNS and PNS work together as a team to monitor, coordinate, and control the activities of the entire body.

The nervous system consists of two types of cells. **Neurons** (NYOOR-ahns)

are the functional cells of the nervous system. Neurons transmit signals through the body. The cell body is the part of a neuron that contains the nucleus, cytoplasm, and organelles.

FIGURE 34.3
How does the nervous system of the human (below) differ from that of the grasshopper?

Brain

Spinal cord

CNS

PNS
Nerves

FIGURE 34.4

Cells of the Nervous System

A neuron, shown in the photo below, transmits nerve signals. How do Schwann cells and astrocytes assist neurons?

Peripheral nervous system

Central nervous system

Neuron

Schwann cells

Capillary

Astrocyte

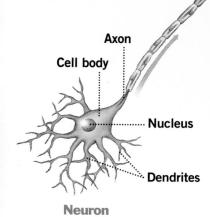

Axon

Cell body

Nucleus

Dendrites

Neuron

Unlike most cells, neurons have fiberlike extensions called axons and dendrites. In the PNS, these fibers are bundled into ropelike structures called nerves. In the CNS, the fibers are bundled into structures called tracts. You will learn more about neurons in the next section.

About 90 percent of the cells that make up the nervous system are not neurons. Instead, they are connective-tissue cells called glial (GLEE-ul) cells. The **glial cells** protect, support, and assist the neurons. There are several kinds of glial cells in the nervous system, including Schwann cells and astrocytes. Schwann cells and astrocytes have different functions.

In the PNS, Schwann cells are the most numerous glial cells. Schwann cells wrap around nerve fibers as they grow. The membranes of Schwann cells contain a fatty substance called myelin (MY-uh-lin), which forms a sheath that insulates and holds the nerve fibers together. Neurons with myelin sheaths can transmit signals faster than neurons without myelin sheaths.

Astrocytes are the most numerous glial cells in the CNS. Astrocytes help maintain a stable chemical environment near neurons, and they supply neurons with oxygen and nutrients from nearby blood vessels. Research indicates that astrocytes may play a role in the transmission of nervous system signals. Look at the illustration of an astrocyte in *Figure 34.4*. How do you think astrocytes got their name?

CHECKPOINT 34.1

1. List the four functions of the nervous system.
2. Compare and contrast the nervous systems of humans and hydras.
3. What are the differences between the central and peripheral nervous systems?
4. **Critical Thinking** Why are most glial cells in the CNS different from the glial cells in the PNS?

Build on What You Know

5. How does it benefit animals such as jellyfish to have sense receptors all around the body? *(Need to jog your memory? Revisit relevant concepts in Chapter 21, Section 21.4.)*

? How do nervous systems function?

34.2 Nerves at Work

Endorphins, the natural painkillers

How does acupuncture work? The needles, which are inserted into the skin at specific points, may stimulate nerves that send messages to the brain to release endorphins. Endorphins lessen the feeling of pain and, by acting on special receptors in brain neurons, give a sense of well-being. Although scientists do not know for certain how or if acupuncture works, many people do feel relief after treatments.

What you'll learn

IDEAS
- To describe a nerve impulse
- To define the different types of neurons
- To explain how a reflex arc functions

WORDS
resting potential, action potential, synapses, sensory neurons, motor neurons, interneurons, reflex arc

NEURONS IN ACTION

Go with the flow

Your nervous system carries thousands of signals through your body every moment in the form of nerve impulses. A nerve impulse is a wave of chemical and electrical change that moves along the membrane of a neuron. When a neuron is stimulated to conduct a nerve impulse, the electrical and chemical states are changed and restored in a few thousandths of a second.

A neuron, like all cells, has a membrane potential—an electrical charge difference across the cell membrane.

The inside of most cells has a negative charge relative to the outside of those cells. This is also true for a neuron in the resting state, before a nerve impulse. The membrane potential of a neuron in the resting state is called the **resting potential.**

When a neuron is stimulated, the electrical charge across the cell membrane reverses. The reversal and restoration of charges across the cell membrane of a neuron is called the **action potential.** Action potential is another name for a nerve impulse. Use *Figure 34.5* to follow the steps involved in the transmission of a nerve impulse.

FIGURE 34.5

Nerve Impulse Transmission

The transmission of a nerve impulse involves the movement of ions across a neural membrane.

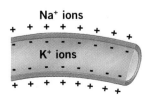

1 A region of a neuron at resting state.

2 Upon stimulation, channels in the membrane of the first region open, and sodium ions (Na⁺) flow into the cell.

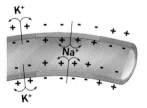

3 After Na⁺ enters the first region, potassium ions (K⁺) flow out of the cell, restoring the first region to its resting potential. The reversal of charge opens the channels in the next region of the neuron.

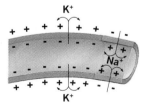

4 A charge reversal in the second region starts a charge reversal in the third region, and so on, as the nerve impulse is transmitted along the neuron.

Can One of Your Reflex Arcs Be Stimulated?

Reflex arcs are nerve pathways carrying automatic, involuntary responses to a stimulus before the stimulus is interpreted by the brain. You can see a reflex arc in action when you . . .

Try This

1 Sit on a table or high stool so that your lower legs dangle from the edge.

2 Have your partner strike the tendon just below your kneecap with the outer edge of his or her hand.

3 Repeat the procedure on your partner.

Analyze Your Results

1 Explain why the leg does not jerk upward unless you apply pressure to a very limited area.

2 Diagram what must be happening in the nervous system when sudden pressure is applied to the tendon just below the kneecap.

A nerve impulse moves through a cell in one direction. A dendrite receives and carries the impulse to the cell body. The axon carries the impulse away from the cell body. Each neuron has one axon, but it can have many dendrites.

FIGURE 34.6
Chemicals called neurotransmitters cross a gap in the synapse and continue the nerve impulse.

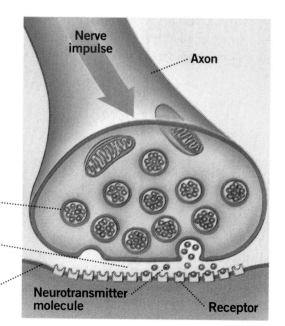

Nerve impulse

Axon

Neurotransmitter sac

Synapse gap

Membrane

Neurotransmitter molecule

Receptor

Most neurons do not actually touch one another, nor do they touch the organs to which they send messages. Nerve impulses move from neurons across synapses. **Synapses** (SIN-ap-sez) are junctions with tiny gaps between adjacent neurons and between neurons and the organs to which they send messages.

When a nerve impulse reaches the end of an axon, it sends information across the synapse. The information stimulates the next neuron or the organ that is to receive the message. Information crosses synapses in the form of chemical messengers called neurotransmitters.

Figure 34.6 shows a diagram of a synapse. Notice the end of the axon, where neurotransmitters are stored in small sacs. When a nerve impulse reaches the end of an axon, the impulse causes some of the sacs to fuse with the axon's membrane. Each fused sac releases its neurotransmitter into the synapse gap. The neurotransmitter diffuses across the gap and binds to receptors on the next neuron or on a cell of the organ that is receiving the message. The binding of the neurotransmitter causes a change in the membrane potential of the receiving cell. This change in membrane potential eventually leads to a new nerve impulse, or a response.

As you know, all neurons have the same basic structures. However, neurons vary greatly in appearance and function. There are three types of neurons, each with a different function.

Sensory neurons conduct nerve impulses toward the central nervous system. Sensory neurons transmit information from cells and organs that gather information about conditions inside and outside the body. Specialized sensory neurons called sensory receptors respond to an environmental stimulus, producing

FIGURE 34.7

A Reflex Arc

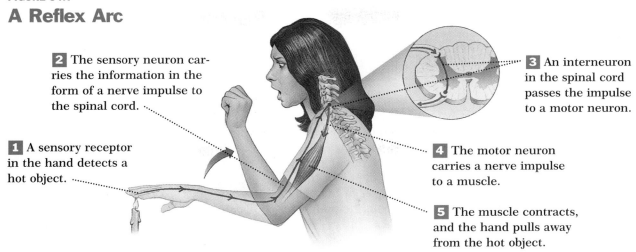

2 The sensory neuron carries the information in the form of a nerve impulse to the spinal cord.

1 A sensory receptor in the hand detects a hot object.

3 An interneuron in the spinal cord passes the impulse to a motor neuron.

4 The motor neuron carries a nerve impulse to a muscle.

5 The muscle contracts, and the hand pulls away from the hot object.

signals. The signals become nerve impulses in sensory neurons.

Motor neurons conduct impulses away from the central nervous system. Impulses that motor neurons transmit cause muscles, organs, and glands to respond.

Interneurons conduct impulses within the central nervous system. Interneurons connect with sensory neurons, motor neurons, or other interneurons. There are about 100 billion interneurons in the brain alone. Interneurons in the central nervous system process and coordinate the nerve impulses coming from and going to the peripheral nervous system.

REFLEX ARCS

Ouch! That's hot!

One of the simplest responses of the nervous system is called a reflex. You may remember from Chapter 28 that a reflex is an automatic response to a change in the environment. For example, your eyes blink if they suddenly see an object coming toward them. Blinking is a reflex. Can you think of other reflexes that you have?

A **reflex arc** is the pathway of neurons that carries the nerve impulses for an automatic, involuntary response to a stimulus. *Figure 34.7* shows how different types of neurons can work together in a reflex arc. The reflex shown is one that involves pulling your hand away from a hot object.

Notice that the interneuron in the spinal cord passes an impulse directly to a motor neuron that leads back to the arm muscles. This impulse does not travel through the brain. A reflex that does not involve the brain is called a spinal reflex. However, the brain does receive information that is interpreted as pain.

CHECKPOINT 34.2

1. How does a nerve impulse occur?

2. Contrast the functions of sensory neurons, motor neurons, and interneurons.

3. List the parts in a reflex arc.

4. Critical Thinking Figure 34.5 shows a neuron section at four consecutive movements during the transmission of a nerve impulse. Diagram what would happen in a Step 5.

Build on What You Know

5. What is exocytosis? When does exocytosis occur during the transmission of a nerve impulse? *(Need to jog your memory? Revisit relevant concepts in Chapter 3, Section 3.5.)*

34.3 Central and Peripheral Nervous Systems

What you'll learn

IDEAS
- To identify brain structures
- To analyze brain functions
- To describe the role of the peripheral nervous system

WORDS

brain stem, cerebellum, cerebrum, somatic nervous system, autonomic nervous system, sympathetic nervous system, parasympathetic nervous system

Food for thought
Eating just before a test may help you get a higher score. Doctors have found that students who have recently eaten perform better on tests of verbal learning and memory. Scientists think that the temporary increase in sugar in the blood right after eating may help the brain work a little better and faster.

CENTRAL NERVOUS SYSTEM

The hub

The central nervous system (CNS), comprising the brain and spinal cord, is the command center of the body. Each part of the CNS has different functions. The spinal cord links the peripheral nerves with the brain, which is the body's main information processing center.

Spinal cord The spinal cord is a tubelike organ consisting of neurons, glial cells, and blood vessels. Located inside the backbone, or spine, the spinal cord is protected by the bones of the spine, three membranes called the meninges (meh-NIN-jeez), and a cushion of fluid.

Figure 34.8 shows part of a spinal cord in cross section. Notice that the spinal cord has two distinct regions. The outer region is called the white matter and the inner region is called the gray matter.

Neurons in CNS white matter are protected by glial cells called oligodendrocytes. As you may recall, Schwann cells form a myelin sheath that surrounds neurons in the PNS. The oligodendrocytes form a myelin sheath that surrounds neurons in the outer layer of the spinal cord, so this layer appears white. Neurons in the inner layer of the spinal cord do not have myelin sheaths, so this layer appears gray.

The spinal cord relays nerve impulses to and from the brain. Impulses from the peripheral nervous system (PNS) travel by sensory neurons to the spinal cord, then move through the spinal cord to the brain. The brain, in turn, sends impulses down the spinal cord to the motor nerves of the PNS. The spinal cord also controls spinal reflexes such as the reflex arc described in the previous section.

Brain The human brain is a complex organ. An average brain weighs about 1500 grams (g) and contains approximately 100 billion neurons and 900 billion glial cells. Like the spinal cord, the brain is protected by bone,

FIGURE 34.8
The spinal cord is the major nerve pathway to the brain. What is the structural difference between white and gray matter?

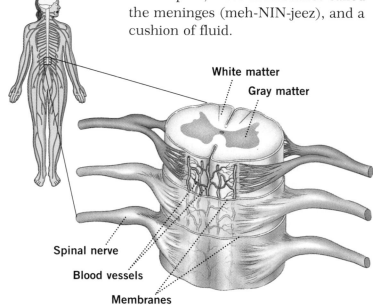

White matter
Gray matter
Spinal nerve
Blood vessels
Membranes

meninges, and a cushion of fluid. The brain also has layers of white matter and gray matter. Unlike the spinal cord, however, the brain has an inner region of white matter and an outer region of gray matter. The brain has three main structural parts: the brain stem, the cerebellum, and the cerebrum. You can find these three parts in *Figure 34.9.*

The **brain stem,** which connects the spinal cord to the rest of the brain, coordinates many of the body's survival functions, such as breathing, heart rate, sleep, and wakefulness. Three distinct regions make up the brain stem: the midbrain, the pons, and the medulla oblongata.

Just above the brain stem are two important structures called the thalamus and the hypothalamus. The thalamus serves as a relay station. It directs incoming messages from the spinal cord to the appropriate parts of the brain. The hypothalamus monitors homeostasis of the body, such as water content and temperature. As you learned in Chapter 33, the hypothalamus is a link between the endocrine and nervous systems.

Located behind the brain stem, the cerebellum (sayr-uh-BEL-uhm) is the second largest part of the brain. The **cerebellum** coordinates muscle activities, enabling the body to move in a smooth, steady, and efficient manner. The cerebellum also controls balance, equilibrium, and posture.

The cerebrum (seh-REE-bruhm) constitues about 85 percent of the human brain. The **cerebrum** is responsible for all voluntary, or conscious, activity in the brain. Its surface, called the cerebral cortex, is covered with folds and creases. These folds give the brain a very large surface area. The cerebrum is divided into right and left halves, or hemispheres. For both hemispheres, the surface of the cerebral cortex is divided into four lobes, as shown

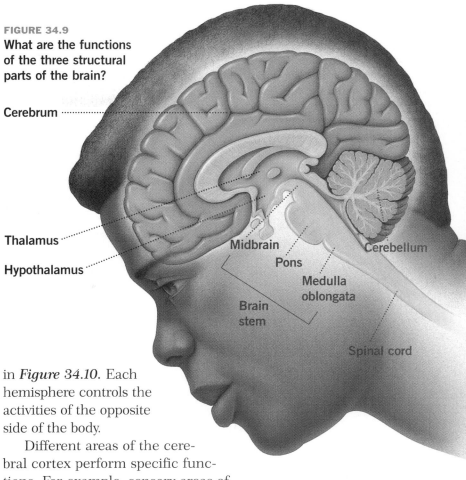

FIGURE 34.9

What are the functions of the three structural parts of the brain?

Cerebrum

Thalamus

Hypothalamus

Midbrain

Pons

Cerebellum

Medulla oblongata

Brain stem

Spinal cord

in *Figure 34.10.* Each hemisphere controls the activities of the opposite side of the body.

Different areas of the cerebral cortex perform specific functions. For example, sensory areas of the cortex receive incoming information from sensory neurons. Motor areas control voluntary muscle movements. Association areas coordinate complex activities, such as speech, language, and memory.

FIGURE 34.10

Each hemisphere of the cerebral cortex is divided into four lobes. Different functions of the body are controlled by different association areas of the cerebral cortex.

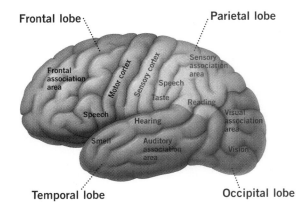

Frontal lobe

Parietal lobe

Frontal association area

Motor cortex

Sensory cortex

Sensory association area

Speech

Taste

Reading

Speech

Hearing

Visual association area

Smell

Auditory association area

Vision

Temporal lobe

Occipital lobe

FIGURE 34.11

The limbic system is the working center of human emotions and memory. It includes the thalamus, the hypothalamus, the amygdala, and the hippocampus. The Broca's and Wernicke's areas on the cerebrum are important for speech.

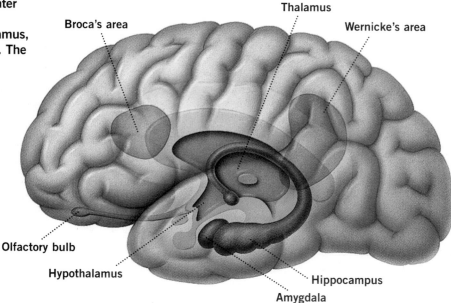

Broca's area
Thalamus
Wernicke's area
Olfactory bulb
Hypothalamus
Hippocampus
Amygdala

MEMORY, EMOTIONS, SPEECH

Integrated circuits

What processes are involved in feeling emotions? What parts of your brain are involved in memory and speech? Scientists have been trying to answer these questions for a long time. By using animal models, studying brain-damaged humans, and analyzing the effects on human brains of various stimulations, researchers have been able to create some partial maps of the human brain.

Human emotions, such as anger, love, and joy, involve the brain's limbic system. The parts of the limbic system are shown in *Figure 34.11*. The limbic system connects directly to the area of the brain used for complex reasoning, called the prefrontal cortex.

The limbic system is also involved in the formation of memories. The amygdala can connect incoming information with an emotion or an event. The hippocampus functions in memory storage and learning.

Where are memories stored? In the 1920s Canadian neurosurgeon Wilder Penfield found that his patients recalled specific memories when he stimulated different parts of the cerebral cortex. Further research has shown that memories are distributed throughout the cerebral cortex.

The process of speech involves several areas of the cerebrum. Two important regions are Broca's area and Wernicke's area. These regions are located on the left side of the cerebral cortex. Broca's area translates thoughts into speech and coordinates the muscles used for speaking. A person with an injury to Broca's area can understand language but cannot speak. Wernicke's area stores the information needed to understand

FIGURE 34.12

A PET scan of a sleeping human brain shows areas of activity even during sleep. Brightly colored areas are the most active.

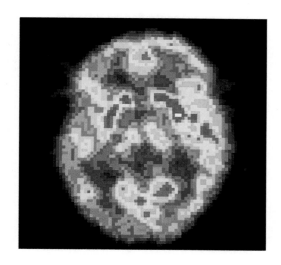

language. A person with damage to Wernicke's area can speak, but the words make little or no sense.

Watching a movie?

Scientists can observe the processes of the conscious brain in action. Using a technique called positron-emission tomography (PET), researchers can see which parts of the brain are used for different activities. PET scanning involves labeling a blood component such as sugar or oxygen with a radioactive element that emits tiny particles called positrons. When the positrons of a labeled blood component collide with electrons in body molecules, gamma rays are released. The gamma rays can be detected by a sensor. The information detected by the sensor is fed to a computer and converted to an image on a screen.

In the brain, the blood flow to a particular area greatly increases when the area is used. Therefore, every time an area of the brain is used during a PET scan, the area releases a burst of gamma rays and the computer produces an image of the area being used. Researchers instruct the patient to perform such activities as speaking, reading, or abstract thinking, and then watch the active areas of the brain light up on-screen. In *Figure 34.12,* you can see the results of a PET scan used to map areas of the brain that are active during sleep.

Since its introduction in 1988, PET scanning has provided a great deal of information about the normal function of the brain. This technique can be used to diagnose and treat brain disorders such as Alzheimer's disease, strokes, and cancer. In addition, PET scanning can be used to monitor and diagnose other parts of the body, including the heart.

PERIPHERAL NERVOUS SYSTEM

Outreach

Imagine you are trying on a new pair of shoes. Sensory nerves enable you to see and sense the texture of the shoes and to feel pressure in your toes. Motor nerves enable you to hold the shoes and slip them on. You may recall that sensory and motor nerves are part of the peripheral nervous system (PNS). Sensory nerves carry impulses from sensory receptors to the CNS. Motor nerves deliver impulses from the CNS to the rest of the body. The body's response to the impulses can be voluntary or involuntary. In general, the nerve impulses for voluntary and involuntary responses are carried by motor nerves in different areas of the PNS. *Figure 34.13* shows the organization of the PNS.

The **somatic nervous system** is part of the PNS and includes the motor nerves that control voluntary responses. For example, skeletal muscles respond to impulses from the somatic nervous system. However, some involuntary reflexes involving skeletal muscles also occur through the nerves of the somatic nervous system.

FIGURE 34.13
An organizational chart of the nervous systems.

FIGURE 34.14

Two sets of motor nerves in the autonomic nervous system—the sympathetic and parasympathetic—work in balance to control the functioning of the body's organs and glands.

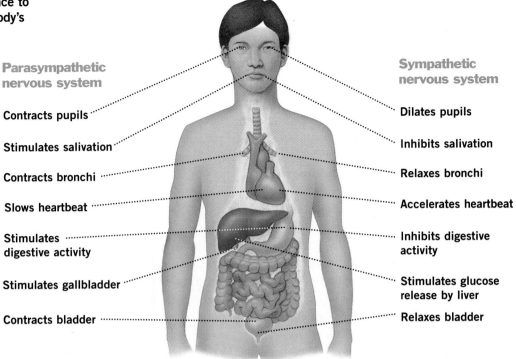

Parasympathetic nervous system

Contracts pupils

Stimulates salivation

Contracts bronchi

Slows heartbeat

Stimulates digestive activity

Stimulates gallbladder

Contracts bladder

Sympathetic nervous system

Dilates pupils

Inhibits salivation

Relaxes bronchi

Accelerates heartbeat

Inhibits digestive activity

Stimulates glucose release by liver

Relaxes bladder

The part of the PNS called the **autonomic nervous system** controls many involuntary responses. For example, smooth muscles, organs, and glands respond automatically to changes inside and outside the body.

The autonomic nervous system is divided into two parts. The **sympathetic nervous system** controls the responses of the body to stressful situations. It consists of motor nerves originating in the central section of the spine. The **parasympathetic nervous system** controls body functions associated with rest and digestion. It consists of motor nerves originating in the brain stem and in the base of the spine.

Nerves from these two systems have opposite effects on organs and glands. Stimulating a sympathetic nerve speeds heart rate; stimulating a parasympathetic nerve slows the heart down. The opposing effects of these two systems help the body maintain homeostasis

despite constant changes in internal and external environments. *Figure 34.14* compares the effects of sympathetic and parasympathetic nerve stimulation on some organs.

CHECKPOINT 34.3

1. What part or parts of the brain coordinate breathing and heartbeat? Balance and posture? Speech and emotions?

2. The limbic system plays a role in what two functions?

3. Critical Thinking Based on the information in Figure 34.14, how do you think stress and relaxation are handled by your sympathetic and/or parasympathetic nervous systems? Explain.

Build on What You Know

4. Compare the ways the nervous systems and the endocrine system help the body maintain homeostasis. *(Need to jog your memory? Revisit relevant concepts in Chapter 33, Section 33.2.)*

LAB ZONE Investigate It!

Analyzing Response Time

WHAT YOU WILL DO Measure and analyze your response times by catching a falling object when you are distracted and when you are focused

SKILLS YOU WILL USE Observing, measuring, collecting and recording data, calculating

WHAT YOU WILL NEED Metric ruler

Propose a Hypothesis

Can your response time vary depending on external distractions? How? Propose a hypothesis.

Conduct Your Experiment

1 Face your partner while he or she holds a metric ruler at the end with the highest measurement. Place your thumb and index finger at the opposite end of the ruler, but do not touch the ruler, as shown in the photo above.

2 Tell your partner when you are ready. Keep your eyes on your partner's hand and try to catch the ruler with your thumb and index finger as soon as your partner releases it. Record the centimeter mark at which you caught the ruler.

3 Repeat step 2 four times. Find and record the average of the five trial runs.

4 Repeat steps 1–3 while your partner creates environmental distractions. Your partner could ask you questions about homework, sing a song, whistle, or do some other distracting activity.

Analyze Your Data

1 How did your average distance with no distractions compare with your average distance with distractions?

2 How did your average distances compare with your classmates' averages?

3 Create a graph that shows the average distances for everyone in your class under both conditions.

Draw Conclusions

1 Was your hypothesis supported by the data? Why or why not?

2 Based on your findings, what would you recommend to a person doing something that requires quick response time, such as driving a car?

Design a Related Experiment

Internal distractions might affect your response time differently than external distractions. Propose a hypothesis and explain how you would test this in an experiment.

Lab: Analyzing Response Time

Objective: To measure response time by catching a falling object

	Focused	Distracted
Trial 1		
Trial 2		
Trial 3		
Trial 4		
Trial 5		
Average		

34.4 The Senses

What you'll learn

IDEAS
• To compare the structures and functions of the eye and ear
• To explain the relationship between taste and smell
• To describe the skin's sensitivity to pressure, temperature, and pain

WORDS
retina, cochlea

A blink in time

Blinking does more work than you may think. Humans blink to keep the eye's surface clean, moist, and comfortable. In one year, we blink about 8 million times. Since the average blink closes our eyes for one sixth of a second, blinking closes our eyes for more than 170 hours a year.

VISION

To see . . . to believe

How do you see? Your body has structures to sense and interpret patterns of light. Structures that make vision possible include the eye, the optic nerve, and a part of the brain's cerebral cortex called the visual cortex. Follow the steps in *Figure 34.15* to trace the path of light as it passes through the eye. The eye's structures help to produce a sharp image on the retina.

The **retina** (REH-tin-uh) contains receptor cells that respond to light energy. These receptors are called photoreceptors. The retina contains two types of photoreceptors: rods and cones. Rods can function with very little light but cannot detect color. Cones, on the other hand, can distinguish colors but require bright light. What do you think happens when you try to identify colors at dusk or in pale moonlight?

FIGURE 34.15
An Eye and Vision

Cornea
1 Light from an object passes through a transparent cornea.

Iris
2 Light passes through an opening in the iris, a ring of muscle that can vary the amount of light that passes through it. The pupil is the opening in the center of the iris.

Lens
3 The lens focuses the light onto the retina.

Retina
4 Photoreceptors in the retina respond to light energy, producing signals that become nerve impulses.

Optic nerve
5 The optic nerve contains sensory neurons that carry nerve impulses to the brain's visual cortex. The brain interprets the impulses as an image of the object.

FIGURE 34.16
An Ear and Hearing

1 The outer ear collects sound waves, which travel through the auditory canal and vibrate the eardrum.

2 Eardrum vibrations move three bones in the middle ear: the hammer, anvil, and stirrup.

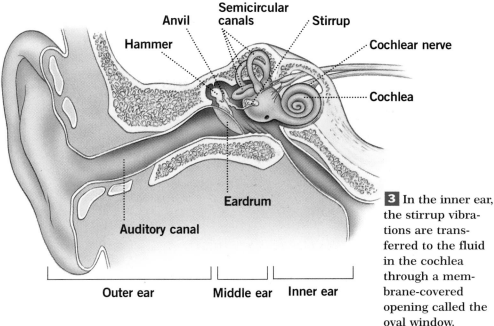

3 In the inner ear, the stirrup vibrations are transferred to the fluid in the cochlea through a membrane-covered opening called the oval window.

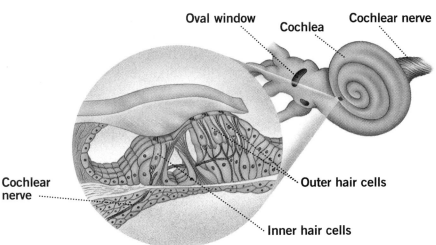

4 The fluid vibrations in the cochlea bend hair cells, which transmit nerve impulses to the cochlear nerve. The brain interprets the impulses as sounds.

HEARING AND BALANCE

Did you hear that!

Your ear is a complex organ that enables you to hear sound and maintain balance. The receptor cells for both hearing and balance are called mechanoreceptors. Mechanoreceptors detect movement and are stimulated to transmit nerve impulses.

The **cochlea** (KOH-klee-uh) is the organ of the inner ear that contains the mechanoreceptors for hearing. This structure is filled with fluid. Sound waves cause vibrations in the fluid. The vibrations cause mechanoreceptors called hair cells to bend, sending impulses to the cochlear nerve. The cochlear nerve transmits the impulses to the brain. Follow the steps in *Figure 34.16* to see how the ear collects sound waves and converts them to nerve impulses.

The semicircular canals of the ear contain mechanoreceptors that help maintain balance. Like the cochlea, the semicircular canals are filled with fluid. The three canals are oriented at right angles (90°) to each other. Whenever your body moves, mechanoreceptors in the canals detect the direction in which the fluid is moving. The brain uses this information to help you maintain balance.

FIGURE 34.17

Taste and Smell

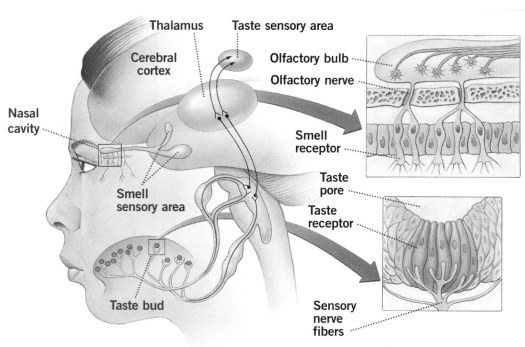

TASTE AND SMELL

A little goes a long way

Taste and smell are closely related senses that often work together. Both senses rely on receptor cells called chemoreceptors. A chemoreceptor responds to a specific kind of chemical and sends impulses to the brain through sensory nerves. The brain interprets the impulses from taste and smell chemoreceptors and decides whether foods are safe to eat. You can use *Figure 34.17* to trace the pathways from taste and smell receptors to the corresponding areas of the brain.

The chemoreceptors that detect taste are located in structures called taste buds. Most taste buds are on the tongue. Each taste bud has about 50 taste receptors surrounded by supporting cells. To reach these taste receptors, a chemical must be dissolved in liquid. Three pairs of salivary glands in the mouth secrete a liquid called saliva when you are about to eat. You experience taste when molecules dissolved in saliva are detected by the receptors in the taste buds.

There are four primary tastes: sour, salty, bitter, and sweet. Other tastes are combinations of the primary tastes. Different taste receptors that detect each primary taste are located in different areas of the tongue. Look again at *Figure 34.17.* Which taste areas overlap?

Smell, or olfactory, receptors are chemoreceptors located on mucous membranes in the upper cavity of the nose. Smell receptors respond to odor molecules that dissolve in the mucus. Sniffing increases the airflow into the nose and enhances the sense of smell. Smell receptors can detect tiny amounts of some molecules. For example, the molecule that gives garlic its odor can be detected at a concentration of 1/25,000,000,000 milligrams (mg) per milliliter of air.

Your sense of smell plays a role in your ability to taste. Think about what happens when you have a cold and your smell receptors are blocked. Food has little flavor. The characteristic flavors of foods result from a complex combination of smells and the four primary tastes.

EVERYDAY BIOLOGY

Protective Pain

Feeling pain is essential to our self-protection. One of the effects of Hansen's disease, or leprosy, is an inability to feel pain. People with leprosy can cut or burn their fingers, toes, or even limbs and feel no pain.

OTHER SENSES

Hot, heavy, and hurtful

Various types of receptor cells sense changes inside and outside the body. Your skin is a sensory organ for touch, temperature, and pain. Each type of sensation involves a different type of receptor cell. The figure at right illustrates types of receptor cells in the skin.

Heat and cold are detected by thermoreceptors. Touch and pressure are detected by mechanoreceptors. Pain receptor cells, called nociceptors (NOH-sih-sep-terz), are located in most tissues in the body. Pain alerts the body to damage being done and helps prevent further damage. Nociceptors can respond to many kinds of strong stimuli.

Chemoreceptors in the brain can detect changes in the concentration of substances dissolved in the blood. When the blood is too concentrated, chemoreceptors send impulses that trigger thirst. Chemoreceptors are also present in arteries, where they detect the buildup of carbon dioxide in the blood. These chemoreceptors send impulses that trigger rapid breathing to release the carbon dioxide and bring in oxygen.

Do It!

Where Are Your Temperature Receptors?

Your skin has receptor cells for both hot and cold temperatures. You can map the site of the receptors when you . . .

Try This

1 Use a marker to draw a 2-centimeter square box on the back of your hand.
2 Use a cold nail to touch different spots in the boxed area on your hand. Mark the spots that feel cold with the marker. **Caution:** Nails are sharp.
3 Repeat the process, using the same boxed area on your hand and a heated nail. Mark spots that feel hot with a different colored marker.

Analyze Your Results

1 Do you see a pattern to the location of your skin's temperature receptors?
2 Did you find more heat-sensitive spots or cold-sensitive spots? Explain your results.
3 Design an experiment that would allow you to map the pressure-sensitive areas of your skin.

CHECKPOINT 34.4

1. Describe the location and function of the two kinds of photoreceptors in the eye.
2. What is the cochlea? Briefly describe its shape and explain its function.
3. How can you stimulate the thermoreceptors, chemoreceptors, and nociceptors in your skin?
4. Critical Thinking A friend has stated that smell is a more valuable sense than taste. Do you agree? Explain your answer.

Build on What You Know

5. What groups of molecules are detected by the four kinds of taste receptors? *(Need to jog your memory? Revisit relevant concepts in Chapter 2, Sections 2.1 and 2.2.)*

What makes up the nervous system?

34.5 Nervous System Health and Substance Abuse

What you'll learn

IDEAS
- To identify various nervous system disorders
- To compare the effects of alcohol and tobacco

WORDS
concussion, Alzheimer's disease, stimulants, depressants, hallucinogens, narcotics

The most common addiction?
The caffeine in cola drinks, coffee, tea, and chocolate has mild effects. The most noticeable effect is a feeling of being awake. A surprisingly small amount of regular caffeine use can lead to a dependency. People who drink only two cups of coffee or three colas a day can get headaches if they suddenly give up the habit.

FIGURE 34.18
These electron micrographs show normal brain tissue (top) and diseased tissue from a patient with Alzheimer's disease (bottom). What differences do you see between the two tissues?

NERVOUS SYSTEM DISORDERS

System down!

Although well protected, your nervous system is still susceptible to injuries and diseases. Injuries and diseases that strike the nervous system are particularly serious because the parts of the nervous system cannot heal as other parts of the body can.

Most mature neurons cannot undergo mitotic cell division, so these cells cannot replace themselves if they are damaged or destroyed. If a neuron's cell body is damaged, the neuron will die. However, if a neuron's axon is damaged, the cell may survive. Under proper conditions, damaged axons that make up peripheral nerves can regenerate. If the axon's connections are not too far away, and if the axon's path is not blocked by other tissue, neurons can re-establish axon-dendrite connections. Axons that make up tracts in the central nervous system, however, do not regenerate under normal conditions.

Neurons and nerve tissue can be damaged either by injury or by disease. A blow to the head, such as a fall, can cause a brain injury called a

concussion. The blow knocks the brain against the inside of the skull, causing a bruise to the brain. The person may feel dizzy, see "stars," or become unconscious. Minor concussions usually do not result in permanent brain damage, but more serious injuries can cause permanent paralysis and coma. Injuries to sense organs, such as the eyes and ears, can also have permanent results, including blindness and deafness.

Damage to the brain's circulatory vessels can also result in neuron death. A blockage in one of the brain's blood vessels can lead to a stroke. The blockage may be the result of a blood clot or of narrowing of the blood vessels due to atherosclerosis. Because blood flow is interrupted, vital brain tissue dies from lack of oxygen. Symptoms of a stroke include paralysis, slurred speech, numbness, and blurred vision.

Another problem related to blood circulation is shock. In shock, significant blood loss or other serious injury suddenly reduces the amount of blood reaching the body's vital organs—including the brain. Symptoms of shock include weakness, dizziness, and loss of consciousness. A person in shock has pale, clammy skin; shallow, rapid breathing; and a weak, rapid pulse.

There are additional diseases that affect the brain. As you can see in *Figure 34.18*, in **Alzheimer's disease** the brain tissue deteriorates. Abnormal protein deposits build up in brain tissue, and parts of the brain waste away. People with Alzheimer's disease lose their memory, become disoriented, and may undergo a complete personality change.

Other diseases attack the nerves and spinal cord. A disease called multiple sclerosis affects the myelin sheaths that protect neurons and assist in transmitting nerve impulses. Damage to the myelin sheaths can slow or stop nerve impulses. A person with multiple sclerosis may experience impaired vision and speech, muscle weakness, tremors, and paralysis. Polio, a disease that can be prevented by vaccination, is caused by a virus that affects the gray matter of the spinal cord, damaging motor neurons and eventually causing paralysis.

AN OVERVIEW OF DRUGS

Aspirin to Xanax

A drug is a nonfood chemical substance that changes the way the body functions. Many drugs are used to treat illnesses. Other drugs have no medicinal use, and though many of these are illegal, some are legally available. Caffeine is the drug in coffee, tea, cola drinks, and even chocolate. Beer, wine, and liquor contain the drug alcohol. And cigarettes contain the powerful drug nicotine.

Of course, all drugs—from caffeine to street drugs such as crack and heroin—can be misused or abused. But any use of a medicinal drug other than for its intended purpose and in

LAB ZONE ? Think About It!

Analyzing Pain Pills and Their Cost

Do you know what the active ingredient is in the last pill you took for a headache or a sore muscle? The vast majority of popular over-the-counter pain medications contain one of just three drugs: aspirin, acetaminophen, or ibuprofen. Check pain medication labels the next time you are in a drugstore.

For example, Brand A is a widely advertised name brand. Each tablet contains 200 mg of ibuprofen. Brand A costs $4.99 for a 100-tablet bottle. Brand B is generic; it is just called ibuprofen. Each tablet contains 200 mg of ibuprofen; the bottle contains 200 tablets; and it costs $1.99.

Analyze Your Results

1 If a dose is one tablet, calculate the cost per dose for each brand.
2 If you take six pain pills per week for the next 30 years, how much money would you save by using a generic brand instead of Brand A?

the recommended amount is a misuse. Drugs taken without a prescription or for a nonmedical purpose are illegal, and use of them constitutes drug abuse.

Many drugs, legal and illegal, cause drug dependency. People with a drug dependency crave the drug and may endanger themselves or others in order to get more of the drug. Drug dependency can be psychological, physical, or both. Physical dependency on a drug is called addiction.

Many of the drugs for sale at pharmacies are over-the-counter drugs. These drugs are safe and effective when used according to the label instructions. Even then, some over-the-counter drugs have dangerous side effects. For example, over-the-counter diet aids may cause an abnormal heartbeat.

Prescription drugs are those that can be purchased only with a written order from a doctor. You should never take a prescription drug that was prescribed for someone else, because your unique condition may cause the drug to harm you. Abusing drugs prescribed for you can also be very dangerous. For example, abuse of prescription drugs over many years contributed to the death of Elvis Presley, the "king" of rock 'n' roll.

Chemical manipulators

Drugs can be classified according to their effect on the body. The following paragraphs describe some of the most commonly abused drugs. Nicotine and alcohol, also common drugs of abuse, will be described later in this section.

Drugs that increase the central nervous system's activity are called **stimulants.** Stimulants speed up the heart rate and transmission of nerve impulses. They also increase blood pressure. Caffeine is a mild stimulant. Cocaine is a stimulant derived from the leaves of the coca plant. Cocaine, a very addictive drug, is used legally as a painkiller for nasal surgery. However, cocaine is sold illegally as a white powder that is sniffed, or as white chunks called "crack" that are smoked.

Crack and other forms of cocaine strain the nervous and circulatory systems. Even a young, healthy person who uses cocaine can suffer a heart attack or stroke. Basketball player Len Bias died from a heart attack brought on by a single use of cocaine. "Speed," or amphetamine, is another strong stimulant that damages the body in a way similar to cocaine.

Drugs that slow down the central nervous system's activity are called **depressants.** Doctors prescribe depressants such as barbiturates or tranquilizers to relieve anxiety or sleeplessness. An overdose of depressants can lead to coma or death.

Drugs that affect the sensory perceptions of the central nervous system are called **hallucinogens.** LSD, PCP, and mescaline are examples of hallucinogens. People using hallucinogens may imagine sights and sounds and react unpredictably to things in their surroundings. PCP users have frequently committed acts of violence.

Opiates are drugs derived from opium—a substance in the fruit of the Asian poppy. Heroin is a powerful, addictive opiate. Heroin users usually inject the drug into their bloodstream, and they may share needles. Sharing needles can transmit diseases such as AIDS and hepatitis B.

Those drugs that relieve pain or induce sleep are called **narcotics.** Narcotics—which include many

FIGURE 34.19
The coca plant is the source of the drug cocaine.

FIGURE 34.20
The hallucinogen mescaline is derived from the peyote cactus.

FIGURE 34.21
Opium is derived from the sap that oozes from the pod of the Asian poppy flower.

FIGURE 34.22
Dried leaves of the marijuana plant are smoked in pipes or cigarettes.

depressants, heroin, and cocaine—are very addictive drugs. Many crimes are committed by narcotics addicts because the need to get money to buy drugs overrides an addict's sense of right and wrong.

Marijuana is the most commonly abused illegal substance in the United States. Marijuana consists of the dried leaves and flowers of the *Cannabis sativa* plant. Smoking marijuana alters one's sense of reality. Mental confusion and short-term memory loss may occur. In addition, smoking marijuana is believed to have long-term risks including lung damage, reduction of sperm count in men, and reduction of sex hormones in both men and women. People who regularly smoke marijuana often have less motivation and interest in hobbies and careers.

Steroids—lipid hormones—are used to stimulate the growth of muscles and to increase strength and performance. They are also used medically to alleviate joint pain from arthritis. The most common abuse of steriods occurs among athletes. Overuse or long-term use of steroids can be harmful to the heart, liver, and endocrine system.

ALCOHOL

Dangerous and legal

Alcoholic beverages contain a type of alcohol called ethanol (C_2H_5OH), a product of yeast fermentation. In the United States alcohol can be used legally by people of the drinking age set by each state. In most states, the drinking age is 21. Although some people falsely believe that alcohol is less dangerous than illegal drugs, many people die from alcohol consumption each day. Alcohol-related car accidents are the number-one cause of death among teenagers.

Alcohol is a depressant that affects the brain and liver. The effect of alcohol on the brain depends on the blood-alcohol concentration, or BAC. Some body effects of BAC concentrations are shown in *Table 34.23*. Two to three drinks in one hour can raise the BAC to the level of 0.06–0.08 percent.

People who drink alcohol in excess often suffer liver damage. The liver of a heavy alcohol drinker accumulates fat and bands of scar tissue that impair normal

Wrong!

Recently 35 percent of American teens thought that black coffee, fresh air, or a cold shower could sober up an alcohol-intoxicated person. They were wrong. In fact, only the body's elimination of alcohol over time restores normal brain function.

FIGURE 34.23

This table shows the effects of blood-alcohol concentrations. Which of the effects would probably influence a person's ability to drive?

Effects of Blood-Alcohol Concentrations (BAC)	
BAC (%)	**Effects**
0.02–0.03	Slight feeling of relaxation and mood elevation
0.05–0.06	Slight decrease in reaction time; slight loss of coordination
0.08–0.09	Slight speech, vision, and balance impairment
0.10–0.12	Coordination and balance impairment; some loss of judgment
0.13–0.15	Serious impairment of vision, speech, and coordination
0.20	Significant mental confusion; inability to walk
0.30	Loss of control over body and mind
0.40	Loss of consciousness
0.50	Coma
0.60	Death from respiratory failure

FIGURE 34.24

What differences do you see in the three livers in the photo above? The liver on the left is normal; the liver in the center has fatty deposits from alcohol abuse; and the liver on the right is cirrhotic.

functioning. This condition of the liver is called cirrhosis. Many people who seriously abuse alcohol die from cirrhosis. Compare the healthy liver tissue to the liver tissue with cirrhosis in *Figure 34.24.*

Many other health risks are associated with alcohol abuse. Alcohol is an addictive drug that produces both psychological and physical dependency. Alcohol dependency is called alcoholism. Symptoms of alcoholism may include a "need" for a drink to feel normal, drinking all day, and memory blackouts. Research suggests that a tendency to develop alcoholism is inherited. However, no one can become dependent on alcohol unless they drink it.

When alcoholics and heavy drinkers stop drinking, they experience a withdrawal period. Symptoms of alcohol withdrawal can be severe, especially if the drinker stops suddenly. In cases of severe alcoholism, withdrawal can cause delirium tremens, or DTs. This condition produces hallucinations, seizures, and sometimes death. Medically supervised withdrawal can help an alcoholic to successfully stop drinking alcohol.

Fetal alcohol syndrome

Although alcohol can be damaging to anyone, unborn babies are particularly vulnerable to its harmful effects. When a pregnant woman drinks alcohol, alcohol passes from the mother to the developing fetus through the placenta, slowing the growth of fetal tissue. Brain tissue, which grows very quickly in developing fetuses, is particularly susceptible. With heavy drinking, fetal damage can be quite serious, resulting in a condition called fetal alcohol syndrome (FAS).

This syndrome includes physical, mental, and behavioral defects. Typically, babies born with FAS are smaller than normal. They also have smaller heads and some degree of mental retardation. As they grow up and start school, they tend to have trouble due to a short attention span and poor coordination. These children may also have trouble adjusting socially due to jittery or impulsive behavior. In some cases FAS children eventually catch up in their development and lead a normal life. In other cases, however, the damage is permanent.

Labels on alcoholic beverages include warnings to pregnant women. Public service announcements warn

FIGURE 34.25

The developing brain tissue of this child was damaged by alcohol prior to the child's birth.

future parents about the dangers of alcohol. Should more be done? What do you think would help solve the problem?

TOBACCO

A pack of trouble

Because of the large number of smoking-related deaths each year, some consider nicotine to be the most deadly drug. A highly addictive stimulant, nicotine increases the heart rate and narrows blood vessels. Tobacco smoke contains many other harmful chemicals, such as carbon monoxide, hydrogen cyanide, ammonia gas, and tar. Tar is a thick, dark, sticky substance that is carcinogenic, or cancer-causing. All these substances can directly damage the respiratory and circulatory systems.

Smoking can paralyze or destroy the cilia that line respiratory structures. You may recall from Chapter 32 that cilia move the mucus that traps pathogens and particles out of the air passages. When the cilia are not working properly, mucus accumulates in the lungs, producing a "smoker's cough." Smoking eventually destroys the cilia completely.

Smoking is a recognized cause of lung cancer. Other cancers are also associated with tobacco use. For example, people who chew or sniff tobacco run a high risk of getting cancer of the mouth and throat. These cancers have been detected even in teenagers.

Years of smoking can destroy the lungs' alveoli, causing emphysema. As scar tissue develops in the lungs, the alveoli lose their elasticity and exhaling becomes difficult. There is no cure for emphysema.

You may be surprised to know that heart attacks are the number-one cause of death among smokers. The narrowing of blood vessels caused by nicotine reduces the amount of blood that circulates throughout the body. The heart has to pump harder to force the blood through the system, so blood pressure rises.

Carbon monoxide, a by-product of smoking, complicates the work of the circulatory system by binding to hemoglobin at the sites used by oxygen and carbon dioxide. As a result, the blood delivers less oxygen to body tissues. During exercise, smokers tend to tire more easily than nonsmokers.

For people who quit smoking, the risk of heart attack returns to normal after about one year. However, quitting smoking is very difficult. Most people try to quit three to five times before they are successful. The addiction to nicotine and the habit of lighting and

FIGURE 34.26
Emphysema results when scar tissue forms in the lungs. People with emphysema must often rely on oxygen tanks to breathe.

FIGURE 34.27
What differences do you see between the healthy lung tissue on the left and the lung tissue of a person who smoked cigarettes on the right?

smoking a cigarette are a hard combination to break. No one ever regrets having stopped smoking, so if you do not smoke, do not start.

CARE OF YOUR NERVOUS SYSTEM

Helmet on and buckle up

FIGURE 34.28
What are the laws in your state about wearing helmets while biking or participating in other sports?

Your nervous system makes all your activities possible. So taking care of it is a good investment. Always wear a helmet when you ride a bike or a motorcycle, or when you are skateboarding or rollerblading. Fasten your seat belt whenever you ride in a car. Do not dive into water unless you know the water is deep enough to do so safely. If you participate in sports in which falling is likely, learn to fall safely.

Like other body systems, your nervous system benefits from proper food, rest, and exercise. Avoid abusing your body with drugs, including alcohol and tobacco. Also, make sure that you get enough sleep so that your brain can work at its peak performance level. Sleep deprivation affects memory and slows response time, which can lead to many kinds of accidents.

Protecting your sense organs is also important. Wear foam earplugs or other hearing protectors in noisy areas. To protect your eyes, wear protective goggles in the lab or workshop, and wear sunglasses while outside in bright sunlight. While working with chemicals or dust, wear a mask to protect your nose.

CHECKPOINT 34.5

1. Name three different disorders of the nervous system.
2. What are the harmful effects of alcohol and tobacco?
3. **Critical Thinking** Morphine is a prescription drug derived from opium. What type of drug is morphine? What are the effects of this type of drug?

Build on What You Know

4. What functions of the body could be affected if the liver is damaged by cirrhosis? *(Need to jog your memory? Revisit relevant concepts in Chapter 30, Section 30.2.)*

 What factors affect the health of the nervous system?

Chapter 34 Review

34.1 Nervous systems control our detection of and response to the environment.

34.2 – 34.4 The human nervous system consists of the brain, spinal cord, nerves, and sensory organs.

34.5 The health of the nervous system can be affected by injury, disease, and substance abuse.

Sum It Up

Use the following summary to review the main concepts in this chapter.

34.1 Sensing and Control

- Nervous systems gather and respond to information from the environment.
- The peripheral nervous system (PNS) supplies data to the central nervous system (CNS); the CNS responds with instructions to the PNS.
- Neurons are cells that transmit nerve impulses.
- Glial cells protect and support neurons.

34.2 Nerves at Work

- During nerve impulse transmission, ions move across the neuron membrane.
- Chemicals carry messages across the synapse.
- Different types of neurons carry impulses to the CNS, from the CNS, and within the CNS.

34.3 Central and Peripheral Nervous Systems

- The spinal cord relays impulses between the PNS and the brain.
- The brain stem controls survival functions; the cerebellum coordinates muscle activity; the cerebrum controls conscious activities. Emotions, memory, and learning involve the limbic system.

- Some responses of the PNS are voluntary. Involuntary, or autonomic, PNS responses are controlled by opposing systems—the sympathetic and parasympathetic nervous systems—that function together to maintain homeostasis.

34.4 The Senses

- Receptors on the eye's retina and in the ear's cochlea change light and sound waves into nerve impulses, respectively.
- Chemoreceptors in taste buds and the nasal passages detect taste and smell.
- Skin has receptors for touch, temperature, and pain.

34.5 Nervous System Health and Substance Abuse

- Nerve tissue can be damaged by physical injury, a lack of oxygen, or disease.
- Drugs can speed up or slow down nerve impulses, alter perceptions, and damage organs.
- There are many health risks associated with alcohol and tobacco.

Use Terms and Concepts

Use each of the following words or terms in a complete sentence. If you need to review a meaning, turn to the page indicated.

ganglia (p. 822)

central nervous system (p. 823)

peripheral nervous system (p. 823)

neurons (p. 823)

glial cells (p. 824)

resting potential (p. 825)

action potential (p. 825)

synapses (p. 826)

sensory neurons (p. 826)

motor neurons (p. 827)

interneurons (p. 827)

reflex arc (p. 827)

brain stem (p. 829)

cerebellum (p. 829)

cerebrum (p. 829)

somatic nervous system (p. 831)

autonomic nervous system (p. 832)

sympathetic nervous system (p. 832)

parasympathetic nervous system (p. 832)

retina (p. 834)

cochlea (p. 835)

concussion (p. 838)

Alzheimer's disease (p. 839)

stimulants (p. 840)

depressants (p. 840)

hallucinogens (p. 840)

narcotics (p. 840)

Use Your Word Power

COMPLETION **Write the word or phrase that best completes each statement.**

1. A loss of memory can be a key symptom of _____ .

2. Drugs that are _____ slow down impulses; drugs that are _____ speed up impulses.

3. Schwann cells and astrocytes are two kinds of _____ , which support and protect _____.

4. The _____ contains mechano-receptors; the _____ contains photoreceptors.

5. The _____ controls balance; the _____ controls breathing; the _____ controls speech.

6. Involuntary responses are controlled by the _____ .

7. A blow to the head can cause a(n) _____ .

TRUE-FALSE **Write true if the statement is true. If the statement is false, replace the underlined word(s) to make the statement true.**

8. Skeletal muscles are stimulated by the <u>somatic nervous system</u>.

9. Digestion is inhibited by the <u>sympathetic nervous system</u>.

10. <u>Neurotransmitters</u> carry messages across synapses.

11. The nerve pathway used for a <u>voluntary response</u> to a stimulus is a reflex arc.

12. The electrical charge across the membrane of a neuron prior to transmission is the <u>action potential</u>.

13. The brains of some <u>invertebrates</u> are clusters of nerve cells called ganglia.

14. Drugs such as LSD and mescaline are <u>narcotics</u>.

Show What You Know

15. What is the difference between a stimulant and a depressant?

16. Compare the functions of Schwann cells and astrocytes in the human nervous system.

17. What is the key difference between the functions of the cerebrum and the brain stem?

18. How do the structures in an ear change a sound wave into nerve impulses?

19. Give an example of how the sympathetic and parasympathetic nervous systems work together to maintain homeostasis.

20. What roles do the iris, retina, and optic nerve play in vision?

21. How does the flow of sodium and potassium ions across a neuron cell membrane affect the membrane potential?

22. What role does water play in the identification of tastes and smells?

23. **Make a Concept Map** As you walk by a plate of cookies, you smell them and decide to pick one up. Make a concept map to describe the interactions of the different parts of your nervous system that are involved in smelling the cookies and responding to this stimulus.

Take It Further

24. **Applying Concepts** Why are barbiturates and alcohol a life-threatening combination?

25. **Developing a Hypothesis** Acetylcholine is the neurotransmitter that relays signals between motor neurons and skeletal muscles. Muscles respond after acetylcholine binds to receptors on the muscles. The drug curare also binds to muscle receptors but cannot activate them. Hunters in South America have used curare on the tips of darts and arrows. What effect does curare have on an animal?

26. Interpreting a Graph This graph is based on data from the U.S. Department of Health and Human Services. How often is alcohol involved in highway deaths? What percent of murders are alcohol related? What is the incidence of alcohol-related accidents at work?

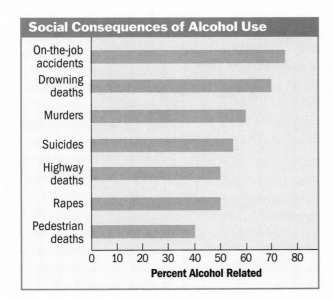

Social Consequences of Alcohol Use

Percent Alcohol Related

27. Analyzing Data The following table shows the percent of brain neurons lost, on average, from different parts of the brain during aging. Which region of the brain shows the greatest loss of neurons? Which region shows the least? What functions could be affected by neuron loss in the cerebellum? In the hippocampus?

Neuron Loss and Aging	
Region of the Brain	**Percent Loss**
Cerebellum	25
Visual association area	50
Auditory association area	30–50
Hippocampus	30
Thalamus	0

28. Designing an Experiment What factors can affect the ability to learn? Do physical stresses such as hunger or lack of sleep have an effect on learning? What effect do distractions such as noise or music have on the ability to learn? Choose one factor, propose a hypothesis, and design an experiment to test your hypothesis.

29. Applying Concepts During an asthma attack, the respiratory passages become narrower. Which division of the nervous system should an asthma-treating drug target?

30. Making an Analogy Describe two characteristics that a neuron and an extension cord have in common. How do they differ?

Consider the Issues

31. Alternative Therapies Many people seek alternatives to conventional medicine to combat diseases or disorders. These therapies include ancient, traditional treatments, such as Chinese acupuncture, and many other nonconventional options. How can a consumer determine if an alternative treatment is safe and effective? What role should physicians play in evaluating alternative treatments?

Make New Connections

32. Biology and Language Speakers of English use words related to the senses in many descriptive phrases. For example, working hard may be described as keeping your "nose to the grindstone." Find as many of these phrases as you can and classify them according to each of the five senses.

33. Biology and History Report on the contributions to our knowledge of the nervous system made by Charles Sherrington, Joseph Erlanger, Edgar Adrian, Bernard Katz, A. F. Huxley, and Alan Hodgkin.

FAST-FORWARD TO CHAPTER 35

The nervous system provides an organism with information about its environment. Chapter 35 will describe the range of environments and the factors that organisms must adapt to in a given environment.

Unit 8 Review

Connect the Chapters

1. What key feature do the alveoli in lungs share with the villi in intestines? How does this feature support the functions of lungs and small intestines?

2. What do skeletal muscles and the motor nerves of the autonomic nervous system have in common?

3. Where can you find connective tissue in the nervous and circulatory systems?

4. Explain why drugs that suppress the immune system might be used in treating arthritis.

5. Compare the roles of the liver, kidneys, and lymph nodes in cleansing body fluids.

6. Describe a method used by both antibodies and protein hormones to accomplish their respective functions.

7. Compare the functions of the three types of blood vessels and the three types of neurons.

Connect the Units

8. Is active transport involved in nerve transmission? Explain.

9. What could fossils reveal about the skeletal, muscular, digestive, nervous, and reproductive systems?

10. Describe the first step in the replication of the retrovirus HIV by T4 cells.

11. What structures and functions do leaves and skin share?

12. Compare the respiratory systems of birds and humans, including the flow of air into the lungs.

Connect to Themes

13. Unity and Diversity Compare the role of antigens in blood transfusions and in the immune response.

14. Energy Describe how the differences in animals' excretory and respiratory systems are adaptations for life in different environments.

15. Scale and Structure Explain how the relative sizes of egg and sperm cells are related to their functions.

project plans

1 The medical professions are not the only professions that focus on human body systems. For example, dancers are concerned with muscles, joints, ligaments, and tendons. Select a nonmedical career and determine what knowledge of the human body would be required for that career.

2 Unlike the doctor characterized in Mary Shelley's Frankenstein, doctors do not create living creatures. They can, however, surgically repair and rebuild many organs and structures. Research how much of the human body can be reconstructed using currently available medical procedures and devices.

3 Companies often have job descriptions so that employees will know the criteria against which their performance will be evaluated. The "Help Wanted" ads in the paper usually include a brief job description. As a class, write job descriptions for each of the twelve systems in the human body. How could you measure each system's performance?

A.D.A.M.
The Inside Story
User's Guide

CRITIC'S CORNER

A CD-ROM REVIEW BY MAYA S. LEE MENLO PARK, CA

A.D.A.M. The Inside Story, is an excellent way to learn about the human body. The software allows one to explore any part of the body, from pectoral muscles to the skull, and to observe it from the front, back, or side. The software can also transform organs, muscles, and bone structures into 3-D figures, making it possible to observe the body on several levels simultaneously. I found this software gave me the freedom to explore what most interests me about the human body.

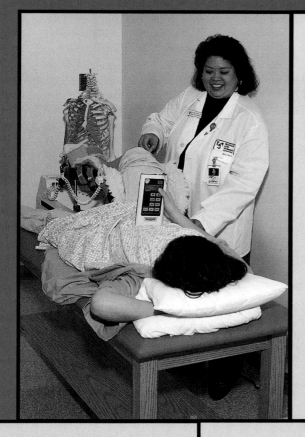

BARBARA ODAKA
Physical therapist and clinical supervisor

EDUCATION: B.S. in allied health sciences; certificate in physical therapy

" Biology is essential to anyone interested in a health career. It's important for a physical therapist to know about human development. We need to know how the body works normally, so someone with a disease or some kind of injury can be given the right kind of therapy. Most people come to a physical therapist for orthopedics after an injury, to regain the use of an injured limb, or to learn to walk again. We usually do manual therapy, using physical agents like heat, cold, and electricity. We also see cardiovascular patients to provide them with appropriate exercise programs to help them recuperate. These days, there's great research being done, making new therapies available. It's a challenge to keep up, but it's a good challenge . . . ."

bioSURF Visit the Internet site *http://body_systems.biosurf.com* to find out more about physical therapy.

JEAN DRISCOLL
Assistant coach

EDUCATION: B.S. in speech communication; M.S. in rehabilitation administration

"When I go on speaking tours, I talk about 'dreaming big and working hard.'"
—JEAN DRISCOLL

" I was born with spina bifida, which is an opening in the spine. . . . When I was growing up, for someone with a disability, fitness was never stressed. . . . I was recruited to play wheelchair basketball at the University of Illinois, and started doing racing just for fun. Then, when I started winning races, I got really interested in fitness. . . . The only muscles I have to work with are in my upper body, so I have to understand how the muscle groups work. . . . I do about 15–20 races per year, from track meet events to 10K races to marathons. . . . I work as an assistant to my coach, Marty Morse. I do administrative and coaching duties for him, and he trains me for races."

bioSURF Explore *http://body_systems.biosurf.com* for more information on biology careers.

Organisms and the Environment

Which of these amazing statements about the environment are fact, and which are fiction?

Hit *or* Myth?

Some fishes do the work of **dentists.**

(Fact. They may not have gone to dentistry school, but wrasse fishes clean fungi and bacteria from the teeth and skin of larger fishes.)

Wetlands are not always wet.

(Fact. A wetland's dry cycle, which occurs in winter, does not completely remove moisture as a clothes dryer does, but it does remove enough to enable the wetland to absorb spring waters.)

The average amount of trash three Americans throw away in one year weighs nearly as much as a male **African elephant.**

(Fact. The average American throws away 1.85 tons of trash each year; the average African bull elephant weighs 6 tons.)

There is a 99 percent chance that some of the air you have inhaled contained a molecule from **Julius Caesar's last breath.**

(Fact. The molecules in air are part of chemical cycles that might have brought a molecule of 2000-year-old air to you.)

Only big cities have **smog.**

(Fiction. The wind can carry smog to remote areas. Some days, the smog in the Arctic rivals that of Los Angeles.)

All **deserts** are hot.

(Fiction. Deserts are characterized by lack of moisture, not high temperatures. For example, in the Great Basin Desert, temperatures range from -30° to 30° Celsius.)

Toads form knots.

(Fact. A group, or population, of toads is called a knot.)

bioSURF

You can find out more about the biosphere by exploring the following Internet address:
http://ecology.biosurf.com

In this chapter . . .

FEATURES

Everyday Biology
• Making Soil
• Taking Water to the Cleaners

In the Community
Freshwater Field Day

 Issues in Biology
Help for Wetlands

LAB ZONES

Discover It!
• How Do Abiotic Factors Affect You

Do It!
• Modeling Seasons
• How Does Salt Water Affect Organisms?

Think About It!
• Predicting Weather in Your Biome

Investigate It!
• Testing the Water Capacity of Soils

HERE COMES THE RAIN

Every culture throughout history has valued rain. In an attempt to control rainfall, people from cultures native to North and South America, Europe, and Africa engaged in rituals. A rain dance in New Guinea included the use of long grasses, which were believed to pierce the sun's eyes, so that the sun would weep—making rain fall on Earth. In ancient Egypt, rain dances were memorialized in tomb paintings.

Rain is so valued because it determines climate, and climate affects the habitability of an area. Too little rain renders an area difficult to inhabit, as many organisms cannot survive the harsh conditions. Yet heavy rains can cause flooding, which may harm many organisms and destroy their habitats. Additional nonliving, or abiotic, factors that affect organisms in an environment are the amount of sunlight, the temperature, and the type of soil. How do these factors affect the organisms in a particular environment?

How Do Abiotic Factors Affect You?

1. List several abiotic factors, such as rain and temperature.
2. Record how each factor affects your day-to-day activities. For example, if you live in an area that receives little rain, you may have to abide by water conservation laws.

Nonliving, or abiotic, factors determine your environment –for example, whether it is hot and dry, humid and tropical, or cold and snowy. Each environment has its own characteristics, to which its inhabitants are adapted. The variety of environments on Earth create its incredible biodiversity.

WRITE ABOUT IT!

In your science journal, write about the abiotic factors of your favorite climate. What do you like about each of these factors? What are some disadvantages?

35.1 Characteristics of the Biosphere

Not a typical office job

Ecologists are scientists who study environments all over the world, both in the water and on the land. This ecologist is studying an environment that is intermediate between land and water, called a marsh. She is especially interested in the organisms and food sources she may find in the water.

STUDYING ECOLOGY

Looking for life in all the right places

In the world of science, **ecology** is the study of organisms and their interactions with the environment. Biologists who specialize in this area are called ecologists. Ecologists, such as the one in the photograph above, work in every setting imaginable, from rain forests to prairie wetlands and from deserts to coral reefs.

There is no shortage of organisms for ecologists to study. Scientists have identified and classified more than 1.5 million different types of living things. How many millions more do you think await discovery? All these organisms live in a region of the Earth that extends from the darkest depths of the ocean floor to about 8 kilometers (km) into the atmosphere. This life-supporting region of Earth is called the **biosphere** (BY-uh-sfir). The biosphere includes all the land, water, and air in which organisms live.

Within Earth's biosphere are many different kinds of environments, including places as diverse as a bubbling

FIGURE 35.1

Earth is composed of a variety of regions. A computer compiled this cloudless image from several satellite photographs. What regions can you identify in this image?

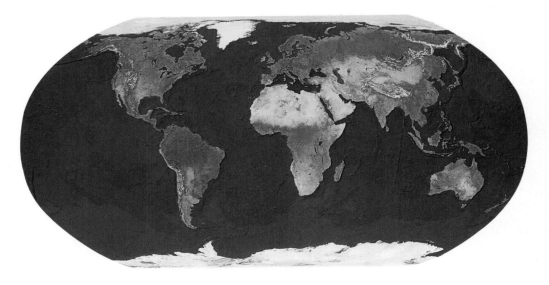

stream, a windswept mountain peak, and a vacant lot in a city. Although no two environments are exactly alike, every environment consists of both living and nonliving parts. The living parts of an environment are called **biotic** (by-OT-ic) **factors.** Examples of biotic factors are plants, animals, and other organisms. The nonliving parts of the environment are called **abiotic factors.** Abiotic factors include water, soil, light, temperature, wind, and physical space. Organisms obtain everything they need from the biosphere, and they depend on both biotic and abiotic factors to survive in their environments.

In Chapter 29 you learned that the human body has many levels of organization—cells, tissues, organs, and organ systems. The biosphere, too, has levels of organization—individuals, populations, communities, and ecosystems.

In the photos in *Figure 35.2*, you can identify the biotic and abiotic factors in the wildebeests' (WIL-duh-beests) environment. How does each factor affect the wildebeests? Could you learn about wildebeests by studying individual wildebeests? To get a more complete idea of how wildebeests interact with each other and their environment, you would probably study a group, or population, of wildebeests. A **population** consists of all the members of a single species that live in one area. A herd of wildebeests is a population, as is the grass growing in a field. What are some ways that the wildebeest population is interacting with its environment, as shown in *Figure 35.2*?

A population does not live alone in its environment. In any region of the biosphere, populations of many different organisms share a living space and interact with one another in a variety of ways. All the populations that live and interact in one environment make

up a **community.** How many members of the community can you identify in *Figure 35.2*?

All the populations and abiotic factors in an area make up its **ecosystem.** An ecosystem can be a large area, such as a forest, a desert, or an ocean. It can also be a much smaller area, such as a sand dune, a quiet pond, or a backyard garden. What parts of an ecosystem can you identify in *Figure 35.2*? A healthy ecosystem usually includes a wide variety of species, a characteristic known as biodiversity. You will learn more about biodiversity in Chapter 36.

Like you, wildebeests also have a "home," or habitat. The type of environment in which a particular species lives is its **habitat.** Every species in a habitat has characteristics that enable it to function in the unique abiotic and biotic factors there. A habitat provides the members of a species with food, shelter, water, and whatever else they need to survive. What parts of the wildebeests' habitat are shown in *Figure 35.2*?

FIGURE 35.2
The vulture (top) and wildebeests (bottom) belong to two of the many populations in this ecosystem (center). What abiotic factors can you see?

EVERYDAY
BIOLOGY

Making Soil

In a typical climate, it takes more than 100 years for just 2.5 centimeters (cm) of soil to be formed. In some climates, it may take hundreds of thousands of years to form 10 cm of soil!

FIGURE 35.3
Abiotic Factors

Temperature ▲
Different organisms tolerate different temperature ranges. Some living things, such as the white spruce, can survive harsh environments, where temperatures are extreme.

Water and oxygen ▶
Most living things cannot survive without water and oxygen. These two abiotic factors are both present in the waterfall.

◄ Wind
Wind affects weather. It shapes landforms (such as these sand dunes) and creates waves and currents that stir up nutrients in ponds, lakes, and oceans.

Soil ▲
Soils differ in texture, in the minerals and nutrients they contain, and in how well they hold water. Most land-dwelling organisms have adaptations that help them conserve water. The desert cacti shown here have a waxy coating that keeps them from drying out.

Fire ▶
Fire is a natural event that helps maintain conditions crucial for life in some ecosystems. After a fire sweeps across grasslands, grass plants quickly regrow, filling in the burned area before other types of plants can begin growing.

THE PHYSICAL ENVIRONMENT
Forces that shape life

As you just learned, the abiotic factors of an ecosystem include components such as light, water, temperature, oxygen, fire, wind, and soil. The degree to which these factors are present in an area affects the type and distribution of organisms that live in that area. The photographs above show examples of how abiotic factors affect ecosystems. How does sunlight affect a pond ecosystem? Why is fire sometimes beneficial to an ecosystem?

CHECKPOINT 35.1

1. Identify the components that make up the biosphere.
2. Explain the difference between populations, communities, and ecosystems.
3. **Critical Thinking** How might fire be beneficial to the animals that live in a grassland?

Build on What You Know

4. How might changes in abiotic factors in an area lead to speciation? *(Need to jog your memory? Revisit relevant concepts in Chapter 10, Section 10.4.)*

LAB ZONE Investigate It!

Testing the Water Capacity of Soils

WHAT YOU WILL DO Measure the water-holding capacity of three types of soil and estimate their rate of drainage

SKILLS YOU WILL USE Observing, measuring, collecting and recording data

WHAT YOU WILL NEED 3 funnels, filter paper, 3 glass beakers, a 100-mL graduated cylinder, grease pencil, sand, loam, clay, water

Propose a Hypothesis

Propose a hypothesis that predicts which type of soil holds the greatest amount of water and estimates the relative rate of drainage of each type.

Conduct Your Experiment

1 In your notebook, write the name of each soil type and record your observations of each, including the color.
2 Roll a small sample of each soil between your thumb and finger. In your notebook, describe the texture, or consistency, of each soil.
3 Line each of the three funnels with filter paper, and place each one in a glass beaker. **Caution:** Glass beakers are dangerous when broken.
4 Using a graduated cylinder, measure 40 mL of sand. Place the sand in one funnel, and use the grease pencil to label the glass beaker *Sand*.
5 Repeat step 2 for the clay and loam.

6 Use the graduated cylinder to pour 75 mL of water into each funnel.
7 Allow the water to drain for 15 minutes. Note the relative rates at which water drains through the samples. Record your observations.
8 Measure and record the volume of water in each beaker.
9 Calculate the water-holding capacity of each sample. Subtract the data from step 8 from the 75 mL of water added to each sample. Record your data.

Analyze Your Data

1 Make a graph of the data you collected.
2 Which sample had the highest water-holding capacity? The lowest?

3 Through which sample did water drain fastest? Slowest?

Draw Conclusions

Water moves quickly through permeable, or penetrable, soils. Which soil sample is the most permeable? The least permeable? Was your hypothesis correct? Why or why not?

Design a Related Experiment

Based on your observations and data, which type of soil might be best for growing crops? What other soil characteristics might influence crop growth? Design an investigation to answer one of these questions.

Lab: Testing the Water Capacity of Soils

9. Water-Holding Capacity
   Sand: 75 mL - 65 mL = 10 mL

   Loam:

   Clay:

35.2 Climate

What you'll learn

IDEAS

• To identify the factors that shape global and regional climates

• To explain the climate conditions that cause rain shadows

WORDS

climate, tropical zone, temperate zone, arctic zone, rain shadow, altitude

Land of the midnight sun

If you lived at the North Pole, you would enjoy 24 hours of daylight every day during the summer. The sun never drops below the horizon. This phenomenon is shown in the time-lapse photo. During the winter, however, the sun never rises above the horizon, so you would have to get accustomed to several months of continual darkness.

GLOBAL CLIMATE

How's the weather?

Sunlight, water, temperature, and wind are all abiotic factors that affect the survival of organisms in an ecosystem. These factors also affect the climate. **Climate** is the typical weather pattern of an area over time.

Many different factors—especially temperature and precipitation—interact to shape global and regional climates. You will learn that climate plays a major role in determining how ecosystems are distributed throughout the biosphere.

Earth's primary source of heat is radiation from the sun—solar radiation. Because Earth is a sphere, however, different levels of solar radiation reach different parts of its curved surface. As you can see in *Figure 35.4*, the sun's rays strike the Earth most directly at the equator. Land and water areas near the equator receive more solar radiation—and heat—than other regions do.

Because Earth's axis is in a continuous cycle of tilting toward and away from the sun, the amount of solar radiation that reaches different parts of Earth's surface change throughout the year. This leads to variations in weather and climate. Seasonal changes in climate are most pronounced in areas farthest from the equator.

In June, the Northern Hemisphere is tilted toward the sun, and the Southern Hemisphere is tilted away. In the Northern Hemisphere, summer begins in June. There are more hours of daylight in summer, and the temperatures are higher. In the southern hemisphere, June marks the beginning of winter, with the daylight shorter and temperatures lower.

The latitude at the equator is 0°. As you move away from the equator, latitude increases and temperature decreases. Imagine

FIGURE 35.4

The sun's rays strike different regions of Earth at different angles, affecting climate zones. What zone do you live in?

North Pole
60°N
30°N
Equator
30°S
60°S
South Pole

SUNLIGHT DIRECTLY OVERHEAD

Atmosphere

Arctic Zone
Temperate Zone
Tropical Zone
Temperate Zone
Arctic Zone

you are traveling from the equator toward one of the poles. As you travel, you will cross several climate zones. At the equator, you are in the heart of the tropical zone. As you can see in *Figure 35.4*, the **tropical zone** is the region that extends from the equator to about 30° north and south latitudes.

Temperatures in most areas of the tropical zone are hot and fluctuate very little between summer and winter. As warm, moist air rises from equatorial regions, it cools. Clouds form and the moisture in the air falls back to Earth. The rain forests that grow in the tropical zone receive several meters of rain per year.

As you move north or south beyond the tropical zone, you enter the temperate zone. The general boundaries of the **temperate zone** extend from about 30° to about 60° north and south latitudes. Overall, temperatures are cooler than in the tropical zone, and they change with the seasons. Summers are warm to hot, and winters are cool to cold. During summer in the temperate zone, most precipitation falls as rain or drizzle. In winter, precipitation falls mainly as snow, sleet, and freezing rain.

Beyond 60° north or south latitude, you enter the **arctic zone.** At these high latitudes, summers are short and cool, and winters are long and severely cold. The poles are located at the northernmost and southernmost points in the arctic zones. At the poles, temperatures rarely get above freezing. All precipitation is frozen. Ice and snow cover exists year-round and can be very thick.

FIGURE 35.5
Same Latitude, Different Climate

San Diego and Dallas are located at the same latitude, yet they have very different climates. How do the climates of these two cities differ? Why?

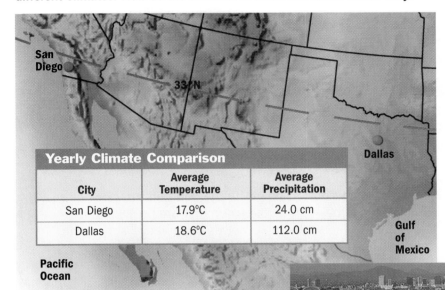

Yearly Climate Comparison

City	Average Temperature	Average Precipitation
San Diego	17.9°C	24.0 cm
Dallas	18.6°C	112.0 cm

San Diego

Dallas

REGIONAL CLIMATE

Climate closer to home

Dallas, Texas, and San Diego, California, are at roughly the same latitude in the temperate zone. However, their climates are quite different. Why? Global climate patterns tell only part of the climate story. There are a variety of other factors—and three important ones—that can affect regional climate.

The distance to the nearest body of water is one factor that affects the

FIGURE 35.6
The rain-shadow effect is caused by mountain ranges.

West

Pacific Ocean

Wind direction

Coast Range

Cascade Range

East

Modeling Seasons

You can model seasonal changes in climate if you. . .

Try This

1 Obtain a world globe that has a tilted axis. Place the globe in a darkened room as shown, with the North Pole tilted away from you.

2 Direct the light of a flashlight to the point on the globe closest to you. Observe the areas of the globe that are lit. Which half— the northern or the southern—receives the greatest amount of direct light? Sketch and record your observations.

3 Shift the globe so that the North Pole tilts toward you. Repeat step 2. Record your observations.

Analyze Your Results

1 In which direction was the North Pole pointing when the northern half of the globe received the most light? The least light?

2 Assuming that the area receiving the most direct light is also the hottest, which position models summer for the northern half of the globe? What season is it in the southern half? Why?

3 What factors determine the seasons on Earth?

regional climate of an area. Breezes from an ocean or a lake, for example, tend to cause cooler summers and milder winters in nearby land areas. As you can see in *Figure 35.5* on page 859, San Diego is on the West Coast, close to the Pacific Ocean. Which city—Dallas or San Diego—do you think would be more likely to have cooler summers?

Land formations, such as mountains and valleys, also affect regional climate. Mountain ranges affect rainfall patterns. When winds coming off the Pacific coast in the northwestern United States reach the western slopes of the coastal mountains, the moist air rises, cools, and drops its moisture as rain or snow. Enough precipitation falls on the western slopes of the mountains to support a cool, temperate rain forest of tall trees, ferns, and mosses.

What happens as the air continues eastward? As you can see in *Figure 35.6* on page 859, air flows over the mountain tops and down the eastern slopes. Having already given up most of its moisture, this air is dry. As a result, it rarely rains on the eastern side of the mountains. The lack of rainfall on one side of a mountain range is called a **rain shadow**. Rain shadows can result in almost desert-like conditions.

Altitude is a third factor that influences regional climate. **Altitude** is the height above sea level. As altitude increases, temperature tends to decrease. Climate varies with changes in altitude. The climate zones created by altitude are similar but not identical to those created by latitude.

CHECKPOINT 35.2

1. What two major factors shape global and regional climates?

2. Explain climate conditions that form rain shadows.

3. Critical Thinking What similarities and differences are likely to exist between the climate at the top of a mountain near the equator and the climate at sea level near one of Earth's poles?

Build on What You Know

4. What events might have caused Earth's climate to change during its history? *(Need to jog your memory? Revisit relevant concepts in Chapter 11, Section 11.3.)*

In what ways does life depend on the connections between living and nonliving parts of the environment?

35.3 Land Biomes

Home sweet biome

Humans inhabit almost every land environment on Earth. Different environments have led to different functional styles of architecture. Low ceilings and thick walls trap heat, while white buildings with many windows reduce temperatures. How is this architecture in Venice suited to its function in a watery environment?

What you'll learn

IDEAS
• To define the elements of a biome
• To compare land biomes

WORD
biome

CHARACTERISTICS OF LAND BIOMES

Natural real estate

No two places on Earth are exactly alike. But many regions of the world do have similar climate conditions, which support similar kinds of ecosystems. Ecologists use the term **biome** to describe a large group of similar ecosystems, usually identified by the abundance of certain types of plants.

Figure 35.7 shows the locations of some of the major land biomes. As you look at the map, keep in mind that, in nature, biomes rarely have neatly defined boundaries. Because of climate differences, regions of one type of biome overlap with those of another. What are some of the biomes in Africa? Asia?

Figures 35.8–35.14 show these biomes in more detail. Each figure includes a graph that shows rainfall (in bars) and temperature (in a line).

FIGURE 35.7
The major land biomes are shown on this world map. In which type of biome do you live?

- Tundra
- Taiga
- Temperate forest
- Chaparral
- Tropical rain forest
- Desert
- Grassland (temperate)
- Grassland (tropical savanna)
- Polar and high-mountain ice

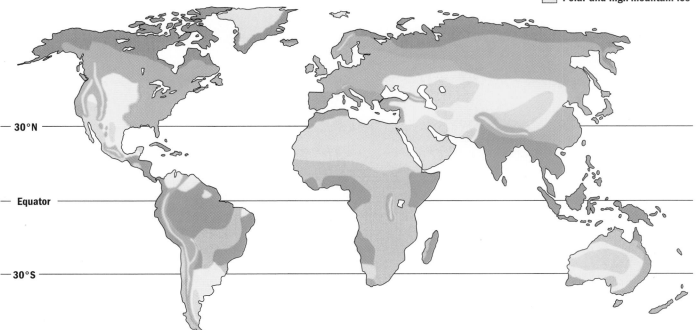

- 30°N
- Equator
- 30°S

FIGURE 35.8
Tundra

A tundra is cold and treeless, and most of the soil is permanently frozen. A thin layer of soil thaws briefly during short, cool summers. Winters are long, dark, and very cold. Where are tundras located?

Weasels (below) prey on small rodents such as lemmings. Other lemming predators include snowy owls and arctic foxes.

Caribou or reindeer (right), musk ox, and arctic wolves are some of the larger animals that roam the tundra.

The ground is carpeted with a spongy mat of lichens, mosses, short grasses, and low-growing shrubs. Soil nutrients are limited because cold conditions slow decay.

There is little precipitation on the tundra, but during summer the landscape is dotted with shallow ponds in which millions of insects breed.

Insects are food for many species of birds that migrate to the tundra for the summer.

(Climate graph: Degrees Celsius axis from -20 to 30; Rainfall in cm axis from 0 to 50; months J M M J S N (Every other month))

FIGURE 35.9
Taiga

The taiga (TY-guh) biome is located south of the tundra, at the northern edge of the temperate zone. Winters in the taiga are long and cold, and summers are relatively mild. How do taigas differ from tundras?

Perched in the trees, owls (above) and eagles keep a lookout for squirrels, rabbits (below), and small rodents.

(Climate graph: Degrees Celsius axis from -20 to 30; Rainfall in cm axis from 0 to 50; months J M M J S N (Every other month))

Moose (above), elk, bears, and lynx are some of the large animals living in this biome.

Coniferous trees grow close together in taiga forests. On the forest floor, a dense mat of pine needles covers the acidic soil.

FIGURE 35.10
Temperate Forest

Temperate forests grow where summers are pleasantly warm with frequent rains, and winters are somewhat cold. What type of trees make up a temperate forest?

Tall deciduous trees, such as maple, beech, oak, hickory, and chestnut dominate this forest biome.

Black bears (right), deer, mice, and squirrels are common in temperate forests because berries and nuts are plentiful.

Blue jays (above) and dozens of species of birds flit through the trees. Snakes, salamanders, and frogs make their homes on the ground.

The leaf litter is an ideal habitat for a wide variety of insects, spiders, and worms.

The top layer of soil in a temperate forest is rich in minerals and humus.

FIGURE 35.11
Chaparral

A chaparral (sha-puh-REL) is a warm region that has a rainy winter season, followed by a long dry summer. How do chaparral organisms adapt to these extremes in precipitation?

Dense stands of tough, stunted plants such as shrub oak and manzanita (below) are drought-resistant.

Skunks (above), mice, deer, and birds like this roadrunner (left) live in chaparrals.

Reptiles, such as the lizard, and insects, have thick, watertight body coverings to help prevent dehydration.

FIGURE 35.12
Tropical Rain Forest

Tropical rain forests are characterized by warm, wet weather, lush plant life, and diverse animal life. What abiotic factors contribute to this biodiversity?

Tall trees with their leafy tops form a dense canopy about 50 m above the ground.

Rain forest soils are poor; most of the nutrients are in the vegetation. When leaves, animal waste, and dead organisms fall to the forest floor, they quickly decompose and the nutrients are recycled.

The diversity of plant life in rain forests is astounding. Ferns, vines, orchids, and other brilliantly colored flowers are everywhere.

Sloths (above), monkeys, eagles, and parrots are just a few of the animals that make their home in the canopy.

On the forest floor, leaf-cutter ants (left) and giant centipedes share space with peccaries and poison dart frogs.

FIGURE 35.13
Desert

Too little precipitation creates deserts, arid regions with sparse plant life. Extremely dry, hot deserts may consist only of shifting sand dunes. How do desert plants conserve water?

Small desert animals, such as gila monsters (below), must conserve water. Active only at night or early in the morning, they avoid the scorching daylight by hiding in rocky crevices.

Although most deserts are hot, some are cold. The interior of Antarctica is a cold polar desert that receives as little precipitation as the Sahara. However, it is covered with ice that melts very slowly because of the temperature.

A cactus has a thick, succulent stem in which water is stored. Sharp spines protect the cactus from animals.

Surprisingly, many desert soils are rich in nutrients and only need water to become productive.

FIGURE 35.14
Grassland

Grasslands are widespread communities characterized by grasses and small plants. There are two kinds of grasslands: temperate grasslands (shown) and tropical savannas.

Long dry spells and occasional fires prevent the growth of most trees and shrubs, despite the presence of very rich soil.

Large predators such as wolves and lions share their environment with many types of small mammals, such as the badger (below), birds, and insects.

Tropical savannas are generally warm year-round. Rather than winter and summer, savannas have alternating wet and dry seasons.

In temperate grasslands (graph shown), summers are hot and winters are cold and windy.

Lush grass supports a great diversity of grazing animals, including antelopes (below).

CHECKPOINT 35.3

1. What are the elements of a biome?
2. Make a table that compares and contrasts the land biomes.
3. **Critical Thinking** Animals in hot climates have larger ears and longer, thinner legs than do similar species in colder climates. How might these adaptations enable the animals to survive in the different climates?

Build on What You Know

4. Choose one of the biomes and describe the niches that may be found there. *(Need to jog your memory? Revisit relevant concepts in Chapter 10, Section 10.1.)*

LAB ZONE — Think About It!

Predicting Weather in Your Biome

Biomes differ according to the amount of precipitation and range of temperatures. Research the average monthly temperature and precipitation your area receives over the year. Make a line-bar graph of your data.

Analyze Your Data

1 Based on your data, what type of biome do you live in?
2 Predict the weather for the next month, based on your graph. Observe the weather. Was your prediction correct?
3 How do the amount of precipitation and the temperature affect the organisms in your biome? How are these organisms adapted to the conditions in your biome?

35.4 Water Biomes

What you'll learn

IDEAS
- To distinguish between the water biomes
- To describe the zones in the marine biome

WORDS
wetlands, estuary

Bring your own "chinlight"
This deep-ocean fish has a type of "flashlight" dangling from its chin. It lives in the total blackness of the ocean depths. Why light up the darkness? Deep-ocean fishes probably carry their own light, less for seeing than for being seen. The light may lure prey to a predator or signal a prospective mate.

EVERYDAY BIOLOGY

Taking Water to the Cleaners

Wetland areas provide water storage and flood protection by soaking up rainwater like a sponge. They also function as natural water-treatment facilities by filtering out toxic chemicals and various pollutants.

CHARACTERISTICS OF WATER BIOMES

It's a watery world

Water in all forms covers roughly 75 percent of Earth's surface. Consequently, most of the biosphere is composed of aquatic, or water, biomes. The two major water biomes are the freshwater biomes and the marine, or saltwater, biomes. Each biome contains ecosystems that are differentiated by abiotic factors such as light, temperature, and the amount of salt, oxygen, and nutrients in the water. Organisms that live in aquatic biomes have characteristics that enable them to live with these diverse and changing abiotic factors.

When ecologists study aquatic biomes, they examine specific zones within a particular system. In most large bodies of water there are three zones: photic, aphotic, and benthic.

The photic (light) zone is the uppermost portion of aquatic biomes through which light can penetrate to support photosynthesis. Beneath the photic zone is an aphotic (without light) zone where light does not penetrate. The bottom of a body of water is the benthic zone. The seafloor, a lake bottom, and a riverbed are all benthic zones.

FIGURE 35.17
Flowing Water

Problems facing organisms that live in flowing-water biomes include moving against the current and simply staying in one place. What adaptations might prevent animals that live in rivers and streams from being washed away?

Moving water picks up sediment and carries it downstream. Where streams slow down or widen into rivers, sediment tends to settle out of the water.

Over long periods of time, flowing water can level mountains, cut deep canyons, and deposit enough sediment to create new landforms.

Insect larvae have tiny hooks that they use to attach to underwater objects.

Fishes such as salmon (left) and trout have streamlined bodies, allowing them to move through currents.

FRESHWATER BIOMES
Go with the flow

Freshwater biomes include everything from cold mountain streams and muddy rivers to lakes and marshes. Many freshwater biomes undergo significant changes during a year, such as seasonal variations in water temperature or nutrient levels. The ability to adapt to changing conditions is a characteristic that many freshwater organisms have in order to survive.

Ecologists further divide freshwater biomes into three major categories: flowing-water biomes, standing-water biomes, and wetlands. Flowing-water biomes are rivers and streams in which currents are created. *Figure 35.17* shows some of the characteristics of this type of biome. Lakes and

IN THE COMMUNITY
Freshwater Field Day

Find a body of fresh water in, or near, your own neighborhood. What type of body of water is it—a lake, a pond, a river, or a stream? Where does the water come from? Is it a natural accumulation of water, or is it an artificial one, like an irrigation channel or a catch basin? If wading is permitted, use a dipnet or jar to collect and release small organisms. Caution: Never go wading alone. Make a chart of all the organisms you can find in the water. Can you make connections between the organisms and their surroundings? Do you think the types of organisms in the water might vary at different times of the year? Why? To learn more about freshwater resources, log on to *http://ecology.biosurf.com.*

FIGURE 35.18
Standing Water

Standing-water biomes include ponds and lakes. Ponds are smaller and usually shallower than lakes. How does light availability affect plant life in ponds and lakes?

Pond animals include a variety of fishes, frogs, birds, and insects, including mosquito larvae (above). Algae, together with rooted and floating plants, make up the vegetation.

Seeds and small organisms are often carried into ponds by wind and rain. As a result, ponds tend to have a large variety of plant and animal life.

Ponds often do not have an aphotic zone. They are usually shallow enough for light to reach all the way to the bottom.

Away from shore, plankton live in the lake's photic zone.

On the lake bottom—the benthic zone—are organisms such as catfish (right) that live on decaying plant and animal remains.

Many of the same types of animals, such as the turtle (right), and plants in ponds are also found in the shallow lake waters near shore.

ponds are examples of standing-water biomes and their characteristics can be seen in *Figure 35.18* on page 867. A third freshwater biome is a wetland. **Wetlands** develop where fresh or salt water and land meet. Wetlands are categorized as either inland or coastal. Inland wetlands include marshes, swamps, and bogs. Coastal wetlands include mangrove swamps and salt marshes. You can see examples of these biomes in *Figure 35.19* and *Figure 35.20*.

ISSUES IN BIOLOGY

Help for wetlands

The Everglades in Florida was once the largest inland wetland in the continental United States. Agriculture and urban development led to the damming and draining of the natural waterways that ran through this wetland system. The effect on wildlife was devastating. Efforts now being made to restore this area to its natural state have been significantly successful.

Wildlife corridors have been established throughout the United States to protect endangered species. These corridors allow threatened species to travel between tracts of protected land, thereby increasing their range. Such increases in range result in better access to resources and reduce the threat of extinction. Ecologists have planned corridors in Florida, southern California, and the Pacific Northwest.

Some ecologists, however, think that these corridor plans are unjustifiable because there is little evidence of their effectiveness. Many ecologists emphasize the difficulty of studying complex ecological interactions in the field. To understand fully the importance of wildlife corridors, populations

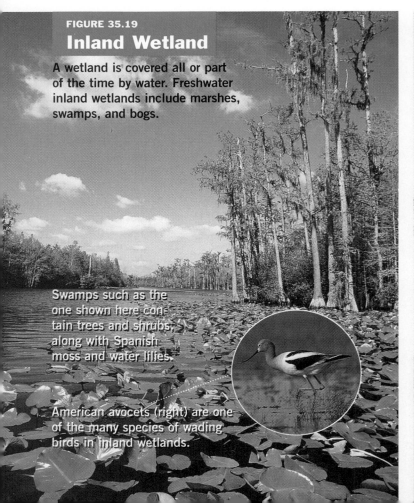

FIGURE 35.19
Inland Wetland

A wetland is covered all or part of the time by water. Freshwater inland wetlands include marshes, swamps, and bogs.

Swamps such as the one shown here contain trees and shrubs, along with Spanish moss and water lilies.

American avocets (right) are one of the many species of wading birds in inland wetlands.

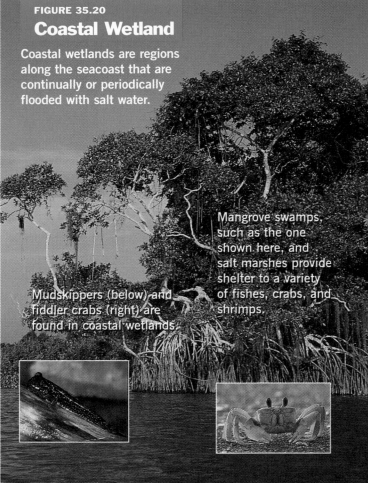

FIGURE 35.20
Coastal Wetland

Coastal wetlands are regions along the seacoast that are continually or periodically flooded with salt water.

Mangrove swamps, such as the one shown here, and salt marshes provide shelter to a variety of fishes, crabs, and shrimps.

Mudskippers (below) and fiddler crabs (right) are found in coastal wetlands.

FIGURE 35.21
Estuary

Estuaries are areas where fresh water and salt water mix. They form where rivers containing large amounts of nutrient-rich sediment meet the sea and deposit the sediment.

The water in an estuary is brackish—never completely fresh, but less salty than sea water. Estuaries can support a large number of organisms because of their nutrient-rich environments.

Many kinds of fishes, mollusks, and crustaceans, such as this blue crab (left), live in estuaries. These organisms attract birds, such as the osprey (above) that feed on them.

in a large geographical area would have to be studied over long periods of time.

The mouth of a river is the place where a river empties into the ocean. Sediment—particles of rock and soil that are carried by a river—often settles near the river's mouth, making the region shallow. A shallow area where fresh water and salt water mix is called an **estuary** (ES-choo-ayr-ee). An estuary biome is shown in *Figure 35.21.*

THE MARINE BIOME

Pass the salt

More than 70 percent of Earth's surface is covered by the marine biome. Physical conditions within this biome vary tremendously. Light, temperature, and water pressure all change with depth. The salinity, or salt content, of the ocean also varies from place to place.

The organisms that inhabit the marine biome are remarkably

LAB ZONE ▶ Do It!

How Does Salt Water Affect Organisms?

What happens to your skin when you stay in the water a long time? Do salt water and fresh water affect your body the same way? You can find out how fresh water and salt water affect organisms if you . . .

Try This

1 Fill six identical glass jars with the same amount of tap water. Label three jars tap water, and three jars salt water. Put two spoonfuls of salt into each of the saltwater jars and stir.
2 Collect two small equal-sized pieces of apple, two raisins, and two grapes. Record the size and texture of each fruit sample.
3 Place one sample of each fruit in a jar of salt water and one sample of each in a jar of fresh water. Predict the effects of salt water and fresh water on each fruit.
4 Examine each sample after one hour. Record your observations and results in a data table. Be sure to record the size and texture of each fruit sample.

Analyze Your Results

1 What happened to the fruit? What might have caused the results?
2 What characteristics might an organism need to survive in a saltwater environment such as the ocean?

FIGURE 35.22

Marine Zones

The marine biome is a saltwater environment that includes the oceans and their shorelines. What characteristics enable organisms to live in the different marine zones?

① Intertidal zone
At the ocean's edge lies the intertidal zone. Organisms in this zone must survive extreme variation in both temperature and salinity. The organisms are repeatedly covered then exposed by the tides.

② Neritic zone
The neritic zone lies over the continental shelf and is rich in mineral nutrients washed from the land. Light usually penetrates to the bottom of the neritic zone, allowing the growth of phytoplankton and algae.

③ Oceanic zone
In the oceanic zone, mineral nutrients are scarce. As a result, the populations of organisms are far less dense than in the neritic zone.

④ Photic zone
Here, light can penetrate ocean waters to a depth of about 200 m. The photic zone is home to phytoplankton, which are eaten by zooplankton, which are then eaten by larger animals, such as grunts (below), other fishes, and squids.

⑤ Aphotic zone
So little light penetrates this zone that photosynthesis cannot take place. Inhabitants live in complete darkness. Many deep-sea squids (below) and fishes make their own light.

⑥ Benthic zone
In the benthic zone are common bottom-dwelling organisms, such as sea stars, (left) shrimps, crabs, clams, worms, urchins, sponges, and sea anemones.

diverse. And new species—especially from the deep sea—are being discovered continually. Although coastal zones make up only about 10 percent of the marine biome, they contain almost 90 percent of marine life. Coastal zones contain several distinct features.

The open ocean has several zones. The zones are classified according to water depth, presence of light, and distance from shore. You can locate each of the marine zones in *Figure 35.22*. Which zone supports the most organisms? Why?

CHECKPOINT 35.4

1. How do freshwater biomes differ from marine biomes?
2. List and describe the zones in a marine biome.
3. **Critical Thinking** Predict how damming a river would affect an estuary at the river's mouth.

Build on What You Know

4. In which marine zones are heterotrophs located? Autotrophs? Explain your answers. *(Need to jog your memory? Review relevant concepts in Chapter 4, Section 4.1.)*

What are the distinguishing characteristics of Earth's land and water biomes?

Chapter 35 Review

35.1–35.2 Life depends on the relationships between living and nonliving parts of the environment.
35.3–35.4 Regions of the biosphere have distinguishing characteristics.

Sum It Up

Use the following summary to review the main concepts in this chapter.

35.1 Characteristics of the Biosphere

- Ecologists study the interactions of organisms with their physical environments.
- Levels of organization in the biosphere increase in complexity from individuals to populations, communities, and ecosystems.
- Every environment is comprised of living (biotic) factors and nonliving (abiotic) factors.

35.2 Climate

- Temperature and precipitation are abiotic factors that distinguish climate patterns.
- Because Earth's surface is curved, the distribution of solar radiation is not uniform. Because Earth is tilted on its axis, the amount of radiation that reaches Earth varies by season.
- Earth can be divided into three large climate zones by latitude.
- The proximity to large bodies of water and the location of mountains affect regional climates.

35.3 Land Biomes

- Regions with similar climates support similar ecosystems.

- A tundra is a treeless plain with permanently frozen soil.
- The taiga biome has long, cold winters and relatively mild summers, which support conifers.
- Tall deciduous trees dominate the temperate forest biome.
- The chaparral's rainy seasons alternate with dry seasons to produce hardy, stunted plants.
- The humidity and warmth of tropical rain forests supports biodiversity.
- Plants and animals that live in arid deserts must be able to conserve water.
- Both temperate and tropical grasslands support diverse populations of grazing animals.

35.4 Water Biomes

- Most of Earth consists of aquatic biomes.
- Freshwater biomes include those with flowing water, those with standing water, and wetlands.
- Inland and coastal wetlands develop where freshwater or saltwater meets land.
- Marine zones are classified by the water depth, the presence of light, and the distance from shore.

Using Terms and Concepts

Use each of the following words in a complete sentence. If you need to review a meaning, turn to the page indicated.

ecology (p. 854)
biosphere (p. 854)
biotic factors (p. 855)
abiotic factors (p. 855)
population (p. 855)
community (p. 855)

ecosystem (p. 855)
habitat (p. 855)
climate (p. 858)
tropical zone (p. 859)
temperate zone (p. 859)
arctic zone (p. 859)

rain shadow (p. 860)
altitude (p.860)
biome (p. 861)
wetlands (p. 868)
estuary (p. 869)

Use Your Word Power

COMPLETION **Write the word or phrase that best completes each statement below.**

1. The _____ is the typical weather pattern in an area over time.

2. The environment consists of a unique set of _____ factors that support a specific species.

3. A large group of ecosystems that share similar conditions of temperature and precipitation is called a(n) _____.

4. All the communities and abiotic factors in a given area are a(n) _____.

5. The shallow area near the mouth of a river where freshwater and saltwater mix is called a(n) _____.

6. _____ is the study of organisms and their environments.

7. _____ is defined as height above sea level.

TRUE-FALSE **Write true if the statement is true. If the statement is false, replace the underlined word(s) to make the statement true.**

8. All the members of a species that live in a particular area are called a <u>community</u>.

9. The <u>tundra</u> is located in the arctic zone.

10. The amount of sunlight and oxygen are two of the <u>biotic</u> factors in marine environments.

11. The life-supporting region of Earth is called the <u>biosphere</u>.

12. A <u>rain shadow</u> forms on the eastern slopes of a mountain range.

13. Temperatures in the <u>temperate zone</u> vary little from season to season.

14. Mangrove swamps and salt marshes are examples of coastal <u>wetlands</u>.

Show What You Know

15. What characteristics do altitude and latitude have in common?

16. How is a tropical savanna similar to a chaparral? How are the two different?

17. What is the characteristic that cold deserts and hot deserts have in common?

18. How do the hours of available daylight change, from January to June at the equator? At the North Pole?

19. What is the primary difference between the neritic zone and the oceanic zone?

20. How does the climate in tropical rain forests and temperate forests differ? How do the trees in the temperate forest respond to the change in climate?

21. Explain how a benthic zone could be photic or aphotic.

22. **Make a Concept Map** Create a concept map that relates different climates and biomes.

Take It Further

23. **Developing a Hypothesis** Make a prediction about the degree of biodiversity at the boundary between two biomes.

24. **Applying Concepts** Suppose you had two locations: one 40° north of the equator, the other 40° south of the equator—and each at the same longitude. Would they have the same climate? Give reasons for your answer.

25. **Making an Analogy** A shadow occurs when an object blocks light from a surface, thereby "casting" a shadow. How is a light shadow similar to a rain shadow? Explain.

26. **Identifying Cause and Effect** Although the level of precipitation is low, most tundra ecosystems are very wet. What characteristic would explain this apparent contradiction?

27. Designing an Experiment Is there a minimum amount of precipitation that grass needs to survive? Do different species of grass need different amounts of water? How does the amount of precipitation affect the growth rate of grass? Does mowing a lawn affect the growth rate? Design an experiment to answer each of these questions.

28. Analyzing Data Graph the data below, using the x-axis for the location and the y-axis for the amount of rainfall. When labeling your locations, keep them in the order they appear in the table (Quinault nearest the origin and Spokane furthest from the origin).

Annual Rainfall in Washington State	
Location	**Rainfall (cm)**
Quinault	343
Sequim	43
Seattle	86
Snoqualimie Pass	257
Yakima	18
Spokane	38

29. Interpreting a Graph The locations in the table and your graph are listed in order from west to east. Washington has two mountain ranges—the Olympic Mountains near the coast and the inland Cascade Range. Use the information in your graph to describe where the locations are in relation to the mountains.

Consider the Issues

30. Wetlands or Paved Lands? Each year many wetlands are filled and paved over to provide land for homes and recreation. Although these actions provide valuable human resources, they also have their consequences. Wetlands are beneficial because they control pollution and flooding, and provide habitats for many organisms. What can be done to provide resources for humans while ensuring that wetlands are not completely destroyed?

Make New Connections

31. Biology and Cartoons Explain the joke in this cartoon. What did the artist need to know about biomes to create the cartoon? Use what you have learned in the chapter to create your own cartoon.

THE FAR SIDE   By GARY LARSON

"I love the desert"

32. Biology and Physics When warm, moist air travels up and over a mountain range, clouds form. These clouds contain water in its liquid state. Look up *condensation*, and explain how water changes from the gaseous state to the liquid state. How does condensation affect the temperature at the top of a mountain?

33. Biology and Oceanography Research the Gulf Stream in the North Atlantic. What causes this warm ocean current? What is its effect on the climate of Iceland and Great Britain?

FAST-FORWARD TO CHAPTER 36

Chapter 35 focused on the abiotic factors that determine the location of communities. In Chapter 36, you will learn how both abiotic and biotic factors affect the survival of populations within communities.

You can find out more about populations and communities by exploring the following Internet address:
http://biosurf.ecology.com

In this chapter . . .

FEATURES

Everyday Biology
- Limits
- Mutual Feelings

In the Community
What Is a Community?

 Issues in Biology
Missing Members

LAB ZONES

Discover It!
- Comparing Populations

Do It!
- Analyzing Interactions in Your Community
- Studying Human Causes of Succession

Think About It!
- Would You Work for Pennies?

Investigate It!
- Observing Population Growth

Little Dogs on the Prairie

On the Great Plains of the United States, many black-tailed prairie dogs live together in large groups. Prairie dogs build networks of underground tunnels that can be compared to towns. These "towns" consist of family units called coteries, which have neighboring territories with defined boundaries. Each coterie territory has several entrances, allowing quick access into and out of the protective tunnels. Prairie dogs spend much of their day above ground eating grass. When a predator is spotted, they warn each other, and the population scurries underground. Their system is so effective that a scientific research team witnessed only 22 successful attacks on prairie dogs in 73,000 hours of observation.

Other animals benefit from prairie-dog towns. As many as 171 different animal species have been associated with an underground prairie-dog town, and some of these animals use the tunnels as shelter. For example, the endangered black-footed ferret would be extinct if it were not for the shelter provided by prairie-dog towns. Scientists have concluded that prairie dogs and the animals that share their towns have a very social community. But what is a community, and what are the relationships in a community?

LAB ZONE Discover It!

Comparing Populations

1. Observe a population of living things in your area. Populations to choose from can include people, birds, grasses, or insects. Estimate and record the size of the population.
2. What other living things interact with the population you have observed?
3. What abiotic factors affect this population?

Many different factors affect a population's size and growth. Changes in the environment can benefit some populations and harm others.

WRITE ABOUT IT!

Like many scientific terms, *community* has an everyday meaning in addition to its scientific definition. What does the word *community* mean to you? In your science journal, write about your community and how it affects your life.

36.1 Population Growth

Animal mobs

You may know that many fish make up a school, but did you know that a group of frogs is called an army? Other interesting names of groups of animals include a crash of rhinos, a mob of kangaroos, a smack of jellyfish, a drift of hogs, and a pod of whales. Birds also have unique group names: a murder of ravens, an exaltation of larks, and a parliament of owls.

STUDYING POPULATIONS

Getting the big picture

What comes to mind when you hear the word *population*? You are part of a population in your community. The school you attend also has a population.

A **population** is a group of organisms of the same species that live in a particular area. For example, the honeybees that live together in a hive are members of the same species. All the honeybees in a hive make up a colony and a population.

During the course of a year, the size of a honeybee population may change dramatically. When flowers are blooming and food is plentiful, the colony may grow very quickly. Twenty, forty, or even sixty thousand bees may crowd together in the hive. During severe environmental conditions, however, the number of bees in the colony can decrease drastically. A cold winter or a mite infestation can kill thousands of bees.

Population ecology is the study of how and why populations change. In their research, ecologists try to determine what factors influence the size, density, distribution, and growth of various populations of organisms. Once the ecologists have identified the factors that affect a population, they can predict how that population may change in the future.

For populations to survive, many different environmental factors must be in balance. This balance can be upset by natural disasters. Think of what a prolonged drought can do to plant and animal populations in a forest or on a prairie. Human activities,

FIGURE 36.1
How is a honeybee colony an example of a population?

such as pollution and habitat destruction, can also upset the balance of environmental factors that must exist in order for populations to survive.

Populations can change—sometimes permanently—as a result of human activities. For example, cod used to be abundant in the ocean off the coast of Newfoundland. But during the 1980s, the number of cod dropped dramatically due to overfishing. By the early 1990s, cod had all but disappeared. Studying these changes in populations can help people understand and reduce the negative impact of their activities.

EXPONENTIAL GROWTH

Growing by leaps and bounds

To understand how populations grow, think about what happens to a population under ideal conditions. Suppose you put a single bacterium in a nutrient-rich culture dish then incubate the culture under conditions ideal for bacterial growth. Each bacterium can divide every 20 minutes. How large would the population of bacteria be after one day?

The graph in *Figure 36.2* shows how a population of bacteria can increase in size. In the first 20 minutes, the single bacterium would divide to produce 2 bacteria. After 40 minutes, there would be 4 bacteria. After the first hour, there would be 8 bacteria. After 10 generations, there would be 1024 bacteria, and after 20 generations, 1,048,576 bacteria. After 72 generations—only 24 hours later—your culture dish would be teeming with 4.72×10^{21} bacteria!

The growth pattern of bacteria is an example of exponential (eks-poh-NEN-shul) growth. **Exponential growth** occurs when the rate of population growth in each new generation is a multiple of the previous generation. If you graph the exponential growth of a population, the result is a J-shaped curve, as shown in *Figure 36.2*.

The model of exponential growth in bacteria includes two assumptions. The first assumption is that no bacteria die, and the second is that all of the bacteria in the population reproduce. These assumptions make it possible for there to be a 100-percent

Population Growth in Bacteria

Number of Generations	Number of Bacterial Cells
0	1
1	2
2	4
3	8
4	16
10	1024
20	1,048,576
72	4.72×10^{21}

Number of Bacterial Cells (vertical axis)

Number of Generations (horizontal axis)

FIGURE 36.2
Bacterial growth occurs in an exponential, or J-shaped, curve. What assumptions are included in this growth curve?

LAB ZONE — Think About It!

Would You Work for Pennies?

Would you rather have a job that paid $100 a week, or one that paid you one penny the first day, two pennies the second day, four pennies the third day, and so on for thirty days?

Analyzing the Information

1 Calculate the amount pay you would receive after thirty days for both methods of payment.
2 Make a graph to show your pay each day for the second method of payment. How does your graph compare with the graph of bacterial growth?
3 Which method of payment would you prefer? Explain your answer using your calculations and graph.

increase in every generation. In other words, the population of bacteria doubles with every generation.

In nature, of course, not all of the offspring in a population survive to reproduce. Suppose a rabbit population begins with 100 rabbits. The population size of each new generation may increase by only 5 percent. Will this population growth produce an exponential growth curve? You can see in *Figure 36.3* that it will. But because the percentage increase in each rabbit generation is only 5 percent, compared to 100 percent in the bacteria, the curve looks different. It takes more generations for the growth curve of the rabbit population to become steep. Nevertheless, you can see that even a small percentage increase in the size of each generation can lead to exponential growth.

The total change in a population's size over time is its growth rate. You can calculate growth rate by using the following equation:

$$\text{Growth rate} = \frac{\text{Change in number of individuals}}{\text{Time period}}$$

Four factors play a role in growth rate: birth rate, immigration, death rate, and emigration. Immigration is the movement of organisms into an area occupied by an existing population. Emigration is the movement of organisms out of an area where a population is located. The combined effects of these four factors determine whether a population grows, shrinks, or stays the same size.

It is also possible to use the age structure of a population to make predictions about changes in population size. The age structure means the proportion of individuals in a population that are young, old, and in between. For example, what is the growth potential in a human population in which most people are over age 80? How about in one composed primarily of young adults? If most members of a population are young and able to reproduce, that population has the potential to grow rapidly. On the other hand, a population of mostly older individuals has less growth potential, and that potential may decrease as the death rate increases.

FIGURE 36.3

This graph shows the growth rate of a rabbit population. How does the shape of this graph differ from that in *Figure 36.2*?

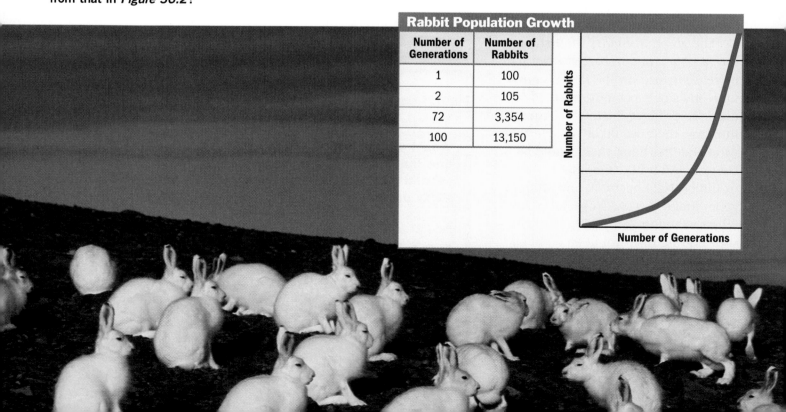

Rabbit Population Growth

Number of Generations	Number of Rabbits
1	100
2	105
72	3,354
100	13,150

Number of Rabbits

Number of Generations

CARRYING CAPACITY

Exponential growth meets the real world

Study the graph of population growth in *Figure 36.4*. This graph shows the growth of a fruit fly population. Notice that the population first goes through a stage of exponential growth. But after a while, the population growth slows down. Eventually the number of fruit flies in the population levels off. Why does this happen?

As you may recall from Chapter 35, organisms obtain all of the biotic and abiotic resources they need from their environment. When a population first begins to grow, resources such as food, water, and living space are plentiful. The birth rate is high, the death rate is low, and the population increases exponentially. But as growth continues, the environment's resources are shared by more and more individuals. Eventually, some resources are in short supply and become limiting factors. A **limiting factor** is any biotic or abiotic resource in the environment that limits the size of a population.

Limiting factors determine an environment's carrying capacity. **Carrying capacity** is the number of individuals in a population that an environment can support over a relatively long period of time. The graph in *Figure 36.4* shows how carrying capacity works. Assume that food is a limiting factor. As food supplies dwindle, the birth rate drops and the death rate rises, causing population growth to slow down. Eventually, the population levels off as the carrying capacity of the environment is reached. When the birth rate and the death rate of the population become roughly equal, the population size stabilizes.

The growth pattern of the fruit fly population forms an S-shaped curve. This growth pattern is typical of many populations in nature. Population

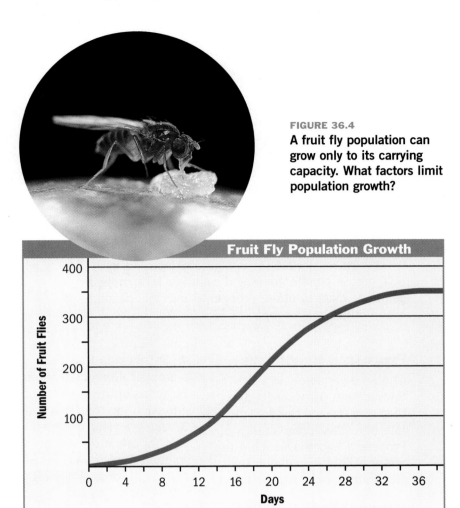

FIGURE 36.4
A fruit fly population can grow only to its carrying capacity. What factors limit population growth?

growth is rapid at first, but then slows and levels off as the population reaches the environment's carrying capacity.

CHECKPOINT 36.1

1. What is a population? Give two examples of a population.
2. What is exponential growth? What causes a population to stop growing exponentially?
3. Critical Thinking How might a change in the water level of a river affect the fish populations living in the river?

Build on What You Know

4. Compare the factors that affect growth rate with the factors that affect the gene pool of a population. *(Need to jog your memory? Revisit relevant concepts in Chapter 10, Section 10.5.)*

Chapter 36 Populations and Communities **879**

Observing Population Growth

WHAT YOU WILL DO Observe the effect of a variable on a yeast cell population

SKILLS YOU WILL USE Observing, collecting and recording data, measuring, designing an experiment

WHAT YOU WILL NEED 6 empty baby-food jars with lids, grease pencil, graduated cylinder, 10% molasses solution, yeast solution, dropper, 6 microscope slides, 6 coverslips, microscope

Propose a Hypothesis

Choose a variable (such as temperature, light, or food) that may change the growth rate of a yeast population. Propose a hypothesis about the effect of that variable on the growth of a yeast population.

Conduct Your Experiment

DAY 1

1 Label two jars *A,* two jars *B,* and two jars *C.* Then number each pair *1* and *2.* A1 and A2 are your control jars. Add 10 milliliters (mL) of molasses solution to each of your control jars. Add 10 mL of molasses solution or 10 mL of water to jars B1, B2, C1, and C2 depending on whether food is your chosen variable.

2 Stir the yeast solution with a dropper. Immediately transfer 10 drops of the yeast solution into each jar, then mix again.
3 Using a clean dropper, transfer one drop of the solution from jar A1, jar B1, and jar C1 onto slides with coverslips.
4 Observe the slides under a microscope at high power. Count the number of individual yeast cells in each of five different fields per slide. Buds also count as individual cells.
5 Make a table to record the five counts for each slide. Average the five counts for each slide and record your results. Empty and clean jars A1, B1, and C1 when you have completed this step.

6 Place jar A2 (the control) in a warm, dark place. Place jars B2 and C2 in places where you can test your chosen variables.

DAY 6

7 Repeat steps 3, 4, and 5 for jars A2, B2, and C2. Gently mix the yeast solution before transferring the drops to the slides. Record your data in the table.

Analyze Your Data

1 Make three line graphs to plot the changes in yeast cell populations A, B, and C.
2 Describe the shape of your graphs. How do these graphs differ? What do your graphs reveal about yeast population growth?

Draw Conclusions

How did your variable affect the rate of growth of the yeast population?

Design a Related Experiment

Design an experiment to test the effect of another variable on yeast population growth.

Lab: Observing Population Growth

5. Average Count per Slide
  jar A1 average:
  jar B1 average:
  jar C1 average:

36.2 Limits on Population Growth

Disappearance of the cliff dwellers
Between A.D. 1000 and 1300, the people of what is now the southwestern United States lived in cliff dwellings. These dwellings could house up to 1500 people and were constructed from stone, adobe, and timber. However, the cliff dwellers left their homes for unknown reasons—perhaps because of war or climate changes. What factors affect human populations today?

What you'll learn

IDEAS
• To distinguish between exponential growth and a boom-and-bust curve
• To compare and contrast limiting factors

WORDS
density-dependent limiting factors, predation, density-independent limiting factors

DENSITY-DEPENDENT LIMITING FACTORS

Too close for comfort

Limiting factors in the environment keep the population size in check in two ways: They either cause a decrease in the birth rate or an increase in the death rate. Some factors become limiting only when the population density—the number of organisms per unit of space—reaches a certain level. These factors are called **density-dependent limiting factors.**

One density-dependent limiting factor is living space. For example, mice that live together under stressful, crowded conditions often neglect their young. Neglected baby mice have a high death rate, and this limits population growth. Three other common density-dependent limiting factors are disease, competition, and predation.

Disease As a population becomes more dense, disease often limits growth. During the fourteenth century, for example, bubonic plague killed more than 25 million people in Europe. The disease spread through crowded villages and towns, killing people with frightening speed. In rural areas, however, where the human population was sparse, fewer people contracted the disease. Today, bubonic plague is rare and treatable. What diseases affect the human population today?

Competition You probably know what it is like to compete for something. Other organisms also compete with each other for resources. Competition is an interaction in which organisms try to obtain a share of the same limited resources. Animals compete for food, water, mates, and territories. Plants compete for water, minerals, pollinators, and sunlight. Within a population, competition for any resource is a density-dependent limiting factor.

FIGURE 36.5
This community watering hole is drying up. How is this change an example of a density-dependent limiting factor?

881

FIGURE 36.6

Population Cycles

The graph (right) illustrates how the lynx population cycle changes as the snowshoe hare population fluctuates. The series of photos (below) illustrates why the size of the lynx population varies with the size of the hare population.

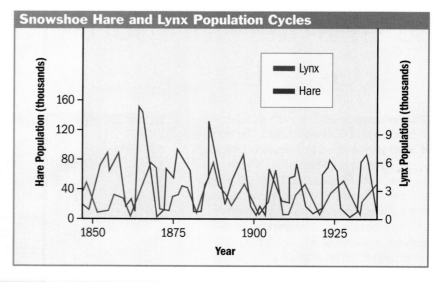

Snowshoe Hare and Lynx Population Cycles

When population density increases, resources must be shared among more individuals.

Predation An interaction in which one species (a predator) feeds on another species (prey) is called **predation.** The lynx shown in *Figure 36.6* is a catlike predator of the northern forests that stalks and eats snowshoe hares. When snowshoe hares are plentiful, the lynx in the area are well fed, and many of their young survive. As a result, the lynx population grows. As the number of lynx increases, more snowshoe hares are killed and eaten, and the size of the snowshoe hare population decreases. As snowshoe hares become scarce, the lynx population will begin to decline as well.

Predation is a density-dependent limiting factor because its effects on a population change as the numbers of predators or prey increase or decrease.

In general, when a population grows beyond the carrying capacity of the environment, density-dependent limiting factors act to reduce the population. The population's size grows and shrinks, resulting in the cycles shown in *Figure 36.6*.

Changes in the size of predator-prey populations often occur in cycles. Determine the length of each population cycle shown in *Figure 36.6*. Can you explain the changes in hare and lynx populations?

A similar interaction takes place between snowshoe hares and the plants they eat. When the snowshoe hare population increases, more plants are eaten, decreasing the plant population and the hares' food supply. Because there is less food available, the number of hares declines. With fewer hares around, the plant population increases and the cycle starts again.

Predator-prey relationships are a strong force in natural selection. Prey that escape predators can reproduce and pass on to their offspring traits that enabled them to escape. At the same time, predators that capture the most prey are likely to be stronger and to produce more offspring. Their offspring inherit traits that made their parents efficient predators. In this way, predators and their prey may coevolve.

DENSITY-INDEPENDENT LIMITING FACTORS

Just bad luck

Some environmental factors can disrupt or destroy all sorts of populations. Factors that affect all populations in the same way, regardless of their density, are called **density-independent limiting factors.** Weather, seasonal cycles, natural disasters, and many human activities are density-independent limiting factors. These factors can cause growing or stable populations to collapse suddenly. For example, when Mount St. Helens erupted in 1980, many populations died within minutes.

Some density-independent disturbances happen regularly. In places where there are severe winters, large numbers of insects die every year. In some areas, periodic droughts wipe out entire grass populations.

Populations that live in areas of seasonal cold and drought seldom approach the environment's carrying capacity. Instead, they have a population growth pattern called a boom-and-bust curve. As you can see in *Figure 36.7*, a boom-and-bust curve represents a period of exponential growth followed by a sudden collapse of the population.

Environments are always changing, and most populations can adapt to a certain amount of change. Populations grow or shrink in response to changes in the environment until balance is restored.

Major upsets in the natural balance, however, can lead to extinction. Extinction occurs when populations cannot adapt to changing conditions in the environment. Human activities can upset the balance in natural systems so quickly that populations of organisms do not have time to adapt. Overhunting, overfishing, clear-cutting of forests, damming of rivers, and pollution all can lead to extinction. Although extinction can occur naturally, human activities have greatly accelerated the rate of extinction worldwide.

HUMAN POPULATION

Growing . . . growing . . .

In 1798 the English economist Thomas Malthus wrote that the human population was increasing at a much faster rate than its food supply. Malthus thought that population growth caused resource shortages that

Limits

Some scientists hypothesize that Earth's total carrying capacity for humans is 15 to 20 billion people—three to four times the size of today's population. With current rates of growth, the human population could reach that size in 75 to 80 years.

FIGURE 36.7

Native to Australia, thrips are insects with a seasonal boom-and-bust cycle. The thrip's population peaks during the summer months of December and January. When would you find the fewest thrips per flower?

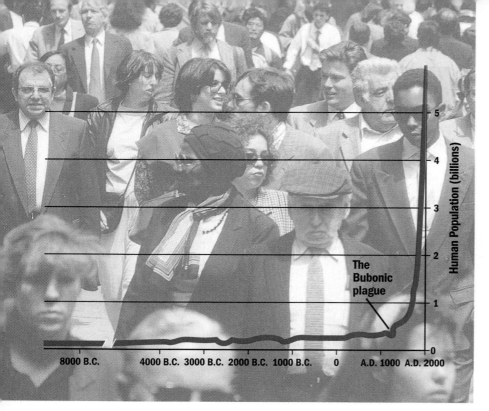

The Bubonic plague

Human Population (billions)

5
4
3
2
1
0

8000 B.C.   4000 B.C. 3000 B.C. 2000 B.C. 1000 B.C.   0   A.D. 1000 A.D. 2000

rapid growth is due to the increasing gap between birth rates and death rates—far more people are born than die each year. Exponential growth of the human population cannot continue indefinitely. The same factors that limit population size for bacteria, lynx, or any other organism also apply to humans.

Population ecologists are not sure what the world's carrying capacity is for humans. They hope that population growth will level out in an S-shaped curve and become stable at some point. In the meantime, the expanding human population is placing huge demands on natural resources. As our population has grown, humans have developed medical, agricultural, and other technologies that enable more people to survive. Do you think there is a limit to our population?

FIGURE 36.8

The human population is growing rapidly. What factors affect this growth curve? How does human population growth affect other populations?

led to famines and wars. As you learned in Chapter 10, Charles Darwin later concluded that all populations could outgrow their resources.

How much has the human population increased over time? The J-shaped curve in *Figure 36.8* represents human population growth. As you can see, for thousands of years the population growth was very slow. Then, between 1650 and 1850, the population doubled—passing the one billion mark. And the population's doubling time is becoming shorter and shorter. After 1850 it took only 80 years for the population to double to 2 billion. It reached 4 billion just 45 years later. Population ecologists estimate that the human population now increases by 90 million people every year!

At the moment, the human population is growing exponentially. This

CHECKPOINT 36.2

1. What causes a boom-and-bust growth pattern? How is this pattern different from the growth patterns of the fly and bacteria discussed in Section 36.1?

2. Compare and contrast density-dependent limiting factors with density-independent limiting factors. Give examples of each.

3. **Critical Thinking** What will happen to a population of predators if there is a sudden increase in food for its prey? Explain.

Build on What You Know

4. Relate Malthus' theories to Darwin's theory of natural selection. *(Need to jog your memory? Revisit relevant concepts in Chapter 10, Section 10.2.)*

What factors affect population size?

36.3 Communities

Birds and beasts

African red-billed oxpeckers have a unique relationship with grazing animals. These birds eat ticks and other harmful insects found on rhinos, giraffes, and water buffalo. Not only are the grazers free of pests, but they also gain a built-in alarm system—the birds make noise when predators approach.

What you'll learn

IDEAS
- To describe a community
- To compare community interactions

WORDS

community, symbiosis, mutualism, parasitism, commensalism

ROLES IN THE COMMUNITY

All together

Picture a meadow full of tall grass and wildflowers. Honeybees flit from flower to flower. Dragonflies zoom around hunting for insects. Mice scurry through the grass looking for seeds. High overhead, a hawk circles. All the organisms living in and around this meadow form a community.

A **community** is a collection of populations that interact with each other in a given area. Populations in a community compete for resources, prey on one another, and interact in many other ways.

Different communities vary in the types of species they contain and in the abundance of each species. An Amazon rain forest community contains thousands of different kinds of plants and animals. Some species may be represented by only a handful of individuals, however. In contrast, a pine forest community in northern Canada might contain only a few dozen species, but most of those species would be very abundant. For example, there could be many thousands of individuals of one pine tree species.

In any community, each species is unique in what it does and in how it interacts with other community members and the physical environment. As you may recall from Chapter 10, the particular role that a population plays in its community is called its niche. In the meadow example, a honeybee population pollinates flowering plants. A population of mice eats seeds and is prey for other animals. Hawks are predators that feed on mice and other small animals.

A population's niche includes all its interactions with other species in its community, as well as interactions with abiotic parts of the community. Understanding a species' niche helps

FIGURE 36.9

The hawk and the mouse occupy different niches in the same community. What are their niches?

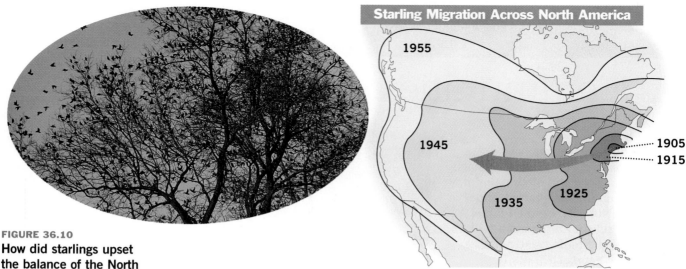

Starling Migration Across North America

1955

1945

1935

1925

1905

1915

FIGURE 36.10
How did starlings upset the balance of the North American bird community?

ecologists predict how changing conditions might affect that species and other living organisms with which it interacts. How might plowing a meadow affect the niches of the different species living there?

COMMUNITY INTERACTIONS

Tough competition

In any community, you will find organisms interacting in many different ways—so many, in fact, that studying interactions can be a bit bewildering. But the interactions in a community fall into a few general categories.

As you read earlier in this chapter, most species in a community compete with other species for food, water, sunlight, nesting material—even places to perch or hide. Competition can occur between populations of different species or between members of the same species.

When a resource is in short supply, competition can become fierce. Sometimes foreign species move in and outcompete native species for limited resources. For example, 60 European starlings were released in New York City's Central Park in 1890. Now there are more than 200 million starlings in North America. Starlings compete with bluebirds, redheaded woodpeckers, flickers, and flycatchers for nesting sites. The growth in the starling population has had a negative impact on these native species.

Competition is not the only type of interaction between species. You have also read about predator-prey relationships. The lynx, for example, depends on the hare for survival. Can you suggest other examples of predator-prey relationships?

Natural selection constantly acts to fine-tune predator-prey relationships.

LAB ZONE Do It!

Analyzing Interactions in Your Community

The inside of your home is a dwelling place, not just for humans but for a whole community of species. You can investigate their interactions if you . . .

Try This

1 Make a list of organisms that can be found living in your house or apartment. Some may be invited, such as pets or houseplants. Others may be uninvited, such as insects or molds.
2 Make a table and record information about the food relationships among members in this community.

Analyze Your Results

1 What do the animals eat? Do they rely on the human food supply, or do they have their own sources of food?
2 Are there predators and prey in this community?
3 Describe how the community members compete for resources.

Many predators and prey have evolved sharp claws, teeth, and beaks. Prey have acquired defenses such as spines and shells. Both predators and prey have camouflaging body colors and patterns that make them less visible to each other.

Predator-prey relationships are one of the many types of interactions among populations. Another type of interaction, called **symbiosis,** occurs when one species lives in close association with another species over a period of time. There are three types of symbiotic relationships: mutualism, parasitism, and commensalism. What are some of the symbiotic relationships you read about in Units 4, 5, 6, and 7?

In **mutualism,** two species interact closely in a way that benefits both species. Honeybees and other insect pollinators have a mutualistic relationship with many flowers. Flowers attract bees with sweet nectar. As bees feed, they pick up pollen that they transfer to other flowers, pollinating them in the process.

Many animals, including cows and termites, have microorganisms in their digestive tracts. In this type of mutualism, the microorganisms help the host digest grass, wood, or other plant materials. In return, the microorganisms have a habitat with a constant food supply.

In **parasitism,** a parasite lives on or in another organism—its host. Parasites suck blood or obtain nutrients in some way from the host's body. Parasites may weaken their hosts, but they usually don't kill them like predators do. Parasites may live

FIGURE 36.11
Symbiosis

How do these photographs represent the three types of symbiosis?

Parasitism
Ticks (right), fleas, leeches, lice, and mites are examples of parasites that live outside the host, attached to skin or scales.

Mutualism
The ants and acacia trees in Central and South America have an unusual mutualistic relationship. The ants live in the acacia's thorns and eat their leaves. The acacias benefit, too, because ants protect them from predators, and will even destroy other plants that shade the acacias from the sun.

Commensalism
The clown fish and sea anemone illustrate commensalism in a coral reef community. The clown fish lives on scraps from the sea anemone's meals. When danger threatens, it retreats into the sea anemone's waving tentacles. Most fish are instantly paralyzed by the tentacles, but the clown fish seems to be immune to the sea anemone's touch.

Chapter 36 Populations and Communities **887**

FIGURE 36.12
Cheetahs are genetically very similar. How does this low genetic variability render them vulnerable to extinction?

outside or inside a host's body. Parasites that live inside a host include tapeworms, pinworms, and liver flukes.

In **commensalism,** one organism benefits from the interaction, and the other organism is neither helped nor harmed. Barnacles that live on the skin of whales or sea turtles are examples of commensalism. Barnacles benefit because they are moved from place to place, increasing their access to food. The whales or sea turtles are not affected by the barnacles.

BALANCE IN A COMMUNITY

Everything in its place

An ecological community is a highly organized natural system in which all parts exist in a delicate balance. Every species occupies its own special niche. The complex interactions that take place between different species help maintain the balance and lead to stability in the community.

An important connection exists between biodiversity—the degree of species variety—and balance in ecological communities. To see this connection, compare a naturally diverse forest and a tree plantation.

In a forest, different species of trees grow side by side. Two spruce trees, for example, might be separated by a fir tree and several pines. If disease or insects attack a particular tree, neighboring trees of a different species may be resistant to the attack. In this way, species diversity in a forest acts as a natural barrier to the spread of disease or insect infestation.

In comparison, a tree plantation is more vulnerable to disease. All the trees are of the same species, so pests and disease spread from tree to tree much more easily.

Genetic diversity within populations is also important in maintaining ecological balance in a community. When a population of genetically diverse organisms is infected by a disease, some individuals will die, but others may survive because their different genetic makeup makes them more resistant to the disease. This is not the case in populations where all the organisms are genetically very similar, such as the cheetahs in *Figure 36.12*. A disease that affects one individual will most likely affect all the others. Species with low genetic variability are especially vulnerable to extinction.

Worldwide, between 10 and 200 species become extinct every day as a result of human activities. Adding or removing just one species from a community can have unpredictable and wide-ranging consequences.

The introduction of foreign species into existing communities is a global problem. Some introductions have been accidental, others intentional. In 1859, for example, two dozen rabbits were released into the Australian countryside. Within ten years, millions of rabbits had overrun the land.

The water hyacinth, a blue-flowered floating plant from South America, has been introduced into

IN THE COMMUNITY

What Is a Community?

Now that you have learned the scientific definition of a community, analyze your own community from a biological perspective. What different species occupy your community, and what niches do they occupy? How do the different species interact with each other? Draw a diagram that includes the different species in your community, and use arrows to indicate interactions. Do any species upset the balance of the community? Log on to *http://ecology.biosurf.com* to investigate other types of communities.

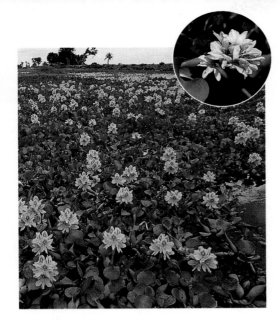

FIGURE 36.13
These water hyacinths have overrun their water habitat. How have they upset the balance in the ecosystem?

many countries. Once established, the water hyacinth's growth is almost unstoppable. You can see water hyacinths in *Figure 36.13*. They choke rivers, destroy lakes, and crowd out other species. Waterways in Florida and nearby states are overrun by water hyacinths, as is Lake Victoria in East Africa—Africa's largest lake. Can you think of other species that have upset the balance in an ecosystem?

ISSUES IN BIOLOGY

Missing members

Many large predators, such as lions, tigers, leopards, and wolves, have been removed from their habitats or hunted nearly to extinction. For example, wolves were systematically eliminated throughout most of the United States. Without predators to control their numbers, deer populations grew exponentially. Large deer populations are now a serious problem in many areas.

The deer destroy crops, damage trees and shrubs, and compete with other species for resources.

Wolves, bald eagles, and other predators are returning or being reintroduced into parts of their former ranges. In 1995 biologists released 29 gray wolves into Yellowstone National Park, the first phase of a program to restore wolf populations in the Rocky Mountains.

Some ranchers and area residents disagree with this reintroduction, as predators may kill pets or livestock. Human communities are working together to make predator reintroduction safe and successful for all.

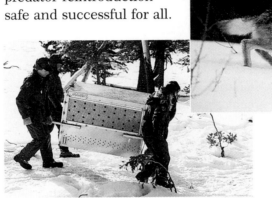

FIGURE 36.14
Gray wolves have recently been released into the wild. How did their absence affect their community?

CHECKPOINT 36.3

1. What is a community? Give two examples.
2. Describe three types of interactions in a community.
3. **Critical Thinking** Classify the relationship between oxpeckers and grazing animals as predator-prey, mutualism, parasitism, or commensalism. Explain.

Build on What You Know

4. What type of symbiosis can be found in lichens? *(Need to jog your memory? Revisit relevant concepts in Chapter 16, Section 16.3.)*

How are the structure and characteristics of a community determined?

?

36.4 Ecological Succession

Fertilizer for the sea
In 1995 a research ship dumped 450 kilograms of dissolved iron into the Pacific Ocean. Within weeks the area was filled with phytoplankton that use iron as a nutrient. Scientists hope that other community members will also increase—including species of fishes. How else might this ecosystem be affected?

FIGURE 36.15
Ecological succession has begun in this recently burned area. What new community will develop?

THE PROCESS OF SUCCESSION

Success in change

Change is a natural part of life in any ecological community. Competition for limited resources may eliminate one or more of a community's populations. Some populations may move to a new location, or a disease may wipe them out. Extreme weather or a natural disaster may drastically reduce some populations, yet enable others to thrive.

Whenever change occurs in a community, some habitats may be destroyed while new ones are created. For example, a forest fire might eliminate the habitats of some tree-dwelling birds. At the same time, however, the once-dark forest floor would be flooded with sunlight, creating a habitat suitable for grasses and small flowering plants. These plants could thrive in great numbers along with the animals, such as insects and rodents, that feed on them. Animals that feed on the rodents and insects, such as birds and large predators, could also move into the area.

In addition to fires, other natural disasters such as floods, earthquakes, and volcanic eruptions can destroy or alter niches. Wherever change occurs, opportunities arise for new species to move in and for new communities to develop. Over time, new communities of organisms may gradually replace existing ones in a process called **ecological succession.**

Natural disturbances can set the stage for ecological succession by emptying habitats that were previously occupied. Succession may occur as new species occupy the area and establish new niches. Human activities such as mining, logging, building, and farming can change environments and lead to ecological succession. Succession can also occur after humans have left an area. What might you observe during the first stages of ecological succession in a newly vacant lot?

The barren slopes of a recently erupted volcano and an area of rock exposed by a recent landslide are places where primary succession occurs. **Primary succession** occurs when communities begin to form where none existed before.

The first organisms to occupy an area undergoing primary succession are called pioneer species. A group of pioneer species eventually forms a **pioneer community.** As succession continues, a **climax community** becomes established. A climax community is one that has achieved relative stability and species diversity.

The interactions between the different species help keep the community stable. Unless disturbed by outside factors, such as a natural disaster, a climax community can remain stable for many generations.

Climax communities do not develop everywhere. Sometimes frequent disturbances prevent succession from proceeding beyond a certain point. In grasslands, for example, succession is continually occurring due to frequent fires.

A type of succession that occurs more rapidly than primary succession is secondary succession. **Secondary succession** occurs where a community has been cleared by a disturbance that did not destroy the soil. A vacant lot in a city, abandoned farmland, and a forest area where trees have been cut down are examples of places where secondary succession might occur.

ISLAND SUCCESSION

Colonists in a new land

How do new islands that form in the ocean, far from other lands, become populated with living things? In most cases, communities of organisms are slowly established on new islands through rare and "lucky" accidents. Seed pods can travel thousands of kilometers across the sea. Small animals and plants can be carried long distances on logs or floating debris.

FIGURE 36.16

Ecological Succession

During the establishment of a climax community, succession occurs in steps. In what biome is succession occurring here?

Pioneer community

1 Lichens, which grow on bare rock, and other pioneer species form a pioneer community. Lichens produce acids that break down rock and begin the process of soil formation.

Growing grass

2 In time, enough soil accumulates to support the growth of grasses. As grasses grow and decompose season after season, the soil becomes deep enough for weeds and shrubs to grow.

Shallow trees

3 Over time, enough soil accumulates to support the growth of shallow-rooted trees, such as pines.

Climax community

4 In the shade of the pines, conditions may favor the growth of broadleaf trees such as maple and beech. As succession continues, a more stable community—a climax community—becomes established.

LAB ZONE Do It!

Studying Human Causes of Succession

Secondary succession often occurs after human disturbances. When lots, buildings, and farmland are abandoned, or large sections of forest are cleared, the soil is not destroyed and rapid succession results. You can observe secondary succession in action if you . . .

Try This

1 Find a vacant lot or abandoned farm or field in your community. Obtain permission to study the area.
2 Study the plants that have colonized the disturbed area. Compare these plants to the plants found in comparable areas, such as a park or working farmland. Record your observations.

Analyze Your Results

1 How tall are the plants in the disturbed area? Are they grasses and weeds, shrubs, or trees?
2 How does this plant community differ from those in the surrounding area? Describe your findings in terms of succession.

FIGURE 36.17
What factors determine the rate of island colonization?

Insects and birds can be blown off course by storms and end up on a new island. New arrivals can carry seeds on their feet, fur, or feathers.

Two factors determine the rate of colonization and succession on an island: its distance from other land

and its size. If an island is close to other land, a colonizing plant or animal will more likely survive the short trip than if the island is far away. If an island is large, it is more likely that drifting plants and animals will wash ashore.

Organisms colonizing an island can find themselves without competitors or predators. Island populations often thrive and may evolve into new species. For example, recall from Chapter 10 that many finch species have evolved from a single common ancestor. While new species evolve on islands, their mainland relatives may become extinct. For this reason, islands are often home to species that do not exist anywhere else on Earth.

Any land area that is surrounded by a natural barrier can be thought of as an island. A desert oasis or a city park can be as isolated as an island. Island environments tend to be delicate and easily disturbed. New organisms can easily upset the balance of the island ecosystem.

CHECKPOINT 36.4

1. What is a climax community?
2. What are the similarities and differences between primary and secondary succession?
3. Critical Thinking In 1883 a volcanic eruption destroyed all life on the tropical island of Krakatoa in Indonesia. Describe how you think succession may have occurred on Krakatoa.

Build on What You Know

4. How do plants affect ecosystems in succession? *(Need to jog your memory? Revisit relevant concepts in Chapter 19, Section 19.2.)*

 How do biotic and abiotic changes alter community structure?

Chapter 36 Review

THE BIG IDEA!

36.1–36.2 The size of a population is affected by living and nonliving factors.

36.3 How populations interact determines the structure and characteristics of a community.

36.4 Biotic and abiotic changes in a community alter the community structure.

Sum It Up

Use the following summary to review the main concepts in this chapter.

36.1 Population Growth

- If all individuals in a bacterial population survived and reproduced, the population would double in each generation. Even smaller percentage increases can lead to exponential growth.
- Four factors that affect growth rate are birth rate, death rate, immigration, and emigration.
- A population's carrying capacity is determined by limiting factors.

36.2 Limits on Population Growth

- Living space, disease, competition, and predation are density-dependent limiting factors. These factors reduce populations that have exceeded their carrying capacity.
- Seasonal climate changes, natural disasters, and human activity can affect populations regardless of their density. Seasonal changes can produce a boom-and-bust growth pattern. Major upsets can lead to species extinctions.
- The growth rate of the human population has increased dramatically in the last few centuries.

36.3 Communities

- In communities with a large number of species, some species may have few members. Where the number of species is limited, most of the species will have many members.
- Two species may have symbiotic relationships in which both species benefit, in which one species benefits while harming the other, or in which one species benefits without harming the other.
- Biodiversity and genetic diversity help maintain ecological balance in a community.

36.4 Ecological Succession

- Natural disasters, competition among species, and human activity can change environments and lead to ecological succession.
- The absence or presence of soil determines the type of succession that occurs in a disturbed habitat.
- Colonization and succession on islands often leads to speciation.

Use Terms and Concepts

Use each of the following words or terms in a complete sentence.
If you need to review a meaning, turn to the page indicated.

population (p. 876)

exponential growth (p. 877)

limiting factor (p. 879)

carrying capacity (p. 879)

density-dependent limiting factors (p. 881)

predation (p. 882)

density-independent limiting factors (p. 883)

community (p. 885)

symbiosis (p. 887)

mutualism (p. 887)

parasitism (p. 887)

commensalism (p. 888)

ecological succession (p. 890)

primary succession (p. 891)

pioneer community (p. 891)

climax community (p. 891)

secondary succession (p. 891)

Use Your Word Power

COMPLETION **Write the word or phrase that best completes each statement.**

1. The interaction between a lynx and a snowshoe hare is an example of _____ .

2. Both parasitism and commensalism are examples of _____ .

3. Any resource that may be depleted is a(n) _____ .

4. A group of organisms of the same species that live in a particular area form a(n) _____ .

5. A(n) _____ in a tropical rain forest contains thousands of species.

6. The process in which new communities replace existing communities is called _____ .

7. The number of individuals that a population's environment can support is called its _____ .

8. When a population graph has a steep J-shaped curve, the population is experiencing _____ .

MULTIPLE CHOICE **Choose the letter of the word or phrase that best completes each statement.**

9. An example of a density-dependent limiting factor is (a) a killing frost; (b) a drought; (c) a tuberculosis epidemic; (d) a new dam.

10. A lifeless habitat can form a climax community by (a) secondary succession; (b) exponential growth; (c) competition; (d) primary succession.

11. An example of a density-independent limiting factor for human populations is (a) depletion of the ozone layer; (b) the cultivation of farmland; (c) an influenza epidemic; (d) the water available for irrigation.

12. In a pioneer community, one could find (a) shrubs; (b) trees; (c) lichens; (d) weeds.

13. The relationship between honeybees and flowers is an example of (a) parasitism; (b) mutualism; (c) commensalism; (d) predation.

Show What You Know

14. Explain why the changes in population size for a predator and its prey often occur in cycles.

15. What causes the growth curve of a population to change from a J-curve to an S-curve?

16. How were deer populations in North America affected by the removal of large predators?

17. How does the age structure of a population affect its growth rate?

18. How can a forest fire be both harmful and beneficial at the same time?

19. Explain why an infectious disease is classified as a density-dependent limiting factor.

20. Why do thrips experience a boom-and-bust growth pattern?

21. **Make a Concept Map** Create a concept map that shows the relationship among populations, communities, and ecological succession.

Take It Further

22. **Developing a Hypothesis** Temperate forests have more biodiversity than temperate grasslands. Tropical rain forests have more biodiversity than tropical grasslands. Propose an explanation for these differences.

23. **Designing an Experiment** As cattle graze in the grasslands of East Africa, they stir up insects living in the grass. Birds known as cattle egrets eat insects and capture more food when they hunt near the cattle than when they hunt on their own. Design an experiment that would determine if the relationship between cattle and egrets is mutualism, parasitism, or commensalism.

24. **Interpreting a Graph** Hawks prey on wood pigeons. The following graph compares the size of the pigeon population with the hawks' success rate. How does population size affect the hawks' success rate?

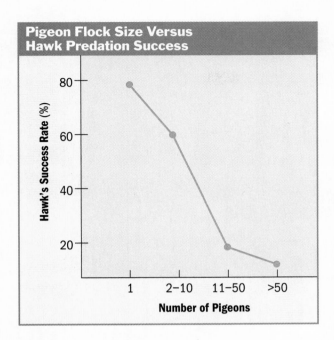

Pigeon Flock Size Versus Hawk Predation Success

Hawk's Success Rate (%)

Number of Pigeons: 1, 2–10, 11–50, >50

25. Analyzing Data The table below shows death rates for red deer on Rhum Island in Scotland. The rates are the percent of each age group that die during the year. Female deer are capable of reproduction when they are 2–3 years old. How do the death rates change as the deer age? What happens to the death rates of female and male deer as they age? Propose an explanation for sex-specific differences.

Red Deer Death Rate		
Age	Females (%)	Males (%)
0–6 months	12.4	12.4
6–12 months	13.0	20.8
1 year	7.4	13.0
2 years	1.1	1.8
3–4 years	3.6	1.7
5–6 years	3.8	2.2
7–8 years	2.3	6.1
9–10 years	2.8	16.3
11–12 years	8.7	37.3

Consider the Issues

26. No Building Permit Like humans, beavers can have a major effect on their environment. When beavers cut down trees to build dams, they produce beaver ponds. Their activities can also increase the amount of seasonally flooded land in a neighborhood. Home owners who live near newly created beaver ponds may find their basements full of water. The neighbors whose properties are affected may suggest setting traps. Animal rights activists often object to the use of traps to control beavers. What would you do to address the problem?

Make New Connections

27. Biology and Art Identify a local site that was disturbed by a natural disaster such as a fire or earthquake. Make a drawing of the site as it looks today. Make a second drawing of what it might look like 10 years from now.

28. Biology and Social Studies Most communities in the United States do not produce all the resources they need to survive. For example, much of the food in local grocery stores is imported from other places. However, as the population of a town or city grows, the need for local resources increases. What resources might limit growth in your community? Can these resources be expanded?

FAST-FORWARD TO CHAPTER 37

As populations interact with one another, energy flows through the community. Chapter 37 will describe the flow of energy and chemicals through ecosystems.

You can find out more about ecosystem dynamics by exploring the following Internet address:
http://ecology.biosurf.com

In this chapter . . .

FEATURES

Everyday Biology
- Our Food Chain
- Losing Lichens

In the Community
Beyond the Faucet

 Environmental Awareness
Gasoline-free Cars

LAB ZONES

Discover It!
- Theorizing About How Organisms Interact

Do It!
- How Do Decomposers Grow?
- How Do Chemical Cycles Affect Ecosystems?

Think About It!
- Discovering Where Humans Belong in Energy Pyramids

Investigate It!
- Investigating the Water Cycle

WANTED:
Tree-climbing
Ecologists

If you have ever climbed a tree, you could perform ecology research! In the early 1970s ecologists began exploring the treetops of ancient forests in the northwestern United States. But they had one important obstacle to overcome. The old Douglas firs, giant sequoias, and redwoods grow to 100 meters (m) tall, with the lowest branches looming 30 m above the forest floor.

Researchers developed a system of pulleys to make their way to the top of a forest, and there they discovered a previously unknown world. They found hundreds of new animal, plant, and fungal species and investigated how these organisms interacted with their environment. For example, ecologists discovered that the needles of these ancient trees block so much light that they lower the temperature of the ground and streams below. In these low stream temperatures, salmon thrive. Therefore, the loss of these ancient trees would result in a smaller salmon population—a surprising relationship. The treetops and their inhabitants also play an important role in the water and chemical cycles that affect the entire planet. What are these cycles, and what effect do they have on Earth's ecosystems?

Theorizing About How Organisms Interact

You need a houseplant and a hand lens

1. Observe how the plant interacts with the environment. Using the hand lens, determine if any organisms inhabit the soil, stem, or leaves of the plant. Record your observations.
2. Using your knowledge of plants, theorize about the other interactions occurring among the plant, the air, and the light. How might these interactions be part of a cycle?

Every organism on Earth interacts with and changes its environment. Ecologists who study these interactions are researching ecosystem dynamics. What are some ways you change your environment?

WRITE ABOUT IT!

Select one of the biomes that you studied in Chapter 35. In your science journal, write a short story about an imaginary new organism in that biome. How does it affect the other organisms in the biome? How does it change the environment? Include biotic and abiotic factors in your story.

37.1 Ecosystem Structure

What you'll learn

IDEAS
• To describe the flow of energy in an ecosystem
• To distinguish between food chains and trophic levels
• To explain the danger of biological magnification

WORDS
autotroph, producers, heterotroph, consumers, food chain, trophic level, herbivore, carnivore, omnivore, scavenger, decomposer, biological magnification

You are my sunshine
At dawn, rays of golden summer sunshine spill across a field of sunflowers. Almost imperceptibly, the plants begin to move. Broad green leaves and yellow-rimmed flowers slowly turn toward their source of energy—the rising sun.
The sun is the ultimate source of energy for nearly all of Earth's ecosystems.

ENERGY FOR LIFE

Pass it on

As sunlight pours down on the planet, plants and other photosynthetic organisms capture its radiant energy. They use the sun's energy to transform inorganic compounds into energy-rich organic compounds during photosynthesis. These photosynthetic organisms then use the energy stored in the organic compounds as food to fuel all of their life processes. This energy moves through the ecosystem as one organism consumes another for food. The flow of energy is one-way—moving from the sun through photosynthetic organisms, then through other organisms in the ecosystem.

A plant or other organism that converts the sun's energy into energy-rich compounds is called an **autotroph.** Because autotrophs make food that is used by the entire community, they are also called **producers.** Algae in a pond, phytoplankton in the ocean, and grasses, shrubs, and trees on land are all producers in their ecosystems.

Although most of the producers in the biosphere are photosynthetic organisms, there are a few exceptions. As you learned in Chapter 14, chemosynthetic organisms use inorganic compounds, rather than sunlight, as sources of energy. Some types of chemosynthetic bacteria live around hydrothermal vents on the ocean floor. Chemosynthetic bacteria are the producers in these deep-sea communities, just as plants and algae are the producers in the sunlit world far above.

FIGURE 37.1
How is the blackbird obtaining energy from the caterpillar?

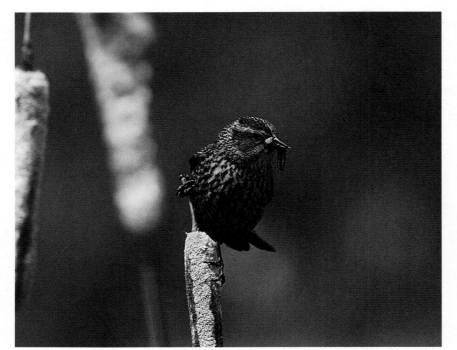

FOOD CHAINS AND TROPHIC LEVELS

Living links

Some of the energy captured by a producer is passed on to the organism that consumes it. Such an organism is called a **heterotroph.** It obtains energy and nutrients by consuming other organisms. Heterotrophs are the **consumers** in an ecosystem.

As an example, in a field of sunflowers, the sunflower plants are the producers. A consumer such as a caterpillar eats sunflower leaves. Another consumer such as a red-winged blackbird eats the caterpillar. Still another consumer, perhaps a fox, may eat the blackbird. Eventually, bacteria and fungi consume the remains of any dead organisms. This overall feeding pattern is an example of a food chain. A **food chain** models the flow of energy through organisms in a community.

In the food chain shown in *Figure 37.2,* arrows show the energy flow from one organism to the next. For example, when the caterpillar eats the leaf, some of the energy and organic compounds stored in the leaf are transferred to the caterpillar. When the caterpillar is eaten by the red-winged blackbird, some of the energy and organic compounds from the caterpillar are transferred to the bird. This pattern continues through the food chain.

Notice that only some of the energy and matter is transferred each time one organism consumes another. At every link in a food chain, part of the energy is lost (as heat) to the environment. Because of energy loss, most food chains can support no more than four or five links.

FIGURE 37.2

A Food Chain

A food chain models the energy flow in a community. How do decomposers affect energy flow?

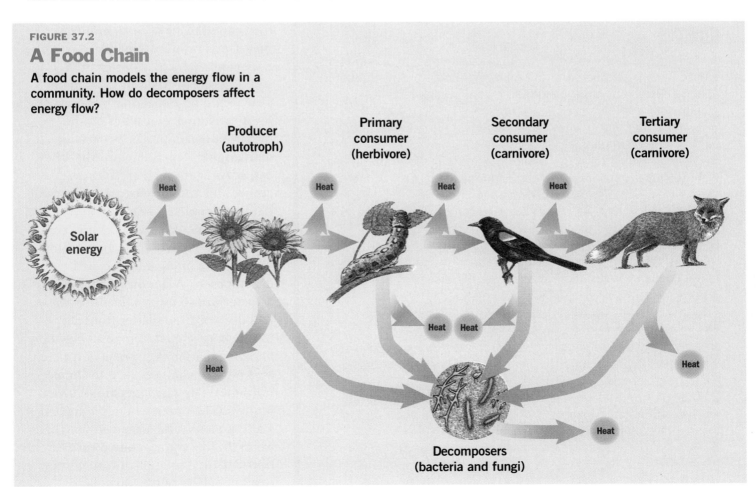

Producer (autotroph) Primary consumer (herbivore) Secondary consumer (carnivore) Tertiary consumer (carnivore)

Solar energy

Heat

Decomposers (bacteria and fungi)

Each step in the transfer of energy and matter in an ecological community is called a **trophic level** (TROH-fik). Producers such as plants form the community's first trophic level and are the base of all food chains. Primary consumers, which feed directly on producers, make up the second trophic level. In the sunflower-field food-chain example, the leaf-eating caterpillar is a primary consumer. A primary consumer that eats only plants is called an **herbivore.**

The third and fourth trophic levels in a food chain are composed of carnivores. A **carnivore** is an organism that eats only meat. The third trophic level is composed of secondary consumers, which feed on primary consumers. The blackbird in our food-chain example is a secondary consumer. The fourth trophic level is composed of tertiary consumers, which feed on secondary consumers. Which animal in the sunflower-field example is a tertiary consumer?

Some organisms can be part of more than one trophic level, depending on what they eat. For example, a fox that eats an insect-eating bird is a tertiary consumer. But that fox could also eat a primary consumer, such as a mouse or a rabbit. In that case, the fox would be a secondary consumer. Consumers called **omnivores,** such as bears and humans, eat both producers and other consumers. Because they eat all types of food, omnivores may act as primary, secondary, or tertiary consumers in an ecosystem. Can you describe a situation in which a bear would be a secondary consumer?

A consumer that feeds on the tissues of dead animals is called a **scavenger.** Depending on what they eat, scavengers such as vultures, crows, and ants may be part of several different trophic levels.

In addition to producers and consumers, every food chain has a third major group of organisms called decomposers. A **decomposer,** such as a bacterium or fungus, feeds on wastes and dead organic matter from all trophic levels. As decomposers feed on decaying matter, they break down complex organic compounds into simpler nutrients. The nutrients are returned to the soil or water, where producers such as plants and algae can use them again. In this way, decomposers recycle nutrients that are critically important to all members of the food chain.

How Do Decomposers Grow?

You can find out which decomposers favor specific types of food if you . . .

Try This

1 Obtain five petri dishes (with lids), blotting paper, a hand lens, grease pencil, scissors, and the following foods: bread, Roquefort cheese, a piece of a dill pickle, an orange wedge, and several grapes cut in half.
2 Number the petri dishes #1 through 5. Line the bottoms of the petri dishes with moist blotting paper.
3 Moisten (don't soak) the bread. Place the bread in petri dish 1. Place the cheese in dish 2, the pickle in dish 3, the orange wedge in dish 4, and the grapes in dish 5.
4 Leave the uncovered dishes exposed for 24 hours. Then cover the petri dishes and place in a cool, dark place.
5 Observe the petri dishes every day for one or two weeks. Use the hand lens and record your observations of the dishes' contents. **Caution**: Do not remove lids from the dishes at any time. Wash your hands after handling petri dishes.

Analyze Your Results

1 How many different types of decomposers did you observe? What physical characteristics distinguished one type of decomposer from another?
2 Did you find that one type of decomposer can grow on different types of organic material? What evidence did you find that organic molecules were being decomposed?
3 Based on your observations, what is the role of decomposers in the food chain? How would an ecosystem differ if no decomposers were present?

BIOLOGICAL MAGNIFICATION

A food chain's deadly links

You have just learned how energy moves from one organism to another in a food chain. But harmful substances can also move through food chains. DDT is one such substance.

Beginning in the late 1940s, the pesticide DDT was widely used to kill insects that spread disease and damaged crops. At first, the pesticide appeared to have no negative effects on other organisms. As time passed, however, people noticed that the populations of bald eagles and other large fish-eating birds were declining.

Ecologists discovered that DDT settled into the soil and got into the groundwater. Eventually, the DDT found its way into rivers and lakes, contaminating tiny planktonic organisms. Small fishes that ate the plankton stored DDT in their tissues. When larger fishes ate the contaminated fishes, they accumulated even higher concentrations of DDT in their tissues. This buildup of a pollutant in organisms at higher trophic levels in a food chain is called **biological magnification.**

When bald eagles ate the large contaminated fishes, they took DDT into their bodies. As a result of biological magnification, the DDT in the birds' tissues was ten million times the original concentration of DDT in the water and it interfered with the depositing of calcium in the shells of the eggs. The eggs' shells were thin and broke easily, so the eagle embryos inside did not survive. The eagle population began to decline, and this was one of the reasons DDT was banned in the United States in 1971. Although the populations of bald eagles and other affected birds have gradually recovered, DDT is still being used in some other countries.

FIGURE 37.3
Biological Magnification

Biological magnification can have devastating results. How did DDT affect the bald eagle populations?

DDT concentration increases 10 million times

DDT in fish-eating birds: 25 ppm

DDT in large fishes: 2 ppm

DDT in small fishes: 0.5 ppm

DDT in zooplankton: 0.04 ppm

DDT in water: 0.000003 parts per million (ppm)

CHECKPOINT 37.1

1. Describe the flow of energy in an ecosystem.
2. What is a food chain? How does it relate to trophic levels?
3. Explain biological magnification and its dangers.
4. **Critical Thinking** Are you a primary, secondary, or tertiary consumer? Explain.

Build on What You Know

5. How is the energy from ingested food stored in the body of a consumer? *(Need to jog your memory? Revisit relevant concepts in Chapter 30, Section 30.3.)*

37.2 Energy Levels

What you'll learn

IDEAS

- To identify the relationships illustrated by an ecological pyramid
- To define and illustrate a food web

WORDS

biomass, ecological pyramid, food web

What kills killer whales?
Killer whales (right), eagles, and adult lions have no natural predators. Why are these animals the last stop in their food chains? The reason does not lie only in their ferocity and hunting ability. Because there is a limited amount of energy available to these organisms, their communities can only support a few trophic levels.

ECOLOGICAL PYRAMIDS

Community building

The total mass of all the organisms in a food chain or an ecological community is called the **biomass.** The biomass at each trophic level contains stored energy representing the potential food available to the organisms at the next trophic level. For example, the biomass of a community's producers contains energy-rich compounds and many other compounds that the producers make. When consumers eat the producers, they ingest both matter and energy. The consumers use this ingested energy and matter to build their own bodies and perform essential life functions.

The transfer of matter and energy from one trophic level to the next is not very efficient. Only a small fraction of the biomass from one trophic level moves on to the next. One reason for the inefficiency is that many of the organisms are not consumed by the organisms at the next trophic level. As a result, this energy is not available for transfer. A second reason is that some of the biomass at each trophic level consists of materials that consumers at the next level are not likely to eat: wood, bones, teeth, beaks, hooves, claws, and shells. Even if consumers do eat

these materials, they usually cannot digest them to release their stored energy.

A diagram called an **ecological pyramid** shows the relationships between producers and consumers at the trophic levels in an ecosystem. The energy available at each trophic level is about one-tenth the energy available from the trophic level below it. This pattern of energy transfer is sometimes called the 10 percent law.

FIGURE 37.4

Ecological Pyramids

These ecological pyramids represent the relationships between producers and consumers in three different ways. What pattern do all three pyramids share?

50 g

500 g

5000 g

If the producers in the energy pyramid in *Figure 37.4* supply 200,000 kilocalories of energy, how many kilocalories will be passed on to each higher trophic level, assuming the 10 percent law applies?

In most food chains, fewer organisms occupy each higher trophic level. For example, a meadow is covered by a thick layer of grasses and other plants. These plants are the producers. The meadow has many primary consumers, including mice, seed-eating birds, and a variety of insects. But it has fewer secondary consumers, including robins, other insect-eating birds, and snakes. There are very few tertiary consumers, including hawks and bobcats, at the highest trophic level.

The number of organisms at each trophic level is proportional to the amount of biomass and energy available at the level below it. In fact, the biomass and energy from the producers at the lowest trophic level determine the number of organisms a community can support. The more biomass and energy the producers supply, the larger the total number of organisms that the community can support.

LAB ZONE Think About It!

Discovering Where Humans Belong in Energy Pyramids

Humans can be placed in many different energy pyramids. Draw the energy pyramids that would result from the following activities: humans consuming corn, consuming cattle, and consuming salmon.

Analyzing the Diagram

1 In which pyramid is the greatest amount of energy available to humans? In which activity is the least amount of energy available? Explain your answer, using percentages.

2 As the population grows, how might human diets be affected? Why?

Energy
An ecological pyramid can represent the energy contained in biomass. Organisms at each trophic level use some of this energy for their life processes, but much of it is lost as heat.

Number of organisms
An ecological pyramid can show the relative number of organisms at each trophic level. As you move up the pyramid, the number of organisms usually decreases.

Biomass
An ecological pyramid can represent the amount of biomass at each trophic level. The greatest biomass is at the base of the pyramid. Each higher trophic level contains less biomass.

FIGURE 37.5

The Salt-Marsh Food Web

This food web shows the energy flow in a salt-marsh community. Which organisms are herbivores?

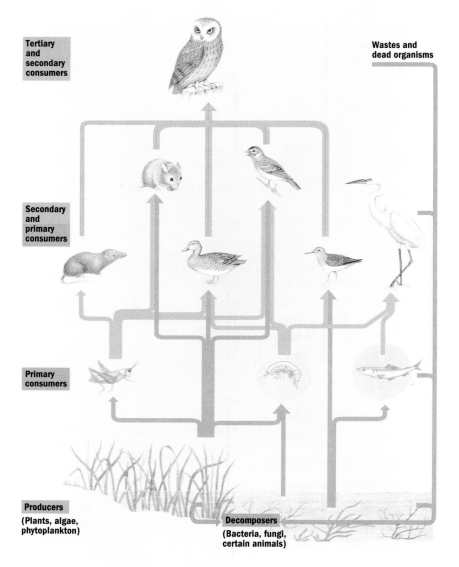

Tertiary and secondary consumers

Wastes and dead organisms

Secondary and primary consumers

Primary consumers

Producers
(Plants, algae, phytoplankton)

Decomposers
(Bacteria, fungi, certain animals)

Tying it all together

The feeding relationships in a community are far more complex than a simple food chain containing a few organisms. Most organisms in a community eat more than just one kind of food. If we look at how food chains combine to form a food web, a more complete picture emerges. A **food web** demonstrates the interconnectedness of food chains in a community or an ecosystem. An example of a food web in a salt marsh community is shown in *Figure* 37.5. Which organisms are the producers?

Food webs in one community may be connected to food webs in others. For example, a river that meets the sea at a salt marsh may have flowed through forest and grassland communities. Organisms that move with the river may play a role in the food webs of each community the river meets.

CHECKPOINT 37.2

1. What types of organisms are always at the base of an ecological pyramid? At the top?

2. What is a food web? Draw a diagram of a food web that includes one producer, two primary consumers, two secondary consumers, and two decomposers.

3. **Critical Thinking** What would happen to a community if the biomass of producers increased greatly? Decreased greatly?

Build on What You Know

4. How could you estimate the number of kilocalories available in a given biomass of producers? (*Need to jog your memory? Revisit relevant concepts in Chapter 30, Section 30.3.*)

How does energy flow in an ecosystem?

37.3 Chemical Cycles

Water, water everywhere

How much water do you use every day? Probably more than you think! Humans use water for drinking, cooking, washing, cleaning, agriculture, and watering lawns. Cities often use more water than the environment can supply. Water is involved in one of the chemical cycles essential to the ecosystem.

What you'll learn

IDEAS

• To explain the importance of chemical cycles to an ecosystem

• To describe the carbon cycle, the nitrogen cycle, and the water cycle

WORDS

carbon cycle, fossil fuel, nitrogen cycle, nitrogen fixation, denitrification, water cycle

CHEMICAL CYCLES

Recycled and reused

In any ecosystem, living organisms need energy and chemical nutrients. In the previous sections you learned about energy—how it enters an ecosystem and is captured by producers, and how it flows from one organism to another through the trophic levels in a food chain. At each step, energy is lost to the environment. Energy cannot be recycled; it must continually be replenished by the sun. As a result, the flow of energy through natural systems is a one-way process. Nutrients, on the other hand, do not move in one direction through an ecosystem.

Nutrients are the chemical elements and compounds that organisms must have to live and grow. Carbon, oxygen, and nitrogen are examples of nutrients. Unlike energy, nutrients are not constantly replenished from an outside source such as the sun. The supply of nutrients is limited, and they must be recycled in ecosystems again and again.

Sometimes nutrients cycle rapidly through an ecosystem. In a rain forest, for example, carbon in fallen leaves is rapidly cycled through the forest's complex food web. Other times, nutrients cycle very slowly and may be "tied up" in living organisms, in soil or rock, in the air, or in the oceans for long periods of time. For example, marine organisms deposit atoms of carbon in their shells, which eventually become limestone. The limestone may remain intact and undisturbed for millions of years.

Nutrients and water also cycle on a global scale. Earth's various nutrient

FIGURE 37.6
How do nutrients and energy flow in this terrarium?

Light energy

Chemical cycling

Heat energy

cycles are closely connected—what happens in one cycle can affect all the others. By studying Earth's complex nutrient cycles, we can gain a better understanding of how human activities impact them.

THE CARBON CYCLE

It's a gas

Organisms exchange carbon and oxygen with the air or water around them. These elements cycle mainly in the form of carbon dioxide gas (CO_2). Carbon dioxide moves from the air or water through living things, and back to the air or water again. The movement of carbon through the environment is called the **carbon cycle.** This cycle is illustrated in *Figure 37.7*.

How carbon cycles The driving forces behind the carbon cycle are the processes of photosynthesis and cellular respiration. Following are the chemical equations for both processes. Notice how each reaction depends on the products of the other.

Photosynthesis
$$6H_2O + 6CO_2 + energy \rightarrow C_6H_{12}O_6 + 6O_2$$

Respiration
$$C_6H_{12}O_6 + 6O_2 \rightarrow 6H_2O + 6CO_2 + energy$$

During photosynthesis, producers such as plants and algae take up CO_2 from the air or water around them. The producers use CO_2 and water (H_2O) to manufacture glucose ($C_6H_{12}O_6$), an energy-rich organic compound. During this reaction, oxygen (O_2) is released.

FIGURE 37.7

The Carbon Cycle

Photosynthesis and cellular respiration are the two main processes of the carbon cycle.

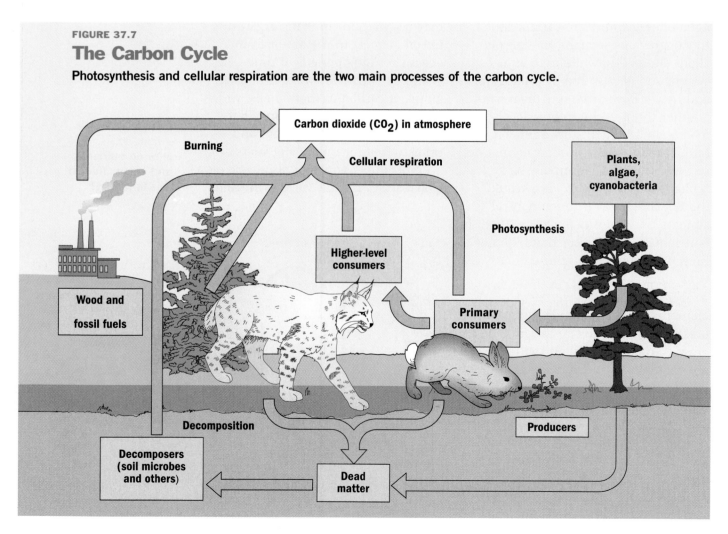

Producers and consumers use glucose to fuel the process of cellular respiration. In cellular respiration, glucose breaks down as it undergoes a chemical reaction with O_2. The reaction releases energy and produces H_2O and CO_2. The CO_2 produced by the reaction is released into the air or water surrounding the organism. In other words, carbon and oxygen cycle through the environment, while photosynthesis and cellular respiration alternately build glucose and break it down. *Figure 37.8* shows how carbon is stored in the carbon cycle.

Humans and the carbon cycle
Over the last few hundred years, humans have begun to interfere with the global carbon cycle. For example, people have cut down many forests around the world. Fewer forests means fewer trees and other plants that can absorb CO_2. Human activities are increasing the levels of CO_2 in the atmosphere. People have burned large amounts of fossil fuels for energy, releasing huge amounts of CO_2. A **fossil fuel** is an energy-rich compound formed from organic matter by a geological process.

There is evidence that increased levels of CO_2 may lead to changes in Earth's climate. These climate changes are possible because carbon dioxide in the atmosphere traps heat, as does glass in a greenhouse. If carbon dioxide levels continue to increase, global warming may occur. You will learn more about global warming and the greenhouse effect in Chapter 38.

ENVIRONMENTAL AWARENESS

Gasoline-free cars

In an effort to decrease fossil-fuel burning in automobiles and to reduce the amount of CO_2 released into the environment, scientists are developing

FIGURE 37.8
Carbon Storage

All carbon is not cycling through the environment at one time. Instead, some carbon is stored in various ways.

Organic compounds
1 Large amounts of carbon are stored in the organic compounds of trees. When the trees decay or are burned, the carbon is released as CO_2.

Fossil fuels
2 Fossil fuels—oil, coal, and natural gas—store carbon. Fossil fuels formed over millions of years as organisms were compressed by geological processes. When fossil fuels are burned, energy and CO_2 are released.

Limestone
3 Many marine organisms have calcium carbonate shells. When these organisms die, their shells sink and form carbon-rich sediments. Eventually, these sediments form limestone rock. When geological processes elevate and expose the limestone, it may break down and release stored carbon.

vehicles that are powered by alternative fuels. Among these alternative fuels are electricity and solar energy. The environmental advantage of these fuels is that they do not directly release CO_2.

Solar-powered cars run on electricity that is converted from the sun's energy and stored in batteries. Electric vehicles are powered by electricity stored in batteries, which are recharged by plugging them into electrical outlets. Many of these gasoline-free automobiles are in the early stages of development, and they continue to improve. One new electric sports car accelerates faster than most gas-powered cars and has a top speed of nearly 160 kilometers per hour (100 miles per hour). Best of all, it releases no CO_2!

THE NITROGEN CYCLE

Fixed on nitrogen

Air contains about 78 percent free-nitrogen gas (N_2). But N_2 must be converted into other compounds before it can be used by most living things. This conversion occurs during the **nitrogen cycle,** the pathway by which nitrogen moves through the environment. *Figure 37.9* illustrates the nitrogen cycle.

How nitrogen cycles N_2 in the air is converted to usable nitrogen compounds in a process called **nitrogen fixation.** Lightning causes some nitrogen fixation by forming nitrogen oxides from nitrogen and oxygen in the air. But most nitrogen fixation is carried out by bacteria.

Some nitrogen-fixing bacteria live in soil or water. Others live in nodules on the roots of plants that belong to the legume family. Alfalfa, peanuts, soybeans, clover, and peas are all legumes that could support these bacteria.

Nitrogen-fixing bacteria convert N_2 to ammonia (NH_3), which quickly dissolves in water to produce ammonium ions (NH_4^+). Some plants can take up ammonium ions directly. Other plants can only take up nitrogen in the form of nitrates. Certain bacteria convert ammonium ions to nitrates in a two-step process. The nitrates can then be absorbed by the roots of plants.

Plants use the nitrogen compounds they absorb to make amino acids, proteins, and other needed substances. Animals get the nitrogen they need by

FIGURE 37.9

The Nitrogen Cycle

Nitrogen is converted into many compounds throughout the nitrogen cycle. What are some of these nitrogen compounds?

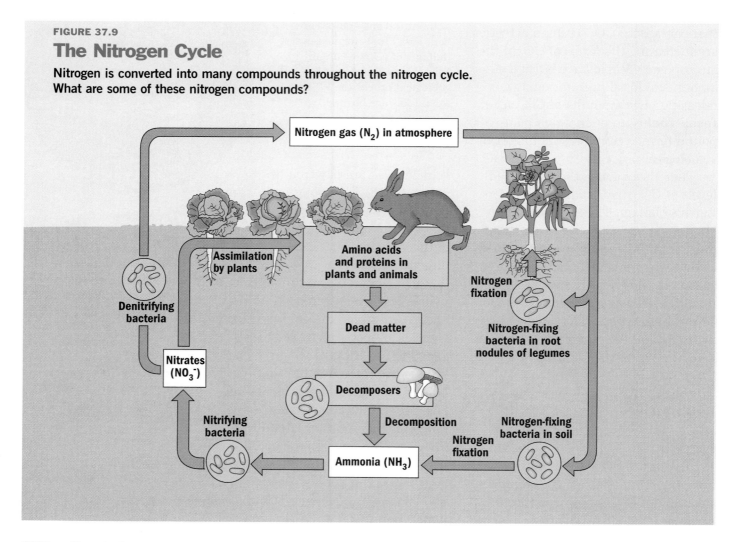

eating plants or the organisms that consume plants. All the amino acids that comprise your body's proteins contain the nitrogen you obtained by consuming other organisms or their products.

Decomposers play an important role in the nitrogen cycle. They break down nitrogen-containing animal wastes and the remains of dead organisms. The breakdown of these materials releases ammonia, which dissolves to produce ammonium ions. As just described, bacteria convert some ammonium ions to nitrates. Plants take up ammonium ions and nitrates, and the cycle starts over again. Another group of bacteria converts some of the ammonia and nitrates into free nitrogen gas. This process of returning nitrogen gas to the atmosphere is called **denitrification.**

Humans and the nitrogen cycle
Human activities interfere with the nitrogen cycle in several ways. Many nitrogen compounds dissolve easily in water, so erosion and extensive irrigation can wash nitrogen out of the soil. Sewage and nitrogen-fertilizer runoff can add excess nitrogen to rivers, lakes, and ponds. When this happens, plants and algae can grow out of control, disrupting aquatic ecosystems.

Crop plants such as corn and cotton absorb nitrogen compounds from the soil as they grow. When the crops are harvested, the nitrogen they contain is removed from the environment. If crops are grown repeatedly in the same soil, the soil can quickly become nitrogen-depleted.

Farmers can use several strategies to return nitrogen to the soil. Crop rotation is an ancient and effective method of restoring nitrogen to farmland. Farmers rotate crops such as corn or cotton with soybeans or other legumes that support nitrogen-fixing bacteria in their roots. In modern

agriculture, however, farmers often replace lost nitrogen by adding commercially produced nitrogen fertilizers. Although the use of commercial fertilizers is effective, it is expensive. Large amounts of energy, usually from fossil fuels, are needed to make nitrogen fertilizers. What links can you see between the manufacture of nitrogen fertilizer and the carbon cycle?

FIGURE 37.10
Excess nitrogen in bodies of water can spur plant and algae overgrowth. What can cause excess nitrogen to collect in a body of water?

LAB ZONE Do It!

How Do Chemical Cycles Affect Ecosystems?

Through various processes, resources in an ecosystem move back and forth between organisms and the environment. You can discover how if you . . .

Try This

1 Design and construct a model ecosystem. For example, you could model an aquatic ecosystem by using dechlorinated water, a glass jar, small fish, and aquatic plants. For any ecosystem, you must include soil or sand or gravel, plants, and animals.
2 Observe your ecosystem for one week and record any changes that occur.

Analyze Your Results

1 Describe a food chain in your ecosystem.
2 What chemical cycles did you observe? How did they affect your ecosystem?

THE WATER CYCLE

Puddle to cloud to rain

If you have ever noticed how quickly a puddle of water evaporates on a sunny day, you are already familiar with the water cycle. The **water cycle** is the continual movement of water from the Earth's surface to the atmosphere and back to the surface again. The water cycle is powered by solar energy, which causes evaporation. As you can see in *Figure 37.11,* water may take several paths as it moves through the environment.

How water cycles When water evaporates from oceans, lakes, or other bodies of water, it enters the atmosphere as a gas—water vapor. In the atmosphere, the water vapor cools and condenses to form clouds.

Eventually, clouds release the water they contain, and the water returns to Earth's surface as precipitation—rain, snow, hail, or sleet.

Water from precipitation may collect on the Earth's surface to form streams, rivers, and lakes. Most of the water eventually flows back to the ocean, carrying nutrients and sediments with it.

Some water, however, seeps into the ground instead of running off. It slowly percolates through soil and rock layers and is being filtered and purified along the way. Eventually, water moving down through the soil reaches groundwater deep beneath the surface. In some places, this water returns to the surface—bubbling up in clear, sparkling springs that fill wells, lakes, and ponds.

FIGURE 37.11

The Water Cycle

Solar radiation powers the water cycle. How does the water cycle affect the weather?

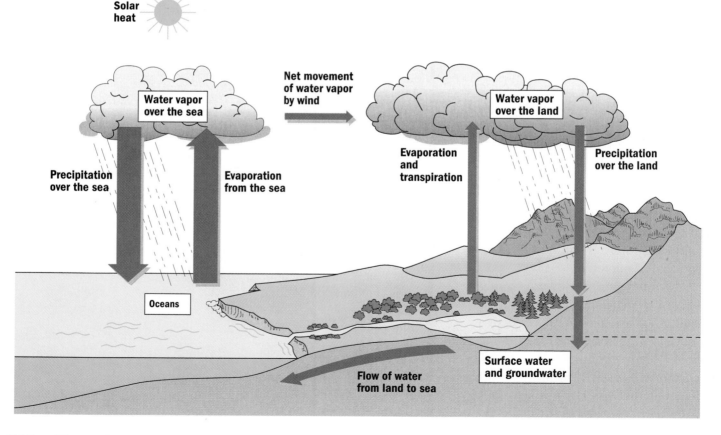

Beyond the Faucet

Communities need a reliable fresh water supply. Research the sources and uses of fresh water in your area. Every town and city has a water department or is affiliated with a regional agency. Locate the source of the water you use. Is it above or below ground? If it comes from a reservoir, is it a natural formation, an artificial one, or a combination (such as a dammed river)? Find out how water is brought to your area and how it is used in homes, industry, and agriculture. Is water conservation underway in your area? You can find out more about water conservation at this Internet address: *http://ecology.biosurf.com.*

Water cycles through living things as well as through the physical environment. For example, plants take up water through their root systems. Some of this water evaporates from plant leaves during transpiration. Animals also cycle water through their bodies. They take in water by eating and drinking, and they return some of the water to the environment when they perspire, urinate, or exhale water vapor.

Humans and the water cycle
Many human activities pollute water supplies. Chemicals, sewage, trash, and toxic wastes find their way into rivers, ponds, and lakes all over the world. Chemicals and toxic wastes contaminate groundwater. Deforestation can also affect the water cycle. For example, tropical rain forests transpire huge quantities of water up from the soil and into the atmosphere. When humans remove the trees and vegetation, this transpiration stops, and the land becomes susceptible to flooding and erosion. Soil and nutrients wash away, seriously changing the landscape.

FIGURE 37.12
Deforestation makes this tropical rain forest more susceptible to flooding. Why? What effect does the deforestation have?

CHECKPOINT 37.3

1. How are chemical cycles important to an ecosystem?
2. Describe the carbon, nitrogen, and water cycles.
3. Critical Thinking Is water frozen in the polar ice caps during part of the water cycle? What might happen if the ice caps melted?

Build on What You Know

4. What step in cellular respiration produces carbon dioxide? What step in photosynthesis produces oxygen? *(Need to jog your memory? Revisit relevant concepts in Chapter 4, Section 4.2 and Section 4.3.)*

How are nutrients recycled in ecosystems?

Investigating the Water Cycle

Cobalt chloride paper

Waxed paper

Stem

Petroleum jelly seal

Cups filled with water

WHAT YOU WILL DO Investigate the role of plants in the water cycle

SKILLS YOU WILL USE Controlling variables, observing, collecting and recording data

WHAT YOU WILL NEED 4 large clear cups, two 15-cm squares of waxed paper, 2 strips of blue cobalt-chloride paper, paper clip, petroleum jelly, 2 geranium-plant leaves with stems, tape

Propose a Hypothesis

Propose a hypothesis that explains the role of plants in the water cycle.

Conduct Your Experiment

1 Fill two cups (A and B) with water, and apply petroleum jelly to the rims.
2 Straighten the paper clip, and poke a hole in the center of each waxed paper square.
3 Insert a geranium-leaf stem through the hole in each waxed paper square. Apply petroleum jelly around each stem where it emerges from the waxed paper.
4 Apply a coat of petroleum jelly to both surfaces of one of the leaves.

5 Position the uncoated leaf over cup A. Gently press on the waxed paper so that it is held in place by the petroleum jelly around the rim. The stem should be in the water.
6 Repeat step 5 with the coated leaf and cup B. Be sure the stem is in the water.
7 Tape a piece of cobalt-chloride paper to the inside of each of the two other cups. Apply petroleum jelly around the rims of these cups.
8 Invert one of these cups over cup A and the other over cup B. Gently press them together. Do not allow the leaf to touch the cobalt-chloride paper.
9 Observe both setups for 10 minutes. After each minute,

record your observations in a data table, paying particular attention to the color of the cobalt chloride paper.
10 After 24 hours make your final observations and record them.

Analyze Results

1 What is the purpose of coating the leaf in setup B with petroleum jelly? Which setup is the control?
2 Did the color of either piece of chloride paper change? What does this change indicate?
3 What changes did you observe after 24 hours? Explain your answer.

Draw Conclusions

1 How are green plants involved in the water cycle?
2 What is the plant process you observed in this experiment, and how might it affect local climates?

Design a Related Lab

Design a related lab to determine the role of plants in the carbon cycle.

Lab: Investigating the Water Cycle

1. Propose a hypothesis: Plants take up water in the ground through their root systems.

Minute	Cup A	Cup B
1		

Chapter 37 Review

THE BIG IDEA!   **37.1–37.2** In an ecosystem, the flow of energy moves in one direction.

37.3 Nutrients are recycled in ecosystems.

Sum It Up

Use the following summary to review the main concepts in this chapter.

37.1 Ecosystem Structure

- Energy flows from the sun to autotrophs, which are consumed by heterotrophs. As energy is transferred in a food chain, some energy is lost as heat.
- Heterotrophs with varied diets can function at different trophic levels in different food chains.
- As decomposers feed on wastes and dead organisms, they recycle nutrients.
- When pollutants such as DDT move to higher levels in food chains, they become concentrated and their impact is magnified.

37.2 Energy Levels

- The transfer of matter and energy to higher trophic levels is inefficient. Only about 10 percent of energy is transferred between trophic levels.
- There are fewer organisms at higher trophic levels. The number of organisms at a given level depends on the biomass and energy supplied by the level below.
- Food webs show the connections between food chains in a community or an ecosystem.

37.3 Chemical Cycles

- Unlike energy, nutrients are not replenished by the sun. They must be recycled.
- Photosynthesis and cellular respiration are the processes responsible for the recycling of carbon and oxygen. Carbon also may be stored in organisms, fossil fuels, or limestone.
- The burning of fossil fuels and the destruction of forests interfere with the carbon cycle.
- Nitrogen must be converted into compounds by nitrogen-fixing bacteria before it can be used by other organisms. Decomposers release nitrogen from animal wastes and dead organisms.
- The nitrogen removed from the soil by plants can be restored through crop rotation or fertilizers. If nitrogen fertilizer or sewage is washed into a body of water, the water can become choked with overnourished plants and algae.
- Solar radiation evaporates water, which returns to Earth's surface as precipitation. Water also cycles through living organisms.
- Human activities can result in both surface and ground-water contamination.

Use Terms and Concepts

Use each of the following words or terms in a complete sentence. If you need to review a meaning, turn to the page indicated.

autotroph (p. 898)
producers (p. 898)
heterotroph (p. 899)
consumers (p. 899)
food chain (p. 899)
trophic level (p. 900)

herbivore (p. 900)
carnivore (p. 900)
omnivore (p. 900)
scavenger (p. 900)
decomposer (p. 900)
biological magnification (p. 901)

biomass (p. 902)
ecological pyramid (p. 902)
food web (p. 904)
carbon cycle (p. 906)
fossil fuel (p. 907)

nitrogen cycle (p. 908)
nitrogen fixation (p. 908)
denitrification (p. 909)
water cycle (p. 910)

Use Your Word Power

COMPLETION Write the word or phrase that best completes each statement.

1. The primary consumers in an ecosystem have a smaller _____ than do the producers.

2. A(n) _____ provides a model of the flow of energy through a biological community.

3. Decomposers play a key role in the _____ and _____ cycles.

4. Primary consumers make up the second _____ in an ecological community.

5. Evaporation is one step in the _____ .

6. Consumers that eat only plants are _____ ; consumers that eat meat are _____ .

7. The buildup of pollutants in higher-level consumers is called _____ .

MULTIPLE CHOICE Choose the letter of the word or phrase that best completes each statement.

8. The number of organisms at each trophic level can be represented by (a) food chains; (b) biological magnifications; (c) food webs; (d) ecological pyramids.

9. Chemosynthetic bacteria are (a) autotrophs; (b) heterotrophs; (c) consumers; (d) producers.

10. The burning of fossil fuels produces some of the same end products as (a) photosynthesis; (b) nitrogen fixation; (c) denitrification; (d) cellular respiration.

11. Denitrifying bacteria are (a) scavengers; (b) decomposers; (c) producers; (d) omnivores.

Show What You Know

12. How are the roles of scavengers and decomposers similar? How are they different?

13. What information do ecological pyramids provide that is not provided by food chains and food webs?

14. What is the role of glucose in the carbon cycle?

15. Explain why the number of levels in a food chain is limited.

16. What is the relationship between producers and nitrogen-fixing bacteria?

17. What is the difference between a primary and secondary consumer?

18. What is the relationship between biomass and trophic level?

19. Describe how solar radiation affects the water cycle and ecological pyramids.

20. Why are forests included in the carbon and water cycles?

21. **Make a Concept Map** Create a concept map that shows the relationships between producers and consumers in an ecosystem of your choice.

Take It Further

22. **Developing a Hypothesis** In a lake, organisms sink to the bottom when they die. In temperate climates, the water at the lake surface cools in autumn. Why is it important for organisms living near the surface of temperate lakes that cool water is denser than warm water?

23. **Organizing and Classifying** In terms of trophic level, how would you classify a Venus-flytrap—a plant that traps insects? Explain.

24. **Applying Concepts** Apply what you have learned about biomass, energy, and ecological pyramids to the USDA food pyramid.

25. **Designing an Experiment** Design an experiment that would enable a cattle rancher to determine the average biomass required to produce a 1000-kilogram cow.

26. Interpreting a Graph The graph shows the effect of precipitation on the production of plant biomass. What happens to biomass as annual precipitation increases? What factors other than water might affect plant growth? Suggest reasons why the graph levels off at high levels of precipitation.

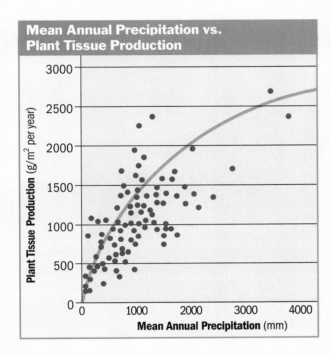

27. Analyzing Data Living organisms need phosphorus for structures such as cell membranes. The table below shows the distribution of available phosphorus in the global ecosystem. In which location is the most phosphorus stored? In which location is the least stored? Create a graph using these data.

Global Distribution of Phosphorus Storage	
Storage Location	**Metric Tons**
Atmosphere	2.8×10^3
Land organisms	3.0×10^9
Land	2.0×10^{12}
Shallow ocean water	2.71×10^9
Ocean organisms	1.38×10^8
Deep ocean water	8.71×10^{10}
Ocean sediments	4×10^{15}

Consider the Issues

28. Water Pollution Water contamination by chemical pollutants poses a serious health risk for many organisms, including humans. These chemical pollutants include automobile emissions, fertilizers, and pesticides that are washed from the air and land into the water. Although harmful, we depend on the products and processes that produce these pollutants. Suggest several ways to minimize water pollution.

Make New Connections

29. Biology and Art Construct a food web with yourself at the center. Select foods that you enjoy eating and trace their energy back through the web. For example, if you drink milk, you would need to include a dairy cow in your web as well as the food eaten by the cow. Try to make as many connections as possible.

30. Biology and Economics Do a comparative study of cars that are fueled by gasoline and by electricity. How do the two car models compare in terms of initial cost, maintenance, speed, and range before refueling?

31. Biology and History Find a library or local historical society that keeps copies of old cookbooks. If possible, compare ingredient lists from recipes published about 100 years ago and today. Are any of the ingredients unfamiliar? How have the expectations about available foods changed over the century?

FAST-FORWARD TO CHAPTER 38

You now know that the water that organisms take in must not be polluted for the water cycle to be life sustaining. In Chapter 38, you will learn how humans affect the quality and quantity of all Earth's resources.

People and the Environment

You can find out more about people and the environment by exploring the following Internet address:
http://ecology.biosurf.com

In this chapter . . .

FEATURES

Everyday Biology
- Natural Filters
- Fluoride Inside

In the Community
Your Success Story

 Environmental Awareness
Biodiversity

LAB ZONES

Discover It!
- Changing the Environment

Do It!
- What Is the Quality of Local Water?
- Where Is Air Pollution?

Think About It!
- Making Decisions About Land Use

Investigate It!
- Recycling Paper

Many people consider Alaska to be the "last frontier" of the United States. This large and sparsely populated state contains vast tracts of federally protected wilderness. Each year, over half a million tourists visit Alaska to enjoy the incredible sights—wolves, moose, grizzly bears, and the towering peak of Mount McKinley in Denali National Park; caribou, polar bears, and glaciers along the coast of the remote Arctic National Wildlife Refuge. Although many people have never visited Alaska, they feel strongly about protecting the splendor of its natural treasures. Many conservation groups are working toward this goal.

Alaska is rich in natural resources. Below its surface lie oil and coal. Most valuable is the timber of the temperate forests located in the southern regions of the state. Mining, oil exploration, and logging have long constituted a significant portion of the Alaskan economy, providing employment for many residents. Will expanding these operations harm the Alaskan wilderness? How will these activities affect the ecosystem? These questions are not unique to Alaska, but are considered in many regions around the world, as humans try to balance their need for natural resources with the preservation of Earth's ecosystems.

The Last Frontier?

Discover It!

Changing the Environment

1. Select a plant species and an animal species (not human) that live in your community.
2. On a sheet of paper, make three columns, one for the plant, one for the animal, and one for humans.
3. Under each column, list some characteristics of that species that help it to survive in its environment. Do these characteristics change the environment?

We humans are far more able to change our environment than other species. This ability can lead to conflicts about the use of natural resources and the protection of other species. How have these conflicts been resolved in your community? Do you agree or disagree with the methods of resolution?

WRITE ABOUT IT!

In your science journal, write about the ways that your environment has changed in the last year. What activities have you taken part in that might have contributed to the changes in your environment?

917

38.1 Earth's Resources

Wasting electricity?
Many different energy sources may be used in the future. Bacterial degradation of biological waste produces methane gas. Sawdust, old paper, tree bark, and sewage can be burned to produce electricity. Using waste products as fuel is nothing new. For example, dried cattle dung has long been a cooking fuel in south Asia.

TYPES OF NATURAL RESOURCES

Nature's bank

Humans, like all living things, need food, water, shelter, and space for survival. All of these needs are met by the natural resources of Earth. The quality of our natural resources is a major concern, because healthy soil, clean air, and drinkable water are essential for human survival. In addition, the quantity of resources available is critical.

When evaluating a natural resource, scientists consider whether or not it is replaceable. A **renewable resource** is a resource that can be replaced by natural processes. For example, oxygen in the air is a renewable resource because it is continuously replenished by plants and algae during photosynthesis. Trees are a renewable resource because new trees can grow after older trees are harvested. What are some other examples of renewable resources?

Different time periods are needed to replenish different renewable resources. Oxygen is replaced continuously. Trees, on the other hand, can take hundreds of years to replace. Changing environmental conditions affect the rate of replenishment. When renewable resources are used faster than natural processes can replenish them, they are depleted.

There are only limited amounts of nonrenewable resources. A **nonrenewable resource** is a resource that cannot be replenished by natural processes. Fossil fuels and minerals such as copper are examples of nonrenewable resources. Many nonrenewable resources, such as fossil fuels, can be used only once. When these resources are depleted, they are gone forever. However, some nonrenewable resources can be used more than once. For example, the copper in electrical wires can be melted down and reused in other copper products.

FIGURE 38.1
Fossil fuels, such as oil, are nonrenewable resources. Wind is a renewable resource. Why?

THE EFFECTS OF HUMAN USE

All used up

How are natural resources affected by human use? Human use of a natural resource greatly affects the quantity of the resource. **Sustainable development** means using renewable resources at a rate that does not deplete them. Renewable resources can be used over long periods of time if their short-term use is controlled. For example, farmers practice sustainable development by managing soil use to ensure that the soil will be fertile in the future. Switching from a nonrenewable resource to a renewable resource, such as from fossil fuels to wind power, is another example of sustainable development.

The quality of natural resources can also be changed by humans. The quality of drinking water depends on how people use water and dispose of waste. How is the quality of other natural resources affected by humans? Human use of natural resources can affect chemical cycles, food webs, biodiversity, and ecological succession. As you learned in Chapter 37, humans are part of an ecosystem. We have a dramatic effect on the ecological balance of our ecosystem.

The human effect on Earth's natural resources is proportional to the size of the population. For example, the exhaust fumes from one car might not be a problem. But when several million cars produce the same exhaust, it creates a harmful effect on air quality. Recall that the human population is growing exponentially, and scientists are uncertain about Earth's carrying capacity for humans. In order to meet the needs of a growing

population, humans must sustain both the quality and quantity of natural resources.

Behavioral adaptations enable humans to obtain the resources they need for survival. As you learned in Chapter 12, we are able to survive in most of Earth's ecological zones because of our ability to adapt to different environments. Most of these adaptations are behavioral, rather than physical, and behavior can be modified. The human capacity for changing behavior allows each of us to decide on the best way to use and preserve natural resources.

CHECKPOINT 38.1

1. Explain the difference between renewable and nonrenewable resources.
2. What are the effects of human use of natural resources?
3. **Critical Thinking** How could a lumber or fishing company practice sustainable development?

Build on What You Know

4. Why are fossil fuels a nonrenewable resource? *(Need to jog your memory? Revisit relevant concepts in Chapter 37, Section 37.3.)*

FIGURE 38.2
For decades, Spectacle Island was a city dump. Now the land is being restored and turned into a national park. How is Spectacle Island an example of humans restoring natural resources?

How is the web of life affected by human use of natural resources?

38.2 Land in the Biosphere

What you'll learn

IDEAS
• To describe the processes that alter forests and soil
• To appraise energy sources and waste buildup

WORDS
soil erosion, desertification, deforestation, biodegradable, nonbiodegradable

A rosy treatment

The rosy periwinkle, a flower found only in the tropical rain forests of Madagascar, is a source of two substances used in the treatment of Hodgkin's disease and other forms of cancer. Ecologists fear that the destruction of rain forests and other biomes may prevent the discovery of other species that have medicinal uses.

FORESTS, SOILS, AND MINERALS

A base for life

Land is essential for life on Earth. It provides resources and living space for many organisms, including humans. The soil that covers the land serves as a home for producers, decomposers, and burrowing animals. Forests and soil also provide a home for many populations. Humans depend on land for its valuable resources. For example, forests provide lumber for building materials. How do human activities affect these essential resources?

Poor farming and ranching practices can lead to soil erosion.

Soil erosion is the wearing away of surface soil by water and wind. In dry regions of the world, erosion and overgrazing can lead to desertification. **Desertification** is the reduction of a soil's ability to retain water and nutrients, both of which are essential for plant growth. Productive farms and grasslands can change into barren deserts because of desertification.

Many farmers and ranchers use techniques that protect the soil. Farmers reduce soil erosion with terracing, contour plowing, and reduced irrigation. Planting trees as windbreaks also slows soil erosion. Ranchers avoid overgrazing of land in an effort to stop desertification.

FIGURE 38.3
Fields terraced in this manner help prevent soil erosion (left). Recycling newspapers can help prevent deforestation (right). What effects do erosion and deforestation have on the biosphere?

Human activities can also change forests. **Deforestation** is the removal of large numbers of trees from a forest. During deforestation many species lose their habitats. Because trees use carbon dioxide, deforestation can also contribute to the buildup of carbon dioxide in the air.

Deforestation is proceeding rapidly all over the world. An estimated 11 million hectares of tropical rain forest are cleared each year. Environmentally sensitive methods of lumber harvesting can help prevent deforestation. Everyone can help limit deforestation by recycling paper and choosing alternatives to wood products.

Minerals are mined for a variety of products used by humans. Unfortunately, mining of these valuable minerals can scar the landscape, destroy habitats, and pollute the air and water. Restoration of mining sites has reversed some of the damages. Newer, environmentally sensitive mining techniques are preventing future problems. Minerals are a nonrenewable resource. Recycling is an important method for conservation of key mineral resources. Aluminum, copper, and lead are now commonly recycled.

ENERGY

The power to live

Energy resources from the land—coal, oil, and natural gas—heat and light our homes, power our appliances, and run our vehicles. We rely on these energy sources because they are relatively accessible and inexpensive. But reliance on these fossil fuels is costly in terms of damage to our environment. Coal mining can cause severe soil erosion. Oil spills destroy plant and animal life. The burning of fossil fuels pollutes the air.

As you may know, fossil fuels are formed over a time period of millions of years from the remains of ancient organisms. Some day the supplies of oil, coal, and natural gas will be depleted. Since fossil fuels are nonrenewable and can harm our environment, it is extremely important that renewable and environmentally safe energy sources be developed.

Solar energy is one of the most promising alternatives to fossil fuels. Simple, nonpolluting devices called photovoltaic cells can make electricity from sunlight almost anywhere the sun shines. However, solar energy technology is still relatively expensive.

Other alternatives to fossil fuels include nuclear energy, hydroelectric power, wind power, geothermal power, and tidal power. Each of these energy sources has advantages and disadvantages.

The raw materials for nuclear energy are essentially unlimited, and nuclear energy does not pollute the air. However, it produces dangerous radioactive waste that is difficult to dispose of. Hydroelectric power plants use moving water to generate electricity, requiring dams and reservoirs that flood plant and animal habitats. Wind drives windmills that can generate electricity on large "wind farms," but only a few locations have the steady winds needed for this technology. Geothermal energy,

FIGURE 38.4
The solar power generated by these solar panels is a renewable alternative to fossil fuels. What is the drawback of solar power?

which comes from hot water or steam deep inside Earth, is available in only a few locations. Tidal or wave power also has limited availability. Other alternatives to fossil fuels are being studied in the hope they will help meet fuel needs.

WASTE

Reduce, reuse, recycle

The United States produces 19 percent of the world's solid waste. Most of the household solid waste ends up buried in landfills. Thousands of hectares of land are used for this purpose. What happens to the waste?

Some solid wastes, such as food scraps, leaves, and grass clippings, are biodegradable (BY-oh-dee-GRAY-duh-bul). **Biodegradable** wastes can be broken down and recycled by decomposers. **Nonbiodegradable** wastes,

FIGURE 38.6
Landfills are now lined with clay and plastic to prevent soil and water contamination by waste materials.

such as plastics, metals, and pesticides, cannot be broken down.

Unfortunately, very little decomposition takes place at a landfill. The wastes at a landfill are tightly packed and there is not enough oxygen for decomposers to survive. Chemical wastes buried in landfills can contaminate groundwater. In some places, solid wastes are burned in incinerators at very high temperatures. Although incinerators reduce waste volume, they are expensive to operate.

We can all take actions to help reduce the number and size of landfills. Reusing items and purchasing products with less packaging can keep household wastes to a minimum. Biodegradable wastes can be composted, or turned into a rich organic humus, and added to garden soil. Recycling paper, glass, certain plastics, and aluminum can reduce waste, and conserve valuable resources.

Some of the waste produced by industries such as manufacturing, mining, and agriculture is hazardous.

FIGURE 38.5
In deep well injection, hazardous liquid wastes are pumped through lined pipes to rocks located far below water sources.

Water table

Porous rock layer

Waste

Nonporous rock layer

Hazardous wastes may contain toxic or cancer-causing chemicals, heavy metals, or substances that are explosive, flammable, or corrosive. Strict government regulations exist to control disposal of hazardous wastes. These regulations protect humans and other living things in the environment.

Some hazardous wastes are stored far underground by deep well injection, as illustrated in *Figure 38.5*. In theory, deep well injection is safe. But if the stored wastes move in unpredictable ways, groundwater could be contaminated.

ENVIRONMENTAL AWARENESS

Biodiversity

Some human activities are changing Earth's environment. Some of these changes result in the extinction of other species and are causing an alarming decrease in biodiversity. You may recall from Chapter 36 that biodiversity is important for ecological stability. The ecological balance of an ecosystem—for example, our own—can be disrupted if biodiversity decreases rapidly.

In addition to maintaining ecological stability, the biodiversity of Earth is an important resource for humans. We depend on various species for foods, medicines, chemicals, and other useful materials. And only a fraction of the species on Earth have been studied. Cures for cancer and other diseases may exist in plants and animals that have not been discovered or analyzed.

Some of the ecosystems with the greatest biodiversity are most at risk. For example, tropical rain forests are home to between 50 and 90 percent of the total number of species on Earth. Other diverse ecosystems at risk include coral reefs, estuaries, wetlands, and temperate forests.

Habitat destruction is the greatest threat to biodiversity today. Cutting forests, filling in wetlands, and plowing up grasslands can destroy habitats. Pollution, commercial hunting, trade in exotic plants and animals, and introduction of foreign species also threaten biodiversity.

Steps are being taken to preserve biodiversity. Wildlife reserves and wilderness areas have been set aside in many countries. Laws such as the Endangered Species Act are being used to protect species and preserve habitats.

CHECKPOINT 38.2

1. Describe two processes that alter forests and soils.
2. What are some energy alternatives to fossil fuels? Explain the benefits of at least three alternatives.
3. **Critical Thinking** Explain why removing species from ecosystems is like "removing bricks from a wall."

Build on What You Know

4. Explain how genetic drift can affect biodiversity. (**Need to jog your memory? Revisit relevant concepts in Chapter 10, Section 10.5.**)

FIGURE 38.7
Clearing the rain forest can provide new areas for people to live in and farm, but it also causes loss of biodiversity.

EVERYDAY BIOLOGY

Natural Filters

Salt marshes are often targeted for draining and development because of their desirable coastal location. However, salt marshes have an important function—they can filter pollutants from coastal waters as effectively as waste-treatment plants.

38.3 Water in the Biosphere

What you'll learn

IDEAS

• To describe three different ways water can become polluted

• To explain the modern sewage treatment process

When carp rule
Each year, the use of fossil fuels and fertilizers releases more than 272 million metric tons of nitrogen compounds into the biosphere. These compounds encourage the growth of plankton in lakes and rivers. Excessive plankton growth depletes the oxygen in water. Only certain fish, such as goldfish and carp, can survive in water with little oxygen.

SEDIMENT AND SEWAGE POLLUTION

Muddying the waters

Humans use water for drinking, cooking, and washing, and in agriculture, recreation, and industry. In addition, aquatic ecosystems provide food and much of the biodiversity on Earth. For these reasons, water pollution is a major concern today.

As you learned in the previous section, soil erosion is the carrying away of exposed soil by wind and water. The soil, or sediment, is carried from the land to streams, lakes, and other waterways. Rivers in the United States carry 3.6 billion metric tons of sediment per year.

Excessive sediment in waterways can harm or kill aquatic organisms. Small particles of sediment suspended in water block the light needed by aquatic plants for photosynthesis. Heavier particles settle to the bottom of lakes and rivers and bury bottom-dwelling organisms. In tropical regions, sediments that flow from rivers into the ocean can destroy coral reefs. You have learned that farming techniques such as contour plowing help prevent soil erosion. Avoiding soil erosion can prevent pollution of water.

Sewage is another major source of water pollution. In many parts of the world, raw untreated sewage is discharged directly into streams and lakes. Untreated sewage may contain disease-causing organisms that make the water unsafe to drink. In most developed nations, however, sewage is usually treated in some way before being discharged into waterways.

Basic sewage treatment involves filtering out debris and allowing solid materials to settle out. Next, bacterial decomposers are added to the mix. These bacteria break down most of the biodegradable wastes. The treated sewage, or sludge, passes on to sedimentation tanks, where the bacteria

FIGURE 38.8
This computer-enhanced satellite photograph shows how topsoil (green) is carried away by the Mississippi River and dumped into the Gulf of Mexico. How does this process affect the Mississippi delta?

and sludge settle out. The sludge may eventually be burned, used as fertilizer, or dumped in landfills.

Advanced sewage treatment takes the process one step further by removing heavy metals and other chemicals, such as phosphates and nitrates. The result is clean water from which 95 percent of all pollutants have been removed. Chlorine is usually added to the treated water to kill any remaining bacteria and viruses.

CHEMICAL POLLUTION

Compound problems

Chemical pollutants from a variety of different sources can end up in the water supply. Mining and manufacturing wastes may contain toxic heavy metals, such as lead and mercury. Rainwater leaching through waste dumps can carry these substances into groundwater. Pesticides and fertilizers can enter waterways in runoff from agricultural lands. Organic compounds such as oil, plastics, detergents, and solvents wash into streams, rivers, and lakes through storm drains and sewers.

Oil spills are a major source of chemical pollution. For example, one of the largest spills occurred in 1989 when the *Exxon Valdez* oil tanker accidentally released millions of liters of oil into the ocean near Alaska. Such large oil spills pollute the spill area for years, in spite of cleanup efforts. Smaller-scale oil spills occur frequently. Even more oil pollution

LAB ZONE Do It!

What Is the Quality of Local Water?

You can evaluate your local waterways and identify water pollution if you . . .

Try This

1 Take a field trip to a river, stream, lake, or other water source near your school.
2 Survey the site for water pollution. Make a table classifying the types of pollution you see.

Analyze Your Results

1 Try to identify the source of each pollutant. How might the pollutants affect the biome? The chemical cycles?
2 Write a short essay describing your observations. What can you do to help solve the problems you have identified?

comes from waste oil spilled on land or into storm drains that empty into lakes and rivers.

Most chemical pollutants are toxic to humans and other species. Oil spills threaten water quality, destroy habitats, and kill wildlife. Compounds in pesticides and other industrial chemicals can disrupt the endocrine system. Sterility, birth defects, and rapidly declining reproductive rates have been linked to these chemical pollutants. As you learned in Chapter 37, some toxic chemicals become concentrated—and more deadly— through biological magnification.

Not all chemicals found in the water supply are harmful. Fluoride helps prevent tooth decay. In most cities, chlorine is used to purify drinking water and wastewater.

You can follow certain guidelines to help keep harmful chemicals out of your water supply. Limit the use of lawn and garden pesticides. Never pour oil, paint, or solvents down the drain, or throw pesticides or other toxic chemicals into the garbage. Instead, discard these substances at your community's household toxic-waste disposal center.

THERMAL POLLUTION

Turning up the heat

The release of heat into a body of water is called thermal pollution.

Many industrial processes use large amounts of water for cooling, then release the heated water into rivers and lakes. Nuclear power plants use large amounts of water to cool reactors. Steel mills, oil refineries, and paper mills also use large amounts of water for cooling.

When heated water is released into lake and stream

FIGURE 38.11
This tower at a nuclear power plant cools water before recycling it back to open water. How might warmer water adversely affect a freshwater biome?

FIGURE 38.10
These toxic chemicals are being handled in a responsible manner. Where can you safely dispose of such materials in your community?

ecosystems, the temperature of the water increases. Temperature is a limiting factor in ecosystems. Each species has a particular range of temperatures in which it survives and reproduces best. Even a slight increase in the temperature of a river or lake can make the water uninhabitable for some species. They will die or move away to cooler waters.

Some types of fishes will not spawn in warmer-than-normal water, and some fish eggs will not hatch if the temperature is above a certain point. Warm water can also make many aquatic animals more vulnerable to disease, parasites, and the harmful effects of toxic chemicals.

Raising the water temperature lowers the water's oxygen content, because warm water holds less dissolved oxygen than cold water does. Low oxygen levels can harm fishes and other aquatic organisms or interfere with reproduction.

There are solutions to thermal pollution. Cooling towers like those in *Figure 38.11* allow heat from nuclear reactors and factories to dissipate in the air. Heated water from power plants and other industries can be pumped into artificial cooling ponds. After the water in the ponds has cooled down, it can be discharged safely into rivers and lakes.

BIODIVERSITY NEAR SHORE

No day at the beach

You may recall that biodiversity is an important feature in our environment. In waters near shore, biodiversity is abundant. For example, coral reefs are second only to tropical rain forests in the number of species found in a given area. Estuaries are nurseries for mollusks, fishes, and many other aquatic species. Because these wetland areas are near shorelines—and human populations—their biodiversity is particularly vulnerable to water pollution.

To survive, coral reefs need clear, shallow ocean waters. Sediment runoff can cloud the water, starving the coral by blocking the light to the symbiotic algae that live in coral tissues. Toxic chemicals in the water can kill coral or disrupt the coral ecosystem. Thermal pollution can cause coral to whiten and die. Strict environmental laws are helping to preserve some coral reefs, such as Australia's Great Barrier Reef.

Estuary ecosystems are vulnerable to pollutants carried by the rivers that flow into them. For example, pesticides and other toxic wastes have flowed into the Chesapeake Bay estuary for many years. High levels of nitrates and phosphates have led to algal blooms and oxygen depletion. Fish and crab populations, once sources of income for fishing fleets, have been devastated by pollution and disease. Oysters and other mollusks contain so many toxins that they are considered unsafe to eat. Restoration efforts are underway to improve the water quality in Chesapeake Bay.

The Everglades, a wetland area in south Florida, has been disrupted

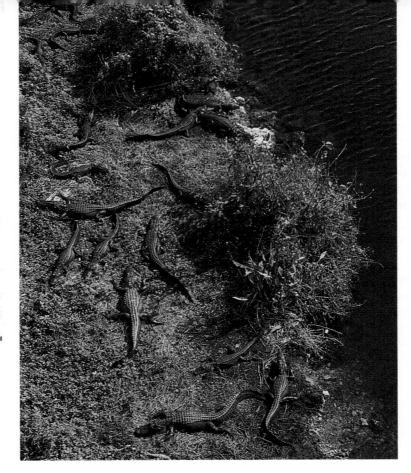

and polluted for many years. A multimillion-dollar restoration project, which includes a huge water retention pond, has begun there. The pond will trap pollutants and release clean water into the wetlands, which are home to a wide variety of unique species.

FIGURE 38.12
Alligators and other species may benefit from efforts to preserve the Florida Everglades.

CHECKPOINT 38.3

1. Identify three types of water pollution. Where does each type come from?

2. Describe the process of modern sewage treatment. Explain the purpose of each step.

3. Critical Thinking What might happen if a container or pond holding hazardous waste were to rupture or leak?

Build on What You Know

4. What environmental factors make high levels of biodiversity possible in the waters near shore? *(Need to jog your memory? Revisit relevant concepts in Chapter 35, Section 35.4.)*

38.4 Air in the Biosphere

What you'll learn

IDEAS
• To identify several sources of air pollution
• To describe the cause and effects of acid rain, global warming, and ozone layer depletion

WORDS
acid rain, greenhouse effect, global warming, chlorofluorocarbons

Dark shark
Humans are not the only animals who need protection from the burning effects of the sun. The sun darkens the skin of other animals, too. Researchers recently discovered that when hammerhead sharks were moved to water with increased light, their backs turned a deep brownish-black. Although sharks seem to have "tanning" ability, they do not seem to get skin cancer.

AIR QUALITY

Breathe free and easy

Take a deep breath and exhale. You probably do not think of air as a natural resource, but the gases in air (O_2, CO_2, N_2) are essential natural resources. Recall that the carbon cycle and the nitrogen cycle are both vital chemical cycles. Air is a renewable resource, but harmful substances in air can make it an unusable resource. Unfortunately, air pollution is a serious problem all over the world.

The main source of air pollution is the burning of fossil fuels. Smog (from the words SMoke and fOG) is a haze of pollutants that hangs in the air above many cities. Smog contains several harmful chemicals, including nitrogen dioxide, carbon monoxide, sulfur dioxide, and ozone. Smog also may contain particulates—tiny particles of soot, ash, or dust.

Volcanic eruptions are a natural source of air pollution. A major eruption, such as the 1991 eruption of Mount Pinatubo in the Philippines, releases large amounts of particulates. Particulates block sunlight and can cause a noticeable cooling of Earth's surface. Volcanoes also release chemical pollutants, such as sulfur dioxide.

Air pollution can cause respiratory problems, burning and watery eyes, and increased susceptibility to disease. Permanent lung damage can result from breathing polluted air over a long period of time. Air pollution contributes to an estimated 50,000 deaths per year in the United States.

Industries can reduce air pollution by switching to fuels that emit fewer harmful substances. Pollution-control devices, such as scrubbers on smokestacks, can help reduce the amount of air pollution caused by industry. Scrubbers remove pollutants before they are released into the air. In the late 1960s, Japan's sulfur dioxide levels were some of the highest in the world. By installing scrubbers on industrial smokestacks, Japan was able to cut sulfur dioxide levels by 75 percent in just fifteen years.

The passing and enforcement of laws can also reduce air pollution. In the United States, the 1990 Clean Air Act Amendments set aggressive standards for reducing air pollution. For example, according to this legislation, by the year 2000 sulfur dioxide levels must be reduced to half of what they were in 1980.

You can help reduce pollution by reducing motor vehicle exhaust. Walk, bike, carpool, or use mass transit. At home, try to use less electricity—it is primarily produced by power plants that burn fossil fuels.

FIGURE 38.13
Idling commuters are adding to this city's smog problem. What is smog?

ACID PRECIPITATION

Deadly rain

Some air pollutants do more than irritate your eyes and lungs. The nitrogen dioxide and sulfur dioxide in smog dissolve in water to form nitric acid and sulfuric acid. These strong acids fall to earth as **acid rain.**

How acidic is acid rain? Normal rain is slightly acidic, with a pH of 5.0 to 5.6. Rain in some parts of the eastern United States has a pH close to 4.3. This decrease of about 1 on the pH scale means that rain is ten times more acidic than it should be! Some areas of the world receive acid rain with a pH of 2.3 or less, rain that is nearly a thousand times more acidic than normal.

Acid rain has damaged many ecosystems in North America, Europe, and Asia. Acid rain changes soil chemistry, disrupting chemical cycles. Some of the greatest effects of acid rain are seen in rivers and lakes. When snowpack formed from acid rain melts and flows into bodies of water, the organisms living in these rivers and lakes are often unable to survive the high acidity. The tissues of most organisms, including trees, are very sensitive to strong acid levels. Metal and limestone can also be damaged by acid rain. Buildings, bridges, and statues are all vulnerable. Acid rain can cause these structures to weather quickly and fall apart. The most effective way to reduce acid rain is to reduce emissions of nitrogen dioxide and sulfur dioxide. Scientists predict

FIGURE 38.14
Acid rain can damage statues and destroy forests. How is acid rain formed?

 Do It!

Where Is Air Pollution?

You can determine the numbers and types of air particulates in your school if you . . .

Try This

1 Obtain the following: five microscope slides, petroleum jelly, five petri dishes with lids, and a hand lens. Smear the center of each slide with a thin layer of petroleum jelly. Place each slide inside a petri dish, jelly side up.
2 Take four of the petri dishes to four different areas in your school. Remove the cover from each dish. Keep the fifth dish covered as a control.
3 Three to five days later, retrieve the slides. Examine the slides with a hand lens. Count the number of particulates on each slide and record your results.

Analyze Your Results

1 Identify five particulates that landed on the slides. Which of these would you classify as pollutants? Explain.
2 Describe the locations you chose. Which location showed the greatest number of air particulates? The least?

that reducing air pollution caused by fossil-fuel consumption will result in the reduction of acid rain levels.

THE GREENHOUSE EFFECT
Heating up

Carbon dioxide (CO_2) and other gases in the atmosphere act like a blanket over Earth. They hold in heat from the sun that would otherwise radiate back into space. The trapping of heat in the atmosphere is the **greenhouse effect.** The greenhouse effect is a natural phenomenon that has warmed Earth enough to make life possible. Without it, Earth's surface temperature would average about –18°C.

CO_2 and other heat-trapping gases, such as methane (CH_4), are called greenhouse gases. The amount of CO_2 in Earth's atmosphere has increased more than 21 percent since the year 1750. This increase is a result of the burning of fossil fuels. As CO_2 levels increase in the atmosphere, the greenhouse effect gets stronger. The result may be **global warming,** an increase in Earth's average surface temperature.

If CO_2 levels keep increasing at the present rate, scientists hypothesize Earth's temperature may increase by 2°C to 4°C by the year 2050. Scientists predict that global warming of just a few degrees could bring about major climate changes. It could cause the oceans to warm and expand, raising sea levels by about 50 centimeters. If the polar ice caps melt, sea levels could rise by many meters, flooding

FIGURE 38.15
The Greenhouse Effect

The greenhouse effect is the trapping of heat by Earth's atmosphere. This effect increases as the amount of CO_2 in the atmosphere increases. How might increases in the greenhouse effect change Earth's average temperature and climates?

Changes in CO₂ Concentration and Temperature

coastal cities and causing low-lying islands to disappear. Global warming could change rainfall patterns and increase the amount of violent weather, such as hurricanes and tornadoes, that occurs.

Reducing the buildup of CO_2 and other greenhouse gases can prevent or slow global warming. This reduction can be accomplished by reducing the use of fossil fuels. Preserving forests can also help slow global warming. Recall that trees and plants remove CO_2 from the atmosphere.

THE OZONE LAYER

Saving the protective shield

Between 20 and 50 kilometers (km) above Earth, in a part of the atmosphere called the stratosphere, is a global sunscreen—the ozone layer. The ozone layer is a band of ozone molecules (O_3) that shields Earth from much of the sun's harmful ultraviolet (UV) radiation. Worldwide, the ozone layer is "thinning" as the total amount of ozone decreases. At certain times of year, enormous holes form in the ozone layer, particularly over Antarctica and the North Pole.

The main cause of the thinning of the ozone layer is a group of chlorine-containing chemicals known as **chlorofluorocarbons** (CLOR-oh-FLOR-oh-kar-bunz), or CFCs. These odorless, noncorrosive compounds were once widely used as propellants in aerosol cans and in the production of plastic foam. CFCs were also used as coolants in air conditioners, refrigerators, and freezers. In the lower

atmosphere, CFCs are stable. But when CFCs are released into the environment, they are carried up into the stratosphere. In the stratosphere, they are bombarded by ultraviolet rays and they break apart. This process releases chlorine atoms that react with ozone and deplete the ozone layer.

Depletion of the ozone layer increases Earth's exposure to UV radiation. This exposure can cause cataracts and skin cancer. It may also decrease resistance to disease. In areas of the Southern Hemisphere where ozone depletion is severe, cases of skin cancer and cataracts are increasing. Increased UV radiation can lead to reductions in crop yields and disruptions of food webs.

CFCs have been banned in the United States and many other nations. Substitutes are being developed for some types of CFCs. However, CFCs persist in the atmosphere for many years. So even though CFC use has dropped dramatically, ozone destruction will continue for many years.

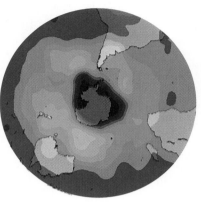

FIGURE 38.16
This computer-enhanced satellite image shows the ozone hole over Antarctica. What causes the ozone hole?

CHECKPOINT 38.4

1. What causes air pollution? Describe at least two sources.
2. What effects do acid rain, global warming, and ozone depletion have on the environment?
3. **Critical Thinking** What are the three types of invaluable natural resources? Why are they important?

Build on What You Know

4. How can ultraviolet radiation cause cancer? **(Need to jog your memory? Revisit relevant concepts in Chapter 8, Section 8.4.)**

Why are land, water, and air invaluable natural resources?

38.5 Environmental Success Stories

Ferreting out black-footed ferrets

The black-footed ferret was once a common sight in America's western plains. Their habitat was destroyed, however, and the ferrets were considered extinct until 18 ferrets were found in the 1970s. Bred in captivity, black-footed ferrets now number in the hundreds and have been returned to their habitat in prairie-dog towns.

FIGURE 38.17

Peregrine falcons, such as this falcon living in Los Angeles, were a rare sight in the 1970s. They have since been brought back from the brink of extinction. How was this achieved?

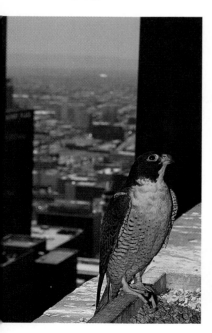

PEREGRINE FALCONS RETURN

Saved from extinction

In this chapter you have learned how humans' use of natural resources has changed our environment. People now realize that these changes frequently have negative effects on biodiversity, chemical cycles, food webs, and the stability of ecosystems. In recent years, many people have worked hard to avoid or reverse these negative effects on our environment. Some of this work has focused on alternative uses of natural resources—for example, recycling instead of disposing of waste. Other work has successfully restored damaged ecosystems, such as those of the black-footed ferrets and the peregrine falcons.

Peregrine falcons once hunted in the skies over much of North America. As predators at the top of a food chain, peregrine falcons ingested DDT, a pesticide that was present in the tissues of their prey. Due to biological magnification, the DDT became concentrated in the falcons' tissues. The DDT caused the falcons to lay eggs with very thin shells, which broke before hatching.

Unable to successfully reproduce, peregrine falcons became an endangered species. By 1970 they had vanished from the eastern United States, and only 19 pairs remained in western states.

In the 1970s the use of DDT was banned in the United States. At the same time, conservation groups began breeding peregrine falcons in captivity. When young falcons were old enough to survive on their own, they were released into the wild at selected sites all over the United States and Canada.

Gradually, the peregrine falcon population began to increase. By 1991, conservation groups stopped releasing captive-raised birds in the eastern United States. They were hopeful that the 90 or more pairs of falcons that had become established there would reproduce at a steady rate.

By 1996 more than 1000 breeding pairs of peregrine falcons were living in the continental United States. Not only did the birds make a remarkable comeback, but a surprising number have become adapted to big-city life. In the wild, peregrine falcons are cliff-nesting birds. In cities, they nest on skyscrapers—hunting pigeons and starlings from high above the city streets. New York City alone has 15 nesting pairs of peregrine falcons. The successful return of the peregrine falcon has caused its status to be upgraded from endangered to threatened.

THE GREEN BELT MOVEMENT

Forests from seven trees

In 1977 a young Kenyan woman named Wangari Maathai planted seven trees in her nation's capital of Nairobi in honor of World Environment Day. She went on to found a nationwide reforestation program in Kenya called the Green Belt Movement.

The Green Belt Movement has three main goals. The first goal is to halt erosion and desertification in rural Kenya. The second goal is to promote tree planting for firewood. The third goal is to educate people about environmental conservation and sustainable development.

Tree seedlings were made available to many villages, and women and children were paid a small fee to plant them. Tree nurseries were set up to raise more seedlings. People were educated about the causes and effects of ecological destruction, deforestation, and desertification.

Within 10 years the Green Belt Movement grew into a self-help community action program that involved 80,000 women and 500,000 children. By 1990 more than 10 million trees had been planted. The long-term goal is to plant one tree for each of Kenya's 27 million inhabitants.

In 1991 Wangari Maathai was awarded the Africa Prize for creating a successful program that combined community development with environmental protection. The Green Belt

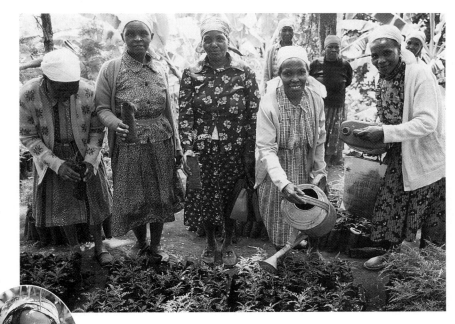

Movement has helped thousands of people become self-reliant while protecting their environment. The success of the Green Belt Movement has led to the creation of similar reforestation programs in more than a dozen other African countries.

FIGURE 38.18
Wangari Maathai (left) began the Green Belt Movement in an effort to halt the desertification of Kenya.

LAB ZONE Think About It!

Making Decisions About Land Use

The use of community-owned land can be a controversial issue. You can consider both arguments—development vs. open space—by walking around your community. Make a scale map of your neighborhood, shading the areas that are open spaces. Record the approximate percentage of land that is open space. In addition, do library research to determine what species, if any, would be affected by building on this open space.

Analyzing Your Results

1 If the open space in your neighborhood was chosen as the site of a much-needed community medical clinic, would you be in favor of or opposed to its development?
2 What would be the economic advantages of building a clinic on this site? What would be the economic disadvantages?
3 How would the community ecosystem be affected by building a clinic?

COSTA RICA'S FORESTS

A catalog of 500,000

Costa Rica, sandwiched between Nicaragua and Panama, is a small Central American country about the size of West Virginia. Along Costa Rica's northwestern coast, in the lowlands of the Guanacaste National Park, lies one of the few remaining patches of tropical dry forest. Unlike a rain forest, a tropical dry forest consists of sparse, flat-topped trees and an understory of thorny shrubs. Tropical dry forests once stretched along the Pacific coast from Mexico to Panama. The small sections that remain are far more rare—and more endangered—than tropical rain forests.

Daniel Janzen, a professor of biology at the University of Pennsylvania, has devoted much of his life to protecting and restoring about 750 square km of tropical dry forest in the Guanacaste region. Since 1963, he and his wife have raised more than $10 million for the restoration project. Their project, like the Kenyan Green Belt Movement, has involved local people at every step of the way. Farmers living nearby were hired to sow tree seeds and to plant new tree seedlings. Education programs in local schools were designed to teach young people about the forest and how important it is to the region.

Much progress has been made in restoring Guanacaste's tropical dry forest. But it is a project that will probably take more than 100 years to complete. By involving the local people, including the children, the project can continue for the time it will take to restore the ecosystem. The rare ecosystem will continue to thrive under the care of the people who live in and around it.

In 1989 Professor Janzen also helped found the Costa Rican

FIGURE 38.19
This Costa Rican tropical dry forest may be more endangered than tropical rain forests. How do the rain forests and dry forests differ?

FIGURE 38.20
This rain forest preserve in Costa Rica is being cataloged for such diverse species as poison arrow frogs (below) and quetzal birds (left). Why are pharmaceutical companies interested in this project?

National Biodiversity Institute (INBio). He recruited and trained hundreds of Costa Ricans to collect, identify, and store specimens of the country's approximately 500,000 species of plants and animals. The result of INBio's project will be a complete inventory of Costa Rica's biological resources—a catalog of the country's rich biodiversity.

Some of the organisms being collected may be sources of unique chemical compounds. These compounds may be used to create new medicines and other useful products. Recently, INBio signed an unusual contract with the world's largest pharmaceutical company. INBio agreed to supply the drug company with samples of plant and insect species from Costa Rican forests. If any compounds in those organisms are used to make new drugs or other products, the drug company agreed to return a percentage of the profits to

Costa Rica. There the money will be used to pay for other conservation projects and to protect the country's rich biodiversity.

CHECKPOINT 38.5

1. What human efforts have reversed the negative effects of humans on the environment?

2. What human efforts make it possible to preserve and protect the Earth's environments?

3. Critical Thinking What role does economic development play in environmental protection? How can it be successfully balanced with the needs of living things?

Build on What You Know

4. What have you learned about the interactions of living things with one another and with their environments? *(Need to jog your memory? Revisit relevant concepts in Chapters 1 through 38.)*

What type of effects can humans have on the biosphere?

Investigate It!

Recycling Paper

WHAT YOU WILL DO Develop a method of recycling paper

SKILLS YOU WILL USE Collecting and recording data, observing, estimating

WHAT YOU WILL NEED Sheets of newspaper, large mixing bowl, eggbeater, water, liquid laundry starch, hand lens, large square pan, screen, four sheets of blotting paper, rolling pin

Propose a Hypothesis

Propose a hypothesis about how paper is recycled. Develop a procedure using the materials listed. Consider the following information when developing your procedure: Liquid laundry starch acts as a glue, and the screen and rolling pin can be used to remove excess liquid.

Conduct Your Experiment

1 After planning your procedure, conduct your experiment. You may want to conduct the experiment more than once to determine the optimum proportion of the three ingredients: newspaper, water, and starch.

2 Use the hand lens to examine your paper mixture at different times throughout your experiment. Record your results.

Analyze Your Data

1 Why is liquid laundry starch needed in this process? Why is water needed?

2 Dense paper has many fibers arranged tightly together. Lighter-weight paper has fibers more loosely arranged. Was your recycled paper more or less dense than the original newspaper?

Draw Conclusions

1 Would you want to read a book that was printed on this type of recycled paper? Write a paragraph that describes how your recycled paper could be improved.

2 As a class, discuss the following question: Do you think you could use this process to recycle plastics?

Design a Related Experiment

Design a procedure for recycling another material that would result in more dense and less dense recycled paper.

Lab: Recycling Paper

1. Propose a Hypothesis: Paper can be recycled by mixing small pieces of newspaper with water and laundry starch, and drying a flat layer of this mixture.

Chapter 38 Review

 THE BIG IDEA!

38.1 Human use of essential natural resources can affect the web of life.

38.2–38.4 Land, water, and air are invaluable natural resources.

38.5 Humans can affect the future of the biosphere in a positive way.

Sum It Up

Use the following summary to review the main concepts in this chapter.

38.1 Earth's Resources

- Some of Earth's resources are renewable and can be replenished by natural processes. Other resources are limited and nonrenewable.
- In order to preserve natural resources, humans need to practice sustainable development—control the rate at which the resources are used.
- Humans are part of an ecosystem; we can change our behaviors to preserve the quality and quantity of Earth's natural resources.

38.2 Land in the Biosphere

- Farmers and ranchers need soils that retain water and nutrients.
- Paper recycling and careful lumber harvesting can help minimize deforestation.
- Mining nonrenewable mineral resources can destroy habitats and cause pollution.
- Each alternative to fossil fuels has advantages and disadvantages.
- Reducing solid wastes frees up the land used by landfills, which can threaten groundwater.
- Habitat destruction threatens biodiversity.

38.3 Water in the Biosphere

- Soil erosion contributes to water pollution, as does the release of untreated sewage.

- Chemical pollutants can threaten Earth's water supply. Oil spills are a major source of chemical pollution.
- Aquatic species are sensitive to thermal pollution. Coral reefs and estuaries are especially vulnerable to all forms of water pollution.

38.4 Air in the Biosphere

- Emission devices on cars and scrubbers on smokestacks help control air pollution.
- Acid rain damages ecosystems, changing soil chemicals; it also damages structures such as buildings.
- Reducing the level of greenhouse gases can help prevent or reduce global warming.
- CFCs damage the ozone layer, which protects organisms from UV radiation.

38.5 Environmental Success Stories

- The banning of DDT helped save peregrine falcons from extinction.
- The Green Belt Movement in Kenya is aimed at reforestation and helping to stop erosion and desertification.
- People in Costa Rica are working to save the endangered tropical dry forest.

Use Terms and Concepts

Use each of the following words or terms in a complete sentence. If you need to review a meaning, turn to the page indicated.

renewable resource (p. 918)

nonrenewable resource (p. 918)

sustainable development (p. 919)

soil erosion (p. 920)

desertification (p. 920)

deforestation (p. 921)

biodegradable (p. 922)

nonbiodegradable (p. 922)

acid rain (p. 929)

greenhouse effect (p. 930)

global warming (p. 930)

chlorofluorocarbons (p. 931)

Use Your Word Power

MATCHING **Write the term from the list of key terms that best matches each of the phrases below.**

1. Wastes that cannot be recycled by natural processes.

2. Compounds that are capable of destroying ozone when released into the atmosphere.

3. The use of natural resources at a rate that does not deplete them.

4. A practice responsible for the destruction of many tropical habitats.

5. The predicted increase in Earth's average surface temperature.

6. The reduction in a soil's ability to retain water and nutrients.

7. The retention of atmospheric heat that would normally radiate back into space.

TRUE-FALSE **Write true if the statement is true. If the statement is false, replace the underlined word(s) to make the statement true.**

8. Recycling can help prevent <u>deforestation</u>.

9. Forests are <u>nonrenewable</u> resources.

10. Nitrogen oxide and <u>carbon dioxide</u> dissolve in water to form acid rain.

11. Contour plowing and terracing can help prevent <u>soil erosion</u>.

12. <u>Biodegradable wastes</u> can be composted to form humus.

Show What You Know

13. What danger does runoff from agricultural lands pose to living organisms?

14. How do volcanoes contribute to acid rain?

15. Describe an effect that soil erosion can have on aquatic organisms.

16. What effect might global warming have on coastal communities?

17. Explain why biodegradable wastes do not necessarily decompose at landfills.

18. What role do bacteria play at sewage treatment plants?

19. Describe the processes of deforestation, desertification, and soil erosion. What impact can these processes have on each other?

20. Explain why ozone destruction continues even though chlorofluorocarbons are banned.

21. **Make a Concept Map** Create a concept map that identifies different types of pollutants and shows how they affect air, water, and land.

Take It Further

22. **Applying Concepts** Gardeners who construct and keep a compost heap periodically turn over the materials in the pile. How does this action promote decomposition?

23. **Developing a Hypothesis** Ecologists are concerned about the effects of habitat fragmentation. For example, when land is cleared for agriculture or for homes, isolated sections of the original habitat may remain. How might fragmentation or a reduction in the size of an ecosystem affect its inhabitants?

24. **Applying Concepts** Explain why forest ecosystems can be described as a threatened habitat, despite the fact that trees are a renewable resource.

25. **Developing a Hypothesis** Different grades of coal contain different amounts of sulfur. Explain why burning low-sulfur coal can reduce acid rain.

26. **Designing an Experiment** Determine which commonly discarded items contribute most to the bulk of solid waste. Design an experiment to find out which of these bulky items are biodegradable and, if they are, how long they might take to degrade in a typical landfill.

27. Interpreting a Graph The graph below illustrates how thermal pollution might affect fish. What happens to the oxygen (O_2) consumption of fish as the temperature of the water rises? What happens to the O_2 content of the water as its temperature rises? Why might a fish become less active as the water temperature rises?

Effects of Water Temperature on Oxygen Consumption of Fish

Active fish

O_2 content of water

Resting fish

Oxygen Consumption of Fish

Oxygen Content of Water

Water Temperature (°C)

0   10   20   30   40

28. Analyzing Data The total biomass of primary producers on Earth, or net primary production, is about 132 petagrams. The table below shows amounts of primary production used by humans in several habitats. What is the total mass of primary production used by humans? What percent of Earth's net primary production does this represent? What percent of Earth's net primary production is available for all other species? How does the amount of primary production used by humans affect biodiversity?

Primary Producers Used by Humans	
Habitat Category	Net Primary Production
Cultivated land	15.0
Grazing land	11.6
Forest land	13.6
Human-occupied areas	0.4

*Values are in petagrams (one petagram = 10^{15} grams)

Consider the Issues

29. Triage for Ecosystems After a disastrous occurrence, such as an earthquake or multi-car accident, doctors use a system called triage to treat the injured. They divide patients into three categories—those likely to recover without assistance, those most likely to benefit from medical treatment, and those whose injuries are most probably fatal. Could such a system be applied to ecosystems and species? Who could make the determinations? What criteria could they use?

Make New Connections

30. Biology and Literature Oklahoma during the Great Depression of the 1930s inspired John Steinbeck to write *The Grapes of Wrath*. Read Steinbeck's novel and find out how drought and soil erosion affected so many lives.

31. Biology and Government If your state periodically tests automobile emissions, visit a local testing center. Find out how often vehicles are tested. What equipment is used, and what does it measure? What are the criteria for passing the test? What happens when an automobile fails the test?

32. Biology and Anthropology Urban anthropologists study the lifestyle of city residents. One method of research includes analyzing their trash. What information might urban anthropologists be seeking? Investigate how anthropologists use waste products to research a community's lifestyle.

FAST-FORWARD

We are all a part of the web of life. In your continued studies and in your day-to-day activities, use what you have learned to strengthen and preserve the fragile connections and delicate strands that constitute the web of life.

Unit 9 Review

THE BIG IDEA! Answering the following questions will help you to link ideas and grasp the core concepts.

Connect the Chapters

1. How does crop rotation contribute to sustainable development?

2. Describe three ways in which nonhuman populations might respond to global warming.

3. What human activities might increase the range of desert biomes?

4. Explain how soil erosion could affect the photic zone in an aquatic biome.

5. In which types of biomes would a population be most likely to experience a boom-or-bust growth curve?

6. Which would be better for sustainable development: a human-population growth curve that is S-shaped or one that is J-shaped?

7. Are human activities that contribute to water pollution density-dependent or density-independent limiting factors? Explain your answer.

Connect the Units

8. What compounds in the human body contain nitrogen? How is nitrogen recycled from humans to the environment?

9. How is photosynthesis important in helping to reduce gases that contribute to the greenhouse effect?

10. How can poor air quality affect the human respiratory system?

Connect to Themes

11. Patterns of Change/Cycles Will primary or secondary succession occur in a habitat that has been deforested? Explain your answer.

12. Stability and Equilibrium How might introducing non-native species into an ecosystem affect native populations?

13. Systems and Interactions What effect does burning fossil fuels have on the carbon cycle and the water cycle?

project plans

1 Select one of the major latitude lines on a world map or globe. List at least six cities that are located on or near the latitude you have chosen. Include cities on at least two different continents. Make travel brochures that identify the cities' climates and biomes.

2 Select a habitat restoration project other than the ones described in Chapter 38. Research the history of the project. What factors contributed to the habitat's destruction? What motivated people to restore the habitat? What methods were used? What progress has been made?

3 Some people suggest that the way to deal with population growth and limited resources on Earth is to colonize outer space. Some think that the moon would be a good destination. As a class, research conditions on the moon. What resources would be available for human life? What resources would people need to transport from Earth?

CRITIC'S CORNER

A BOOK REVIEW BY ANN K.D. MYERS ST. PAUL, MN

Last Chance to See is a humorous account of Douglas Adams's worldwide travels to observe endangered species. The book does have a serious message: Unless we do something *NOW*, we may never see any of these animals—mountain gorillas, Komodo dragons, white rhinos, Yangtze river dolphins, and many others—again. I recommend this book to anyone who wants to know more about rare species and have a good laugh at the same time.

JOYCE PONSELL
Volunteer at a bird-rescue sanctuary

EDUCATION: B.A. in speech therapy; interested in bird watching and ecology

" Before I retired, my job was to gather a team for cleanups. Now, I'm on the volunteer list. My volunteer work gives back to the wild.

Sometimes animals get hurt when nature and humans interact. Birds can be harmed by cars, by eating bugs or plants covered with pesticides, or by oil spills. We treat birds covered with oil. Oil is removed from feathers by washing them very gently.

We try to save each and every bird we find, no matter what species it is. For example, there are a lot of Canada geese on the East Coast and some people think they're a nuisance because they are noisy and can make a mess of ponds and golf courses. But all of the different shorebirds contribute to biodiversity, and all of them are a link in the chain of the ecosystem."

bioSURF Explore the Internet site *http://ecology.biosurf.com* to find out how communities protect the environment.

"We try to save each and every bird we find, no matter what species it is." — JOYCE PONSELL

CAROL PADDEN
Chief conservation ranger

EDUCATION: M.S. in environmental science

" My job is to care for town conservation land, including fields, wetlands, and about 90 miles (144 km) of hiking trails. Last summer we studied Flint's Pond, our drinking water supply. We look at whether ponds are affected by animals or humans—either from septic systems or road runoff.

I try to raise awareness about natural resources. For example, people who don't understand the ecology of water systems can damage our drinking supply. Any kind of wetland is valuable because it helps filter our water. We all need to understand how we effect the land and that our abuses may come back and affect us later."

bioSURF Visit *http://ecology.biosurf.com* to learn more about conservation of natural resources.

Dear Student Biologist:

As you complete your biology course, our fondest hope is that your course and this program have helped you become more curious about the living world. Life is all around us, and the science of biology helps us to understand it.

There are many places you can go from here. Careers in biological research contribute new knowledge about nature's organization and function. The medical and health professions also make invaluable contributions to our lives. Biology can also be important in agriculture, law, art, and many other professions. No matter what career you choose, you are a citizen of the living world. As a citizen, you are a custodian of the environment. The decisions you make every day will affect the web of life now and in the future.

This course is the beginning of what can be a lifelong journey of discovery about the living world. Seize the opportunity to learn more. Visit natural areas, go to museums, and find life wherever you are. Immerse yourself in the wonder of the natural world. You will not be disappointed.

Good luck and enjoy your future journeys!

Eric G. Strauss

Marylin Lisowski

Metric Conversions

Metric Units	Metric to English	English to Metric
LENGTH		
meter (m) = 100 cm	1 m = 3.28 ft	1 ft = 0.31 m
kilometer (km) = 1000 m	1 km = 0.62 mi	1 mi = 1.61 km
centimeter (cm) = 0.01 m	1 cm = 0.39 in	1 in = 2.54 cm
millimeter (mm) = 0.001 m	1 mm = 0.039 in	1 in = 25.4 mm
micrometer (μm) = 10^{-6} m	1 μm = 3.9×10^{-5} in	1 in = 25,400 μm
nanometer (nm) = 10^{-9} m	1nm=3.9×10^{-8} in	1 in = 2.54×10^7 nm
AREA		
square meter (m^2) = 10,000 cm^2	1 m^2 = 10.76 sq ft	1 sq ft = 0.09 m^2
square kilometer (km^2) = 10,000 m^2	1 km^2 = 0.39 sq mi	1 sq mi = 2.59 km^2
hectare (ha) = 10,000 m^2	1 ha = 2.47 acres	1 acre = 0.40 ha
square centimeter (cm^2) = 100 mm^2	1 cm^2 = 0.16 sq in	1 sq in = 6.45 cm^2
MASS		
gram (g) = 1000 mg	1 g = 0.04 oz	1 oz = 28.35 g
kilogram (kg) = 1000 g	1 kg = 2.21 lb	1 lb = 0.45 kg
milligram (mg) = 0.001 g	1 mg = 4×10^{-5} oz	1 oz = 28.350 mg
VOLUME (SOLIDS)		
cubic meter (m^3) = 1,000,000 cm^3	1 m^3 = 35.32 cu ft	1 cu ft = 0.03 m^3
cubic centimeter (cm^3) = 1000 mm^3	1 cm^3 = 0.06 cu in	1 cu in = 16.39 cm^3
VOLUME (LIQUIDS)		
liter (L) = 1000 mL	1 L = 1.06 qt 1 L = 0.27 gal	1 qt = 0.94 L 1 gal = 3.79 L
milliliter (mL) = 0.001 L	1 mL = 0.03 fluid oz	1 fluid oz = 29.57 mL

The Periodic Table

1

1
1
H
Hydrogen
1.0079

1 .... Atomic Number
H .... Symbol
Hydrogen .... Element Name
1.0079 .... Atomic Mass

Alkali Metals · Alkaline earth metals · Transition Metals · Other Metals · Nonmetals · Noble Gases

2

3	4
Li	**Be**
Lithium	Beryllium
6.941	9.0122

11	12
Na	**Mg**
Sodium	Magnesium
22.990	24.305

3	**4**	**5**	**6**	**7**	**8**	**9**

19	20	21	22	23	24	25	26	27
K	**Ca**	**Sc**	**Ti**	**V**	**Cr**	**Mn**	**Fe**	**Co**
Potassium	Calcium	Scandium	Titanium	Vanadium	Chromium	Manganese	Iron	Cobalt
39.098	40.08	44.956	47.90	50.941	51.996	54.938	55.847	58.933
37	38	39	40	41	42	43	44	45
Rb	**Sr**	**Y**	**Zr**	**Nb**	**Mo**	**Tc**	**Ru**	**Rh**
Rubidium	Strontium	Yttrium	Zirconium	Niobium	Molybdenum	Technetium	Ruthenium	Rhodium
85.468	87.62	88.906	91.22	92.906	95.94	(97)	101.07	102.91
55	56	71	72	73	74	75	76	77
Cs	**Ba**	**Lu**	**Hf**	**Ta**	**W**	**Re**	**Os**	**Ir**
Cesium	Barium	Lutetium	Hafnium	Tantalum	Tungsten	Rhenium	Osmium	Iridium
132.91	137.33	174.97	178.49	180.95	183.85	186.21	190.2	192.22
87	88	103	104	105	106	107	108	109
Fr	**Ra**	**Lr**	**Unq**	**Unp**	**Unh**	**Uns**	**Uno**	**Une**
Francium	Radium	Lawrencium						
(223)	226.03	(260)	(261)	(262)	(263)	(264)	(265)	(266)

57	58	59	60	61	62
La	**Ce**	**Pr**	**Nd**	**Pm**	**Sm**
Lanthanum	Cerium	Praseodymium	Neodymium	Promethium	Samarium
138.91	140.12	140.12	144.24	(145)	150.4
89	90	91	92	93	94
Ac	**Th**	**Pa**	**U**	**Np**	**Pu**
Actinum	Thorium	Protactinium	Uranium	Neptunium	Plutonium
(227)	232.04	213.04	238.03	237.05	(244)

Inner transition elements

Periodic table (partial, groups 10–18)

								18
								2 **He** Helium 4.0026

			13	14	15	16	17	
			5 **B** Boron 10.81	6 **C** Carbon 12.011	7 **N** Nitrogen 14.007	8 **O** Oxygen 15.999	9 **F** Fluorine 18.998	10 **Ne** Neon 20.179
			13 **Al** Aluminum 26.982	14 **Si** Silicon 28.086	15 **P** Phosphorus 30.974	16 **S** Sulfur 32.06	17 **Cl** Chlorine 35.453	18 **Ar** Argon 39.948

10	11	12						
28 **Ni** Nickel 58.71	29 **Cu** Copper 63.546	30 **Zn** Zinc 65.38	31 **Ga** Gallium 69.72	32 **Ge** Germanium 72.59	33 **As** Arsenic 74.922	34 **Se** Selenium 78.96	35 **Br** Bromine 79.904	36 **Kr** Krypton 83.80
46 **Pd** Palladium 106.4	47 **Ag** Silver 107.87	48 **Cd** Cadmium 112.41	49 **In** Indium 114.82	50 **Sn** Tin 118.69	51 **Sb** Antimony 121.75	52 **Te** Tellurium 127.60	53 **I** Iodine 126.90	54 **Xe** Xenon 131.30
78 **Pt** Platinum 195.09	79 **Au** Gold 196.97	80 **Hg** Mercury 200.59	81 **Tl** Thallium 204.37	82 **Pb** Lead 207.2	83 **Bi** Bismuth 208.98	84 **Po** Polonium (209)	85 **At** Astatine (210)	86 **Rn** Radon (222)

63 **Eu** Europium 151.96	64 **Gd** Gadolinium 157.25	65 **Tb** Terbium 158.93	66 **Dy** Dysprosium 162.50	67 **Ho** Holmium 164.93	68 **Er** Erbium 167.26	69 **Tm** Thulium 168.93	70 **Yb** Ytterbium 173.04
95 **Am** Americium (243)	96 **Cm** Curium (247)	97 **Bk** Berkelium (247)	98 **Cf** Californium (251)	99 **Es** Einsteinium (254)	100 **Fm** Fermium (257)	101 **Md** Mendelevium (258)	102 **No** Nobilium (259)

Laboratory Safety

A biology laboratory is an environment where exciting experiments and observations can occur. However, it is also an environment filled with dangerous materials and potential hazards. Following sensible safety precautions will help you create a positive laboratory experience. Read the following guidelines before you begin working in the laboratory, and periodically review these precautions throughout the year.

Safety Guidelines

1. Thoroughly read each laboratory procedure before entering the laboratory.

2. Know how to locate and use all safety equipment in the laboratory, including the first aid kit, fume hood, fire blanket, fire extinguisher, safety shower, and eye wash. Also, be able to locate the nearest exit in case of an emergency.

3. Do not engage in dangerous laboratory behavior such as horseplay or running.

4. Always wear safety goggles, unless otherwise instructed.

5. Wear an apron or a lab coat to protect your clothing.

6. Secure any loose-fitting clothing, and tie back long hair.

7. Never eat or drink in the laboratory.

8. Never taste, touch, or smell any chemicals unless instructed.

9. Thoroughly wash your hands before and after each laboratory activity.

10. Keep your work area clear of any unnecessary items.

11. Do not experiment with or mix any chemicals except as instructed during the prescribed laboratory activity. When combined, many chemicals in the laboratory can be explosive or otherwise dangerous.

12. Thoroughly wash all laboratory instruments before and after each use.

13. When using scissors or a scalpel, cut away from yourself and others.

14. When heating substances in a test tube, always slant and aim the mouth of the test tube away from yourself and others.

15. Clearly label all containers with the names of the materials you use during the activity.

16. Report all accidents, no matter how small, immediately to your instructor.

17. Never pick up broken glass with your hands. Sweep broken glass into a dustpan, and dispose of it in the broken glass container.

18. Never return unused chemicals to their original containers. Follow your instructor's directions for the proper disposal and cleanup of all unused materials.

19. Make sure all your materials are washed and put away. Clean your work area before leaving the laboratory.

20. Before leaving the laboratory, be certain that all Bunsen burners, gas outlets, and water faucets are turned off.

These symbols will draw your attention to specific potential hazards.

Safety Symbols	
Live Animals	Plants
Electrical Safety	Hot Object
Protective Clothing	Poison
Eye Protection	Glassware
Sharp Object	

Laboratory Skills

Use of a Compound Microscope

The microscope is an important tool in biology. The type of microscope common to most biology laboratories is the compound microscope. The compound microscope uses two lenses to magnify an image: the eyepiece, or ocular lens, and the objective lens.

Parts of a Microscope

Before you begin, locate the twelve main parts of a compound microscope in the diagram. Become familiar with each part and its specific function.

Eyepiece	Body tube
High-power objective	Stage
Low-power objective	Stage clips
Diaphragm	Mirror
Coarse adjustment	Base
Fine adjustment	Arm

Using a Microscope

Follow these steps each time you use a microscope:

1. Carry the microscope to your table by holding the arm of the microscope with one hand while supporting its base with your other hand. Never carry a microscope with just one hand.

2. Carefully place the microscope on the table with the arm facing toward you.

3. If necessary, gently clean the lenses with lens paper. Do not touch the lenses with your fingers or regular tissue paper.

4. Determine the light source for your microscope. If the microscope has a lamp, plug it in and adjust the light to a comfortable level. If the microscope has a mirror, adjust the mirror to reflect light through the diaphragm. Never use direct sunlight as a light source when using a mirror, because it can damage your eyes.

5. Turn the revolving nosepiece until the low-power objective lens is in line with the body tube and the diaphragm. The lens should click into place.

6. Place a slide on the stage, and secure the slide with the stage clips. Make sure the specimen is directly in line with the light coming through the diaphragm. (See the next page for instructions on preparing slides.)

7. While watching from the side, not through the eyepiece, use the coarse adjustment to lower the objective toward the slide. Stop the objective just above, but not touching, the slide.

8. While looking through the eyepiece, slowly raise the objective with the coarse adjustment. When the specimen comes into view, turn the fine adjustment knob to focus sharply on the specimen. If you cannot find the specimen, repeat step 7.

947

Preparing a Wet-Mount Slide

You can use a wet-mount slide to view a specimen through a compound microscope. Use the following steps to successfully prepare a wet-mount slide:

1. Obtain a slide and a coverslip. If necessary, clean each with lens paper. Use extreme care when cleaning coverslips, because they break easily.

2. Place the specimen you want to observe in the center of the slide. Using an eyedropper, place one drop of water on the specimen.

3. Holding the coverslip at a 45° angle (as shown above), touch its edge to the droplet of water. The water should spread evenly along the edge of the coverslip.

4. Slowly lower the coverslip over the specimen, avoiding air bubbles. If air bubbles become trapped under the coverslip, gently tap the coverslip with a pencil eraser until the bubbles disappear.

5. Remove excess water with a paper towel placed at the edge of the slide.

6. If the specimen begins to dry out over time, place another drop of water at the edge of the coverslip. Never lift the coverslip to add water.

Using a Triple-Beam Balance

There are many types of balances used to determine mass. However, the triple-beam balance is often used in biology laboratories. It can accurately measure the mass of an object to within 0.1 gram. Follow these steps every time you use the triple-beam balance:

1. Place the balance on a level surface.

2. Move all the weights to the left, and turn the adjustment screw so that the pointer rests at the zero mark.

3. Place the object to be measured on the pan.

4. Locate the beam with the heaviest weight. Slide the weight to the right until the pointer falls below the zero mark. Then slide the weight one notch to the left.

5. Locate the beam with the next-heaviest weight. Position the weight using the same procedure used in step 4.

6. Slide the lightest weight to the right until the pointer rests at zero. The mass of the object is the total of the masses shown on all three beams.

7. When measuring liquids, powders, and hot objects, place the substance in a container, rather than directly on the pan. To determine the mass of the substance, be sure to subtract the mass of the container from the total mass.

Adjustment screw   Weights   Pointer

Pan

Problem-Solving Skills
Observing and Interpreting

The scientific method involves making observations and interpreting them. An observation is something that can be made with the senses or with instruments that extend the senses. When conducting a scientific experiment, a scientist must be careful to observe the effects of only one variable at a time. A scientist must also repeat the experiment under the same set of conditions in order to confirm that there has been no error in observation.

An interpretation is a possible explanation of what might have produced the observations that were made. There are often several possible interpretations of the same set of observations. A scientist's task is to identify all the reasonable interpretations and then determine which interpretation is most probable.

Like all problem-solving tasks, observing and interpreting can be organized into a series of steps. Here are a few simple steps to help you:

- Think about the definitions of the words *observation* and *interpretation*.

- Divide the information given into small pieces.

- Apply the definitions of "observation" and "interpretion" to each piece of information.

- Look at the conditions under which the observations and interpretations were made. Decide whether the observations were made carefully and whether the interpretations are reasonable.

Everyday Applications

1. You check your mailbox and observe that it contains no mail. State two interpretations for this observation. How could you test each of your interpretations?

2. The kitchen flashlight does not light. State three ways to interpret this observation. What further observations might be useful?

Biology Applications

On a separate sheet of paper, identify the observations and interpretations in the following passage:

The Montero family notices that their lawn is turning brown. They suspect that the cause is insufficient water. To determine the cause, they divide the lawn into two sections. Section A is given an increased amount of water; section B is watered with the usual amount. After a few days, they also decide to add fertilizer to section A. Two weeks later, section A is green and section B is still brown. The Monteros decide that increased watering caused section A to turn green.

The Tran family has the same problem. They divide their lawn into three sections. Section A receives increased water, section B receives fertilizer and the usual amount of water, and section C is treated as usual. The Trans find that only section A becomes green; sections B and C remain brown. They, too, conclude that increased watering was the factor that improved the appearance of the lawn.

1. Which family was observing the results of two variables at one time?

2. Do you think the interpretations of both families are equally good? Why or why not?

3. Did both families use the correct procedures? How would you improve the experiments?

4. What other factors might have affected the experiments?

Lab Zone Applications

Practice the skills of observing and interpreting by doing these Lab Zone activities:

- **Think About It:** Analyzing Firefly Behavior, *Chapter 28, page 670*

- **Do It:** What Happens When You Exhale?, *Chapter 31, page 746*

Problem-Solving Skills
Analyzing

When people analyze information, they break it down into its parts and then determine how the parts relate to each other and to the whole. Analyzing helps to develop an understanding of how something works. When you analyze information rather than memorize it, you are more likely to remember the information and use it. Analyzing helps you to link new information to things you already know.

You can analyze many things—data, processes, diagrams, graphs, and more. When you are analyzing a subject that is complex, there are a few things to keep in mind. First, it is important to know the overall purpose of the subject you are analyzing. Once you understand the purpose, keep it in mind as you study the subject.

If the subject of your analysis has several parts, look at it one part at a time. Think about how each part contributes to the overall purpose. Also think about how the parts are related to one another.

After you have made observations, try to explain your subject aloud or in writing. If you truly understand the process, you will be able to explain it to someone else. If you are unable to explain the subject clearly, you should review your notes and repeat the process described below.

Here are a few simple steps to help you to analyze:

- Decide on the overall purpose of the subject.

- Break it down into parts.

- Review by explaining it in your own words aloud or on paper.

Everyday Applications

Your favorite music group has just released a new compact disc (CD), and you want to buy a copy. Some of the steps involved in your purchase are listed below, but they are not in the correct order. Place the steps in the correct order, and answer the accompanying questions.

A. Find out if your local music store has the CD in stock.

B. Pay for the CD.

C. Ride your bike to the store.

D. Check your wallet to see if you have enough money to buy the CD.

E. Find the CD in the store.

F. Ride your bike home.

G. Check the tires of your bike to make sure they are not flat.

H. Put the CD in your backpack.

1. Which step did you list first, and why?

2. What might have happened if you placed step H before step B?

3. What was the function of step G?

Biology Applications

Analyze the diagrams of photosynthesis described in Chapter 4 and answer the following questions:

1. What is the function of the Calvin cycle?

2. Why must the light-dependent reactions occur before the carbon-fixing reactions?

3. What is the function of light in photosynthesis? What would happen in the absence of light?

4. Could the light-dependent reactions occur in the absence of the Calvin cycle? Why or why not?

Lab Zone Applications

Practice the skill of analyzing by doing these Lab Zone activities:

- **Think About It:** Analyzing Tree Rings, *Chapter 18, page 439*

- **Think About It:** Determining the Age of a Fossil, *Chapter 11, page 265*

Problem-Solving Skills
Stating a Hypothesis

A hypothesis is an interpretation of observations. We all make hypotheses about things in our everyday lives. A scientist makes a hypothesis only after he or she has studied a problem and made observations. Next, the scientist analyzes his or her observations to find patterns and clues. If there are patterns in the data, the scientist uses his or her imagination and knowledge to think of possible explanations for all of the observations. These explanations are the hypotheses.

The best of the hypotheses are selected and tested in experiments that produce new observations or data. A hypothesis that is not consistent with the data must be rejected or changed.

The steps in stating a hypothesis can be summarized as follows:

- Collect all the data that appear to be related to the problem.

- Organize the information, and look for patterns.

- Make a list of explanations of the observations. Identify as many explanations as you can.

- Choose the explanation that is most consistent with all the available data. If two or more hypotheses seem to fit the data equally well, do not decide between them until more data can be collected.

Everyday Applications

You are packing for a camping trip and find that your flashlight does not light. In order to determine why the flashlight does not work, you make the following observations: The flashlight has the correct size and number of batteries; the flashlight worked last week when your younger brother was playing with it; the bulb does not appear broken.

1. Develop a hypothesis to explain why the flashlight does not work. Is your hypothesis consistent with all of your observations?

2. Suppose you also observed that the switch was left in the "on" position. How does this additional information affect your hypothesis?

Biology Applications

You are given the two Petri dishes shown below. Your teacher tells you that both dishes contain tobacco seedlings. The green seedlings in dish A were germinated in the light, and the white seedlings in dish B were germinated in darkness. Your teacher also tells you that there is a genetic condition called albinism in some plants. Plants with albinism cannot make chlorophyll and are therefore white.

A **B**

1. Form one or more hypotheses to explain the differences between the two sets of seedlings.

2. Another student says she would like to test her hypothesis by leaving both dishes in the light for a day. What do you think her hypothesis is?

3. After 24 hours in light, the plants in the two dishes are the same color. Use all the data you now have to choose the best hypothesis or to form a new hypothesis.

Lab Zone Applications

Practice the skill of stating a hypothesis by doing these Lab Zone activities:

- **Think About It:** Solving a Reproduction Puzzle, *Chapter 22, page 527*

- **Investigate It:** Does Temperature Affect Bacterial Growth?, *Chapter 14, page 339*

Problem-Solving Skills
Organizing and Classifying

Quite often, people must deal with large numbers of facts or objects. When dealing with a large collection of different things, it is important to organize and classify the items in the collection. Organizing and classifying make the items easier to find and to use.

When you organize and classify anything, you must first think about your purpose for doing so. Your reasons for organizing and classifying will determine the criteria you use. The most important criterion for organizing things is that the system makes sense to the person who uses the items. After the items are organized into groups according to the appropriate criteria, it may be necessary to form subgroups. Here again, the criterion is usefulness.

Here is a summary of the steps for classifying:

- Decide what your purpose is for classifying.

- Study the characteristics of the things to be classified. Decide on useful criteria for classifying.

- Go through the items, and place them in the appropriate groups.

- Decide if subgroups would be useful. If so, use the same process again.

Everyday Applications

Imagine you are organizing a kitchen that has a square cabinet under the sink, three drawers under the work counter, a shelf by the stove, and a tall, narrow closet by the entrance.

1. Where would you place each of the following items: broom, spice bottle, frying pan, knives, gloves?

2. What criteria did you use to determine where each item should be stored?

3. Name one other item that you would store with each of the four items listed.

Biology Applications

Imagine you are responsible for planning a zoo that will place the following animals in containments:

Lion	Rattlesnake
Alaskan king crab	Baboon
Jaguar	Parrot
Poison arrow frog	Walrus
Tsetse fly	Desert vulture
Collared lizard	Giraffe
Mako shark	Mexican tarantula
Pacific salmon	

1. The zoo is organized to group animals by ecosystems, such as the African plains, the Pacific coast, or the South American rain forests. Decide which animals you would place in neighboring containments.

2. The zoo decides to place the above animals into the following scientific groupings: Mammals, Reptiles, Fish, Amphibians, Birds, and Arthropods. Reorganize the animals on the list into these taxa.

3. Choose another biological charactertistic and group the animals according to your new characteristic. Groups may include predators and prey; herbivores, carnivores, and omnivores; large and small animals; and so on.

Lab Zone Applications

Practice the skills of organizing and classifying by doing these Lab Zone activities:

- **Do It:** Categorizing Plants, *Chapter 17, page 414*

- **Do It:** What is the Quality of Local Water?, *Chapter 38, page 917*

Problem-Solving Skills
Making a Concept Map

Through your study of biology, you will be presented with many new concepts. There are many ways to organize these concepts, but one of the most helpful ways is to create a concept map. In a concept map, ideas and concepts are expressed as words or phrases enclosed in circles. The circles are connected by lines that are accompanied by one or two words that describe the connection. Each main idea is linked to more specific concepts and examples. The following steps will help you to construct a concept map:

- Identify the main idea and concepts.

- Place the main idea at the top of the map and draw a circle around it. Draw lines to connect the main idea to the concepts, and circle each concept.

- Add linking words or phrases that explain the relationship between the circled concepts.

Do not be discouraged if you find concept mapping difficult at first. Remember, there is no one correct concept map for a topic. Your concept map will be correct if it shows the main ideas and general concepts and identifies the relationships among them.

Everyday Applications

The following concept map shows how to write an essay:

1. Where would you add quotations and a bibiography to the concept map? How would you link these concepts?

2. Create a concept map showing the organization of your classroom. Use the following terms in your concept map: teacher, students, desks, chalkboard, erasers, textbooks, bulletin board, computers, paper, principal, school building.

Biology Applications

The concept map below shows the relationships between the main idea–birds–and some general concepts and specific ideas about birds.

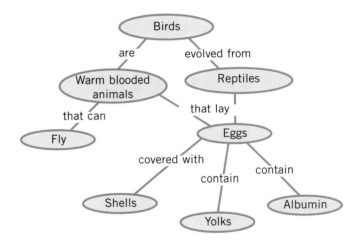

1. What organisms lay eggs? What do eggs contain?

2. Where and how would you add the following terms to the concept map above: wings, feathers, migrate.

Lab Zone Applications

Practice the skill of organizing concepts in other ways by doing these Lab Zone activities:

- **Think About It:** Constructing a Phylogenetic Tree, *Chapter 13, page 309*

- **Investigate It:** Using a Pedigree, *Chapter 6, page 146*

Problem-Solving Skills
Designing an Experiment

An experiment is designed test a hypothesis by investigating the effects of an experimental variable. Any factor that can influence the outcome of an experiment is a variable. Only one variable is analyzed in one experiment. All other variables are kept constant.

An experiment has two parts: the experimental setup and the control setup. In the experimental setup, the experimental variable is present. In the control setup, the experimental variable is missing or changed. The control setup is crucial to the experiment, because one cannot determine the effect of the experimental variable unless one can see what happens when it is changed or removed.

Here are some steps to follow when you design an experiment:

- Follow the procedure for stating an hypothesis (see page 951).
- Determine the variable you want to test.
- Set up an experiment to test your hypothesis.
- Devise an experimental setup and control setup.

Everyday Applications

A convenience store owner has recently purchased a soft-drink machine, but finds that soft-drink sales are slow. The owner hypothesizes that the reason for the slow sales is the location of the machine: a dark corner.

1. Design an experiment to test the store owner's hypothesis.

2. State two other hypotheses that could explain the slow sales.

3. Design an experiment to test each of the alternative hypotheses.

Biology Applications

Raj has an aquarium in which the water is heated to a constant temperature of 18°C. One day, the temperature control in the heater breaks, and the water rises to 22°C. Raj notices that the fishes appear more active than usual and seem to be breathing more rapidly.

Raj has a hypothesis, which he decides to test. He selects three fishes, places each fish in a beaker or water, and sets the beakers down in larger bowls of water. The bowls contain either warm water, ice water, or room-temperature water. During a 10-minute period Raj and several friends measure the water temperature in the beakers and count how many times per minute each fish breathes. After the experiment, the fish are returned to the tank unharmed. The data are organized on a table as shown.

Comparing Fish Breathing Rates						
	BOWL #1		BOWL #2		BOWL #3	
Min.	Temp. (°C)	Breaths (#/min.)	Temp. (°C)	Breaths (#/min.)	Temp. (°C)	Breaths (#/min.)
0	22°C	58	21°C	57	21°C	60
2	22°C	59	24°C	67	19°C	51
4	22°C	57	25°C	81	16°C	32
6	22°C	56	27°C	93	14°C	20
8	22°C	55	29°C	110	10°C	12
10	22°C	56	30°C	110	11°C	13

1. What hypothesis is Raj testing in this experiment?

2. What variable did Raj isolate?

3. Suppose Raj finds out that cold water can dissolve more oxygen than warm water can. Use this information to write a new hypothesis.

Lab Zone Applications

Practice the skill of designing an experiment by doing these Lab Zone activities:

- **Investigate It:** Designing a Scientific Experiment, *Chapter 1, page 26*

- **Investigate It:** Observing Population Growth, *Chapter 36, page 880*

Problem-Solving Skills
Making Analogies

If you are trying to understand a new idea, it sometimes helps to compare the new idea to something with which you are already familiar. Such a comparison is called an analogy. For example, you could compare an airplane to a bird. Both objects fly and they are similar in shape. Of course, an airplane and a bird are not alike in most ways. But they do have some similarities in structure that reflect their common functions. Like all analogies, the comparison between an airplane and a bird is limited by the differences between the two items.

Analogies are also often used in making models. Whenever you use an analogy to create a model, keep in mind the differences between the two objects. For example, an airplane might be useful if you are examining bird flight, but it would not be useful if you were planning to study bird songs.

Reasoning by analogy uses the skills of comparing and contrasting. It also uses the skill of analyzing, because finding a good analogy requires that you understand all the parts of the things you are comparing. Analogies can also help you understand new ideas because they help structure and focus your thinking. By understanding how things are alike, you can hypothesize about unknown features of the unfamiliar item. However, you must also remain aware of the ways that the items are different.

To make and use analogies, follow these steps:

- Look at the new concept or information, and think about its parts and its function.

- Think, "Is this like anything I already know about?" List anything you can think of, however silly, that seems like it might be similar.

- Try out each analogy. Identify the one that has the most similarities.

- Compare and contrast your analogy with the new concept. See how far you can take the analogy.

Everyday Applications

1. Develop an analogy between each word listed on the left and the word opposite it on the right. Explain the basis for each analogy.

Bird	**Factory**
Ship	**Theater**
Supermarket	**Airplane**

2. Choose four familiar nouns at random from the dictionary. Exchange your list with another student. From the list given to you by your classmate, find and explain as many analogies among the words as you can.

3. Explain the limitations of each analogy that you developed in questions 1 and 2.

Biology Applications

1. Use your comparing and contrasting skills to explain the following analogies:

   a. A cell is like a factory.

   b. A cell membrane is like a sieve.

   c. A circulatory system is like a railroad.

   d. The brain is like a telephone system.

   e. The xylem of a plant is like a straw.

2. Explain the limitations of each analogy used in question 1.

Lab Zone Applications

Practice the skill of making analogies by doing these Lab Zone Activities:

- **Think About It:** Modeling Fungal Growth, *Chapter 16, page 376*

- **Think About It:** From Milk to Wasp: Modeling Mutations, *Chapter 8, page 195*

Problem-Solving Skills
Making Generalizations

When people make generalizations, they draw conclusions about a broad category of things based on a number of experiences. Scientists make generalizations when they draw conclusions about the world based on the observations made in experiments. The scientist understands, however, that there are always possible exceptions to a generalization.

One way a generalization is helpful to a scientist is that it enables him or her to make predictions. Generalizations lead to assumptions, which form the basis of the prediction. Part of the purpose of conducting an experiment may be to test the generalization. The generalization, therefore, can be a starting point for developing a hypothesis.

To make useful generalizations, follow these steps:

- Collect all the related examples you can find of the situation you are studying.

- Analyze the examples and note patterns or similar parts.

- Make all the generalizations you can about the examples.

- List the significant exceptions to the generalizations you have made.

Everyday Applications

1. Finish the following statement: "Ten-year-olds always. . . ."

2. Now imagine you are 10 years old again, and that someone has just made the previous statement. Explain the reasons why the generalization would be unfair.

3. Make generalizations using examples in each of the following categories: cars, movies, sports, and shopping malls. Indicate whether you think each statement applies to all or most examples in each category.

Biology Applications

1. Suppose there is an animal called a glorpus. A male glorpus comes upon the territory of another male glorpus. Predict the behavior of the two male glorpuses during such an encounter.

   a. What assumptions did you make about the structure, lifestyle, and environment of the glorpuses?

   b. What generalizations did you use to predict the animals' behavior?

   c. If you were to find out that glorpuses are insects, would this information change your prediction? Why or why not?

2. One day, a stray cat appears at your doorstep. Because you like cats and do not like to see them suffer, you go to your kitchen and fill a bowl of milk for the cat. The cat sniffs the bowl, sits down, looks you in the eye and meows, but does not drink the milk.

   a. What generalizations inspired you to get the bowl of milk?

   b. What hypotheses can you make to explain the cat's lack of interest in the milk? List as many hypotheses as you can.

   c. State the generalizations you used to make the hypotheses. Do you think that using generalizations is a good way to make hypotheses? Explain your answer.

Lab Zone Applications

Practice the skill of making generalizations by doing these Lab Zone activities:

- **Think About It:** Finding Examples of Symmetry, *Chapter 21, page 510*

- **Investigate It:** Modeling Disease Transmission, *Chapter 32, page 776*

Classification of Organisms

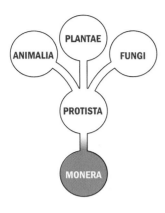

Kingdom: Monera

KEY CHARACTERISTICS: Prokaryotes; most unicellular, but some form filaments or clusters; reproduce asexually by binary fission, some species can exchange genetic information.

Category: Archaebacteria
KEY CHARACTERISTICS: Probably ancestral to other bacteria; most are anaerobic; live in harsh environments.

PHYLUM: METHANOGENS
KEY CHARACTERISTICS: Anaerobic; produce methane.
EXAMPLES: Bacteria found in swamps and in mammalian digestive tracts.

PHYLUM: THERMOPHILES
KEY CHARACTERISTIC: Live in hot, acidic environments.
EXAMPLE: *Sulfolobus*.

PHYLUM: EXTREME HALOPHILES
KEY CHARACTERISTIC: Live in extremely salty environments.
EXAMPLE: *Haloarcula marismortui*.

Category: Eubacteria
KEY CHARACTERISTICS: Known as "true bacteria"; includes heterotrophs and autotrophs; some are aerobic, some are anaerobic.

PHYLUM: GRAM-POSITIVE BACTERIA
KEY CHARACTERISTICS: Cell walls contain a thick layer of protein-sugar complex and a single layer of lipid molecules; many species form endospores.
EXAMPLES: *Staphylococcus, Streptococcus, Bacillus*.

PHYLUM: PROTEOBACTERIA
KEY CHARACTERISTICS: Unicellular eubacteria; many have flagella; some species play key role in nitrogen cycle.
EXAMPLES: *Rhizobium, Escherichia coli, Salmonella*.

PHYLUM: CYANOBACTERIA
KEY CHARACTERISTICS: Many have thick, gel-like cell walls; capable of photosynthesis; most live in fresh-water environments.
EXAMPLES: *Oscillatoria, Gloeocapsa, Nostoc*.

PHYLUM: CHLAMYDIAS
KEY CHARACTERISTICS: Gram-negative; parasitic; limited metabolism.
EXAMPLE: *Chlamydia trachomatis*.

PHYLUM: SPIROCHETES
KEY CHARACTERISTICS: Spiral-shaped; capable of movement; free-living and parasitic species.
EXAMPLE: *Treponema pallidum*.

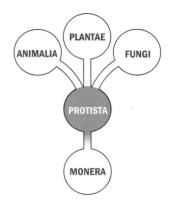

Kingdom: Protista

KEY CHARACTERISTICS: Eukaryotes; may be unicellular, colonial, or multicellular; can reproduce sexually or asexually.

Category: Protozoans
KEY CHARACTERISTICS: Heterotrophic; unicellular; animal-like; many parasitic; methods of reproduction are mostly asexual.

PHYLUM: SARCODINA
(Some classify these organisms into three phyla: Rhizopoda, Anthinopoda, and Foraminifera).
KEY CHARACTERISTICS: Have no definite shape; use pseudopodia for feeding and movement.
EXAMPLE: *Entamoeba histolytica* (causes amebic dysentery).

PHYLUM: ZOOFLAGELLATA
(Some call this phylum Zoomastigophora).
KEY CHARACTERISTICS: Most are unicellular; use flagella for movement.
EXAMPLES: *Trypanosoma, Trychonympha, Giardia*.

Classification of Organisms

PHYLUM: CILIOPHORA (CILIATES)
KEY CHARACTERISTICS: Most are unicellular; use cilia for movement; some reproduce sexually by conjugation; some reproduce asexually by binary fission.
EXAMPLES: *Paramecium, Vorticella, Didinium.*

PHYLUM: SPOROZOA
(Some classify these organisms into the phylum Apicomplexa).
KEY CHARACTERISTICS: Sessile; most are parasites, some species live inside other species in symbiotic relationships, individuals often change hosts throughout life cycle; reproduce in sexual and asexual stages.
EXAMPLES: *Plasmodium* (causes malaria), *Pneumocystis carinii* (causes AIDS-related pneumonia).

Category: Algae
KEY CHARACTERISTICS: Photosynthetic autotrophs; some are unicellular, many are multicellular; plantlike organisms, but all lack the distinct organs of true plants.

PHYLUM: CHRYSOPHYTA (DIATOMS)
(Some classify these organisms into the phylum Baccillariophyta).
KEY CHARACTERISTICS: Unicellular; cell walls made of glassy silicon with intricate patterns; contain yellow and brown photosynthetic pigments; motile; live in saltwater environments.
EXAMPLES: *Thallasiosina, Botrydium.*

PHYLUM: DINOFLAGELLATA (DINOFLAGELLATES)
KEY CHARACTERISTICS: Unicellular; cellulose plates provide unique shape; move using two flagella positioned at right angles to each other; most live in salt water; some species are bioluminescent.
EXAMPLES: *Gonyaulax* (causes "red tide"), *Noctilucans scintillans.*

PHYLUM: EUGLENOPHYTA (EUGLENOIDS)
KEY CHARACTERISTICS: Unicellular; contain a flexible protein covering; two flagella used for movement; reproduce by binary fission; most live in fresh water.
EXAMPLE: *Euglena.*

PHYLUM: CHLOROPHYTA (GREEN ALGAE)
KEY CHARACTERISTICS: Some are unicellular but most are multicellular; cell walls made of cellulose similar to plants; sessile; live in ponds, moist soils, and shallow ocean water.
EXAMPLES: *Volvox, Chlamydomonas, Ulva.*

PHYLUM: RHODOPHYTA (RED ALGAE)
KEY CHARACTERISTICS: Multicellular; contain special pigments that trap sunlight for photosynthesis in deep water; sessile; live in saltwater environments.
EXAMPLES: *Porphyra, Polysiphonia.*

PHYLUM: PHAEOPHYTA (BROWN ALGAE)
KEY CHARACTERISTICS: Large, multicellular; contain a brown photosynthetic pigment; reproduce by alternation of generations; sessile; most live in salt water.
EXAMPLES: *Fucus* (kelp), *Sargassum, Laminaria.*

Category: Molds
KEY CHARACTERISTICS: Unlike fungi, cell walls do not contain chitin; heterotrophs, usually decomposers; most use ameboid movement.

PHYLUM: MYXOMYCOTA (PLASMODIAL SLIME MOLDS)
KEY CHARACTERISTICS: Unicellular; multinucleated; under harsh conditions, form a spore-producing structure called a fruiting body.
EXAMPLE: *Physarum.*

PHYLUM: ACRASIOMYCOTA (CELLULAR SLIME MOLDS)
KEY CHARACTERISTICS: Unicellular; life cycle alternates between a spore-producing fruiting body form and a feeding form; live in fresh water, damp soil, or on decaying plant matter.

PHYLUM: OOMYCOTA (WATER MOLDS)
KEY CHARACTERISTICS: Unicellular; some species are parasitic and attack injured tissues; most live in fresh water.
EXAMPLE: *Phytophthora infestans* (causes potato blight).

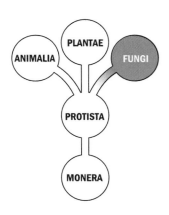

Kingdom: Fungi

KEY CHARACTERISTICS: Eukaryotes; mostly multicellular and multi-nucleated; cell walls contain chitin; body composed of hyphae; sessile; heterotrophic; reproduce sexually or asexually.

DIVISION: ZYGOMYCOTA (COMMON MOLDS)
KEY CHARACTERISTICS: Hyphae lack septa; decomposers of plant and animal matter; usually reproduce asexually by spore production, under harsher conditions most can reproduce sexually by producing zygospores; live in terrestrial environments.
EXAMPLES: *Rhizopus* (causes black bread mold), *Pilobolus.*

DIVISION: ASCOMYCOTA (SAC FUNGI)
KEY CHARACTERISTICS: Largest group of fungi; most are multicellular, yeast species are unicellular; species can be parasitic or free-living; reproduce sexually by forming ascospores in saclike ascus; reproduce asexually by forming spores at the ends of hyphae; yeasts reproduce asexually by budding.
EXAMPLES: Truffles, morels, yeasts.

DIVISION: BASIDIOMYCOTA (CLUB FUNGI)
KEY CHARACTERISTICS: Multicellular; incomplete septa in the hyphae; reproduce sexually by basidiospores formed in the basidium.
EXAMPLES: Bracket fungi, puff balls, rusts, smuts.

DIVISION: DEUTEROMYCOTA (IMPERFECT FUNGI)
KEY CHARACTERISTICS: Diverse group; only reproduce asexually by producing spores in specialized hyphae.
EXAMPLES: *Penicillium,* athlete's foot fungus, ringworm.

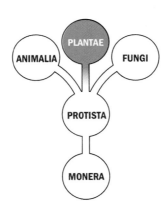

Kingdom: Plantae

KEY CHARACTERISTICS: Eukaryotes; multicellular; photosynthetic autotrophs with chlorophyll *a*, chlorophyll *b*, and other pigments contained in chloroplasts; sessile; cell walls contain cellulose; tissues organized into distinct organs; reproduce asexually by vegetative propagation, or sexually by alternation of generations; most species live in terrestrial environments.

DIVISION: BRYOPHYTA (MOSSES)
KEY CHARACTERISTICS: Nonvascular; reproduce by haploid spores; haploid gametophyte is dominant stage of life cycle; most live in damp terrestrial environments.
EXAMPLE: *Sphagnum* (peat moss).

DIVISION: HEPATOPHYTA (LIVERWORTS)
KEY CHARACTERISTICS: Nonvascular; reproduce by haploid spores; reproduce asexually by fragmentation and by gemmae; haploid gametophyte is dominant stage of life cycle; most live in damp terrestrial environments.

DIVISION: ANTHOCEROPHYTA (HORNWORTS)
KEY CHARACTERISTICS: Nonvascular; reproduce by haploid spores; haploid gametophyte is dominant stage of life cycle; sporophytes perform photosynthesis.

DIVISION: PSILOPHYTA
KEY CHARACTERISTICS: Vascular; branched stems; no true roots or leaves; reproduce by haploid spores; haploid gametophyte is dominant stage of life cycle; live in tropical environments.
EXAMPLE: *Psilotum nudum* (whisk fern).

DIVISION: LYCOPHYTA
KEY CHARACTERISTICS: Vascular; roots and leaves surround a single central taproot; diploid sporophyte is dominant stage of life cycle; reproduce by haploid and diploid spores; live in shady, damp terrestrial environments.
EXAMPLE: *Lycopodium* (club moss).

DIVISION: SPHENOPHYTA (HORSETAILS)

KEY CHARACTERISTICS: Vascular; thick, hollow stem and scaly leaves; reproduce by haploid spores; sporophyte is dominant stage of life cycle.
EXAMPLE: *Equisetum.*

DIVISION: PTEROPHYTA (FERNS)

KEY CHARACTERISTICS: Highly developed vascular system; true roots, leaves, and stems; reproduce by spores; sporophyte is dominant stage of life cycle; most common seedless plant; live in tropical rain forests and moist woodlands.
EXAMPLES: *Polypodium, Azolla, Osmunda.*

Category: Seed Plants

KEY CHARACTERISTICS: Vascular plants; reproduce by seeds; water is not needed for fertilization; diploid sporophyte is dominant stage of life cycle.

Class: Monocotyledones (Monocots)

KEY CHARACTERISTICS: Seeds with one cotyledon; floral parts occur in multiples of three; leaves have parallel veins; most have fibrous roots.
EXAMPLES: Grasses, palm trees, corn, rice, wheat.

Class: Dicotyledones (Dicots)

KEY CHARACTERISTICS: Seeds with two cotyledons; floral parts occur in multiples of four or five; leaves have branching netlike veins; most have a taproot.
EXAMPLES: Fruit trees, roses, tulips, dandelions.

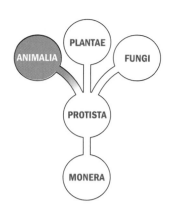

Kingdom: Animalia

KEY CHARACTERISTICS: Eukaryotes; cells lack cell walls; multicellular; most have radial or bilateral symmetry; heterotrophic; most are motile; most reproduce sexually with sperm and eggs; some reproduce asexually by budding or fragmentation.

PHYLUM: PORIFERA (SPONGES)

KEY CHARACTERISTICS: Internal skeleton made of spicules and spongin; two layers of porous tissue with no organ structure; filter-feeders; reproduce sexually or asexually; most live in saltwater environments.

PHYLUM: CNIDARIANS

KEY CHARACTERISTICS: Body consists of two tissue layers with a jellylike material in between; most have radial symmetry; two body forms, a sessile polyp and a free-floating medusa; tentacles with stinging cnidocytes; some species are colonial; most live in saltwater environments.
EXAMPLES: Jellyfish, coral, hydra.

PHYLUM: PLATYHELMINTHES (FLATWORMS)

KEY CHARACTERISTICS: Flat-bodied; acoelomates; digestive tract with one opening; bilateral symmetry; cephalization; parasitic and free-living forms.
EXAMPLES: Planarians, flukes, tapeworms.

PHYLUM: NEMATODA (ROUNDWORMS)

KEY CHARACTERISTICS: Long, slender bodies; pseudocoelomates; unsegmented; digestive tract with two openings; bilateral symmetry; cephalization; common in soil; many species are parasites.
EXAMPLES: *Trichinella spiralis, Ascaris,* pinworms, hookworms, vinegar worms.

PHYLUM: MOLLUSCA (MOLLUSKS)

KEY CHARACTERISTICS: Soft-bodied coelomates; some have shells; all have mantle, visceral mass, and muscular foot; most have open circulatory system; live in salt water, fresh water, or terrestrial environments.
EXAMPLES: Chitons, clams, snails, *Architeuthis* (giant squid), octopuses.

PHYLUM: ANNELIDA (SEGMENTED WORMS)

KEY CHARACTERISTICS: Segmented bodies; coelomates; most species have setae; closed circulatory system; well-developed nervous system.
EXAMPLES: Polychaetes, earthworms, leeches, sand worms.

PHYLUM: ARTHROPODA (ARTHROPODS)

KEY CHARACTERISTICS: Jointed legs or appendages; bilateral symmetry; exoskeleton contains chitin; open circulatory system; ventral nervous system.

EXAMPLES: Insects, spiders, lobsters, crabs.

PHYLUM: ECHINODERMATA (ECHINODERMS)

KEY CHARACTERISTICS: Deuterostomes; water vascular system used for movement, circulation, respiration, and excretion; spiny skin; radial symmetry in adult; bilateral symmetry in larva; live in saltwater environments.

EXAMPLE: Sea stars, brittle stars, sea urchins, sea cucumbers.

PHYLUM: CHORDATA (CHORDATES)

KEY CHARACTERISTICS: Notochord; gill slits; hollow, dorsal nerve tube; post-anal tail; nerve tube and notochord usually replaced by a vertebral column in adults.

Subphylum: Urochordata (Tunicates)

KEY CHARACTERISTICS: Soft, saclike body; no internal skeleton; sessile adult; motile larva; filter-feeders; live in saltwater environments.

EXAMPLES: Sea squirts, salps.

Subphylum: Cephalochordata (Lancelets)

KEY CHARACTERISTICS: No internal skeleton; transparent; thin, fish-like body; segmented; live in saltwater environments.

EXAMPLE: Amphioxus.

Subphylum: Vertebrata (Vertebrates)

KEY CHARACTERISTICS: Notochord develops into a spinal column enclosing dorsal nerve tube; internal skeleton usually made of bone; high degree of cephalization.

Class: Agnatha (Jawless Fishes)

KEY CHARACTERISTICS: Eel-like with smooth body; no scales; no jaws; round, sucking mouth; skeleton made of cartilage; two-chambered heart.

EXAMPLES: Hagfishes, lampreys.

Class: Chondrichthyes (Cartilaginous Fishes)

KEY CHARACTERISTICS: Skeleton made of cartilage; flexible jaw; rigid paired fins; body covered with scales; internal fertilization; two-chambered heart; most live in saltwater environments.

EXAMPLES: Rays, sharks, skates.

Class: Osteichthyes (Bony Fishes)

KEY CHARACTERISTICS: Bony skeleton; flexible jaw; flexible paired fins; air-filled swim bladder; two-chambered heart; live in saltwater and freshwater environments.

EXAMPLES: Salmon, tuna, carp, guppies, trout, bass.

Class: Amphibia (Amphibians)

KEY CHARACTERISTICS: Moist skin; most have lungs and a three-chambered heart; many undergo metamorphosis; most species have aquatic larval and terrestrial adult forms; external fertilization; water needed to reproduce.

EXAMPLES: Frogs, salamanders, newts.

Class: Reptilia (Reptiles)

KEY CHARACTERISTICS: Dry skin; body covered with scales; breathe through lungs; most have four limbs (except for snakes); internal fertilization; amniotic eggs with leathery shells.

EXAMPLES: Alligators, snakes, turtles, lizards.

Class: Aves (Birds)

KEY CHARACTERISTICS: Body covered with feathers; wings; lungs with one-way air flow; four-chambered heart; internal fertilization; eggs covered with hard shell; most species adapted for flight.

EXAMPLES: Ducks, penguins, sparrows, chickens.

Class: Mammalia (Mammals)

KEY CHARACTERISTICS: Body usually covered with hair or fur; four-chambered heart; highly developed brain; internal fertilization; young nourished by milk from the mother; extended period of parental care in many species.

EXAMPLES: Kangaroos, whales, bats, humans.

ARCTIC OCEAN

Severnaya Zemlya
New Siberian Islands
80° N

Barents Sea
Novaya Zemlya
Kamchatka Peninsula
60° N

URAL MTS.
Yenisey
Ob'
SIBERIA
Sea of Okhotsk

Baltic Sea
Volga
Irtysh
Lake Baykal
Amur
Kuril Is.

Northern European Plain
Aral Sea
ASIA
Sea of Japan
Hokkaido

EUROPE
Mt. Elbrus 5642 m (18,510 ft)
Caucasus Mts.
TIEN SHAN
GOBI DESERT
Honshu
40° N

ALPS
Danube
Black Sea
Caspian Sea
HINDU KUSH
Huang
Shikoku
Kyushu

Balkan Peninsula
Asia Minor
Tigris
HIMALAYAS
Plateau of Tibet
East China Sea
PACIFIC OCEAN

Mediterranean Sea
Euphrates
Persian Gulf
Indus
Mt. Everest 8848 m (29,028 ft)
Chang
Taiwan

SAHARA
Nile
Red Sea
Thar Desert
Ganges
Hainan
20° N

Arabian Peninsula
Arabian Sea
Deccan Plateau
South China Sea
Philippine Islands
Micronesia

Lake Chad
Bay of Bengal

AFRICA
Ethiopian Highlands
Sri Lanka
Malay Peninsula
0°

Maldives

CONGO BASIN
Lake Victoria
Seychelles
Sumatra
Borneo
New Guinea

Congo
Kilimanjaro 5895 m (19,340 ft)
Celebes
Melanesia

Lake Tanganyika
Java
20° S

INDIAN OCEAN
Fiji

Lake Nyasa
Madagascar

Kalahari Desert
AUSTRALIA
GREAT VICTORIA DESERT
GREAT DIVIDING RANGE

Cape of Good Hope
Cape Agulhas
Darling
Murray
Mt. Kosciusko 2230 m (7,316 ft)
40°

Tasmania

0   1000   2000 mi
0   1000   2000 km
Robinson Projection
© GeoSystems Global Corp.

60° S

ANTARCTICA
Ross Sea
80° S

20° E 40° E 60° E 80° E 100° E 120° E 140° E 160° E

POPULATIONS OF MAJOR CITIES

Antigua & Barbuda
St. Johns 27,000

Bahamas
Nassau 172,000

Barbados
Bridgetown 6,000

Belize
Belize City 45,000
Belmopan 4,000

Canada (metro)
Toronto 3,893,000
Montréal 3,127,000
Vancouver 1,603,000
Ottawa 921,000

Costa Rica (metro)
San José 1,000,000

Cuba
Havana 2,119,000

Dominica
Roseau 16,000

Dominican Republic
Santo Domingo 2,400,000

El Salvador
San Salvador 423,000

Grenada
St. George's 30,000

Guatemala
Guatemala 1,676,000

Haiti
Port-au-Prince 690,000

Honduras
Tegucigalpa 608,000

Jamaica (metro)
Kingston 587,000

Mexico (metro)
Mexico City 20,000,000
Guadalajara 3,000,000
Monterrey 2,700,000

Nicaragua
Managua 1,000,000

Panama
Panamá 447,000

St. Kitts & Nevis
Basseterre 15,000

St. Lucia
Castries 45,000

St. Vincent & Grenadines
Kingstown 15,000

Trinidad & Tobago
Port of Spain 51,000

United States
New York 7,323,000
Los Angeles 3,485,000
Chicago 2,784,000
Houston 1,631,000
Philadelphia 1,586,000
San Diego 1,111,000
Detroit 1,028,000
Washington, D.C. 607,000

International comparability of city population
data is limited by various data inconsistencies.

NATURAL VEGETATION

Ice Cap
Tundra
Coniferous Forest
Deciduous Forest
Broadleaf Evergreen Forest
Mixed Forest
Midlatitude Scrubland
Midlatitude Grassland
Desert
Tropical Seasonal and Scrub
Tropical Rain Forest

POPULATION

Persons per sq mi	Persons per sq km
Over 520	Over 200
260–519	100–199
130–259	50–99
25–129	10–49
1–24	1–9
0	0

WORLD POPULATION

Asia 61.0%
Europe 12.5%
Africa 12.4%
North America 8.0%
South America 5.6%
Oceania 0.5%

© GeoSystems Global Corp.

964

CITIES
- ⊛ National Capital
- ★ Territorial Capital
- ● Other City

ELEVATIONS

Feet		Meters
13,120		4000
6560		2000
1640		500
656		200
0		0
Below sea level		Below sea level

CLIMATE GRAPHS

Average daily temperature °F range

Average monthly precipitation Inches

100 High
65 Low
32
0

ATLANTA, USA

MEXICO CITY, Mexico

NUUK, Greenland

PHOENIX, USA

SAN FRANCISCO, USA

SAN JUAN, Puerto Rico

FAIRBANKS, USA

MINNEAPOLIS, USA

NEW YORK, USA

ST. JOHN'S, Canada

SAN JOSÉ, Costa Rica

VANCOUVER, Canada

© GeoSystems Global Corp.

POPULATIONS OF MAJOR CITIES

Argentina
Buenos Aires	2,961,000
Córdoba	1,148,000
Rosario	895,000

Bolivia
La Paz	711,000
Santa Cruz	695,000
Sucre	131,000

Brazil
São Paulo	9,480,000
Rio de Janeiro	5,336,000
Salvador	2,056,000
Belo Horizonte	2,049,000
Fortaleza	1,758,000
Brasília	1,596,000
Recife	1,290,000
Curitiba	1,290,000
Pôrto Alegre	1,263,000
Belém	1,246,000
Manaus	1,011,000

Chile
Santiago	4,385,000
Concepción	306,000

Colombia (metro)
Bogotá	3,975,000
Medellín	1,452,000
Cali	1,369,000
Barranquilla	917,000

Ecuador
Guayaquil	1,508,000
Quito	1,101,000

Falkland Islands
Stanley	1,200

French Guiana
Cayenne	41,000

Guyana
Georgetown	195,000

Paraguay
Asunción	502,000

Peru (metro)
Lima	6,415,000
Arequipa	635,000
Trujillo	532,000

Suriname
Paramaribo	192,000

Uruguay
Montevideo	1,360,000

Venezuela
Caracas	1,825,000
Maracaibo	1,208,000
Valencia	903,000
Barquisimeto	603,000

International comparability of city population
data is limited by various data inconsistencies.

NATURAL VEGETATION

- Unclassified Highlands
- Deciduous Forest
- Mixed Forest
- Midlatitude Scrubland
- Midlatitude Grassland
- Desert
- Tropical Seasonal and Scrub
- Tropical Rain Forest
- Tropical Savanna

POPULATION

Persons per sq mi	Persons per sq km
Over 520	Over 200
260–519	100–199
130–259	50–99
25–129	10–49
1–24	1–9
0	0

WORLD POPULATION

- Asia 61.0%
- Europe 12.5%
- Africa 12.4%
- North America 8.0%
- Oceania 0.5%
- **South America 5.6%**

© GeoSystems Global Corp.

CARIBBEAN SEA

Barranquilla
Cartagena
Maracaibo
Barquisimeto
Valencia
Maracay
Caracas
Cumaná
Maturín
Ciudad
Bolívar
Ciudad Guayana
Georgetown
Paramaribo
Cayenne
Bucaramanga
Cúcuta
San Cristóbal
L. Maracaibo
VENEZUELA
GUYANA
SURINAME
FRENCH
GUIANA
(FR.)
ATLANTIC
OCEAN
Medellín
Manizales
Pereira
Ibagué
Bogotá
Cali
COLOMBIA
LLANOS
GUIANA
HIGHLANDS
Pasto
Negro
Ilha
Marajó
Belém
Quito
ECUADOR
Chimborazo
6267 m
(20,561 ft)
Guayaquil
Cuenca
Iquitos
AMAZON
Manaus
Fortaleza
Teresina
Natal
Piura
PERU
SELVAS
BASIN
Juruá
Purús
Amazon
Tapajós
Chiclayo
Trujillo
Chimbote
Huascarán
6768 m
(22,205 ft)
Pucallpa
Pôrto Velho
Madeira
BRAZIL
Recife
Maceió
Callao
Lima
Huancayo
Cuzco
Ica
Titicaca
Beni
Guaporé
Mamoré
Xingu
Tocantins
Araguaia
São Francisco
Salvador
Arequipa
La Paz
Cochabamba
Santa Cruz
BOLIVIA
MATO GROSSO
PLATEAU
Cuiabá
Goiânia
Brasília
BRAZILIAN
HIGHLANDS
Uberlândia
Arica
Oruro
Sucre
Potosí
ALTIPLANO
L. Poopó
Pilcomayo
Campo
Grande
Belo Horizonte
Vitória
Iquique
ATACAMA DESERT
GRAN CHACO
Paraguay
Campinas
São Paulo
Santos
Rio de Janeiro
Antofagasta
Salta
PARAGUAY
Asunción
Ciudad
del Este
Curitiba
Isla San Ambrosio
(CHILE)
Isla San Félix
(CHILE)
Ojos del Salado
6880 m
(22,572 ft)
San Miguel
de Tucumán
Santiago
del Estero
Resistencia
Encarnación
Paraná
Salto
Pôrto Alegre
Aconcagua
6960 m
(22,834 ft)
Córdoba
San Juan
Rosario
Santa
Fe
Salto
Paysandú
CHILE
Islas Juan Fernández
(CHILE)
Valparaíso
Santiago
Mendoza
URUGUAY
ATLANTIC
OCEAN
Rancagua
Buenos
Aires
Montevideo
Talca
Río de la Plata
PACIFIC
OCEAN
Concepción
Temuco
Neuquén
Bahía Blanca
Mar del Plata
ARGENTINA
ANDES
PAMPAS
Puerto Montt
Chiloé
Península
Valdés
N
Archipiélago
de los Chonos
Península
Taitao
Comodoro Rivadavia
PATAGONIA

CITIES

⊕ National Capital
★ Territorial Capital
● Other City

ELEVATIONS

Feet		Meters
13,120		4000
6560		2000
1640		500
656		200
0		0
Below sea level		Below sea level

Falkland Is.
(Islas Malvinas)
(U.K.)
Stanley

Strait of
Magellan

Punta Arenas
Tierra del Fuego
Ushuaia
Cape Horn

0   250   500   750   1000 mi
0   250   500   750   1000   1250   1500 km

© GeoSystems Global Corp.

CLIMATE GRAPHS

Average daily
temperature
°F range

Average monthly
precipitation
Inches

100
65
32
0

High
Low

20
10
0

ASUNCIÓN, Paraguay

BUENOS AIRES, Argentina

CAYENNE, French Guiana

LIMA, Peru

PUNTA ARENAS, Chile

RIO DE JANEIRO, Brazil

BOGOTÁ, Colombia

CARACAS, Venezuela

LA PAZ, Bolivia

MANAUS, Brazil

RECIFE, Brazil

SANTIAGO, Chile

POPULATIONS OF MAJOR CITIES

Albania
Tiranë — 244,000

Andorra
Andorra la Vella — 16,000

Armenia
Yerevan — 1,254,000

Austria
Vienna — 1,539,000

Azerbaijan
Baku — 1,149,000

Belarus
Minsk — 1,613,000

Belgium — (metro)
Brussels — 951,000
Antwerp — 465,000

Bosnia and Herzegovina
Sarajevo — 416,000

Bulgaria
Sofia — 1,141,000

Croatia
Zagreb — 704,000

Czech Republic
Prague — 1,212,000

Denmark
Copenhagen — 617,000

Estonia
Tallinn — 478,000

Finland
Helsinki — 495,000

France
Paris — 2,152,000
Marseille — 800,000
Lyon — 416,000

Georgia
Tbilisi — 1,268,000

Germany
Berlin — 3,438,000
Hamburg — 1,661,000
Munich — 1,237,000
Cologne — 956,000
Frankfurt — 647,000
Essen — 626,000
Dortmund — 600,000
Stuttgart — 584,000
Düsseldorf — 577,000
Leipzig — 508,000

Greece
Athens — 748,000

Hungary
Budapest — 2,017,000

Iceland
Reykjavík — 97,000

Ireland
Dublin — 478,000

Italy
Rome — 2,829,000
Milan — 1,549,000
Naples — 1,208,000
Turin — 1,060,000
Genoa — 742,000
Palermo — 714,000

Latvia
Riga — 909,000

Liechtenstein
Vaduz — 5,000

Lithuania
Vilnius — 591,000

Luxembourg
Luxembourg — 75,000

F.Y.R. Macedonia
Skopje — 393,000

Malta
Valletta — 9,000

Moldova
Chişinău — 667,000

Monaco
Monaco — 27,000

Netherlands
Amsterdam — 713,000
Rotterdam — 590,000

Norway
Oslo — 465,000

Poland
Warsaw — 1,654,000
Łódź — 847,000
Kraków — 751,000
Wrocław — 643,000

Portugal
Lisbon — 678,000

Romania
Bucharest — 2,064,000

Russia (European)
Moscow — 8,747,000
St. Petersburg — 4,437,000
Nizh. Novgorod — 1,441,000
Samara — 1,239,000
Kazan — 1,104,000
Perm' — 1,099,000
Ufa — 1,097,000
Rostov-na-Donu — 1,027,000
Volgograd — 1,006,000

San Marino
San Marino — 3,000

Slovakia
Bratislava — 441,000

Slovenia
Ljubljana — 277,000

Spain
Madrid — 2,991,000
Barcelona — 1,668,000
Valencia — 719,000
Seville — 654,000

Sweden
Stockholm — 679,000

Switzerland
Zürich — 342,000
Bern — 135,000

Turkey (European)
İstanbul — 6,620,000

Ukraine
Kiev — 2,643,000
Kharkiv — 1,622,000
Dnipropetrov'sk — 1,190,000
Donets'k — 1,121,000
Odesa — 1,096,000

United Kingdom
London — 6,803,000
Birmingham — 995,000
Leeds — 706,000
Glasgow — 688,000
Sheffield — 520,000
Liverpool — 475,000
Edinburgh — 439,000
Manchester — 433,000

Yugoslavia
Belgrade — 1,137,000

International comparability of city population data is limited by various data inconsistencies.

© GeoSystems Global Corp.

NATURAL VEGETATION

- Tundra
- Coniferous Forest
- Deciduous Forest
- Mixed Forest
- Midlatitude Scrubland
- Midlatitude Grassland
- Unclassified Highlands or Ice Cap

WORLD POPULATION

- Asia 61.0%
- Oceania 0.5%
- South America 5.6%
- North America 8.0%
- Africa 12.4%
- Europe 12.5%

POPULATION

Persons per sq mi	Persons per sq km
Over 520	Over 200
260–519	100–199
130–259	50–99
25–129	10–49
1–24	1–9
0	0

0   250   500   750 mi

0   250   500   750   1000 km

© GeoSystems Global Corp.

Barents Sea

North Cape

Hammerfest

Tromsø · Murmansk

LAPLAND

White Sea · Arkhangel'sk

URAL MTS.

Perm'

Oulu

Norwegian Sea

Umeå

FINLAND

RUSSIA

Kirov

Ufa

Trondheim

Sundsvall

L. Onega

Rybinsk Reservoir

Kazan

Nizhny Novgorod

Samara

Faeroe Is. (DEN.)

NORWAY

Bergen

SWEDEN

Tampere · Lahti

Turku · Helsinki

L. Ladoga

St. Petersburg

Yaroslavl'

Shetland Is. (U.K.)

Oslo ⊛

Stockholm ⊛

Uppsala

Tallinn ⊛

ESTONIA

⊛ Moscow

Saratov

Aberdeen

Orkney Is.

Stavanger

North Sea

Göteborg

Gotland (SWE.)

Öland

Linköping

Riga ⊛

LATVIA

Daugavpils

Vitsyebsk

Smolensk

Voronezh

Volgograd

Astrakhan'

ATLANTIC OCEAN

Glasgow

Edinburgh

Belfast

UNITED KINGDOM

Newcastle upon Tyne

Jutland

Skagerrak

Copenhagen ⊛

DENMARK

Malmö

Odense

Helsingborg

Baltic Sea

Kaliningrad

Gdańsk

LITHUANIA

Kaunas · Vilnius

RUSSIA

Hrodna

BELARUS ⊛ Minsk

Mahilyow

Homyel'

Kharkiv

Luhans'k

Caspian Sea

Dublin ⊛

IRELAND

Liverpool

Leeds

Manchester

Sheffield

Hamburg

Szczecin

Bremen

Elbe

Poznań

Łódź

Warsaw ⊛

Brest

Kiev ⊛

UKRAINE

Dnipropetrov'sk

Donets'k

Rostov-na-Donu

Krasnodar

Cork

Birmingham

Cardiff

Bristol

NETHERLANDS

Amsterdam

Hannover

Berlin ⊛

NORTHERN EUROPEAN

Leipzig

POLAND

Wrocław

Katowice

Kraków

L'viv

Kryvyy Rih

Zaporizhzhya

Mykolayiv

Mariupol'

Mt. Elbrus 5642 m (18,510 ft)

CAUCASUS

Baku

Portsmouth

English Channel

London ⊛

Rotterdam

Essen

Cologne

GERMANY

Dresden

PLAIN

Ostrava

CZECH REP.

Prague ⊛

Brno

Odesa

Dnieper

Simferopol'

Tbilisi ⊛

GEORGIA

AZERBAIJAN

Channel Is. (U.K.)

Le Havre

Brussels ⊛

BELGIUM

Antwerp

Liège

Bonn

Frankfurt

LUXEMBOURG

CARPATHIAN

SLOVAKIA

Košice

MOLDOVA ⊛

Chisinău

Dniester

Iaşi

ARMENIA

Yerevan ⊛

AZER.

Brest

Rouen

Paris ⊛

Luxembourg ⊛

Mannheim

Stuttgart

Frankfurt

LIECHTENSTEIN

Bratislava ⊛

Brno

MTS.

Debrecen

ROMANIA

Black Sea

Sevastopol'

Nantes

Loire

Strasbourg

Munich

Linz

Vienna ⊛

AUSTRIA

Budapest ⊛

Timişoara

Ploieşti

Constanţa

FRANCE

Bern ⊛

SWITZERLAND

Zürich

Graz

HUNGARY

SLOVENIA

Zagreb ⊛

Novi Sad

Belgrade ⊛

Bucharest ⊛

Varna

Bay of Biscay

Bordeaux

Lyon

Geneva

ALPS

Mont Blanc 4802 m (15,771 ft)

Milan

Verona

Venice

CROATIA

BOSNIA AND HERZEGOVINA

Sarajevo ⊛

YUGOSLAVIA

BULGARIA

Sofia ⊛

Plovdiv

Burgas

Bilbao

Toulouse

Marseille

Nice

MONACO

Turin

Genoa

Bologna

Florence

SAN MARINO

Split

Dubrovnik

Podgorica

Skopje ⊛

F.Y.R. MACEDONIA

Thessaloníki

İstanbul

Vigo

PYRENEES

Ebro

Pico de Aneto (11,169 ft)

ANDORRA

APENNINES

Adriatic Sea

ALBANIA

Tiranë ⊛

Lárisa

TURKEY

Porto

Valladolid

IBERIAN

Zaragoza

Barcelona

CORSICA (FR.)

Elba

VATICAN CITY

Rome ⊛

ITALY

Bari

Kérkira

GREECE

PORTUGAL

Lisbon ⊛

PENINSULA

Madrid ⊛

Valencia

Tagus

SPAIN

Majorca

Minorca

Palma

BALEARIC IS. (SP.)

SARDINIA (IT.)

Cagliari

Naples

Salerno

Tyrrhenian Sea

Ionian Sea

Pátrai

PELOPONNESUS

Athens ⊛

Cyclades

Córdoba

Seville

Granada

Alicante

Cabo São Vicente

Cádiz

Málaga

Strait of Gibraltar

GIBRALTAR (U.K.)

MEDITERRANEAN SEA

SICILY (IT.)

Palermo

Mt. Etna 3369 m (11,053 ft)

Catania

MALTA · Valletta

Sea of Crete

Iráklion

CRETE (GR.)

Rhodes

Aegean Sea

N

Reykjavík

Akureyri

ICELAND

CITIES

⊛ National Capital

★ Territorial Capital

• Other City

ELEVATIONS

Feet		Meters
13,120		4000
6560		2000
1640		500
656		200
0		0
Below sea level		Below sea level

CLIMATE GRAPHS

Average daily temperature °F range

Average monthly precipitation Inches

100 — High

65

32 — Low

0

20

10

0

ARKHANGEL'SK, Russia

COPENHAGEN, Denmark

LISBON, Portugal

NAPLES, Italy

PARIS, France

TROMSØ, Norway

ATHENS, Greece

DUBLIN, Ireland

MOSCOW, Russia

ODESA, Ukraine

REYKJAVÍK, Iceland

VIENNA, Austria

POPULATIONS OF MAJOR CITIES

Afghanistan		Kyrgyzstan	
Kabul	1,424,000	Bishkek	628,000
Bahrain		**Laos**	
Manama	151,000	Vientiane	377,000
Bangladesh	(metro)	**Lebanon**	
Dhaka	3,459,000	Beirut	475,000
Bhutan		**Malaysia**	
Thimphu	8,900	Kuala Lumpur	920,000
Brunei		**Maldives**	
Band. Seri Begawan	51,000	Male	55,000
Burma (Myanmar)		**Mongolia**	
Rangoon	2,513,000	Ulaanbaatar	536,000
Cambodia		**Nepal**	
Phnom Penh	800,000	Kathmandu	419,000
China		**Oman**	
Shanghai	7,500,000	Muscat	85,000
Beijing	5,700,000		
Tianjin	4,500,000	**Pakistan**	(metro)
Shenyang	3,600,000	Karachi	5,181,000
Wuhan	3,200,000	Lahore	2,953,000
Guangzhou	2,900,000	Faisalabad	1,104,000
Chongqing	2,700,000	Islamabad	204,000
Harbin	2,500,000		
Chengdu	2,500,000	**Philippines**	(metro)
Zibo	2,200,000	Manila	1,895,000
Xi'an	2,200,000		
Nanjing	2,091,000	**Qatar**	
		Doha	236,000
Cyprus	(metro)		
Nicosia	167,000	**Russia (Asian)**	
		Novosibirsk	1,442,000
India	(metro)	Yekaterinburg	1,371,000
Mumbai	12,572,000	Omsk	1,169,000
(Bombay)		Chelyabinsk	1,143,000
Calcutta	10,916,000	Krasnoyarsk	925,000
Delhi	8,375,000		
Chennai (Madras)	5,361,000	**Saudi Arabia**	
Hyderabad	4,280,000	Riyadh	1,300,000
Bangalore	4,087,000	Jiddah	1,200,000
Indonesia		**Singapore**	
Jakarta	8,200,000	Singapore	2,818,000
Surabaya	2,400,000		
Bandung	2,000,000	**Sri Lanka**	
Medan	1,700,000	Colombo	615,000
Iran		**Syria**	
Tehran	6,043,000	Damascus	1,451,000
Mashhad	1,464,000	Halab (Aleppo)	1,445,000
Iraq		**Taiwan**	
Baghdad	3,841,000	Taipei	1,770,000
Israel		**Tajikistan**	
Jerusalem	544,000	Dushanbe	602,000
Japan		**Thailand**	
Tokyo	8,164,000	Bangkok	5,876,000
Yokohama	3,220,000		
Osaka	2,624,000	**Turkey (Asian)**	
Nagoya	2,155,000	Ankara	2,559,000
Sapporo	1,672,000	İzmir	1,757,000
Kobe	1,477,000		
Kyoto	1,461,000	**Turkmenistan**	
Fukuoka	1,237,000	Ashgabat	407,000
Kawasaki	1,174,000		
Hiroshima	1,086,000	**United Arab Emirates**	
		Abu Dhabi	722,000
Jordan			
Amman	936,000	**Uzbekistan**	
		Tashkent	2,094,000
Kazakstan			
Almaty	1,147,000	**Vietnam**	
		Ho Chi Minh City	2,900,000
North Korea		Hanoi	1,090,000
P'yŏngyang	2,300,000		
		Yemen	(metro)
South Korea		Sana	427,000
Seoul	10,628,000		
Pusan	3,798,000		
Taegu	2,229,000		
Kuwait			
Kuwait	78,000		

International comparability of city population data is limited by various data inconsistencies.

NATURAL VEGETATION

- Unclassified Highlands and Ice Cap
- Tundra and Alpine Tundra
- Coniferous Forest
- Midlatitude Deciduous Forest
- Subtropical Broadleaf Evergreen Forest
- Mixed Forest
- Midlatitude Scrub
- Midlatitude Grassland
- Desert
- Tropical Seasonal and Scrub
- Tropical Rain Forest
- Tropical Savanna

POPULATION

Persons per sq mi	Persons per sq km
Over 520	Over 200
260–519	100–199
130–259	50–99
25–129	10–49
1–24	1–9
0	0

WORLD POPULATION

- Asia 61.0%
- Oceania 0.5%
- South America 5.6%
- North America 8.0%
- Africa 12.4%
- Europe 12.5%

© GeoSystems Global Corp.

CITIES
⊛ National Capital
★ Territorial Capital
● Other City

ELEVATIONS

Feet	Meters
13,120	4000
6560	2000
1640	500
656	200
0	0
Below sea level	Below sea level

CLIMATE GRAPHS

Average daily temperature °F range
Average monthly precipitation Inches

100
65
32
0
High
Low
20
10
0

ALMATY, Kazakstan

COLOMBO, Sri Lanka

HONG KONG, China

NEW DELHI, India

TEHRAN, Iran

TOKYO, Japan

BEIRUT, Lebanon

DHAKA, Bangladesh

JAKARTA, Indonesia

RIYADH, Saudi Arabia

TIANJIN, China

YAKUTSK, Russia

0   500   1000   1500 mi
0   500   1000   1500   2000 km

© GeoSystems Global Corp.

POPULATIONS OF MAJOR CITIES

Algeria
Algiers 1,483,000
Oran 590,000
Constantine 483,000

Angola
Luanda 1,100,000

Benin
Cotonou 402,000
Porto-Novo 144,000

Botswana
Gaborone 137,000

Burkina Faso
Ouagadougou 442,000

Burundi
Bujumbura 235,440

Cameroon
Douala 852,000
Yaoundé 700,000

Cape Verde
Praia 61,000

Central African Republic
Bangui 474,000

Chad
N'Djamena 687,000

Comoros (metro)
Moroni 30,000

Congo
Brazzaville 596,000

Côte d'Ivoire
Abidjan 2,700,000
Yamoussoukro 107,000

Djibouti (metro)
Djibouti 450,000

Egypt
Cairo 6,800,000
Alexandria 3,380,000
Port Said 460,000
Suez 388,000

Equatorial Guinea
Malabo 38,000

Eritrea
Asmara 358,000

Ethiopia
Addis Ababa 1,913,000

Gabon
Libreville 275,000

The Gambia
Banjul 40,000

Ghana
Accra 949,000

Guinea
Conakry 705,000

Guinea-Bissau
Bissau 138,000

Kenya
Nairobi 959,000
Mombasa 401,000

Lesotho
Maseru 109,000

Liberia
Monrovia 400,000

Libya
Tripoli 591,000

Madagascar
Antananarivo 802,000

Malawi
Blantyre 332,000
Lilongwe 234,000

Mali
Bamako 658,000

Mauritania
Nouakchott 550,000

Mauritius
Port Louis 142,000

Morocco
Casablanca 2,600,000
Fez 852,000
Rabat 556,000

Mozambique
Maputo 931,000

Namibia
Windhoek 114,000

Niger
Niamey 392,000

Nigeria
Lagos 1,300,000
Ibadan 1,300,000
Abuja 250,000

Rwanda
Kigali 237,000

São Tomé & Príncipe
São Tomé 43,000

Senegal
Dakar 1,700,000

Seychelles (metro)
Victoria 24,000

Sierra Leone
Freetown 470,000

Somalia
Mogadishu 700,000

South Africa (metro)
Johannesburg 1,900,000
Cape Town 1,900,000
Durban 1,100,000
Pretoria 1,000,000
Bloemfontein 270,000

Sudan
Khartoum 476,000

Swaziland
Mbabane 38,000

Tanzania
Dar es-Salaam 1,096,000

Togo
Lomé 600,000

Tunisia
Tunis 620,000

Uganda
Kampala 773,000

Western Sahara
Laayoune 90,000

Zaire
Kinshasa 3,800,000
Lubumbashi 739,000

Zambia
Lusaka 982,000

Zimbabwe (metro)
Harare 1,200,000

International comparability of city population data is limited by various data inconsistencies.

NATURAL VEGETATION

- Coniferous Forest
- Mixed Forest
- Midlatitude Scrubland
- Midlatitude Grassland
- Desert
- Tropical Seasonal and Scrub
- Tropical Rain Forest
- Tropical Savanna

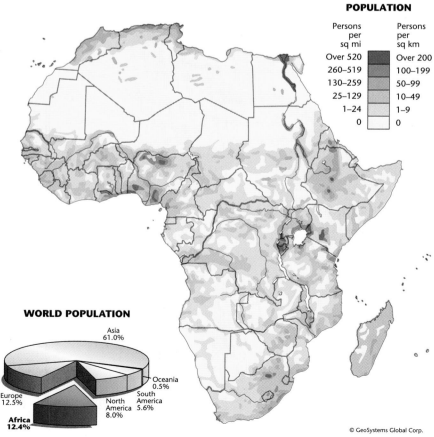

POPULATION

Persons per sq mi	Persons per sq km
Over 520	Over 200
260–519	100–199
130–259	50–99
25–129	10–49
1–24	1–9
0	0

WORLD POPULATION

Asia 61.0%
Europe 12.5%
Africa 12.4%
North America 8.0%
South America 5.6%
Oceania 0.5%

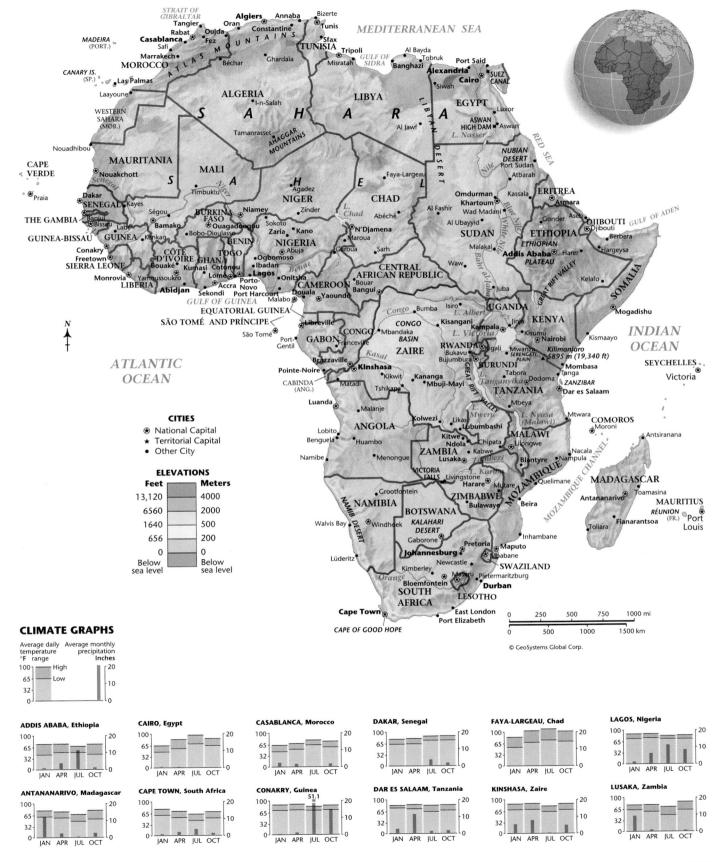

Africa

STRAIT OF GIBRALTAR

MEDITERRANEAN SEA

Tangier • Annaba • Bizerte
Algiers • Oran • Constantine ⊛ **Tunis**
MADEIRA (PORT.) Rabat • Oujda • Fez • Sfax
Casablanca • Safi **TUNISIA** • Tripoli
Marrakech • Béchar • Ghardaïa • Misratah • *GULF OF SIDRA* • Al Bayda • Tobruk • Port Said
CANARY IS. (SP.) • **MOROCCO** • Banghazi • **Alexandria** • **SUEZ CANAL**
Las Palmas • **Cairo** • Siwah
Laayoune **ALGERIA** • I-n-Salah • **LIBYA** • **EGYPT** • Luxor
WESTERN SAHARA (MOR.) • **S A H A R A** • Al Jawf • **ASWAN HIGH DAM** • Aswan
Nouadhibou • Tamanrasset • *L. Nasser*
CAPE VERDE • *AHAGGAR MOUNTAINS* • *NUBIAN DESERT* • *RED SEA*
Praia • **MAURITANIA** • **MALI** • Faya-Largeau • **CHAD** • Port Sudan • Atbarah
Nouakchott • *S* • *A* • *H* • *E* • *L* • Omdurman • Kassala • **ERITREA**
Dakar • Kayes • Agadez • Khartoum • **Asmara**
SENEGAL • Timbuktu • Zinder • *L. Chad* • Abéché • Al Fashir • Wad Madani • Gonder • Aseb • **DJIBOUTI** • *GULF OF ADEN*
THE GAMBIA • Ségou • Niamey • Al Ubayyid • **SUDAN** • **Djibouti** • Berbera
GUINEA-BISSAU • Bamako • **BURKINA FASO** • Sokoto • Kano • N'Djamena • Maroua • **ETHIOPIA** • Harer • Hargeysa
GUINEA • Kankan • **Ouagadougou** • Zaria • **NIGERIA** • Caroua • Sarh • Al Ubayyid • **Addis Ababa** • *ETHIOPIAN PLATEAU*
Conakry • Labé • Bobo-Dioulasso • Abuja • Waw • Juba • Kelafo
Freetown • **CÔTE D'IVOIRE** • **BENIN** • Ogbomoso • **CENTRAL AFRICAN REPUBLIC** • **SOMALIA**
SIERRA LEONE • **GHANA** • **TOGO** • Ibadan • **Lagos** • Onitsha • Bouar • *GREAT RIFT VALLEY*
Monrovia • Bouake • Kumasi • Cotonou • **CAMEROON** • Bangui
LIBERIA • Yamoussoukro • Lome • Porto-Novo • Douala • **Yaounde** • Bumba • Isiro • **UGANDA** • Mogadishu
Abidjan • Accra • Port Harcourt • Malabo • *Congo* • Kisangani • *L. Albert* • **KENYA**
Sekondi • **EQUATORIAL GUINEA** • **Libreville** • *CONGO BASIN* • Mbandaka • *L. Victoria* • **Kampala** • Jinja • Kisumu • **Nairobi**
GULF OF GUINEA • **SÃO TOMÉ AND PRÍNCIPE** • **GABON** • Franceville • **CONGO** • **ZAIRE** • **RWANDA** • Kigali • Mwanza • *Kilimanjaro 5895 m (19,340 ft)* • Kismaayo
São Tomé • Port-Gentil • **Brazzaville** • *Kasai* • Bukavu • *SERENGETI PLAIN* • **INDIAN OCEAN**
ATLANTIC OCEAN • **Kinshasa** • Kikwit • Kananga • **BURUNDI** • Bujumbura • Tabora • Mombasa • **SEYCHELLES**
Pointe-Noire • Matadi • Tshikapa • **Mbuji-Mayi** • *L. Tanganyika* • Dodoma • Tanga • Victoria
CABINDA (ANG.) • Luanda • Malanje • *L. Mweru* • **TANZANIA** • *ZANZIBAR* • **Dar es Salaam**
Kolwezi • Likasi • Mbeya • *L. Nyasa (Malawi)* • Mtwara • **COMOROS**
ANGOLA • Lobito • Kitwe • Lubumbashi • Chipata • Moroni • Antsiranana
Benguela • Huambo • Ndola • Lilongwe • **MALAWI** • Nampula
Namibe • Menongue • **ZAMBIA** • Kabwe • **Lusaka** • Blantyre • Nacala • **MADAGASCAR**
VICTORIA FALLS • *Zambezi* • *L. Kariba* • **MOZAMBIQUE** • Quelimane • **Antananarivo** • Toamasina
Grootfontein • Livingstone • **Harare** • Mutare • Beira • *MOZAMBIQUE CHANNEL* • **MAURITIUS** • *RÉUNION (FR.)* Port Louis
NAMIBIA • **ZIMBABWE** • Bulawayo • Inhambane • Fianarantsoa
Walvis Bay • *NAMIB DESERT* • **BOTSWANA** • *KALAHARI DESERT* • Toliara
Windhoek • Gaborone • **Pretoria** • Maputo • **SWAZILAND**
Lüderitz • **Johannesburg** • Mbabane
Kimberley • Newcastle • **LESOTHO**
Orange • **Bloemfontein** • Maseru • Pietermaritzburg
Cape Town • **SOUTH AFRICA** • East London • **Durban**
CAPE OF GOOD HOPE • Port Elizabeth

CITIES
⊛ National Capital
★ Territorial Capital
• Other City

ELEVATIONS
Feet		Meters
13,120		4000
6560		2000
1640		500
656		200
0		0
Below sea level		Below sea level

N ↑

Scale: 0 250 500 750 1000 mi
0 500 1000 1500 km

© GeoSystems Global Corp.

CLIMATE GRAPHS

Average daily temperature °F range
Average monthly precipitation Inches

°F	Inches
100 High	20
65 Low	10
32	0
0	

ADDIS ABABA, Ethiopia
JAN APR JUL OCT

CAIRO, Egypt
JAN APR JUL OCT

CASABLANCA, Morocco
JAN APR JUL OCT

DAKAR, Senegal
JAN APR JUL OCT

FAYA-LARGEAU, Chad
JAN APR JUL OCT

LAGOS, Nigeria
JAN APR JUL OCT

ANTANANARIVO, Madagascar
JAN APR JUL OCT

CAPE TOWN, South Africa
JAN APR JUL OCT

CONAKRY, Guinea 51.1
JAN APR JUL OCT

DAR ES SALAAM, Tanzania
JAN APR JUL OCT

KINSHASA, Zaire
JAN APR JUL OCT

LUSAKA, Zambia
JAN APR JUL OCT

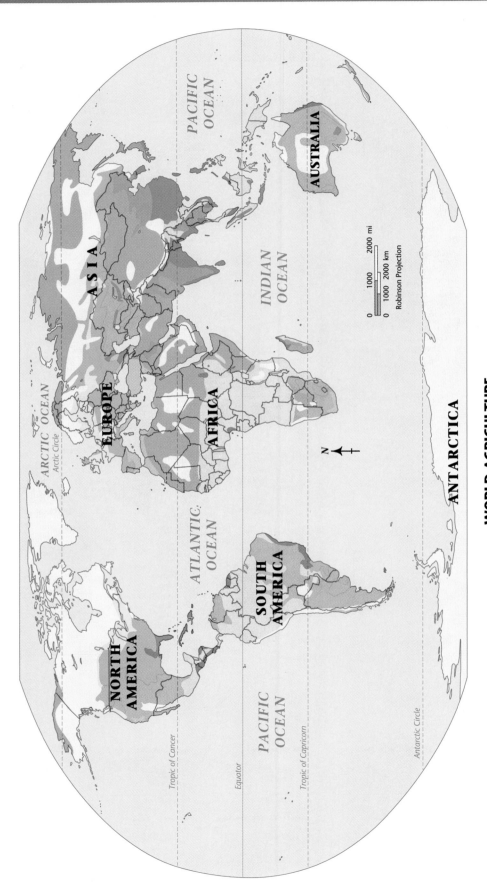

WORLD AGRICULTURE

Nomadic Herding
Primitive Cultivation and Gathering
Subsistence Rice Agriculture
Other Subsistence Agriculture
Mixed Crop/Livestock Farming
Livestock Raising

Grain Farming
Dairy Farming
Mediterranean Agriculture
Plantation Crops
Commercial Horticulture
Little or No Activity

© GeoSystems Global Corp.

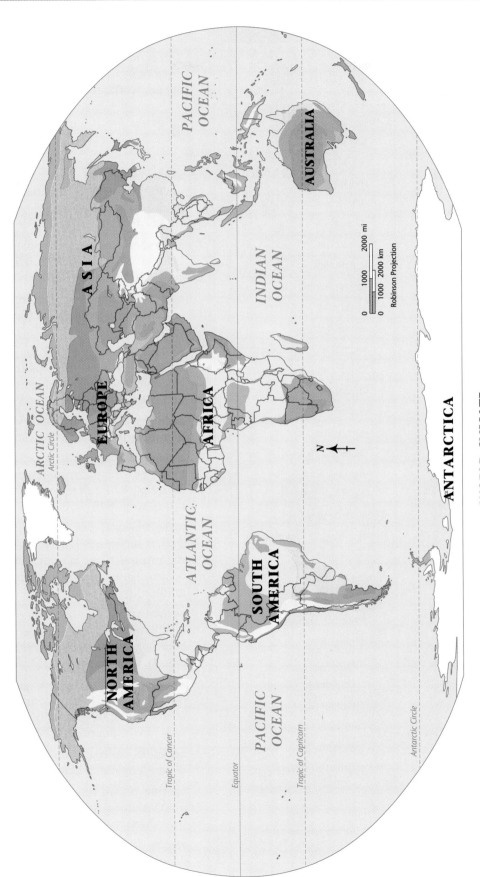

WORLD CLIMATE

Humid Tropical
Tropical Savanna
Desert
Steppe
Mediterranean
Humid Subtropical

Marine West Coast
Humid Continental
Subarctic
Tundra
Ice Cap
Highland

© GeoSystems Global Corp.

ASIA

EUROPE

AFRICA

AUSTRALIA

NORTH AMERICA

SOUTH AMERICA

ANTARCTICA

ARCTIC OCEAN
Arctic Circle

PACIFIC OCEAN

INDIAN OCEAN

ATLANTIC OCEAN

PACIFIC OCEAN

Tropic of Cancer

Equator

Tropic of Capricorn

Antarctic Circle

2000 mi
1000
0
1000 2000 km
0
Robinson Projection

N

Vocabulary Preview

Learning new words can be a challenging part of biology. If you know what the parts of the words mean, however, your job is a lot easier.

Word Part	Meaning	Example
anti-	against	antibody
archae-	ancient, original	archaeologist
auto-	self	autotroph
bi-, di-	two, double	bilateral, disaccharide
bio-	life	biology
cephalo-	head	cephalization
chloro-	green	chlorophyll
chromo-	colored	chromosome
-cyte, cyto-	cell	amebocyte, endocytosis
-derm, derma-	skin, covering	echinoderm
ecto-, exo-	outer, external	ectothermic, exoskeleton
endo-	inner, internal	endodermis, endothermic
epi-	above, top layer	epidermis
eu-	true, modern	eukaryote
gastro-	stomach	gastrointestinal
-gen, gen-	make, produce	genetics, antigen
hemo-	blood	hemoglobin
herb-	plant	herbivore
hetero-	mixed, different	heterotroph
homo-, homeo-	same	homologous, homeostasis
hypo-	under, less	hypotonic
hyper-	over, more	hypertension
iso-	equivalent	isotonic
leuco-, leuko-	white	leucocyte, leukemia
-logy	study	ecology
mono-	one, single	monocot
-ped(e), -pod	foot, leg	centipede, gastropod
-phage, phago-	eat, engulf	macrophage, phagocyte
photo-	light	photosynthesis
-plasm	forming	cytoplasm
poly-	many	polymer, polyploidy
pro-, proto-	first, early	prokaryote, protostome
syn-	combine, together	protein synthesis
-some, soma-	body	chromosome, somatic
-troph	nutrition, feeding	phototrophic

Key terms are defined in the glossary to clarify their meaning in the text. The numbers following the definitions refer to pages on which terms appear in the text.

A

abiotic factor a nonliving part of an environment, such as water, soil, light, temperature, and wind (p. 855)

absorption the digestive process that takes small food molecules into the cells of the body (p. 720)

acid a compound that ionizes to release hydrogen ions (H^+) in water (p. 51)

acid rain nitric and sulfuric acid that fall to Earth as rain; strips the soil of valuable nutrients needed by trees and plants (p. 929)

actin the protein that makes up thin filaments in a myofibril (p. 708)

action potential a depolarization followed by a repolarization across the membrane of a neuron; a nerve impulse (p. 825)

active transport transport of a substance across a cell membrane requiring the use of energy; usually occurs against a concentration gradient (p. 72)

adaptation an inherited biological or behavioral trait that increases a population's chances for survival in a specific environment (p. 231)

adaptive radiation the emergence of diverse species from a common ancestor due to adaptation to many new environments (p. 243)

addiction a physical or psychological dependency on a drug (p. 839)

adenine one of the nitrogenous bases in DNA and RNA; a purine that pairs with thymine or uracil (p. 161)

aerobe an organism that uses oxygen during cellular respiration (p. 343)

albumin the liquid egg white that provides additional nutrients to the embryo (p. 637)

alcoholic fermentation a type of anaerobic respiration that converts pyruvate into carbon dioxide and ethanol (p. 94)

alga a plantlike photosynthetic protist (p. 358)

allantois a membrane that stores waste and provides the site for gas exchange in embryos (p. 622)

allele an alternate form of the same gene for a given trait (p. 133)

allele frequency the fraction of all genes for a particular trait that each allele represents in a given gene pool (p. 246)

allergy the response of the immune system to a normally harmless substance as if it were an antigen (p. 783)

alternation of generations the condition of an organism that alternates, or switches, from diploid ($2n$) spore-producing generations to haploid (n) gamete-producing generations (pp. 361, 412)

altitude the height above sea level (p. 860)

alveolus a tiny air sac of the lung where gas exchange between the circulatory and respiratory systems takes place (p. 747)

Alzheimer's disease a disease that causes the deterioration of the brain; characterized by memory loss, disorientation, or personality change (p. 839)

amebocyte a cell that shuttles nutrients and removes waste from other cells in a sponge (p. 504)

amniotic egg an egg that provides nourishment and protection for an embryo in a terrestrial environment by enclosing it in a shell with a fluid-filled membrane (p. 622)

amphibian a vertebrate adapted for living in water and on land (p. 605)

ampulla in echinoderms, a muscular sac that helps force water into and out of the tube feet (p. 573)

anaerobe an organism that does not use oxygen during cellular respiration (p. 343)

analogous structure characteristic shared by different species that is similar in function but not inherited from a common ancestor (p. 239)

anaphase the third phase of mitosis; replicated chromatids separate and move to opposite ends of the cell (p. 109)

anemia a condition in which a person's blood transports too little oxygen (p. 763)

angiosperm a flowering vascular plant that produces seeds enclosed in fruit (p. 415)

animal a eukaryotic multicellular heterotroph whose cells lack cell walls (p. 500)

annelid an earthworm, leech, or marine worm animal whose body is divided into segments (p. 536)

annual a plant that lives, reproduces, and dies in one year or one growing season (p. 416)

anorexia an eating disorder characterized by a refusal to eat coupled with a tendency to overexercise (p. 731)

anther the structure of the stamen that produces pollen (p. 463)

antheridium the male sperm-producing structure in bryophytes and pteridophytes (p. 476)

anthropoid a humanlike primate; monkeys, apes, and hominids are all anthropoids (p. 281)

antibody a disease-fighting protein produced in response to a specific antigen (p. 780)

anticodon the three-base sequence found on tRNA that binds to a complementary piece of mRNA during protein synthesis (p. 185)

antigen any substance that is identified by a macrophage as foreign to the body; induces the production of antibodies (p. 780)

aphotic zone an area in an aquatic biome in which light does not penetrate (p. 866)

appendicular skeleton the arm bones, leg bones, and bones of the pelvic girdle and shoulder areas; one of the two primary parts of the human skeleton (p. 698)

archaebacteria a group of monerans that live in extremely harsh environments (p. 340)

archegonium the female egg-producing structure in bryophytes and pteridophytes (p. 476)

arctic zone the region beyond 60° north or south latitude (p. 859)

arteriole the smallest of arteries (p. 757)

artery a blood vessel that carries blood away from the heart (p. 757)

arthritis a disease of the joints that causes inflammation and pain (p. 702)

artificial propagation the process whereby humans use asexual methods such as cutting, grafting, and tissue culturing to grow plants (p. 456)

artificial selection the breeding of a domesticated plant or animal to accentuate characteristics favorable to humans; also called selective breeding (pp. 206, 235)

ascus a saclike structure in which the spores of ascomycotes are contained (p. 381)

asexual reproduction the production of offspring by a single parent without combining genes from another individual (p. 105)

GLOSSARY

asthma a respiratory condition characterized by narrowed bronchial tubes; results in breathing difficulties (p. 752)

asymmetry without symmetry, irregular in shape (p. 509)

atherosclerosis a cardiovascular condition characterized by a narrowing of the arteries due to an accumulation of fat deposits (p. 762)

atom the smallest particle of an element that has the properties of the element (p. 38)

ATP (adenosine triphosphate) an energy-storing molecule used by most organisms (p. 82)

atrioventricular node a mass of nerve and muscle cells located in the septum between the atria; sends electrical signals to the ventricles, causing them to contract (p. 758)

atrium an upper chamber of the heart; receives incoming blood (p. 756)

autoimmune disease a disease in which the immune system attacks an organism's own tissues (p. 784)

autonomic nervous system a division of the peripheral nervous system; controls the activities of smooth muscles, organs, and glands (p. 832)

autosome any chromosome other than the sex chromosomes (p. 170)

autotroph an organism that produces its own food from inorganic compounds and sunlight (pp. 83, 898)

auxin a plant hormone that causes cells to elongate (p. 449)

axial skeleton the skull, vertebral column, and ribcage; one of the two primary pieces of the human skeleton (p. 698)

B

bacteriophage a type of virus that infects bacteria (pp. 159, 332)

bacterium a tiny prokaryotic organism from the kingdom Monera (p. 336)

base a compound that yields hydroxide ions (OH$^-$) when dissolved in water (p. 51)

basidium the structure in which the spores of club fungi are produced (p. 382)

behavior the way an organism reacts to a change in its environment (p. 668)

benthic zone area at the bottom of an aquatic biome; seafloor, lake bottom, or riverbed (p. 866)

biennial a plant that completes its life cycle in two years (p. 416)

bilateral symmetry a body plan where the right and left halves of the body are approximate mirror images of each other when divided lengthwise down the central axis (p. 524)

bile a yellow-green liquid formed in the liver that contains cholesterol, pigments, bile salts, and other compounds (p. 728)

binary fission asexual reproduction in prokaryotes; a process in which the chromosome of a moneran replicates, after which the cell divides to form two identical cells (p. 338)

binocular vision the use of both eyes at once in overlapping fields so that objects appear to have depth (p. 282)

binomial nomenclature a system of identifying organisms by their genus and species names; the two-word naming scheme developed by Linnaeus (p. 304)

biodegradable substances that can be broken down and recycled by natural processes (p. 922)

biodiversity the degree of species variety and balance in an ecological community (p. 888)

biogenesis a theory that states that life arises from living things (pp. 5, 256)

bioindicator an organism or species whose health serves as an indicator of the health of the environment or ecosystem (p. 614)

biological magnification the buildup of pollutants in organisms at the higher trophic levels of a food chain (p. 901)

biomass the total mass of all organisms at a given trophic level within an ecosystem (p. 902)

biome a large group of similar ecosystems containing distinctive types of plants and other organisms; determined by the climate (p. 861)

bioremediation a general term used to describe the process of using microorganisms to help restore natural environmental conditions (p. 345)

biosphere the thin layer of air, land, and water that is home to all living things on Earth (pp. 4, 854)

biotic factor a living part of an environment, such as a plant, animal, or other organism (p. 855)

bipedal the ability to walk upright on two legs (p. 286)

blade the broad, flat photosynthetic surface of a leaf (p. 398)

blastopore an opening in an embryo that develops at the point where cells of the blastula move inward to form the cell layers of the gastrula (p. 503)

blastula a hollow ball of cells formed during embryonic development (p. 502)

blood a liquid tissue consisting of plasma and blood cells in suspension (p. 754)

blood vessel a tubular organ through which blood flows (p. 754)

B lymphocyte a white blood cell that produces antibodies (p. 780)

body symmetry the arrangement of body parts around a central point or plane (p. 503)

bone a hard connective tissue made up of living cells and minerals (p. 698)

boom-and-bust curve a population growth pattern characterized by exponential growth followed by a sudden collapse of the population (p. 883)

brain stem the part of the brain that connects the spinal cord to the rest of the brain (p. 829)

Broca's area the portion of the cerebral cortex that translates thoughts into speech and coordinates the muscles used for speaking (p. 830)

bronchiole a small tube branching from a bronchus (p. 747)

bronchitis a condition involving inflammation of bronchial tube membranes; results in increased production of mucus, making breathing difficult (p. 751)

bronchus a respiratory tube that leads to the lungs (p. 746)

bryophyte a nonvascular plant that belongs to the division Bryophyta; includes mosses, liverworts, and hornworts (p. 471)

budding a form of asexual reproduction that begins with the formation of a small budlike cell from a larger cell (p. 505)

bud scale a structure that forms in order to protect buds from cold and infection (p. 450)

bulimia an eating disorder characterized by first consuming a large amount of food and then purging this food from the system (p. 731)

C

calcium an element found in endoskeleton systems; hardens bone and is essential for muscle contraction and nerve impulse transmission (p. 698)

calorie the amount of heat energy needed to raise the temperature of 1 gram of water by 1 degree Celsius (pp. 95, 729)

calorimeter an instrument used to measure the energy value of food; measures the heat given off when a small sample of food is burned (p. 729)

Calvin cycle the process that uses NADPH and ATP to construct carbohydrates from carbon dioxide; the second stage of photosynthesis (p. 89)

cambium in plants, a type of lateral meristem tissue whose function is to produce new cells in plants (p. 438)

cancer uncontrolled, abnormal cell reproduction (p. 196)

canine a long, pointed tooth used for piercing and tearing (p. 649)

capillary a tiny, thin-walled blood vessel across which gases are exchanged (p. 757)

capsid the protein coat of a virus that surrounds the DNA or RNA (p. 326)

capsule the structure of a moss that forms haploid (*n*) spores by meiosis (p. 477)

carapace in crustaceans, a hard shield of chitin that covers the cephalothorax (p. 549)

carbohydrate an organic compound composed of carbon, hydrogen, and oxygen atoms; stores energy and provides shape or structure to organisms (p. 34)

carbon cycle a cycle that describes the movement of carbon and oxygen throughout the environment (p. 906)

carcinogen an agent that causes or tends to cause cancer (p. 198)

cardiac muscle the striated, involuntary muscle tissue that forms the heart (p. 707)

carnivore an animal that eats only other animals (p. 900)

carrier an individual who possesses a particular recessive trait but does not express it (p. 143)

carrier protein a special protein in the membrane that helps specific molecules cross the membrane (p. 73)

carrying capacity the maximum population size that a particular environment can support over time (p. 879)

cell the smallest unit of life capable of carrying out all of the functions of living things (p. 9)

cell cycle the period from one cell division to the start of the next cell division; the sequence of phases in the life cycle of a cell (p. 107)

cell-mediated immunity the response of the immune system to virus-infected body cells (p. 781)

cell membrane a thin layer of lipid and protein separating the cell's contents from the outside environment (p. 62)

cell theory the theory stating that cells are the basic unit of life, that all organisms are made of one or more cells, and that cells arise from existing cells (p. 60)

cellular respiration the process by which food molecules are broken down to release energy (p. 91)

cellulose organic compound made of long fibers, or chains, of glucose molecules; an important structural component of plant cell walls (p. 407)

cell wall a tough, rigid outer covering that provides a cell with protection and maintenance of its shape (p. 69)

central nervous system (CNS) the body's main control center; the brain and the spinal cord (p. 823)

centromere the point where sister chromatids are joined (p. 108)

cephalization the characteristic of a well-developed brain and a group of sensory organs located inside the head (pp. 592, 693)

cephalothorax the fused head and chest region in many arthropods to which legs and other appendages are attached (p. 549)

cereal the edible fruit or seed of grasses (p. 407)

cerebellum the second largest part of the brain; coordinates muscle activities (p. 829)

cerebrum the largest region of the human brain; responsible for all conscious, or voluntary, activity (p. 829)

chalaza in bird eggs, a ropelike strand of tissue that supports the albumin, which connects to the chorion (p. 637)

chaparral a warm biome characterized by a winter rainy season followed by a dry, hot summer (p. 863)

chelicerae the anterior appendage modified into pincers and fangs for food-gathering (p. 552)

chemical bond a force that holds two or more atoms together (p. 39)

chemical digestion a digestive process that breaks food down into smaller, simpler molecules (p. 720)

chemical reaction a reaction characterized by the breaking or forming of chemical bonds (p. 42)

chemoautotroph an organism that obtains energy from inorganic substances (p. 342)

chitin a tough, flexible carbohydrate that makes up the cell walls of fungi and the exoskeleton of arthropods (p. 374)

chlorofluorocarbon (CFC) a chlorine-containing chemical that causes the thinning of the ozone layer; can be discharged through aerosol sprays, air conditioners, and the production of plastic foam (p. 931)

chlorophyll an important group of photosynthetic pigments in plants and algae (p. 85)

chloroplast an organelle common in plants and algae that converts sunlight, carbon dioxide, and water into sugars during the process of photosynthesis; contains chlorophyll (pp. 69, 86)

chorion the outer membrane of an amniotic egg that provides a layer of protection and aids in regulating gas exchange (p. 623)

chromatin a thin, tangled bundle of DNA threads found in the nucleus of cells during interphase (p. 108)

chromosome a structure within a cell that contains a cell's genetic information (p. 64)

chromosome theory of heredity the theory stating that the material of inheritance is carried by genes on chromosomes (p. 134)

chyme a thick liquid made up of partially digested proteins, starches, acids, and undigested sugars and fats; food reduced to a soft pulp after about three hours in the stomach (p. 726)

ciliophoran a protozoan that is covered with cilia; also called ciliate (p. 357)

cilium a short, tiny, hairlike projection that is usually found in large numbers on the surface of cells; aids some eukaryotic cells in movement (pp. 68, 357)

circadian rhythm a rhythm that repeats approximately every 24 hours (p. 681)

class a group within a phylum in the classification system (p. 301)

classical conditioning the training of an animal to respond to a stimulus (p. 677)

climate the average weather pattern of an area over time (p. 858)

climax community an established community that encounters little ecological succession (p. 891)

cloaca in most vertebrates, a chamber where products of the digestive, excretory, and sometimes reproductive systems empty; not found in mammals (p. 606)

clone a product or offspring that is genetically identical to its parent (p. 455)

closed circulatory system a circulatory system in which blood travels through the body inside one continuous network of vessels (p. 534)

cochlea the fluid-filled structure of the inner ear that contains the mechanoreceptors needed for hearing (p. 835)

codominance a pattern of inheritance in which both alleles in a heterozygote are fully expressed (p. 149)

codon the sequence of three nitrogenous bases in mRNA or DNA (p. 184)

coelom in some animals, body cavity completely lined with mesoderm; it develops into the digestive tract and other internal organs (p. 532)

coevolution a process in which two or more populations that closely interact over an extended period of time adapt to one another (p. 243)

cohesion clinging together; shown in hydrogen bonds in water molecules; results in surface tension (p. 50)

collagen a protein made by the dermis layer of the skin; makes skin supple and strong (p. 711)

collar cell one of the flagellated cells lining the interior of a sponge; also called a choanocyte (p. 504)

colonizer the first organism to dwell in an uninhabited area (p. 452)

colony a group of similar cells or organisms living and growing together in close association (p. 353)

commensalism a relationship in which one organism benefits from an interaction and the other organism is neither helped nor harmed by it (p. 888)

community a collection of interacting populations within a given ecosystem; its organisms depend on each other for survival (pp. 855, 885)

compact bone dense bone found in shafts of long bones (p. 699)

companion cell a cell that controls the movement of substances through sieve tubes in plants (p. 431)

compensation point the amount of light a plant needs for photosynthesis to balance its energy use in cellular respiration (p. 425)

competition the struggle between organisms to obtain the same limited resource (p. 886)

compound two or more elements chemically combined in definite proportions (p. 37)

compound eyes multifaceted eyes with many separate lenses that combine to form a single mosaic image (p. 547)

concentration gradient the difference between the concentration of a particular molecule in one area and its concentration in a neighboring area (p. 73)

concussion a brain injury caused by a blow to the head (p. 838)

cone a photoreceptor that can distinguish colors but requires bright light (p. 834)

conjugation a form of sexual reproduction in which single-celled organisms exchange genetic material through cell-to-cell contact(p. 338)

connective tissue tissue that joins together body structures, providing protection and support (p. 692)

consumer a heterotroph (p. 899)

control setup in an experiment, all factors are exactly the same except for the change in the experimental variable (p. 22)

convergent evolution a process in which different species evolve with similar characteristics; often the result of living in a similar environment (p. 243)

cork cambium the tissue between the phloem and the epidermis that replaces the epidermis and cortex with cork (p. 438)

cotyledon a seed leaf in a plant's embryo; used as an organ for food storage (p. 460)

covalent bond a type of chemical bond formed when atoms share electrons (p. 40)

crop a storage area within the digestive tract of annelids and birds (pp. 537, 634)

crossing over the switching of genes between pairs of homologous chromosomes during meiosis I (p. 168)

cuticle a waxy, waterproof layer that coats the outer parts of a plant exposed to air and helps prevent evaporation (pp. 423, 470)

cyanobacteria a group of gram-negative monerans that perform photosynthesis (p. 342)

cytokinesis a step of eukaryotic cell division in which the cytoplasm divides creating two daughter cells (p. 108)

cytoplasm a jellylike substance made up primarily of water and the organelles suspended in it; the center for most of the cell's metabolic activity (p. 63)

cytosine one of four nitrogenous bases in DNA and RNA; a pyrimidine that pairs with guanine (p. 161)

cytoskeleton a network of fibers and tiny tubes throughout the cytoplasm; gives a cell support and helps it to maintain or change its shape (p. 64)

cytotoxic T cell also called killer T cell; an immune cell that produces a protein that ruptures the cell membrane of a specific target cell (p. 781)

D

decomposer an organism that breaks down dead organic materials into food (pp. 344, 900)

deforestation the removal of large numbers of trees from a forest (p. 920)

deletion the loss of a segment of DNA (p. 192)

denitrification the conversion of ammonia, nitrite, or nitrate into free nitrogen gas by bacteria (p. 909)

density-dependent limiting factor a factor that comes into operation only when the number of organisms per unit of space reaches a maximum level (p. 881)

density-independent limiting factor a factor that affects all populations regardless of their population density (p. 883)

depressant a drug that slows down the activity of the central nervous system (p. 840)

dermal tissue the outermost protective layers on leaves and stems (p. 410)

dermis the thick inner layer of the skin (p. 711)

desert an arid region with sparse plant and animal life; annual rainfall in a desert is usually less than 25 centimeters (p. 864)

desertification a process that occurs when a soil loses the ability to retain water and nutrients; can result from deforestation (p. 920)

deuterostome a coelomate whose blastopore develops into an anus; a mouth forms later at the opposite end of the digestive tube (p. 575)

diabetes mellitus a disorder in which the body is unable to control blood sugar levels (p. 801)

diaphragm a sheet of muscle below the lungs that separates the chest cavity from the abdomen; contracts during inhalation and relaxes during exhalation (pp. 650, 748)

diastole the part of the heart beat in which the heart muscle relaxes, enabling blood to flow into the atria and ventricles (p. 758)

diatom a type of alga lacking cilia and flagella, with a glasslike cell wall composed of silica (p. 359)

dichotomous key a guide designed to identify organisms; uses pairs of observable traits as a checklist to pinpoint the organism's identity (p. 313)

dicot an angiosperm whose embryo has two cotyledons (p. 460)

differentiation the development of cells into specialized shapes and functions (p. 105)

diffusion the random movement of molecules from an area of higher concentration (more molecules) to an area of lower concentration (fewer molecules) (p. 72)

digestion the process by which food is broken down by mechnical and chemical processes into smaller, usable molecules of chemical compounds (p. 725)

digestive system a system in humans and other animals that processes food (p. 720)

dinoflagellate a type of alga with two flagella that spin the cell in a corkscrew fashion (p. 358)

diploid referring to a cell having two sets of chromosomes ($2n$) (p. 114)

directional selection a change in the allele frequency of a population that occurs when an environmental change favors an extreme phenotype for a trait (p. 249)

disruptive selection a change in the allele frequency of a population that occurs when an environmental change is not favorable for the most common phenotype (p. 250)

divergent evolution a process in which once-related populations evolve independently; often occurs as the result of geographic isolation (p. 242)

division a major taxonomic group in the plant kingdom and fungi kingdom; equivalent to phylum in other kingdoms (pp. 301, 471)

DNA fingerprint the band patterns that form when DNA fragments are separated by gel electrophoresis (p. 210)

DNA polymerase an enzyme that assembles new strands of DNA during replication (p. 163)

dominant allele the expressed form of a trait that usually masks the recessive allele (p. 133)

dormancy a period of decreased activity that occurs because of structural and chemical changes in a plant (p. 450)

dorsal the back side of the body of an animal with bilateral symmetry (p. 693)

dorsal hollow nerve cord a nerve cord that is located on the back side of a chordate animal (p. 581)

double fertilization a process in angiosperms in which one sperm and egg form a zygote and a second sperm and two polar nuclei form an endosperm (p. 487)

double helix the twisted ladder shape of a DNA molecule formed by two strands of nulceotides (p. 161)

duplication a process that occurs when part of a chromosome breaks off and is incorporated into its homologous chromosome, giving that chromosome an extra copy of a DNA sequence (p. 193)

E

echinoderm a marine invertebrate with an endoskeleton, spiny skin, radial symmetry, and a water vascular system (p. 572)

echolocation the process some species use to find food and avoid objects in the dark; process using high-pitched sound waves to bounce off objects to determine their location (p. 661)

ecological pyramid a diagram that shows the relationships between producers and consumers at different trophic levels within an ecosystem (p. 902)

ecological succession a change in the community resulting in new populations of organisms gradually replacing existing ones (p. 890)

ecology the study of organisms and their interactions with their environment (p. 854)

ecosystem the combination of all the communities and abiotic factors in an environment (p. 855)

ectoderm in animals, the outer layer of embryonic tissue (p. 502)

ectopic pregnancy a pregnancy that occurs when a fertilized egg implants in the Fallopian tube instead of the uterus (p. 815)

ectotherm an animal whose body temperature is determined by its external environment (p. 593)

egestion the process of eliminating undigested food waste from an animal (p. 501)

egg a gamete produced by a female (p. 803)

electron a subatomic particle with a negative charge and a relatively small mass (p. 38)

electron transport the process by which energy is transferred from the electron carriers to ATP (p. 93)

element a substance that cannot be broken down by chemical processes into simpler substances (p. 37)

elongation the lengthening of the amino acid chain during protein synthesis (p. 184)

emigration the movement of organisms out of an area occupied by an existing population (p. 878)

endocrine gland a ductless gland that releases hormones directly into the blood (p. 794)

endocytosis a form of active transport in which a portion of the cell membrane surrounds outside particles and moves them into the cell (p. 76)

endoderm in animals, the inner layer of embryonic tissue (p. 502)

endometriosis a disease characterized by a scarring of the Fallopian tubes resulting in a blocking of an egg entering the uterus; parts of the uterine lining migrate outside the uterus (p. 815)

endoplasmic reticulum an extensive network of membranes that transports materials through a cell (p. 66)

endoskeleton a rigid framework inside an animal that provides support and protection (pp. 546, 697)

endospore a heat-resistant, thick-walled, inactive bacterial cell that develops when conditions are unfavorable (p. 337)

endosymbiosis the hypothesis that eukaryotic cells evolved when the prokaryotic ancestors of mitochondria and chloroplasts were engulfed by larger cells (p. 267)

endotherm an animal that uses food energy to maintain a constant body temperature (p. 593)

energy the ability to perform work (p. 46)

envelope the outer covering of viruses that infect animal cells; surrounds the capsid (p. 327)

enzyme a catalytic protein that speeds up the chemical reactions within an organism (p. 44)

epidermis the outer layer of skin that covers the human body and its organs (p. 711)

epiglottis a flap of elastic tissue forming a lid over the opening of the trachea; protects the larynx when you swallow (p. 746)

epithelial tissue the tissue that covers the body and its organs, includes skin and lining of organs (p. 692)

epoch a subdivision of a period on the geologic time scale (p. 268)

era the largest division of time on the geological time scale: Precambrian, Paleozoic, Mesozoic, and Cenozoic (p. 268)

esophagus the muscular tube that connects the pharynx and the stomach (p. 726)

estuary an area where fresh water and salt water mix; a coastal region that forms where a river meets the sea (p. 869)

eubacteria true bacteria; largest and most common group of monerans (p. 341)

eukaryote an organism whose cells have a nucleus surrounded by a nuclear membrane (p. 64)

evolution the changes in populations over long periods of time; the change within the gene pool of a population (p. 233)

excretion the process of eliminating nitrogen-containing waste products from a cell, organ, or organism (p. 501)

excretory system the system that removes nitrogen-containing wastes from the body (p. 733)

exocytosis a process in which wastes and cell products are secreted out of a cell through the cell membrane (p. 76)

exon the sections of DNA or RNA in eukaryotic cells that code for proteins; joined together during RNA splicing (p. 184)

exoskeleton a hard covering on the outside of an animal that provides support, protection, and a point of attachment for muscles (pp. 546, 697)

exponential growth a form of population growth in which the size of a population in each subsequent generation is a multiple of the previous generation (p. 877)

extensor a muscle that straightens a joint (p. 707)

extinction the destruction of a population because it cannot adapt to changing environmental conditions (p. 883)

F

facilitated diffusion the process of transporting molecules by carrier proteins during diffusion; requires no energy output (p. 73)

family the level below order in the classification system (p. 301)

feces an undigested solid waste matter formed inside the body (p. 727)

feedback control when the rate of a current process is controlled by the outcome of its previous cycle; functions within different systems throughout the body to maintain homeostasis (p. 799)

fermentation the extraction of a small amount of energy from pyruvate in the absence of oxygen; pyruvate is transformed into either alcohol or lactate (p. 94)

fetus a developing embryo (p. 810)

fibrin a substance created when clotting factors react with fibrinogen; forms strands that trap blood cells, creating a clot (p. 760)

fibrous root one of numerous extensively branched roots in a root system; it is efficient at preventing soil erosion (p. 401)

filament the structure of the stamen that supports the anther (p. 463)

filter-feeding a method of feeding in which organic matter and microscopic organisms are filtered from water (p. 504)

fixed-action pattern the mechanism for instinctive behavior triggered by an object or event (p. 672)

flagellum a long hairlike structure growing from a cell; it contracts in a whiplike motion and aids in the movement of organisms (pp. 68, 356)

flame cell a small bulblike structure that excretes water and chemical wastes (p. 525)

flexor a muscle that bends a joint (p. 707)

flower the reproductive structure of an angiosperm (pp. 402, 463)

food chain the pathway for the transfer of energy within an ecosystem; each organism provides food for the next higher organism (p. 899)

food web a web consisting of all interconnected food chains within an ecosystem (p. 904)

fossil the preserved remains or imprints of ancient organisms (p. 232)

fossil fuel an energy-rich compound formed from decayed plant matter (p. 907)

fragmentation a type of asexual reproduction that involves the growth of a new organism from a small piece that breaks off the parent organism (p. 477)

frameshift mutation the deletion or insertion of nucleotides that disrupts a codon (p. 193)

fruit a structure that develops from the ovary in a plant; houses and protects seeds (p. 403)

fruiting body the reproductive structure of fungi and funguslike protists; consists of a stalk that supports the structures in which spores are made (p. 379)

G

gallbladder a small saclike organ connected to the liver; concentrates and stores bile (p. 728)

gamete a specialized haploid (n) cell involved in sexual reproduction. (459)

gametophyte the haploid (n) phase of a plant life cycle; produces gametes (p. 459)

ganglion a cluster of nerve cells (p. 822)

gastrula the three-layered embryo formed during early development (p. 502)

gel electrophoresis a process used by researchers to break apart nucleic acids or proteins and sort the fragments by size (p. 209)

gemmae the tiny pieces of tissue that mosses produce to form new gametophytes (p. 477)

gemmule a dormant mass of amebocytes surrounded by protective layers of spicules; forms during adverse conditions (p. 506)

gene the unit of hereditary information that controls traits of a particular organism; located on a chromosome (p. 133)

gene cloning a process using genetic engineering to make copies of genes (p. 211)

gene mutation the errors within individual genes in a chromosome that occur during DNA replication (p. 193)

gene pool the combined genetic material of all the members of a given population (p. 246)

gene therapy a medical treatment that attempts to change a genome (p. 214)

genetic drift an accidental change in gene frequency that affects small populations only, as the result of chance instead of natural selection (p. 248)

genetic engineering the use of biochemical techniques to identify, study, and modify genes (p. 209)

genetic equilibrium a state of constant allele frequency in a population throughout generations (p. 246)

genetics the scientific study of heredity (p. 130)

genome the base sequence for all of the DNA in an organism (p. 173)

genotype an organism's genetic makeup (p. 134)

genus the level below family in the classification system; a group of closely related species (p. 301)

geotropism the growth of a plant in response to gravity (p. 446)

gestation period the length of time an embryo develops inside the mother's body (p. 652)

gill pouch a fold of tissue in the neck region in all vertebrate embryos (p. 240)

gill slit one of a pair of openings along the pharynx in many chordates (p. 581)

gizzard a digestive organ in annelids and birds that contains muscular walls to grind food (p. 634)

glial cell a nonconducting cell of the nervous system that protect, mechanically support, and assist the neurons (p. 824)

global warming an increase in Earth's average surface temperatures (p. 930)

glomerulus a group of capillaries in a nephron that allow fluid and wastes to seep out while blood and protein stay in (p. 736)

glucagon a hormone that raises the level of glucose in the blood (p. 799)

glycogen a carbohydrate in which animals store energy (p. 35)

glycolysis the process converting glucose to pyruvate; releases energy that can be stored as ATP (p. 92)

Golgi apparatus a membrane-bound organelle that packages and secretes products of the endoplasmic reticulum from the cell (p. 66)

gradualism a theory about the rate of evolution—that the small genetic changes accumulate in a population over long periods of time (p. 236)

grafting the process of inserting a piece of one plant into a slit in a second plant to make the two plants grow as one (p. 457)

grana the stacks of disc-shaped structures inside the chloroplast (p. 86)

grassland a biome with hot, humid summers coupled with cold winters; a large community characterized by grasses and small plants (p. 865)

greenhouse effect the heat-trapping action of gases in the atmosphere that may contribute to global warming (pp. 427, 930)

growth rate the total change in a population's size over time (p. 878)

guanine one of four nitrogenous bases in DNA and RNA; a purine that pairs with cytosine (p. 161)

gymnosperm a nonflowering vascular plant that produces seeds that lack a fruit (pp. 415, 481)

H

habitat the type of environment in which a particular species lives (p. 855)

habituation the process by which an animal learns to ignore an unimportant stimulus (p. 676)

half-life the time it takes for half of the atoms in a sample to undergo radioactive decay (p. 263)

hallucinogen a drug that affects the sensory perceptions of the central nervous system; LSD, PCP, and mescaline are hallucinogens (p. 840)

halophile archaebacteria that live in extremely salty environments (p. 341)

haploid referring to a cell having one set of chromosomes (n) (p. 114)

Hardy-Weinberg Principle the theory that states that if a population is not evolving, the allele frequencies in the population remain constant (p. 246)

Haversian canals the spaces in bone through which nerves and blood vessels pass (p. 699)

heart the main pump of the circulatory system (p. 754)

heartwood the dark-colored layers of xylem at the center of a tree that contain substances like gums, oils, resins, and tannins; its clogged cells are no longer able to carry water (p. 439)

helper T cell a white blood cell that stimulates the immune response at the onset of an infection (p. 781)

hemoglobin a large iron-containing protein in red blood cells that carries oxygen from the lungs to the rest of the body (p. 759)

herbaceous a nonwoody plant composed of a relatively soft green tissue covered with a thin protective layer (p. 400)

herbivore a consumer that only eats plants (p. 900)

hermaphrodite an organism that has functional male and female reproductive systems; capable of producing both eggs and sperm; not necessarily self-fertilizing (p. 506)

heterotroph an organism that cannot make its own food; obtains energy and nutrients by ingesting other organisms (pp. 84, 899)

heterozygous having two different alleles for a given trait (p. 135)

histamine a chemical released by injured cells that triggers an inflammatory response (p. 778)

HIV (human immunodeficiency virus) the virus that causes AIDS; attacks the human immune system and destroys the body's ability to fight infection (p. 785)

homeostasis the maintenance of a stable set of internal conditions within an organism (p. 47)

hominid a family that consists of humans and extinct humanlike primates (p. 286)

homologous pair a similar pair of chromosomes, one from the mother and one from the father (p. 115)

homologous structure a structure or characteristic with similar functions found in different species; thought to be inherited from common ancestors (p. 239)

homozygous having two identical alleles for a given trait (p. 135)

hormone an organic compound released by one part of an organism to affect another part of the organism (pp. 447, 794)

host an organism that shelters and nourishes another organism (p. 327)

humoral immunity the immune response to a disease occurring in bodily fluids (p. 780)

humus a part of soil formed by partially decayed plant material (p. 453)

hybrid an organism that receives different genetic information for a trait from each parent (p. 131)

hydrostatic skeleton a type of skeletal system in which the muscles are supported by a water-filled cavity (pp. 526, 696)

GLOSSARY

hypertension a disease that occurs when the force of blood pumping through blood vessels is too high (p. 763)

hyperthyroidism a disease characterized by a fast metabolism due to the thyroid gland producing too much thyroid hormone (p. 801)

hypertonic solution a solution having a higher concentration of solutes outside a cell than the concentration of solutes inside the cell (p. 74)

hypha a tiny filament filled with cytoplasm and nuclei that collectively form the body of a fungus (p. 374)

hypothalamus the part of the brain that controls basic body functions, such as blood pressure and body temperature (p. 796)

hypothesis a possible explanation for an event or a set of observations (p. 21)

hypothyrodism a disease characterized by the slowing of metabolism as a result of the thyroid gland not producing enough thyroid hormone (p. 801)

hypotonic solution a solution having a lower concentration of solutes outside the cell than the concentration of solutes inside the cell (p. 74)

I

immigration the movement of organisms into an area occupied by an existing population (p. 878)

implantation the process in which the embryo attaches to the uterine wall (p. 809)

imprinting the learning of a behavior that becomes the permanent response to a stimulus (p. 676)

inbreeding the crossing of parents that have similar genotypes (p. 206)

incisor a conelike tooth specialized for stripping and cutting (p. 649)

incomplete dominance a pattern of inheritance in which two alleles in a heterozygote are partially expressed (p. 148)

inflammatory response a nonspecific defense reaction to tissue damage caused by injury or infection; results in redness and swelling (p. 778)

innate behavior a behavior that is genetically determined, that is present and complete without the need for experience (p. 669)

instinct a complex pattern of innate behavior (p. 672)

insulin a hormone produced by the pancreas that causes glucose to move from the blood to the liver (p. 799)

integumentary system the name given to the skin, its surface glands, hair, and nails (p. 710)

interferon a protein that interferes with the replication of viruses (p. 779)

interneuron a neuron that conducts impulses within the central nervous system; connects with sensory neurons, motor neurons, or other interneurons (p. 827)

interphase the longest phase in the cell cycle, during which cells mature and chromosomes are duplicated (p. 107)

intron the sections of DNA or RNA in eukaryotic cells that do not code for proteins (p. 184)

inversion a process that occurs when part of a chromosome breaks off, turns around, and reattaches in the reverse order to the same chromosome (p. 193)

invertebrate an animal without a backbone (p. 503)

ion an atom that has lost or gained electrons (p. 38)

ionic bond a chemical bond formed between ions with opposite charges (p. 40)

isotonic solution a solution whose concentration is equal to the concentration of solutes inside the cell (p. 74)

isotope one of several atoms of the same element that have the same number of protons but different numbers of neutrons (p. 38)

J

joint the point where bones come together (p. 701)

K

karyotype a photograph showing an organism's chromosomes (p. 173)

keratin a protein that makes up skin, hair, feathers, and other animal coverings; insoluble in water (p. 710)

kidney the main organ of the excretory system that removes wastes from the blood and processes these wastes into urine (p. 735)

killer T cell a white blood cell that attacks an infected body cell by poking holes in the cell membrane; binds to a specific antigen on the surface of the infected cell (p. 781)

kingdom the broadest group in the classification system (p. 301)

Krebs cycle a series of oxidation reactions that break down pyruvate; the second phase of aerobic respiration (p. 92)

L

lactic acid fermentation a type of anaerobic respiration in which pyruvate is converted into lactic acid (p. 94)

large intestine the organ that absorbs water and water-soluble vitamins during digestion; also known as the colon (p. 727)

larynx the tube between the pharynx and the trachea containing vocal cords; also known as voice box (p. 747)

lateral line system the sensory organs in most fishes that are used to detect vibrations and water currents (p. 595)

Law of Dominance Mendel's law that states that if two alleles in a gene pair are different, then one allele can control the trait and the other one can be hidden (p. 136)

Law of Independent Assortment Mendel's law that states that gene pairs segregate into gametes randomly and independently of each other (p. 135)

Law of Segregation Mendel's law that states that each pair of genes segregates, or separates, during meiosis and each gamete contains one gene from each gene pair (p. 135)

leaf scar a structure that forms on a stem after a leaf drops (p. 450)

learned behavior a behavior that is acquired as a result of experience (p. 669)

learning a change in behavior that results from experience (p. 675)

leukemia a type of cancer affecting blood in which immature blood cells are produced (p. 763)

leukocytes also called white blood cells (p. 775)

lichen a symbiotic partnership between a fungus and a photosynthetic organism (p. 384)

ligament the connective tissue that joins bones (p. 701)

lignin a hard substance that strengthens cell walls, allowing cells to support additional weight (p. 470)

limiting factor any abiotic or biotic resource that limits the size of a population (p. 879)

linked genes genes located on the same chromosome (p. 167)

lipid an organic compound commonly referred to as fats and oils; tends to be insoluble in water (p. 35)

liver the largest organ inside the body; produces digestive fluids (p. 728)

lung a spongelike organ in which oxygen and carbon dioxide are exchanged (p. 745)

lungfish a fish that has both lungs and gills (p. 602)

lymph the fluid that collects inside the lymphatic vessels (p. 774)

lymphatic system the body system made of vessels, nodes, and organs that collect and clean the fluid around your cells (pp. 755, 774)

lymph node a mass of tissue through which the lymph ducts drain (p. 774)

lymphocyte a leucocyte involved in antibody production and other aspects of the body's specific defense system (p. 775)

lysogenic cycle a type of viral replication in which a virus does not immediately kill a host cell, because the viral DNA becomes incorporated into the host DNA (p. 328)

lysosome a small saclike organelle that contains digestive enzymes that help the cell break down large molecules of carbohydrates, proteins, and lipids (p. 66)

lytic cycle the viral replication process that rapidly kills a host cell by producing many new viruses (p. 328)

macrophage the largest phagocyte that has the ability to engulf hundreds of bacterial cells (p. 775)

Malpighian tubule an excretory organ in the abdomen of arachnids that filters wastes from body fluids (p. 552)

mammal an endothermic vertebrate with mammary glands (p. 648)

mammary gland a gland in females that secretes milk (p. 648)

mandible the jawlike appendage of crustaceans used to chew and crush food (p. 549)

mantle the soft outer tissue layer that, in many mollusks, secretes material to form an external shell (p. 530)

marrow a soft tissue that fills spaces within bone, stores fat, and produces red blood cells (p. 699)

marsupial a mammal producing offspring who initially develop internally but later develop in the mother's external pouch (p. 651)

mechanical digestion a digestive process that breaks food into small pieces without changing its chemical structure (p. 720)

medusa a usually motile, bell-shaped form of cnidarian with a mouth on the ventral surface and tentacles that point downward (p. 509)

meiosis reduction division of a cell; each daughter cell is haploid (n) (p. 114)

melanin the pigment that gives skin its color (p. 712)

menstrual cycle the female reproductive cycle that prepares the lining of the uterus to receive a fertilized egg or discharge an unfertilized egg (p. 807)

menstruation the release of the uterine lining and an unfertilized egg over a period of 5 to 7 days (p. 808)

meristem a growing tissue of a plant (p. 435)

mesoderm in animals, the middle layer of embryonic tissue between the ectoderm and the endoderm (p. 502)

mesophyll a plant tissue made of parenchyma cells; the part of a leaf where most photosynthesis takes place (p. 423)

metabolism the sum of all the chemical processes that occur within an organism (pp. 46, 729)

metamorphosis a series of changes undergone by young animals as they develop into adults (p. 559)

metaphase the second phase of mitosis; homologous chromosomes become arranged in the middle of the cell (p. 109)

methanogen a group of archaebacteria that live in oxygen-free environments and produce methane (p. 341)

microscope a system of lenses that produce an enlarged, focused image of an object (p. 59)

microsphere a bubblelike structure of water and proteins that is somewhat like a cellular membrane (p. 260)

mimicry an adaptation involving structural resemblance to another species or object (p. 562)

mitochondrion an organelle that changes energy found in food compounds into energy, or ATP, necessary to power the cell's functions; the site of cellular respiration (p. 66)

mitosis a step of eukaryotic cell division in which the nucleus divides into two nuclei (p. 108)

molar a broad, flattened tooth adapted for grinding and crushing; located behind the premolar (p. 649)

mold a funguslike protist that lives mostly in damp or watery places and acts as a decomposer (p. 362)

molting in animals, the process in which organisms periodically shed their exoskeleton, skin, or feathers (p. 546)

monocot an angiosperm with one cotyledon in each embryo (p. 460)

monomer a small organic molecule that acts as a building block for large molecules (p. 260)

monosomy a genetic condition in which the zygote receives only one copy of a particular chromosome instead of two (p. 175)

monotreme a mammal that reproduces by laying eggs (p. 651)

motile free-moving (p. 500)

motor neuron a neuron that conducts impulses away from the central nervous system and towards the cells involved in the response (p. 827)

mRNA (messenger RNA) a type of RNA that carries the genetic instructions for protein production from the DNA to the ribosome (p. 184)

multiple alleles the presence of more than two alleles for a gene in a population (p. 149)

muscle tissue tissue made of cells that contract in response to signals from the brain, resulting in movement (p. 692)

mutagen a factor in the environment that can cause mutations (p. 198)

mutation a change in the genes or nucleotides in DNA (p. 192)

mutualism a symbiotic relationship in which both organisms benefit (p. 887)

mycelium the mass of tangled, interwoven hyphae that form the body of a fungus (p. 375)

mycorrhiza a mutualistic association between a fungus and the roots of a plant (p. 385)

myelin sheath the protective wrapping of Schwann cells around an axon (p. 824)

myofibril a tiny structure in muscle, cylindrical in shape; many myofibrils comprise muscle fiber (p. 708)

myosin a protein that makes up a thick filament in a myofibril (p. 708)

N

narcotic any drug that relieves pain or induces sleep; opiates are narcotics (p. 840)

nastic movement a reversible plant response that occurs in the same way regardless of the direction of stimulus (p. 447)

natural killer cell a lymphocyte that attacks virus-infected body cells and causes the infected cells to burst; part of the body's nonspecific defense system (p. 779)

natural selection Charles Darwin's theory of a mechanism for evolution; organisms with traits favorable for their environment are more likely to survive, reproduce, and pass on the favorable traits to offspring (p. 236)

nematocyst a coiled filament with a tiny harpoonlike barb on the end, used by cnidarians to sting prey (p. 510)

nephridium an individual unit of the excretory system that excretes waste in earthworms (p. 536)

nephron the functional unit of the kidney that removes waste from the blood (p. 736)

nervous system a control system that enables the human body to gather information and respond quickly to internal and external changes (p. 822)

nervous tissue tissue composed of neurons and glial cells; carries information throughout the body (p. 693)

neuron a cell that can conduct nerve impulses through the body; the basic functional unit of the nervous system (p. 823)

neutron a subatomic particle located in the nucleus of the atom with about the same mass as a proton and no charge (p. 38)

New World monkeys a group of monkeys that evolved on the American continents; characteristics include broad, flat noses and prehensile tails (p. 281)

niche the specific role an organism plays within its community (p. 231)

nictitating membrane in frogs, a transparent membrane that covers the eyes (p. 605)

nitrogen cycle the pathway by which nitrogen moves through the environment (p. 908)

nitrogen fixation the conversion of atmospheric nitrogen gas into usable nitrogen compounds (p. 908)

nonbiodegradable cannot be broken down or recycled by natural processes (p. 922)

nondisjunction the failure of one or more homologous chromosome pairs to separate during cell division (p. 174)

nonrenewable resource a resource that cannot be replenished through natural processes (p. 918)

nonspecific defense the general cellular or chemical response of the immune system (p. 773)

nonvascular plant a plant lacking the tissues needed for transport and structural support (p. 413)

notochord a firm, flexible supporting rod located below the nerve cord (p. 581)

nucleic acid a large, complex DNA or RNA molecule that carries hereditary, or genetic, information (p. 36)

nucleolus a specialized organelle in the nucleus of cells; the site of ribosome production (p. 64)

nucleotide a part of a nucleic acid; consists of three parts: a five-carbon sugar, a phosphate group, and a nitrogen-containing base (p. 160)

nucleus the control center of a cell (p. 64)

nutrient a substance needed by the body for energy, growth, repair, or maintenance (p. 720)

O

Old World monkeys a group of monkeys that evolved on the African, Asian, and European continents; characteristics include long noses and short tails (p. 281)

omnivore a consumer that eats both producers and other consumers (p. 900)

oncogene a gene that has the ability to cause cancer (p. 196)

open circulatory system a circulatory system whose blood is enclosed in vessels in some places but flows freely over body tissues in other places (p. 530)

operant conditioning a type of training that involves environmental reward or punishment for certain accidental behaviors performed by an animal (p. 677)

operculum a protective flap of tissue that covers the gills in ray-finned fishes (p. 596)

opposable thumb a thumb that can be placed in the opposite direction from the other fingers (p. 281)

order a division of classes in the classification system (p. 301)

organ two or more different types of tissues that work together to perform a specific function (pp. 11, 693)

organic compound a compound that contains carbon; usually associated with living things (p. 37)

organism any living thing (p. 4)

osculum the opening at the top of a sponge where water leaves the body (p. 504)

osmosis the diffusion of water molecules across a semipermeable membrane (p. 73)

osteoblast a cell found in bones that produces new bone cells for growth and repair (p. 699)

osteoporosis a disease that causes bones to become brittle (p. 702)

ostracoderm an extinct fishlike animal without jaws and covered with bony plates; among the earliest known vertebrates (p. 593)

outbreeding the mating of distantly related organisms (p. 207)

ovarian cycle the cycle of changes that takes place in the ovary, including the maturation of the follicle and the release of the egg (p. 807)

ovary in a flower, the structure that contains maturing ovules and develops into a fruit; the female reproductive organ that releases eggs and produces the hormones estrogen and progesterone (pp. 463, 806)

ovulation the release of a mature egg from the ovary (p. 807)

ovule a structure in seed plants consisting of an egg inside protective cells; develops into a seed (pp. 463, 483)

ovum a mature egg cell in the female reproductive cycle (p. 807)

ozone layer the layer of the atmosphere composed of ozone molecules; shields Earth from ultraviolet radiation (p. 931)

P

paleontologist a scientist who studies ancient life through fossils (p. 232)

palmate a dicot leaf characterized by lobes radiating from a central point; resembles the fingers and palm of a hand (p. 399)

pancreas an organ involved in the digestive and endocrine systems; secretes the hormones insulin and glucagon (p. 728)

GLOSSARY

Pangaea the supercontinent once formed when the present world continents were connected (p. 271)

parapodium a paddlelike structure found on some annelids; used in respiration and/or locomotion (p. 538)

parasite an organism or virus that derives its nutrients by living in or on a host, eventually causing harm to the host (p. 329)

parasitism a symbiotic relationship between two organisms in which one species harms the other species (p. 887)

parasympathetic nervous system a division of the autonomic nervous system that controls body functions associated with rest and digestion (p. 832)

passive transport the movement of a substance across a cell membrane without the use of ATP energy (p. 72)

pathogen a substance or organism that causes an infectious disease in other organisms (p. 770)

peat bog a wet ecosystem formed by large mats of sphagnum moss in cold and temperate regions (p. 477)

pedigree a chart that shows how a trait is inherited throughout a family (p. 142)

pedipalp in arachnids, a specialized appendage that helps to hold and chew food (p. 553)

penis the male reproductive organ that delivers sperm during intercourse (p. 805)

perennial a plant that lives, reproduces, and continues to grow year after year (p. 416)

pericardium the double-walled sac surrounding the heart; covers, protects, and anchors the heart to the diaphragm and breast bone (p. 756)

period a subdivision of an era on the geologic time scale (p. 268)

periosteum the membrane covering bones in an endoskeleton (p. 699)

peripheral nervous system (PNS) a network of nerves that extend throughout the body and gather and deliver information to and from the central nervous system (p. 823)

peristalsis successive waves of smooth muscle contractions that move food along the digestive tract (p. 726)

petal the usually colorful, leaflike appendages on a flower that attract pollinators (p. 464)

petiole the stalk that connects a leaf to a stem (p. 399)

phagocyte a leucocyte that engulfs and digests unwanted cells and pathogens in a nonspecific manner (p. 775)

phagocytosis the process in which the cell membrane engulfs a food particle, or other solid substance, and brings it into the cell (p. 76)

pharynx in planarians, a muscular tube used to take in food; the tube in the human respiratory system located where the mouth and nose come together; throat (pp. 525, 746)

phenotype the outward expression of an allele or alleles (p. 135)

pheromone a chemical signal used by an insect or animal to communicate (pp. 48, 560)

phloem the vascular tissue that transports sugars and nutrients upward and downward in a plant (p. 410)

phospholipid a structural substance found in cell membranes (pp. 35, 62)

photic zone the area in an aquatic biome in which light can penetrate and support photosynthetic organisms (p. 866)

photoperiodism a plant response that is linked to day and night length (p. 449)

photoreceptor a receptor within the retina that responds to light energy (p. 834)

photosynthesis the process by which autotrophs convert sunlight into a usable form of energy (p. 85)

photosystem the light-collecting unit of a chloroplast (p. 86)

phototropism a response in which a plant grows towards the light (p. 446)

pH scale the standard measurement of the concentration of hydrogen ions (H^+) in a solution (p. 51)

phylogenetic tree the branching structure taxonomists use to compare relationships between taxa (p. 305)

phylum the level below kingdom in the classification system (p. 301)

phytochrome a blue pigment that controls photoperiodism and other responses, such as flowering, seed germination, and seasonal inactivity in plants (p. 450)

phytoplankton the algae component of plankton (p. 365)

pigment a molecule that absorbs certain wavelengths of light and reflects or transmits others (p. 85)

pinnate a featherlike dicot leaf characterized by smaller veins branching off a main central vein (p. 399)

pinocytosis a process in which the cell membrane encloses a droplet of fluid and its solutes and brings the droplet into the cell (p. 76)

pioneer community the first organisms to occupy an area previously uninhabited by its species (p. 891)

pistil the female structure of a flowering plant that produces eggs (p. 463)

pituitary gland an important endocrine gland that releases hormones that affect many body activities (p. 798)

placenta an organ through which materials are exchanged between the mother and the developing embryo (p. 810)

placental mammal a mammal whose offspring develop inside the mother's body until birth (p. 652)

plankton a collection of mostly microscopic organisms that float near the surface of oceans and lakes (p. 365)

planula a free-swimming, ciliated larva (p. 511)

plasma the thick yellowish fluid component of blood that suspends blood cells and other substances (p. 759)

plasmid a small circular piece of DNA found in bacteria; can serve as a vector in genetic engineering (pp. 211, 336)

plasmodium the feeding stage in the life cycle of a plasmodial slime mold (p. 362)

platelet a small membrane-bound cytoplasmic disk found in plasma; causes blood to clot (p. 760)

plate tectonics a theory that describes the movement of Earth's crustal plates relative to one another (p. 271)

pleiotropy a single gene that affects more than one trait (p. 150)

pneumonia a type of respiratory disease characterized by inflammation of alveoli; results in accumulation of fluid and debris in alveoli and decreased exchange of oxygen and carbon dioxide (p. 751)

point mutation the replacement of a single base pair in a gene (p. 194)

pollen the grains produced by the anther in a plant; the male gametophyte (p. 463)

pollination the transfer of pollen from a male plant part to a female plant part (pp. 402, 464)

pollinator the wind or an animal that carries pollen from plant to plant (p. 488)

polygenic trait a trait controlled by two or more gene pairs (p. 149)

polymer a large molecule composed of a string of monomers (p. 260)

polyp a sessile, tubelike form of cnidarian with a mouth on the dorsal surface and tentacles that point upward (p. 509)

polyploidy a genetic condition in which nondisjunction occurs in all the chromosome pairs; the organism has more than two sets of chromosomes (p. 176)

population a group of organisms of the same species living in a specific area (pp. 855, 876)

population ecology the study of how and why populations change and how those changes affect an environment (p. 876)

population genetics the study of genetic traits and changes in populations (p. 246)

post-anal tail a tail that extends beyond the anus (p. 581)

predation the interaction between organisms in which one species (the predator) captures and eats another species (the prey) (p. 882)

predator an organism that eats other organisms (p. 14)

prehensile tail a tail composed of many muscles that can be used to grip branches while climbing or swinging; characteristic of New World monkeys (p. 283)

premolar a broad, flattened tooth adapted for grinding and crushing; located in front of the molar (p. 649)

pressure-flow hypothesis an explanation of how sugar is transported throughout plant cells (p. 432)

prey an organism eaten by another organism (p. 14)

primary growth the elongation of plant stems and roots (p. 436)

primary immune response the initial response of the immune system to a new pathogen (p. 782)

primary shoot the first stem that emerges from a seed; forms the main stem and leaves (p. 436)

primary succession a process that occurs when a new community arises from a previously lifeless habitat (p. 891)

primate a group of mammals that includes all monkeys, apes, and humans (p. 280)

prion a carbohydrate-protein molecule that causes disease in animals (p. 333)

probability the likelihood of an event or the frequency of an occurrence (p. 138)

producer an autotroph that provides food for a community (p. 898)

prokaryote an organism whose cells do not contain a nucleus or membrane-bound organelles (pp. 64, 336)

promoter a section of DNA that serves as the binding site for the enzyme RNA polymerase (p. 190)

prophage a viral DNA segment that has become part of a host cell's chromosome (p. 328)

prophase the first stage of mitosis, during which the nuclear membrane and nucleolus disappear and chromatin condenses to form visible chromosomes (p. 109)

prosimian a small primate with large forward-facing eyes (p. 281)

protein a complex macromolecule composed of amino acids (p. 35)

protein synthesis the manufacture of proteins; the mechanism that translates an organism's genotype (the information stored in DNA) into its phenotype (the observed traits) (p. 182)

proton a subatomic particle with a positive charge and a relatively large mass (p. 38)

protostome a coelomate whose blastopore develops into a mouth (p. 575)

protozoan a protist with animal-like characteristics (p. 355)

pseudopod a lobe of extended cytoplasm used by sarcodinians for movement and capturing food (p. 356)

puberty a stage in humans between the ages of 10 and 13 when the sexual organs mature and secondary sexual characteristics develop (p. 813)

pulmonary circuit the circulatory loop that carries blood between the heart and lungs (p. 755)

punctuated equilibrium one theory about the rate of evolution—that species are stable for long periods of time followed by short periods of rapid genetic change (p. 237)

Punnett square a grid used to predict the outcome of breeding (p. 139)

purebred any organism that receives the same genetic information from each of its parents (p. 131)

pyrogen a chemical released by macrophages that causes fever by stimulating the hypothalamus to raise body temperature (p. 779)

R

radial symmetry the arrangement of body parts around a central axis in a shape similar to the spokes of a wheel (p. 509)

radioactive isotope an isotope in which the nucleus is highly unstable and breaks apart spontaneously, giving off energy in the form of radiation (p. 39)

radula a tonguelike organ in some mollusks that is used in feeding (p. 533)

rain shadow a region of low rainfall on the sheltered side of a mountain (p. 860)

reasoning thinking of a solution or drawing a conclusion from known information or observations (p. 677)

recessive allele the form of a trait that is typically masked by the dominant allele (p. 133)

recombinant DNA DNA containing fragments derived from different organisms (p. 211)

recombination the process by which new combinations of genes are passed on to offspring (p. 168)

red blood cell a cell that carries oxygen to all cells of the body (p. 759)

red bone marrow marrow producing blood cells (p. 699)

reflex a simple, innate, involuntary response to a specific stimulus; an automatic response to a change in the environment (pp. 672, 827)

reflex arc the pathway of neurons that carries the nerve impulses for an automatic, involuntary response to a stimulus (p. 827)

regeneration the process of growing back a lost body part (p. 379)

renewable resource a resource that can be replenished through natural processes (p. 918)

replication the process by which something makes copies of itself (pp. 107, 163)

repressor a protein that binds to DNA, turning the genes "off," or halting gene expression (p. 189)

respiration the overall process by which a body gets and uses oxygen and gets rid of carbon dioxide (p. 745)

response a reaction to a change (p. 668)

resting potential the electrical charge across the cell membrane of a neuron in the resting state (p. 825)

restriction enzyme the enzyme that "cuts," or breaks, DNA bonds at precise spots within the base sequence (p. 209)

retina the part of the eye that contains photoreceptors (p. 834)

retrovirus a virus containing an RNA core that replicates by first transcribing its RNA into DNA (p. 332)

reverse transcriptase an enzyme which transcribes viral RNA into viral DNA (p. 332)

rhizoid the part of a hypha that anchors a fungus to its nutrient source (p. 380)

rhizome an underground stem in vascular plants that produces shoots above the ground and roots below (p. 479)

ribosome an organelle that helps to assemble proteins from amino acids (p. 66)

ritual a series of communication behaviors performed the same way by all members of a population (p. 680)

RNA (ribonucleic acid) a single-stranded nucleic acid molecule; involved in protein synthesis; nitrogenous bases include cytosine, guanine, adenine, and uracil (p. 182)

RNA polymerase an enzyme that matches RNA bases with the complimentary bases on the DNA template; catalyzes transcription (p. 183)

RNA splicing a step in eukaryote protein synthesis in which introns are removed from mRNA; controls which genetic information leaves the nucleus (p. 184)

rod a photoreceptor in eyes that can function with very little light but cannot detect color (p. 834)

S

salivary gland a gland in the mouth that produces saliva (p. 725)

saprophyte a fungus that digests and absorbs nutrients from dead organisms (p. 376)

sapwood the outer, light-colored layers of secondary xylem that transport water (p. 439)

sarcodinian a protozoan that moves by extending lobes of cytoplasm (p. 355)

sarcomere a unit of layered thick and thin filaments; part of a myofibril (p. 708)

scavenger a consumer that feeds on the remains of dead organisms (p. 900)

scientific method a process that involves making predictions, designing an experiment that tests those predictions, making careful observations about that experiment, and interpreting those observations (p. 20)

sebaceous gland a gland usually found attached to hair follicles in the dermis that produces sebum (p. 712)

sebum an oily substance produced by glands in the dermis layer of the skin; keeps the dermis soft and flexible (p. 711)

secondary growth growth that makes the roots, stems, and branches of a seed plant wider (p. 437)

secondary immune response the rapid response of the immune system to a previously encountered pathogen (p. 782)

secondary succession the development of a new community in a previously occupied habitat (p. 891)

seed a reproductive structure consisting of a plant embryo and its stored food (pp. 402, 459)

selective breeding the breeding of organisms to produce specific traits in the offspring; also called artificial selection (pp. 206, 235)

self-fertilization the process in which an organism receives genetic information from one parent (p. 131)

semipermeable allowing only certain molecules to pass through membrane (p. 72)

sensory neuron a neuron that receives impulses from the environment and relays these messages towards the central nervous system (p. 826)

sepal a leaf at the base of the flower that covers the bud and protects the developing flower parts as they grow (p. 464)

septum a cross-wall that divides fungal hyphae into segments; thick wall of muscle separating right and left halves of the heart (pp. 375, 756)

sessile permanently attached to one spot (p. 500)

seta a bristlelike structure projecting from the body wall of many annelids; used in locomotion (p. 536)

sex chromosome a chromosome responsible for determining sex (p. 170)

sex-influenced trait an autosomal gene expressed differently in different sexes (p. 172)

sex-limited trait an autosomal gene expressed in only one sex (p. 172)

sex-linked gene a gene located on a sex chromosome (p. 170)

sexual reproduction the production of offspring by combining genetic material from two parent organisms (p. 106)

sieve plate in echinoderms, a cluster of openings in which water enters and leaves the body (p. 573)

sieve tube in plants, the tube formed by sieve tube elements stacked end to end (p. 431)

sieve tube element in plants, a cell present in phloem lacking ribosomes and nuclei; allows sap to move through sievelike end walls (p. 431)

sign stimulus an object, event, or behavior that signals a fixed-action pattern of behavior (p. 672)

sinoatrial node a mass of nerve and muscle cells located in the wall of the right atrium; sends electrical signals to the atria, causing them to contract (p. 758)

sister chromatid one of two identical copies of condensed genetic material attached at a point known as the centromere (p. 108)

skeletal muscle voluntary muscle tissue that enables the movement of the arms, legs, and other body parts (p. 706)

skeleton the framework of organs and connective tissues that supports the body, protects internal organs, and allows for movement (p. 696)

sliding filament theory a theory stating that skeletal muscles move because actin filaments travel towards each other during muscle contraction while myosin filaments remain constant (p. 708)

small intestine the organ between the stomach and the large intestine that completes the digestion and absorption of proteins and other nutrients (p. 726)

smog a haze of pollutants that hangs in the air; contains harmful chemicals and particulates (p. 928)

smooth muscle involuntary muscle tissue found in most internal organs (p. 706)

social insect an insect that lives in a colony where individual insects are structurally adapted to perform a specific job (p. 560)

GLOSSARY

soil erosion the slow destruction of land and topsoil by water and wind (p. 920)

solute the dissolved substance in a solution (p. 49)

solution a uniform mixture of two substances (p. 49)

solvent the dissolving substance in a solution (p. 49)

somatic nervous system a division of the peripheral nervous system that controls voluntary response (p. 831)

sorus a spore-containing structure on the underside of a fern leaf (p. 479)

speciation the evolution of one or more new species from a single ancestral species (p. 241)

species an interbreeding population of organisms that can produce healthy, fertile offspring (p. 230)

specific defense the cellular or chemical response of the immune system to a specific pathogen (p. 773)

sperm a small, motile gamete produced by males (p. 803)

spicule a tiny needlelike or starlike structure in a sponge made of silicon dioxide or calcium carbonate (p. 505)

spiracle a small external opening in the exoskeleton of arthropods through which air enters the respiratory system (p. 556)

spongin a network of protein fibers in a sponge (p. 504)

spongy bone bone tissue with many open spaces; found in ends of long bones and in middle parts of short, flat bones (p. 699)

spontaneous generation a theory stating that living organisms are produced from nonliving matter and ethers (pp. 4, 60)

sporangium a hollow reproductive structure that produces spores (p. 380)

spore a haploid (n) reproductive unit of plants that produces the gametophyte phase; its hard outer surface is specialized for dispersal (p. 379)

sporophyte the diploid ($2n$) phase of a plant life cycle that produces spores (p. 459)

sporozoan a spore-forming, parasitic protozoan (p. 357)

stamen the male structure of a flowering plant that produces pollen (p. 463)

steroid a group of lipids that provide structure and control functions for the cell (p. 35)

stigma the sticky structure of the pistil in which pollen grains land and germinate (p. 463)

stimulant a drug that increases the central nervous system's activity (p. 840)

stimulus an environmental condition to which an organism responds (pp. 446, 668)

stolon a hypha that connects groups of rhizoids in a plant or fungus (p. 380)

stoma a pore in the epidermis of a plant that allows for gas exchange (p. 423)

stomach a thick muscular sac with expandable walls that secretes acids and enzymes; it mechanically and chemically digests foods (p. 726)

strain smaller group of bacterial species within the classification system (p. 301)

striated muscle muscle characterized by narrow bands that are visible under a microscope; also known as skeletal muscle (p. 706)

stroke a blockage in one of the brain's blood vessels (p. 838)

stroma a gel-like matrix surrounding the thylakoids; the site of the sugar-producing reactions in photosynthesis (p. 86)

stromatolite a layered geological structure of fossilized bacteria and sediment (p. 266)

style the structure of the pistil connecting the stigma to the ovary (p. 463)

subcutaneous layer the layer of fat under skin layers that stores energy and insulates the body (p. 711)

substrate the reactant in an enzyme-catalyzed reaction (p. 44)

suppressor T cell a white blood cell that slows and then stops the immune response at the end of an infection (p. 781)

sustainable development using natural resources at a rate that does not deplete them (p. 919)

swim bladder in ray-finned fishes, a thin-walled sac that can inflate or deflate to regulate buoyancy (p. 594)

symbiosis a relationship in which two different organisms live in close association (pp. 344, 887)

sympathetic nervous system a division of the autonomic nervous system that controls the body's response to stressful situations (p. 832)

synapse a tiny gap between adjacent neurons and between neurons and effectors (p. 826)

systemic circuit the circulatory loop that transports oxygenated blood to the body and returns deoxygenated blood to the heart (p. 755)

systole the part of the heart beat in which the ventricles contract, pumping the blood out to the body (p. 758)

T

taiga a biome characterized by long, cold winters and short, relatively mild summers; its primary vegetation is spruce and fir (p. 862)

taproot in plants, single large central root with many smaller roots branching out from it (p. 401)

taxonomy the branch of biology that identifies, classifies, and names different types of organisms (p. 300)

telophase the final phase of mitosis in which new nuclear membranes form (p. 109)

temperate forest a biome characterized by warm summers and moderate winters, and approximately the same amount of precipitation in each of the four seasons; large deciduous forest community (p. 863)

temperate zone the region that extends from about 30° to about 60° north and south latitude (p. 859)

tendon connective tissue that attaches muscles to bones (p. 701)

test cross the cross of a homozygous recessive and an unknown genotype resulting in offspring with observable phenotypes (p. 141)

testes the male reproductive organs that produce sperm and the hormone testosterone (p. 804)

tetrad homologous chromosomes that pair up in a set of four chromatids during prophase I of meiosis (p. 168)

theory a hypothesis that is supported by many experiments done over a period of time (p. 23)

thermophile a group of archaebacteria that live in hot water environments (p. 341)

thigmotropism the growth of a plant in response to touch (p. 447)

thylakoid an individual disc-shaped structure within the chloroplast; contains chlorophyll and all other pigments necessary for photosynthesis (p. 86)

thymine one of four nitrogenous bases in DNA; a pyrimidine that pairs with adenine (p. 161)

tissue a group of similar cells that work together to perform a specific function (pp. 11, 692)

tissue culture the process of growing an entire plant from individual cells or from small pieces of leaf, stem, or root (p. 457)

T lymphocyte a white blood cell that participates in cell-mediated immune responses (p. 781)

toxin a poison (p. 730)

trachea the main passageway to the lungs; also called the windpipe (p. 746)

tracheid a long narrow cell found in xylem; forms a thick hollow cylinder that transports water (p. 430)

trait any characteristic that can be passed on from parents to offspring (p. 130)

transcription the process of transferring information from a strand of DNA to a strand of mRNA (p. 182)

transgenic organism a genetically engineered organism that has recombinant DNA from a different species added to its genome (p. 213)

translation the formation of an amino chain from the information provided by mRNA (p. 183)

translocation the process in which part of a chromosome breaks off and attaches to a different, nonhomologous chromosome (p. 193)

transpiration the evaporation of water from the parts of a plant exposed to air (p. 431)

trisomy a genetic condition in which the zygote receives three copies of a particular chromosome instead of two (p. 175)

tRNA (transfer RNA) a form of RNA that carries amino acids to the ribosome during protein synthesis (p. 184)

trophic level a step in the transfer of energy and matter within an ecological community (p. 900)

tropical rain forest a biome characterized by warm, wet weather, lush plant life, and diverse animal communities (p. 864)

tropical zone the region that extends from the equator to about 30° north and south latitudes (p. 859)

tropism the growth of a plant in a certain direction in response to a stimulus (pp. 446)

tube foot a hollow tube with a suction-producing cuplike end; located beneath an ampulla in echinoderms (p. 573)

tumor-suppressor gene a gene responsible for the control of cell reproduction; actions help prevent the growth of tumors (p. 197)

tundra a treeless permanently frozen biome in the arctic and subarctic regions (p. 862)

turgor the rigidity of a plant cell caused by osmotic pressure on the cell's membrane (p. 428)

tympanic membrane a circular structure behind a frog's eye that transmits sound waves to the inner ear (p. 606)

U

uniramian an arthropod that has a single pair of antennae, compound eyes, and highly specialized chewing mouthparts (p. 556)

uracil in RNA, the nitrogenous base that binds with the DNA base adenine (p. 183)

urine a yellow-colored liquid expelled from the body; contains wastes removed from the blood (p. 735)

uterus the female organ with muscular walls in which a fetus develops from a fertilized egg into an individual capable of surviving outside the mother's body (p. 806)

V

vaccination a process of injecting a person with a weakened or dead derivative of a pathogen; stimulates the immune system to produce and store special cells and proteins that will later destroy that type of pathogen if it ever enters the body (p. 335)

vaccine a medicine that contains dead or weakened pathogens that increases a person's immunity (p. 788)

vacuole a membrane-bound sac or compartment within plant cells that absorbs water or may store proteins, ions, and waste products (p. 70)

variable a factor that can change during the course of an experiment (p. 21)

variation a difference between members of the same population (pp. 119, 230)

vascular cambium the area located between the xylem and phloem; produces new xylem and phloem during the plant's secondary growth (p. 438)

vascular plant a plant, such as a tree, a vine, or grass, that has vascular tissue (p. 413)

vector a carrier of genetic material used in genetic engineering (p. 211)

vegetative reproduction the types of asexual reproduction that take place naturally in plants (p. 456)

vein in plants, the vascular bundle that transports water and food throughout a leaf; in animals, a blood vessel that returns blood from the tissues to the heart (pp. 399, 757)

ventral the front side of the body of an animal with bilateral symmetry (p. 693)

ventricle a lower chamber of the heart; pumps blood throughout the body (p. 756)

venule the smallest of veins (p. 757)

vertebrae the series of bones that form the backbone (p. 592)

vertebrate an animal with a backbone (pp. 503, 592)

vessel element in plants, the short wide cell in xylem with no end walls; transports water (p. 430)

vestigial structure a structure or characteristic that is unused but which is homologous with structures or characteristics in other species, suggesting common ancestry (p. 239)

villus a fingerlike projection on the intestinal wall that increases the surface area across which nutrients are absorbed (p. 727)

viroid a strand of pure RNA that causes disease in plants (p. 333)

virus a particle consisting of nucleic acid and a protein coat that causes disease in many organisms (p. 326)

vital capacity the largest volume of air that can be inhaled and exhaled (p. 748)

W

water cycle the continual movement of water from Earth's surface to the atmosphere and back to the surface again (p. 910)

water vascular system in echinoderms, a network of fluid-filled tubes that enable movement, feeding, and respiration (p. 573)

Wernicke's area the portion of the cerebral cortex that stores the information needed to understand language (p. 830)

wetland a region such as a bog, swamp, or marsh that is permanently or occasionally covered with water (p. 868)

white blood cell a cell that helps a body fight disease (p. 760)

X, Y, Z

xylem the vascular tissue that carries water and dissolved minerals from the roots to the leaves in a plant (p. 410)

yellow bone marrow marrow found in cavities within shafts of long bones; made mostly of fat cells (p. 699)

yolk the food source for a developing embryo (p. 622)

Z line an area of dense matter that separates sarcomeres in muscle tissue (p. 708)

zooflagellete a protozoan that moves by means of flagella (p. 356)

zygospore a thick-walled diploid fungal spore containing many nuclei; it is formed during sexual reproduction (p. 381)

Note: **Bold** page number indicates a key word; *italicized* page number indicates a figure.

INDEX

Forensics, 217
Fossil fuel, 17, 408, **907**, 918, 921, 928
Fossil record, 232, 238–239
   comparison of rock layers, 263
   to create geological time scale, 268
   incomplete, 237, 239, 502
Fracture, 702
Fragmentation, 477
Frameshift mutation, **193**–194
Franklin, Rosalind, 161
Fritz, Emanuel, 397
Frog, 607–608, 610, 613–614
Frog fish, *602*
Frond, 479
Fruit, **403**, 415, 474, 487–488
   definition, 407
   as energy source, 488–489
   fleshy vs. dry, 415
Fruiting body, 362, 363, 379, 382
Fuels, 17–18, 907
Fungi, 302
   classification of, 312, 378
   club, 382–383
   disease-causing, 385–386
   ecological roles in, 384–385
   growth of, 376–377
   human uses for, 386–387
   imperfect, 383
   nutrition in, 376
   origin of, 378–379
   parasitic, 376
   reproduction in, 378–379
   sac, 379, 381–382
   structure of, 374–375
Furcula, 633

--------------- G ---------------

Galapagos Islands, 229, 236, 244, 892
Gallbladder, **728**
Gametes, 114, 115, 118–120, 131,
   175–176, 506, 803
Gametophyte, **459**
   angiosperm, 486
   fern, 478, 479
   generation, 361
   hornwort, 471
   moss, 471, 476
   pine, 482
Ganglia, **822**
Gas exchange, 537, 650, 744–745, 749
Gastropods, 533
Gastrula, **502,** 574
Gastrulation, *502*
Gavials, 628
Geese, nesting behavior, 672
Gel electrophoresis, 210
Gemmae, 477
Gemmule, **506**
Gene control, 188–191, 798

Gene expression, 150–151, 182–183,
   189, 190
Gene flow, 247, 311
Gene map, 169
Gene pool, migration and, 272
Gene therapy, 199, 214–215
Genes, **133,** 134, 165. *See also*
   Sex-linked genes
   activation and deactivation, 188
   cloning, 211, *212*
   coding for proteins, 182
   location of, 168–169
   mutations, 193–195
   viral, 326–327
Genetic counseling, 144–145, 168–169,
   174
Genetic disorders, 143–145, 216
Genetic diversity in populations, 888
Genetic drift, **248**
Genetic engineering, 24, 106, 199, **209,**
   213–220, 335, 346, 387
Genetic equilibrium, **246**–247
Genetically Engineered Biological
   Bandage (GEBB), 213
Genetics, **130**–*161*
Genital warts, 816
Genome, **173**
Genotype, **134**–135, 139, 141, 182
Genus, **301**
Geological time scale, 268, *269*
Geothermal energy, 921–922
Geotropism, 446–447
Germ layers, 809–810
Germ theory, 22, 770–771
Germination, *460,* 461
Gestation period, **652**
Giant kelp, 352, 361
Giant puffball, 378
Giardia, 366
Gill pouch, 240
Gill slits, **581,** 592
Gills, 595–596, 744–745
   in arthropods, 547
   in filter feeders, 533
   in mushrooms, *375*
Ginkgos, 474, 482, 484
Gizzard, **634**–635
Glands, function of, 692
Glial cells, 693, **824,** 828–829
Gliding joint, *701*
Global warming, 271, 272, 427, 518,
   907, **930**–931
Glucagon, 799
Glucose
   in cellular respiration, 907
   cellulose formation, 90
   in diabetes mellitus, 801
   as energy source, 90, 94
   in plants, 424–425
   storage of, 90, 94

Glycerol, antifreeze properties, 42
Glycogen, 35, 730
Glycolysis, **92**
Gnetae, 474, 482
Golgi apparatus, **66,** 67
Golgi vesicles, 76
Gonyaulax toxin, 366
Goose bumps, 651
Gorilla, *659*
Gould, Stephen Jay, 237
Gradualism, **237**
Grafting, 457
Gram staining, **342**
Grana, 86
Grasshopper, 556, *557*
Grassland, *865*
Gray matter, 828–829
Grebes, 639
Green Belt Movement, 933
Green gland, 550–551
Greenhouse effect, 427, 907, **930**–931
Griffith, Frederick, 158–159
Growth and development, 7, 47, 103,
   105, 813–814
Growth factor, 196–197
Growth hormone, 106, 802
Growth inhibitors, 451
Growth rings, 439, 440
Guanine, **161**
Guard cells, 423, 426
Gymnosperm, **415,** 473–474, 483–484
   See also Conifers

--------------- H ---------------

Habitat, **855,** 868, 923
Habituation, **676**
Hagfishes, 600
Hair follicle, 712
Half-life, **263,** 264–265
Hallucinogens, **840**
Halophiles, 341
Hansen's disease, 836
Haploid cell, **114,** 115, 459, *482*
Hardy-Weinberg principle, 246–247
Harvey, William, 5–6
Haversian canals, 699
Hazardous wastes, 922–923
HCl. *See* Hydrochloric acid
Hearing, 835
Heart, 650, **754**–746, 762
Heart attack, 762, 843
Heart rate, 758
Heartwood, 439
Helper T cells, 781
Hemoglobin, 37, 749, 759, 760
Hemophilia, 171, 215
Hepatitis, 731
Hepatitis B, 841
Hepatophyta, 471

Acknowledgements

AA—Animals Animals; BA—Bonnier Alba; BC—Bruce Coleman, Inc.; CMS—Custom Medical Stock Photo; GL—Gamma Liaison; GH—Grant Heilman Photography, Inc.; IV—Innerspace Visions; MP—Minden Pictures; MYP—Mo Yung Productions; PA—Peter Arnold, Inc.; PR—Photo Researchers; PT—Phototake; SB—Stock Boston; TSA—Tom Stack & Assoc.; TSI—Tony Stone Images; VU—Visuals Unlimited

PHOTOGRAPHS

iiiB Art Wolfe/TSI; iiiT Norbert Wu/MYP; ixB Robin Kittrell Laughlin; ixC Robin Kittrell Laughlin; ixCR Robin Kittrell Laughlin; ixT Howard Hall/HHP; vBC The Institute of Greatly Endangered and Rare Species, Courtesy, Dr. Antle; vBL Pat Field/BC; vBR Rod Williams/BC; vCR Biophoto Assoc./PR; viBL Gerard Lacz/AA; viCR David M. Dennis/TSA; viT Anthony Mercieca/PR; viiBL Lee D. Simon/Science Source/PR; viiCR Hans Gelderblom/VU; viiiBL Jane Grushow/GH; viiiCL Allan Penn*; viiiT Runk/Schoenberger/GH; xBL Frans Lanting/MP; xBR Tom McHugh/PR; xT E. R. Degginger/PR; xi Dr. Dennis Kunkel/PT; xiiTL Dr. Dennis Kunkel/PT; xiiTR David M. Phillips/PR; xiiiB John Midgley/TSI; xiiiC Dr. Morley Read/Science Photo Library/PR; xiiiTC Alan Carey/PR; xiiiTL Alan Carey/PR; xiiiTR Alan Carey/PR

Chapter 1 1 Allan Penn*; 2–3 Robert & Linda Mitchell; 3BL Dr. Jeremy Burgess/Science Photo Library/PR; 3 TOP BAR E. R. Degginger/PR (firefly); Gustav W. Vergerber/VU (mite); Richard Walters/VU (snow); 4TR (AII79539) The Alchemist by Teniers, David the Elder (1582-1649), Palazzo Pitti, Florence/The Bridgeman Art Library, London; 6TL Richard Walters/VU; 6TR Runk/Schoenberger/GH; 7BC Cheryl Graham/TSI; 7BR E. R. Degginger/AA; 7TL Peter Salek/TSI; 7TR E. R. Degginger/PR; 8BL Raymond G. Barnes/TSI; 8BR Barry L. Runk/GH; 8TC CNRI/Science Photo Library/PR; 8TL Tracey Wheeler*; 10B C. C. Lockwood/AA; 10BL E. R. Degginger/PR; 10CL Michael P. Gadomski/PR; 10CR Cabisco/VU; 10TL NASA/PR; 10TR Dennis Drenner/VU; 12B Art Wolfe; 12T Leroy Simon/VU; 13B Runk/Schoenberger/GH; 13T Rene Sheret/TSI; 14B Kjell Sandved/PR; 14T Tom Brakefield/BC; 15BC L. J. Connor/VU; 15BR Gustav W. Vergerber/VU; 15T Gary Retherford/PR; 16BL Jim Balog/TSI; 16BR PhotoDisc; 16CL Grant Heilman/GH; 16CR John D. Cunningham/VU; 17BL Larry Lefever/GH; 17BR John Elk III/BC; 17CL Grant Heilman/GH; 17CR Chip Henderson/TSI; 18 Peter Ziminski/VU; 19BL Jane Burton/BC; 19CL Gay Bumgarner/TSI; 19CR Frans Lanting/MP; 19R Tom McHugh/PR; 19T Bob Daemmrich/SB; 20TL Cabisco/VU; 20TR Fred Hossler/VU; 21 Len Rue Jr./BC; 24B Gregory G. Dimijian/PR; 24T Tracey Wheeler*; 25 Sherwood Landers/GL; 26 Allan Penn*

Unit 1 30BR Tracey Wheeler*; 30C Roland Birke/OKAPIA/PR; 30CL M. P. Kahl/DRK; 30TR Allan Penn*; 31B PhotoDisc; 31BL Kjell B. Sandved/VU; 31BR Jim Ballard/TSI; 31C David M. Phillips/VU; 31TR David Madison/TSI; 124BL Courtesy, Carlos Contreras; 125B David Powers, 1995; 125T Jerry LeBlond, 1996

Chapter 2 32–33 David Thompson/Oxford Scientific Films/AA; 32C Harry Rogers/PR; 32TR Wolfgang Bayer/BC; 33 TOP BAR George I. Bernard/AA (pond skater); NASA (earth); 34–35 Barry L. Runk/GH; 34BC Barry L. Runk/GH; 34BL D. Wilder/TSA; 35BR Darwin Dale/PR; 36 Grant Heilman/GH; 37BR Michael Rosenfeld/TSI; 37C Dr. Dennis Kunkel/PT; 37TR F. Ruggeri/The Image Bank; 38 Dr. Mitsuo Ohtsuki/Science Photo Library/PR; 39B Hank Morgan/Science Source/PR; 40 Dr. Jeremy Burgess/Science Photo Library/PR; 42 John Gerlach/TSA; 43CR John D. Cunningham/VU; 43TC Thomas and Pat Leeson/PR; 43TL Bert Blokhuis/TSI; 43TR Allan Penn*; 45 Tracey Wheeler*; 46B Gunter Ziesler/PA; 46TR Stephen Dalton/AA; 47BR Ted Clutter/PR; 47T J. H. Robinson/AA; 48 Holt Studios Int'l./Nigel Cattlin/PR; 49 NASA; 49BC Allan Penn*; 49BL Allan Penn*; 49BR Allan Penn*; 50 John Shaw/TSA; 50BC George I. Bernard/AA; 50BL Liz Hymans/TSI; 50C George I. Bernard/AA; 50CL Dr. Jeremy Burgess/Science Photo Library/PR

Chapter 3 56–57 Dr. Gopal Murti/PT; 56C G. Covian/The Image Bank; 57C Art Montes de Oca/FPG; 57 TOP BAR Bruce Iverson/Science Photo Library/PR; 58TC Corbis-Bettmann; 58TR CNRI/Science Photo Library/PR; 59BC Kevin & Betty Collins/VU; 59TC Leonard Lessin/Peter Arnold Inc.; 59TL The Science Museum/Science & Society Picture Library; 60BL David M. Phillips/VU; 61 Courtesy, IBM; 61TR PhotoDisc; 62B VU; 62TR Bruce Iverson/Science Photo Library/PR; 63BR Dr. Dennis Kunkel/PT; 64 Alfred Pasieka/Science Photo Library/CMS; 65TL Institut Pasteur/CNRI/PT; 65TR Don Fawcett/Science Source/PR; 66 Proff. Motta, Correr & Nottola/University "La Sapienza", Rome/Science Photo Library/PR; 67BR K. G. Murti/VU; 67C VU; 68TL Karl Aufderheide/VU; 68TR David M. Phillips/VU; 69BL Dr. Dennis Kunkel/PT; 69BR Don Fawcett/Science Source/PR; 69TR George D. Dodge/BC; 71TC Runk/Schoenberger/GH; 71TR R. Calentine/VU; 72 Runk/Schoenberger/GH; 76 W. J. Johnson/VU

Chapter 4 80–81 Eric Crichton/BC; 80C John Cancalosi/DRK; 81 TOP BAR George B. Chapman/VU; 82 David E. Myers/TSI; 84 Betty Derig/PR; 85 Frans Lanting/TSI; 86BC George B. Chapman/VU; 86BL J. Michael Eichelberger/VU; 86CL Runk/Schoenberger/GH; 87 Tim Davis*; 90 Tracey Wheeler*; 91 Keith Porter/Science Source/PR; 94 David Madison/Duomo; 95 Phillip & Karen Smith/TSI; 96 Tracey Wheeler*; 97B K. & K. Ammann/BC; 97T Michael P. Gadomski/PR; 98 Will & Deni McIntyre/PR; 101 Jason Burns/Ace/PT

Chapter 5 102–103 Art Wolfe/TSI; 102C Clem Haagner/PR; 103 (grass background) Alan Pitcairn/GH; 103 TOP BAR Kent Wood; 104BC Biophoto Assoc./Science Source/PR; 104C Grant Heilman/GH; 104CL Thomas Dressler/DRK; 104TR Gerry Ellis/Ellis Nature Photography; 105 Glenn M. Oliver/VU; 106BC Kent Wood; 107 John D. Cunningham/VU; 108 Gunther F. Bahr/AFIP/TSI; 110BR John D. Cunningham/VU; 110TR M. Abbey/VU; 111L John D. Cunningham/VU; 112 Jason Burns/Ace/PT; 113 Carolina Biological Supply/PT; 114 Oxford Scientific Films/Michael Fogden/AA; 115 CNRI/Science Photo Library/PR; 118 Francois Gohier/PR; 123 CNRI/Science Photo Library/PR; 124BR SimLife ® and © 1992, SimEarth ® and © 1992 Maxis Inc. All Rights Reserved.

Unit 2 126–127 Tracey Wheeler*; 126BL Peter Menzel; 126CR Gary John Norman/TSI; 126T PhotoDisc, photo manipulation by John Scott; 127CR James Gerholdt/PA; 127TL James King-Holmes/Science Photo Library/PR; 224BL Courtesy, Stacie Simmons; 224BR Reprinted with permission of Scribner, a Division of Simon & Schuster from THE DOUBLE HELIX by James D. Watson. Jacket design Jeanyee Wong. Copyright (c) 1968 James D. Watson. 225B Robert Campagna, Courtesy Cornell College; 225T Los Angeles Times. Reprinted by permission.

Chapter 6 128–129 Wayne R. Bilenduke/TSI; 129 TOP BAR Jack M. Bostrack/VU; 130BR Erich Lessing/Art Resource, NY; 130TR Telegraph Colour Library/FPG; 131BR Image Select/Art Resource, NY; 131CR Dwight Kuhn; 132 Mary Evans Picture Library; 134BL Biophoto Assoc./PR; 134TR Jack M. Bostrack/VU; 135 B. Everett Webb; 138 J. D. Schwalm/Stock South; 142BL Ashley Morrison/Uniphoto, Inc.; 142CL Patricia J. Bruno/Positive Images; 142TR Michael Krasowitz/FPG; 143CR CNRI/Science Photo Library/PR; 143TL SIU/PR; 143TR Courtesy, Dr. Eugene J. Mark/Massachusetts General Hospital; 144BR Courtesy, Dr. Jean Paul G. Vonsattel/Massachusetts General Hospital; 144BL CNRI/Science Photo Library/PR; 144TL Nancy M. Hamilton/PR; 145 Peter Menzel/SB; 147 Courtesy, Dr. Erick Greene; 148 CMS; 149 Allan Penn*; 150 Dr. Dennis Kunkel/PT; 150BR Dan McCoy/Rainbow; 150TL Stanley Flegler/VU; 151 R. J. Erwin/PR; 152 Paul Merideth/TSI; 155 Charles Neal/SuperStock

Chapter 7 156C S.N.S./Sipa Press; 156–157 SYGMA; 157 TOP BAR CNRI/Science Photo Library/PR; 158TR Martin Rotker/PT; 160 Dan McCoy/Rainbow; 160TR from "The Double Helix" by J.D. Watson/Cold Spring Harbor Laboratory Archives; 161B A. Barrington Brown/Science Source/PR; 161CR Science Photo Library/PR; 161TR PR; 162 Dr. Gopal Murti/Science Photo Library/PR; 164 Tracey Wheeler*; 165 Gerard Lacz/AA; 170BL Biophoto Assoc./PR; 170CL Biophoto Assoc./PR; 170TR Visual Unlimited; 171 Runk/Schoenberger/GH; 172BL L. West/BC; 172BR L. West/BC; 172TR Bill Ballenberg; 173B CNRI/Science Photo Library/PR; 173T Jeff Greenberg/GL; 174 Shahn Kermani/GL; 175 Jeff Greenberg/VU; 179 Chanan

Chapter 8 180–181 Allan Penn*; 181 TOP BAR David Scharf; 182 Stephen J. Krasemann/PR; 186L Tracey Wheeler*; 186TR Kiselva D. Fawcett/VU; 188B Reprinted with permission from Dr. Bjorn Reino Olsen/Harvard Medical School/1996 American Association for the Advancement of Science; 188T Reprinted with permission from Dr. Lee Niswander (Memorial Sloan Kettering Cancer Institute) 1996 American Association for the Advancement of Science; 191B Professors P. M. Motta, P. M. Andrews, K. R. Porter & J. Vial/Science Photo Library/PR; 191C Steven E. Sutton/Duomo; 191CL Prof. P. Motta/Dept. of Anatomy/University "La Sapienza" Rome/Science Photo Library/PR; 191CR David M. Phillips/VU; 191TL CNRI/Science Photo Library/PR; 191TR Andrew Syred/Science Photo Library/PR; 192BL Kent Wood; 192TR Chanan; 193CL David Scharf; 193TL David Scharf; 193TR Horticultural Photography; 196BC J. Croyle/CMS; 196BL Courtesy, Dr. Bruce Rosen/Massachusetts General Hospital; 196T Corbis-Bettmann; 198BL Heidi Bradner, Courtesy of Dr. Robert Baker /Texas Tech University; 198BR Sovfoto/Eastfoto; 199 Ernest Manewal/FPG; 200CL Grant Le Duc/SB; 200T Franklin Viola; 203 Jon Gordon/PT

Chapter 9 204 Roger/Viollet/GL; 205 Vlastimir Shone/GL; 205 TOP BAR CMS (electrophoresis, left); Jon Gordon/PT (microinjection); Michael Skott/The Image Bank (cat); NIH/CMS (electrophoresis, right); 206BC VU; 206BL David Cavagnaro/PA; 206BR Holt Studios Int'l./Nigel Cattlin/PR; 206T Mitch Kezar/TSI; 207BC Barbara Von Hoffmann/TSA; 207BC Michael Skott/The Image Bank; 207TL Jean-Michel Labat/Jacana/PR; 207TR Victoria Hurst/TSA; 208C The Institute of Greatly Endangered and Rare Species, Courtesy, Dr. Antle; 208TL Pat Field/BC; 208TR Rod Williams/BC; 209 Kjell Sandved/PR; 211BL NIH/CMS; 211CR Courtesy,The Whitehead Institute; 213BC Rick Browne/SB; 213BR Michael P. Gadomski/PR; 213CR Christi Carter/GL; 213T Courtesy, Dr. Daniel Smith, University of Akron; 214 Jon Gordon/PT; 215 Professor P. M. Motta, G. Macchiarelli, S. A. Nottola/Science Photo Library/CMS; 216B Tracey Wheeler*, posters courtesy of The Whitehead Institute; 216TL SIU/VU; 217TL Peter Menzel; 217TR Science Photo Library/CMS; 219B SIU/PR; 219T Dan McCoy/Rainbow; 223BR Kenneth W. Fink/BC; 223TR Drawing by Gahan Wilson; The New Yorker Magazine, Inc.

Unit 3 226BL Francois Gohier/PR; 226BR Tracey Wheeler*; 226TL Frank Rossotto/Stocktrek; 226TR Charles Shotwell; 227BR Tracey Wheeler*; 227CL Keren Su/TSI; 227CR Robin Kittrell Laughlin; 227TL Francois Gohier/PR; 227TR M. P. Kahl/PR; 320BL Courtesy, Dana Denson; 320BR Inherit The Wind © 1960 United Artists Pictures, Inc. All Rights Reserved. Still courtesy of MGM Consumer Products. 321B The Field Museum, photo by John Weinstein, neg # GN 88096; 321T Courtesy, Conneticut College

Chapter 10 228–229 Barry L. Runk/GH; 229BR by permission of the Syndics of Cambridge University Library; 229TL The Granger Collection, New York; 229 TOP BAR David M. Dennis/TSA; 230BL Zig Leszczynski/AA; 230CL Darrell Gulin/TSI; 230T Rudie Kuiter/1985 Discover Magazine; 231BC Kim Taylor/BC; 231BL Tom Brakefield/BC; 232BL Jeff Foott/TSA; 233BR Archive Photos; 233C Science Photo Library/PR; 233CR Illustrated London News/Archive Photos; 233TC Michio Hoshino/MP; 234BL Norman Owen Tomalin/BC; 234BR Tim Davis/PR; 235CL Jane Grushow/GH; 235CR Michael P. Gadomski/PR; 235T Frank T. Awbrey/VU; 235TL Norm Thomas/PR; 235T John Colwell/GH; 236B Karl Ammann/BC; 236T William & Marcia Levy/PR; 238T David M. Dennis/TSA; 239BR Kenneth W. Fink/BC; 239CR John D. Cunningham/VU; 240CL Petit Format/Nestle/Science Source/PR; 240TL Lennart Nilsson/BA; 241BC G. C. Kelley/PR; 241BR Douglas Faulkner/PR; 241CR Charlie Ott/PR; 241TC Dieter & Mary Plage/BC; 241TL Corbis-Bettmann; 242BL Gerard Lacz/AA; 242BR Gerard Lacz/PA; 242TL Bryn Campbell/TSI; 242TR Stephen

1014

Chapter 22   522–523 WHOI-D Foster/VU; 523T © 1993 NSF Oasis Project/Mo Yung Productions; 523 TOP BAR David Scharf/PA (hookworm); L. West/BC (earthworm); Marty Snyderman/VU (polychaeta); Stephen Frink/WaterHouse (mollusk); 524BR M. I. Walker/Science Source/PR; 524T Tom McHugh/PR; 525 Tom E. Adams/PA; 527B A. Kerstitch/VU; 527T R. Calentine/VU; 528C Runk/Schoenberger/GH; 528CL David Scharf/PA; 528T J. H. Robinson/PR; 529TC Fred Marsik/VU; 529TR Science Photo Library/CMS; 530BL Daniel W. Gotshall; 530CL Daniel W. Gotshall; 530T Breck P. Kent/AA; 531 James P. Rowan/TSI; 532BL George I. Bernard/AA; 532BR Polaroid/VU; 533B Fred Bavendam/PA; 533TL Stephen Frink/WaterHouse; 533TR Norbert Wu/MYP; 534 Norbert Wu/MYP; 535 Peter Yates/Science Photo Library/PR; 536BL Marty Snyderman/VU; 536CL L. West/BC; 536T Cabisco/VU; 536TL Y. Lanceau Jacana/PR; 537 David Fox/Oxford Scientific Films/AA; 538 Marty Snyderman/VU; 539 St. Bartholomew's Hospital/Science Photo Library/PR; 543 John Shaw/BC

Chapter 23   544C George Lepp/TSI; 544–545 James L. Amos; 545 TOP BAR Kjell B. Sandved/VU (rhino beetle); Robin Kittrell Laughlin (beetle, dragonfly, pill bugs); 546B Robin Kittrell Laughlin; 546T Kjell B. Sandved/VU; 547BL Barry L. Runk/GH; 547BR Barry L. Runk/GH; 547T Richard Walters/VU; 548 Michael Fogden/BC; 549 Howard Hall/Oxford Scientific Films/AA; 549B Tracey Wheeler*; 550 H. W. Robinson/VU; 551CR Nancy Sefton/PR; 551T Robin Kittrell Laughlin; 552B John Mitchell/PR; 552T Kjell B. Sandved/VU; 553 Heinz Plenge/PA; 554BC Carol Hughes/BC; 554BL Ed Degginger/BC; 554BR Runk/Schoenberger/GH; 554CL William C. Jorgensen/VU; 555BC John Cancalosi/DRK; 555C J. C. Carton/BC; 555CR Joe & Carol McDonald/BC; 556BL Oxford Scientific Films/AA; 556CL Nuridsany et Perennou/PR; 556T Peter Menzel; 556TL Andrew Syred/Science Photo Library/PR; 557 Robin Kittrell Laughlin; 558C Alex Kerstitch/VU; 558CL Robin Kittrell Laughlin; 558CR Robin Kittrell Laughlin; 558TR C. W. Perkins/AA; 559B J. & L. Waldman/BC; 559BC Ken Lucas/VU; 559BR Kevin Byron/BC; 559CL John Shaw/BC; 559CR Michael Fogden/BC; 559TC Robin Kittrell Laughlin; 559TL Robin Kittrell Laughlin; 559TR E. R. Degginger/BC; 560BR Mark Moffett/MP; 560CL Runk/Schoenberger/GH; 560CR Hans Pfletschinger/PA; 561 Grant Heilman/GH; 562BL Stephen J. Krasemann/DRK; 562BR Runk/Schoenberger/GH; 562TL Michael Fogden/BC; 562TR E. R. Degginger/BC; 563 J. Spurr/BC; 564B Runk/Schoenberger/GH; 564TL Nuridsany et Perennou/PR; 564TR Nuridsany et Perennou/PR; 565BL Richard Hutchings/BC; 565CR Robin Kittrell Laughlin; 566BL Zig Leszczynski/AA; 566CL Runk/Schoenberger/GH; 566T D. Cavagnaro/DRK; 568 Robin Kittrell Laughlin; 569 Larry Lipsky/BC

Chapter 24   570C Columbus America Discovery Group; 570–571 Columbus America Discovery Group; 571 TOP BAR Doug Perrine/IV (sea urchin); Norbert Wu/MYP (sun star); 572B Gary Milburn/TSA; 572T Doug Perrine/IV; 573BL Larry Lipsky/BC; 573C Doug Perrine/IV; 574 Peter Parks/Norbert Wu/MYP; 576BL Larry Benvenuti; 576BR Doug Perrine/IV; 576T Norbert Wu/MYP; 577BL Stephen Frink/WaterHouse; 577BR Doug Perrine/IV; 577TL Doug Perrine/IV; 577TR Kjell Sandved/BC; 578 Doug Perrine/IV; 579 E. R. Degginger/AA; 580BL Biophoto Assoc./PR; 580TR Norbert Wu/MYP; 582 Stephen Frink/WaterHouse

Unit 7   588BL Art Wolfe; 588BR Jack Daniels/TSI; 588C G. C. Kelley/PR; 588TR Art Wolfe/TSI; 589BL 1996 Discover Magazine; 589C Clem Haagner/PR; 589CL Kim Taylor/BC; 589T Stephen Dalton/PR; 686BL Courtesy, Michael Leigh; 686BR *Survival Island* Video courtesy of Imax Corporation; 687B Kathi Lamm/TSI; 687T Steven Holt/Aigrette

Chapter 25   590–591 David Fleetham/IV; 591BL Layne Kennedy; 591 TOP BAR Kevin & Betty Collins/VU (salmon); Marty Snyderman (balloonfish); Michael Fogden/BC (frog); 592B E. R. Degginger/PR; 592T Manfred Danegger/TSI; 594 James Watt/MYP; 594 James Watt/MYP; 595 Herbert Schwind/Okapia/PR; 597BR Jen & Des Bartlett/BC; 597T Kevin & Betty Collins/VU; 597TL Brandon Cole/MYP; 597TL Glenn M. Oliver/VU; 597 Brandon Cole/MYP; 598 Tracey Wheeler*; 598BL ibis file photo; 599B Oxford Scientific Films/AA; 599T Norbert Wu/MYP; 600BL Berthoule-Scott/Jacana/PR; 600BR Tom McHugh/Steinhart Aquarium/PR; 601B Tom McHugh/Steinhart Aquarium/PR; 601T Carl Roessler; 602BL Stephen Frink/WaterHouse; 602C Hal Beral/VU; 602CL Carl Roessler; 602TC Norbert Wu/MYP; 603B Tom & Pat Leeson/PR; 603T M. I. Walker/PR; 604C Marty Snyderman; 604T Don Brewster/BC; 605B E. R. Degginger/BC; 605CR E. R. Degginger/BC; 605T Michael Fogden/BC; 608C Herbert Kehrer/Okapia/PR; 608CL Jane Burton/BC; 608TC Kim Taylor/BC; 608TL Jane Burton/BC; 608TR Jane Burton/BC; 609TC Karl H. Switak/PR; 610BL Richard Thom/VU; 610BR Michael P. Gadomski/BC; 611CR Michael Fogden/BC; 611TC Gary Meszaros/BC; 611TL Jane Burton/BC; 612B Tom McHugh/PR; 612CR Michael Fogden/BC; 612TR C. Bradley Simmons/BC; 613B Kim Taylor/BC; 613T Merlin D. Tuttle/Bat Conservation Int'l./PR; 614 Mark Moffett/MP

Chapter 26   618–619 James D. Watt/Earthviews; 619 TOP BAR Klaus Uhlenhut/AA (lizard); Michael Fogden/BC (snake); Schafer & Hill/TSI (toucan); 620B Norman Owen Tomalin/BC; 620T Michael Fogden/AA; 621B Cosmos Blank/NAS/PR; 621T Tom Myers/PR; 622 Fulvio Eccardi/BC; 623 Zig Leszczynski/AA; 624CR Larry West/BC; 624TR Zig Leszczynski/AA; 625 J. Markham/BC; 626B 5794(2), Photo by Denis Finnin Courtesy Dept. of Library Services, American Museum of Natural History; 626T 5800(2), Photo by Denis Finnin Courtesy Dept. of Library Services, American Museum of Natural History; 627 Frans Lanting/MP; 628BL Renee Lynn/PR; 628BR John Darling/TSI; 628TL Tom McHugh/Steinhart Aquarium/PR; 629BL Zig Leszczynski/AA; 629BR Klaus Uhlenhut/AA; 629C Joe & Carol McDonald/BC; 629T Michael Fogden/BC; 630 Carol Hughes/BC; 631 Dade W. Thornton/PR; 632 Alan & Sandy Carey/PR; 634 David E. Myers/TSI; 636B Tom Brakefield/BC; 636T Joe McDonald/AA; 638B 213(2), Photo by Denis Finnin Courtesy Dept. of Library Services, American Museum of Natural History; 638T Bruce M. Wellman/AA; 639BR Rod Planck/TSI; 639C Schafer & Hill/TSI; 639CR John Warden/TSI; 639T Ted Levin/AA; 639TL

Kenneth W. Fink/PR; 639TR Hans Reinhard/BC; 640B Stan Osolinski/TSI; 640T BC; 641C Sid Bahrt/PR; 641CR Tim Davis/TSI; 641TR Darrell Gulin/TSI

Chapter 27   646–647 Daniel J. Cox/TSI; 647 TOP BAR Daniel J. Cox/TSI (gorilla); Dave Watts/Tom Stack & Assoc (koala); Frans Lanting/MP (tarsiers); Nikolas Konstantinou/TSI (manatee); 648B Stephen Dalton/PR; 648T Michael Dick/AA; 649 Frans Lanting/MP; 651B Mike James/PR; 651CR Tom McHugh/PR; 652 William J. Weber/VU; 653 Tim Davis*; 654 Frans Lanting/MP; 655 Norman Owen Tomalin/BC; 656BL Lee Rentz/BC; 656CL Erwin & Peggy Bauer/BC; 656TC Dave Watts/TSA; 656TL John Shaw/BC; 657 Fred Felleman/TSI; 657CR Frans Lanting/MP; 657TL Stephen Dalton/AA; 657TR John Giustina/Wildlife Collection; 658BC Hans Reinhard/BC; 658BR Clem Haagner/BC; 658CL Nikolas Konstantinou/TSI; 658TR Vince Streano/TSI; 659CR Daniel J. Cox/TSI; 659TC Belinda Wright/DRK; 659TL Stephen Krasemann/TSI; 659TR Frans Lanting/MP; 660B Len Rue Jr./BC; 660T Ken Cole/AA; 661B Jeff Foott/BC; 665 Richard Walters/VU

Chapter 28   666–667 Michael Fogden/AA; 667 TOP BAR Barbara Gerlach/VU (birds); Bob Torrez/TSI (dog); John Chellman/AA (chimp); 668B Daryl Balfour/TSI; 668T Barbara Gerlach/VU; 669B Phil Degginger/BC; 669T Michael Murphy/PR; 670 Susan Kuklin/Science Source/PR; 671B Mike Severns/TSI; 671T Hans Reinhard/BC; 672BR Tim Davis/PR; 672T Gerard Lacz/NHPA; 674 Richard Walters/VU; 675B Erwin & Peggy Bauer/BC; 675T Bob Torrez/TSI; 676B Thomas McAvoy, Life Magazine Time Inc.; 676T Mark Stouffer/AA; 677 Runk/Schoenberger/GH; 679B John Chellman/AA; 679T Mark Newman/BC; 680BL Pat & Tom Leeson/PR; 680BR Art Wolfe/TSI; 681 Darrell Gulin/TSI; 682 Ron Sanford/TSI; 685 CNRI/PT

Unit 8   688B NASA; 688C PhotoDisc; 688TL Allan Penn*; 688TR PhotoDisc; 689B Art Wolfe/TSI; 689B Tracey Wheeler*; 689TL Penny Gentieu/TSI; 689TR Tracey Wheeler*; 848BL Courtesy, Maya Lee; 848BR Courtesy A.D.A.M. Software, Inc. All Rights Reserved. 849B Manny Millan/S.I. Picture Collection; 849T Tracey Wheeler*

Chapter 29   690691 NASA; 691C NASA; 691 TOP BAR Biophoto Associates/PR (compact bone); Carolina Biological Supply/PT (stomach cell); CNRI/PT (skull); M. Abbey/PR (skeletal muscle); 692BL Prof. P. Motta/Dept. of Anatomy/University "La Sapienza" , Rome/Science Photo Library/PR; 692CL Carolina Biological Supply/PT; 692T Andrew Martinez/PR; 696B Daniel J. Lyons/BC; 696T K. & K. Ammann/BC; 697CL J. Markham/BC; 697CR Breck P. Kent/AA; 697TC Judy Davidson/Science Photo Library/PR; 698 Laurence Monneret/TSI; 699CL Biophoto Assoc./PR; 699TL George J. Wilder/VU; 700TC Prof. P. Motta/Dept. of Anatomy/University "La Sapienza," Rome/Science Photo Library/PR; 700TL Secchi, Lecaque, Roussel, UCLAF, CNRI/Science Photo Library/PR; 700TR CNRI/PT; 703B Stephen Dalton/PR; 703T Jen & Des Bartlett/BC; 704–705 Tom Brakefield/DRK; 704CL J. H. Robinson/PR; 704CR Runk/Schoenberger/GH; 705TL Anthony Mercieca/PR; 706TL Antonio Ribeiro/GL; 707TC M. I. Walker/Science Source/PR; 707TL M. Abbey/PR; 707TR Biophoto Assoc./ScienceSource/PR; 709 Mark Richards/PhotoEdit; 710BL George I. Bernard/AA; 710CL Bruce Davidson/AA; 710T Gerard Lacz/PA; 710TL J. C. Carton/BC; 711 Biophoto Assoc./PR; 712B Matthew McVay/TSI; 712BL Cabisco/VU; 714 Tracey Wheeler*

Chapter 30   718–719 Michael Webb/VU; 718C CNRI/PT; 719 TOP BAR Microworks/CNRI/PT; 720 C. Allan Morgan; 721 Gregory Ochocki/PR; 725 Tracey Wheeler*; 727 Microworks/CNRI/PT; 729 Lori Adamski Peek/TSI; 730 Myrleen Ferguson/PhotoEdit; 731 Tracey Wheeler*; 732 Tracey Wheeler*; 733 Johnny Johnson/DRK; 735 Tim Lynch/SB; 738 SIU/VU

Chapter 31   742–743 William R. Sallaz/Duomo; 743 Rick Rickman/Duomo; 743 TOP BAR Dr. Dennis Kunkel/PT (platelets); Prof. Aaron Polliack/Science Photo Library/PR (blood cells); 744 Suzanne L. & Joseph T. Collins/PR; 748 Charles Thatcher/TSI; 750 Tim Davis*; 751B Aaron Haupt/SB; 751T Archive Photos; 752B Frank Siteman/SB; 752T Mauritius/Habel/PT; 753B Tony Freeman/PhotoEdit; 753BR PhotoDisc; 753C Bruce Ayres/TSI; 753T Robert E. Daemmrich/TSI; 754 Francisco Chanes/CMS; 756 Biophoto Assoc./Science Source; 757 O. Meckes/Nicole Ottawa/PR; 758 Tracey Wheeler*; 759B Dr. Dennis Kunkel/PT; 759T Will & Deni McIntyre/TSI; 760TL Prof. Aaron Polliack/Science Photo Library/PR; 760TR Dr. Dennis Kunkel/PT; 761 George W. Wilder/VU; 762BL Lennart Nilsson/BA; 762BR Lennart Nilsson/BA; 762T Jonathan Elderfield/GL; 763BR Science Source/PR; 763CR Science Source/PR; 763T CMS; 767BR Dr. Dennis Kunkel/CNRI/PT

Chapter 32   768–769 R. Ellis/SYGMA; 769BR Dr. Jeremy Burgess/Science Photo Library/PR (mold spore); 769 TOP BAR Dr. Dennis Kunkel/CNRI/PT (pollen grain); Dr. Dennis Kunkel/PT (macrophage); Hans Gelderblom/VU (HIV virus); John Kaprielian/PR (poison ivy); 770BL Robert & Linda Mitchell; 770CL CNRI/PT; 770TL Jeff Rotman/TSI; 772C Scott Camazine/PR; 772CL David Young-Wolff/TSI; 772TL Tracey Wheeler*; 774 Dr. Dennis Kunkel/PT; 775 David M. Phillips/VU; 776 Tracey Wheeler*; 777 Allan Penn*; 779 Tracey Wheeler*; 782 Meckes/Ottawa/PR; 783BL Biophoto Assoc./Science Source/PR; 783BR Dr. Jeremy Burgess/Science Photo Library/PR; 783C Dr. Dennis Kunkel/CNRI/PT; 783TL Andrew Syred/Science Photo Library/PR; 784B Dr. Jeremy Burgess/Science Photo Library/PR; 784TC Doug Plummer/PR; 784TL John Kaprielian/PR; 784TR John M. Burnley/PR; 785 Hans Gelderblom/VU; 788 Lawrence Migdale/SB; 791 David M. Phillips/PR

Chapter 33   792–793 Paula Lerner; 793CR Paula Lerner; 793 TOP BAR CNRI/Science Photo Library/PR (healthy sperm); David M. Phillips/PR (sperm swarming egg); J. L. Carson/CMS (sperm); Lennart Nilsson/BA (fetus); 794B Biophoto Assoc./PR; 794T Roger Wilmshurst/BC; 795B Holt Studios Int'l./PR; 795CR C. Rider/PR; 795TC Breck P. Kent/AA; 795TL Breck P. Kent/AA; 795TR Ralph A. Reinhold/AA; 796 Paul Howell/GL; 800 Allan Penn*; 801B Genentech/VU; 801T Rosanne Olson/TSI; 802 Tracey Wheeler*; 803B David J. Wrobel; 803T David M. Phillips/PR; 804B Mike James/PR; 804TL Art Wolfe; 804TR Laura Riley/BC; 805 J.

L. Carson/CMS; 807BR C. Edelmann/La Villette/PR; 807CR C. Edelmann/La Villette/PR; 807TR C. Edelmann/La Villette/PR; 809 Bruce Ayres/TSI; 811 Lennart Nilsson/BA; 812 CMS; 813 Lawrence Migdale/SB; 814B Jay Syverson/SB; 814T TSI; 815BR Dr. Tony Brain/Science Photo Library/PR; 815CR CNRI/Science Photo Library/PR; 815T Lennart Nilsson/BA; 816 Tracey Wheeler*

Chapter 34 820–821 Gary Yeowell/TSI; 821B Gary Yeowell/TSI; 821 TOP BAR David M. Phillips/PR; 822 Pascal Quittemelle/SB; 824 David M. Phillips/PR; 825 CNRI/PT; 828 Michael Newman/PhotoEdit; 830 Hank Morgan/Science Source/PR; 833 Tim Davis*; 834TR Jerome Tisne/TSI; 838BL Biophoto Assoc./Science Source/PR; 838CL R. C. Eager/PR; 838TR Allan Penn*; 839 David Chambers/TSI; 840BC Lefever/Grushow/GH; 840BL M. Viardi Jacana/PR; 840BR Phil Schermeister/TSI; 840CL Wesley Bocxe/PR; 841 Mark Reinstein/GL; 842B Yoav Levy/PT; 842T A. Glauberman/Science Source/PR; 843BL Joseph R. Siebert/CMS; 843BR Martin Rotker/PT; 843T Jeff Zaruba/AllStock; 844B Linc Cornell/SB; 844T Bob Daemmrich/SB; 847 Tom Van Sant/Geosphere Project,Santa Monica/Science Photo Library/PR

Unit 9 850BL Peter Cade/TSI; 850BR James Balog/TSI; 850CL Phil Degginger/BC; 850TR Bill Wood/BC; 851BL E. R. Degginger/BC; 851BR John Kieffer/PA; 851TL SEF/Art Resource, NY; 851TR Johnny Johnson/TSI; 940BL Courtesy, Ann Myers; 940BR "From Last Chance to See" by Douglas Adams and Mark Carwardine. ©1990 by Serias Productions Ltd. Reprinted by Permission of Harmony Books, a division of Crown Publishers, Inc.; 941B John Coletti; 941T Tri-State Bird Rescue

Chapter 35 852–853 Henry Gonzalez/BC; 853B Jean-Paul Manceau/TSI (leopards); 853 TOP BAR Frank Siteman/TSI (fish); Gregory G. Dimijian/PR (ant); Norbert Wu/TSI (sloth); Jean-Paul Manceau/TSI (desert); 854B Tom Van Sant/Geosphere Project,Santa Monica/Science Photo Library/PR; 854T Mark Burnett/PR; 855CR Manoj Shah/TSI; 855TC R.S. Virdee/GH; 855TR Tim Davis/PR; 856BL Grant Heilman/GH; 856BR Jen & Des Bartlett/BC; 856C John Beatty/TSI; 856TL Schafer & Hill/PA; 856TR E. R. Degginger/BC; 858T Arnulf Husmo/TSI; 859BR J. Messerschmidt/BC; 859TR James Blank/TSI; 860 Tracey Wheeler*; 861 Jane Grushow/GH; 862B Charlie Ott/PR; 862BL Mark Newman/PR; 862BR Michael Giannechini/PR; 862C Scott Nielsen/BC; 862T Arthur C. Smith III/GH; 862TC Kim Heacox/TSI; 862TR W. Lankinen/BC; 863B Danilo S. Donadoni/BC; 863BC Larry Brock/TSA; 863BL Robert E. Daemmrich/TSI; 863BR John R. MacGregor/PA; 863T Michael Busselle/TSI; 863TC Michio Hoshino/MP; 863TR Steve & Dave Maslowski/PR; 864B Jean-Paul Manceau/TSI; 864BL Kim Heacox/Petet Arnold, Inc.; 864BR Gary Meszaros/BC; 864T Art Wolfe/TSI; 864TL Gregory G. Dimijian/PR; 864TR Norbert Wu/TSI; 865C Art Wolfe; 865CL William Felger/GH; 865T John Shaw/TSI; 866B John Shaw/TSI; 866BL Dan Guravich/PR; 866T Peter David/Planet Earth Pictures; 867B Grant Heilman/GH; 867BL Runk/Schoenberger/GH; 867BR Runk/Schoenberger/GH; 867C John Shaw/BC; 868B Tom Tietz/TSI; 868BC Runk/Schoenberger/GH; 868BL Randy Wells/TSI; 868BR Jeff Foott/BC; 868CR Patricio Robles Gil/BC; 869C John Gerlach/AA; 869T M. E. Warren/PR; 869TR Fritz Polking/PA; 870CL Randy Morse/TSA; 870CR Tom McHugh/Steinhart Aquarium/PR; 870T Scott Blackman/TSA; 870TR Frank Siteman/TSI; 873 Dr. Morley Read/Science Photo Library/PR; 873CR THE FAR SIDE © FARWORKS, INC./Dist. by UNIVERSAL PRESS SYNDICATE. /reprinted with permission. All rights reserved.

Chapter 36 874–875 Erwin & Peggy Bauer/BC; 875 TOP BAR Art Wolfe/TSI (butterflyfish); Tim Davis/TSI (cheetahs); Leonard Lee Rue III/PR (starlings); 876BL Jane Burton/BC; 876C Kim Taylor/BC; 876TR Hans Reinhard/BC; 877 M. Gabridge/VU; 878B Jim Brandenburg/MP; 879 Kim Taylor/BC; 880 Kent Wood; 881B Clem Haagner/BC; 881T Frank Siteman/TSI; 882 Alan Carey/PR; 883 Dr. Morley Read/Science Photo Library/PR; 884 Jim Pickerell/TSI; 885B Allan Blank/BC; 885T Art Wolfe; 886 Leonard Lee Rue III/PR; 887BC Andrew Drake/TSI; 887BL Robert & Linda Mitchell; 887CR L. West/PR; 888 Tim Davis/TSI; 889C Victoria McCormick/AA; 889CR Lynn M. Stone/DRK; 889T Alan L. Detrick/PR; 889TC Mark N. Boulton/PR; 890B Arthur C. Smith III/GH; 890T Art Wolfe/TSI; 891B Michael Busselle/TSI; 891C Grant Heilman/GH; 891CR Michael P. Gadomski/PR; 891T Grant Heilman/GH; 892 Sylvain Grandadam/TSI

Chapter 37 896–897 Gary Braasch; 897BL Richard Alan Wood/AA; 897BR Gary Braasch; 897 TOP BAR Brandon Cole/MYP (salmon); Grant Heilman/GH (sunflowers); 898B Joe McDonald/BC; 898T Grant Heilman/GH; 901CR Brandon Cole/MYP; 901TR Steve Bly/TSI; 902 Francios Gohier/PR; 905 Jerry Howard/SB; 907C Charlie Ott/PR; 907CR Albert J. Copley/VU; 907TR Grant Heilman/GH; 909 Grant Heilman/GH; 911B Ohlt Studios International/PR; 911T Lawrence Migdale/PR; 915 Richard Parker/PR

Chapter 38 916BC Johnny Johnson/DRK; 916–917 Larry Ulrich/TSI; 917 TOP BAR Billy Hustace/TSI (wind turbine); Johnny Johnson/DRK (grizzly); Larry Ulrich/TSI (mountains); 918BC Billy Hustace/TSI; 918BL Ken Graham/TSI; 918TR Ned Therrien/VU; 919 Courtesy, Central Artery/Tunnel Project, photo by Louis Martin; 920BL John Midgley/TSI; 920BR Ed Degginger/BC; 920TR Richard Parker/PR; 921 Torin Boyd/GL; 922 J. Sarapochiello/BC; 923 Sue Cunningham/TSI; 924BL VU; 924TR Joe Munroe/PR; 925BR John Chiasson/GL; 925TL John S. Lough/VU; 925TR John S. Lough/VU; 926BL Carolyn Schaefer/GL; 926TR Joseph Sohm/TSI; 927 Guido Cozzi/BC; 928BL Ed Pritchard/TSI; 928TR Ron & Valerie Taylor/BC; 929TL Runk/Schoenberger/GH; 929TR Oliver Strewe/TSI; 931 NOAA/Science Photo Library/PR; 932BL Galen Rowell/Mountain Light; 932TR Marty Stouffer/AA; 933 Wendy Stone/GL; 934BL Jack Swenson/Wildlife Collection; 934TR Bob Daemmrich/SB; 935C Michael Fogden/BC; 935R Stephen J. Krasemann/PR; 935TL Michael Fogden/BC; 936 Jose Azel/Aurora; 939 NASA; 942 Allan Penn*

* Photographed expressly for Scott Foresman-Addison Wesley.

1016

ILLUSTRATIONS

From *Biochemistry, Second Edition*, by C.K. Matthews and K.E. vanHolde. Copyright (©) 1996 by the Benjamin/Cummings Publishing Company. Reprinted by permission. 93 (b)

From *Biology* by Neil Campbell. Copyright (©) 1987 by the Benjamin/Cummings Publishing Company. Reprinted by permission. 75 (t)

From *Biology, Concepts & Connections*, by N. Campbell, L. Mitchell and J. Reece. Copyright (©) 1994 by the Benjamin/Cummings Publishing Company. Reprinted by permission. 64 (tc), 135, 169, 183 (cr), 197 (t), 436 (b), 745, 747 (l) , 754 (r), 755 (br), 757, 805, 806, 812, 906

From *Biology, Fourth Edition*, by Neil Campbell. Copyright (©) 1996 by the Benjamin/Cummings Publishing Company. Reprinted by permission. 67 (bc), 73 (t), 87, 183–184, 185, 195, 209, 237, 238, 287, 331, 332, 342 (br), 346, 359, 364, 375 (bc), 384, 717, 720, 721 (bl), 721 (br), 733, 734 (t), 734 (b), 747 (tr), 810, 822, 823 (tl), 823 (tr)

From *Biology, Third Edition* by Neil Campbell. Copyright (©) 1993 by the Benjamin/Cummings Publishing Company. Reprinted by permission. iv (br), 67 (cr), 76 (t), 88 (b), 93 (cr), 131, 184 (tl), 189, 212, 726, 748, 754 (l), 861, 870, 908, 910

From *Biology, Second Edition* by Neil Campbell. Copyright (©) 1990 by the Benjamin/Cummings Publishing Company. Reprinted by permission. 905

From *Ecology and Field Biology*, Fourth Edition, by Robert Leo Smith. Copyright (©) 1990 by Robert Leo Smith. Reprinted by permission of Addison-Wesley Educational Publishers Inc. 904

From *Human Anatomy and Physiology*, Second Edition, by Elaine Marieb. Copyright (©) 1992 by the Benjamin/Cummings Publishing Company. Reprinted by permission 67 (tl), 692, 694–695, 725, 736 (cl), 755 (bl), 824 (tc), 828 (bl)

Reprinted from *Addison-Wesley Biology, Second Edition*, Bernice E. Essenfeld, Carol R. Gontang and Randy Moore 947, 948, 948, 951

Charles Boyter 775
Todd Buck 829, 830
John Burgoyne 244, 269–270, 308, 311 (t), 399, 408, 425, 486, 771, 899
Susan Johnston Carlson 450, 463, 464 (t), 510, 515 (t)
Chuck Carter 257
Diphrent Strokes Inc./Felipe Passalacqua* 645, 649, 649, 727
Jim Dowdalls vii (t), 63 (b,t), 74, 319, 327, 337, 356–357, 511, 778
Mark Foerster* 912
Dale Glasgow 642, 722, 730, 858, 859 (t), 886, 922, 930
Patrick Gnan viii, 215 (Illustration formation provided by Genentech Inc.), 419 (b), 422 (br), 428 (b), 430 (b) 433 (r), 561
Pedro Julio Gonzalez 286
Jackie Heda xi (t), 711, 746, 747, 819, 823 (b)
Marlene May Howerton* 234 (tl), 609
Illustrious Interactive 232, 259, 262, 272 (t), 599, 721 (t), 735, 832, 859 (b)
Caryln Iverson iv (bl), 55, 58, 62, 64 (cr, cl), 65 (cr, cl), 67 (br, bl, tr, cl), 69 (br, bl), 267, 322, 343, 352, 410, 422 (bl), 423, 428 (cl), 430 (l, cl), 432 (r), 433 (l), 435, 436 (c)
John Karapelou xi (c), 698, 702, 737
David F. Kelley 10 (b), 797
Michael Leonard 700, 708
Elizabeth Morales 632
Hilda R. Muinos 692, 693
Jared Schneidman Design iv (cl), v, 10 (t), 29 (tr), 35 (br, cr), 36, 72, 155, 160–161, 182
Laurie O'Keefe* 701, 707, 902, 903, 903
Marcelo Oliver 673
Roberto Osti ix, x, 108, 110, 111, 112 (tr, tl), 116–117, 118, 119, 165, 175 (t), 502, 505, 512, 531, 534, 537, 550, 553, 557, 585, 594–595, 595, 596, 606–607, 617, 621 (cr), 650 (t)
Rolin Graphics* 5, 22, 79, 86 (b), 490, 621 (tl), 623, 637, 650 (b), 654, 706, 728, 736 (b), 749, 758, 760, 780, 781, 825, 827, 836, 857
Patrice Rossi* 704
Wendy Smith-Griswold 133, 136–137, 140, 147 (b), 158, 166 (tl), 213, 375, 377, 380, 381, 382, 443 (br), 460–461, 524, 525, 538–539, 540
Nadine B. Sokol vii (b), 44, 73 (b), 105, 159, 210, 239, 311 (b), 328–329, 330, 333, 367, 426 (t), 432 (l), 438, 448, 449, 526 (bl), 532 (cl), 580, 582
Walter Stuart 627
Stephen Thompson 287, 289, 290
Warren Budd & Assoc.* 493, 607 (b)
Sarah Woodward* xii, 699, 701, 741, 756, 798, 809, 824 (cl), (tr), 826, 828 (bc), 834, 835, 837

*From *Addison-Wesley Biology, Second Edition*, Bernice E. Essenfeld, Carol R. Gontang and Randy Moore

Biology Atlas maps © 1998 GeoSystems Global Corporation. This product contains proprietary property of GeoSystems Global Corporation. Unauthorized use, including copying, of this product is expressly prohibited.